The Periodic Table of Elements (*long form*)

Atomic masses are rounded to three decimals, where available; atomic numbers appear above the symbols. See the facing page for a table of all significant figures.

Periods	1 IA	2 IIA	3 IIIB	4 IVB	5 VB	6 VIB	7 VIIB	8	9 VIIIB	10	11 IB	12 IIB	13 IIIA	14 IVA	15 VA	16 VIA	17 VIIA	18 VIIIA
1	1 **H** 1.008																1 **H** 1.008	2 **He** 4.003
2	3 **Li** 6.941	4 **Be** 9.012											5 **B** 10.811	6 **C** 12.011	7 **N** 14.007	8 **O** 15.999	9 **F** 18.998	10 **Ne** 20.180
3	11 **Na** 22.990	12 **Mg** 24.305											13 **Al** 26.982	14 **Si** 28.086	15 **P** 30.974	16 **S** 32.066	17 **Cl** 35.453	18 **Ar** 39.948
4	19 **K** 39.098	20 **Ca** 40.078	21 **Sc** 44.956	22 **Ti** 47.88	23 **V** 50.942	24 **Cr** 51.996	25 **Mn** 54.938	26 **Fe** 55.847	27 **Co** 58.933	28 **Ni** 58.69	29 **Cu** 63.546	30 **Zn** 65.39	31 **Ga** 69.723	32 **Ge** 72.61	33 **As** 74.922	34 **Se** 78.96	35 **Br** 79.904	36 **Kr** 83.80
5	37 **Rb** 85.468	38 **Sr** 87.62	39 **Y** 88.906	40 **Zr** 91.224	41 **Nb** 92.906	42 **Mo** 95.94	43 **Tc** (98)	44 **Ru** 101.07	45 **Rh** 102.906	46 **Pd** 106.42	47 **Ag** 107.868	48 **Cd** 112.411	49 **In** 114.82	50 **Sn** 118.710	51 **Sb** 121.75	52 **Te** 127.60	53 **I** 126.904	54 **Xe** 131.29
6	55 **Cs** 132.905	56 **Ba** 137.327	* (57–71)	72 **Hf** 178.49	73 **Ta** 180.948	74 **W** 183.85	75 **Re** 186.207	76 **Os** 190.2	77 **Ir** 192.22	78 **Pt** 195.08	79 **Au** 196.966	80 **Hg** 200.59	81 **Tl** 204.383	82 **Pb** 207.2	83 **Bi** 208.980	84 **Po** (209)	85 **At** (210)	86 **Rn** (222)
7	87 **Fr** (223)	88 **Ra** 226.025	† (89–103)	104 **Unq** (261)	105 **Unp** (262)	106 **Unh** (263)	107 **Uns** (262)	108 **Uno** (265)	109 **Une** (266)									

Nonmetals

Metals

Transition metals

Inner transition metals

*Lanthanide series

57 **La** 138.906	58 **Ce** 140.115	59 **Pr** 140.908	60 **Nd** 144.24	61 **Pm** (145)	62 **Sm** 150.36	63 **Eu** 151.965	64 **Gd** 157.25	65 **Tb** 158.925	66 **Dy** 162.50	67 **Ho** 164.930	68 **Er** 167.26	69 **Tm** 168.934	70 **Yb** 173.04	71 **Lu** 174.967

†Actinide series

89 **Ac** 227.028	90 **Th** 232.038	91 **Pa** 231.036	92 **U** 238.029	93 **Np** 237.048	94 **Pu** (244)	95 **Am** (243)	96 **Cm** (247)	97 **Bk** (247)	98 **Cf** (251)	99 **Es** (252)	100 **Fm** (257)	101 **Md** (258)	102 **No** (259)	103 **Lr** (260)

Elements with semi-metallic behavior (Chapter 25) are B, Si, Ge, Sb, and Te.

GENERAL CHEMISTRY

Ninth Edition

GENERAL
CHEMISTRY

Henry F. Holtzclaw, Jr.
University of Nebraska—Lincoln

William R. Robinson
Purdue University

Jerome D. Odom
University of South Carolina

D.C. Heath and Company
Lexington, Massachusetts   Toronto

Address editorial correspondence to:

D.C. Heath
125 Spring Street
Lexington, MA 02173

Acquisitions Editor: Kent Porter Hamann
Developmental Editor: Elizabeth Coolidge-Stolz
Production Editor: Anne Rebecca Starr
Cover and Text Designer: Alwyn R. Velásquez
Production Coordinator: Michael O'Dea
Photo Researcher: Connie Komack, Pictures & Words
Text Permissions Editor: Margaret Roll

Cover photos: (background) Malachite ore, John Urban/*Museum of Science, Boston;* (front) Molten copper, Michael Melford/*The Image Bank;* (back left) Sheets of oxidized copper, Paul Silverman/*Fundamental Photographs;* (back right) Raw copper ore, Mike Schneps/*The Image Bank*

For permission to use photographs, grateful acknowledgment is made to the copyright holders listed on pages A21–A23, which are hereby considered an extension of this copyright page.

Preface

How does a text that is in its ninth edition retain its freshness? With a new author, Professor Jerome D. Odom, who is an inorganic chemist and chair of the Chemistry Department at the University of South Carolina; with new approaches to content that reflect the input of students, instructors, colleagues, and collaborators; with an inviting new design that uses illustrations and photographs to complement the content pedagogically; with close attention paid to both chemical and chemical education literature; and with a commitment on the part of the authors and the publisher to produce the best text available. At the same time, we have not in any way compromised the solid foundation of the previous editions, which are highly recognized and respected for their clarity, accuracy, and concern for the student.

Our Philosophy

As is evident in previous editions, we believe it is essential that the concepts and models of chemical behavior be presented clearly before applying them to various other systems, where additional considerations may mask the chemical principles involved. Thus, we have consistently paid careful attention to the introduction and development of chemical concepts before extending them to different situations. Because the changes in the treatment of several major topics in this revision reflect this philosophy, we will address them individually.

Our philosophy of working from simple to complex in the development of concepts is evident also in the exercises at the end of the chapters; many simple drill-and-practice problems are provided, followed by more complicated or involved exercises. We also believe that it is important to include questions that challenge a student to think about the meaning of the concepts and not simply grind out calculations. As a result, many of the exercises are much more than just calculations or recall questions.

Chemical Behavior

The most obvious organizational change is in Chapter 2, the chapter that introduces the language of chemistry—atoms, molecules, and ions; chemical reactions; and nomenclature. This chapter presents the concepts that students need in order to understand how chemists talk about chemical behavior and reinforces these concepts in a discussion of the chemistry of some important industrial compounds. The way in which molecules, chemical reactions, nomenclature, and supporting concepts are introduced will give students sufficient background for understanding an instructor's use of these concepts as well as their laboratory applications. Because this material is presented near the beginning of the text, we took a great deal of care to describe it at a level that is appropriate to the early part of a general course. Consequently, some topics are, of necessity, covered again in subsequent sections of the text in more detail.

Stoichiometry

Stoichiometry remains early in the text so it, too, is available for laboratory use. Because atoms, molecules, and chemical equations are introduced in Chapter 2, the discussion of stoichiometry is consolidated into Chapter 3 without losing any content. This chapter retains the style of problem solving that was well received by students using the text. In particular, we are careful to discuss how to solve the problems in the examples before the calculations themselves are presented. It is well established that students who are successful with mathematical problems usually can describe the steps in the solution of a problem without using the numbers in the problem. We present two different techniques (written and schematic) that students can use to describe the logic of a problem before carrying out the calculations.

Atomic Structure, Periodicity, and Bonding

In this edition, we cover atomic structure and chemical periodicity in two separate chapters: Chapter 5 on atomic structure, and Chapter 6 on the periodic behavior of the physical and chemical properties of the elements. Both chapters are completely coordinated with the introduction in Chapter 2. As in previous editions, a discussion of chemical bonding follows the introduction of atomic theory and periodicity. Chapters 7, 8, and 9 discuss Lewis structures, valence shell electron-pair repulsion and valence bond theory, and molecular orbital theory, respectively. In addition, we present in Chapter 7 a general procedure for use in predicting the products of simple chemical reactions, based on acid–base behavior, oxidation–reduction behavior, common oxidation numbers, and the metallic or nonmetallic nature of the elements involved. This procedure provides a framework that enables students to begin to master a subject that can often seem uncoordinated or incomprehensible. This can be a source of considerable satisfaction and encouragement for students.

Intermolecular Forces

The concept of intermolecular forces is important in discussions of biochemistry, polymers, soil science, materials science, and other areas that draw on chemical principles. We have expanded our discussion of these forces in the introductory sections of Chapter 11 and have used them in Chapter 12 to describe the energy factors responsible for dissolution.

Equilibrium

The discussion of equilibrium in Chapters 15, 17, and 18 is significantly different from that in the previous editions. The introduction to the state of equilibrium is now presented in terms of constant concentrations at equilibrium rather than equality of forward and reverse rates. A change in concentration is a more concrete concept (you can see color changes as some concentrations change, for example); equality of rates is a more formal, abstract concept. In this edition, we present the idea of equality of rates specifically to explain why the concentrations do not appear to change at equilibrium.

The discussion of the reaction quotient has been strengthened. It is very helpful in predicting which way a reaction will shift to reach equilibrium. Moreover, the concept of a reaction quotient is very important in thermodynamics and electrochemistry.

Many introductions to equilibrium treat the subject in a way that makes various kinds of equilibria seem unrelated and each type of equilibrium calculation seem different. Our introduction discusses equilibrium in a way that can be readily extended to all types of equilibria and equilibrium problems. The presentation in the three chapters on equilibrium is consistent. Thus, a new solution process does not have to be learned for each type of system.

We have focused on the change in concentration (or pressure) as the general approach for solving all problems in which the student is given initial concentrations and asked to calculate equilibrium concentrations. Change lines are used in all examples. In addition, the introduction to equilibrium presents the mathematical strategies for solving equilibrium problems in a separate section, with the strategies presented from the simplest to the most complex. If the easy solution strategy proves satisfactory, students can stop there. If not, they can move up to the next strategy.

In the discussion of acid–base equilibria in aqueous solution, we are careful to point out that water can contribute to the hydronium or hydroxide concentrations in solutions of very dilute or very weak acids or bases. Students should develop the understanding that in most circumstances the ionization of water need not be taken into account, but that in some cases it can be a significant factor and must be taken into account.

It appears to be a small point, but we believe it is important to distinguish carefully the statement ''assume $x = 0$'' from ''assume $1.00 - x = 1.00$'' in solving equilibrium equations. The latter assumption is the correct statement and avoids confusion; students are often puzzled by the question, ''How can I solve for x if I assume that it is 0?''

Descriptive Chemistry

Examples and applications in the descriptive chemistry chapters have been updated. In addition, these chapters now recall the principles involved in the chemistry discussed. Environmental chemistry has been retained as a separate chapter, not just mentioned in passing in other chapters, and the chapter has been wholly revised. The nuclear chemistry chapter has been expanded and now includes radioactive dating; applications of nuclear chemistry in medicine, agriculture, and industry; environmental concerns; and biological effects of radiation.

Additional Changes in Topical Coverage

There are also many smaller, less obvious changes. The concept of oxidation number, introduced in Chapter 2, is expanded in terms of the distribution of electrons in bonds in Chapter 7. We added a section on formal charge to Chapter 7. The discussion of polar molecules occurs in Chapter 8 after molecular structures have been discussed. We added brief introductions to infrared spectroscopy to illustrate an experimental means of identifying relative bond strengths (Section 7.10) and to NMR to illustrate an experimental technique for determining structure and hybridization (Section 8.12). Chapter 8 now contains a more specific introduction to valence bond theory in addition to hybridization and molecular structure; it precedes the molecular orbital chapter (Chapter 9), which now contains an application of MO theory as a way of explaining the conductivity of metals, semiconductors, and insulators. The introduction to electrochemistry in Chapter 20 starts with galvanic cells using spontaneous reactions; this approach fits better with the students' understanding because they are familiar with spontaneous reactions and batteries. Additionally, we pay close attention to relating the behavior in a galvanic cell to half-reactions, which is important in making the half-reactions used in balancing oxidation–reduction reactions seem less abstract.

Supplements for the Texts

The following comprehensive teaching and learning package accompanies both *General Chemistry,* Ninth Edition, and *General Chemistry with Qualitative Analysis,* Ninth Edition.

- **Instructor's Guide,** William H. Breazeale, Jr., *Francis Marion College*
- **Study Guide,** Norman E. Griswold, *Nebraska Wesleyan University*
- **Solutions,** John H. Meiser and Frederick K. Ault, *Ball State University*
- **Complete Solutions,** John H. Meiser; Christian A. Clausen III, *University of Central Florida;* and Frederick K. Ault
- **Basic Laboratory Studies in General Chemistry with Semimicro Qualitative Analysis,** Grace R. Hered, *Olive-Harvey College, City College of Chicago*
- **Instructor's Guide for Basic Laboratory Studies in General Chemistry with Semimicro Qualitative Analysis,** Grace R. Hered
- **D. C. Heath Exam: Computerized Testing for IBM PC, Apple II, and Macintosh**
- **Test Item File,** Christian A. Clausen III
- **Chemical Lecture Demonstrations** (Videotape), Paul B. Kelter, *University of Wisconsin—Oshkosh*
- **Transparencies**

Acknowledgments

No author can take the entire credit for the success of a text; many others played an important role in its development. We are particularly indebted to the following reviewers who read all or part of the manuscript and made thoughtful suggestions:

John E. Bauman, *University of Missouri—Columbia*
J. M. Bellama, *University of Maryland*
Ruth J. Bowen, *California State Polytechnical University, Pomona*
Albert W. Burgstahler, *University of Kansas*
James D. Carr, *University of Nebraska—Lincoln*
Ronald J. Clark, *Florida State University*
Christian A. Clausen III, *University of Central Florida*
David V. Frank, *Ferris State University*
Larry W. Houk, *Memphis State University*
B. I. Naddy, *Columbia State University College*
Gordon A. Parker, *University of Toledo*
Krish Rengan, *Eastern Michigan University*
Frank J. Torre, *Springfield College*
Rupert Wentworth, *Indiana University*
George C. Williams, *Judson College*

In addition, many users of the text submitted helpful ideas. They include:

Cliff Kubiak, *Purdue University*
Fred Lytle, *Purdue University*
Dave McMillin, *Purdue University*
Patricia Metz, *Texas Tech University*
Susan Nurrenbern, *University of Wisonsin—Stout*

We appreciate the valuable contributions of Chris Holliman and Tony Boccanfuso who checked our examples and exercises. Finally, we wish to acknowledge and to thank our colleagues at D.C. Heath for their thoughtful assistance and support.

Henry F. Holtzclaw, Jr.
William R. Robinson
Jerome D. Odom

About the Authors

Henry F. Holtzclaw, Jr. is Foundation Regents Professor of Chemistry Emeritus at the University of Nebraska—Lincoln. He received the A.B. degree from the University of Kansas and M.S. and Ph.D. degrees in inorganic chemistry from the University of Illinois. He served as Guest Professor at the University of Konstanz (Germany) in 1973–74. He was Dean for Graduate Studies at the University of Nebraska for nine years (1976–85) and was Interim Chairman of the Department of Chemistry in 1985–86.

His research is in synthesis, stereochemistry, and bonding of metal chelates, including metal chelates of 1,3-diketones and nitrogen- and sulfur-substituted 1,3-diketones. He has also worked with metal chelate polymers of various dihydroxyquinoid ligands.

Professor Holtzclaw has served as a member of the National Committee of Examiners (Advanced Chemistry Test) for the Graduate Record Examination and as a member of the Graduate Record Examination Board. He has also served on the TOEFL Policy Committee (Test of English as a Foreign Language) and on its Executive Committee and Research Committee, including a term as Chairman of the Research Committee. In the American Chemical Society, he is a Councilor and has served on the Publications Committee, the Committee on Committees, and the Nominations and Elections Committee.

He recently completed a term as President of *Inorganic Syntheses* and was Editor-in-Chief of Volume VIII of that series. He is a member of the American Chemical Society and Sigma Xi, an Associate Member of the Committee on Chemical Abstracts (for the American Chemical Society), and a Fellow in the American Association for the Advancement of Science.

William R. Robinson is a Professor of Chemistry at Purdue University. He received his B.S. and M.S. degrees in chemistry from Texas Technological College (now Texas Tech University) and the Ph.D. degree from the Massachusetts Institute of Technology. In 1973 he spent six months as an Adjunct Associate Professor in the Department of Earth and Space Sciences at the State University of New York at Stony Brook.

Professor Robinson has been active in the General Chemistry program at Purdue since joining the faculty in 1967. He has served as Director of General Chemistry and has assisted with preliminary and developmental reviews of freshman texts. He has published in *The Journal of Chemical Education*. He is a member of the American Chemical Society General Chemistry Examinations Committee. As a consequence of his interest in how students learn chemistry, he has joined the Division of Chemical Education in Purdue's Department of Chemistry and has an active research program in this area.

Professor Robinson's other interests include the structure, properties, and reactivity of transition metal compounds. His published research includes thermal studies of classical coordination compounds of cobalt and chromium, synthetic and structural studies of heavy transition metal compounds containing metal–metal bonds, and synthetic and structural studies of organometallic compounds. At present he is engaged in the study of the solid state chemistry and structure of transition metal oxides, sulfides, and phosphates. He is on the Editorial Board of *The Journal of Solid State Chemistry,* and a member of the American Association for the Advancement of Science, the American Chemical Society, the American Crystallographic Association, National Association for Research in Science Teaching, and Sigma Xi.

Jerome D. Odom is Professor and Chairman of Chemistry at the University of South Carolina. He received his B.S. degree from the University of North Carolina—Chapel Hill and the Ph.D. degree from Indiana University. He spent a postdoctoral year at Bristol University in Bristol, England, and in 1975–76 was a Fellow of the Alexander von Humboldt Foundation at the University of Stuttgart, Germany.

Professor Odom has taught general chemistry at the University of South Carolina since joining the faculty in 1969. In 1984 he was awarded the Amoco Foundation Award for Outstanding Teaching, the university's highest award for undergraduate teaching. He has also been an instructor for many years in National Science Foundation workshops for small-college and high school chemistry teachers. He has served as a member of the Inorganic Subcommittee of the American Chemical Society Examinations Committee.

His research involves syntheses and studies of compounds of the representative elements, particularly compounds of boron, germanium, selenium, and tellurium. Professor Odom has been instrumental in developing and using selenium-77 nuclear magnetic resonance spectroscopy in the study of organoselenium compounds as well as biological molecules containing selenium. At present he is engaged in studies directed toward the incorporation of selenium and tellurium into biochemical systems and the use of the derivatized systems as structural probes. He has written over 125 refereed publications and has also published numerous review articles and book chapters.

He is a member of the American Chemical Society, Sigma Xi, Phi Lambda Upsilon, and Alpha Chi Sigma. He is an avid water skier, snow skier, and racquetball player.

Brief Contents

Contents

Structure of the Atom 127

Chemical and Physical Properties of the Elements and the Periodic Table 157

Chemical Bonding: General Concepts 177

Molecular Structure, Valence Bond Theory, and Hybridization 213

Molecular Orbitals 237

The Gaseous State and the Kinetic-Molecular Theory 259

Intermolecular Forces, Liquids, and Solids 297

Solutions; Colloids   335

The Active Metals   379

Chemical Kinetics 415

An Introduction to Chemical Equilibrium 447

Acids and Bases 489

Ionic Equilibria of Weak Electrolytes   517

The Solubility Product Principle   577

Chemical Thermodynamics   603

Electrochemistry and Oxidation–Reduction 639

A Survey of the Nonmetals 687

The Nonmetals, Part 1: Hydrogen, Oxygen, Sulfur, and the Halogens 711

The Nonmetals, Part 2: Carbon, Nitrogen, Phosphorus, and the Noble Gases 747

Nuclear Chemistry 775

The Semi-Metals 811

Coordination Compounds 833

The Transition Elements 859

The Post-Transition Metals 897

The Atmosphere and Natural Waters 921

Organic Chemistry 943

Biochemistry 973

Appendixes A1

Photo Credits A21

Glossary A25

Answers to Selected Even-Numbered Exercises A37

Index A43

GENERAL
CHEMISTRY

1 Some Fundamental Concepts

Silicon computer chips, chips of elemental silicon, and sugar crystals.

A movie that was made in 1966 and starred Clint Eastwood popularized the phrase "the good, the bad, and the ugly." Those words can also be used to describe the world in which we live and, for our particular concern in this book, the way chemistry can affect our lives. The words *chemistry* and *chemical* mean different things to different people, but to many they have rather unpleasant associations. In fact, a well-known chemical company that once used the slogan "Better Things For Better Living through Chemistry" recently dropped the last two words from that phrase, perhaps to avoid the negative connotations of *chemistry*. (It is not our purpose to analyze how this situation came about, but perhaps chemicals are equated in some people's minds with addictive drugs, and others may assume that what is "chemical" is somehow not "natural.'' And not all the connotations are negative, as we notice when we hear people speak of the ''chemistry'' between themselves and someone they are attracted to!)

However strong our associations with the term *chemistry,* the positive effects of its applications surround us. High-impact plastics and shatterproof glass have improved the safety of transportation. Pharmacy and medicine have also benefited greatly from chemistry. Pain-killing medications are chemicals: acetylsalicylic acid (aspirin), acetaminophen (Tylenol), and ibuprofen (Motrin) are examples. The development of specific plastics has enabled doctors to perform kidney dialysis, which can save victims of kidney failure. In many respects, chemistry also feeds the people of the world. Safe agrochemicals, effective fertilizers, and efficient fuels have increased food production world-wide. Synthetic fabrics (such as Dacron, Nylon, and Rayon), permanent dyes, and flame-retardant materials all help clothe us safely and attractively. Those of us who wear soft contact lenses can be thankful for hydroxyethylmethacrylate polymers. Molecularly incorporated dyes in these polymers can even appear to change the color of our eyes! Those of us interested in money (and who isn't?) can think of special papers and long-lasting inks that are essential to producing money from paper. The point is that ''good'' chemistry is involved in almost every aspect of our lives. Indeed, all matter is chemical. A living being is a chemical factory wherein numerous reactions occur at all times.

Just as chemistry can be ''good,'' it can also be ''bad.'' Toxic chemicals can be dumped into the environment, seep into our water supply, or vaporize into the atmosphere to cause severe health problems. Pollution of both air and water is a serious problem in nearly all industrialized countries. *Chemical dependency* is a well-known term associated with the alcoholism and drug addiction that cause untold sadness and consume vast resources in our society. Insecticides and pesticides, which can be very helpful, can also be very harmful; their use must be carefully monitored and controlled.

How is chemistry ''ugly''? The incredible destruction of life and property that occurred in Japan when the United States dropped nuclear bombs on Hiroshima and Nagasaki demonstrates how chemistry can be ugly. (Nuclear chemistry can also be ''good'' in a variety of peacetime uses—such as the generation of energy—provided that proper safety procedures and mechanisms for nuclear waste disposal are installed and scrupulously maintained.) The thousands of lives that were lost in Bhopal, India, in 1984 as a result of a chemical reaction that should not have been allowed to occur offer another example of how chemistry might be viewed as ''ugly.'' The apparent assault on Earth's protective ozone layer resulting from our heavy use of a class of compounds known as chlorofluorocarbons (CFCs) is a chemical problem to some degree, and it has the potential to become an extremely ''ugly'' one.

Even with these severe problems, we must recognize the importance of the human factor in decision making. The best solutions are usually found by educated individuals prepared to make rational decisions and armed with at least some understanding of chemistry. Chemistry can indeed be good, bad, and ugly. But the good in chemistry *can* often be used to eliminate the bad and the ugly.

Introduction

❶.1 Chemistry

Oil and Nylon, gasoline and water, salt and sugar, and iron and gold are all forms of matter that differ strikingly from each other in many ways. These differences are due to differences in the composition and structure of these substances.

(a)

(b)

Figure 1.1

(a) Extraction of metals from minerals such as this sample of wulfenite, a molybdenum ore, is a chemical process. (b) Copper and nitric acid react, forming copper nitrate and gaseous brown nitrogen dioxide.

Most forms of matter can be converted into other forms (Fig. 1.1). For example, iron is converted into rust when it combines with oxygen and water; gasoline is converted into water, carbon dioxide, and other substances when it burns; and oil can be converted into Nylon via a series of chemical reactions. Our very existence depends on changes that occur in matter. Plants convert simple forms of matter into more complex forms, which serve as food for animals. The chemical changes that take place when this food is digested and assimilated by the body are essential to life processes.

During our study of chemistry, we will examine many different changes in the composition and structure of matter, the causes that produce these changes, the changes in energy that accompany them, and the principles and laws involved in these changes. In brief, then, the science of **chemistry** may be defined **as the study of the composition, structure, and properties of matter and of the reactions by which one form of matter may be produced from or converted into other forms.**

Knowledge about chemistry has increased so much during the last century that chemists usually specialize in one of the field's several principal branches. **Physical chemistry** is primarily concerned with the structure of matter, energy changes, and the laws, principles, and theories that explain the transformation of one form of matter into another. **Analytical chemistry** is concerned with the identification, separation, and quantitative determination of the composition of different substances. **Organic chemistry** deals with the synthesis and reactions of the compounds of carbon. (Life on earth is based on carbon compounds.) **Inorganic chemistry** is concerned with the chemistry of elements other than carbon and with their compounds. **Biochemistry** is the study of the specific molecular basis of life. The boundaries between the branches of chemistry are arbitrary, however, and much work in chemistry today occurs at the borders of two or more branches.

1.2 Matter and Energy

Matter, by definition, is anything that occupies space and has mass. All the objects in the universe occupy space and have mass; they are matter. The property of occupying space is often easily perceived by our senses of sight and touch. The **mass** of an object

Figure 1.2

The three states of matter as illustrated by water; ice is solid water, the lake is liquid water, and the clouds form when gaseous water (which is invisible) condenses to form very small drops of liquid water.

pertains to the quantity of matter that the object contains. The force required to change the speed at which an object moves, or to change the direction in which it moves, is a measure of its mass. An object's weight is also a measure of its mass (Section 1.12).

Matter can exist in three different physical states: solid, liquid, and gas (Fig. 1.2). A **solid** is rigid, possesses a definite shape, and has a volume that is very nearly independent of changes in temperature and pressure. A **liquid** flows and thus takes the shape of its container, except that it assumes a horizontal upper surface. Like solids, liquids are only slightly compressible and so, for practical purposes, have definite volumes. A **gas** takes both the shape and the volume of its container. Gases are readily compressible and capable of infinite expansion.

Energy can be defined as the capacity for doing work, where **work** is simply the process of causing matter to move against an opposing force. For example, when we pump up a bicycle tire, we are doing work—we are moving matter (the air in the pump) against the opposing force of the air already in the tire.

Like matter, energy exists in different forms. The energy for running the pump to carry out the work of pumping up a tire could be chemical energy released in our muscles as we use a hand pump, electrical energy used to drive an electric motor on a compressor, or heat used in a steam engine running a compressor. Light is also a form of energy. Solar cells can convert light into electrical energy, which could run our compressor or do other work.

Energy can be further classified as either potential energy or kinetic energy. Because one definition of energy is the capacity for doing work, **potential energy** is the potential for doing work. A piece of matter is said to possess potential energy by virtue of its position, condition, or composition. Water at the top of a waterfall possesses potential energy because of its position; if it falls in a hydroelectric plant, it does work that leads to the production of electricity. A compressed spring possesses potential energy because of its condition; it can do work such as making a clock run. Sugar possesses potential energy because of its chemical composition. When it enters our bodies, it undergoes a series of chemical reactions that release energy. We will find later that energy changes involved in the combination of breaking and creating chemical bonds in chemical reactions can serve as a source of energy. When a body is in motion, it also has energy, or the capacity for doing work. The energy that a body possesses because of its motion is called **kinetic energy.** As water falls from the top of a waterfall, its potential energy decreases as its kinetic energy increases.

❶.3 Laws of Conservation of Matter and Energy

When a piece of calcium metal is exposed to dry air, it unites with oxygen in the air (Fig. 1.3). If the product (calcium oxide) is collected and weighed, it is found to have a mass greater than that of the original piece of metal. When the mass of the oxygen that combined with the metal is taken into consideration, however, the final mass is found to be equal to the sum of the masses of the calcium metal and the oxygen. This behavior of matter reflects the **law of conservation of matter: During a chemical change, there is no detectable increase or decrease in the total quantity of matter from that initially present.**

The conversion of one type of matter into another (chemical change) is always accompanied by the conversion of one form of energy into another. Usually heat is

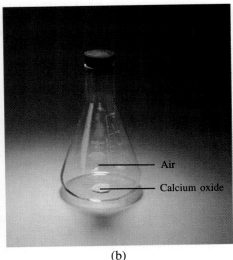

(a)   (b)

Figure 1.3

(a) A closed 1-liter flask filled with air and containing 0.646 g of calcium. (b) The same flask after the calcium has reacted with 0.258 g of oxygen from the air in the flask and formed 0.904 g of calcium oxide. The total weight of the flask and its contents has not changed.

evolved or absorbed, but sometimes the conversion involves light or electrical energy instead of, or in addition to, heat. When calcium metal combines with oxygen, chemical energy is converted into heat. Under certain conditions the calcium may actually burn, producing light as well. Many transformations of energy, of course, do not involve chemical changes. Electrical energy can be changed into light, heat, or potential energy without any chemical change. Potential and kinetic energy can each be converted into the other. Many other conversions are possible, but all of the energy involved in any change always exists in some form after the change is completed. This fact is expressed in the **law of conservation of energy: During an ordinary chemical change, energy can be neither created nor destroyed, although it can be changed in form.**

When applied to chemical changes, the laws of conservation of matter and energy hold very well. During nuclear changes, however, these laws are violated. Both conversion of matter into energy and conversion of energy into matter can occur in nuclear reactions. So, to encompass both chemical and nuclear changes, we combine these two laws into one statement: **The total quantity of matter and energy available in the universe is fixed.**

1.4   Chemical and Physical Properties

The characteristics that enable us to distinguish one substance from another are known as properties. **Chemical properties** involve the way one kind of matter transforms into another kind. Iron exhibits a chemical property when it combines with oxygen in the presence of water to form the reddish-brown iron oxide we call rust. A chemical property of chromium is that it does not rust (Fig. 1.4). The **physical properties** of a particular kind of matter are those characteristics that do not involve a change in the chemical identity of the matter. Familiar physical properties include color, hardness, physical state, melting temperature, boiling temperature, and electrical conductivity (Fig. 1.5). Iron, for example, melts at a temperature of 1535°C; chromium melts at a different temperature, 1900°C. As they melt, the metals change from solids to liquids, but they remain iron and chromium because no change in chemical identity has occurred.

Figure 1.4

You can distinguish iron from chromium because they exhibit different chemical properties. Iron reacts with oxygen in the air to form rust, but chromium does not.

Figure 1.5

You can distinguish these elements by their physical properties. Mercury is the metallic-looking liquid. Bromine is the dark orange liquid that forms an orange gas. Chlorine is the pale yellow-green gas. Copper is the orange-colored solid. Aluminum is the metallic-looking solid.

A **physical change** is one that does not involve a change of one kind of matter into another. The melting of iron, the freezing of water, the conversion of liquid water to steam, and the condensation of steam to liquid water are all examples of physical changes. In each of these there is a change in one or more properties, but there is no alteration of the chemical composition of the substance. Water maintains the same chemical composition, whether it is in the solid, liquid, or gaseous state. Iron, whether molten or solid, is the same kind of matter. Some physical properties can be observed only when matter undergoes a physical change. The freezing temperature of water, for example, is determined by measuring the temperature as water changes from a liquid to a solid. Other physical properties (an example is color) can be determined even though no physical change is taking place.

In order to identify a chemical property, we look for a chemical change. A **chemical change** always produces one or more different kinds of matter from those that were present before the change occurred. Iron rust contains oxygen as well as iron, and it is therefore a different kind of matter from the iron, air, and water from which it formed. Thus the formation of iron rust is a chemical change. When milk sours, the sugar (lactose) in the milk is converted into lactic acid via a chemical change, and the composition and properties of the acid differ from those of the sugar.

The absence of a chemical change is also a chemical property. Because chromium does not rust, one of its chemical properties is that it does *not* undergo this chemical change.

The properties of various kinds of matter enable us to distinguish one kind from another. We can distinguish between iron wire and chromium wire by their physical properties (their colors, for example) or by their chemical properties (for example, iron rusts but chromium does not).

Any property of matter that we can measure can be classified into one of two categories. If the property we measure does *not* depend on the amount of matter present, we have measured an **intensive property.** Temperature is a good example of an intensive property. A measured value that does depend on the amount of matter present is an

extensive property. Length, mass, and volume are all extensive properties. A good rule of thumb to use to distinguish between intensive and extensive properties is that extensive properties are additive, whereas intensive properties are not. If you stand on a scale that indicates a weight of 150 pounds, and then a friend who weighs 120 pounds stands on the scale with you, the scale should register 270 pounds. The value is additive, so you have measured an extensive property (mass). If you have just fixed a cup of coffee for you and a friend, and you combine the two cups, the volume of the coffee (an extensive property) increases, but its temperature remains the same. Temperature, then, is not additive and is therefore an intensive property.

1.5 The Classification of Matter

Matter, as we have said, is anything that occupies space and has mass, and the three states of matter are solid, liquid, and gas. All samples of matter can also be classified as either pure substances or mixtures (Fig. 1.6). A **mixture** is composed of two or more kinds of matter that can be separated by physical means. Moreover, the composition of

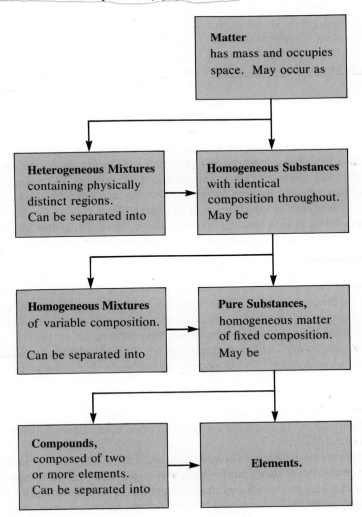

Matter
has mass and occupies space. May occur as

Heterogeneous Mixtures
containing physically distinct regions.
Can be separated into

Homogeneous Substances
with identical composition throughout.
May be

Homogeneous Mixtures
of variable composition.

Can be separated into

Pure Substances,
homogeneous matter of fixed composition.
May be

Compounds,
composed of two or more elements.
Can be separated into

Elements.

Figure 1.6
The classification of matter.

a mixture can be varied continuously. Blood consists of varying amounts of proteins, sugar, salt, oxygen, carbon dioxide, and other components mixed in water. It can be recognized as a mixture because it can be separated into solids and plasma by centrifugation, a physical method of separation. Air is a mixture of oxygen, nitrogen, carbon dioxide, water vapor, and small amounts of other gases.

When sugar dissolves in water it forms a **homogeneous mixture,** a mixture with a composition that is uniform throughout. In a homogeneous mixture of sugar dissolved in water, the amount of sugar is always the same from place to place within the mixture; so is the amount of water. Homogeneous mixtures are often called **solutions.** Other examples of homogeneous mixtures include syrup, air, soft drinks, gasoline, and a solution of salt in water. A mixture whose composition differs from point to point is a **heterogeneous mixture.** A type of salad dressing commonly known as Italian dressing is an example of a heterogeneous mixture (Fig. 1.7). It consists of salad oil, vinegar, and herbs. After the bottle is shaken, the oil and vinegar separate, and the herbs gradually settle to the bottom of the mixture. Other heterogeneous mixtures include granite (you can often see the separate bits of mica, quartz, and feldspar), sand in water, blood, and concrete.

Pure substances are similar to homogeneous mixtures in that both are of uniform composition throughout. However, whereas the composition of a homogeneous mixture can vary from one sample to another, a specific pure substance always has the same composition. Thus a **pure substance** is defined as a homogeneous sample of matter, all specimens of which have identical compositions as well as identical chemical and physical properties.

A carbonated soft drink is a homogeneous mixture, typically of water, sugar, coloring and flavoring agents, and carbon dioxide. It is not a pure substance by our definition, because its composition can vary. The amount of carbon dioxide in the drink decreases after the bottle is opened and the drink begins to lose its fizz. A sample of carbon dioxide alone, however, is a pure substance. Any sample of carbon dioxide that weighs 44 grams always contains 12 grams of carbon and 32 grams of oxygen. Any sample of carbon dioxide also has the same melting temperature, color, and other properties, no matter what brand of beverage or other source it is isolated from.

Chemists divide pure substances into two classes: those that cannot be decomposed by a chemical change and those that can. Pure substances that cannot be decomposed by a chemical change are called **elements.** (Although this is a good historical definition, we will offer a more rigorous definition of an element in Chapter 3 when we discuss isotopes.) Familiar examples of elements are iron, silver, gold, aluminum, sulfur, oxygen, and carbon. At the present time, 109 elements are known; a list of these is printed on the inside front cover of this book. Of these elements, 88 occur naturally on the earth, and the other 21 have been created in laboratories (the most recent in 1984).

Pure substances that can be decomposed by chemical changes are called **compounds.** The decomposition of a compound may produce either elements or other compounds, or both. Mercury oxide can be broken down by heat into the elements mercury and oxygen (Fig. 1.8). When heated sufficiently in the absence of air, the compound sucrose decomposes into the element carbon and the compound water (Fig. 1.9). Water can be decomposed by an electric current into its two constituent elements, hydrogen and oxygen.

The properties of elements in combination are different from those in the free, or uncombined, state. For example, white crystalline sugar (sucrose) is a compound resulting from the chemical combination of the element carbon, which is usually a black solid when free, and the two elements hydrogen and oxygen, which are colorless gases when uncombined. Free sodium, an element that is a soft shiny metallic solid, and free chlo-

Figure 1.7

Italian salad dressing is a heterogeneous mixture of salad oil, vinegar, and herbs. The salad oil and vinegar (without herbs present) in it are both homogeneous mixtures.

Figure 1.8

Mercury oxide is a compound. When heated, it decomposes into silvery drops of mercury and oxygen gas (which is not visible).

rine, an element that is a yellow-green gas, combine to form sodium chloride, a white crystalline solid.

Although there are only 109 known elements, several million chemical compounds result from different combinations of these elements. Each compound possesses definite chemical and physical properties by which chemists can distinguish it from all other compounds.

Eleven elements make up about 99% of the earth's crust and of the atmosphere (Table 1.1). Oxygen constitutes nearly one-half and silicon about one-fourth of the total quantity of these elements. Only about one-fourth of the elements are found on the earth in the free state; the others occur only in chemical combinations with other elements.

(a)

Table 1.1	Percentages of Elements in the Atmosphere and in the Earth's Crust, by Mass			
Oxygen	49.20%		Chlorine	0.19%
Silicon	25.67		Phosphorus	0.11
Aluminum	7.50		Manganese	0.09
Iron	4.71		Carbon	0.08
Calcium	3.39		Sulfur	0.06
Sodium	2.63		Barium	0.04
Potassium	2.40		Nitrogen	0.03
Magnesium	1.93		Fluorine	0.03
Hydrogen	0.87		Strontium	0.02
Titanium	0.58		All others	0.47

(b)

❶.6 Atoms and Molecules

An atom is the smallest particle of an element that can enter into a chemical combination. Silicon is an element. If we could take a piece of silicon, from which computer chips are made (see photo at the beginning of this chapter), and divide it into smaller and smaller pieces, eventually we would have a single atom of silicon. This atom would no longer be silicon if it were divided. Such a single atom of silicon is incredibly small. It would require about 110 million silicon atoms lying side by side to make a line 1 inch long.

The first suggestion that matter is composed of atoms is attributed to early Greek philosophers, notably Democritus. Indeed, the word *atom* comes from the Greek word *atomos,* which means "indivisible." However, it was not until the early nineteenth century that John Dalton (1766–1844), an English chemist and physicist, presented an atomic theory *and* supported it with quantitative measurements. Since that time, repeated experiments have confirmed his theory, which is still used with only minor revisions.

Only a few elements, such as the gases helium, neon, and argon, consist of a collection of individual atoms that move about independently of one another (Fig. 1.10). Other elements, such as the gases nitrogen, oxygen, and chlorine, exist as pairs of atoms, each pair moving as a single unit. The element phosphorus consists of units composed of four phosphorus atoms; sulfur, of units composed of eight sulfur atoms. These units are called **molecules.**

(c)

Figure 1.9

(a) Sucrose (table sugar) before it is heated. (b) After some heating, sugar begins to lose water and become a dark, caramel-like substance.
(c) After more heating, the sucrose totally decomposes to elemental carbon and water.

Figure 1.10

Representations of molecules of the elements oxygen, phosphorus, and sulfur, and of the compound water.

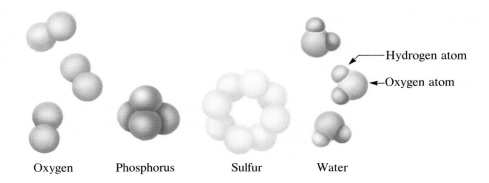

Hydrogen atom

Oxygen atom

Oxygen   Phosphorus   Sulfur   Water

A molecule consists of two or more atoms joined by strong forces called chemical bonds. A molecule may consist of two or more identical atoms, as in oxygen and sulfur, or of two or more different atoms, as in water. Water has a definite composition and a set of chemical properties that enable us to recognize it as a distinct substance. Each water molecule is a unit that contains two hydrogen atoms and one oxygen atom (Fig. 1.10). Subdivision of a water molecule results in the formation of the gases hydrogen and oxygen, each of which has properties quite different from those of water and those of each other.

To appreciate the minute size of molecules, consider that if a glass of water were enlarged to the size of the earth, the water molecules would be about the size of golf balls.

❶.7   The Scientific Method

Your study of chemistry will be concerned with the observations, theories, and laws that give this science its foundation and that form a unified framework of knowledge. This framework develops from the pursuit of answers to many questions, each of which can be subjected to experimental investigation by an approach often called the **scientific method.**

Scientists identify problems or questions through their own observations and experiments or from the observations, experiments, and conclusions of others. The first step in applying the scientific method to a problem involves carefully planning experiments to gather facts and obtain information about all phases of the problem. The results are examined for general relationships that will unify the observations. A **hypothesis,** which is a tentative explanation, is advanced to explain the experimental data. The hypothesis is tested by means of further experiments, and, if it is capable of explaining the large body of experimental data, it is dignified by the name **theory.** For instance, Dalton attempted to explain why mass is conserved in a chemical reaction when he first presented his ideas, which were really hypotheses, of the atomic nature of matter. Those hypotheses have been so extensively tested that we now refer to them as Dalton's atomic theory. Theories themselves can prompt new questions or suggest new directions in which additional information can be sought. Thus, when a theory is extensively tested and no exceptions are known, it is called a **law.** One example is the law of conservation of matter (Section 1.3), which summarizes the results of thousands of experimental observations.

Measurement in Chemistry

❶.8 Units of Measurement

The hypotheses, theories, and laws that describe the behavior of matter and energy are usually based on quantitative measurements. When properly reported, these measurements convey three kinds of information: the size or magnitude of the measurement (a number), an indication of the possible error or uncertainty (Section 1.10) in the measurement, and the units of the measurement (Fig. 1.11).

Units provide a standard of comparison for a measurement. A well-known sandwich is prepared from a quarter-pound of hamburger meat (0.250 pound). The mass of the meat has a magnitude of 0.250 times the mass of the arbitrary standard of 1 pound. Even if the unit of reference is changed for some reason, what is being measured (in this case, the mass) does not change. The same mass of hamburger meat can be reported as being a quarter-pound, 4.00 ounces, or 0.000125 ton (a 0.000125-tonner?); the actual amount of meat is the same, no matter what the unit of measurement.

The results of scientific measurements are usually reported in an updated version of the metric system, in which the units for length, mass, and time, respectively, are the meter, the kilogram, and the second. The standards of measurement are based on *natural* universal constants provided for in an international agreement and called the **International System of Units** or **SI units** (from the French, *Le Système International d'Unités*). These units have been used by the National Institute of Standards and Technology (formerly the National Bureau of Standards) since 1964. The SI consists of the following seven base units, from which other units of mass and measure can be derived.

Figure 1.11

Units of degrees Celsius, degrees Fahrenheit, or kelvins are used to measure the temperature of this molten gold.

Physical Property	Name of Unit	Symbol
Length	meter	m
Mass	kilogram	kg
Time	second	s
Electric current	ampere	A
Temperature	kelvin	K
Luminous intensity	candela	cd
Amount of substance	mole	mol

In both the SI and other metric systems, we may report measurements as fractions or multiples of 10 times a base unit by using the appropriate prefix with the name of the base unit. For example, a length can be reported in units of meters, kilometers (10^3 meters), millimeters (10^{-3} meter), or picometers (10^{-12} meter). The prefixes and their symbols denoting the powers to which 10 is raised are given in Table 1.2.

Because both SI and older metric units are currently in use by scientists, it is necessary to be familiar with both systems. Consequently, both systems of units will be used in this text.

what is the other metric units used?

Table 1.2		Common Prefixes Used in the Metric System	
Prefix	Symbol	Factor	Example
pico	p	10^{-12}	1 picometer (pm) = 1×10^{-12} m (0.000000000001 m)
nano	n	10^{-9}	1 nanogram (ng) = 1×10^{-9} g (0.000000001 g)
micro	μ*	10^{-6}	1 microliter (μL) = 1×10^{-6} L (0.000001 L)
milli	m	10^{-3}	2 milliseconds (ms) = 2×10^{-3} s (0.002 s)
centi	c	10^{-2}	5 centimeters (cm) = 5×10^{-2} m (0.05 m)
deci	d	10^{-1}	1 deciliter (dL) = 1×10^{-1} L (0.1 L)
kilo	k	10^{3}	1 kilometer (km) = 1×10^{3} m (1000 m)
mega	M	10^{6}	3 megagrams (Mg) = 3×10^{6} g (3,000,000 g)
giga	G	10^{9}	5 gigameters (Gm) = 5×10^{9} m (5,000,000,000 m)
tera	T	10^{12}	1 teraliter (TL) = 1×10^{12} L (1,000,000,000,000 L)

*Greek letter mu.

❶.9 Conversion of Units; Dimensional Analysis

In addition to the units in use within the scientific community, many other units are employed by other disciplines. For example, units of mass range from grams and kilograms in science, to pounds and tons in engineering, to grains and drams in medicine. The relationships between some common units are given in Table 1.3. More such relationships are given in Appendix B.

Consider the conversion of a length from meters to yards. As given in Table 1.3, 1 meter = 1.094 yards. This may be read as indicating that there is 1 meter per 1.094 yards or, alternatively, that there are 1.094 yards per 1 meter. Very often a slash (/) or a division line is used instead of the word *per*. This gives the following unit conversion factors:

$$1 \text{ meter per } 1.094 \text{ yards}, \quad 1 \text{ meter}/1.094 \text{ yards}, \quad \text{or} \quad \frac{1 \text{ meter}}{1.094 \text{ yards}}$$

$$1.094 \text{ yards per } 1 \text{ meter}, \quad 1.094 \text{ yards}/1 \text{ meter}, \quad \text{or} \quad \frac{1.094 \text{ yards}}{1 \text{ meter}}$$

Table 1.3	Common Conversion Factors (to four significant figures)
Length	
1 meter = 1.094 yards	1 inch = 2.540 centimeters
Volume	
1 liter = 1.057 quarts	1 cubic foot = 28.32 liters
Mass	
1 kilogram = 2.205 pounds	1 ounce = 28.35 grams

A **unit conversion factor** is used to convert a quantity in one system of units to the corresponding quantity in another system of units. For example, 1.094 yards/1 meter can be used to convert a length given in meters to the corresponding length in yards. We simply multiply the quantity in meters by the conversion factor.

$$\text{meters} \times \frac{\text{yards}}{\text{meters}} = \text{yards}$$

If an incorrect unit conversion factor is used, an incorrect unit is obtained. For example,

$$\text{meters} \times \frac{\text{meters}}{\text{yards}} = \frac{\text{meters}^2}{\text{yards}}$$

This unit conversion factor clearly is incorrect because it does not convert meters into yards; the units do not cancel to give yards.

The use of unit conversion factors plays a very important part in solving many of the problems we shall encounter in this course. In many numerical problems in chemistry, we need to ask ourselves carefully what is given to us in the problem, what we are trying to find, and what relationships we know that will be useful. These relationships are often in the form of unit conversion factors. For example, we know that there will always be 1.094 yards in 1 meter. Whether we use 1 meter/1.094 yards or 1.094 yards/1 meter depends on the type of conversion we need to make.

Example 1.1

A 100.0-meter dash is how many yards long?

From the relationship 1 meter = 1.094 yards, we can get the unit conversion factor 1.094 yards/1 meter. Multiplication gives

$$100.0 \text{ meters} \times \frac{1.094 \text{ yards}}{1 \text{ meter}} = 109.4 \text{ yards}$$

The distance covered by the runner does not change when we switch from units of meters to units of yards. There are two points to remember when performing conversions. First, *always include the units* when working a problem. It will be immediately obvious that you have worked the problem incorrectly if the proper units are not obtained in the answer. Second, *ask yourself whether the answer makes sense.* In the foregoing problem, we should realize from examining our unit conversion factor that there is slightly more than 1 yard in every meter. Thus, if we have 100 meters, our answer should be slightly more than 100 yards. If our answer is less than 100 yards or much more than 100 yards, we should recognize that something is wrong and we need to reevaluate our answer.

A technique called **dimensional analysis** has been used in Example 1.1. In dimensional analysis, units are treated like algebraic quantities. Unit conversion factors can be multiplied by another, one divided into the other, or two or more canceled. It is also important to realize that, because a unit conversion factor consists of equivalent quantities in different units, multiplying by a unit conversion factor is the same as multiplying by 1. In this book, we emphasize how conversion factors cancel out by coloring the cancellation lines and drawing the lines for different units at different (and usually distinct) angles.

1.10 Uncertainty in Measurements and Significant Figures

Suppose you weigh an object on a balance and find, as best you can determine, that its mass is closer to 13.4 grams than to either 13.3 or 13.5 grams. You would report the mass as 13.4 grams. The uncertainty in this measurement is about 0.1 gram, because the true mass of the object could lie anywhere between 13.35 and 13.45 grams. If the same object were weighed on a more sensitive balance in your laboratory, your best efforts might show that its mass is 13.384 grams; that is, the mass is closer to 13.384 grams than to either 13.383 or 13.385 grams. The uncertainty in this case would be about 0.001 gram, because the true mass could lie anywhere between 13.3835 and 13.3845 grams. Any experimental measurement, no matter how carefully made, contains uncertainty. **All measurements may be taken to have an uncertainty of at least one unit in the last digit of the measured quantity.**

The mass 13.4 grams has an uncertainty of 0.1 gram; 13.384 grams, an uncertainty of 0.001 gram; a measured volume of 25 milliliters, an uncertainty of 1 milliliter; and a measured length of 0.001378 meter, an uncertainty of 0.000001 meter. All of the measured digits in the determination, including the uncertain last digit, are called **significant figures.**

Results calculated from measurements are as uncertain as the measurement itself. Suppose a sample weighs 78.7 grams and exactly one-third of it is iron. In order to calculate how much iron is in the sample, we need only multiply 78.7 grams by one-third. On a calculator, this comes out to 26.233333 grams. This is not the correct answer, however. To report the mass of iron as 26.233333 grams indicates an uncertainty of 0.000001 gram. The mass of iron should be reported as 26.2 grams (three significant figures). In calculations involving experimental quantities, we must take into account the number of significant figures in these quantities in order not to misrepresent the uncertainty in the calculated result.

The following two rules may be used to determine the number of significant figures in a measured quantity:

1. Find the first nonzero digit on the left and count to the right, including this first nonzero digit and all remaining digits. Unless the last digit is a zero lying immediately to the left of the decimal point (which is covered in Rule 2), this is the number of significant figures in the measured quantity.

First nonzero digit on the left

0.00<u>120530</u>

Six significant figures

First nonzero digit on the left

<u>10.00120530</u>

Ten significant figures

First nonzero digit on the left

<u>126.7309</u>

Seven significant figures

First nonzero digit on the left

$\underline{97}$

Two significant figures

The first three zeros on the left in the first example above, 0.00120530, are not significant. They merely tell us where the decimal point is located. We could equally well express this number in exponential notation as 1.20530×10^{-3}. In this case the number 1.20530 contains all six significant figures, and 10^{-3} locates the decimal.

2. When a number ends in zeros that are to the left of a decimal point, the trailing zeros may or may not be significant. A mass given as 1300 grams may indicate a mass closer to 1300 grams than to 1200 or 1400 grams. In this case the zeros serve only to locate the decimal point and are not significant. If the mass is closer to 1300 grams than to 1290 or 1310 grams, then the zero to the right of the 3 is significant. If the mass is closer to 1300 grams than to 1299 or 1301 grams, both zeros are significant. The ambiguity can be avoided by using exponential notation: 1.3×10^3 (two significant figures), 1.30×10^3 (three significant figures), 1.300×10^3 (four significant figures). For convenience in this text, *we will assume that when a number ends in zeros that are to the left of a decimal point, these trailing zeros are significant unless otherwise specified.*

The two rules given above apply to measured quantities. If we count items rather than measure them, the result is exact, with no uncertainty. If we count eggs in a carton, we know, without any uncertainty, exactly how many eggs the carton contains. Defined quantities are also exact. By definition, 1 foot is exactly 12 inches, 1 kilogram is exactly 1000 grams, and 1 inch equals exactly 2.54 centimeters. These exact numbers, numbers with no uncertainty, can be considered to have an infinite number of significant figures.

The correct use of significant figures in a calculation carries the uncertainty of measured quantities into the result. The following two rules govern the number of significant figures that should be reported in an answer:

1. When adding or subtracting, report the results with the same number of decimal places as that of the number with the least number of decimal places.

Example 1.2

(a) Add 4.383 g and 1.0023 g.   (b) Subtract 421 g from 486.39 g.

(a) $\begin{array}{r} 4.383 \text{ g} \\ +1.0023 \text{ g} \\ \hline 5.3853 \text{ g} = 5.385 \end{array}$ } 3 decimal places

(b) $\begin{array}{r} 486.39 \text{ g} \\ -421 \quad\;\; \text{g} \\ \hline 65.39 \text{ g} = 65 \end{array}$ } No decimal places

---

2. When multiplying or dividing, report the product or quotient with no more digits than the least number of significant figures in the numbers involved in the computation.

Example 1.3

Multiply 0.6238 cm by 6.6.

$$0.6238 \text{ cm} \times 6.6 = 4.1 \text{ cm}$$

In rounding numbers off at a certain point, simply drop the digits that follow if the first of them is less than 5. To two significant figures, 8.7235 rounds off to 8.7; to three significant figures, it rounds off to 8.72. If the first digit to be dropped is greater than 5 or if it is 5 followed by other nonzero digits, increase the preceding digit by 1. To three significant figures, 23.3501 rounds off to 23.4. To three significant figures, 3.8689 rounds off to 3.87. If the digit to be dropped is 5 or 5 followed *only* by zeros, a common practice is to increase the preceding digit by 1 if it is odd and to leave it unchanged if it is even. Dropping a 5 in this manner always leaves an even number. Thus, to three significant figures, 3.425 rounds off to 3.42, and 7.53500 rounds off to 7.54.

❶.11 Length and Volume

The standard unit of **length** in both metric and SI units is the **meter (m).** In the SI system, the meter is defined as the length equal to exactly 1,650,763.73 wavelengths, in vacuum, of the orange line in the emission spectrum of ^{86}Kr, a particular isotope of krypton (spectra and isotopes will be discussed in subsequent chapters).

In more familiar frames of reference, a meter is about 3 inches longer than a yard, 1 meter is approximately 1.094 yards, and 1 meter equals 100 centimeters or 1000 millimeters (Fig. 1.12).

Volumes are defined in terms of the standard lengths cubed. The standard SI volume, a **cubic meter (m^3),** is the volume of a cube that is exactly 1 meter on an edge. A more convenient unit is the volume of a cube with an edge length of exactly 10 centimeters (cm), or 1 decimeter (10 cm = 1 dm). This volume of 1000 cm^3, or 1 dm^3, is often called a **liter (L)** and is 0.001 times the volume of a cubic meter; 1 liter is about 1.06 quarts. A **milliliter (mL)** is the volume of a cube with an edge length of exactly 1 centimeter (Fig. 1.13) and thus is equal in volume to 1 cubic centimeter (cm^3); 1 liter contains 1000 milliliters.

Example 1.4

What is the volume in liters of 1.000 oz, given that 1 L = 1.057 qt and that 32 oz = 1 qt?

From the two relationships given, it is possible to determine the exact unit conversion factor 1 qt/32 oz and the unit conversion factor 1 L/1.057 qt. First convert ounces to quarts.

$$1.000 \text{ oz} \times \frac{1 \text{ qt}}{32 \text{ oz}} = 0.03125 \text{ qt}$$

Then convert quarts to liters.

$$0.03125 \text{ qt} \times \frac{1 \text{ L}}{1.057 \text{ qt}} = 2.956 \times 10^{-2} \text{ L}$$

Thus

$$1.000 \text{ oz} = 2.956 \times 10^{-2} \text{ L}$$

These two steps could have been combined into one operation as follows:

$$1.000 \text{ oz} \times \frac{1 \text{ qt}}{32 \text{ oz}} \times \frac{1 \text{ L}}{1.057 \text{ qt}} = 2.956 \times 10^{-2} \text{ L}$$

(a) 1 meter
(b) 1 yard
(c) 1 centimeter
(d) 1 inch

1 cm   2 cm

1

cm   10   20   30   40   50   60   70   80   90   100

1ft   2ft   3ft

1 m = 1.094 yd

1 in. = 2.54 cm

Figure 1.12

Relative lengths of (a) 1 m, (b) 1 yd, (c) 1 cm, and (d) 1 in. (not actual size) and a comparison of 1 in. and 2.54 cm (actual size) and 1 m and 1.094 yd. A meter is exactly 100 times longer than 1 cm.

| ← 1.8 cm → | 1 cubic centimeter
Dime   = 1 milliliter

Figure 1.13

Comparison between a dime (actual size) and a cubic-centimeter block. A cubic centimeter is equal to 1 mL; 1 cubic centimeter of water has a mass of 1 g at 4°C.

❶.12 Mass and Weight

We said in Section 1.2 that the mass of an object is the quantity of matter that it contains. The mass of a body of matter is an invariable quantity. On the other hand, the weight of a body is the force that gravity exerts on the body; it is variable because that attraction depends on the distance from a planet's center. If this book were taken up in an airplane, it would weigh slightly less than it does at sea level. However, the mass of the book does not change as the distance from the center of the earth changes. Scientists measure quantities of matter in terms of mass rather than weight because the mass of a body remains constant, whereas its weight is an accident of its environment. It should be noted, however, that the term *weight* is often used loosely for the mass of a substance.

The mass of an object is found by comparing it to other objects of known mass. The instrument used to make this comparison is called a **balance**. Figure 1.14(a) shows a triple-beam balance. The object to be weighed is placed on the pan and weights are moved along the scales on the three beams until the masses balance, bringing the pointer to the center of the scale. At this point, the weights on the three beams balance the mass of the object on the pan. Weighing on a balance makes use of the fact that the gravita-

Figure 1.14

These three laboratory balances all determine mass. (a) The triple-beam balance is the least accurate, and is not usually used in research laboratories. (b) The top-loading balance is accurate to ±0.01 g. (c) The single-pan analytical balance is accurate to ±0.0001 g.

(a)

(b)

(c)

tional attraction for objects of equal mass is the same; that is, their weights are equal. A modern research analytical balance is shown in Fig. 1.14(c).

The standard object to which all SI and other metric units of mass are referred is a cylinder of platinum–iridium alloy, which is kept in France. The unit of mass, the **kilogram (kg),** is defined as the mass of this cylinder; 1 kilogram is about 2.2 pounds. The **gram (g)** is equal to exactly 0.001 times the mass of the standard kilogram (1×10^{-3} kg) and is very nearly equal to the weight of 1 cubic centimeter of water at 4°C, the temperature at which water has its maximum density. A dime has a mass of about 2.3 grams.

❶.13 Density

One of the important physical properties of a solid, a liquid, or a gas is its density. **The mass of a unit volume of a substance is called its density.** This may be expressed mathematically as

$$\text{Density} = \frac{\text{mass}}{\text{volume}} \quad \text{or} \quad D = \frac{M}{V}$$

Density is an intensive property and is independent of the quantity of matter being studied. However, because volume varies with temperature, density is a function of temperature. We can often distinguish between substances by measuring their densities, because two different substances usually have different densities. Generally, the density of a gas is taken as the mass (in grams) of a liter of the gas, and the density of a liquid or a solid is the mass (in grams) of a milliliter or cubic centimeter of the liquid or solid (Table 1.4).

Table 1.4	Densities of Common Materials at 25°C and 1 atm
Air	1.29 g/L
Helium gas	0.179 g/L
Water	0.997 g/cm³
Glycerin	1.26 g/cm³
Mercury	13.6 g/cm³
Salt	2.17 g/cm³
Iron	7.86 g/cm³
Silver	10.5 g/cm³

Example 1.5 Calculate the density of a body that has a mass of 321 g and a volume of 45.0 cm³ at 25°C.

The density of the body is the mass of 1 cm³. This can be determined by dividing the mass of the body by its volume.

$$\text{Density} = \frac{\text{mass}}{\text{volume}} = \frac{321 \text{ g}}{45.0 \text{ cm}^3} = 7.13 \text{ g/cm}^3$$

What is the mass in kilograms of 10.5 gal (39.7 L) of gasoline with a density of 0.82 g/mL?

Example 1.6

Converting 39.7 L to milliliters and then multiplying by the mass of 1 mL of gasoline gives the total mass.

$$\text{Volume} = 39.7 \text{ L} \times \frac{1000 \text{ mL}}{1 \text{ L}}$$

$$= 39,700 \text{ mL}$$

$$\text{Mass} = \text{density} \times \text{volume}$$

$$= 0.82 \text{ g/mL} \times 39,700 \text{ mL}$$

$$= 33,000 \text{ g} = 33 \text{ kg}$$

What is the density in pounds per quart and in grams per milliliter for the common antifreeze ethylene glycol? A 5.600-qt sample of ethylene glycol weighs 12.953 lb.

Example 1.7

$$\text{Density} = \frac{\text{mass}}{\text{volume}} = \frac{12.953 \text{ lb}}{5.600 \text{ qt}}$$

$$= 2.313 \text{ lb/qt}$$

To determine the density in grams per milliliter, we need the mass in grams and the volume in milliliters. The necessary conversion factors are given in Table 1.3 and in Appendix B: 1 L = 1.057 qt; 1 kg = 2.205 lb.

$$12.953 \text{ lb} \times \frac{1 \text{ kg}}{2.205 \text{ lb}} \times \frac{1000 \text{ g}}{1 \text{ kg}} = 5874.4 \text{ g}$$

$$5.600 \text{ qt} \times \frac{1 \text{ L}}{1.057 \text{ qt}} \times \frac{1000 \text{ mL}}{1 \text{ L}} = 5298 \text{ mL}$$

$$\text{Density} = \frac{5874.4 \text{ g}}{5298 \text{ mL}} = 1.109 \text{ g/mL}$$

Alternatively, the calculation could be set up in one equation as follows:

$$\frac{12.953 \text{ lb}}{5.600 \text{ qt}} \times \frac{1.057 \text{ qt}}{1 \text{ L}} \times \frac{1 \text{ L}}{1000 \text{ mL}} \times \frac{1 \text{ kg}}{2.205 \text{ lb}} \times \frac{1000 \text{ g}}{1 \text{ kg}} = 1.109 \text{ g/mL}$$

❶.14 Temperature and Its Measurement

The word **temperature** refers to the hotness or coldness of a body of matter. In order to measure a change in temperature, we must use some physical property of a substance that varies with temperature. Practically all substances expand when temperature increases and contract when it decreases. This property is the basis for the common glass thermometer. The mercury or alcohol in the hollow glass tube rises when the temperature increases because the volume of the mercury or alcohol increases as the substance expands.

Figure 1.15

The relationships among the Kelvin, Celsius, and Fahrenheit temperature scales.

To agree on a set of temperature values, we need **standard reference temperatures** that can be readily determined. Two such temperatures are the freezing and boiling points of water at a pressure of 1 atmosphere. On the **Celsius** scale the freezing point of water is defined as 0° and the boiling point as 100°. The heights of the mercury column at these two reference temperatures determine the 0° and 100° points on a thermometer. The space between these two points is divided into 100 equal intervals, or degrees. On the **Fahrenheit** scale the freezing point of water is defined as 32° and the boiling point as 212°. The space between these two points on a thermometer is divided into 180 equal parts, or degrees. Thus a degree Fahrenheit is exactly $\frac{100}{180}$, or $\frac{5}{9}$, of a degree Celsius (Fig. 1.15). The relationships are shown by the equations

$$\frac{°F - 32}{180} = \frac{°C}{100}, \qquad °C = \frac{5}{9}(°F - 32), \qquad °F = \frac{9}{5}°C + 32$$

The readings below 0° on either scale are treated as negative.

The SI unit of temperature is called the **kelvin (K),** named after Lord Kelvin, a British physicist. The zero point on the Kelvin scale corresponds to $-273.15°C$. The size of the degree on the Kelvin scale is the same as that on the Celsius scale. The freezing temperature of water on the Kelvin scale is 273.15 K (0°C), and the boiling temperature is 373.15 K (100°C). We convert a temperature on the Celsius scale to its equivalent on the Kelvin scale by adding 273.15 to the Celsius reading; we convert a temperature on the Kelvin scale to its equivalent on the Celsius scale by subtracting 273.15 from the Kelvin reading. (Note that temperatures on the Kelvin scale are, by convention, reported without the degree sign. The units of temperature on the Kelvin scale are kelvins; K is read "kelvins.")

$$K = °C + 273.15, \qquad °C = K - 273.15$$

Figure 1.15 shows the relationships among the three temperature scales. Temperatures in this book are in Celsius unless otherwise specified. The following examples demonstrate conversions among the three scales.

The boiling temperature of ethanol (ethyl alcohol) is 78.5°C at 1 atmosphere of pressure. What is its boiling point on the Fahrenheit scale and on the Kelvin scale? **Example 1.8**

$$°F = \frac{9}{5}°C + 32 = \left(\frac{9}{5} \times 78.5\right) + 32 = 141 + 32 = 173°F$$

$$K = °C + 273.15 = 78.5 + 273.15 = 351.6 \text{ K}$$

Convert 50°F to the Celsius scale and the Kelvin scale. **Example 1.9**

$$°C = \frac{5}{9}(°F - 32) = \frac{5}{9}(50 - 32) = \frac{5}{9} \times 18 = 10°C$$

$$K = °C + 273.15 = 10 + 273.15 = 283 \text{ K}$$

For Review

Summary

Because chemistry deals with the composition, structure, and properties of matter and with the reactions by which various forms of matter may be interconverted, it occupies a central place in the study of science and technology.

Matter is anything that occupies space and has **mass.** The basic building block of matter is the **atom,** the smallest unit of an element that can combine with other elements. In many substances, atoms are combined into **molecules.** Matter exists in three states: **solids,** of fixed shape and essentially incompressible; **liquids,** of variable shape but essentially incompressible; and **gases,** of variable shape and compressible or expansible. Most matter is a **mixture** of substances. These mixtures can be **heterogeneous** or **homogeneous.** Homogeneous mixtures are called **solutions.** Pure substances are also homogeneous. A **pure substance** may be an **element,** which cannot be decomposed by a chemical change, or a **compound,** which consists of two or more types of atoms. A pure substance exhibits characteristic **chemical and physical properties** by which it can be identified. Any property of a substance that does not depend on the amount of that substance is an **intensive property,** and any property that does depend on the amount is an **extensive property.**

Chemistry is a science based on laws and theories that are derived from observations via the **scientific method.** Quantitative measurements utilize the metric system, generally with **SI units.** Common units in use include the **gram** and **kilogram** for mass, the **centimeter** and **meter** for length, the **liter** (cubic decimeter) and **milliliter** (cubic centimeter) for volume, and **degrees Celsius** or **kelvins** for temperature. Experimental measurements have an associated error that can be expressed by attention to the number of significant figures. When using quantities in calculations, you must keep track of the units involved.

Key Terms and Concepts

Note: Section numbers are given for each term.

atom (1.6)
chemical change (1.4)
chemical properties (1.4)
compound (1.5)
density (1.13)
element (1.5)
energy (1.2)
extensive property (1.4)
gas (1.2)
gram (1.12)
intensive property (1.4)

International System of Units
  (SI units) (1.8)
kelvins (1.14)
kilogram (1.12)
length (1.11)
liquid (1.2)
liter (1.11)
mass (1.2)
matter (1.2)
meter (1.11)
mixture (1.5)

molecule (1.6)
physical change (1.4)
physical properties (1.4)
scientific method (1.7)
significant figures (1.10)
solid (1.2)
solutions (1.5)
temperature (1.14)
unit conversion factor (1.9)
volume (1.11)

Exercises

Note: The answers to selected even-numbered exercises marked by red numbers appear at the end of the book. The solutions to all even-numbered exercises are worked out in the manual prepared by J. H. Meiser and F. K. Ault, titled *Solutions Guide for General Chemistry,* 9th edition, by Holtzclaw, Robinson, and Odom.

You should make a special effort to develop good habits in expressing answers to exercises to the correct number of significant figures. To this end, we have paid careful attention to significant figures in the answers provided. Our answers were obtained by carrying all figures in the calculator and rounding the final answer. If you choose to do the exercise in steps, rounding after each step, you may get answers that differ from ours by one or two units in the least significant figure. These differences do not indicate an error; they simply reflect the two equally acceptable, but different, ways of rounding.

1. With what is the science of chemistry concerned?
2. What properties distinguish solids from liquids? Solids from gases? Liquids from gases?
3. Describe a chemical change that illustrates the law of conservation of matter.
4. Why is an object's mass, rather than its weight, used as a measure of the amount of matter it contains?
5. Describe how a scientist would proceed from the formulation of a question to the establishment of a theory.

Classification of Matter

6. How can one distinguish between an element, a compound, and a mixture?
7. In what ways do heterogeneous mixtures differ from homogeneous mixtures? In what ways are they alike?
8. Classify each of the following as a heterogeneous mixture or a homogeneous mixture: air, blood, ginger ale, kerosene, mustard, scrambled eggs, chicken noodle soup, perfume.

9. In what ways does a pure substance differ from a homogeneous mixture? In what ways are they alike?
10. Classify each of the following homogeneous materials as a solution, an element, or a compound: copper, pancake syrup, water, the brown gas in Fig. 1.1(b), the two decomposition products mentioned in Fig. 1.8, ozone, vitamin C, ocean water.
11. Classify each of the following as a physical or a chemical change: the rotting of leaves, the boiling of water, the dissolving of salt in water, the tarnishing of silver, the freezing of water, the sublimation of dry ice (if you do not know the meaning of "sublimation," check the Glossary at the end of the book), photosynthesis, the condensation of steam.
12. In what ways does an atom differ from a molecule? In what ways are they alike?
13. What is the difference between a molecule of oxygen and a molecule of sulfur? Between a molecule of oxygen and a molecule of water? Fig. 1.10 may help.
14. How do molecules of elements and molecules of compounds differ?
15. Are any of the substances shown in Fig. 1.5 mixtures? Explain why or why not.
16. Molecules of water consist of atoms of hydrogen and atoms of oxygen. Is water a mixture? Explain why or why not.
17. Refer to Fig. 1.2. Is ice floating in liquid water a mixture? Explain why or why not.

Significant Figures

18. How many significant figures are there in each of the following numbers?
  (a) 1.0055   (c) 0.00550
  (b) 0.0055   (d) 105.50
19. Indicate whether each of the following can be determined exactly or must be measured with some degree of uncertainty.

(a) The number of pine cones in a bushel.

(b) The mass of a pumpkin.

(c) The time required to drive from San Francisco to New York at an average speed of 56 miles per hour (mph).

(d) The number of centimeters in exactly 3 millimeters.

(e) The mass of your notebook for this class.

(f) The number of seconds in 3 weeks.

(g) The number of quarts of oil necessary to change the oil in your automobile.

20. How many significant figures are there in each of the following measurements?

(a) 53 cm

(b) 1.0075 g

(c) 0.008 g

(d) 0.0730 m

(e) 30.00 mL

(f) 4.5×10^8 atoms

(g) 9.74130×10^{-4} kg

21. Round off each of the following to two significant figures:
(a) 517; (b) 86.3; (c) 6.382×10^3; (d) 5.0008; (e) 175; (f) 0.885.

22. Report the results of each of the following calculations to the correct number of significant figures.

(a) $25.0 \times 3.0 \times 4.88$

(b) $0.147 + 0.0066 + 0.012$

(c) $38 \times 95 \times 1.792$

(d) $15 - 0.15 - 0.015$

(e) $8.78 \times 0.0500/0.478$

(f) $140 + 7.68 + 0.014$

(g) $30 \times 740/6.5$

23. Express each of the following numbers in exponential notation.

(a) 527.0

(b) 0.789

(c) 36572

(d) 111.8

(e) 0.03722

(f) 100000.0

(g) 0.00000637482

24. In a 1950 handbook, 1 in. was given as equal to 2.540005 cm. Since that time, 1 in. has been defined as exactly 2.54 cm. Are there more, fewer, or the same number of significant figures in the newer value?

25. It is necessary to determine the density of a liquid to four significant figures. The volume of solution can be measured to the nearest 0.01 cm³.

(a) What is the minimum volume of sample that can be used for the measurement?

(b) Assuming the minimum-volume sample determined in (a), how accurately must the sample be weighed (to the nearest 0.1 g, or 0.01 g, or . . .), if the density of the solution is greater than 1.00 g/cm³?

26. Refer to Fig. 3.3. Suppose the volumes that you read for water and butyl alcohol in the volumetric cylinders are 18.0 mL and 91.5 mL, respectively. Calculate the density of each of these liquids.

Metric System; SI Units

27. Much of Chapter 1 deals with measurement. Why is measurement so important in chemistry?

28. What is the difference between mass and weight?

29. Even though a body "weighs" less on the moon than on Earth, a triple-beam balance, such as the one described in Section 1.12, indicates that the mass of an object is the same on the moon and on Earth. Why?

30. Complete the following conversions.

(a) 3.58 mg = _____ g

(b) 37.12 cm = _____ km

(c) 1.344 L = _____ mL

(d) 83.5 cm³ = _____ mL

(e) 174.3 mm = _____ m

(f) 34.51 g = _____ mg

(g) 2.78×10^2 L = _____ m³

(h) 1.3 kg = _____ g

31. Indicate the SI base unit appropriate to express each of the following.

(a) The length of a marathon.

(b) The mass of an automobile.

(c) The area of a basketball court.

(d) The volume of a bathtub.

(e) The density of the nonmetal selenium.

(f) The speed of a downhill skier.

(g) The maximum temperature at the equator on October 12, 1492.

32. Give the prefix used with SI units to indicate multiplication by each of the following exact quantities: 10^3; 10^{-1}; 10^6; 10^{-9}; 10^{-3}; 10^{-6}.

33. A tetanus injection for a puncture wound has a volume of 0.5 mL. What is this volume in liters and in microliters?

Conversion of Units

34. A two-person sailplane with a wingspan of 52 ft is considered a safe aircraft. What is this wingspan in meters?

35. The America's Cup may be sailed in monohulled vessels 75 ft in length with 110-ft masts in the future. What are these measurements in kilometers?

36. A recent article in the *Journal of the American Medical Association* reported that in 1989, boys aged 14–17 weighed an average of 142 pounds (lb). Express this weight in kilograms.

37. If an automobile has a top speed of 140 miles per hour (mph), what is its speed in kilometers per hour?

38. A 5000-m women's cross-country race is how many yards long? How many miles?

39. If 1000 pages of a book are 2.0 in. thick, what is the thickness of 1 page in meters?

40. A 2.3-L automobile engine contains how many pints?

41. If a cigarette contains 0.9 mg of nicotine, how many ounces of nicotine does it contain?

42. A Hawaiian-born sumo wrestler weighed 488 lb when he won Japan's most prestigious sumo championship. What was his weight in kilograms?

43. The final time trial in the bicycle race known as the *Tour de France* is from Versailles to Paris, a distance of 24.5 km. What is this distance in miles?

44. The Kentucky Derby is 1.25 miles (mi) long. If the record time for this race is 1 minute (min), 59-2/5 seconds (s), what

was the average speed of the record-breaking horse in kilometers per hour?

45. Complete the following conversions.
 (a) 6.5 dm = _____ m
 (b) 160 lb = _____ mg
 (c) 6.3 m³ = _____ cm³
 (d) 25.4 mg = _____ kg
 (e) 1.05 × 10⁶ cm = _____ mi
 (f) 1 dm³ = _____ cm³

46. A nautical mile is 1.15 land miles. How many kilometers are there in a nautical mile?

47. There are 29.6 mL in one fluid ounce (oz) and 16 fluid ounces in a pint. How many fluid ounces are in 5 gallons (gal)? How many milliliters?

48. A hectometer is 100 m. How many feet are there in a hectometer?

49. A long ton is 2240 lb. How many milligrams are there in a long ton?

50. In dry measure, a peck is 8.0 quarts and a bushel consists of 4 pecks. How many milliliters are there in a bushel?

51. If a solution prepared in the laboratory fills a 250-mL flask, what is the volume of the solution in fluid ounces? In pints?

52. The distance between the centers of two nitrogen atoms in a nitrogen molecule is 1.10 Å. What is this distance in picometers? In inches?

53. The density of liquid bromine is 2.928 g/cm³. What is the mass of 100 mL of bromine? What is the volume of 25 g of bromine?

54. Calculate the density of magnesium if 18.9 cm³ has a mass of 32.85 g.

55. Osmium is one of the most dense elements known. What is its density if 0.318 cm³ has a mass of 7.16 g?

56. What is the volume of each of the following?
 (a) 27.6 g of aluminum; density = 2.70 g/cm³
 (b) 225 g of silicon; density = 2.34 g/cm³
 (c) 3.0 g of gaseous neon; density = 0.899 g/L

57. What is the mass of each of the following?
 (a) 425 mL of gaseous xenon; density = 5.90 g/L
 (b) 50 mL of liquid ammonia; density = 0.683 g/cm³
 (c) 3.00 cm³ of boron; density = 2.35 g/cm³

Temperature

58. Normal human body temperature is 37.0°C. What is this temperature in degrees Fahrenheit and in kelvins?

59. A Tennessee Valley Authority steam-driven turbogenerator is driven by 8 million pounds of steam per hour, which enters the turbine at 1003°F. What is the temperature of this steam in degrees Celsius and in kelvins?

60. If we keep the thermostat in our home set at 67°F in the winter, what is the setting in degrees Celsius?

61. If the temperature is −40°C, what is the temperature on the Fahrenheit scale?

62. Air can be cooled and eventually liquefied by a series of compressions and expansions. Nitrogen and oxygen can then be separated by a process known as fractional distillation, which uses the difference in boiling point between the two liquids. Nitrogen boils at −196°C and oxygen boils at −183°C. Express these temperatures in degrees Fahrenheit and in kelvins.

63. Convert:
 (a) 80°C to degrees Fahrenheit
 (b) 136°F to degrees Celsius
 (c) 21.0°F to kelvins
 (d) −45°C to degrees Fahrenheit
 (e) −65°F to kelvins

Additional Exercises

64. How do the densities of most substances change as a result of an increase in temperature?

65. Explain how you could determine whether the outside temperature is warmer or cooler than 0°C, without using a thermometer.

66. In a laboratory experiment to determine the density of materials, a student reported the following measurements of a metal bar: height, 2.5 cm; width, 2.5 cm; length, 6.0 cm; weight, 42.383 g. What is the density of this metal?

67. An excellent method of volumetrically calibrating glassware uses an accurate balance and density tables for water as a function of temperature. If a flask weighs 63.24 g dry and empty and 96.58 g filled with water at 21°C (density = 0.9979 g/cm³), what is the volume of the flask?

68. The speed of sound in air is approximately 767 mph. Calculate this speed in meters per second.

69. Mercury is a very heavy metal that is commonly used in thermometers. At 0°C, its density is 13.5955 g/mL; at 10°C, 13.5708 g/mL; at 25°C, 13.5340 g/mL; at 60°C, 13.4468 g/mL; and at 100°C, 13.3522 g/mL.
 (a) Convert the five temperatures to kelvins.
 (b) What is the volume of 6.857 g of mercury at each of the five temperatures?
 (c) Make a graph, plotting temperature (in kelvins) against volume.
 (d) Does the plot suggest a property of mercury that makes it a suitable choice for use in thermometers? If so, what property?
 (e) Can the same graph be adapted to both Celsius and Fahrenheit temperatures? If so, revise the plot to show both.
 (f) Calculate the density of mercury at 100°C in pounds per cubic inch.

70. Which of the following amounts of lead (density = 11.3 g/cm³) occupies the greatest volume: 1.0 lb, 1.0 kg, or 1.0 L?

71. A new technique for generating ultrathin light beams may make it possible to do light microscopy with resolution on a molecular scale. If the beam is 1.0 nm across, what is its width in inches?

Chemical Equations and Reactions

Crystals of vitamin C, ascorbic acid, which has the formula $C_6H_8O_6$.

When speaking and writing about matter and the changes it undergoes, chemists use symbols, formulas, and equations to indicate what elements are present, the relative amounts of each, and how the combinations of elements change during a chemical reaction. They can use this information, along with the masses of the substances involved, to determine how much product should form during the course of a reaction or how much of the starting materials will be consumed, a topic that will be considered in Chapter 3.

In this chapter we will introduce symbols and formulas, the particles contained in atoms, the periodic table, the formation of ions, ionic and covalent compounds, equa-

Figure 2.1

(top) The gaseous element chlorine, Cl_2. (middle) The solid element sodium, Na. (bottom) These two elements react vigorously to form sodium chloride, NaCl, which contains an equal number of atoms of each.

Table 2.1	Some Common Elements and Their Symbols
Aluminum	Al
Bromine	Br
Calcium	Ca
Carbon	C
Chlorine	Cl
Chromium	Cr
Cobalt	Co
Copper	Cu (from *cuprum*)
Fluorine	F
Gold	Au (from *aurum*)
Helium	He
Hydrogen	H
Iodine	I
Iron	Fe (from *ferrum*)
Lead	Pb (from *plumbum*)
Magnesium	Mg
Mercury	Hg (from *hydrargyrum*)
Nitrogen	N
Oxygen	O
Potassium	K (from *kalium*)
Silicon	Si
Silver	Ag (from *argentum*)
Sodium	Na (from *natrium*)
Sulfur	S
Tin	Sn (from *stannum*)
Zinc	Zn

tions, oxidation numbers, and nomenclature of simple compounds. In connection with these topics, we will consider classifications of compounds and of reactions and delve into the chemistry of a few important industrial chemicals.

❷.1   Symbols and Formulas

A chemical **symbol** is an abbreviation that chemists use to represent a specific element. Symbols for several common elements are listed in Table 2.1. Some are derived from the common name of the element; others are abbreviations of the name in another language. Most symbols have one or two letters. Three-letter symbols are used to describe some elements that have recently been prepared in the laboratory. To avoid confusion with other notations, only the first letter of a symbol is capitalized—Co is the symbol for the element cobalt; CO is the notation for the compound carbon monoxide, which contains the elements carbon (C) and oxygen (O). The symbols for all known elements are given on the inside front cover of this book.

A **formula** is an abbreviation used to represent a compound. For example, NaCl is the abbreviation for sodium chloride (common table salt). A formula also shows the composition of a compound. The formula NaCl identifies atoms of the elements sodium (Na) and chlorine (Cl) as the constituents of sodium chloride (Fig. 2.1). Subscripts are

(a)

(b)

Figure 2.2

Photographs of two kinds of models of the benzene molecule, C_6H_6. (a) A ball-and-stick model, which uses balls of different colors (black for carbon and white for hydrogen) to represent each kind of atom and sticks to represent bonds. Ball-and-stick models show the relationships of the atoms and bonds, but are not to scale. (b) A space-filling model, which is approximately to scale based on the atomic radii of the atoms. Space-filling models show the relative sizes of atoms and geometric shapes of molecules more accurately than do ball-and-stick models. As in the ball-and-stick model, a different color is used for each kind of atom.

used to indicate the relative numbers of atoms of each type in the compound, but only when more than one atom of a given element is present. For example, the formula for water, H_2O, indicates that each molecule contains two atoms of hydrogen and one atom of oxygen. The formula for sodium chloride, NaCl, indicates the presence of equal numbers of atoms of the elements sodium and chlorine.

Parentheses in a formula indicate a group of atoms that behave as a unit. The formula for aluminum sulfate, $Al_2(SO_4)_3$, indicates that there are two atoms of aluminum (Al) for each three sulfate (SO_4) groups. In most reactions of $Al_2(SO_4)_3$, the SO_4 units remain combined as a discrete unit consisting of one S (sulfur) atom and four O (oxygen) atoms. The formula shows a total of two atoms of aluminum, three atoms of sulfur, and twelve atoms of oxygen. The numbers of atoms obtained from such formulas are whole numbers that are exact to any number of significant figures.

A **molecular formula** gives the actual numbers of atoms of each element in a molecule. An **empirical formula** (sometimes called a **simplest formula**) gives the *simplest* whole-number ratio of atoms. For example, the molecular formula of benzene, C_6H_6, identifies the benzene molecule as composed of exactly six carbon atoms and six hydrogen atoms (Fig. 2.2). The simplest ratio of these atoms is 1 to 1. Thus the empirical formula of benzene is CH. The molecular formula H_2O indicates that water has exactly two atoms of hydrogen and one atom of oxygen in one molecule (2 atoms H/ 1 atom O). The simplest whole-number ratio of atoms is 2 to 1, so the empirical formula is also H_2O. The following example illustrates empirical and molecular formulas.

A molecule of blood sugar, glucose, contains 6 carbon atoms, 12 hydrogen atoms, and 6 oxygen atoms. What are the empirical and molecular formulas of glucose?

Example 2.1

The molecular formula is $C_6H_{12}O_6$, because one molecule actually contains 6C, 12H, and 6O atoms. The simplest whole-number ratio of C to H to O atoms in glucose is 1:2:1, so the empirical formula is CH_2O.

Some elements can consist of molecules that contain more than one atom of the element. For example, the most common form of elemental sulfur consists of eight atoms of sulfur (see Fig. 1.10); its molecular formula is S_8. Other examples are elemental hydrogen, oxygen, and nitrogen (diatomic molecules), which have the molecular formulas H_2, O_2, and N_2, respectively.

Note that H_2 and 2H do not mean the same thing. The formula H_2 represents a molecule of hydrogen consisting of two atoms of the element, chemically combined.

Figure 2.3

Illustration of the difference in meaning between the symbols H, 2H, and H_2.

H	2H	H_2
One H atom	Two H atoms	One H_2 molecule

The expression 2H, on the other hand, indicates that the two hydrogen atoms are not combined as a unit but are separate (Fig. 2.3).

❷.2 Atomic Mass Units

The mass of an atom is very small. Rather than describe such a small mass in grams, chemists use an arbitrary unit called the **atomic mass unit (amu)** or the **dalton** (named after a famous chemist, John Dalton). By international agreement, an atomic mass unit (or dalton) is taken to be exactly $\frac{1}{12}$ of the mass of a particular kind of carbon atom known as carbon-12. Hence carbon-12 has a mass of exactly 12 amu, a much more convenient number to work with than its mass in grams, 1.99×10^{-23} grams. One atomic mass unit = 1.6606×10^{-24} grams.

❷.3 The Composition of Atoms

Atoms are assemblies of protons, neutrons, and electrons. The **proton** is a particle that has a mass of 1.0073 amu and a charge of $+1$; it is one of the fundamental components of all atoms. The **neutron** is a particle that has a mass of 1.0087 amu, almost the same as that of a proton, but has a charge of zero (it is a neutral particle); the neutron is a fundamental component of all atoms except for the lightest and most common kind of hydrogen atom. The **electron** is a much lighter particle that has a mass of 0.00055 amu and a charge of -1; the electron is a fundamental component of all atoms. The fundamental particles present in an atom are summarized in Table 2.2.

The atom consists of a very small positively charged **nucleus,** in which most of the mass of the atom is concentrated. The nucleus contains the protons and the neutrons (the heavier particles) present in the atom.

The nucleus in an atom is surrounded by the electrons necessary to balance the positive charge of the nucleus and produce an electrically neutral atom. Thus the number

Table 2.2	Fundamental Particles in an Atom	
Particle	Mass, amu	Charge
Electron	0.00055	-1
Proton	1.0073	$+1$
Neutron	1.0087	0

of protons (charge of $+1$ each) in the nucleus of an atom equals the number of electrons (charge of -1 each) outside the nucleus (remember that the neutrons have zero charge).

The number of protons in the nucleus is called the **atomic number** of the element. Because an atom contains the same number of protons as of electrons, the atomic number of an atom represents the number of electrons as well as the number of protons. The sum of the numbers of protons and neutrons in the nucleus is approximately equal to the mass of the nucleus in amu and, without units, is referred to as the **mass number.** The mass number, expressed in amu, is also approximately equal to the mass of the atom, since the mass of the electrons in an atom is negligibly small compared to that of the protons and neutrons. The total mass of an atom in atomic mass units is called its **atomic mass.**

The following example illustrates the composition of the aluminum atom.

An atom of aluminum of mass number 27 has an atomic number of 13. Determine the numbers of protons, neutrons, and electrons within the atom.

Example 2.2

The atomic number of 13 tells us that the atom contains 13 protons within the nucleus and 13 electrons outside the nucleus. Because the sum of the numbers of protons and neutrons equals the mass number, 27, the number of neutrons in the nucleus is 14.

The diameter of the nucleus has been determined to be at least 100,000 times smaller than the diameter of the atom. (The diameter of an atom is on the order of 10^{-8} centimeter, whereas the diameter of a nucleus is on the order of 10^{-13} centimeter.) Thus a nucleus is almost unbelievably small. If the nucleus of an atom were as large as the period at the end of this sentence, the atom would have a diameter of about 40 yards. It is apparent then that the volume occupied by the electrons, outside the nucleus, is very large compared to the volume of the nucleus.

❷.4 The Periodic Table

It became evident early in the development of chemistry that various elements could be grouped together by reason of their similar chemical behavior. The members of one such grouping are lithium (Li), sodium (Na), and potassium (K). These elements all look like metals, all conduct electricity well, and all have similar chemical properties. A second grouping includes calcium (Ca), strontium (Sr), and barium (Ba), which also look like metals, conduct electricity well, and have similar chemical properties (but somewhat different chemical and physical properties than lithium, sodium, and potassium). Fluorine (F), chlorine (Cl), bromine (Br), and iodine (I) also exhibit similar properties. They do not conduct electricity well and are considered nonmetallic.

Dimitri Mendeleev in Russia and Lothar Meyer in Germany, working independently, observed the relationship between the properties of the elements and their atomic masses. As a better understanding of the structure of the atom and of electron configuration (discussed in Chapter 5) developed, however, it became apparent that the properties of atoms were actually periodic functions of their atomic numbers rather than their atomic masses. The modern statement of this periodic relationship, the **periodic law,** is: **The properties of the elements are periodic functions of their atomic numbers.**

The **periodic table** is an arrangement of the atoms in increasing order of their atomic numbers that collects atoms with similar properties in vertical columns. Figure 2.4 gives one common form of the periodic table. A copy of the periodic table is also presented on the page facing the inside front cover of this book.

All elements except those shaded in green are called **metals.** The metals are subdivided into the **representative** (or **main group**) **metals,** shaded red; the **transition metals,** shaded yellow; and the **inner transition metals,** shaded blue. The elements on the right, shaded in green, are called the **nonmetals.**

The periodic table consists of 7 horizontal rows of elements (often referred to as **periods** or **series**) and 32 vertical columns of elements (referred to as **groups** or **families**). In order that the table fit on a single page, some of the elements have been written below the main body of the table. The **lanthanide series** fits between elements 56 (barium, Ba) and 72 (hafnium, Hf). The **actinide series** fits between elements 88 (radium, Ra) and 104 (unnilquadium, Unq).

In the United States, the designation of the groups in the periodic table has traditionally used Roman numerals with capital letters (Fig. 2.4). However, a recent proposal from the International Union of Pure and Applied Chemistry (IUPAC) has recommended a new form in which the groups are numbered 1 through 18 from left to right. The proposal has attracted considerable attention, and its advantages and disadvantages are currently the subject of heated discussion internationally among chemists. We will use primarily the Roman numeral system.

Some of the groups in the periodic table have special names. As we mentioned, lithium (Li), sodium (Na), and potassium (K) exhibit similar chemical properties. These elements, located in the leftmost vertical column in the table (Group 1, or IA) along with rubidium (Rb), cesium (Cs), and francium (Fr), make up a group known as the **alkali metals,** all of which have similar chemical properties. [Hydrogen (H) is listed in both column IA and column VIIA because it exhibits a few similarities to elements in those two columns. However, it is considered a nonmetal.] The elements in Group 2, or IIA, in the periodic table are referred to as the **alkaline earth metals.** The elements located in the third vertical column from the right in the table (Group 16, or VIA) are known as the **chalcogens.** The elements in Group 17, or VIIA, are the **halogens.** Those in Group 18, or VIIIA, are the **noble gases.**

The properties of the elements in any vertical column do differ somewhat, so the elements in a group are similar but not identical in chemical behavior. Adjacent elements in each horizontal row (period) differ decidedly in both chemical and physical properties, but these properties change in a regular way across each period. The horizontal and vertical variations in behavior will be discussed more fully in Chapter 6.

❷.5 Formation of Ions

The noble gas elements (Group VIIIA of the periodic table) are especially stable. Metals (particularly those in Groups IA and IIA, but also certain other metals) tend to lose the number of electrons necessary to leave them with the same number of electrons as the preceding noble gas in the periodic table. By this process, a positively charged particle called an **ion** is formed. Ions are atoms or groups of atoms that are electrically charged, positively or negatively. For example, the neutral sodium atom, with 11 protons and 11 electrons, readily loses 1 electron, leaving it with 10 electrons, the same number as in the neon (Ne) atom. The sodium species with 10 electrons still has 11 protons in the

Figure 2.4 — The periodic table

Periods	1 IA	2 IIA	3 IIIB	4 IVB	5 VB	6 VIB	7 VIIB	8 VIIIB	9 VIIIB	10	11 IB	12 IIB	13 IIIA	14 IVA	15 VA	16 VIA	17 VIIA	18 VIIIA
1	1 H 1.008																1 H 1.008	2 He 4.003
2	3 Li 6.941	4 Be 9.012											5 B 10.811	6 C 12.011	7 N 14.007	8 O 15.999	9 F 18.998	10 Ne 20.180
3	11 Na 22.990	12 Mg 24.305											13 Al 26.982	14 Si 28.086	15 P 30.974	16 S 32.066	17 Cl 35.453	18 Ar 39.948
4	19 K 39.098	20 Ca 40.078	21 Sc 44.956	22 Ti 47.88	23 V 50.942	24 Cr 51.996	25 Mn 54.938	26 Fe 55.847	27 Co 58.933	28 Ni 58.69	29 Cu 63.546	30 Zn 65.39	31 Ga 69.723	32 Ge 72.61	33 As 74.922	34 Se 78.96	35 Br 79.904	36 Kr 83.80
5	37 Rb 85.468	38 Sr 87.62	39 Y 88.906	40 Zr 91.224	41 Nb 92.906	42 Mo 95.94	43 Tc (98)	44 Ru 101.07	45 Rh 102.906	46 Pd 106.42	47 Ag 107.868	48 Cd 112.411	49 In 114.82	50 Sn 118.710	51 Sb 121.75	52 Te 127.60	53 I 126.904	54 Xe 131.29
6	55 Cs 132.905	56 Ba 137.327	* (57–71)	72 Hf 178.49	73 Ta 180.948	74 W 183.85	75 Re 186.207	76 Os 190.2	77 Ir 192.22	78 Pt 195.08	79 Au 196.966	80 Hg 200.59	81 Tl 204.383	82 Pb 207.2	83 Bi 208.980	84 Po (209)	85 At (210)	86 Rn (222)
7	87 Fr (223)	88 Ra 226.025	† (89–103)	104 Unq (261)	105 Unp (262)	106 Unh (263)	107 Uns (262)	108 Uno (265)	109 Une (266)									

Metals — Transition metals

Nonmetals

*Lanthanide series

57 La 138.906	58 Ce 140.115	59 Pr 140.908	60 Nd 144.24	61 Pm (145)	62 Sm 150.36	63 Eu 151.965	64 Gd 157.25	65 Tb 158.925	66 Dy 162.50	67 Ho 164.930	68 Er 167.26	69 Tm 168.934	70 Yb 173.04	71 Lu 174.967

†Actinide series

89 Ac 227.028	90 Th 232.038	91 Pa 231.036	92 U 238.029	93 Np 237.048	94 Pu (244)	95 Am (243)	96 Cm (247)	97 Bk (247)	98 Cf (251)	99 Es (252)	100 Fm (257)	101 Md (258)	102 No (259)	103 Lr (260)

Inner transition metals

Figure 2.4

The periodic table. For each element the atomic number is given above the symbol for the element, and the atomic mass is given below the symbol. Representative metals are shown in red, transition metals in yellow, and inner transition metals in blue. Nonmetals are shown in green. Two systems of numbering the columns (groups or families of elements) from left to right are commonly used. One system uses Roman numerals I through VIII with letters; the other system uses the numbers 1 through 18.

Table 2.3 **Some of the More Common Polyatomic Ions**

Name	Formula	Name	Formula
Peroxide ion	O_2^{2-}	Sulfate ion	SO_4^{2-}
Triiodide ion	I_3^-	Sulfite ion	SO_3^{2-}
Ammonium ion	NH_4^+	Phosphate ion	PO_4^{3-}
Nitrate ion	NO_3^-	Acetate ion	$CH_3CO_2^-$
Nitrite ion	NO_2^-	Perchlorate ion	ClO_4^-
Hydroxide ion	OH^-	Permanganate ion	MnO_4^-
Carbonate ion	CO_3^{2-}	Dichromate ion	$Cr_2O_7^{2-}$

nucleus and hence has assumed a charge of $+1$; it is the sodium ion, Na^+. The neutral calcium atom, with 20 protons and 20 electrons, readily loses 2 electrons and thus has 18 electrons remaining, the same number as in the argon (Ar) atom; by this means the calcium atom produces a calcium ion, Ca^{2+}.

Similarly, nonmetals (especially those in Groups VIIA and VIA, and to a lesser extent those in Group VA) can gain the number of electrons necessary to provide them with the same number of electrons as in the next noble gas in the periodic table. This is how negative ions are formed. For example, the neutral bromine atom, with 35 protons and 35 electrons, can gain 1 electron to provide it with 36 electrons, the same number as in the krypton (Kr) atom. By doing this it forms the bromide ion, Br^- (35 protons and 36 electrons).

Thus metals normally form positive ions, which are known as **cations.** Nonmetals normally form negative ions, which are known as **anions.** In general, binary compounds containing a metal and a nonmetal consist of **monatomic ions** (ions that contain only one atom). For example, calcium chloride, $CaCl_2$, contains Ca^{2+} (the monatomic cation formed from the metal calcium) and Cl^- (the monatomic anion formed from the nonmetal chlorine). Ionic compounds that contain three or more elements may contain **polyatomic ions** (ions containing more than one atom). For example, potassium nitrate, KNO_3, contains the monatomic K^+ ion and the polyatomic NO_3^- ion. Examples of common polyatomic ions are given in Table 2.3.

2.6 Ionic and Covalent Compounds

In ordinary chemical reactions the nucleus of each atom remains unchanged. Electrons, however, can be added by transfer from other atoms, lost by transfer to other atoms, or shared with other atoms. These interactions of electrons among atoms govern the chemistry of the elements.

Ionic Compounds

When an element that readily loses electrons (a metal) reacts with an element that readily gains electrons (a nonmetal), one or more than one electron is completely transferred from one atom to another and two ions are produced. A compound formed by this transfer is stabilized by **ionic bonds,** which involve strong electrostatic attractions between the ions of opposite charge present in the compound. For example, a sodium atom gives up one electron readily to form the sodium ion, Na^+, and can transfer that electron to a chlorine atom, which accepts one electron easily to form the chloride ion, Cl^-. The resulting compound, NaCl, is composed of sodium ions and chloride ions in the ratio of one Na^+ ion for each Cl^- ion. Similarly, a calcium atom can give up two electrons readily and can transfer one to each of two chlorine atoms to form $CaCl_2$, which is made up of Ca^{2+} ions and Cl^- ions in the ratio of one Ca^{2+} ion to two Cl^- ions.

A compound that contains ions is called an **ionic compound.** Such compounds are electrically neutral, even though they contain positive and negative ions. In each ionic compound, the total number of positive charges on the positive ions equals the total number of negative charges on the negative ions. Ionic compounds can include polyatomic ions as well as monatomic ions.

Typical examples of ionic compounds are calcium chloride, $CaCl_2$ (one Ca^{2+} ion for every two Cl^- ions); ammonium bromide, NH_4Br (one NH_4^+ ion for each Br^- ion); calcium phosphate, $Ca_3(PO_4)_2$ (three Ca^{2+} ions for every two PO_4^{3-} ions); aluminum sulfate, $Al_2(SO_4)_3$ (two Al^{3+} ions for every three SO_4^{2-} ions); ammonium nitrate, NH_4NO_3 (one NH_4^+ ion for each NO_3^- ion); and copper sulfate, $CuSO_4$ (one Cu^{2+} ion for each SO_4^{2-} ion). In each case, note that the number of ions of each type is such that, when the number of ions and the charge on each ion are taken into account, the *total* positive charge on the positive ions equals the *total* negative charge on the negative ions.

Ionic compounds such as NaCl, $CuSO_4$, and $Al_2(SO_4)_3$ cannot be identified in terms of a molecule, but only in terms of a *formula unit,* because these compounds do not contain physically distinct molecules (see Fig. 2.7 for NaCl). With the exception of a very small number of ionic compounds such as Hg_2Cl_2 (which contains the ion Hg_2^{2+}), the formula units of such compounds are empirical formulas because they give only the simplest whole-number ratios of the atoms in the compounds. The formula for copper sulfate, $CuSO_4$, indicates that there is one atom of copper for each atom of sulfur and for every four atoms of oxygen in a sample of the compound. The total numbers of atoms of the three elements in any sample of copper sulfate will be proportional to these numbers, but the formula is an empirical formula because there are no individual molecules of $CuSO_4$.

The negative ion in $CuSO_4$ is the polyatomic sulfate ion, SO_4^{2-}. A sample of copper sulfate thus consists of many copper ions (Cu^{2+}) and sulfate ions (SO_4^{2-}) in the ratio 1:1. Likewise, a sample of aluminum sulfate, $Al_2(SO_4)_3$, consists of many aluminum ions (Al^{3+}) and sulfate ions always in the ratio of 2:3.

Covalent Compounds

Many compounds do not contain ions but instead consist of atoms bonded tightly together in molecules that result when atoms *share* electrons instead of transferring electrons from one atom to another. These molecules are uncharged groups of atoms that can behave as single discrete units. Compounds made up of molecules are **covalent compounds,** and the bonds that hold the atoms together in such molecules are **covalent bonds.** Nonmetal atoms form covalent bonds with each other. Diatomic molecules such as H_2 and O_2 are covalent molecules, as are compounds containing more than one kind of nonmetal, such as carbon dioxide (CO_2) and ammonia (NH_3).

❷.7 Oxidation Numbers

The **oxidation number** of an atom, sometimes called the **oxidation state,** is a book-keeping concept. It provides a number that is useful in naming compounds, classifying chemical reactions, writing chemical formulas, and keeping track of the redistributions of electrons that occur during a chemical reaction.

The following rules are used to determine the oxidation number of an atom:

1. The oxidation number of an atom of molecule of any element in its elemental form is considered to be zero. Examples include Na, N_2, P_4, and S_8.

2. The oxidation number of an ion that contains only one atom (a monatomic ion) is equal to the charge on the ion. For example, the ions of the alkali metals, Group IA of the periodic table (Na^+, K^+, Rb^+, Cs^+, and Fr^+), always have an oxidation number of $+1$, corresponding to their charge. The ions of the alkaline earth metals, Group IIA (Be^{2+}, Mg^{2+}, Ca^{2+}, Sr^{2+}, Ba^{2+}, and Ra^{2+}), always have an oxidation number of $+2$. The monatomic ions of the halogens, Group VIIA (F^-, Cl^-, Br^-, I^-, and At^-), have an oxidation number of -1. The monatomic negative ions of the chalcogens, Group VIA (O^{2-}, S^{2-}, Se^{2-}, Te^{2-}, and Po^{2-}), have an oxidation number of -2. Each of the lighter elements of Group VA (N, P, and As) can form monatomic negative ions with an oxidation number of -3 (N^{3-}, P^{3-} and As^{3-}).

3. The oxidation number of oxygen, whether as the monatomic ion or in a polyatomic ion, is commonly -2. Oxygen can occasionally exhibit additional oxidation numbers, but such cases are few. For now, assume that oxygen in a compound has an oxidation number of -2 unless you are told otherwise.

4. The oxidation number of hydrogen is $+1$ when it is in a compound with one or more than one other nonmetal (HCl and $HClO_4$, for example) and -1 when it is combined with a metal (NaH, for example).

The sum of the oxidation numbers of all atoms in a neutral compound is zero. The sum of the oxidation numbers of all atoms in a polyatomic ion is equal to the charge on the ion.

If the oxidation numbers are known for all but one kind of atom in a compound or in a polyatomic ion, that unknown oxidation number can be calculated.

The following examples illustrate the calculation of oxidation numbers.

Example 2.3

Calculate the oxidation numbers for potassium and fluorine in potassium fluoride, KF.

Potassium fluoride is an ionic substance in which the potassium ion has a charge of $+1$ (K^+) and the fluoride ion has a charge of -1 (F^-). Hence the oxidation numbers of potassium and fluorine are $+1$ and -1, respectively (Rule 2).

Example 2.4

Calculate the oxidation number of mercury in HgO and in Hg_2O.

The oxidation number of mercury can be calculated from the oxidation number of oxygen, which is -2 (Rule 3).

In HgO, the Hg must have an oxidation number of $+2$ (to balance the oxidation number of -2 for the O) so that the sum of the oxidation numbers in the neutral compound will be zero.

In Hg_2O, the *two* Hg atoms must have the *total* sum of their oxidation numbers equal to $+2$ in order to balance the oxidation number of -2 for the O in the compound.

Because the total sum of the oxidation numbers for the *two* Hg atoms is +2, each must have a charge of +1; hence the oxidation number for mercury in Hg_2O is +1.

Calculate the oxidation number of nitrogen in the nitrate ion, NO_3^-.

Oxygen has an oxidation number of −2 (Rule 3). Hence for the three oxygen atoms, the total sum of the oxidation numbers is −6. Because the overall charge for the entire ion is −1, the oxidation number for nitrogen must be +5 (+5 and −6 produce the overall −1 charge on the ion).

Example 2.5

❷.8 Naming of Compounds (Nomenclature)

Binary compounds contain two different elements. We will consider here the naming, or **nomenclature,** of some binary compounds and a few compounds that are named as though they were binary compounds. In subsequent chapters, we will discuss how to name compounds that contain more than two different kinds of elements.

1. Binary Compounds Containing a Metal and a Nonmetal. The name consists of the name of the metal followed by the name of the nonmetal with its ending replaced by the suffix *-ide*. Some examples are

NaCl, sodium chloride Na_2O, sodium oxide
KBr, potassium bromide   CdS, cadmium sulfide
CaI_2, calcium iodide Mg_3N_2, magnesium nitride
AgF, silver fluoride Ca_3P_2, calcium phosphide
HCl, hydrogen chloride Al_4C_3, aluminum carbide
LiH, lithium hydride Mg_2Si, magnesium silicide

Compounds that contain polyatomic ions such as those listed in Section 2.5 are named similarly to binary compounds—the name of the positive ion is followed by the name of the negative ion. (The *-ide* ending, which is characteristic of the naming of true binary compounds, is not used here unless the name of the negative ion happens to end in *-ide*.) Thus, for example, NaOH is named sodium hydroxide (it contains the sodium ion, Na^+, and the hydroxide ion, OH^-); NH_4Cl is called ammonium chloride; $Ca(NO_3)_2$, calcium nitrate; and $NaCH_3CO_2$, sodium acetate.

2. Inorganic Binary Compounds Containing Hydrogen and a Nonmetal. Inorganic hydrogen-containing binary compounds are named like binary compounds that contain a metal and a nonmetal, with hydrogen named first. Thus HF is hydrogen fluoride. If a binary hydrogen compound is an acid (gives up hydrogen ions in water solution—Section 2.10), the prefix *hydro-* is used instead of the word *hydrogen* and the suffix *-ic* replaces the suffix *-ide* when we are referring to the water solution. Note that in the following examples (*g*) refers to a gas and (*aq*) refers to a water (aqueous) solution.

HF(*g*), hydrogen fluoride   HF(*aq*), hydrofluoric acid
HCl(*g*), hydrogen chloride   HCl(*aq*), hydrochloric acid
HBr(*g*), hydrogen bromide   HBr(*aq*), hydrobromic acid
H_2S(*g*), hydrogen sulfide H_2S(*aq*), hydrosulfuric acid

Some binary compounds have common names. For example, H_2O is called water and NH_3 is called ammonia.

3. Binary Compounds Containing Two Nonmetals. The name consists of the name of the nonmetal that is farther to the left or farther toward the bottom in the periodic table, followed by the name of the nonmetal that is farther to the right or farther toward the top in the periodic table. The name of the second-named nonmetal is given the suffix *-ide*. If a nonmetallic element can unite with another nonmetallic element to form more than one compound, the compounds can be distinguished by the Greek prefixes *mono-* (meaning one), *di-* (two), *tri-* (three), *tetra-* (four), *penta-* (five), *hexa-* (six), *hepta-* (seven), *octa-* (eight), *nona-* (nine), and *deca-* (ten). The prefixes precede the name of the constituent to which they refer.

CO, carbon monoxide
CO_2, carbon dioxide
NO_2, nitrogen dioxide
N_2O_4, dinitrogen tetraoxide
N_2O_5, dinitrogen pentaoxide

SO_2, sulfur dioxide
SO_3, sulfur trioxide
BCl_3, boron trichloride
PCl_5, phosphorus pentachloride
IF_7, iodine heptafluoride

A second method of naming binary compounds containing elements that can have more than one oxidation number is to place Roman numerals in parentheses after the name of the first-named element to indicate its oxidation number.

$FeCl_2$, iron(II) chloride
$FeCl_3$, iron(III) chloride
Hg_2O, mercury(I) oxide
HgO, mercury(II) oxide
$CuSO_4$, copper(II) sulfate

SO_2, sulfur(IV) oxide
SO_3, sulfur(VI) oxide
NO, nitrogen(II) oxide
NO_2, nitrogen(IV) oxide
IF_7, iodine(VII) fluoride

❷.9 Chemical Equations

When atoms, molecules, or ions regroup to form other substances, chemists use a shorthand type of expression called a **chemical equation** to describe the chemical change. Symbols and formulas are used in equations to describe all substances involved and their compositions. Numbers preceding each symbol or formula are called **coefficients** and are used to indicate the simplest whole-number ratios of the atoms, molecules, or ions involved. The substances to the left of the arrow in the equation are referred to as **reactants;** those to the right are called **products.** The following example shows the equation for the reaction of methane with oxygen to form carbon dioxide and water (also see Fig. 2.5).

$$CH_4 + 2O_2 \longrightarrow CO_2 + 2H_2O \qquad\qquad (1)$$

The arrow is read "to give," "to produce," "to yield," or "to form." A plus sign on the left side of an equation is read "reacts with," and a plus sign on the right side is read "and."

In the equation for the reaction of CH_4 and O_2 [Equation (1)], the simplest whole-number ratios of molecules involved in the reaction are shown to be one CH_4 molecule to two O_2 molecules for the reactants and one CO_2 molecule to two H_2O molecules for the products. Because the law of conservation of matter states that matter can be neither created nor destroyed in a chemical reaction (Section 1.3), a chemical equation must be "balanced"; that is, it must show the same number of atoms in the products as in the reactants. In Equation (1) and in the corresponding Fig. 2.5, we can see that one carbon atom, four hydrogen atoms, and four oxygen atoms are present in both the reactants and the products. In actual practice, of course, vast numbers of each kind of molecule would be involved, but they would always react in the ratios of one molecule of CH_4 to two molecules of O_2 to produce one molecule of CO_2 and two molecules of H_2O.

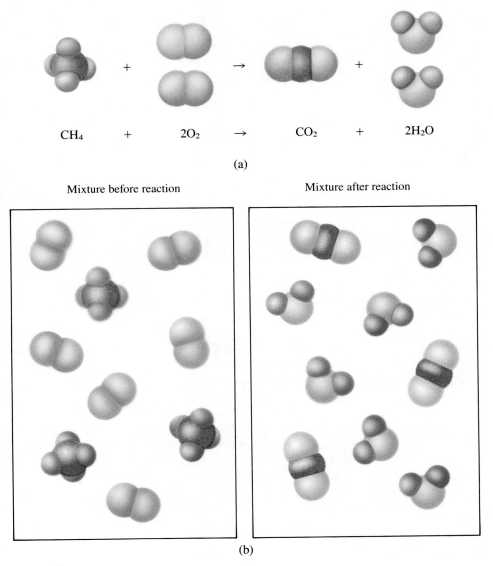

$$CH_4 \quad + \quad 2O_2 \quad \rightarrow \quad CO_2 \quad + \quad 2H_2O$$

(a)

Mixture before reaction   Mixture after reaction

(b)

Figure 2.5

Methane, CH_4, and oxygen, O_2, react to produce carbon dioxide, CO_2, and water, H_2O. One molecule of methane reacts for every two molecules of oxygen that react; one molecule of carbon dioxide and two molecules of water are produced for every methane molecule that reacts. The chemical equation for this reaction is given below part (a). The drawing illustrates how the atoms are redistributed during the reaction. (a) Diagram showing the minimum number of molecules that can react, according to the balanced equation. Carbon atoms are shown in gray; hydrogen atoms in brown; oxygen atoms in red. (b) Diagram showing the same ratios of molecules but beginning with three molecules of methane. In actual fact, huge numbers of each kind of molecule are involved, but they always react in the proportions of two molecules of O_2 for each molecule of CH_4 to produce one molecule of CO_2 and two molecules of H_2O.

Figure 2.6

When an electric current is passed through water, two volumes of hydrogen are produced for each volume of oxygen.

The statement "when water is decomposed by an electric current, hydrogen and oxygen are formed" (Fig. 2.6) can be expressed by the chemical equation

$$H_2O \longrightarrow H_2 + O_2 \qquad \text{(unbalanced)} \qquad (2)$$

However, this equation is not complete because it does not contain the same number of atoms on both sides of the arrow. One molecule of water, which contains only one atom of oxygen, cannot be rearranged into a product that contains two atoms of oxygen. Two molecules of water, however, can provide two atoms of oxygen, but two molecules of water also contain a total of four atoms of hydrogen. We can complete the equation by placing the proper coefficients on each side of the arrow.

$$2H_2O \longrightarrow 2H_2 + O_2 \qquad (3)$$

This procedure is referred to as **balancing** the equation. The subscripts in a formula cannot be changed to make an equation balance; subscripts indicate the atomic composition of a substance. The balanced equation now indicates that when H_2 and O_2 form from the decomposition of H_2O, two molecules of H_2 and one molecule of O_2 must be formed for every two molecules of H_2O that decompose.

Most simple chemical equations can be balanced by inspection. This procedure involves looking at the equation and adjusting the coefficients so that equal numbers of atoms of each type are present on both sides of the arrow. Let's consider the reaction of aluminum, Al, with hydrogen chloride, HCl, producing aluminum chloride, $AlCl_3$, and hydrogen, H_2. First we write the unbalanced equation:

$$Al + HCl \longrightarrow AlCl_3 + H_2 \qquad \text{(unbalanced)} \qquad (4)$$

Now we determine the number of atoms of each type on both sides. This equation is not balanced because it shows one Al, one H, and one Cl atom on the left and one Al, two H, and three Cl atoms on the right. Hence the numbers of atoms of each type are not the same on both sides. To find the coefficients that balance the equation, it is usually best to consider the substance with the most atoms first, which in this case is $AlCl_3$. This molecule contains three Cl atoms, which must all come from HCl. Therefore, we place a coefficient of 3 in front of HCl. At this stage we have

$$Al + 3HCl \longrightarrow AlCl_3 + H_2 \qquad \text{(unbalanced)} \qquad (5)$$

Although the Cl and Al atoms are now balanced, the H atoms are not. Three HCl molecules, which collectively contain three hydrogen atoms, would give $1\frac{1}{2}$ H_2 molecules. Thus we have

$$Al + 3HCl \longrightarrow AlCl_3 + 1\frac{1}{2} H_2 \qquad (6)$$

Although now balanced, this equation is not in its most conventional form, because it indicates that $1\frac{1}{2}$ molecules of hydrogen are formed, and half-molecules do not exist. Therefore, we must multiply each coefficient by 2 to obtain a balanced equation with the simplest whole-number coefficients.

$$2Al + 6HCl \longrightarrow 2AlCl_3 + 3H_2 \qquad (7)$$

There are two Al, six H, and six Cl atoms on each side of the balanced equation.

Balancing equations by inspection is a trial-and-error process; you may have to try several sets of coefficients before you find the correct ones.

In addition to identifying reactants and products, chemical equations often give other information, such as the state of the reactants and products. For example, the formula for a gaseous reactant or product is followed by (*g*); a liquid by (*l*); a solid by (s); and a reactant or product that is dissolved in water by (*aq*). The reaction of solid sodium, Na, with liquid water to give hydrogen gas, H_2, and a solution of sodium hydroxide, NaOH, in water would be indicated by the equation

$$2Na(s) + 2H_2O(l) \longrightarrow H_2(g) + 2NaOH(aq) \tag{8}$$

Special conditions, such as temperature or any other special circumstances that characterize the reaction, may be written above or below the arrow. The electrolysis of water, described earlier in this section, is sometimes written as follows:

$$2H_2O(l) \xrightarrow{\text{Elect.}} 2H_2(g) + O_2(g) \tag{9}$$

where the abbreviation *Elect.* over the arrow indicates that the reaction occurs by means of an electric current. A reaction carried out by heating may be indicated with a triangle ($\triangle$) over the arrow:

$$CaCO_3(s) \xrightarrow{\triangle} CaO(s) + CO_2(g) \tag{10}$$

Ionic Equations

Equations are often written in ionic form, wherein it is customary to show *as ions* the ions formed by any *soluble ionic species* that goes predominantly into solution as ions and to show any ionic substance that remains relatively intact by giving its *empirical formula*. A molecular covalent compound that retains its form as a molecule in solution is written as its molecular formula. Thus, **in an ionic equation, each substance is written in the predominant form in which it occurs in the reaction solution.**

For the equation

$$NaCl(aq) + AgNO_3(aq) \longrightarrow NaNO_3(aq) + AgCl(s) \tag{11}$$

the ionic equation is

$$\underbrace{Na^+(aq) + Cl^-(aq)}_{\text{Solution of NaCl}} + \underbrace{Ag^+(aq) + NO_3^-(aq)}_{\text{Solution of AgNO}_3} \longrightarrow$$

$$\underbrace{Na^+(aq) + NO_3^-(aq)}_{\text{Solution of NaNO}_3} + \underbrace{AgCl(s)}_{\text{Solid AgCl}} \tag{12}$$

Sometimes a **net ionic equation** is written, in which only the species that take part in the reaction are included. In Equation (12), both $Na^+(aq)$ and $NO_3^-(aq)$ are present in the solution, but neither ion takes part in the reaction. Both ions appear in exactly the same form on both sides of the equation. Such ions are often called **spectator ions.** The other two ions, $Ag^+(aq)$ and $Cl^-(aq)$, do *not* appear in the same form on the two sides of the equation. These two ions do take part in the reaction, combining to form solid silver chloride, $AgCl(s)$. The *net* ionic equation, therefore, is

$$Ag^+(aq) + Cl^-(aq) \longrightarrow AgCl(s) \tag{13}$$

It shows only those species that undergo a change during the reaction. The net ionic equation tells us that silver ion from *any* soluble ionic silver compound will combine with chloride ion from *any* soluble ionic chloride compound to form a precipitate of silver chloride. The full molecular or ionic equation tells us what *specific* substances furnish the reacting ions in a particular reaction. These different methods of writing an equation are thus useful in different ways.

NaCl(s)

(a)

$Na^+(aq) + Cl^-(aq)$

(b)

Figure 2.7
The dissolution of solid sodium chloride in water. (a) The distribution of ions in solid sodium chloride. Red spheres represent Na^+; green spheres represent Cl^-. Each ion is in contact with six ions of opposite charge. (b) The distribution of ions in an aqueous solution of sodium chloride. Each ion is free to move independently because it is surrounded by water molecules that help separate the ions of opposite charge, which otherwise would be strongly attracted to each other. Brown spheres represent hydrogen atoms of the water molecules; yellow spheres represent oxygen atoms of the water.

One further important point should be made. **For an ionic equation, the sum of the total ion charges on each side, as well as the numbers of each kind of atom on each side, must balance.** In Equation (13), the sum of the charges on each side is zero. The sum of the charges on each side of a net ionic equation, however, does not have to be zero (and often is not), but *the sums of the charges on both sides must be the same.*

❷.10 Classification of Chemical Compounds

Chemical compounds exhibit a variety of properties. It is possible to classify compounds on the basis of these properties.

1. Salts. A **salt** is an ionic compound composed of positive ions (cations) and negative ions (anions). Simple salts are formed by the combination of a metal and a nonmetal—the metal forms the cation and the nonmetal forms the anion. In more complex salts the cation may be a polyatomic positive ion such as NH_4^+ or PCl_4^+, and the anion a polyatomic negative ion such as NO_3^- or SO_4^{2-}. Ionic compounds that contain hydroxide or oxide ions are called bases rather than salts. (See Part 2 of this section.)

Compounds that are composed of ions are held together in the solid state by ionic bonds, strong electrostatic attractions between oppositely charged ions (Sections 2.6 and 7.1). When soluble salts dissolve in water, the ions separate (Fig. 2.7) and are free to move about independently. The process for the dissolution (dissolving) of the salt sodium chloride in water may be represented by the following equation, in which the abbreviation *aq* indicates that the ions are separated, surrounded by water molecules, and moving independently:

$$NaCl(s) \xrightarrow{H_2O(l)} Na^+(aq) + Cl^-(aq) \qquad (1)$$

2. Acids and Bases. A compound that donates a hydrogen ion (H^+), a proton, to another compound is called a **Brønsted acid,** or simply an **acid,** after Johannes Brønsted, a Danish chemist. A compound that accepts a hydrogen ion is called a **Brønsted base,** or simply a **base.** Other definitions have been developed that emphasize other aspects of the behavior of acids and bases, as will be discussed in Section 16.14, but for now we will concentrate on this one. The following reactions illustrate the transfer of a hydrogen ion from a Brønsted acid to a Brønsted base:

$$\begin{array}{ccc} \text{Acid} & \text{Base} & \text{Salt} \\ HCl(g) + NH_3(g) & \longrightarrow & NH_4Cl(s) \end{array} \qquad (2)$$

$$H_2SO_4(l) + NaOH(s) \longrightarrow NaHSO_4(s) + H_2O(l) \qquad (3)$$

Salts are produced in these reactions: NH_4Cl contains the ions NH_4^+ and Cl^-, and $NaHSO_4$ contains Na^+ and HSO_4^-.

When dissolved in water, acids donate hydrogen ions to water molecules, forming **hydronium ions, H_3O^+,** plus whatever anion is produced when the acid loses a hydrogen ion (Fig. 2.8). Note that water accepts a hydrogen ion from the acid and thereby acts as a base.

$$HCl(g) + H_2O(l) \longrightarrow H_3O^+(aq) + Cl^-(aq) \qquad (4)$$

$$H_2SO_4(l) + H_2O(l) \longrightarrow H_3O^+(aq) + HSO_4^-(aq) \qquad (5)$$

$$HSO_4^-(aq) + H_2O(l) \longrightarrow H_3O^+(aq) + SO_4^{2-}(aq) \qquad (6)$$

Thus an acid forms hydronium ions when dissolved in water. For convenience the hydronium ion is sometimes written as H^+ or $H^+(aq)$, but remember that H^+ and $H^+(aq)$ are abbreviations; a hydrogen ion in water is always associated with at least one water molecule. We will discuss H_3O^+ as a reactive species later (Chapter 16).

When dissolved in water, bases either provide OH^- ions directly to the solution, or they accept hydrogen ions from water molecules, thereby releasing to the solution hydroxide ions plus whatever cation is produced. Examples include

$$NaOH(aq) \xrightarrow{H_2O(l)} Na^+(aq) + OH^-(aq) \quad (7)$$

$$NH_3(aq) + H_2O(l) \longrightarrow NH_4^+(aq) + OH^-(aq) \quad (8)$$

$$CaO(s) + H_2O(l) \longrightarrow Ca^{2+}(aq) + 2OH^-(aq) \quad (9)$$

In Equation (8), water acts as an acid by donating a hydrogen ion to the base, NH_3.

Note that water can behave as either a base [Equations (4) through (6)] or as an acid [Equation (8)], depending on the nature of the substance dissolved in it. This dual behavior is characteristic of some other compounds, too. A compound that can behave either as an acid or as a base is referred to as an **amphoteric compound.**

Some common laboratory acids and bases, and the products that result when they dissolve in water, are listed in Table 2.4.

3. Electrolytes and Nonelectrolytes. Electrolytes are compounds that dissolve in water and give solutions that contain ions. Ionic compounds such as sodium hydroxide and potassium nitrate (which dissolve in water giving solutions of ions) and covalent compounds such as hydrogen chloride and ammonia (which react with water to form ions) are electrolytes. Ionic compounds and those covalent compounds that give essentially a 100% yield of ions are called **strong electrolytes.** Compounds (such as acetic acid and ammonia) that give a low percentage yield of ions in water are called **weak electrolytes. Nonelectrolytes** are compounds that do not ionize when they dissolve in water. Only covalent compounds can be nonelectrolytes. Many compounds of carbon, such as methane, CH_4, benzene, C_6H_6, ethanol, C_2H_5OH, ether, $(C_2H_5)_2O$, and formaldehyde, CH_2O, are nonelectrolytes. A few inorganic compounds are nonelectrolytes;

HCl molecule

$HCl(g)$

(a)

$H_2O(l)$

$Cl^-(aq)$

$H_3O^+(aq)$

$H_3O^+(aq) + Cl^-(aq)$

(b)

Figure 2.8

The dissolution of gaseous covalent hydrogen chloride in water. (a) Molecules of hydrogen chloride in the gas phase. Each chlorine atom (green sphere) is bonded to a hydrogen atom (brown sphere) by a covalent bond. (b) A solution of hydrogen chloride in water (a hydrochloric acid solution). The hydrogen ions are donated to water molecules, giving a solution of H_3O^+ and Cl^- ions.

Table 2.4	Some Common Laboratory Acids and Bases, with the Products that Result When They Dissolve in Water	
Formula of Acid or Base	Name of Compound	Ions Produced in Water
Acids		
HCl	Hydrogen chloride	$H_3O^+(aq) + Cl^-(aq)$
HNO_3	Nitric acid	$H_3O^+(aq) + NO_3^-(aq)$
H_2SO_4	Sulfuric acid	$H_3O^+(aq) + HSO_4^-(aq)$
CH_3CO_2H	Acetic acid	$H_3O^+(aq) + CH_3CO_2^-(aq)$
Bases		
NaOH	Sodium hydroxide	$Na^+(aq) + OH^-(aq)$
KOH	Potassium hydroxide	$K^+(aq) + OH^-(aq)$
$Ca(OH)_2$	Calcium hydroxide	$Ca^{2+}(aq) + 2OH^-(aq)$
NH_3	Ammonia	$NH_4^+(aq) + OH^-(aq)$
CaO	Calcium oxide	$Ca^{2+}(aq) + 2OH^-(aq)$

examples include nitrogen(I) oxide (sometimes called nitrous oxide), N_2O; phosphine, PH_3; and nitrogen(III) chloride (sometimes called nitrogen trichloride), NCl_3.

4. Polymers. A **polymer** (Fig. 2.9) is a very large molecule that is built by the bonding together of many smaller units referred to as **monomers.**

Polymers include many familiar materials, such as polyethylene and polypropylene in plastic bottles and bags for fruits and vegetables; polyvinyl chloride in insulation and plumbing pipes; polystyrene in foam containers; polyurethane in foam cups; polymethyl α-cyanoacrylate ("super glue"); Teflon in valves and nonstick coatings on kitchen utensils; Orlon, Acrilan, Nylon, and Dacron in textiles; Plexiglas and Lucite in molded articles and paints; synthetic rubber in automobile tires; and Saran Wrap for food packaging.

More will be said about polymers in Section 2.12 and in Chapter 30. Perhaps no other single class of synthetic chemical compounds has had a more profound effect on our lives.

❷.11 Classification of Chemical Reactions

Just as it is convenient to classify the elements as metals and nonmetals and to classify compounds as discussed in the preceding section, it is convenient to classify chemical reactions. Several common types of reactions are discussed below. However, note that the classifications overlap, and some reactions fall into more than one class.

1. Addition, or Combination, Reactions. An **addition reaction** occurs when two or more substances combine to give another substance.

$$S + O_2 \xrightarrow{\triangle} SO_2 \tag{1}$$

$$Ca + Br_2 \longrightarrow CaBr_2 \tag{2}$$

$$2K_2S + 3O_2 \xrightarrow{\triangle} 2K_2SO_3 \tag{3}$$

$$CaO + SO_3 \longrightarrow CaSO_4 \tag{4}$$

Remember that most compounds that contain both metals and nonmetals are ionic. Thus the products in Equations (2), (3), and (4) are salts.

2. Decomposition Reactions. A **decomposition reaction** occurs when one compound breaks down (decomposes) into two or more substances.

Figure 2.9

(a) An electric LGB G-gauge model train made of a polymer called Luran S Plastic, a tough, rigid, antistatic polymer that is highly resistant to ultraviolet rays, moisture, and wide temperature variations. It can be used indoors or outdoors in all weather conditions. (b) A 1990 Oldsmobile Silhouette APV, in which the body is completely made of polymer instead of steel. Upper body panels are made of glass-reinforced thermoset polyester; front, rear, and side panels are polyurethane; and fenders are made of a resilient composite polymer called Enduraflex Plus.

(a)

(b)

$$2HgO \xrightarrow{\triangle} 2Hg + O_2 \tag{5}$$

$$CaCO_3 \xrightarrow{\triangle} CaO + CO_2 \tag{6}$$

$$2Cu(NO_3)_2 \xrightarrow{\triangle} 2CuO + 4NO_2 + O_2 \tag{7}$$

$$2NaHSO_4 \xrightarrow{\triangle} Na_2SO_4 + SO_3 + H_2O \tag{8}$$

3. Metathesis Reactions. A **metathesis reaction** is a reaction in which two compounds exchange parts. We can expect a metathesis reaction to occur when an insoluble compound, a gas, a nonelectrolyte, or a weak electrolyte is formed as a product. The formation of any of these kinds of products is referred to as a **driving force** for a reaction. Let us look at examples of each.

(a) *Formation of an Insoluble Compound.*

$$CaCl_2(aq) + 2AgNO_3(aq) \longrightarrow 2AgCl(s) + Ca(NO_3)_2(aq) \tag{9}$$

Calcium chloride, silver nitrate, and calcium nitrate all are ionic compounds that are soluble in water. Silver chloride is also ionic, but it is quite insoluble in water and its formation serves as an effective driving force for the reaction. The ionic equation and net ionic equation are as follows:

Ionic: $[Ca^{2+}(aq)] + 2Cl^-(aq) + 2Ag^+(aq) + [2NO_3^-(aq)] \longrightarrow$

$$2AgCl(s) + [Ca^{2+}(aq)] + [2NO_3^-(aq)] \tag{10}$$

(The brackets, which are optional, indicate spectator ions—ions that are present but do not participate in the reaction.)

Net Ionic: $2Cl^-(aq) + 2Ag^+(aq) \longrightarrow 2AgCl(s)$

Dividing each coefficient by 2 to get the lowest whole-number coefficients yields

$$Cl^-(aq) + Ag^+(aq) \longrightarrow AgCl(s) \tag{11}$$

A solid substance resulting from a reaction is called a **precipitate,** and the reaction can be called a **precipitation reaction,** which is one kind of metathesis reaction.

(b) *Formation of a Gas.* Consider the following metathesis reaction between solid sodium chloride and sulfuric acid in the absence of water:

$$NaCl(s) + H_2SO_4(l) \longrightarrow HCl(g) + NaHSO_4(s) \tag{12}$$

The formation of the gas, hydrogen chloride, serves as a driving force for the reaction.

(c) *Formation of a Nonelectrolyte or a Weak Electrolyte.* A solution of KNO_2, the potassium salt of the acid HNO_2 (nitrous acid) reacts with a solution of HCl to give a solution containing HNO_2 molecules and the salt KCl (potassium chloride).

$$\underbrace{[K^+(aq)] + NO_2^-(aq)}_{\text{Solution of } KNO_2} + \underbrace{H_3O^+(aq) + [Cl^-(aq)]}_{\text{Solution of HCl}} \longrightarrow$$

$$\underbrace{HNO_2(aq) + [K^+(aq)] + [Cl^-(aq)] + H_2O(l)}_{\text{Solution of } HNO_2 \text{ and KCl}} \tag{13}$$

How can you tell it is weak?

The formation of HNO_2, a weak electrolyte, is a driving force for the reaction. It is soluble in water but does not ionize appreciably. It remains largely as HNO_2 molecules when it dissolves and hence is shown in Equation (13) as the HNO_2 molecule.

4. Oxidation–Reduction Reactions. Many of the reactions we have just described can also be classified as oxidation–reduction reactions, reactions involving changes in oxidation numbers. When an atom, either free or in a molecule or ion, loses electrons, it is **oxidized**, and its oxidation number increases. When an atom, either free or in a molecule or ion, gains electrons, it is **reduced**, and its oxidation number decreases.

Oxidation and reduction always occur simultaneously, for if one atom gains electrons and is reduced, a second atom must provide the electrons and thereby be oxidized. Thus the substance that is oxidized (loses electrons) transfers electrons to the substance that is reduced (gains electrons). Reactions involving oxidation and reduction are referred to as **oxidation–reduction,** or **redox, reactions.** An example is the reaction between sodium and chlorine, in which sodium is oxidized and chlorine is reduced.

$$\overset{0}{2Na} + \overset{0}{Cl_2} \longrightarrow \overset{+1\,-1}{2NaCl} \tag{14}$$

As sodium is oxidized, its oxidation number increases from 0 to +1, as indicated by the numbers above the symbols in Equation (14). As chlorine is reduced, its oxidation number decreases from 0 to −1. Other examples of oxidation–reduction reactions follow. In each case, the species that is oxidized is written first.

$$\overset{0}{Zn} + \overset{+1}{H_2SO_4} \longrightarrow \overset{+2}{ZnSO_4} + \overset{0}{H_2} \tag{15}$$

$$\overset{+2}{SnCl_2} + \overset{+4}{PbCl_4} \longrightarrow \overset{+4}{SnCl_4} + \overset{+2}{PbCl_2} \tag{16}$$

$$\overset{+2}{2CO} + \overset{+2}{2NO} \longrightarrow \overset{+4}{2CO_2} + \overset{0}{N_2} \tag{17}$$

The **reducing agent** in an oxidation–reduction reaction gives up electrons to another reactant and causes the other reactant to be reduced. In Equations (14) through (17) the first reactant is the reducing agent. Because a reducing agent loses electrons, it is oxidized. The **oxidizing agent** in a redox reaction gains electrons and causes the reducing agent to be oxidized. The oxidizing agent picks up electrons during a redox reaction, so it is reduced.

Although Equation (14) is an oxidation–reduction reaction, it can also be classified as an addition reaction. Other oxidation–reduction reactions that are also addition reactions include Equations (1), (2), and (3) in this section. Oxidation–reduction reactions may also be decomposition reactions, as illustrated in Equations (5) and (7) in this section. These reactions are examples of the overlap of classifications noted at the beginning of this section.

Reactions of an element or a compound with oxygen at an elevated temperature are called **combustion reactions,** which constitute one type of oxidation–reduction reaction. Examples are the combustion of methane to give carbon dioxide and water (Fig. 2.5) and Equations (1) and (3) in this section.

5. Acid–Base Reactions. An **acid–base reaction** occurs when a hydrogen ion is transferred from a Brønsted acid to a Brønsted base. The reaction of H_2SO_4 with $Mg(OH)_2$ is an acid–base reaction. An acid–base reaction in water always results in formation of a salt and water.

$$H_2SO_4 + Mg(OH)_2 \longrightarrow MgSO_4 + 2H_2O \qquad (18)$$

$$\underset{\text{An acid}}{} \quad \underset{\text{A base}}{} \qquad \underset{\text{A salt}}{} \quad \underset{\text{Water}}{}$$

Hydrogen ions are transferred from H_2SO_4 to the hydroxide ions in $Mg(OH)_2$ in this acid–base reaction.

6. Reversible Reactions. A **reversible reaction** is a reaction that can proceed in either direction. When acetic acid, CH_3CO_2H, is added to water, the acetic acid reacts to form hydronium ions, H_3O^+, and acetate ions, $CH_3CO_2^-$, in small amounts (acetic acid is a weak electrolyte). As soon as any hydronium ions and acetate ions form, some of them react with each other to give acetic acid. This reaction is the reverse of that which occurs when acetic acid is added to water. Both reactions, forward and reverse, then proceed simultaneously. Equations describing reactions that can proceed in either direction are written with a double arrow ($\rightleftharpoons$).

$$CH_3CO_2H(aq) + H_2O(l) \rightleftharpoons H_3O^+(aq) + CH_3CO_2^-(aq) \qquad (19)$$

The oxidation–reduction reaction of nitrogen with hydrogen to produce ammonia is also a reversible reaction.

$$N_2(g) + 3H_2(g) \overset{\triangle}{\rightleftharpoons} 2NH_3(g) \qquad (20)$$

When a closed container of nitrogen and hydrogen at high pressure is heated at 300°C, about 50% of the N_2 and H_2 is converted to NH_3 once the reaction is complete (when the amount of ammonia stops changing). If the container is then heated to 400°C, the reverse reaction occurs and some of the ammonia decomposes to nitrogen and hydrogen. The percentage of ammonia in the container is reduced to about 35% by the time the amount of ammonia again stops changing. The extent to which each of the two opposite reactions takes place can be varied by changing the quantities of the reactants or by changing the temperature, pressure, or volume.

The properties of reversible reactions will be considered more fully in Chapter 15. At this stage of your study, it is sufficient for you to recognize that a reversible reaction is one that can proceed in two opposing directions and that the two opposing reactions proceed simultaneously. Many reactions have at least some tendency toward reversibility.

❷.12 Chemistry of Some Important Industrial Chemicals

The compounds and elements listed in Table 2.5 constituted about 72% of the industrial chemicals produced in the United States during 1989. In this section, we will survey some of the chemistry of six of the top ten chemicals—four inorganic elements and compounds (nitrogen, oxygen, sulfuric acid, and ammonia), which show some of the differences between the chemistry of some elements and compounds, and two organic compounds (ethylene and propylene) that are important in the polymer industry. The

(a)

(b)

(c)

Figure 2.10

Models of sulfuric acid, H_2SO_4
(a) The molecular structure. (b) A ball-and-stick model. (c) A space-filling model.

Table 2.5	Important Industrial Chemicals
Element or Compound	1989 U.S. Production (in billion-lb units)
H_2SO_4	86.80
N_2	53.77
O_2	37.75
C_2H_4	34.95
NH_3	33.76
CaO, $Ca(OH)_2$	32.99
H_3PO_4	23.12
Cl_2	22.32
NaOH	22.15
C_3H_6	20.23
Na_2CO_3	19.79
HNO_3	15.98
NH_4NO_3	15.11
CO_2	10.83
HCl	5.26
$(NH_4)_2SO_4$	4.71

Reprinted in part with permission from *Chemical and Engineering News,* April 9, 1990, p. 12. Copyright 1990 American Chemical Society.

section will illustrate many of the topics we have discussed in this chapter, such as symbols and formulas, ionic and covalent compounds, oxidation numbers, nomenclature, chemical equations, and types of compounds and reactions.

1. Sulfuric Acid. (Ranks number 1 in U.S. industrial chemical production.) With 14% of the industrial chemical production of the United States devoted to its manufacture, sulfuric acid (Fig. 2.10) ranks as the most significant industrial chemical. Per capita use of sulfuric acid has been taken as one index of the technical development of a nation.

Sulfuric acid is used extensively as an acid (a source of hydrogen ions) because it is the cheapest strong acid. It is used to manufacture fertilizer, leather, tin plate, and other chemicals; to purify petroleum; and to make and dye fabrics.

Sulfuric acid is prepared from elemental sulfur (Fig. 2.11). When sulfur is burned in air, it is oxidized in an oxidation–reduction reaction by the oxygen in the air. Covalent molecules of gaseous sulfur dioxide result, wherein sulfur has an oxidation number of +4.

$$\overset{0}{S_8} + \overset{0}{8O_2} \longrightarrow \overset{+4\ -2}{8SO_2} \tag{1}$$

The sulfur in the sulfur dioxide is then further oxidized by oxygen to an oxidation number of +6, producing sulfur trioxide in a reversible reaction.

$$\overset{+4\ -2}{2SO_2} + \overset{0}{O_2} \overset{\triangle}{\rightleftharpoons} \overset{+6\ -2}{2SO_3} \tag{2}$$

Even though the percentage of SO_2 that reacts to give SO_3 is highest at lower temperatures, SO_3 forms slowly at these temperatures. At higher temperatures it forms more rapidly, but the conversion of SO_2 to SO_3 is less complete. In order to get as high a conversion to SO_3 as possible, the reaction is run at lower temperatures with vanadium(V) oxide, V_2O_5, as a catalyst. A **catalyst** is a substance that increases the speed of a chemical reaction without affecting the amount of product produced and without undergoing a permanent chemical change itself.

Sulfur trioxide reacts with water to form sulfuric acid. (This is not an oxidation–reduction reaction.)

$$\overset{+6}{SO_3} + H_2O \longrightarrow \overset{+6}{H_2SO_4} \tag{3}$$

(a)

This addition reaction also occurs in nature when SO_3 from polluted air dissolves in raindrops to give acid rain.

Sulfuric acid is a strong electrolyte. Its greatest use is as a source of hydrogen ions. About 65% of the sulfuric acid produced in the United States is used to manufacture fertilizers via an acid–base reaction with ammonia and via reaction with calcium phosphates.

The reaction of sulfuric acid with ammonia is an acid–base reaction (also an addition reaction) used to prepare ammonium sulfate, $(NH_4)_2SO_4$, a soluble fertilizer that is applied to provide nitrogen to plants.

(b)

Figure 2.11
(a) A sulfuric acid plant, including a partial view of the mound of elemental sulfur to be used as a starting material in the process. (b) A closeup view of elemental sulfur to show its nature.

$$H_2SO_4(l) + 2NH_3(g) \longrightarrow (NH_4)_2SO_4(s) \tag{4}$$

In 1989 about 4.7 billion pounds of $(NH_4)_2SO_4$ were produced in the United States.

The reaction with calcium phosphates is typically accomplished with a calcium fluorophosphate such as $Ca_5(PO_4)_3F$, found principally in North Carolina and Florida as phosphate rock (Fig. 2.12). It is a metathesis reaction that converts the extremely insoluble fluorophosphate compound into a somewhat soluble form of calcium dihydrogen phosphate, $Ca(H_2PO_4)_2 \cdot H_2O$, that can enter a plant's roots and provide it with necessary phosphorus.

$$2Ca_5(PO_4)_3F(s) + 7H_2SO_4(l) + 3H_2O(l) \longrightarrow$$
$$3Ca(H_2PO_4)_2 \cdot H_2O(s) + 2HF(g) + 7CaSO_4(s) \tag{5}$$

The centered dot in the formula $Ca(H_2PO_4)_2 \cdot H_2O$ indicates that the solid contains molecular water surrounded by the ions of the solid; such water-containing compounds are called **hydrates.**

(a)

(b)

Figure 2.12
(a) The insoluble phosphate rock from phosphate mines is converted to soluble phosphates by treatment with sulfuric acid in the plant shown.
(b) The phosphate rock from a mine is typically fluoroapatite, $Ca_5(PO_4)_3F$; chloroapatite, $Ca_5(PO_4)_3Cl$; or a mixture of these, as in the sample shown.

The solid mixture of the salts $Ca(H_2PO_4)_2 \cdot H_2O$ and $CaSO_4$ is used directly as the fertilizer. The hydrogen fluoride is recovered and used in the preparation of Freon, Teflon, and other fluorine compounds. However, as we will discuss in Chapter 29, release of the Freon class of compounds causes significant problems in the environment; much research is being devoted to discovering suitable substitutes.

Many metal oxides behave as bases, reacting with sulfuric acid in acid–base reactions to form ionic sulfate salts and water. For example, copper sulfate (used as a fungicide and in electroplating), aluminum sulfate (used in water treatment and in papermaking), and magnesium sulfate (Epsom salts) are prepared this way.

$$CuO(s) + H_2SO_4(aq) \longrightarrow Cu^{2+}(aq) + SO_4^{2-}(aq) + H_2O(l) \tag{6}$$

$$Al_2O_3(s) + 3H_2SO_4(aq) \longrightarrow 2Al^{3+}(aq) + 3SO_4^{2-}(aq) + 3H_2O(l) \tag{7}$$

$$MgO(s) + H_2SO_4(aq) \longrightarrow Mg^{2+}(aq) + SO_4^{2-}(aq) + H_2O(l) \tag{8}$$

Because these products are ionic, they exist in solution as ions. They can be recovered as solids by evaporating the water.

Sulfuric acid also undergoes a metathesis reaction with sodium chloride, giving hydrogen chloride and sodium hydrogen sulfate. The sodium hydrogen sulfate then reacts with additional sodium chloride if the mixture is heated.

$$H_2SO_4(l) + NaCl(s) \longrightarrow NaHSO_4(s) + HCl(g) \tag{9}$$

$$NaHSO_4(s) + NaCl(s) \xrightarrow{\triangle} Na_2SO_4(s) + HCl(g) \tag{10}$$

The gaseous HCl that is formed serves as a driving force for the reactions.

2. Nitrogen and Oxygen. (Rank 2 and 3, respectively, in U.S. industrial chemical production.) Both pure nitrogen and pure oxygen can be isolated from air. Nitrogen is quite unreactive, and its principal uses are actually based on this nonreactivity. It is used as an inert atmosphere blanket in the food industry to prevent spoilage due to oxidation. Liquid nitrogen boils at 77 K ($-196°C$). It is used as a means of storing biological materials such as blood and tissue samples at very low temperatures and as a coolant to produce low temperatures (Fig. 2.13).

Oxygen is a strong oxidizing agent. One of its principal uses is in oxidations to form metal oxides in the steel industry. During steel production, oxygen is blown through hot liquid iron to oxidize metallic impurities. Two common reactions are

$$\overset{0}{C} + \overset{0}{O_2} \longrightarrow \overset{+4\ -2}{CO_2} \tag{11}$$

$$\overset{0}{Si} + \overset{0}{O_2} \longrightarrow \overset{+4\ -2}{SiO_2} \tag{12}$$

Silicon dioxide, SiO_2, is less dense than liquid iron and floats to the surface where it is removed; CO_2 escapes as a gas. Note that the two Group IVA elements carbon and silicon are both oxidized to the oxidation number $+4$ and that oxygen is reduced to the oxidation number -2.

3. Ethylene and Propylene. (Rank 4 and 10, respectively, in U.S. industrial chemical production.) Ethylene, C_2H_4, and propylene, C_3H_6, are organic compounds that are vital in the production of polymers because of their ability to link themselves together in the presence of certain catalysts. Polymers contain long chains of atoms and so are very large molecules. They are used in many different applications, including clothing, fibers, insulation, construction materials, automobiles, and aircraft (Fig. 2.9).

Figure 2.13

Liquid nitrogen boiling at $-196°C$, cools a high-temperature superconductor, above which floats a magnet. The liquid nitrogen is used to cool the superconductor to the temperature at which it can exhibit its superconducting properties. It is called a high-temperature superconductor because $-196°C$ is a relatively high temperature for superconductor properties. Earlier superconductors required much lower temperatures. The much more expensive liquid helium (which remains liquid clear down to absolute zero, $-273°C$) was used to cool them.

When molecules of ethylene add together, polyethylene is produced. When molecules of propylene add together, polypropylene is produced.

$$n\left(\begin{array}{c}H \\ \diagdown \\ H\end{array}C=C\begin{array}{c}H \\ \diagup \\ H\end{array}\right) \xrightarrow{\text{Catalyst}} \left(\begin{array}{cc}H & H \\ | & | \\ -C-C- \\ | & | \\ H & H\end{array}\right)_n \qquad (13)$$

$$\text{Ethylene} \qquad\qquad \text{Polyethylene}$$

$$n\left(\begin{array}{c}H \\ \diagdown \\ H\end{array}C=C\begin{array}{c}H \\ \diagup \\ CH_3\end{array}\right) \xrightarrow{\text{Catalyst}} \left(\begin{array}{cc}H & H \\ | & | \\ -C-C- \\ | & | \\ H & CH_3\end{array}\right)_n \qquad (14)$$

$$\text{Propylene} \qquad\qquad \text{Polypropylene}$$

In these equations, n is large and represents the number of repeating groups. For polyethylene, n is approximately 400, but it can be 20,000 or even higher for some polymers.

Covalent bonds holding atoms together are represented above by single lines for single bonds and by double lines for double bonds. Covalent bonds will be explained in more detail later in Section 7.3; for now, just remember that atoms in all covalent molecules are held together quite tightly by such bonds and that this is a convenient way to represent these bonds.

A key element in these processes is the catalyst. Much study and experimentation has gone into developing better, more efficient catalysts for this kind of reaction.

Polyethylene is a flexible, tough polymer that is very water-resistant and has excellent insulating properties. It is used in plastic bottles, bags for fruits and vegetables, insulators, and many other items.

Most of the ethylene used to make polyethylene or used in other industrial reactions is produced by **pyrolysis** (heating) of ethane, C_2H_6, a component of natural gas, at temperatures of 500–800°C.

$$C_2H_6 \xrightarrow{\triangle} C_2H_4 + H_2 \qquad (15)$$

The importance of ethylene is emphasized by the fact that only three chemical substances are produced industrially in greater quantity in the United States.

The preparation of propylene is analogous to that of ethylene and is accomplished by pyrolysis of propane, C_3H_8.

$$C_3H_8 \xrightarrow{\triangle} C_3H_6 + H_2 \qquad (16)$$

4. Ammonia. (Ranks 5 in U.S. industrial chemical production.) Ammonia (Fig. 2.14) is one of the few compounds that can be prepared readily from elemental nitrogen. It is prepared by the reversible reaction of a mixture of hydrogen and nitrogen at high pressure and temperature (400–600°C) in the presence of a catalyst containing iron.

$$N_2(g) + 3H_2(g) \underset{\substack{\text{High pressure} \\ \text{400–600°C} \\ \text{Fe catalyst}}}{\rightleftharpoons} 2NH_3(g) \qquad (17)$$

This reaction is simply the oxidation of hydrogen by nitrogen, producing the covalent compound ammonia.

106.8°
(a)

(b)

(c)

Figure 2.14

Models of ammonia, NH_3. (a) The molecular structure. (b) A ball-and-stick model. (c) A space-filling model.

Figure 2.15

Ammonia is used as a fertilizer. Pure ammonia is a gas at room temperature and pressure; for convenience, it is transported in the liquid form in a pressurized tank. The ammonia is retained in the soil because it is very soluble in the water there and because it reacts with acids present in the soil.

Pure ammonia is a gas that is very soluble in water. The uses of ammonia can be attributed to two principal chemical properties of the molecule: (1) ammonia is a base, and (2) the nitrogen atom in ammonia is reactive and can readily be oxidized to higher oxidation numbers, particularly by plants, in the production of other nitrogen-containing compounds. Thus ammonia and its derivatives form an important source of nitrogen fertilizers such as ammonium nitrate and ammonium sulfate.

Approximately 15 billion pounds of ammonium salts are prepared each year in the United States. Most of this is used for fertilizer. The reactions are acid–base reactions that give salts containing the NH_4^+ ion. The principal reactions involve nitric acid, HNO_3, sulfuric acid, H_2SO_4, and phosphoric acid, H_3PO_4.

$$NH_3(g) + HNO_3(l) \longrightarrow NH_4NO_3(s) \tag{18}$$

$$2NH_3(g) + H_2SO_4(l) \longrightarrow (NH_4)_2SO_4(s) \tag{19}$$

$$NH_3(g) + H_3PO_4(l) \longrightarrow NH_4H_2PO_4(s) \tag{20}$$

Pure ammonia is also used as a fertilizer, applied from tanks in which the ammonia is in the liquid form under pressure (Fig. 2.15).

The nitrogen in ammonia can be oxidized by oxygen. Ammonia burns in oxygen, forming nitrogen(II) oxide, NO, which can then react with additional oxygen to give nitrogen(IV) oxide, NO_2. The latter oxide reacts with water to give nitric acid. This reaction is more complex than most reactions of water with nonmetal oxides because oxidation–reduction is also involved. The series of reactions is the primary method of production of nitric acid, HNO_3.

$$4NH_3 + 5O_2 \longrightarrow 4NO + 6H_2O \tag{21}$$

$$2NO + O_2 \longrightarrow 2NO_2 \tag{22}$$

$$3NO_2 + H_2O \longrightarrow 2HNO_3 + NO \tag{23}$$

For Review

Summary

A chemical **formula** identifies the atoms in a substance using **symbols,** which are one-, two-, or three-letter abbreviations for the atoms. Subscripts in formulas indicate the relative numbers of the different atoms. A **molecular formula** indicates the exact number of each type of atom in a molecule. An **empirical formula** gives the simplest whole-number ratio of atoms in a substance.

The mass of an atom is usually expressed in **atomic mass units (amu)** and is referred to as the **atomic mass.** An amu is defined as exactly $\frac{1}{12}$ the mass of a carbon-12 atom.

Atoms are composed of protons, neutrons, and electrons. **Protons** are relatively heavy particles with a charge of +1 and a mass of 1.0073 amu. **Neutrons** are relatively heavy particles with no charge and a mass of 1.0087 amu, very close to that of protons. **Electrons** are light particles with a mass of 0.00055 amu and a charge of −1. The atom contains a small positively charged nucleus surrounded by electrons. The nucleus is at least 100,000 times smaller than the atom. The nucleus consists of protons and neutrons. The number of protons in the nucleus is called the **atomic number.** The sum of the numbers of protons and neutrons in the nucleus is called the **mass number** and, expressed in amu, is approximately equal to the mass of the nucleus. It is also approximately equal to the mass of the atom, because the mass of the electrons in an atom is negligibly small compared to that of the protons and neutrons. Because an atom is neutral, the number of electrons in an atom must be equal to the number of protons.

The periodic recurrence of similar properties among the elements led to formulation of the **periodic table,** in which the elements are arranged in order of increasing atomic number in rows (known as **periods** or **series**) and columns (known as **groups** or **families**). Elements in the same group of the periodic table have similar chemical properties. Elements can be classified as **metals** and **nonmetals.** Metals appear to the left in the table and nonmetals to the right. Metals are subdivided into **representative,** or **main group, metals; transition metals;** and **inner transition metals.**

Groups are numbered, from left to right, either 1 through 18, or I through VIII along with the letter A or B, as shown in Fig. 2.4. The elements in Group 1, or IA, are known as the **alkali metals;** those in Group 2, or IIA, the **alkaline earth metals;** those in Group 16, or VIA, the **chalcogens;** those in Group 17, or VIIA, the **halogens;** and those in Group 18, or VIIIA, the **noble gases.**

The noble gases are especially stable elements. Metals (particularly those in Groups IA and IIA, but also certain other metals) tend to lose the number of electrons that would leave them with the same number of electrons as occur in the preceding noble gas in the periodic table. By this means a positively charged particle called an **ion** is formed. Similarly, nonmetals (especially those in groups VIIA and VIA, and to a lesser extent those in Group VA) can gain the number of electrons needed to provide the atoms with the same number of electrons as occur in the nearest noble gas in the periodic table. This is how negative ions are formed. Thus ions are atoms or groups of atoms that are electrically charged (some positively and some negatively). Ions can be either **monatomic** (contain only one atom) or **polyatomic** (contain more than one atom).

Compounds that contain ions are called **ionic compounds.** Compounds that do not contain ions, but instead consist of atoms bonded tightly together in molecules (uncharged groups of atoms that move about as a single unit), are called **covalent compounds.**

Oxidation numbers are assigned to atoms in molecules in accordance with the rules cited in this chapter. Oxidation numbers are used in naming compounds, classifying chemical reactions, writing chemical formulas, and keeping track of the redistribution of electrons that occurs during chemical reactions.

Most chemical compounds can be classified as **salts,** as **acids** or **bases,** as **electrolytes** or **nonelectrolytes,** or as **polymers.**

Most chemical reactions can be classified within the categories of **addition reactions, decomposition reactions, metathesis reactions, oxidation–reduction reactions,** and **reversible reactions.** Formation of an insoluble compound, a gas, a nonelectrolyte, or a weak electrolyte can serve as a driving force for a reaction.

When atoms, molecules, or ions regroup to form other substances, a shorthand type of expression called a **chemical equation** is used to describe the chemical reaction. Because matter can be neither created nor destroyed in a chemical reaction (Section 1.3), the same number of atoms of each type must appear among both the reactants and the products of a reaction. The coefficients in a balanced chemical equation indicate the relative numbers of atoms, molecules, and ions involved in a reaction.

Discussion, at the end of this chapter, of the chemistry of six of the most widely produced industrial chemicals illustrates many of the concepts introduced in the chapter.

Key Terms and Concepts

acid (2.10)
acid–base reaction (2.11)
addition reaction (2.11)
alkali metal (2.4, 2.5)
alkaline earth metal (2.4, 2.5)
amphoteric compound (2.10)
atomic mass (2.2)
atomic mass unit, amu (2.2)
atomic number (2.3)
base (2.10)
chalcogen (2.4, 2.5)
chemical equation (2.9, 2.11)
combustion reaction (2.11)
covalent compound (2.6)
dalton (2.2)
decomposition reaction (2.11)
driving force (2.11)
electrolyte (2.10)

electron (2.3)
empirical formula (2.1)
equation (2.9, 2.11)
formula (2.1)
halogen (2.4, 2.5)
hydronium ion (2.10)
inner transition metal (2.4)
ion (2.5)
ionic compound (2.6)
ionic equation (2.9)
main group metal (2.4)
mass number (2.3)
metal (2.4)
metathesis reaction (2.11)
molecular formula (2.1)
monatomic ion (2.5)
neutron (2.3)
noble gas (2.4, 2.5)

nomenclature (2.8)
nonelectrolyte (2.10)
nonmetal (2.4)
nucleus (2.3)
oxidation (2.11)
oxidation number (2.7)
oxidation–reduction reaction (2.11)
periodic table (2.4)
polyatomic ion (2.5)
polymer (2.10, 2.12)
precipitation reaction (2.11)
proton (2.3)
reduction (2.11)
representative metal (2.4)
reversible reaction (2.11)
symbol (2.1)
transition metal (2.4)

Exercises

Answers for selected even-numbered exercises marked by red numbers appear at the end of the book. The worked-out solutions to all even-numbered exercises appear in the Solutions Guide.

Symbols and Formulas

1. Distinguish among the following: symbol, formula, empirical formula.
2. Name the following elements: Ti, Mg, Ge, Tc, Ag, Mn, Sn, W, Au, Hg, Sb, Cu, Pb, Cl, Ne, Ar, Ta.
3. Name the following elements found in your body: C, H, O, N, P, S, I, Na, Cl, K, Ca, Fe, Br, Cu, Zn, Co, Mg.
4. Write the symbol for each of the following chemical elements: tin, oxygen, molybdenum, gallium, lawrencium, sodium, antimony, gold, xenon, lanthanum, uranium, nobelium, silver, fluorine, samarium.
5. Write the symbol for each of the following chemical elements: thallium, tungsten, nitrogen, mercury, sulfur, phosphorus, chlorine, copper, arsenic, chromium, iron, californium, lead, lithium, titanium.
6. Why do we use both molecular and empirical formulas?
7. Determine the empirical formula of each of the following compounds: (a) vitamin C, $C_6H_8O_6$; (b) octane, C_8H_{18}; (c) hexane, C_6H_{14}; (d) phosphorous acid, H_3PO_3; (e) tetraphosphorus hexaoxide, P_4O_6; (f) tetraphosphorus decasulfide, P_4S_{10}; (g) cystine, $C_6H_{12}S_2O_4$; (h) oxalic acid, $C_2H_2O_4$.
8. What information is needed to determine the molecular formula of a compound if the empirical formula is known?

Composition of Atoms; Isotopes

9. Indicate whether the numbers of protons, neutrons, and electrons must be the same or different in each of the following: (a) two atoms of the same element with the same mass number, (b) two atoms of the same element with different mass numbers, (c) two atoms of different elements with the same mass number.
10. Identify the following elements, and determine the number of protons, neutrons, and electrons in each. (You will find it useful to refer to the table on the inside front cover of the book and to the periodic table.) (a) atomic number 6, mass number 14; (b) atomic number 83, mass number 212; (c) atomic number 58, mass number 142; (d) atomic number 82, mass number 210; (e) atomic number 82, mass number 214.
11. Determine the atomic number and the number of protons, neutrons, and electrons in each of the following. (You will find it helpful to refer to the table on the inside front cover of the book and to the periodic table.) (a) potassium atom with mass number 40; (b) strontium atom with mass number 90; (c) cadmium atom with mass number 112; (d) radium atom with mass number 226; (e) unnilseptium atom with mass number 262.

Periodic Table

12. (a) Metals are what percentage of the total number of elements in the periodic table? Nonmetals are what percentage? (For our purposes here, count hydrogen as a

nonmetal, although it is sometimes placed both in Group IA of the metals and Group VIIA of the nonmetals.)

(b) Calculate the percentages for representative metals, for transition metals, and for inner transition metals within the total number of elements in the periodic table.

13. Using the periodic table (Fig. 2.4), state the atomic numbers of each element in each of the following categories. To make your lists as concise as possible, use ranges of atomic numbers (for example, 21–29) when appropriate.
    (a) Representative (main group) metals
    (b) Transition metals
    (c) Inner transition metals
    (d) Nonmetals
    (e) Alkali metals
    (f) Chalcogens
    (g) Noble gases
    (h) Halogens
    (i) Alkaline earth metals

Ions and Electrolytes

14. (a) How does a cation form from a neutral atom?
    (b) How does an anion form from a neutral atom?

15. Which of the following atoms would be expected to form positive ions in binary ionic compounds, and which would be expected to form negative ions? P, I, Mg, Cl, Cs, N, O, S, Al, Ra.

16. Predict the charge on the monatomic ions formed from each of the following atoms in binary ionic compounds: P, I, Mg, Cl, Al, K, N, O, S, Ca, Cs.

17. (a) Which group containing representative metals in the periodic table should form cations with an oxidation number of +3? Explain your answer.
    (b) Which group of nonmetals in the periodic table should form monatomic anions with an oxidation number of −3? Explain your answer.

18. Name each compound and identify the cations and anions in each.
    (a) $RbOH$
    (b) $RaCl_2$
    (c) $Ca(H_2PO_4)_2$
    (d) $SrHPO_4$
    (e) In_2O_3
    (f) $NaBr$
    (g) $(NH_4)_2SO_4$
    (h) $Ca_3(PO_4)_2$

19. Consider one of the atoms of uranium used in nuclear fission, the uranium atom with mass number 235.
    (a) How many protons, neutrons, and electrons does this atom contain?
    (b) How many protons, neutrons, and electrons are contained in an ion of this atom with a charge of +3?

20. Atoms of nitrogen can form ions with a charge of −3. How many protons, neutrons, and electrons are contained in a N^{3-} ion with a mass number 14?

21. Indicate whether each of the following compounds and elements dissolves in water to give a solution of an electrolyte or a nonelectrolyte.
    (a) KBr
    (b) BaI_2
    (c) HCl
    (d) $KClO_3$
    (e) Ar
    (f) NH_3
    (g) H_3PO_4
    (h) $Sr(OH)_2$
    (i) NH_4NO_3
    (j) $Sr_3(PO_4)_2$

Ionic and Covalent Compounds

22. How does an ionic compound differ from a covalent compound?

23. Predict which of the following compounds are ionic, and which are covalent, on the basis of the location of their constituent atoms in the periodic table: NCl_3, $FeBr_2$, K_2O, NO, $MgCl_2$, CaO, IBr, CO_2.

24. For each of the following compounds, state (a) whether the compound is ionic or covalent, (b) if it is ionic, the symbols for the ions and the number of ions of each type that you would predict to be present in one formula unit, and (c) if it is covalent, the formula of the molecule: $NO(g)$, $CaO(s)$, $NH_3(g)$, $HCl(g)$, $SO_2(g)$, $(NH_4)_3PO_4(s)$, $Al_2(SO_4)_3(s)$.

Oxidation Numbers

25. (a) Explain how the oxidation number of an element in a monatomic ion is related to the charge of the ion.
    (b) Explain how the oxidation number of each element in a polyatomic ion is related to the charge on the ion.

26. From their positions in the periodic table, predict the common oxidation number for each of the following elements in binary compounds: Cl, Li, Mg, S, Cs, Al, O, Ca. Explain your answers.

27. From their positions in the periodic table, predict the common oxidation number for each of the following elements in binary compounds: Be, I, N, P, K, S, B, Ra. Explain your answers.

28. Determine the oxidation number of each element in each of the polyatomic ions listed in Table 2.3.

29. Determine the oxidation number of each element in each of the following: Na, Ca, Fe, N_2, O_2, Cl_2, P_4, S_8, NO, $MgCl_2$, HBr.

30. Determine the oxidation number of each element in each of the following: HCl, NaH, NH_4^+, NO_3^-, NH_4NO_3, KNO_3, $Ca(NO_3)_2$, $Al(NO_3)_3$, BF_4^-, SO_4^{2-}, PCl_5.

31. Determine the oxidation number for each element in each of the following: PCl_3, CF_4, NH_3, PCl_3, PCl_5, H_3O^+, H_2SO_3, H_2SO_4, PO_4^{3-}, ClO_3^-, $KClO_4$.

32. Some elements can exhibit more than one oxidation number. The following oxidation numbers are not necessarily ones you would predict at this stage in your study. Write the formula of a binary compound for each of the following elements so that the element has the indicated oxidation number.
    (a) Mn, +2
    (b) N, −3
    (c) N, +3
    (d) Pb, +2
    (e) Co, +2
    (f) Fe, +3
    (g) Cu, +1 (formula for the oxide)
    (h) P, +5 (the oxide)
    (i) P, +3 (the oxide)
    (j) C, +4 (the oxide)

33. Determine the oxidation number of each element in each of the following. (*Note:* Fluorine *always* exhibits an oxidation number of −1 in its compounds.)

(a) Cl_2, ClO^-, ClO_2^-, ClO_3^-, ClO_4^-
(b) NH_3, N_2, N_2O, NO, N_2O_3, NO_2, N_2O_4, N_2O_5
(c) BeF_2
(d) ClF_3
(e) SeF_6

Naming of Compounds

34. Name the following binary compounds: $LiCl$, MgO, Na_2S, $CaCl_2$, HI, NaF.

35. Name the following compounds, each of which contains a polyatomic ion: NH_4Cl, $LiOH$, Na_3PO_4, $MgSO_4$, $KClO_4$, $Al(NO_3)_3$, $Ca(CH_3CO_2)_2$, $(NH_4)_2SO_4$.

36. Each of the following compounds contains a metal atom that can exhibit more than one oxidation number. Name each, using the Roman numeral system to indicate the oxidation number of the metal.

    (a) CoF_3 (e) $TiNO_3$
    (b) CuS (f) $Co(NO_3)_2$
    (c) $FeBr_2$ (g) $Fe_2(SO_4)_3$
    (d) $Mn(OH)_2$ (h) $PbCl_2$

37. Name the following compounds, using Greek prefixes as needed.

    (a) NO_2 (e) PCl_5
    (b) CCl_4 (f) PCl_3
    (c) N_2O_5 (g) N_2O_3
    (d) SF_6 (h) IF_7

38. The following compounds are some that have been approved by the Food and Drug Administration (FDA) for use in foods or food preparation. What is the name of each compound?

    (a) SO_2 (i) $CaCl_2$
    (b) CaO (j) Na_2SO_3
    (c) KI (k) $FeSO_4$
    (d) CO_2 (l) $FePO_4$
    (e) $(NH_4)_2CO_3$ (m) $Al_2(SO_4)_3$
    (f) $MgCO_3$ (n) K_2SO_4
    (g) $NaOH$ (o) CuI
    (h) HCl

Formulas of Compounds

39. Why must a sample of sodium oxide, Na_2O, contain two sodium ions for each oxide ion?

40. Write the formulas of the following compounds:

    (a) Sodium fluoride   (i) Hydrogen bromide
    (b) Calcium sulfide   (j) Aluminum nitride
    (c) Potassium oxide   (k) Aluminum chloride
    (d) Magnesium chloride   (l) Aluminum sulfate
    (e) Lithium nitrate   (m) Ammonium sulfate
    (f) Calcium perchlorate   (n) Aluminum phosphate
    (g) Potassium sulfate   (o) Ammonium phosphate
    (h) Calcium hydroxide   (p) Calcium phosphate

41. Write the formulas of the following compounds:

    (a) Iron(II) sulfate   (i) Nitrogen dioxide
    (b) Lead(II) bromide   (j) Dinitrogen trioxide
    (c) Mercury(II) sulfide   (k) Dinitrogen tetraoxide
    (d) Manganese(II) nitrate (l) Chlorine dioxide
    (e) Copper(I) oxide   (m) Dichlorine heptaoxide
    (f) Tin(II) fluoride   (n) Phosphorus
    (g) Vanadium(IV) chloride   pentachloride
    (h) Chromium(III)   (o) Sulfur hexafluoride
        phosphate   (p) Iron(III) sulfate

Chemical Equations

42. Distinguish among the following: reaction, equation, ionic equation.

43. Write out in words the meaning of each of the following chemical equations. (You should be able to name each substance, using the information given in Section 2.8.)

    (a) $S_8(s) + O_2(g) \longrightarrow SO_2(g)$
    (b) $2SO_2(g) + O_2(g) \longrightarrow 2SO_3(g)$
    (c) $SO_3(g) + H_2O(l) \longrightarrow H_2SO_4(aq)$
    (d) $MgCO_3(s) \longrightarrow MgO(s) + CO_2(g)$

44. Write out in words the meaning of each of the following chemical equations. (Note that $NaHSO_4$ is sodium hydrogen sulfate. You should be able to name the other substances, using the information given in Section 2.8.)

    (a) $NaCl(aq) + H_2SO_4(aq) \longrightarrow HCl(aq) + NaHSO_4(aq)$
    (b) $HBr(aq) + NaOH(aq) \longrightarrow NaBr(aq) + H_2O(l)$
    (c) $2KClO_3(s) \xrightarrow{\Delta} 2KCl(s) + 3O_2(g)$
    (d) $2NaCl(l) \xrightarrow{\text{elect.}} 2Na(l) + Cl_2(g)$

    (*Note:* Both sodium chloride and sodium metal are solids at room temperature. However, at the high temperatures used for the reaction, both melt and give liquids.)

45. Balance the following equations:

    (a) $CaCO_3 \longrightarrow CaO + CO_2$
    (b) $N_2 + H_2 \longrightarrow NH_3$
    (c) $NH_4NO_3 \longrightarrow N_2O + H_2O$
    (d) $Cu(NO_3)_2 \longrightarrow CuO + NO_2 + O_2$
    (e) $H_3PO_3 \longrightarrow H_3PO_4 + PH_3$
    (f) $KClO_3 \longrightarrow KCl + KClO_4$
    (g) $TiCl_4 + H_2O \longrightarrow TiO_2 + HCl$
    (h) $H_2 + Br_2 \longrightarrow HBr$
    (i) $C_6H_{12}O_6 \longrightarrow C_2H_5OH + CO_2$

46. Balance the following equations:

    (a) $PCl_3 + Cl_2 \longrightarrow PCl_5$
    (b) $P_4 + O_2 \longrightarrow P_4O_{10}$
    (c) $(NH_4)_2Cr_2O_7 \longrightarrow Cr_2O_3 + H_2O + N_2$
    (d) $Pb + H_2O + O_2 \longrightarrow Pb(OH)_2$
    (e) $Ca_3(PO_4)_2 + H_3PO_4 \longrightarrow Ca(H_2PO_4)_2$
    (f) $PtCl_4 \longrightarrow Pt + Cl_2$
    (g) $Sc_2O_3 + SO_3 \longrightarrow Sc_2(SO_4)_3$
    (h) $Sb + O_2 \longrightarrow Sb_4O_6$
    (i) $PCl_5 + H_2O \longrightarrow POCl_3 + HCl$

47. Write a balanced equation that describes each of the following chemical reactions.
   (a) Carbon burns in oxygen, O_2, to produce carbon monoxide gas.
   (b) Water and hot carbon react to form hydrogen gas and carbon monoxide gas.
   (c) Water vapor reacts with potassium metal to produce hydrogen gas, H_2, and potassium hydroxide.
   (d) Magnesium carbonate is heated to drive off carbon dioxide, leaving behind a white residue of magnesium oxide.
   (e) During photosynthesis in plants, carbon dioxide and water are converted into glucose, $C_6H_{12}O_6$, and oxygen, O_2.
   (f) Propane gas, C_3H_8, burns in air, forming gaseous carbon dioxide and water.
   (g) An aqueous solution of sulfurous acid, $H_2SO_3(aq)$, forms when sulfur dioxide reacts with water.
   (h) Copper(II) sulfate tetrahydrate, $CuSO_4 \cdot 4H_2O$, decomposes when heated, giving copper(II) sulfate and water.

Classification of Chemical Compounds

48. Write the formula and name for an example of each of the following:
   (a) A salt   (d) An electrolyte
   (b) An acid   (e) A nonelectrolyte
   (c) A base
49. Explain what is meant by the term *polymer*.

Classification of Chemical Reactions

50. Indicate what type, or types, of reaction each of the following represents (many reactions can be classified in more than one category). (See Section 2.11.)
   (a) $2Na + 2HCl \longrightarrow 2NaCl + H_2$
   (b) $Na_2S + 2HCl \longrightarrow 2NaCl + H_2S$
   (c) $MgO + 2HCl \longrightarrow MgCl_2 + H_2O$
   (d) $3KOH + H_3PO_4 \longrightarrow K_3PO_4 + 3H_2O$
   (e) $K_3P + 2O_2 \longrightarrow K_3PO_4$
   (f) $Mg + Cl_2 \longrightarrow MgCl_2$
51. Identify the atoms that are oxidized and reduced, the change in oxidation number for each, and the oxidizing and reducing agents in each of the following reactions:
   (a) $Zn + H_2SO_4 \longrightarrow ZnSO_4 + H_2$
   (b) $C_2H_4 + 3O_2 \longrightarrow 2CO_2 + 2H_2O$
   (c) $Mg + NiCl_2 \longrightarrow MgCl_2 + Ni$
   (d) $PCl_3 + Cl_2 \longrightarrow PCl_5$
   (e) $3Cu + 8HNO_3 \longrightarrow 3Cu(NO_3)_2 + 2NO + 4H_2O$
   (f) $2K_2S_2O_3 + I_2 \longrightarrow K_2S_4O_6 + 2KI$
52. Explain what a reversible reaction is.
53. Classify each of the following reactions as to type or types.
   (a) The reaction shown in Fig. 2.1

   (b) The reaction described in Fig. 2.5
   (c) The reaction shown in Fig. 2.8
   (d) The reaction shown in Example 3.27 of Chapter 3
54. Classify each of the reactions in Exercise 44 as to type or types of reaction. Note that some can be classified in more than one category.
55. Classify each of the reactions in Exercise 45.
56. Classify each of the reactions in Exercise 46.
57. Classify each of the reactions in Exercise 47.
58. Balance the following equations, and classify each according to type or types of reaction.
   (a) $HI + Cl_2 \longrightarrow HCl + I_2$
   (b) $MgO + Si \longrightarrow Mg + SiO_2$
   (c) $Al_2O_3 + Cl_2 + C \longrightarrow AlCl_3 + CO$
   (d) $Fe + H_2O \longrightarrow Fe_3O_4 + H_2$
   (e) $Al + H_2SO_4 \longrightarrow Al_2(SO_4)_3 + H_2$
   (f) $Ag + H_2S + O_2 \longrightarrow Ag_2S + H_2O$
   (g) $Ca_3(PO_4)_2 + C \longrightarrow Ca_3P_2 + CO$
   (h) $NH_3 + O_2 \longrightarrow H_2O + NO$
59. Write the complete balanced ionic equation and the net balanced ionic equation for each of the following reactions, each of which occurs in water. Classify each as to type or types of reaction. (*Note:* In balancing an ionic equation, check to be sure that the total numbers of each kind of atom are the same on both sides of the net ionic equation and also that the total charges are the same on both sides of the net ionic equation. Note also that $K_2Cr_2O_7$ is an ionic compound containing the polyatomic ion $Cr_2O_7^{2-}$.)
   (a) $Br_2 + 2KI \longrightarrow I_2 + 2KBr$
   (b) $2FeCl_2 + Cl_2 \longrightarrow 2FeCl_3$
   (c) $6FeCl_2 + K_2Cr_2O_7 + 14HCl \longrightarrow$
       $2CrCl_3 + 6FeCl_3 + 2KCl + 7H_2O$
60. Write the *net* balanced ionic equation for each of the following reactions, each of which occurs in water, and classify each as to type or types of reaction. (Note that H_2O_2 is predominantly covalent and that MnO_4^- is a polyatomic ion.)
   (a) $Zn + 2HCl \longrightarrow ZnCl_2 + H_2$
   (b) $H_2O_2 + 2HBr + 2FeBr_2 \longrightarrow 2H_2O + 2FeBr_3$
   (c) $5H_2O_2 + 2KMnO_4 + 6HCl \longrightarrow$
       $2MnCl_2 + 8H_2O + 5O_2 + 2KCl$
61. State whether an ionic equation can be written for each of the following; if it can, write the balanced ionic equation.
   (a) The reaction shown in Fig. 2.5
   (b) The reaction in Fig. 2.6
   (c) Equation (4) of Section 2.11
   (d) Equation (20) of Section 2.11
   (e) Equation (1) of Section 2.12
   (f) The reaction shown in Fig. 3.1 of Chapter 3
   (g) The reaction shown in Fig. 3.5 of Chapter 3
62. Specify the driving force, or forces, for each of the following reactions. Explain the reason for your choice.
   (a) $MgCO_3(s) \longrightarrow MgO(s) + CO_2(g)$
   (b) $2KClO_3(s) \longrightarrow 2KCl(s) + 3O_2(g)$

(c) $C_6H_{12}O_6(s) \longrightarrow 2C_2H_5OH(l) + 2CO_2(g)$
(d) $Pb^{2+}(aq) + 2Cl^-(aq) \longrightarrow PbCl_2(s)$
(e) $2H_2(g) + O_2(g) \longrightarrow 2H_2O(l)$

Industrial Chemicals

63. For the chemical reactions relating to industrial chemicals in Section 2.12, classify Equations (1) through (12) and (15) through (23) as to the type or types of reactions they represent. (*Note:* Equations (13) and (14) are difficult to classify in the categories described in Section 2.11, although they can be classified as addition reactions. Such reactions are often referred to simply as polymerization reactions.)

64. The following reactions are either similar to those of the industrial chemicals described in Section 2.12 or related to subjects discussed elsewhere in the chapter. Complete and balance the equations for these reactions.

(a) Reaction of a base and an acid.

$$NH_3 + CH_2CO_2H \longrightarrow$$

(b) "Pickling" of steel in hydrochloric acid.

$$Fe_2O_3 + HCl \longrightarrow$$

(c) Formation of an air pollutant, SO_2, when coal that contains iron(II) sulfide is burned.

$$FeS + O_2 \longrightarrow$$

(d) Preparation of a soluble silver salt for silver plating.

$$Ag_2O + HNO_3 \longrightarrow$$

(e) Neutralization of a basic solution containing nylon in order to precipitate the nylon.

$$Na^+(aq) + OH^-(aq) + H_2SO_4(aq) \longrightarrow$$

(f) Preparation of pure phosphoric acid, H_3PO_4, for use in soft drinks such as cherry phosphate or "Green River" (two reactions). Note the oxidation number of phosphorus in phosphoric acid in order to help determine the product in the first equation.

$$P_4 + O_2 \longrightarrow$$

$$X + H_2O \longrightarrow$$

Additional Exercises

65. (a) Write the balanced equation for the combustion reaction (reaction with oxygen) of methane, CH_4 (Fig. 2.5).

(b) How many water molecules would be produced from 4 CH_4 molecules and 14 O_2 molecules? (Note that one reactant is in excess; therefore, there is not enough of the other reactant to react with all of the one that is in excess.)

(c) How many water molecules would be produced from 8 CH_4 molecules and 14 O_2 molecules?

66. (a) Write the balanced equation for the combustion reaction (reaction with oxygen) of octane, C_8H_{18}, using the empirical formula for octane rather than the molecular formula.

(b) Write the balanced equation for the combustion of octane, using the molecular formula for octane.

(c) Using the molecular formula for octane, calculate how many water molecules would be produced from 15 molecules of C_8H_{18} and 50 molecules of O_2.

67. Balance the following equations and classify each according to type or types of reaction.

(a) $Ca + S_8 \longrightarrow CaS$
(b) $H_2 + Br_2 \longrightarrow HBr$
(c) $Ca(CH_3CO_2)_2 + H_2SO_4 \longrightarrow CaSO_4 + CH_3CO_2H$
(d) $Sb + S_8 \longrightarrow Sb_2S_3$
(e) $NaF + HNO_3 \longrightarrow HF + NaNO_3$
(f) $Cs_2O + SO_3 \longrightarrow Cs_2SO_4$
(g) $P_4 + F_2 \longrightarrow PF_3$
(h) $Cs + P_4 \longrightarrow Cs_3P$

68. (a) Explain why hydrogen chloride, which is a covalent compound, behaves as an electrolyte when it is dissolved in water. Include a balanced equation in your explanation.

(b) Explain why ammonia, which is a covalent compound, behaves as an electrolyte when it is dissolved in water. Include a balanced equation in your explanation.

69. When the following compounds dissolve in water, do they give solutions of acids, bases, or salts?

(a) NaI   (e) $HClO_3$
(b) HNO_3 (f) NH_3
(c) $NaClO_4$ (g) $Ba(OH)_2$
(d) NH_4NO_3 (h) LiOH

3 Chemical Stoichiometry

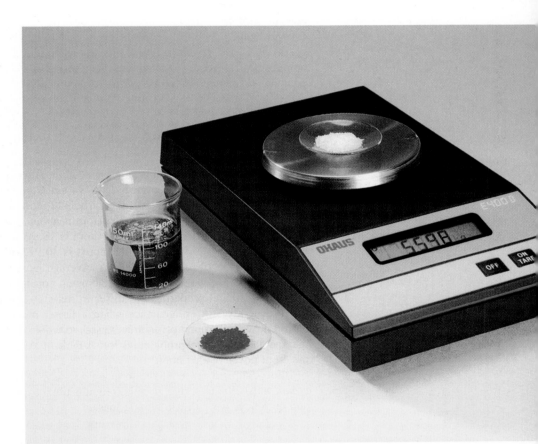

Stoichiometric quantities of copper(II) nitrate (on the watchglass beside the balance) and potassium iodide (on the balance). When dissolved in water, they react to form a stoichiometric ratio of three products (in the beaker), solid copper(I) iodide and solid iodine, precipitated in a solution of dissolved potassium nitrate. (The color of the solution is due to small dissolved quantities of I_2; KNO_3 in solution is almost colorless.)

$$2Cu(NO_3)_2(aq) + 4KI(aq) \longrightarrow 2CuI(s) + I_2(s) + 4KNO_3(aq)$$

In Chapter 2 we discussed symbols, formulas, and other subjects related to chemical equations and reactions. In this chapter, we shall expand our study to include quantitative calculations related to formulas, and we shall describe how chemical equations can be used to compare quantities of chemical substances involved in chemical reactions. These calculations, involving *material balances* in chemical systems, fall into a category of calculations called chemical stoichiometry. Another part of chemical stoichiometry, which will be discussed in future chapters, is concerned with *energy balances* in chemical systems. Thus **chemical stoichiometry** includes the calculation of both material balances and energy balances in chemical systems.

Chemistry is a quantitative science, largely based on laboratory experiments, that involves many mathematical calculations. However, the purpose of these calculations is not merely to obtain a number but also to provide quantitative predictions or descriptions of how matter behaves. A correct calculation suggests that the theory underlying the calculation is correct. For example, the ability to calculate accurate volumes of gas samples using the gas laws (Chapter 10) is one reason for believing that those laws are correct. Similarly, the fact that we can correctly calculate the amount of product that is formed from a chemical reaction shows that we understand something about what is occurring in the reaction, and it enables us to use the reaction to produce a desired amount of a product. Calculations are tools that chemists use in understanding the behavior of matter.

❸.1   Atomic Mass

The **atomic mass** of an atom is its mass in atomic mass units (amu). On the average, the mass of a single hydrogen atom is 1.00794 amu, a quantity derived from the arbitrary standard that assigns the mass of the carbon-12 atom as exactly 12 amu (Section 2.2). Thus the average mass of a hydrogen atom is about $\frac{1}{12}$ the mass of the carbon-12 atom. The average mass of a single fluorine atom is 18.9984032 amu (about 19 times that of a hydrogen atom), and that of phosphorus is 30.973762 amu (approximately 31 times the average mass of a hydrogen atom). Average masses are given here because, as we shall discuss in Section 3.3, many elements consist of mixtures of atoms that have identical chemical properties but differ in mass.

Frequently, for convenience when a larger number of significant figures is not required, we will round off atomic masses to whole numbers or to the number of digits that the data given in a problem justify. A table of average atomic masses appears inside the front cover of this book.

For historical reasons, the term *atomic weight* still is sometimes used instead of *atomic mass*. In that usage, atomic weight is often expressed without units. For accuracy and currency, we will use atomic mass.

❸.2   Molecular Mass

The **molecular mass** of a molecule, analogous to the atomic mass of a single atom (Section 3.1), is the mass of the molecule in atomic mass units (amu). (The term *molecular weight* is also sometimes used, often without units, instead of *molecular mass*.) The molecular mass of a molecule is the sum of the atomic masses of all the atoms in the molecule. For example, the molecular mass of chloroform, $CHCl_3$, equals the sum of the atomic masses of one carbon atom, one hydrogen atom, and three chlorine atoms. The molecular mass of aspirin, $C_9H_8O_4$, equals the sum of the atomic masses of nine carbon atoms, eight hydrogen atoms, and four oxygen atoms.

For CHCl₃

$1C = 1 \times 12.011 \ \text{amu} = 12.011 \ \text{amu}$
$1H = 1 \times 1.008 \ \text{amu} = 1.008 \ \text{amu}$
$3Cl = 3 \times 35.4527 \ \text{amu} = 106.358 \ \text{amu}$
Molecular mass $= 119.377 \ \text{amu}$

For C₉H₈O₄

$9C = 9 \times 12.011 \ \text{amu} = 108.099 \ \text{amu}$
$8H = 8 \times 1.008 \ \text{amu} = 8.064 \ \text{amu}$
$4O = 4 \times 15.999 \ \text{amu} = 63.996 \ \text{amu}$
Molecular mass $= 180.159 \ \text{amu}$

Thus the masses of *single* molecules of $CHCl_3$ and $C_9H_8O_4$ are 119.377 amu and 180.159 amu, respectively.

Because ionic compounds do not contain discrete molecules, they cannot be characterized properly by a molecular mass. For such compounds, we can calculate the **formula mass,** which is the sum of the atomic masses of the atoms found in one formula unit, as indicated by the empirical formula. Calculation of the formula masses of two typical ionic compounds, $KClO_3$ and $Al_2(SO_4)_3$, follows.

For KClO₃

$1K = 1 \times 39.098 \ \text{amu} = 39.098 \ \text{amu}$
$1Cl = 1 \times 35.453 \ \text{amu} = 35.453 \ \text{amu}$
$3O = 3 \times 15.999 \ \text{amu} = 47.997 \ \text{amu}$
Formula mass $= 122.548 \ \text{amu}$

For Al₂(SO₄)₃

$2Al = 2 \times 26.982 \ \text{amu} = 53.964 \ \text{amu}$
$3S = 3 \times 32.067 \ \text{amu} = 96.201 \ \text{amu}$
$12O = 12 \times 15.999 \ \text{amu} = 191.988 \ \text{amu}$
Formula mass $= 342.153 \ \text{amu}$

❸.3   Isotopes

Some atoms of a given element can exhibit the same chemical properties but differ in mass. Inasmuch as all atoms of the same element must have the same atomic number, and hence the same number of protons and electrons (Section 2.3), the difference in mass has to be in the number of neutrons present. Atoms of a particular element that differ only in the number of neutrons in the nucleus are called **isotopes.**

Isotopes are identified with the atomic number as a subscript and the mass number as a superscript to the left of the symbol for the element. For example, the naturally occurring isotopes of magnesium are indicated as $^{24}_{12}Mg$, $^{25}_{12}Mg$, and $^{26}_{12}Mg$. Note that all three isotopes of the element magnesium have 12 protons in the nucleus and 12 electrons outside the nucleus. They differ only in the fact that $^{24}_{12}Mg$ has 12 neutrons in the nucleus, $^{25}_{12}Mg$ has 13, and $^{26}_{12}Mg$ has 14.

The number of protons and neutrons in the nuclei of the naturally occurring elements with atomic numbers 1 through 10 are given in Table 3.1. (Note that the heavier of the two hydrogen isotopes listed has the symbol $^{2}_{1}D$. It is often referred to by the special name *deuterium,* which is given the symbol D. It could also be designated $^{2}_{1}H$.)

Because each proton and each neutron contributes approximately one mass unit to the atomic mass of an atom and each electron contributes far less, the mass of a single atom is approximately equal to its mass number (a whole number). However, the average masses of atoms of most elements are not whole numbers, because most elements exist as mixtures of two or more isotopes. For example, 98.89% of naturally occurring carbon atoms are ^{12}C atoms with a mass of exactly 12 amu (by definition). The remainder have different masses, 1.11% possessing a mass of 13.0033 amu, and less than $10^{-8}\%$ having a mass of 14.0032 amu. The average mass of all of the carbon atoms in the naturally occurring mixture is 12.011 amu. The values listed in tables of atomic masses are the weighted averages of the masses of all isotopes present in a natural sample of an element. That is, a given value is equal to the sum of the masses of all isotopes in an element, each mass first multiplied by the fraction of that isotope present in the element. The following example illustrates this point.

	Symbol	Atomic Number	Number of Protons	Number of Neutrons	Mass, amu	% Natural Abundance
Hydrogen	^1_1H	1	1	0	1.0078	99.985
	^2_1D	1	1	1	2.0141	0.015
	^3_1T	1	1	2	3.01605	—
Helium	^3_2He	2	2	1	3.01603	0.00013
	^4_2He	2	2	2	4.0026	100
Lithium	^6_3Li	3	3	3	6.0151	7.42
	^7_3Li	3	3	4	7.0160	92.58
Beryllium	^9_4Be	4	4	5	9.0122	100
Boron	$^{10}_5B$	5	5	5	10.0129	19.6
	$^{11}_5B$	5	5	6	11.0093	80.4
Carbon	$^{12}_6C$	6	6	6	12.0000[a]	98.89
	$^{13}_6C$	6	6	7	13.0033	1.11
	$^{14}_6C$	6	6	8	14.0032	—
Nitrogen	$^{14}_7N$	7	7	7	14.0031	99.63
	$^{15}_7N$	7	7	8	15.0001	0.37
Oxygen	$^{16}_8O$	8	8	8	15.9949	99.759
	$^{17}_8O$	8	8	9	16.9991	0.037
	$^{18}_8O$	8	8	10	17.9992	0.204
Fluorine	$^{19}_9F$	9	9	10	18.9984	100
Neon	$^{20}_{10}Ne$	10	10	10	19.9924	90.92
	$^{21}_{10}Ne$	10	10	11	20.9940	0.257
	$^{22}_{10}Ne$	10	10	12	21.9914	8.82

Table 3.1 **Nuclear Compositions of Atoms of the Very Light Elements**

[a] Mass assigned as exactly 12 by international agreement.

Example 3.1

A chemist named Dempster found that magnesium contains 78.70% $^{24}_{12}Mg$ atoms (mass = 23.98 amu), 10.13% $^{25}_{12}Mg$ atoms (mass = 24.99 amu), and 11.17% $^{26}_{12}Mg$ atoms (mass = 25.98 amu). Calculate the weighted average mass of a Mg atom.

$$\text{Weighted average mass} = \left(\frac{78.70 \ ^{24}_{12}Mg \ \text{atoms}}{100 \ Mg \ \text{atoms}} \times \frac{23.98 \ \text{amu}}{1 \ ^{24}_{12}Mg \ \text{atom}} \right)$$

$$+ \left(\frac{10.13 \ ^{25}_{12}Mg \ \text{atoms}}{100 \ Mg \ \text{atoms}} \times \frac{24.99 \ \text{amu}}{1 \ ^{25}_{12}Mg \ \text{atom}} \right) + \left(\frac{11.17 \ ^{26}_{12}Mg \ \text{atoms}}{100 \ Mg \ \text{atoms}} \times \frac{25.98 \ \text{amu}}{1 \ ^{26}_{12}Mg \ \text{atom}} \right)$$

$$= 24.31 \ \text{amu/Mg atom}$$

More precise measurements have shown this value to be 24.3050 amu. (Compare this with the atomic mass of magnesium listed inside the front cover of the text.)

In Chapter 1 (Section 1.5), we defined an element as a pure substance that cannot be decomposed by a chemical change. Now, having discussed the fundamental structure of atoms and the subject of isotopes, we are in a position to define an element more rigorously in terms of its atomic number (number of protons in the nucleus). The more rigorous definition takes into account the fact that methods are now known by which isotopes of some elements can be separated chemically. We can thus say that an **element** consists of atoms all of which have the same number of protons in their nuclei. For example, every atom with 8 protons in its nucleus is oxygen, whether it is $^{16}_{8}O$, $^{17}_{8}O$, or $^{18}_{8}O$ in O, O_2, O_3, or a mixture of any of these. Likewise, every atom with 17 protons in its nucleus is chlorine, and every atom with 29 protons in its nucleus is copper.

❸.4 Moles of Atoms and Avogadro's Number

As noted in Chapter 2, a chemical formula tells a chemist the *relative numbers* of atoms of each type that must be assembled to make a particular compound. However, we do not have to count out the actual number of atoms, which is enormous, required to produce a sample of that compound. We need only get the correct ratios of the numbers of atoms. For example, to make carbon tetrachloride, CCl_4, we simply need to use four times as many chlorine atoms as carbon atoms.

Numbers of atoms are conveniently measured in units of the same number of atoms as there are in exactly 12 grams of $^{12}_{6}C$. This is the unit that chemists call **one mole of atoms (1 mol)**. [Recall that the atomic mass unit also is defined in terms of the $^{12}_{6}C$ isotope (Section 2.2).] It has been determined by experiment that the number of atoms in 12 grams of carbon-12, and hence **the number of atoms in one mole of atoms of any element,** is 6.022×10^{23} atoms. This number is called **Avogadro's number** in honor of the Italian professor of physics Amedeo Avogadro (1776–1856).

We could make a sample of carbon tetrachloride by combining 1 mole of carbon atoms (1 mol of C atoms = 6.022×10^{23} C atoms) with 4 moles of chlorine atoms ($4 \times 6.022 \times 10^{23}$ Cl atoms). This would produce 1 mole (6.022×10^{23} molecules) of CCl_4. We could make a smaller sample of CCl_4 by using fewer moles of carbon and chlorine atoms (smaller numbers of C and Cl atoms), as long as there were four times as many moles of chlorine atoms as moles of carbon atoms.

The following examples illustrate calculations that make use of Avogadro's number with atoms and molecules.

How many CCl_4 molecules can be made by the combination of 0.050 mol of carbon atoms with chlorine atoms?

Example 3.2

The formula CCl_4 tells us that one CCl_4 molecule contains one carbon atom (1 molecule CCl_4/1 atom C). If we can determine the number of carbon atoms present, we can determine the number of CCl_4 molecules that can be made. One mol of C atoms contains 6.022×10^{23} C atoms; 0.050 mol of C atoms contains

$$0.050 \text{ mol C atoms} \times \frac{6.022 \times 10^{23} \text{ C atoms}}{1 \text{ mol C atoms}} = 3.0 \times 10^{22} \text{ C atoms}$$

A single CCl_4 molecule contains 1 atom of carbon, so we can make 1 molecule of CCl_4 for each carbon atom. Because we have 3.0×10^{22} atoms of carbon, we can make

$$3.0 \times 10^{22} \text{ C atoms} \times \frac{1 \text{ CCl}_4 \text{ molecule}}{1 \text{ C atom}} = 3.0 \times 10^{22} \text{ CCl}_4 \text{ molecules}$$

Example 3.3

How many moles of chlorine atoms are required to react with 0.050 mol of carbon atoms to convert all of the carbon atoms to CCl_4?

The formula CCl_4 indicates that there are 4 Cl atoms for each C atom in a molecule; thus we must take four times as many Cl atoms as C atoms, or

$$0.050 \text{ mol C atoms} \times \frac{6.022 \times 10^{23} \text{ C atoms}}{1 \text{ mol C atoms}} = 3.0 \times 10^{22} \text{ C atoms}$$

$$3.0 \times 10^{22} \text{ C atoms} \times \frac{4 \text{ Cl atoms}}{1 \text{ C atom}} = 1.2 \times 10^{23} \text{ Cl atoms}$$

We can calculate the number of moles of Cl atoms from the definition of a mole: 1 mol of Cl atoms = 6.022×10^{23} Cl atoms (1 mol Cl atoms/6.022×10^{23} Cl atoms).

$$1.2 \times 10^{23} \text{ Cl atoms} \times \frac{1 \text{ mol Cl atoms}}{6.022 \times 10^{23} \text{ Cl atoms}} = 0.20 \text{ mol Cl atoms}$$

Note that the number of moles of chlorine atoms is indeed four times the number of moles of carbon atoms.

The number of atoms in a mole of atoms is so large that it is difficult to appreciate exactly how big it really is. As a guide to the size of the number, consider that if the entire population of the United States (approximately 250,000,000 people) spent 12 hours a day, 365 days a year, counting atoms at the rate of one atom per second, they would need about 153 million years to count the atoms in a mole.

The mass of a single atom can be calculated from the mass of one mole of atoms and the number of atoms in a mole of atoms.

Example 3.4

Calculate the mass of a carbon-12 atom.

The mass of 1 mol of carbon-12 atoms is exactly 12 grams. The mass of a single atom of carbon-12 is

$$\frac{12 \text{ g}}{1 \text{ mol}} \times \frac{1 \text{ mol}}{6.022 \times 10^{23} \text{ atoms}} = 1.993 \times 10^{-23} \text{ g}$$

Significant figures in this answer are determined by the number of significant figures in Avogadro's number, because the mass of 1 mol of carbon-12 is a defined quantity.

Thus we can see that the following relationship applies to the calculation of the mass of one atom.

$$\text{Mass of one atom} = \frac{\text{mass of one mole of atoms}}{\text{Avogadro's number}}$$

Let us now look at the relationship between masses of atoms and numbers of atoms. A mass of 19 amu of fluorine (note that the value has been rounded) contains one atom of fluorine; a mass of 31 amu of phosphorus contains one atom of phosphorus. A mass of 76 amu (4×19) of fluorine contains four fluorine atoms. Similarly, a mass of 124 amu (4×31) of phosphorus contains four phosphorus atoms. The ratio of the mass of the sample of fluorine to the mass of the sample of phosphorus (76 amu to 124 amu) is the same as the ratio of their atomic masses (19 to 31), and the samples contain the same number of atoms—four. The following is true of any pair of elements: **If the masses of samples of two elements have the same ratio as the ratio of their atomic masses, the samples contain identical numbers of atoms** (Fig. 3.1).

Balances in chemical laboratories measure in units of grams, not atomic mass units, but this is of little consequence in weighing out relative numbers of atoms. Just as 76 amu of fluorine and 124 amu of phosphorus contain the same number of atoms, 76 grams of fluorine and 124 grams of phosphorus also contain identical numbers of atoms, because the ratio of the masses is still 19 to 31.

The **mass of one mole of atoms** in grams is numerically equal to the atomic mass of the atom, and we can get a mole of atoms of any element by weighing out a mass of the element, in grams, equal to its atomic mass. A sample of 31 grams of phosphorus contains one mole of phosphorus atoms. Similarly, 19 grams of fluorine constitutes one mole of fluorine atoms, and 12 grams of carbon contains one mole of carbon atoms. All of these quantities contain the same number of atoms. **A mole of atoms of any element contains the same number of atoms as a mole of atoms of any other element.**

Now we can see that it is easy to count out relative numbers of atoms in the laboratory (Fig. 3.2). Suppose, for example, that we have 32.1 grams of sulfur atoms and want an equal number of zinc atoms. From the atomic mass of sulfur, 32.1 amu, we can recognize that 32.1 grams of sulfur atoms is one mole of sulfur atoms. To get one mole of zinc atoms, we simply look up the atomic mass of zinc (65.4 amu) and then weigh out one mole of zinc atoms—65.4 grams. Finding fractional amounts of moles just requires an extra arithmetic step.

Figure 3.1

The reaction of sodium with water. Each atom of sodium that reacts releases one atom of hydrogen. Because the ratio of the atomic mass of sodium to that of hydrogen is 23 to 1, 1.0 g of sodium releases 0.043 g of hydrogen; 1.0 g of sodium contains the same number of sodium atoms as the number of atoms of hydrogen in 0.043 g of hydrogen.

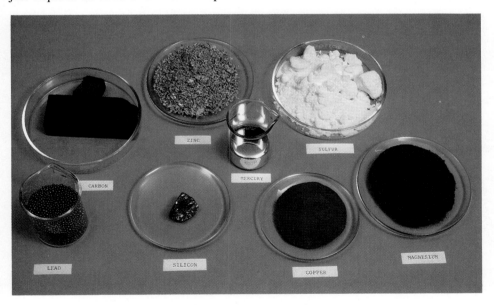

Figure 3.2

Each sample contains 6.02×10^{23} atoms—1.00 mol of atoms: 12.0 g of carbon (at. mass 12.0 amu), 65.4 g of zinc (at. mass 65.4 amu), 201 g of mercury (at. mass 201 amu), 32.1 g of sulfur (at. mass 32.1 amu), 24.3 g of magnesium (at. mass 24.3 amu), 63.5 g of copper (at. mass 63.5 amu), 28.1 g of silicon (at. mass 28.1 amu), and 207 g of lead (at. mass 207 amu). (All values are given to three significant figures.)

The following examples illustrate calculations involving relationships among numbers of atoms, grams, and moles of elements.

How many moles of nitrogen atoms are contained in 9.34 g of nitrogen?

The atomic masses on the inside front cover indicate that the atomic mass of nitrogen is 14.00674; hence 1 mol of nitrogen atoms weighs 14.00674 g, or there is 1 mol of

**Example
3.5**

Example 3.5 continued

nitrogen atoms per 14.00674 g (1 mol N atoms/14.00674 g N atoms). The quantity of nitrogen in 9.34 g can be converted to moles of nitrogen atoms as follows:

$$9.34 \text{ g N atoms} \times \frac{1 \text{ mol N atoms}}{14.00674 \text{ g N atoms}} = 0.667 \text{ mol N atoms}$$

Note that the gram units cancel, indicating that the correct conversion factor has been used. Three significant figures in the answer are justified by the mass of nitrogen given (9.34 g).

Example 3.6

How much sodium contains the same number of atoms as are in 18.29 g of chlorine?

From the periodic table, we find that 1 mol of sodium atoms weighs 22.990 g (22.990 g Na atoms/1 mol Na atoms) and 1 mol of chlorine atoms weighs 35.453 g (1 mol Cl atoms/35.453 g). First find the number of moles of chlorine atoms present.

$$18.29 \text{ g Cl atoms} \times \frac{1 \text{ mol Cl atoms}}{35.453 \text{ g Cl atoms}} = 0.5159 \text{ mol Cl atoms}$$

A quantity of 0.5159 mol of Cl atoms contains the same number of atoms as are in 0.5159 mol of Na atoms. The next step, then, is to find the mass of 0.5159 mol of Na atoms.

$$0.5159 \text{ mol Na atoms} \times \frac{22.990 \text{ g}}{1 \text{ mol Na atoms}} = 11.86 \text{ g}$$

Example 3.7

How many chlorine atoms are contained in 18.29 g of chlorine?

In Example 3.6 it was shown that 18.29 g of chlorine contains 0.5159 mol of chlorine atoms. Because 1 mol contains 6.022×10^{23} atoms, the conversion factor is 6.022×10^{23} Cl atoms/1 mol Cl atoms.

$$0.5159 \text{ mol Cl atoms} \times \frac{6.022 \times 10^{23} \text{ Cl atoms}}{1 \text{ mol Cl atoms}} = 3.107 \times 10^{23} \text{ Cl atoms}$$

❸.5 Moles of Molecules

Analogously to the definition of a mole of atoms (Section 3.4), a **mole of molecules** contains the same number of molecules as there are atoms in exactly 12 grams of ^{12}C. Thus a mole of molecules contains 6.022×10^{23} molecules. To weigh out a mole of molecules, weigh out a mass in grams numerically equal to the molecular mass of the molecule. This mass is sometimes called the **molar mass** of the substance. The unit for molar mass is grams per mole. Thus the molar mass of chloroform, $CHCl_3$, is 119.377 grams per mole; that of aspirin, $C_9H_8O_4$, is 180.160 grams per mole (Fig. 3.3). Because a mole of molecules contains Avogadro's number of molecules, 119.377 g of $CHCl_3$ and 180.160 g of $C_9H_8O_4$ each contain 6.022×10^{23} molecules.

It is also possible to weigh out a mole of an ionic compound such as NaCl or KOH. A mole of an ionic compound contains 6.022×10^{23} of the units described by the formula. A mole of NaCl therefore contains Avogadro's number of NaCl units, each unit being composed of one sodium ion and one chloride ion. The mass of a mole of an ionic

Figure 3.3
Each sample contains 6.02×10^{23} molecules or formula units— 1.00 mol of the compound. From left to right: 58.5 g of NaCl (sodium chloride, formula mass 58.5 amu), 18.0 g of H_2O (water, mol. mass 18.0 amu), 74.1 g of C_4H_9OH (butyl alcohol, mol. mass 74.1 amu), 342 g of $C_{12}H_{22}O_{11}$ (sucrose, or common sugar, mol. mass 342 amu), and 180 g of $C_9H_8O_4$ (aspirin, mol. mass 180 amu). One mole of carbon atoms (black) is also shown. (All values are given to three significant figures.)

compound in grams is numerically equal to the formula mass and is also called the molar mass. The molar masses of sodium chloride and aluminum sulfate are 58.443 grams per mole and 342.157 grams per mole, respectively.

We said earlier that a chemical formula indicates the number of atoms of each element in one molecular or empirical unit of that compound (Section 2.1). **A chemical formula also indicates the number of moles of atoms in 1 mole of the compound.** Ethanol (C_2H_5OH, often called ethyl alcohol) contains two carbon atoms in one molecule. It also contains two moles of carbon atoms in one mole of ethanol molecules ($2 \times 6.022 \times 10^{23}$ C atoms in 6.022×10^{23} C_2H_5OH molecules).

The following examples illustrate the use of the concepts of chemical formulas, atomic masses, molecular masses, and moles of atoms and molecules.

How many moles of sulfur atoms are contained in 80.3 g of sulfur?

Example 3.8

The atomic mass of sulfur is 32.066 amu, so 1 mol of S atoms = 32.066 g of sulfur (1 mol S atoms/32.066 g sulfur).

$$80.3 \text{ g sulfur} \times \frac{1 \text{ mol S atoms}}{32.066 \text{ g sulfur}} = 2.50 \text{ mol S atoms}$$

How many moles of sulfur molecules are contained in 80.3 g of sulfur if the molecular formula is S_8?

Example 3.9

The molecular mass of S_8 is $8 \times 32.066 = 256.53$ amu; hence 1 mol of S_8 = 256.53 g of sulfur (1 mol S_8/256.53 g sulfur).

$$80.3 \text{ g sulfur} \times \frac{1 \text{ mol } S_8}{256.53 \text{ g sulfur}} = 0.313 \text{ mol } S_8$$

Example 3.10

The recommended minimum daily dietary allowance of vitamin C, $C_6H_8O_6$, for a young woman of average weight is 4.6×10^{-4} mol. What is this allowance in grams?

The molecular mass of $C_6H_8O_6$ is 176.1 amu, to one decimal place. Hence 1 mol $C_6H_8O_6 = 176.1$ g (176.1 g $C_6H_8O_6$/1 mol $C_6H_8O_6$).

$$4.6 \times 10^{-4} \text{ mol } C_6H_8O_6 \times \frac{176.1 \text{ g } C_6H_8O_6}{1 \text{ mol } C_6H_8O_6} = 0.081 \text{ g } C_6H_8O_6$$

Example 3.11

How many moles of hydrogen atoms are contained in 500 mg of vitamin C?

First convert milligrams to grams and calculate the number of moles of vitamin C, $C_6H_8O_6$; then use the information from the chemical formula, which indicates exactly 8 mol of H atoms per 1 mol of $C_6H_8O_6$.

$$500 \text{ mg} \times \frac{1 \text{ g}}{1000 \text{ mg}} \times \frac{1 \text{ mol } C_6H_8O_6}{176.1 \text{ g } C_6H_8O_6} = 2.84 \times 10^{-3} \text{ mol } C_6H_8O_6$$

$$2.84 \times 10^{-3} \text{ mol } C_6H_8O_6 \times \frac{8 \text{ mol H atoms}}{1 \text{ mol } C_6H_8O_6} = 2.27 \times 10^{-2} \text{ mol H atoms}$$

③.6 Percent Composition from Formulas

All samples of a pure compound contain the same elements in the same proportion by mass. For example, 11% of the mass of any sample of pure water is always hydrogen; 89% of the mass is always oxygen. This **law of definite proportion,** or **law of definite composition,** helped convince Dalton of the atomic nature of matter and led him to outline his atomic theory.

Because all samples of a pure compound contain the same relative amounts of elements by mass, the proportion of each element present in a compound can be used to identify the compound. The proportion commonly used is the **percent composition**— that is, the percent by mass of the element in the sample, or the fraction of the total mass of the sample that is due to the element, multiplied by 100.

$$\text{Percent by mass of } X = \frac{\text{mass of } X}{\text{mass of sample}} \times 100$$

The following example illustrates the calculation of percent composition of a compound from the formula.

Example 3.12

Calculate the percent by mass of hydrogen and of oxygen in the compound water, H_2O.

To calculate the percent hydrogen and percent oxygen in water, we need to know the masses of hydrogen and oxygen in a sample of water with a known mass. A convenient quantity of water is 1 mol of water, which has a mass of 18.0 g. This mass of water contains 1 mol of oxygen and 2 mol of hydrogen. The percentages of H and O can be calculated as follows:

$$\text{Percent hydrogen by mass in } H_2O = \frac{2 \times \text{atomic mass of H}}{\text{molecular mass of } H_2O} \times 100$$

$$= \frac{2 \times 1.01 \text{ amu}}{(2 \times 1.01 \text{ amu}) + (1 \times 16.0 \text{ amu})} \times 100 = 11.2\%$$

$$\text{Percent oxygen by mass in } H_2O = \frac{1 \times \text{atomic mass of O}}{\text{molecular mass of } H_2O} \times 100$$

$$= \frac{1 \times 16.0 \text{ amu}}{(2 \times 1.01 \text{ amu}) + (1 \times 16.0 \text{ amu})} \times 100 = 88.8\%$$

Note that the percentages of all elements present in a compound total 100.0%. One easy way to check a calculation of percent composition is to determine whether the percentages of the elements add up to 100%.

❸.7 Derivation of Formulas

An empirical formula shows the relative numbers of atoms in a compound. In order to write the empirical formula of a compound, we must know the relative numbers of atoms in a sample of it. In the following example, we are given the numbers of moles of C and of H atoms in a sample of methane (which are proportional to the numbers of atoms) and are asked to determine the empirical formula.

Example 3.13

A sample of the principal component of natural gas, methane, contains 0.090 mol of carbon and 0.36 mol of hydrogen. What is the empirical formula of this compound?

For every 0.090 mol of C in the compound, there is 0.36 mol of H; thus the formula might be written as $C_{0.090}H_{0.36}$. But chemical formulas are customarily written in terms of whole-number ratios, so this formula must be reduced. The ratio of C to H is 1:4, so the *empirical* formula of the compound must be CH_4.

Note: To reduce two nonintegers to integers, first divide each by the smaller noninteger. (Sometimes another step is necessary, as will be illustrated in Example 3.15. For this present example, the first step produces integers.)

$$\frac{0.090}{0.090} = 1; \qquad \frac{0.36}{0.090} = 4$$

In chemistry problems, information about the composition of a compound is usually given in terms of either the masses of the elements in a sample or the percents by mass of the elements. To find the empirical formula when the masses of the elements are given, convert these masses to the numbers of moles and reduce the mole ratio to the simplest whole numbers. When percents by mass are given, find the masses of all elements present in some specific mass of the sample (100 grams is a convenient mass), convert to the numbers of moles, and reduce the mole ratios to the simplest whole numbers.

The following example shows how to determine the empirical formula for a compound from the percent composition.

Example 3.14

A sample of the gaseous compound formed during bacterial fermentation of grain is found to consist of 27.29% carbon and 72.71% oxygen. What is the empirical formula of the compound?

Percent composition of an element in a compound indicates the percent by mass. The mass of an element in a 100.0-g sample of a compound is equal in grams to the percent of that element in the sample; hence 100.0 g of this sample would contain 27.29 g of carbon and 72.71 g of oxygen.

$$100.0 \text{ g sample} \times \frac{27.29 \text{ g C}}{100 \text{ g sample}} = 27.29 \text{ g C}$$

$$100.0 \text{ g sample} \times \frac{72.71 \text{ g O}}{100 \text{ g sample}} = 72.71 \text{ g O}$$

The relative number of moles of carbon and oxygen atoms in the compound can be obtained by converting grams to moles, as shown in the following table.

Element	Mass of Element in 100.0 g of Sample	Relative Number of Moles	Divide by the Smaller Number	Smallest Integral Number of Moles
Carbon	27.29 g	$27.29 \text{ g C} \times \frac{1 \text{ mol C}}{12.01 \text{ g C}} = 2.272 \text{ mol C}$	$\frac{2.272}{2.272} = 1.000$	1
Oxygen	72.71 g	$72.71 \text{ g O} \times \frac{1 \text{ mol O}}{16.00 \text{ g O}} = 4.544 \text{ mol O}$	$\frac{4.544}{2.272} = 2.000$	2

For every 2.272 mol of carbon, there are 4.544 mol of oxygen. Reduced to the smallest whole numbers, the number of moles of oxygen is twice the number of moles of carbon. Hence the number of oxygen *atoms* in the compound is also twice the number of carbon *atoms*. The simplest formula for the gaseous compound produced during fermentation must therefore be CO_2.

The empirical formula CO_2 indicates a formula mass of 44 amu. It can be shown by experiment that the gas actually has a molecular mass of 44 amu. Thus the empirical formula and the molecular formula of CO_2 are the same. If the molecular mass for the gas were 88 amu, then the molecular formula would be C_2O_4, indicating twice as many atoms as in the simplest formula, CO_2.

The next example shows the determination of an empirical formula for a compound, given the number of grams of each element in a sample of the compound.

Example 3.15

A sample of the mineral hematite, an oxide of iron found in iron ores and shown in the photograph, contains 34.97 g of iron and 15.03 g of oxygen. What is the empirical formula of hematite?

The steps in the solution of this problem are outlined in the following table.

Element	Mass of Element	Relative Number of Moles	Divide by the Smaller Number	Smallest Integral Number of Moles
Iron	34.97 g	$34.97 \text{ g Fe} \times \dfrac{1 \text{ mol Fe}}{55.85 \text{ g Fe}} = 0.6261 \text{ mol Fe}$	$\dfrac{0.6261}{0.6261} = 1.00$	$2 \times 1.00 = 2$
Oxygen	15.03 g	$15.03 \text{ g O} \times \dfrac{1 \text{ mol O}}{16.00 \text{ g O}} = 0.9394 \text{ mol O}$	$\dfrac{0.9394}{0.6261} = 1.50$	$2 \times 1.50 = 3$

A sample of black hematite and white quartz crystals.

Here, division by the smaller number of moles does not give two integers, so a third step is necessary. We must multiply by the smallest whole number that will give whole numbers for the relative numbers of moles, and hence of atoms, of each element: $2 \times 1.00 = 2$ and $2 \times 1.50 = 3$. The simplest whole-number mole ratio (and whole-number atom ratio) is $2:3$, and the empirical formula of hematite is Fe_2O_3.

The following example differs from the preceding one in providing the total mass of the sample and the mass of one of the two products of the reaction.

Example 3.16

Pure oxygen is often prepared in a general chemistry laboratory by heating a compound containing potassium, chlorine, and oxygen. What is the empirical formula of this compound if a 3.22-g sample decomposes to give gaseous oxygen and 1.96 g of KCl?

The mass of oxygen produced, and therefore the mass of oxygen atoms in the 3.22-g sample, is $3.22 \text{ g} - 1.96 \text{ g} = 1.26 \text{ g}$. We can determine the number of moles of oxygen atoms by converting 1.26 g of oxygen atoms to moles of oxygen atoms. The moles of potassium atoms and of chlorine atoms can be determined from the number of moles of KCl, because there are 1 mol of K and 1 mol of Cl per 1 mol of KCl. The steps in the solution of this problem are outlined in the following table:

Atom	Relative Number of Moles	Divide by the Smaller Number	Smallest Integral Number of Moles
O	$1.26 \text{ g O} \times \dfrac{1 \text{ mol O}}{16.0 \text{ g O}} = 0.0788 \text{ mol O}$	$\dfrac{0.0788}{0.0263} = 3.00$	3
K	$1.96 \text{ g KCl} \times \dfrac{1 \text{ mol KCl}}{74.6 \text{ g KCl}} \times \dfrac{1 \text{ mol K}}{1 \text{ mol KCl}} = 0.0263 \text{ mol K}$	$\dfrac{0.0263}{0.0263} = 1.00$	1
Cl	$1.96 \text{ g KCl} \times \dfrac{1 \text{ mol KCl}}{74.6 \text{ g KCl}} \times \dfrac{1 \text{ mol Cl}}{1 \text{ mol KCl}} = 0.0263 \text{ mol Cl}$	$\dfrac{0.0263}{0.0263} = 1.00$	1

The ratio of K to Cl to O is $1:1:3$, so the simplest formula of the compound is $KClO_3$.

(a)

(b)

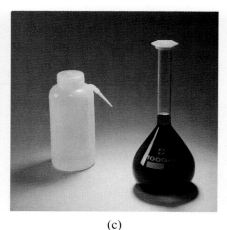
(c)

Figure 3.4

Preparation of a 0.0300 M solution of potassium permanganate, $KMnO_4$. (a) A carefully weighed quantity of 4.74 g of $KMnO_4$ (0.0300 mol), an empty 1.000-L volumetric flask, and a wash bottle containing distilled water. (b) The $KMnO_4$ dissolved in about 700 mL of water after transfer of the solid to the volumetric flask and the addition of distilled water. (c) The volumetric flask containing the 0.0300 M $KMnO_4$ solution after the volumetric flask is carefully filled with distilled water to the 1.000-L mark on the neck of the flask, the flask is stoppered, and the solution is thoroughly mixed. The final solution contains 0.0300 mol of $KMnO_4$ in 1.000 L of solution and is thus 0.0300 M.

3.8 Solutions

When table sugar, sucrose ($C_{12}H_{22}O_{11}$), is stirred into water, the sugar dissolves and a clear mixture, or solution, of sugar in water is formed. This solution consists of the solute (the dissolved sugar) and the solvent (the water). A **solute** is the substance that dissolves, and a **solvent** is the substance in which the solute dissolves. A **solution** is a homogeneous mixture of the solute and the solvent (Section 1.5).

A solution that contains only a small amount of solute compared to the amount of solvent is said to be **dilute;** the addition of more solute makes the solution more **concentrated.** The maximum amount of solute that can be dissolved in a particular amount of solvent depends on the nature of the solute and of the solvent. The solute or the solvent can be a gas, a liquid, or a solid, but in this chapter we will limit our attention to solid solutes dissolved in liquids.

The relative amounts of solute and solvent present in a solution—that is, its **concentration**—can be expressed in different ways. A commonly used method of expressing concentration is as the molarity of the solution. The **molarity (M)** of a solution is the number of moles of solute in exactly one liter (1 L), or one cubic decimeter (1 dm^3), of solution (Fig. 3.4). To calculate molarity, divide the number of moles of solute in a given volume of solution by the volume in liters.

$$\text{Molarity} = \frac{\text{moles of solute}}{\text{liters of solution}} \qquad (1)$$

The following examples illustrate concentration calculations involving molarity.

The maximum solubility of lead chromate, $PbCrO_4$, the artist's pigment *chrome yellow*, is 4.3×10^{-5} g L^{-1} at 25°C. Calculate the molarity of such a solution of $PbCrO_4$.

Example 3.17

We must determine the number of moles of $PbCrO_4$ dissolved in 1 L of solution. The formula mass of $PbCrO_4$ is

$$207.2 \text{ amu} + 52.0 \text{ amu} + 4(16.0 \text{ amu}) = 323.2 \text{ amu}$$

Hence the molar mass of $PbCrO_4 = 323.2$ g mol^{-1}.

$$\text{Molarity} = \frac{4.3 \times 10^{-5} \text{ g PbCrO}_4}{1 \text{ L}} \times \frac{1 \text{ mol PbCrO}_4}{323.2 \text{ g PbCrO}_4}$$

$$= \frac{1.33 \times 10^{-7} \text{ mol PbCrO}_4}{1 \text{ L}} = 1.3 \times 10^{-7} \text{ M}$$

Yellow lead chromate, $PbCrO_4$, is not appreciably soluble in water.

How many moles of sulfuric acid, H_2SO_4, are contained in 0.80 L of a 0.050 M solution of sulfuric acid?

Example 3.18

Equation (1) can be rearranged so that we can solve for moles of solute:

$$\text{Molarity} \times \text{liters of solution} = \text{moles of solute}$$

$$\frac{0.050 \text{ mol H}_2SO_4}{1 \text{ L}} \times 0.80 \text{ L} = 0.040 \text{ mol H}_2SO_4$$

Calculate the concentration of the solution that results when enough water is added to 250.0 mL of a 0.60 M NaOH solution to make 300.0 mL of solution.

Example 3.19

The initial 0.60 M NaOH solution contains 0.60 mol of NaOH in each liter of solution. Hence we can calculate the number of moles of NaOH in the 250.0 mL (0.2500 L) of the initial solution as follows:

$$\frac{0.60 \text{ mol}}{1.000 \text{ L}} \times 0.2500 \text{ L} = 0.15 \text{ mol NaOH}$$

(in the initial solution and also in the final solution after the water is added).

The volume of the final solution is = 300.0 mL, or 0.3000 L. Thus the final solution has 0.15 mol of NaOH in 0.3000 L of solution.

$$\text{Molarity} = \frac{\text{moles of solute}}{\text{liters of solution}} = \frac{0.15 \text{ mol NaOH}}{0.3000 \text{ L solution}}$$

$$= 0.50 \text{ mol NaOH per liter} = 0.50 \text{ M}$$

The addition of water diluted the solution from 0.60 M to 0.50 M.

③.9 Mole Relationships Based on Equations

The chemical reaction

$$2H_2O \longrightarrow 2H_2 + O_2$$

gives the simplest whole-number ratio of the molecules involved. It indicates that when two molecules of H_2O decompose, two molecules of H_2 and one molecule of O_2 are formed. The ratios of molecules, atoms, or ions are identical to the ratios of *moles* of molecules, atoms, or ions. Thus the equation also indicates the ratios of moles. Various ways of indicating the ratios of the numbers of molecules or moles of the substances in the reaction are shown below the following equation.

$2H_2O$	$\longrightarrow$	$2H_2$	$+$	O_2
2 molecules		2 molecules		1 molecule
$2 \times 6.022 \times 10^{23}$ molecules		$2 \times 6.022 \times 10^{23}$ molecules		6.022×10^{23} molecules
2 moles		2 moles		1 mole

The coefficients in a chemical equation indicate the ratios of moles of atoms, molecules, and ions that react or are formed. The foregoing equation indicates that 2 moles of H_2 are formed for every 2 moles of H_2O decomposed (2 mol H_2/2 mol H_2O), that 1 mole of O_2 is formed for every 2 moles of H_2O decomposed (1 mol O_2/2 mol H_2O), and that 1 mole of O_2 forms for every 2 moles of H_2 formed (1 mol O_2/2 mol H_2). These unit conversion factors are exact to any number of significant figures.

It is therefore quite straightforward to determine, from the information provided by a chemical equation, the numbers of atoms and molecules, or the numbers of moles of these atoms and molecules, that react or are produced in a chemical process. The following two examples illustrate how we do this.

The reaction of aluminum with iodine produces aluminum iodide. The purple vapor is iodine gas, produced via the vaporization of some solid iodine by the heat of the reaction.

Example 3.20

As shown in the photograph above, aluminum reacts with iodine. How many moles of Al_2I_6 are produced by the reaction of 4.0 mol of aluminum according to the following equation?

$$2Al(s) + 3I_2(s) \longrightarrow Al_2I_6(s)$$

The balanced equation indicates that exactly 1 mol of Al_2I_6 is produced for every 2 mol of Al consumed (the ratio is 1 mol Al_2I_6/2 mol Al). This relationship can be used to convert the number of moles of Al reacting to the number of moles of Al_2I_6 produced.

$$4.0 \text{ mol Al} \times \frac{1 \text{ mol } Al_2I_6}{2 \text{ mol Al}} = 2.0 \text{ mol } Al_2I_6$$

The unwanted units cancel, so the correct factor was used. The number of significant figures in the answer was determined by the amount of Al, because conversion factors determined from equations are exact.

Example 3.21

How many moles of I_2 are required to react exactly with 0.429 mol of aluminum?

The balanced equation indicates that exactly 3 mol of I_2 react with 2 mol of Al. This gives us the conversion factor 3 mol I_2/2 mol Al.

$$0.429 \text{ mol Al} \times \frac{3 \text{ mol I}_2}{2 \text{ mol Al}} = 0.644 \text{ mol I}_2$$

❸.10 Calculations Based on Equations

In this section we shall introduce a stoichiometry calculation that is related to the quantities of substances involved in chemical reactions. All such calculations proceed from the law of conservation of matter (Section 1.3) and from the facts that (1) balanced equations give the ratios of moles of reactants and products involved in chemical reactions and (2) we can determine the masses of the reactants and products from the numbers of moles involved, using the atomic, molecular, or formula masses of the substances participating in the reaction. The following examples illustrate these calculations.

Calculate the moles of oxygen produced during the thermal decomposition of 100.0 g of potassium chlorate to form potassium chloride and oxygen in the following reaction: **Example 3.22**

$$2KClO_3(s) \xrightarrow{\Delta} 2KCl(s) + 3O_2(g)$$

We are asked to calculate the number of moles of O_2 produced from 100.0 g of $KClO_3$, and we are given the equation for the reaction by which O_2 forms from $KClO_3$. If we can determine the number of moles of $KClO_3$ that react, we can also determine the number of moles of O_2 produced, because the equation indicates that exactly 3 mol of O_2 are produced for each 2 mol of $KClO_3$ that reacts (the conversion factor is 3 mol O_2/2 mol $KClO_3$). The number of moles of $KClO_3$ used can be found from the mass of $KClO_3$ and its formula mass.

$$1 \text{ mol KClO}_3 = 122.55 \text{ g KClO}_3$$

$$100.0 \text{ g KClO}_3 \times \frac{1 \text{ mol KClO}_3}{122.55 \text{ g KClO}_3} = 0.8160 \text{ mol KClO}_3$$

$$0.8160 \text{ mol KClO}_3 \times \frac{3 \text{ mol O}_2}{2 \text{ mol KClO}_3} = 1.224 \text{ mol O}_2$$

Thus 100.0 g of $KClO_3$ is 0.8160 mol $KClO_3$, and 0.8160 mol $KClO_3$ will produce 1.224 mol of O_2. In this case, the chain of calculations involves the following unit conversions:

$$\boxed{\begin{array}{c}\text{Mass of} \\ \text{KClO}_3\end{array}} \longrightarrow \boxed{\begin{array}{c}\text{Moles of} \\ \text{KClO}_3\end{array}} \longrightarrow \boxed{\begin{array}{c}\text{Moles of} \\ \text{O}_2\end{array}}$$

Note how dimensional analysis with the resulting cancellation of units is helpful in checking to see whether you have used the correct conversion factors.

It is not necessary to write each step of the calculations separately. The calculations could have been written in one step, as follows:

$$100.0 \text{ g KClO}_3 \times \frac{1 \text{ mol KClO}_3}{122.55 \text{ g KClO}_3} \times \frac{3 \text{ mol O}_2}{2 \text{ mol KClO}_3} = 1.224 \text{ mol O}_2$$

Example 3.23

What mass of sodium hydroxide, NaOH, would be required to produce 16 g of the antacid milk of magnesia [magnesium hydroxide, $Mg(OH)_2$] by the reaction of magnesium chloride, $MgCl_2$, with NaOH?

$$MgCl_2(aq) + 2NaOH(aq) \longrightarrow Mg(OH)_2(s) + 2NaCl(aq)$$

The equation tells us that 2 mol of NaOH are required to form 1 mol of $Mg(OH)_2$. If we calculate the number of moles of $Mg(OH)_2$ in 16 g of $Mg(OH)_2$, we can determine the moles of NaOH necessary and then the mass of NaOH required.

From the formula mass of $Mg(OH)_2$, 58.3 g of $Mg(OH)_2$ = 1 mol of $Mg(OH)_2$. Therefore

$$16 \text{ g Mg(OH)}_2 \times \frac{1 \text{ mol Mg(OH)}_2}{58.3 \text{ g Mg(OH)}_2} = 0.274 \text{ mol Mg(OH)}_2$$

From the chemical equation, 2 mol of NaOH reacts to give 1 mol of $Mg(OH)_2$ [the conversion factor is 2 mol NaOH/1 mol $Mg(OH)_2$]. Hence

$$0.274 \text{ mol Mg(OH)}_2 \times \frac{2 \text{ mol NaOH}}{1 \text{ mol Mg(OH)}_2} = 0.548 \text{ mol NaOH}$$

From the formula mass of NaOH, 40.0 g of NaOH = 1 mol of NaOH. Thus

$$0.548 \text{ mol NaOH} \times \frac{40.0 \text{ g NaOH}}{1 \text{ mol NaOH}} = 22 \text{ g NaOH}$$

The mass, 16 g of $Mg(OH)_2$, requires two significant figures for the answer.

These calculations could have been handled in one step, as demonstrated in the previous example.

The fundamental principle in this type of calculation is to determine the number of moles of the reactant or product for which data are given and then, from the balanced equation, to calculate the number of moles of the other reactant or product involved in the problem. The relative numbers of moles of the various species participating in a reaction are provided by the balanced equation that describes the system (Section 3.9). The number of grams of the second reactant or product can be calculated from the number of moles of the substance, if required.

Most stoichiometry problems that are concerned with material balances in a chemical reaction involve the basic transformations, or conversions, illustrated in the following general diagram. The arrows indicate that one quantity is converted to the next. As in Examples 3.22 and 3.23, the "mole boxes" are in a different color to emphasize the fundamental importance of the mole concept in these calculations.

Stoichiometry is the calculation of both material balances and energy balances in a chemical system. We will discuss material balances in this chapter and energy balances in Chapter 19. Most stoichiometry problems involve the basic transformations, or conversions, illustrated below. The arrows indicate that one quantity is converted to the next.

The overall conversion from Quantity A to Quantity B requires three steps (each of which may require one or more unit conversion factors of the types we have previously discussed):

1. Conversion of a quantity measured in units such as grams or liters into a quantity measured in moles
2. Determination, from the balanced equation, of how many moles of a second substance are equivalent to the number of moles of the first
3. Conversion of the number of moles of the second substance into a mass of that substance or a volume of a solution of a certain molarity

Although Examples 3.22 and 3.23 illustrate the basic flow of almost any stoichiometry problem involving material balances, such calculations often involve several additional steps. These may result from the nature of the material used in a reaction (a mixture rather than a pure compound, for example) or from the various ways of measuring it (measuring a volume rather than a mass, for example). In such cases the additional steps usually involve relating measured quantities to moles. Additional examples follow.

Calculate the mass of oxygen gas, O_2, required for the combustion of 702 g of octane, C_8H_{18}.

Example 3.24

$$2C_8H_{18} + 25O_2 \longrightarrow 16CO_2 + 18H_2O$$

In this example we are asked to calculate the mass of O_2 that reacts with 702 g of octane, C_8H_{18}, in a reaction indicated by the balanced equation. We can calculate the number of grams of O_2 required (by using the molecular mass of O_2) if we know the number of moles of O_2 required. The equation indicates that 25 moles of O_2 are required for reaction with 2 moles of C_8H_{18}, so we can find the number of moles of O_2 if we can determine the number of moles of C_8H_{18} present. We can determine the number of moles of C_8H_{18} from the mass of C_8H_{18} used and its molecular mass. Thus the chain of calculations requires the following conversions:

$$\boxed{\text{Mass of } C_8H_{18}} \longrightarrow \boxed{\text{Moles of } C_8H_{18}} \longrightarrow \boxed{\text{Moles of } O_2} \longrightarrow \boxed{\text{Mass of } O_2}$$

From the molecular mass of C_8H_{18}, 1 mol C_8H_{18} = 114.2 g C_8H_{18} [(8 × 12.011) + (18 × 1.0079), rounded to one decimal place].

$$702 \text{ g } C_8H_{18} \times \frac{1 \text{ mol } C_8H_{18}}{114.2 \text{ g } C_8H_{18}} = 6.147 \text{ mol } C_8H_{18}$$

From the balanced chemical equation, 25 mol of O_2 reacts for each 2 mol of C_8H_{18} (the conversion factor is 25 mol O_2/2 mol C_8H_{18}), so

$$6.147 \text{ mol } C_8H_{18} \times \frac{25 \text{ mol } O_2}{2 \text{ mol } C_8H_{18}} = 76.84 \text{ mol } O_2$$

From the molecular mass of O_2, 1 mol O_2 = 32.00 g O_2. Hence

$$76.84 \text{ mol } O_2 \times \frac{32.00 \text{ g } O_2}{1 \text{ mol } O_2} = 2459 \text{ g } O_2 = 2.46 \times 10^3 \text{ g } O_2$$

Example 3.24 continued

In this example one more digit than is justified by the data was carried through the calculations, and the final answer was rounded off to three significant figures, as required by the fact that the quantity of C_8H_{18} was given to only three significant figures. Although the logic of the problem involves three steps, the calculations could have been handled in one step, as follows:

$$702 \text{ g } C_8H_{18} \times \frac{1 \text{ mol } C_8H_{18}}{114.2 \text{ g } C_8H_{18}} \times \frac{25 \text{ mol } O_2}{2 \text{ mol } C_8H_{18}} \times \frac{32.00 \text{ g } O_2}{1 \text{ mol } O_2} = 2.46 \times 10^3 \text{ g } O_2$$

Example 3.25

What volume of a 0.750 M solution of hydrochloric acid can be prepared from the HCl produced by the reaction of 25.0 g of NaCl with an excess of sulfuric acid?

$$NaCl(s) + H_2SO_4(l) \longrightarrow HCl(g) + NaHSO_4(s)$$

In order to determine the volume of 0.750 M solution that we can prepare, we need the number of moles of HCl(g) that are available to make the solution. The chemical equation tells us the relationship between the number of moles of gaseous HCl produced and the number of moles of NaCl reacting. The number of moles of NaCl can be determined from the mass of NaCl used and its formula mass. Solution of the problem requires the following steps, each of which uses a single unit conversion factor.

Mass of NaCl	$\longrightarrow$	Moles of NaCl	$\longrightarrow$	Moles of HCl	$\longrightarrow$	Volume of solution

Convert the quantity of NaCl in grams to moles of NaCl. As described in Section 3.5, this conversion requires calculating the formula mass of NaCl, 58.44; thus 1 mol NaCl = 58.44 g NaCl. The conversion is then

$$25.0 \text{ g } NaCl \times \frac{1 \text{ mol } NaCl}{58.44 \text{ g } NaCl} = 0.4278 \text{ mol } NaCl$$

Convert moles of NaCl to moles of HCl. The chemical equation indicates that 1 mol of HCl is produced for every 1 mol of NaCl that reacts. The unit conversion factor is 1 mol HCl/1 mol NaCl (Section 3.9).

$$0.4278 \text{ mol } NaCl \times \frac{1 \text{ mol } HCl}{1 \text{ mol } NaCl} = 0.4278 \text{ mol } HCl$$

Convert moles of HCl to the volume of a 0.750 M solution of HCl. As shown in Section 3.8,

$$\text{Molarity} = \frac{\text{moles of solute}}{\text{liters of solution}}$$

We can rearrange this to solve for the volume of solution:

$$\text{Liters of solution} = \text{moles of solute} \times \frac{1}{\text{molarity}}$$

Because a 0.750 M solution contains 0.750 mol HCl per 1 L (the unit conversion factor is 0.750 mol HCl/1 L), the reciprocal of the molarity (1/M) is expressed as follows:

$$\frac{1}{\text{Molarity}} = \frac{1 \text{ L}}{0.750 \text{ mol } HCl}$$

Thus

$$0.4278 \text{ mol HCl} \times \frac{1 \text{ L}}{0.750 \text{ mol HCl}} = 0.570 \text{ L}$$

As shown in the photograph, potassium iodide, KI, reacts with copper nitrate, $Cu(NO_3)_2$, to form a mixture of copper iodide, CuI, and iodine, I_2. What volume of a 0.2089 M solution of KI will contain enough KI to react exactly with the $Cu(NO_3)_2$ in 43.88 mL of a 0.3842 M $Cu(NO_3)_2$ solution according to the following equation?

Example 3.26

$$2Cu(NO_3)_2(aq) + 4KI(aq) \longrightarrow 2CuI(s) + I_2(s) + 4KNO_3(aq)$$

This problem asks us to use the volume of a $Cu(NO_3)_2$ solution of known concentration to calculate the volume of a KI solution of known concentration. The overall conversion is

To determine the necessary volume of the KI solution, we need to know the moles of KI required to react. This can be determined from the moles of $Cu(NO_3)_2$ that react [the moles of $Cu(NO_3)_2$ present in 43.88 mL of the $Cu(NO_3)_2$ solution], which we can find by using the conversion factor obtained from the equation. The calculation involves the following steps:

Note that the volumes must be expressed in liters. The calculations for each step follow.

$$\frac{0.3842 \text{ mol Cu(NO}_3)_2}{1 \text{ L}} \times 0.04388 \text{ L} = 1.686 \times 10^{-2} \text{ mol Cu(NO}_3)_2$$

$$1.686 \times 10^{-2} \text{ mol Cu(NO}_3)_2 \times \frac{4 \text{ mol KI}}{2 \text{ mol Cu(NO}_3)_2} = 3.372 \times 10^{-2} \text{ mol KI}$$

$$3.372 \times 10^{-2} \text{ mol KI} \times \frac{1 \text{ L}}{0.2089 \text{ mol KI}} = 0.1614 \text{ L}$$

The reaction requires 0.1614 L, or 161.4 mL, of KI solution.

The addition of a solution of KI to a solution of $(CuNO_3)_2$ produces two solids, CuI(s) and $I_2(s)$.

Density can be used in the conversion of either the mass of a substance to its volume or the volume of a substance to its mass. The following example illustrates the interconversion between volume and mass by means of density.

The reaction of chlorobenzene, C_6H_5Cl, with a solution of ammonia containing 28.2% NH_3 by mass is used in the preparation of aniline, $C_6H_5NH_2$, a key ingredient in the preparation of dyes for fabrics. What mass of NH_3 is required to prepare 125 mL of the ammonia solution with a density of 0.899 g/cm^3?

Example 3.27

**Example
3.27
continued**

Two steps are required to solve this problem: a conversion from the volume and density to the mass of a mixture (the solution of NH_3), and a conversion from the mass of a mixture (the solution of NH_3) to the mass of a pure substance (NH_3).

Find the mass of 125 mL of NH_3 solution (interconversion between volume and mass using density). Because 1 mL is the same as 1 cm^3, we express the volume in cubic centimeters.

$$125 \text{ cm}^3 \text{ solution} \times \frac{0.899 \text{ g solution}}{1 \text{ cm}^3 \text{ solution}} = 112.4 \text{ g solution}$$

Now we find the mass of NH_3 in the solution (interconversion between mass of a mixture and mass of a component). A 28.2% NH_3 solution by mass contains 28.2 g NH_3 per 100 g of solution.

$$112.4 \text{ g solution} \times \frac{28.2 \text{ g } NH_3}{100 \text{ g solution}} = 31.7 \text{ g } NH_3$$

③.11 Theoretical Yield, Actual Yield, and Percent Yield

In the preceding sections we have shown how to calculate the amount of product produced by a chemical reaction. These calculations are based on the assumptions that the reaction is the only one involved, that all of the reactant is converted into product, and that all of the product can be collected. The calculated amount of product based on these assumptions is called the **theoretical yield.** We rarely find these conditions satisfied either in the laboratory or in industrial production; the actual amount of product isolated (the **actual yield**) from a reaction is usually less than the theoretical yield. We can calculate the **percent yield** of a reaction from the following relationship:

$$\text{Percent yield} = \frac{\text{actual yield}}{\text{theoretical yield}} \times 100$$

The following example illustrates the calculation of percent yield.

**Example
3.28**

A general chemistry student, preparing copper metal by the reaction of 1.274 g of copper sulfate with zinc metal, obtained a yield of 0.392 g of copper. What was the percent yield?

$$CuSO_4(aq) + Zn(s) \longrightarrow Cu(s) + ZnSO_4(aq)$$

To calculate percent yield, we need both the theoretical yield of copper and the actual yield. The actual yield is 0.392 g; the theoretical yield is the amount of copper that would have been obtained if all of the $CuSO_4$ had been converted into Cu and recovered. The theoretical yield can be calculated by the following steps:

$$\boxed{\text{Mass of} \atop \text{CuSO}_4} \longrightarrow \boxed{\text{Moles of} \atop \text{CuSO}_4} \longrightarrow \boxed{\text{Moles of} \atop \text{Cu}} \longrightarrow \boxed{\text{Mass of} \atop \text{Cu}}$$

$$1.274 \text{ g CuSO}_4 \times \frac{1 \text{ mol CuSO}_4}{159.6 \text{ g CuSO}_4} = 7.982 \times 10^{-3} \text{ mol CuSO}_4$$

$$7.982 \times 10^{-3} \text{ mol CuSO}_4 \times \frac{1 \text{ mol Cu}}{1 \text{ mol CuSO}_4} = 7.982 \times 10^{-3} \text{ mol Cu}$$

$$7.982 \times 10^{-3} \text{ mol Cu} \times \frac{63.546 \text{ g Cu}}{1 \text{ mol Cu}} = 0.5072 \text{ g Cu}$$

The theoretical yield of Cu is 0.5072 g. The percent yield can now be calculated.

$$\text{Percent yield} = \frac{\text{actual yield}}{\text{theoretical yield}} \times 100 = \frac{0.392 \text{ g}}{0.5072 \text{ g}} \times 100 = 77.3\%$$

❸.12 Limiting Reagents

Under certain conditions, all of the reactants in a chemical reaction may not be completely consumed. Consider, for example, the reaction of silver nitrate with copper metal (Fig. 3.5).

$$2AgNO_3 + Cu \longrightarrow 2Ag + Cu(NO_3)_2$$

The equation indicates that exactly 2 moles of $AgNO_3$ must react per mole of Cu that reacts. If the ratio of reactants actually used in this reaction differs from $2:1$, then one of the reactants will be present in excess and not all of it will be consumed. If, for example, we have 2 moles of $AgNO_3$ and 2 moles of Cu, then 1 mole of Cu must remain unreacted at the end of the reaction because 2 moles of $AgNO_3$ can react with only 1 mole of Cu.

Figure 3.5

The photograph on the left shows a copper wire shortly after it is placed in a solution of silver nitrate. On the right the reaction is complete. Silver crystals cover the wire, and the blue color of copper nitrate is evident in the solution. Silver nitrate is the limiting reagent in this reaction because some copper wire remains unconsumed.

The reactant that is completely consumed ($AgNO_3$ in this case) is called the **limiting reagent.** This reactant limits the amount of product that can be formed and determines the theoretical yield of the reaction. Other reactants are said to be present in excess.

To determine which reagent is the limiting reagent, calculate the amount of product expected from each reactant. The reactant that gives the smallest amount of product is the limiting reagent. The following example illustrates a calculation to determine the limiting reagent.

Example 3.29

A mixture of 5.0 g of $H_2(g)$ and 10.0 g of $O_2(g)$ is ignited. Water forms according to the following addition reaction:

$$2H_2(g) + O_2(g) \longrightarrow 2H_2O(g)$$

Which reactant is limiting? How much water will the reaction produce?

First, assume that all of the H_2 will react and calculate the theoretical yield of water (to the two significant figures justified), using the following steps:

$$\boxed{\text{Mass of } H_2} \longrightarrow \boxed{\text{Moles of } H_2} \longrightarrow \boxed{\text{Moles of } H_2O}$$

$$5.0 \text{ g } H_2 \times \frac{1 \text{ mol } H_2}{2.02 \text{ g } H_2} = 2.48 \text{ mol } H_2$$

$$2.48 \text{ mol } H_2 \times \frac{2 \text{ mol } H_2O}{2 \text{ mol } H_2} = 2.5 \text{ mol } H_2O$$

Now, assume that all of the O_2 will react, and calculate the theoretical yield of water (to the three significant numbers justified), using the following steps:

$$\boxed{\text{Mass of } O_2} \longrightarrow \boxed{\text{Moles of } O_2} \longrightarrow \boxed{\text{Moles of } H_2O}$$

$$10.0 \text{ g } O_2 \times \frac{1 \text{ mol } O_2}{32.00 \text{ g } O_2} = 0.3125 \text{ mol } O_2$$

$$0.3125 \text{ mol } O_2 \times \frac{2 \text{ mol } H_2O}{1 \text{ mol } O_2} = 0.625 \text{ mol } H_2O$$

At this point, it is clear that O_2 is the limiting reactant, because 10.0 g of O_2 gives 0.625 mol of H_2O, whereas 5.0 g of H_2 would give 2.5 mol of H_2O if the hydrogen were all converted to water. Thus not enough oxygen is present to convert all the hydrogen to water. The following expression gives the mass of water that is equal to 0.625 mol of water:

$$0.625 \text{ mol } H_2O \times \frac{18.02 \text{ g } H_2O}{1 \text{ mol } H_2O} = 11.3 \text{ g } H_2O$$

The following example illustrates a slightly different method of determining the limiting reagent: by calculating the quantity of one reactant that is needed to react with the available quantity of the other. Then the calculated quantity is compared to the quantity of that reactant that is actually available.

(a) When 0.21 L of 1.00 M H_2SO_4 solution and 0.82 L of 0.750 M KOH are mixed, is the resulting solution acidic or basic?

Example 3.30

$$H_2SO_4 + 2KOH \longrightarrow K_2SO_4 + 2H_2O$$

$$\frac{1.00 \text{ mol } H_2SO_4}{1 \text{ L}} \times 0.21 \text{ L} = 0.21 \text{ mol } H_2SO_4$$

$$\frac{0.750 \text{ mol KOH}}{1 \text{ L}} \times 0.82 \text{ L} = 0.62 \text{ mol KOH}$$

$$0.21 \text{ mol } H_2SO_4 \times \frac{2 \text{ mol KOH}}{1 \text{ mol } H_2SO_4} = 0.42 \text{ mol KOH}$$

Inasmuch as 0.42 mol of KOH would be required for reaction with 0.21 mol of H_2SO_4, but 0.62 mol of KOH is actually present, the KOH (a base) is in excess. The resulting solution is basic.

(b) Which reagent is the limiting reagent?

Not enough H_2SO_4 is present to react with the available KOH, so H_2SO_4 is the limiting reagent.

(c) What is the molarity of KOH in the final solution, assuming that no contraction or expansion in volume takes place when the two initial solutions are mixed together?

The final volume of the solution is 0.21 L + 0.82 L = 1.03 L. The quantity of KOH that reacts with the available H_2SO_4 is 0.42 mol, which leaves (0.62 − 0.42) mol, or 0.20 mol, of excess KOH in the final solution.

$$\frac{0.20 \text{ mol KOH}}{1.03 \text{ L solution}} = 0.19 \text{ M KOH}$$

(d) What is the molarity of H_2SO_4 in the final solution?

All of the H_2SO_4 reacts with KOH to form K_2SO_4. Hence the molarity of H_2SO_4 in the final solution is zero.

(e) What is the molarity of K_2SO_4 in the final solution?

$$0.21 \text{ mol } H_2SO_4 \times \frac{1 \text{ mol } K_2SO_4}{1 \text{ mol } H_2SO_4} = 0.21 \text{ mol } K_2SO_4$$

$$\frac{0.21 \text{ mol } K_2SO_4}{1.03 \text{ L solution}} = 0.20 \text{ M } K_2SO_4$$

③.13 Titration

A known volume of a solution is usually measured with a pipet or a buret. A **pipet** is a tube that will deliver a known fixed volume of a liquid when filled to a reference line (Fig. 3.6). A **buret** is a cylinder (Fig. 3.7) that is graduated in fractions of a milliliter so that the volume of a liquid delivered from it can be accurately measured.

Figure 3.6   (left)

A pipet will deliver a precise volume if it is filled to a reference line and allowed to drain. Various sizes of pipets are available. The one pictured here is a 5.0-mL pipet.

Figure 3.7   (right)

A buret is used for accurately measuring the volume of a solution of known concentration added during a titration.

Burets and pipets are used to determine the concentrations of solutions (to standardize solutions) by **titration** (Fig. 3.8). During a titration, a buret is used to add a solution of a reactant of known concentration to a solution of a sample of unknown concentration. When the exact amount of reactant necessary to react completely with the sample

Figure 3.8

The end point of the titration of an acid with a base where phenolphthalein is the indicator. (left) As the end point is approached, streaks of color are observed that disappear with mixing. (right) At the end point, one drop from the buret produces a permanent color change.

has been added, a chemical indicator or, in some cases the color of the solution itself (see Example 3.32), marks the **end point** of the titration. A **chemical indicator** is a substance that is added to the titration sample to mark the end point of the titration, usually by a change of color. At the end point, the titration is stopped, and the amount of solution added is determined by reading the volume of solution delivered from the buret. This volume is used in determining the concentration of the sample solution. More will be said about titrations and indicators in Chapter 17.

A chemical equation gives the ratios of moles of reactants and moles of products entering into a chemical reaction. If these reactants or products are dissolved, Equation (1) in Section 3.8 can be used to relate the molarity and volume of the solution to the number of moles present.

$$\text{Molarity} = \frac{\text{moles of solute}}{\text{liters of solution}}$$

The following are examples of titration calculations.

Example 3.31

A solution of HCl in water is standardized by titrating a solution that contains a 0.5015-g sample of pure sodium carbonate, Na_2CO_3, dissolved in water. What is the concentration of the HCl solution if 48.47 mL is added from a buret to reach the end point?

$$Na_2CO_3 + 2HCl \longrightarrow 2NaCl + CO_2 + H_2O$$

To determine the concentration of the HCl solution, we need to know the number of moles of HCl in some volume of the solution. At the end of the titration, we know that we have added 48.47 mL of the solution and that the HCl in it has reacted exactly with 0.5015 g of NaOH. The balanced equation tells us that 2 mol of HCl has been added for every 1 mol of NaOH present. The number of moles of HCl present in 48.47 mL of solution can be determined from the number of moles of NaOH titrated. The concentration of the solution can be determined by the following steps:

| Mass of NaOH | $\longrightarrow$ | Moles of NaOH | $\longrightarrow$ | Moles of HCl | $\longrightarrow$ | Molarity of solution |

Titration of a NaOH solution with a HCl solution. (left) The solution in the buret is a solution of HCl for which the concentration is to be determined by titration into a known quantity of NaOH in the flask. The end point of the titration occurs when just enough HCl solution has been titrated into the NaOH solution to neutralize the NaOH exactly. A few drops of phenolphthalein indicator, which has a pink color in basic solution and is colorless in acid solution, have been added to the NaOH solution to indicate the end point. (right) The titration at the exact end point. The buret shows that 48.47 mL of HCl solution has been added to the NaOH solution to reach the end point. The phenolphthalein indicator in the NaOH solution has changed from pink to colorless with the neutralization of the NaOH.

Example
3.31
continued

$$0.5015 \text{ g NaOH} \times \frac{1 \text{ mol NaOH}}{39.997 \text{ g NaOH}} = 1.2538 \times 10^{-2} \text{ mol NaOH}$$

$$1.2538 \times 10^{-2} \text{ mol NaOH} \times \frac{1 \text{ mol HCl}}{1 \text{ mol NaOH}} = 1.2538 \times 10^{-2} \text{ mol HCl}$$

$$\frac{1.2538 \times 10^{-2} \text{ mol HCl}}{0.04847 \text{ L}} = 0.2587$$

The concentration of the HCl solution is 0.2587 M.

Example
3.32

A solution of oxalic acid, $H_2C_2O_4$, was added to a flask by means of a 20.00-mL pipet. After acidifying with sulfuric acid, H_2SO_4, the sample was titrated with a 0.09113 M solution of potassium permanganate, $KMnO_4$. A volume of 23.24 mL was required to reach the end point. What was the concentration of the $H_2C_2O_4$ solution?

$$5H_2C_2O_4 + 2KMnO_4 + 3H_2SO_4 \longrightarrow 2MnSO_4 + K_2SO_4 + 10CO_2 + 8H_2O$$

To determine the concentration of $H_2C_2O_4$ in the solution, we need to know the number of moles of $H_2C_2O_4$ in 0.02000 L (20.00 mL) of the solution, the amount delivered by the pipet. The equation tells us that for every 5 mol of $H_2C_2O_4$ present, 2 mol of $KMnO_4$ reacts. The moles of $KMnO_4$ reacting can be determined from the volume and molarity of the $KMnO_4$ solution added during the titration.

The titration of a solution of $H_2C_2O_4$ (Erlenmeyer flask) by addition of a solution of $KMnO_4$ (buret). As the purple $KMnO_4$ solution is added to the colorless $H_2C_2O_4$ solution, the $KMnO_4$ is converted to essentially colorless $MnSO_4$ by the oxidation–reduction reaction with colorless $H_2C_2O_4$. At the instant when all the $H_2C_2O_4$ has been consumed, addition of the next drop of $KMnO_4$ turns the solution in the flask purple; this indicates the end point of the titration.

$$0.02324 \text{ L KMnO}_4 \times \frac{0.09113 \text{ mol KMnO}_4}{1 \text{ L KMnO}_4} = 2.1179 \times 10^{-3} \text{ mol KMnO}_4$$

$$2.1179 \times 10^{-3} \text{ mol KMnO}_4 \times \frac{5 \text{ mol H}_2\text{C}_2\text{O}_4}{2 \text{ mol KMnO}_4} = 5.2948 \times 10^{-3} \text{ mol H}_2\text{C}_2\text{O}_4$$

$$\frac{5.2948 \times 10^{-3} \text{ mol H}_2\text{C}_2\text{O}_4}{0.02000 \text{ L}} = 0.2647 \text{ M}$$

3.14 Common Relationships in Stoichiometry Calculations

The following diagram summarizes several of the possible relationships in stoichiometry calculations.

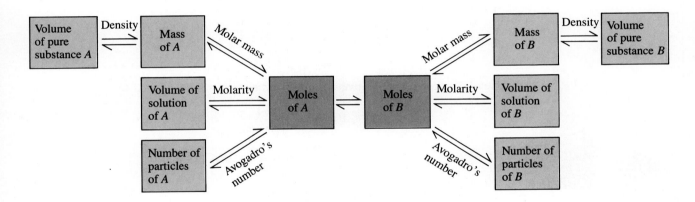

The core of the procedure is the number of moles of A and the number of moles of B. The words over the arrows indicate physical properties that are involved in the interconversion calculations. The double arrows indicate that the calculations can proceed in either direction.

3.15 Additional Examples of Chemical Stoichiometry

Many of the stoichiometry problems that a student sees at the beginning of a chemistry course appear formidable. However, the majority of these problems involve nothing more complicated than applying the conversions shown in the diagram. In most of these problems, the first step or steps use unit conversions to transform a quantity of a substance to moles of the substance. The numbers of moles of additional substances that are equivalent to the first are then usually found, and, finally, the amount of one of these additional substances in some unit other than moles is determined.

The difficulty with stoichiometry problems is usually in finding the order in which to do the conversions. Unfortunately, no single technique can be used to string together these conversions for all types of problems. However, there are some useful guidelines. Many problems require that we determine the quantity of B that is equivalent to a given amount of A. In most of these cases, we need a mole-to-mole conversion (to convert moles of A to moles of B). First we identify the substances (A and B) to be interconverted. We then find the information that tells how much of substance A is present and the information that tells how to report the amount of substance B. After the problem is broken down into these large steps, we work on the conversions necessary to carry them out. For example, the conversion of a quantity of A to moles of A may require only one conversion or it may require several.

One final hint: Be certain that you understand how to do each of the various types of single conversions before you combine them in complicated problems.

Example 3.33

What mass of iodine is required to make 5.00×10^2 mL of a 0.250 M solution of I_2 with chloroform, $CHCl_3$, as the solvent?

The moles of I_2 necessary to make a 0.250 M solution can be found by rearranging Equation (1) as shown in Section 3.8. The mass of I_2 required can then be calculated. The following steps are involved in the calculation:

Note that the volume is given in milliliters and must be converted to liters.

$$5.00 \times 10^2 \text{ mL} \times \frac{1 \text{ L}}{1000 \text{ mL}} = 0.500 \text{ L}$$

$$\frac{0.250 \text{ mol } I_2}{1 \text{ L}} \times 0.500 \text{ L} = 0.125 \text{ mol } I_2$$

$$0.125 \text{ mol } I_2 \times \frac{253.8 \text{ g } I_2}{1 \text{ mol } I_2} = 31.7 \text{ g } I_2$$

A photograph of 31.7 g of solid I_2 (0.125 mol of I_2) and of a 500-mL volume of a 0.250 M I_2 solution in chloroform, $CHCl_3$, made by dissolving 31.7 g of solid I_2 (0.125 mol) in enough chloroform to prepare 500 mL of solution. The resulting I_2 solution is 0.250 M.

Although the logic of this problem is perhaps best approached in three steps, the calculations could have been written in one step, as follows:

$$5.00 \times 10^2 \text{ mL} \times \frac{1 \text{ L}}{1000 \text{ mL}} \times \frac{0.250 \text{ mol } I_2}{1 \text{ L}} \times \frac{253.8 \text{ g } I_2}{1 \text{ mol } I_2} = 31.7 \text{ g } I_2$$

All of the examples in this chapter have the calculations written as separate steps to help show the logic involved in solving them. However, all of these calculations could be written as a single step. When writing single-step calculations, it is particularly important to check that the units cancel properly.

Example 3.34

The toxic pigment called white lead, $Pb_3(OH)_2(CO_3)_2$, has been replaced by rutile, TiO_2, in white paints. How much rutile can be prepared from 379 g of an ore containing ilmenite, $FeTiO_3$, if the ore is 88.3% ilmenite by mass? TiO_2 is prepared by the reaction

$$2FeTiO_3 + 4HCl + Cl_2 \longrightarrow 2FeCl_3 + 2TiO_2 + 2H_2O$$

This problem asks how much rutile, TiO_2, can be prepared from an ore containing ilmenite, $FeTiO_3$. The overall conversion is

$$\boxed{\begin{array}{c}\text{Mass of}\\\text{ore}\end{array}} \longrightarrow \boxed{\begin{array}{c}\text{Mass of}\\TiO_2\end{array}}$$

Most conversions of this type involve mole-to-mole conversions, so the chain of conversions for this problem probably includes one, too. The problem states that the $FeTiO_3$ in an ore is converted into TiO_2, so the chain of conversions should include a conversion of moles of $FeTiO_3$ to moles of TiO_2.

$$\boxed{\begin{array}{c}\text{Mass of}\\\text{ore}\end{array}} \longrightarrow \boxed{\begin{array}{c}\text{Moles of}\\FeTiO_3\end{array}} \longrightarrow \boxed{\begin{array}{c}\text{Moles of}\\TiO_2\end{array}} \longrightarrow \boxed{\begin{array}{c}\text{Mass of}\\TiO_2\end{array}}$$

Now it remains only to convert the mass of ore to the mass of $FeTiO_3$ in the ore. The final calculation involves the following unit conversions:

$$\boxed{\begin{array}{c}\text{Mass of}\\\text{ore}\end{array}} \longrightarrow \boxed{\begin{array}{c}\text{Mass of}\\FeTiO_3\end{array}} \longrightarrow \boxed{\begin{array}{c}\text{Moles of}\\FeTiO_3\end{array}} \longrightarrow \boxed{\begin{array}{c}\text{Moles of}\\TiO_2\end{array}} \longrightarrow \boxed{\begin{array}{c}\text{Mass of}\\TiO_2\end{array}}$$

The calculations for each step follow.

$$379 \text{ g ore} \times \frac{88.3 \text{ g } FeTiO_3}{100 \text{ g ore}} = 334.7 \text{ g } FeTiO_3$$

$$334.7 \text{ g } FeTiO_3 \times \frac{1 \text{ mol } FeTiO_3}{151.7 \text{ g } FeTiO_3} = 2.206 \text{ mol } FeTiO_3$$

$$2.206 \text{ mol } FeTiO_3 \times \frac{2 \text{ mol } TiO_2}{2 \text{ mol } FeTiO_3} = 2.206 \text{ mol } TiO_2$$

$$2.206 \text{ mol } TiO_2 \times \frac{79.88 \text{ g } TiO_2}{1 \text{ mol } TiO_2} = 176 \text{ g } TiO_2$$

Thus 176 g of TiO_2 can be prepared from the 379-g sample of ore.

Example 3.35

Phosphorus(V) chloride, PCl_5, is an important intermediate in the production of one class of insecticides. It can be prepared by the reaction of the nonmetal phosphorus, P_4, with the nonmetal chlorine, Cl_2.

$$P_4(s) + 10Cl_2(g) \longrightarrow 4PCl_5(s)$$

How many grams of PCl_5 can be obtained from the reaction of 1,565,000 molecules of Cl_2 with P_4?

The steps involved in solving the problem are

$$\boxed{\begin{array}{c}\text{Molecules}\\\text{of } Cl_2\end{array}} \longrightarrow \boxed{\begin{array}{c}\text{Moles of}\\Cl_2\end{array}} \longrightarrow \boxed{\begin{array}{c}\text{Moles of}\\PCl_5\end{array}} \longrightarrow \boxed{\begin{array}{c}\text{Mass of}\\PCl_5\end{array}}$$

We know from Avogadro's number that 1 mol of Cl_2 contains 6.022×10^{23} molecules.

Example 3.35
continued

$$\frac{1.565 \times 10^6 \text{ molecules Cl}_2}{\left(\dfrac{6.022 \times 10^{23} \text{ molecules Cl}_2}{1 \text{ mol Cl}_2}\right)} = 2.599 \times 10^{-18} \text{ mol Cl}_2$$

$$2.599 \times 10^{-18} \text{ mol Cl}_2 \times \frac{4 \text{ mol PCl}_5}{10 \text{ mol Cl}_2} = 1.040 \times 10^{-18} \text{ mol PCl}_5$$

$$1.040 \times 10^{-18} \text{ mol PCl}_5 \times \frac{208.24 \text{ g PCl}_5}{1 \text{ mol PCl}_5} = 2.166 \times 10^{-16} \text{ g PCl}_5$$

The problem can also be solved by combining the three steps into one, a system that can be used in all of these types of problems.

$$\frac{1.565 \times 10^6 \text{ molecules Cl}_2}{\left(\dfrac{6.022 \times 10^{23} \text{ molecules Cl}_2}{1 \text{ mol Cl}_2}\right)} \times \frac{4 \text{ mol PCl}_5}{10 \text{ mol Cl}_2} \times \frac{208.24 \text{ g PCl}_5}{1 \text{ mol PCl}_5} = 2.165 \times 10^{-16} \text{ g PCl}_5$$

(The difference of 1 in the fourth significant figure is due to our having rounded three times in the three-step calculation and only once in the one-step calculation.)

Example 3.36

Calcium acetate, $Ca(CH_3CO_2)_2$, is used as a mordant during the dyeing of fabric. (A mordant is a substance that combines with a dye to form an insoluble compound, known as a "lake," that produces a stable fixed color in a textile fiber.) The calcium acetate forms according to the equation

$$Ca(OH)_2 + 2CH_3CO_2H \longrightarrow Ca(CH_3CO_2)_2 + 2H_2O$$

How many grams of a sample containing 75.0% calcium hydroxide, $Ca(OH)_2$, by mass is required to react with the acetic acid, CH_3CO_2H, in 25.0 mL of a solution having a density of 1.065 g/mL and containing 58.0% acetic acid by mass?

Overall, this problem asks us to find the mass of a $Ca(OH)_2$ sample that will react with a given volume of CH_3CO_2H solution.

Because the solution contains CH_3CO_2H that reacts with the $Ca(OH)_2$ in the sample, we need a mole-to-mole conversion.

The density of the solution and the percent by mass of acetic acid in the solution are given, so we can calculate the mass of the solution and, from that, the mass of acetic acid in the solution. This will give us the steps necessary to convert from volume of solution to moles of acetic acid. To convert from moles of $Ca(OH)_2$ to mass of sample, we need to use the percent by mass of $Ca(OH)_2$ in the sample. The overall string of conversions is

The calculations for each step follow.

$$25.0 \text{ mL solution} \times \frac{1.065 \text{ g solution}}{1 \text{ mL solution}} = 26.62 \text{ g solution}$$

$$26.62 \text{ g solution} \times \frac{58.0 \text{ g CH}_3\text{CO}_2\text{H}}{100 \text{ g solution}} = 15.44 \text{ g CH}_3\text{CO}_2\text{H}$$

$$15.44 \text{ g CH}_3\text{CO}_2\text{H} \times \frac{1 \text{ mol CH}_3\text{CO}_2\text{H}}{60.05 \text{ g CH}_3\text{CO}_2\text{H}} = 0.2571 \text{ mol CH}_3\text{CO}_2\text{H}$$

$$0.2571 \text{ mol CH}_3\text{CO}_2\text{H} \times \frac{1 \text{ mol Ca(OH)}_2}{2 \text{ mol CH}_3\text{CO}_2\text{H}} = 0.1286 \text{ mol Ca(OH)}_2$$

$$0.1286 \text{ mol Ca(OH)}_2 \times \frac{74.09 \text{ g Ca(OH)}_2}{1 \text{ mol Ca(OH)}_2} = 9.528 \text{ g Ca(OH)}_2$$

$$9.528 \text{ g Ca(OH)}_2 \times \frac{100 \text{ g sample}}{75.0 \text{ g Ca(OH)}_2} = 12.7 \text{ g sample}$$

Example 3.37

What is the molar concentration of acetic acid in the solution described in Example 3.36?

This problem asks that we find the molarity of the acetic acid solution described in the preceding problem. Thus we must proceed from the volume of that solution to its molarity.

A reaction is not involved, so we do not need to do a mole-to-mole conversion. We should remember, however, that if we know the moles of acetic acid in a given volume of solution, we can calculate the molarity of the solution. The problem gives the volume of acetic acid solution (25.0 mL), so moles of acetic acid enter the chain of calculations.

The first three steps were worked in Example 3.36, which shows that the sample contains 0.2571 mol of CH_3CO_2H.

Example 3.37
continued

$$\text{Molarity} = \frac{\text{moles of CH}_3\text{CO}_2\text{H}}{\text{liters of solution}}$$

$$= \frac{0.2571 \text{ mol}}{0.0250 \text{ L}} = 10.3 \text{ mol/L} = 10.3 \text{ M}$$

Note that molarity is expressed in moles per liter; hence the volume of the solution must be expressed in liters.

Example 3.38

Small amounts of sulfuric acid, H_2SO_4, are prepared industrially by the oxidation of metal sulfides. The following sequence of reactions illustrates the manufacture of sulfuric acid from pyrite, FeS_2.

$$4FeS_2(s) + 11O_2(g) \longrightarrow 2Fe_2O_3(s) + 8SO_2(g) \qquad (1)$$

$$2SO_2(g) + O_2(g) \longrightarrow 2SO_3(g) \qquad (2)$$

$$SO_3(g) + H_2O(l) \longrightarrow H_2SO_4(l) \qquad (3)$$

What mass of FeS_2 is required to prepare 1.00 L of H_2SO_4 (density = 1.85 g/mL)?

We solve this problem by converting the volume of H_2SO_4 into the mass of FeS_2 required to produce it. The following conversions are required:

Volume of H_2SO_4 $\longrightarrow$ Mass of H_2SO_4 $\longrightarrow$ Moles of H_2SO_4 $\longrightarrow$ Moles of SO_3 $\longrightarrow$

Moles of SO_2 $\longrightarrow$ Moles of FeS_2 $\longrightarrow$ Mass of FeS_2

$$1.00 \text{ L } H_2SO_4 \times \frac{1000 \text{ mL}}{1 \text{ L}} \times \frac{1.85 \text{ g}}{1 \text{ mL}} = 1850 \text{ g } H_2SO_4$$

$$1850 \text{ g } H_2SO_4 \times \frac{1 \text{ mol } H_2SO_4}{98.07 \text{ g } H_2SO_4} = 18.86 \text{ mol } H_2SO_4$$

From Equation (3):

$$18.86 \text{ mol } H_2SO_4 \times \frac{1 \text{ mol } SO_3}{1 \text{ mol } H_2SO_4} = 18.86 \text{ mol } SO_3$$

From Equation (2):

$$18.86 \text{ mol } SO_3 \times \frac{2 \text{ mol } SO_2}{2 \text{ mol } SO_3} = 18.86 \text{ mol } SO_2$$

From Equation (1):

$$18.86 \text{ mol } SO_2 \times \frac{4 \text{ mol } FeS_2}{8 \text{ mol } SO_2} = 9.430 \text{ mol } FeS_2$$

$$9.430 \text{ mol } FeS_2 \times \frac{120.0 \text{ g } FeS_2}{1 \text{ mol } FeS_2} = 1.13 \times 10^3 \text{ g } FeS_2$$

For Review

Summary

Calculations of (1) quantitative relationships among atoms in compounds, (2) percent composition of a compound from its chemical formula, (3) empirical and molecular formulas from percent composition, (4) the quantities of reactants and products involved in chemical reactions on the basis of the coefficients in the balanced equation, and (5) the concentration of a solution—all these fall into a category of calculations called chemical stoichiometry. These concepts involve *material balances* in a chemical system and are the subject of this chapter. Another part of chemical stoichiometry (which will be discussed in Chapters 4 and 19) is concerned with *energy balances* in a chemical system. **Chemical stoichiometry** includes the calculation of both material balances and energy balances in a chemical system.

The **atomic mass** of an atom is the mass of a single atom in atomic mass units (amu). The mass of a molecule, in atomic mass units, is equal to the sum of the masses of its constituent atoms. Analogous to atomic mass, the **molecular mass** of a molecule is the mass of a single molecule in atomic mass units. Compounds that do not consist of individual molecules are characterized by a **formula mass,** which is equal to the sum of the atomic masses of the atoms as shown by the empirical formula. The empirical formula of a substance can be determined from the relative numbers of the various types of atoms that make up the substance.

Isotopes of an element are atoms with the same atomic number but different mass numbers; isotopes of an element, therefore, differ from each other only in the number of neutrons within the nucleus. A naturally occurring element is usually composed of several isotopes, and atomic mass is also the term for the weighted average of the masses of the isotopes involved.

We are now in a position to define an **element** (more rigorously than we could in Chapter 1) as consisting of atoms all of which have the same number of protons in their nuclei. For example, every atom with 28 protons in its nucleus is nickel.

A **mole of atoms** of any substance contains the same number of atoms as are found in exactly 12 grams of $^{12}_{6}C$. A mole of any type of atoms contains **Avogadro's number** of atoms, 6.022×10^{23} atoms. The mass, in grams, of a mole of atoms is numerically equal to the atomic mass of the atom.

A **mole of molecules** contains 6.022×10^{23} molecules, and the mass of a mole of molecules, in grams, is numerically equal to the molecular mass. The subscripts in a molecular formula indicate the number of moles of each type of atom in a mole of molecules. A mole of an ionic compound, which does not consist of individual molecules, is equal to 6.022×10^{23} formula units, as described by the empirical formula.

The amount of a substance, in moles, can be determined from its mass, and the mass can be determined from the number of moles. A given quantity of a substance, in moles, can be obtained by weighing. The empirical formula of a substance can be determined from the relative numbers of the various types of atoms that make up the substance. If the **percent composition** is known, then the relative numbers of atoms—and hence the empirical formula—can be calculated. When the molecular mass of a molecular compound is known, the molecular formula can be calculated from the empirical formula.

If a substance is dissolved, forming a solution, a given quantity of the substance, in moles, can be obtained by measuring out a calculated volume of the solution, provided that the molarity of the solution is known. The **molarity** of a solution, one common designation of the concentration of a solution, is equal to the number of moles of solute dissolved in exactly 1 liter of solution.

Stoichiometric calculations involving material balances reflect the fact that the relative numbers of moles of reactants and products involved in a chemical reaction are given by the balanced chemical equation that describes the reaction. Thus a balanced equation can be used to determine unit conversion factors relating moles of reactants and/or products. The quantity of a substance is commonly given as the mass of a pure sample of the substance, as the mass of a mixture containing a certain percent by mass of the substance, as the volume of a substance with its density, or as the volume of a solution with the molarity of the solution. The amount of product produced by complete conversion of a reactant in a reaction is called the **theoretical yield** of the reaction. To calculate the theoretical yield of a reaction, we must know which reagent acts as the **limiting reagent.** The amount of product that is actually isolated from a reaction, either in the laboratory or in an industrial process, is called the **actual yield** of the reaction. The **percent yield** can be calculated from the actual yield and the theoretical yield.

Volumes are often measured by use of a **pipet,** which delivers a fixed volume of a liquid, or by use of a **buret,** which delivers a variable volume that can be measured. Burets are used in **titrations.**

Key Terms and Concepts

actual yield (3.11)
atomic mass (3.1)
atomic weight (3.1)
Avogadro's number (3.4)
buret (3.13)
concentrated solution (3.8)
concentration (3.8)
dilute solution (3.8)
element (3.3)
empirical formula (3.7)

end point (3.13)
formula derivation (3.7)
formula mass (3.2)
indicator (3.13)
isotope (3.3)
limiting reagent (3.12)
molarity (3.8)
molar mass (3.5)
mole (3.4, 3.5)
molecular mass (3.2)

molecular weight (3.2)
percent composition (3.6)
percent yield (3.11)
pipet (3.13)
solute (3.8)
solution (3.8)
solvent (3.8)
theoretical yield (3.11)
titration (3.13)

Exercises

Note: Students sometimes get answers that differ in the last decimal place from the answers given. This generally reflects different ways of rounding off intermediate steps in the calculation. The answers given have been determined by rounding off to the correct number of significant figures at the end of the calculation. Molecular masses have been calculated by using all or most of the significant figures in the atomic masses of the constituent atoms. Answers for selected even-numbered exercises marked by red numbers appear at the end of the book. The worked-out solutions to all even-numbered exercises appear in the *Solutions Guide.*

Atomic and Molecular Masses

1. (a) Calculate the molecular masses of H_2, O_2, Cl_2, H_2O, CH_3CO_2H (acetic acid), and $C_{12}H_{22}O_{11}$ (sugar).
   (b) Are the molecular masses the same as the molar masses

for the substances listed in part (a)? Explain your answer.

2. Calculate the formula mass and the molar mass of each of the following:
   (a) S_8
   (b) H_3PO_4
   (c) $Li_4P_2O_7$
   (d) C_5H_{12}
   (e) $Sc_2(SO_4)_3$
   (f) $[Cr(NH_3)_6][Co(CN)_6]$

3. Calculate the formula mass and the molar mass of each of the following minerals:
   (a) Beryl, $Be_3Al_2Si_6O_{18}$
   (b) Malachite, $Cu_2(OH)_2CO_3$
   (c) Dolomite, $CaCO_3 \cdot MgCO_3$
   (d) Carnallite, $KCl \cdot MgCl_2 \cdot 6H_2O$
   (e) Tschermigite, $(NH_4)Al(SO_4)_2 \cdot 12H_2O$
   (f) Turquoise, $CuAl_6(PO_4)_4(OH)_8 \cdot 4H_2O$

4. Which contains the greatest mass of oxygen: one molecule

of ethanol (C_2H_5OH), one molecule of carbon dioxide, or one molecule of water? Explain your answer.

5. If the mass of a ^{12}C atom were redefined to be exactly 21 nmu (''new mass units''), what would the mass of an average argon atom be in nmu?

6. How many molecules of glucose, $C_6H_{12}O_6$, can be prepared from 18 C atoms? From 30 C atoms?

Moles

7. (a) Which contains the greatest mass in 1 mol of atoms: hydrogen, oxygen, nitrogen, or chlorine? Explain why.
   (b) Which contains the greatest mass in 1 mol of molecules: hydrogen gas (H_2), oxygen gas (O_2), nitrogen gas (N_2), or chlorine gas (Cl_2)? Explain why.

8. (a) Which contains the greatest mass of oxygen: 1 mol of ethanol (C_2H_5OH), 1 mol of carbon dioxide (CO_2), or 1 mol of water? Explain why.
   (b) Which contains the greatest number of moles of oxygen atoms: 1 mol of ethanol, 1 mol of carbon dioxide, or 1 mol of water? Explain why.

9. Which of the following amounts contains the greatest number of atoms of any type: 1.0 g of sodium metal, 0.20 mol of hydrogen atoms, $\frac{1}{8}$ mol of hydrogen molecules, 1.0×10^{23} atoms of mercury, or 100 mmol of hydrogen atoms? Explain why.

10. (a) Calculate the number of moles represented by 4.50 kg of glycerine, $C_3H_5(OH)_3$.
    (b) Calculate the mass of 0.0400 mol of $(NH_4)_2CO_3$.

11. Calculate the mass of 1 mol of P atoms and the mass of 1 mol P_4 molecules.

12. Why do 3.1 g of P_4 and 3.2 g of S_8 contain the same number of atoms? Do they contain the same number of molecules?

13. Why do 7.0 g of CO and 4.0 g of CH_4 contain the same number of C atoms?

14. What information is needed to determine the molecular formula of methane, whose empirical formula is determined in Example 3.13?

15. What mass of CH_4 is consumed in the reaction shown in Fig. 2.5 if 4.0×10^{24} molecules of O_2 react with an excess of CH_4?

16. How would the number of moles of I_2 required for reaction with four grams of Al change if the equation in Example 3.20 were written as follows?

$$4Al + 6I_2 \longrightarrow 2Al_2I_6$$

17. A sample of KBr contains 4.88729 g of K and 9.9880 g of Br. From this information, calculate the atomic mass of Br, using 39.0983 amu as the atomic mass of K.

18. Calculate the mass of one atom of lead.

19. The approximate minimum human daily nutritional requirement of the amino acid lysine, $C_6H_{14}N_2O_2$, is 8.0 mg. What is the requirement in millimoles?

20. Determine the number of moles in each of the following:

(a) 25.0 g of propylene, C_3H_6
(b) 3.06×10^{-3} g of the amino acid leucine, $C_6H_{13}NO_2$
(c) 40 lb of the herbicide Treflan, $C_{13}H_{16}N_2O_4F$ (1 lb = 454 g)
(d) 125 g of the insecticide Paris Green, $Cu_3(AsO_3)_2 \cdot Cu(CH_3CO_2)_2$
(e) 1.0 g of aspirin, $C_6H_4(CO_2H)(CO_2CH_3)$

21. Determine the mass in grams of each of the following:
(a) 4.6 mol KCN
(b) 10.2 mol ethane, C_2H_6
(c) 1.6×10^{-3} mol Na_2SO_4
(d) 6.85×10^3 mol glucose, $C_6H_{12}O_6$
(e) 5.86 mol $[Co(NH_3)_6]Cl_3$

22. Calculate which of the following contains more grams of calcium: 4.6×10^{20} atoms of calcium or 0.050 mol of calcium.

Isotopes

23. Determine the number of protons and neutrons in the nuclei of each of the following isotopes: ^{12}C, ^{13}C, ^{14}C, ^{234}U, ^{235}U, ^{238}U, ^{239}Pu, ^{239}Cm.

24. Identify the element for each of the following isotopes, and determine the number of protons, neutrons, and electrons in each: $^{55}_{25}X$, $^{48}_{22}X$, $^{20}_{10}X$, $^{21}_{10}X$, $^{22}_{10}X$, $^{235}_{92}X$, $^{266}_{109}X$, $^{181}_{73}X$.

25. From the data given in Table 3.1, calculate the atomic mass of naturally occurring oxygen and that of naturally occurring lithium. Compare these with the values in the table of atomic masses inside the front cover. State how many significant figures are justified for these values and show why.

26. Explain why atomic masses of elements often differ markedly from whole numbers, although each proton and each neutron has a mass that is very nearly 1 amu.

Percent Composition and Empirical Formulas

27. Calculate each of the following:
(a) The percent composition of ammonia, NH_3
(b) The percent composition of hydrazoic acid, HN_3
(c) The percent composition of magnesium sulfate, $MgSO_4$
(d) The percent ammonia in $CoCl_3 \cdot 6NH_3$
(e) The percent water in $CuSO_4 \cdot 5H_2O$

28. Calculate the percent composition of each of the following:
(a) $Li_2S_2O_3$
(b) $(BiO)_2CO_3$
(c) $C_6H_2(CH_3)(NO_2)_3$
(d) Caffeine, $C_8H_{10}N_4O_2$
(e) Aspirin, $C_6H_4(CO_2H)(CO_2CH_3)$

29. (a) Determine which of the following fertilizers contains the highest percentage of nitrogen: urea, N_2H_4CO; ammonium nitrate, NH_4NO_3; or ammonium sulfate, $(NH_4)_2SO_4$.
    (b) Calculate which contains the greatest number of grams of nitrogen per formula mass.

30. Determine each of the following to three significant figures:
    (a) The percent of calcium in $Ca_3(PO_4)_2$
    (b) The percent of SO_4^{2-} in $Al_2(SO_4)_3$
    (c) The percent of $MgCO_3$ in $Mg(OH)_2 \cdot 3MgCO_3 \cdot 3H_2O$

31. Determine the empirical formulas for compounds with the following percent compositions:
    (a) 15.8% carbon and 84.2% sulfur
    (b) 43.6% phosphorus and 56.4% oxygen
    (c) 40.0% carbon, 6.7% hydrogen, and 53.3% oxygen
    (d) 28.7% K, 1.5% H, 22.8% P, and 47.0% O

32. (a) A compound has the following percent composition: 92.3% C and 7.7% H. Calculate the empirical formula.
    (b) The molecular mass of the compound is 78.1 amu. What is the molecular formula?

33. Dichloroethane, a compound that is often used for dry cleaning, contains carbon, hydrogen, and chlorine. It has a molecular mass of 99 amu. Analysis of a sample shows that it contains 24.3% carbon and 4.1% hydrogen. What is its molecular formula?

34. Determine the empirical and molecular formulas for a compound that has a molecular mass of 30 amu and a percent composition of 80% C and 20% H.

35. A 5.00-g sample of an oxide of lead contains 4.53 g of lead. Determine the empirical formula for the compound.

36. Determine the empirical formula of a compound that has the following analysis: Na, 16.78%; NH_4, 13.16%; H (in addition to that in NH_4), 0.74%; PO_4, 69.32%.

37. In the industrial process for the production of aluminum metal, molten (melted) cryolite is used to dissolve aluminum oxide. This forms the molten solution through which an electric current is passed to obtain the aluminum metal by electrolysis. The percent composition of cryolite is 32.79% sodium, 13.02% aluminum, and 54.19% fluorine. Calculate the empirical formula for cryolite.

38. Calculate the empirical formula of a crystalline salt that has the following percent composition: Na, 18.5%; S, 25.8%; O (except for that in the water), 19.3%; H_2O, 36.4%.

39. The light-emitting diode used in some calculator displays contains a compound composed of 69.24% Ga and 30.76% P. What is the empirical formula of this compound?

40. Nicotine contains 74.0% C, 8.7% H, and 17.3% N. This compound contains two nitrogen atoms per molecule. What are the empirical and molecular formulas of nicotine?

41. A 27.5-g sample of a compound containing carbon and hydrogen contains 5.5 g of hydrogen. The molecular mass of the compound is approximately 30 amu. What are the empirical and molecular formulas for this compound?

42. Most polymers are very large molecules composed of simple units repeated many times. Thus they often have relatively simple empirical formulas. Calculate the empirical formulas of the following polymers:
    (a) Lucite (Plexiglas); 59.9% C, 8.06% H, 32.0% O
    (b) Saran; 24.8% C, 2.0% H, 73.1% Cl

    (c) Polyethylene; 86% C, 14% H
    (d) Polystyrene; 92.3% C, 7.7% H
    (e) Orlon; 67.9% C, 5.70% H, 26.4% N

43. A gaseous compound that contains 27% C and 73% O is important in the respiration of plants and animals, is used in soft drinks, and is a by-product of winemaking. What is the empirical formula of this gas?

44. What is the product formed when 1.418 g of iron reacts with $Cl_2(g)$ to give 3.220 g of a sample containing iron and chlorine? Identify the product, and write the balanced equation for its formation.

45. The 3.220-g sample of iron(II) chloride described in Exercise 44 reacts with 0.900 g of chlorine to give another iron chloride with a different formula. Determine the empirical formula of this second iron chloride, and write the balanced equation for its formation.

46. A 0.864-g sample of magnesium carbonate decomposes upon heating, giving gaseous CO_2 and a white residue of 0.4105 g of MgO. Determine the empirical formula of this compound.

47. Hemoglobin (molecular mass = 64,456 amu) contains 0.35% iron by mass. How many iron atoms are present in a hemoglobin molecule?

Molarity and Solutions

48. Calculate the mass of solute present in each of the following solutions:
    (a) 2.0 L of 0.050 M sodium hydroxide, NaOH
    (b) 100.0 mL of 0.0020 M barium hydroxide, $Ba(OH)_2$
    (c) 0.080 L of 0.050 M sulfuric acid, H_2SO_4
    (d) 1.50 L of 0.850 M phosphoric acid, H_3PO_4
    (e) 50.0 mL of 0.0300 M glucose, $C_{12}H_{22}O_{11}$

49. Determine the concentration in moles per liter for each of the following solutions:
    (a) 98.0 g of phosphoric acid, H_3PO_4, in 1.00 L of solution
    (b) 0.207 g of calcium hydroxide, $Ca(OH)_2$, in 40.0 mL of solution
    (c) 10.5 kg of $Na_2SO_4 \cdot 10H_2O$ in 18.60 L of solution
    (d) 7.0 millimol of I_2 in 100.0 mL of solution
    (e) 1.8×10^4 mg of HCl in 0.075 L of solution

50. Determine the moles of solute and the grams of solute required to make the indicated amount of solution.
    (a) 1.00 L of 1.00 M $Ca(NO_3)_2$ solution
    (b) 465 mL of 0.2543 M C_3H_7OH solution
    (c) 0.075 L of 0.1625 M $KClO_3$ solution
    (d) 0.075 L of 0.1625 M H_3PO_4 solution
    (e) 0.075 L of 0.1625 M $C_{12}H_{22}O_{11}$ solution

51. What mass of solid sodium hydroxide, NaOH, of 97.0% purity by mass would be required to prepare 0.500 L of a 0.46 M NaOH solution?

52. Calculate the molarity of a concentrated H_2SO_4 solution of density 1.84 g/mL and containing 98.0% H_2SO_4 solute by mass.

Chemical Calculations
Involving Equations

53. How many moles of hydrochloric acid, HCl, are required to react with the potassium hydroxide in 65.0 mL of a 0.250 M KOH solution?

$$KOH(aq) + HCl(aq) \longrightarrow KCl(aq) + H_2O(l)$$

54. How many grams of mercury(II) nitrate, $Hg(NO_3)_2$, is required to react with the calcium chloride, $CaCl_2$, in 16.82 mL of a 1.136 M solution of $CaCl_2$?

$$Hg(NO_3)_2(aq) + CaCl_2(aq) \longrightarrow$$
$$HgCl_2(aq) + Ca(NO_3)_2(aq)$$

55. The aluminum sulfate, $Al_2(SO_4)_3$, in 32.45 mL of a 0.156 M solution reacts with all of the lead nitrate, $Pb(NO_3)_2$, in 42.00 mL of a $Pb(NO_3)_2$ solution. What is the molar concentration of the lead nitrate in the original lead nitrate solution?

$$3Pb(NO_3)_2(aq) + Al_2(SO_4)_3(aq) \longrightarrow$$
$$3PbSO_4(s) + 2Al(NO_3)_3(aq)$$

56. An excess of solid silver nitrate, $AgNO_3$, reacts with 0.4682 L of a solution of calcium chloride, $CaCl_2$, producing calcium nitrate, $Ca(NO_3)_2$, and 2.623 g of silver chloride, AgCl. What is the molarity of the $CaCl_2$ in the $CaCl_2$ solution?

57. What is the molarity of a hydrochloric acid, HCl, solution if 27.5 mL of the solution is required to react with 0.403 g of calcium oxide, CaO?

$$CaO + 2HCl \longrightarrow CaCl_2 + H_2O$$

58. Write the balanced equation and calculate the number of moles of chlorine, Cl_2, required to react with 10.0 g of sodium metal, Na, to produce sodium chloride, NaCl. How many grams of chlorine is this?

59. What mass of oxygen, in grams, is formed by the decomposition of 100 g of mercury(II) oxide?

$$2HgO \longrightarrow 2Hg + O_2$$

60. Calculate the mass of sodium nitrate, $NaNO_3$, required to produce 128 g of oxygen.

$$2NaNO_3 \longrightarrow 2NaNO_2 + O_2$$

61. What mass of carbon dioxide, in pounds, will be formed by the combustion of 20.0 lb of carbon in an excess of oxygen ($C + O_2 \longrightarrow CO_2$)? What mass of impure oxygen (90.0% pure oxygen by mass) will be required for the actual reaction?

62. (a) What mass of copper(II) nitrate, $Cu(NO_3)_2$, must be decomposed to produce 1500 g of copper(II) oxide, CuO?

$$Cu(NO_3)_2 \longrightarrow CuO + NO_2 + O_2 \quad \text{(unbalanced)}$$

(b) What mass of nitrogen dioxide, NO_2, is produced by the decomposition of 75.0 g of copper(II) nitrate?

(c) How many moles of oxygen, O_2, are produced by the decomposition of 75.0 g of copper(II) nitrate?

63. A 12.0-g sample of phosphorus(III) chloride, PCl_3, is allowed to react with water ($PCl_3 + 3H_2O \longrightarrow H_3PO_3 + 3HCl$). What mass of HCl is produced, and what mass of water enters the reaction?

64. (a) Balance the following equation and calculate the mass of oxygen that is required to react with 37.0 g of butane, C_4H_{10}.

$$C_4H_{10} + O_2 \longrightarrow CO_2 + H_2O \quad \text{(unbalanced)}$$

(b) How many moles of CO_2 are produced?

65. For the following reaction, 110.0 g of aluminum oxide, Al_2O_3, 60 g of carbon, C, and 200 g of chlorine, Cl_2, are present.

$$Al_2O_3 + C + Cl_2 \longrightarrow AlCl_3 + CO \quad \text{(unbalanced)}$$

(a) Which substance is in greatest excess in terms of the quantities required for reaction? Show why by calculation.

(b) Calculate the maximum amount of aluminum chloride, $AlCl_3$, that can be produced.

66. (a) How many moles of H_2 are produced by the reaction of 118.5 g of H_3PO_4 in the following reaction?

$$2Cr + 2H_3PO_4 \longrightarrow 3H_2 + 2CrPO_4$$

(b) What mass of H_2, in grams, is produced?

67. (a) Determine how many moles of gallium chloride are formed by the reaction of 2.6 mol of HCl according to the following equation:

$$2Ga + 6HCl \longrightarrow 2GaCl_3 + 3H_2$$

(b) What mass of $GaCl_3$, in grams, is produced?

68. (a) How many molecules of I_2 are produced by the reaction of 0.4235 mol of $CuCl_2$ in the following reaction?

$$2CuCl_2 + 4KI \longrightarrow 2CuI + 4KCl + I_2$$

(b) What mass of I_2 is produced?

69. Tooth enamel consists of hydroxyapatite, $Ca_5(PO_4)_3(OH)$. The substance is converted to fluorapatite, $Ca_5(PO_4)_3F$, by treatment with tin(II) fluoride, SnF_2 (known as stannous fluoride when used as an ingredient in toothpaste). Products of this reaction are SnO and water. What mass of hydroxyapatite can be converted to fluorapatite by reaction with 0.150 g of SnF_2?

$$2Ca_5(PO_4)_3OH + SnF_2 \longrightarrow 2Ca_5(PO_4)_3F + SnO + H_2O$$

70. Silver sulfadiazine burn cream creates a barrier against bacterial invasion and releases antimicrobial agents directly into a wound. What mass of silver sulfadiazine, $AgC_{10}H_9N_4SO_2$, can be produced from the reaction of

73.0 g of silver oxide, Ag_2O, and sulfadiazine, $C_{10}H_{10}N_4SO_2$?

$$Ag_2O + 2C_{10}H_{10}N_4SO_2 \longrightarrow 2AgC_{10}H_9N_4SO_2 + H_2O$$

71. Calcium chloride 6-hydrate, $CaCl_2 \cdot 6H_2O$, is a solid that is used to melt ice and snow. What mass, in kilograms, of $CaCl_2 \cdot 6H_2O$ can be prepared from 250 lb of $CaCO_3$ (limestone)? (1 lb = 0.4536 kg)

$$CaCO_3 + 2HCl + 5H_2O \longrightarrow CaCl_2 \cdot 6H_2O + CO_2$$

72. Silicon carbide, SiC, a very hard material used as an abrasive on sandpaper and in other applications, is prepared by the reaction of pure sand, SiO_2, with carbon at high temperature. Carbon monoxide, CO, is the other product of this reaction. Write the balanced equation for the reaction, and calculate how much SiO_2 is required to produce 3.00 kg of SiC.

73. Silver is often extracted from ores as $K[Ag(CN)_2]$ and then recovered by the reaction

$$2K[Ag(CN)_2](aq) + Zn(s) \longrightarrow$$
$$2Ag(s) + Zn(CN)_2(aq) + 2KCN(aq)$$

What mass of zinc, in grams, is required to produce exactly 1 ounce of silver? (1 g = 0.03527 oz)

74. Thin films of silicon, Si, used for fabrication of electronic components, can be prepared by the decomposition of silane, SiH_4.

$$SiH_4(g) \xrightarrow{\triangle} Si(s) + 2H_2(g)$$

What mass of SiH_4 is required to prepare 0.1842 g of Si by this technique?

Percent Yield

75. In a laboratory experiment, the reaction of 3.0 mol of H_2 with 2.0 mol of I_2 produced 1.0 mol of HI ($H_2 + I_2 \longrightarrow 2HI$). Determine the theoretical yield in moles and the percent yield for this reaction.

76. A sample of calcium oxide, CaO, weighing 0.69 g was prepared by heating 1.31 g of calcium carbonate. What is the percent yield of the reaction?

$$CaCO_3(s) \xrightarrow{\triangle} CaO(s) + CO_2(g)$$

77. A student spilled his ethanol preparation and consequently isolated only 25 g instead of the 81 g theoretically possible. What was his percent yield?

78. Freon-12, CCl_2F_2, is prepared from CCl_4 by reaction with HF. The other product of this reaction is HCl. What is the percent yield of a reaction that produces 12.5 g of CCl_2F_2 from 32.9 g of CCl_4?

79. Citric acid, $C_6H_8O_7$, a component of jams, jellies, and fruity soft drinks, is prepared industrially via fermentation of sucrose by the mold *Aspergillus niger*. The overall reaction is

$$C_{12}H_{22}O_{11} + H_2O + 3O_2 \longrightarrow 2C_6H_8O_7 + 4H_2O$$

What is the amount, in kilograms, of citric acid produced from exactly 1 metric ton (1.000×10^3 kg) of sucrose in a reaction if the yield is 92.30%?

80. Ether, $(C_2H_5)_2O$, for anesthetic use is prepared by the reaction of ethanol with sulfuric acid.

$$2C_2H_5OH + H_2SO_4 \longrightarrow (C_2H_5)_2O + H_2SO_4 \cdot H_2O$$

What is the yield of $(C_2H_5)_2O$ if a reaction beginning with 1.00 kg of C_2H_5OH results in a percent yield of 95.2%?

81. Toluene, $C_6H_5CH_3$, is oxidized by air under carefully controlled conditions to benzoic acid, $C_6H_5CO_2H$, which is used to prepare the food preservative sodium benzoate, $C_6H_5CO_2Na$. What is the percent yield of a reaction that converts 1.000 kg of toluene to 1.21 kg of benzoic acid?

$$2C_6H_5CH_3 + 3O_2 \longrightarrow 2C_6H_5CO_2H + 2H_2O$$

82. What is the percent yield of $NaClO_2$ if 106 g is isolated from the reaction of 202.3 g of ClO_2 with a solution containing 3.22 mol of NaOH?

$$2ClO_2(g) + 2NaOH(aq) \longrightarrow$$
$$NaClO_2(aq) + NaClO_3(aq) + H_2O(l)$$

Limiting Reagents

83. What is the limiting reagent when 30.0 g of propane, C_3H_8, is burned with 75 g of oxygen?

$$C_3H_8(g) + O_2(g) \longrightarrow CO_2(g) + H_2O(g) \quad \text{(unbalanced)}$$

84. (a) What is the limiting reagent when 0.50 mol of Cr and 1.00 mol of H_3PO_4 react according to the following chemical equation?

$$2Cr + 2H_3PO_4 \longrightarrow 2CrPO_4 + 3H_2$$

(b) If 0.20 mol of $CrPO_4$ is recovered from the reaction described in part (a), what is the percent yield?

85. (a) What is the limiting reagent when 1.50 g of silicon and 1.50 g of nitrogen combine according to the following reaction?

$$3Si + 2N_2 \longrightarrow Si_3N_4$$

(b) If the yield of Si_3N_4 recovered from the reaction described in part (a) is 98%, what mass of Si_3N_4 is recovered?

86. Addition of 0.403 g of sodium oxalate, $Na_2C_2O_4$, to a solution containing 1.48 g of uranyl nitrate, $UO_2(NO_3)_2$, yields 1.073 g of solid $UO_2(C_2O_4) \cdot 3H_2O$.

$$UO_2(NO_3)_2(aq) + Na_2C_2O_4(aq) + 3H_2O(l) \longrightarrow$$
$$UO_2(C_2O_4) \cdot 3H_2O(s) + 2NaNO_3(aq)$$

Determine the limiting reagent and the percent yield of this reaction.

87. (a) What is the limiting reagent when 0.20 mol of P_4 and 0.20 mol of O_2 react according to the following chemical equation?

$$P_4 + 5O_2 \longrightarrow P_4O_{10}$$

(b) Calculate the percent yield if 10.0 g of P_4O_{10} results from the reaction.

88. (a) What mass of $[Cr(H_2O)_6]Cl_3$ is produced when a solution containing 5.0×10^{-3} mol of $H_2Cr_2O_7$ is added to a solution containing 15.0×10^{-3} mol of H_2FeCl_4? The two react according to the following chemical equation:

$$H_2Cr_2O_7 + 6H_2FeCl_4 + 5H_2O \longrightarrow$$
$$2[Cr(H_2O)_6]Cl_3 + 6FeCl_3$$

(b) Explain why three significant figures are justified in the answer.

Titrations

89. How many milliliters of 0.560 M H_2SO_4 solution is required to titrate 2.474 g of K_2CO_3?

$$H_2SO_4(aq) + K_2CO_3(s) \longrightarrow$$
$$K_2SO_4(aq) + H_2O(l) + CO_2(g)$$

90. What is the concentration of NaCl in a solution if titration of 15.00 mL of the solution with 0.250 M $AgNO_3$ requires 20.22 mL of the $AgNO_3$ solution to reach the end point?

$$AgNO_3(aq) + NaCl(aq) \longrightarrow AgCl(s) + NaNO_3(aq)$$

91. Titration of 20.00 mL of a 0.222 M solution of HCl with a solution of LiSH required 31.2 mL of the LiSH solution to reach the end point. What is the molar concentration of LiSH?

$$HCl(aq) + LiSH(aq) \longrightarrow LiCl(aq) + H_2S(aq)$$

92. What volume of 0.0125 M HBr solution is required to titrate 250 mL of a 0.0100 M $Ca(OH)_2$ solution?

$$Ca(OH)_2(aq) + 2HBr(aq) \longrightarrow CaBr_2(aq) + 2H_2O(l)$$

93. In a common medical laboratory determination of the concentration of free chloride ion in blood serum, a serum sample is titrated with a $Hg(NO_3)_2$ solution.

$$2Cl^-(aq) + Hg(NO_3)_2(aq) \longrightarrow$$
$$HgCl_2(aq) + 2NO_3^-(aq)$$

What is the Cl^- concentration in a 0.25-mL sample of normal serum that requires 1.46 mL of 8.25×10^{-4} M $Hg(NO_3)_2$ to reach the end point?

94. Crystalline potassium hydrogen phthalate, $KHC_8H_4O_4$, is often used as an acid for standardizing basic solutions because it is easy to purify and to weigh. If 1.9233 g of this salt is titrated with a solution of $Ba(OH)_2$, the reaction is complete when 18.75 mL of the solution has been added. What is the concentration of the $Ba(OH)_2$ solution?

$$2KHC_8H_4O_4 + Ba(OH)_2 \longrightarrow BaK_2(C_8H_4O_4)_2 + 2H_2O$$

95. Potatoes are peeled commercially by soaking them in a 3 to 6 M solution of sodium hydroxide, then removing the loosened skins by spraying them with water. Does a sodium hydroxide solution have a suitable concentration if titration

of 12.00 mL of the solution requires 30.6 mL of 1.65 M HCl to reach the end point?

96. (a) A 7.00-mL sample of vinegar, a solution of acetic acid (CH_3CO_2H), was titrated with a 0.352 M NaOH solution. If 14.25 mL was required to reach the end point, what was the molar concentration of the acetic acid in the vinegar?

$$CH_3CO_2H + NaOH \longrightarrow CH_3CO_2Na + H_2O$$

(b) If the density of the vinegar is 1.005 g/cm^3, what is the percent of acetic acid by mass in the vinegar?

97. Titration of a 20.0-mL sample of a particularly acidic rain required 1.7 mL of 0.0811 M NaOH to reach the end point. If we assume that the acidity of the rain is due to the presence of sulfuric acid, what was the concentration of this sulfuric acid solution?

$$H_2SO_4(aq) + 2NaOH(aq) \longrightarrow Na_2SO_4(aq) + 2H_2O(l)$$

98. A common oven cleaner contains a very caustic metal hydroxide, which we can represent as MOH. Titration of 1.4268 g of MOH with 1.000 M HNO_3 requires 35.70 mL to reach the end point.

$$MOH(aq) + HNO_3(aq) \longrightarrow MNO_3(aq) + H_2O(l)$$

What is the element M, and what is the formula of the hydroxide?

Additional Exercises

99. The acid secreted by the cells of the stomach lining is a hydrochloric acid solution that typically contains 0.282 g of HCl per 50.00 mL of solution. What is the concentration of this acid?

100. How many molecules of $C_2H_4Cl_2$ can be prepared from 15 C_2H_4 molecules and 8 Cl_2 molecules?

101. How many molecules of CH_2O can be prepared from 20 C atoms, 15 H_2 molecules, and 8 O_2 molecules?

102. What mass of $PbSO_4$ is produced when 30.0 mL of 0.1020 M $Al_2(SO_4)_3$ solution is added to 30.0 mL of 0.2442 M $Pb(NO_3)_2$ solution, forming $PbSO_4(s)$ and $Al(NO_3)_3(aq)$?

103. The following quantities are placed in three separate containers: 1.2×10^{24} atoms of hydrogen, 1.0 mol of sulfur, and 88 g of oxygen.
(a) What is the total mass in grams for the collection of all three elements?
(b) What is the total number of moles for the three elements?
(c) If these three quantities of the three elements were used to form a compound that has a formula with two hydrogen atoms, one sulfur atom, and four oxygen atoms, how many grams of material would remain unreacted?

104. As discussed in Section 2.12, sulfuric acid is the industrial chemical that is produced in greatest quantity in the United States. Most of it is produced via the following sequence of chemical reactions:

$$S + O_2 \longrightarrow SO_2$$

$$2SO_2 + O_2 \longrightarrow 2SO_3$$

$$SO_3 + H_2O \longrightarrow H_2SO_4$$

(a) What mass of sulfur would be required in the production of 75.0 kg of H_2SO_4?

(b) What mass of impure sulfur that is 98.0% pure sulfur would be required?

105. The empirical formula for an ion-exchange resin used in water softeners is $C_8H_7SO_3Na$. The resin softens water by removing calcium ion, Ca^{2+}, by the reaction

$$Ca^{2+} + 2C_8H_7SO_3Na \longrightarrow (C_8H_7SO_3)_2Ca + 2Na^+$$

What mass of ion-exchange resin, in grams, is required to soften 1000 gal of water with a Ca^{2+} content of 2.25 ppm (parts per million)? This means that there is 2.25 g of Ca^{2+} per 1,000,000 g of water. One gal of water has a mass of 8.0 lb. (See Appendix B for units and conversion factors.)

106. A volume of 3.42 mL of $SiCl_4$ (density = 1.483 g/mL) reacts with an excess of $H_2S(g)$, giving $HSSiCl_3$ according to the reaction

$$SiCl_4(l) + H_2S(g) \longrightarrow HSSiCl_3(l) + HCl(g)$$

The HCl produced reacts with 1.123×10^{-2} mol of NaOH according to the reaction

$$HCl + NaOH \longrightarrow NaCl + H_2O$$

What is the percent yield of $HSSiCl_3$?

107. The equation for the preparation of phosphorus, P_4, in an electric furnace is

$$2Ca_3(PO_4)_2 + 6SiO_2 + 10C \longrightarrow 6CaSiO_3 + 10CO + P_4$$

What mass of SiO_2 is required to prepare 3.560 kg of P_4?

108. Concentrated sulfuric acid with a density of 1.64 g/cm³ contains 97.5% H_2SO_4 by mass. Determine how many liters of this acid is required to manufacture 6500 kg of phosphate fertilizer, $Ca(H_2PO_4)_2$, according to the reaction

$$2Ca_5(PO_4)_3F + 7H_2SO_4 + 14H_2O \longrightarrow$$
$$3Ca(H_2PO_4)_2 + 7(CaSO_4 \cdot 2H_2O) + 2HF$$

109. The principal component of mothballs is naphthalene, a compound with a molecular mass of about 130 amu, containing only carbon and hydrogen. A 3.000-mg sample of naphthalene burns to give 10.3 mg of CO_2. Determine its empirical and molecular formulas.

110. Sulfur can be removed from coal by washing powdered coal with NaOH(aq). The reaction can be represented as

$$R_2S(s) + 2NaOH(aq) \longrightarrow R_2O(s) + Na_2S(aq) + H_2O(l)$$

where R_2S represents the organic sulfur present in the coal. What mass of NaOH(s), in kilograms, is required to react with the sulfur in 2.00 metric tons (2000 kg) of coal that contains 1.9% S by mass?

111. Sodium bicarbonate (baking soda), $NaHCO_3$, can be purified by dissolving it in hot water (60°C), filtering to remove insoluble impurities, cooling to 0°C to precipitate solid $NaHCO_3$, and then filtering to remove the solid $NaHCO_3$, leaving soluble impurities in solution. Any $NaHCO_3$ that remains in solution is not recovered. The solubility of $NaHCO_3$ in hot water at 60°C is 164 g/L. Its solubility in cold water at 0°C is 69 g/L. What is the percent yield of $NaHCO_3$ when it is purified by this method?

112. Determine the simplest formula of gallium bromide if a sample of gallium bromide weighing 0.165 g reacts with silver nitrate, $AgNO_3$, giving gallium nitrate and 0.299 g of AgBr.

113. Assume that 45.0 g of Si reacts with N_2, giving 0.533 mol of Si_3N_4, according to the equation

$$3Si + 2N_2 \longrightarrow Si_3N_4$$

State which of the following can be determined by using only the information given in this exercise: (a) the moles of Si reacting, (b) the moles of N_2 reacting, (c) the atomic mass of N, (d) the atomic mass of Si, (e) the mass of Si_3N_4 produced.

Thermochemistry

The brilliant effects of the aurora result when chemical reactions in the upper atmosphere release energy as light.

How do we know that "a teaspoon of sugar contains only 16 Calories"? For that matter, what is a Calorie? A Calorie is one of the units of heat. The amount of heat produced when your body metabolizes a teaspoon of sugar is 16 Calories. How do we know? Simple: Someone burned a sample of sugar and determined experimentally how much heat is produced when it combines with oxygen.

Heat is either released or absorbed during the course of almost all chemical and physical changes. Your body temperature is 37°C because many of its chemical reactions, such as the metabolic oxidation of sugar to carbon dioxide and water, produce heat. Heat is also released when charcoal, which essentially is pure carbon, burns and forms carbon dioxide. Ice melts when it absorbs heat. Heat must also be added to convert limestone into quicklime.

In Chapter 3 relationships between the amounts of reactants and products in chemical reactions were discussed. For example, we found out how to calculate the masses of carbon dioxide and water produced when one gram of sugar is oxidized. In this chapter we will focus on the relationships between the amount of heat released or absorbed by a reaction and the amounts of reactants and products present. We will discuss how we could, for example, determine the amount of heat produced when one gram of sugar is oxidized.

This chapter introduces **thermochemistry,** the determination and study of the heat absorbed or evolved in the formation and dissociation of compounds in chemical reactions and in changes of phase (conversion of a liquid to a gas, a solid to a liquid, etc.). The chapter discusses how to measure the amount of heat a chemical reaction produces or absorbs and how to use this information to determine the heat changes associated with other, related reactions.

④.1   Heat and Its Measurement

Figure 4.1

An oxyacetylene torch. Heat produced by the combustion of acetylene in oxygen enters the metal, heats it, and melts it. The sparks result when the molten metal is blown away by the gases in the flame.

Heat is what chemists call the form of energy contained by a substance that gives the substance its temperature. Heat also can cause a substance to melt or to evaporate. When the amount of heat in a substance increases, either the temperature of the substance increases, or the substance melts (if it is a solid) or evaporates (if a liquid). When the amount of heat decreases, either the temperature of the substance decreases, or the substance condenses (from a gas to a liquid or a solid) or freezes (if it is a liquid).

Heat moves spontaneously from a warmer substance to a colder substance until the temperatures of the two substances are equal. However, heat can be forced to move from a cooler to a warmer substance, as in a refrigerator. We can detect a change in the amount of heat in a substance by observing a temperature change or a phase change (melting, freezing, evaporation, and so on).

A chemical reaction or a physical change that produces heat is called an **exothermic** process. The burning of charcoal, for example, is an exothermic process. A reaction or change that absorbs heat is an **endothermic** process. The melting of ice is an endothermic process, because heat is absorbed when ice melts.

The temperature change an object undergoes often reflects whether heat has moved into or out of it. In the absence of a phase change, we can increase the temperature of an object by adding heat, or some other form of energy, to it (Fig. 4.1). Removing heat, or some other form of energy, reduces the temperature. For example, when hot coffee is poured into a mug, the coffee becomes cooler and the mug warmer as heat moves from the hot coffee into the cooler mug.

One unit of heat and other forms of energy is the calorie. A **calorie (cal)** is the amount of heat or other energy necessary to raise the temperature of 1 gram of water by 1 degree Celsius (Fig. 4.2). A **kilocalorie (kcal)** is 1000 calories. The SI unit of heat is the **joule (J)**. There are 4.184 joules in one calorie*. A **kilojoule (kJ)** is 1000 joules. The amount of heat produced or consumed by chemical reactions in the body is usually reported in **nutritional Calories** (note that this unit of heat is capitalized). One Calorie equals 1000 calories, or 1 kilocalorie.

Specific heat is a physical property of a substance that can be used to measure quantities of heat. The **specific heat** is the quantity of heat required to raise the temperature of 1 gram of a substance 1 degree Celsius (1 kelvin). The specific heat of water, which is one of the largest, is 4.184 joules per gram per degree. The unit joules per gram per degree (J/g °C) can be written as $J\ g^{-1}\ °C^{-1}$, because $1/X = X^{-1}$, according to the mathematical rules for exponents. The specific heat of water can be written $4.184\ J\ g^{-1}\ °C^{-1}$. The specific heat of copper is 0.38 joule per gram per degree, that of aluminum is 0.88 joule per gram per degree, and that of zinc is 0.39 joule per gram per degree. Thus if a 1-gram sample of aluminum picks up enough heat to raise its temperature by 1 degree, it must have absorbed 0.88 joule.

The specific heat of a substance is a property of 1 gram of the substance. The heat capacity of a given quantity of matter describes a property of the entire quantity of matter. The **heat capacity** of a body of matter is the quantity of heat required to increase its temperature by 1 degree Celsius (1 kelvin).

$$\text{Heat capacity} = \text{specific heat } (J\ g^{-1}\ °C^{-1}) \times \text{mass (g)}$$

For example, 10 grams of aluminum (specific heat = $0.88\ J\ g^{-1}\ °C^{-1}$) has a heat capacity of $8.8\ J\ °C^{-1}$; 25 grams of aluminum, a heat capacity of $22\ J\ °C^{-1}$. The greater the mass of a substance, the greater its heat capacity.

If we know the mass of a substance and its specific heat, we can determine the amount of heat, q, entering or leaving the substance by measuring the temperature change before and after the heat is gained or lost.

$$q = cm\Delta T$$

where c is the specific heat of the substance, m is its mass, and ΔT (which is read "delta T") is the temperature change, $T_{final} - T_{initial}$. If heat enters a substance, its temperature increases and its final temperature is higher than its initial temperature, $T_{final} - T_{initial}$ has a positive value, and the value of q is positive. If heat flows out of a substance, the final temperature is less than the initial temperature, $T_{final} - T_{initial}$ has a negative value, and q is negative. The following example shows how to calculate the amount of heat that enters a sample of water.

Figure 4.2

Heat from the hot flame of the Bunsen burner enters the cooler water, and the temperature of the water increases. If 800 g of water are present, its temperature will increase by 1°C for each 800 cal it absorbs.

A flask containing 800 g of water is heated over a Bunsen burner as shown in Fig. 4.2. If the temperature of the water increases from 20°C to 85°C, how much heat (in calories) did the water absorb?

Example 4.1

---

*Although a calorie is the same amount of energy as 4.184 joules, the joule is not defined this way in the SI system. In that system, a joule is defined as the amount of heat or other energy equal to the kinetic energy ($\frac{1}{2}\ mv^2$) of an object with a mass m of exactly 2 kilograms moving with a velocity v of exactly 1 meter per second. One joule is equivalent to $1\ kg\ m^2\ s^{-2}$, which is 1 newton-meter.

Example 4.1 continued

The specific heat of water is 4.184 J g^{-1} °C^{-1}, or 1.000 cal g^{-1} °C^{-1}. Thus 1 cal of heat will increase the temperature of 1 g of water by 1°C, and 800 cal will increase the temperature of 800 g of water by 1°C. To increase the temperature of 800 g of water by 65° will require 800 × 65 or 52,000 cal.

$$q = cm\Delta T = cm(T_{final} - T_{initial})$$
$$= 1.000 \text{ cal g}^{-1} \text{ °C}^{-1} \times 800 \text{ g} \times (85 - 20)\text{°C}$$
$$= 52,000 \text{ cal } (=52 \text{ kcal})$$

Because the temperature increased, $T_{final} - T_{initial}$ is greater than zero and q is positive, indicating that heat moved into the water.

Example 4.2

Calculate the temperature change that results when 1625 J are removed from 75 g of ethanol initially at 25.0°C. The specific heat of ethanol is 2.4 J g^{-1} °C^{-1}.

When heat is removed from a substance, the temperature of the substance decreases and q has a negative value. Here $q = -1625$ J. The relationship between q and the temperature change is

$$q = cm\Delta T$$

We can rearrange this equation to solve for the temperature change, ΔT, which is the quantity necessary to determine the final temperature.

$$\text{Temperature change} = \Delta T = \frac{q}{cm}$$

$$= \frac{-1625 \text{ J}}{2.4 \text{ J g}^{-1} \text{ °C}^{-1} \times 75 \text{ g}}$$
$$= -9.0\text{°C}$$

The new temperature is not −9.0°C; this is the change in temperature, ΔT. We can calculate the final temperature as follows:

$$\Delta T = T_{final} - T_{initial}$$
$$-9\text{°C} = T_{final} - 25\text{°C}$$
$$T_{final} = 25\text{°C} - 9\text{°C} = 16\text{°C}$$

4.2 Calorimetry

The process of measuring the amount of heat involved in a chemical or physical change is called **calorimetry.** The simplest form of calorimetry is based on measuring the change in temperature as heat is transferred into or out of a known quantity of water. The amount of heat can be determined from the temperature change of the water, as shown in Example 4.1. Of course, you must be sure that no heat other than that to be measured enters the water and that no heat is lost before the measurement is complete.

A **calorimeter** is a device used to measure heats of reactions. Two polystyrene cups can be used to construct a simple calorimeter. Such ''coffee cup calorimeters'' (Fig. 4.3) are often used in general chemistry laboratories. Because the cups are good insulators, they prevent the loss (or gain) of heat to (or from) the surroundings. When an exothermic reaction occurs in solution in such a calorimeter, the heat produced by the reaction is trapped in the solution and increases its temperature. When an endothermic reaction occurs, the heat required is absorbed from the solution and decreases its temperature. The change in temperature can be used to calculate the amount of heat involved in either case.

If the cups, thermometer, and stirrer used to construct the calorimeter had no heat capacity, the amount of heat produced in the reaction, $q_{reaction}$, would equal the amount of heat absorbed by the solution, q_{soln}. Because energy can be neither created nor destroyed in a chemical reaction,

$$q_{reaction} + q_{soln} = 0$$

and

$$q_{reaction} = -q_{soln}$$

Figure 4.3
A calorimeter constructed from two polystyrene cups. A thermometer and stirrer extend through the cork into the reaction mixture.

In some cases the amount of heat absorbed by the calorimeter is small enough to be neglected, and this equation is used to calculate the approximate amount of heat involved in a reaction. The following example shows how to determine the heat produced by the acid–base reaction of 0.0500 mole of HCl(aq) with 0.0500 mole of NaOH(aq).

Example 4.3

When 50.0 mL (50 g) of 1.00 M HCl at 22.00°C is added to 50.0 mL (50 g) of 1.00 M NaOH at 22.00°C in a coffee cup calorimeter, the temperature increases to 28.87°C. Ignore the specific heat of the calorimeter and calculate the approximate amount of heat produced by the acid–base reaction between the HCl and NaOH.

$$HCl(aq) + NaOH(aq) \longrightarrow NaCl(aq) + H_2O(l)$$

The specific heat of the solution produced is 4.18 J g^{-1} °C^{-1}.

At the instant of mixing, we have 100 g of a mixture of 0.500 M HCl and 0.500 M NaOH at 22.00°C. The mixture undergoes an immediate change as the HCl reacts with NaOH. This exothermic reaction produces heat, which is trapped in the solution by the calorimeter and which raises its temperature to 28.87°C. The amount of heat, q_{soln}, can be calculated from the increase in temperature of the solution.

$$q_{reaction} + q_{soln} = 0$$

and

$$q_{soln} = cm\Delta T$$

therefore

$$q_{reaction} = -q_{soln} = -cm\Delta T$$

The specific heat of the solution, c, is given as 4.18 J g^{-1} °C^{-1}. The mass of the solution is 100 g. ΔT is (28.87°C − 22.00°C).

$$q_{reaction} = -q_{soln} = -cm\Delta T = -[cm(T_{final} - T_{initial})]$$

$$= -[4.18 \text{ J g}^{-1} °C^{-1} \times 100 \text{ g} \times (28.87 - 22.00)°C]$$

$$= -2870 \text{ J}$$

This reaction produces 2870 J of heat. (It is an exothermic reaction.)

The next example shows that not all changes release heat.

Example 4.4

The temperature of 50.0 g of water at 25.00°C contained in a coffee cup calorimeter decreases to 24.39°C when 1.00 g of solid $KClO_3$ is added and the mixture is stirred until all of the solid is dissolved. Ignore the heat capacity of the calorimeter and calculate the heat involved in this change if the specific heat of the resulting solution is 4.18 J g^{-1} °C^{-1}.

In this case, we start with solid $KClO_3$ and liquid water at 25.00°C. When we run the reaction in a calorimeter, no heat can enter the system from the surroundings, so the heat necessary to dissolve the $KClO_3$ is extracted from the solution, and the temperature of the solution is lowered. From the specific heat of the solution, we can calculate the amount of heat that is removed from the solution.

Be careful to note that the mass of the final solution is 51.0 g, the mass of the added $KClO_3$ plus that of the water.

$$q_{reaction} + q_{soln} = 0$$

$$q_{reaction} = -q_{soln} = -cm \, \Delta T$$

$$q_{reaction} = -cm(T_{final} - T_{initial})$$

$$= -[4.18 \text{ J g}^{-1} \text{ °C}^{-1} \times 51.0 \text{ g} \times (24.39 - 25.00)\text{°C}]$$

$$= -[4.18 \text{ J g}^{-1} \text{ °C}^{-1} \times 51.0 \text{ g} \times (-0.61\text{°C})]$$

$$= -(-130 \text{ J}) = 130 \text{ J} \qquad \text{(2 significant figures justified by the data)}$$

A total of 130 J was absorbed by the reaction. (It is an endothermic reaction.)

If the amount of heat absorbed by a calorimeter is not small or if we want more accurate results, then we must take into account the heat absorbed both by the solution, q_{soln}, and by the calorimeter, q_{cal}. Thus

$$q_{reaction} + q_{soln} + q_{cal} = 0$$

and

$$q_{reaction} = -[q_{soln} + q_{cal}]$$

where q_{soln} is determined as shown in Examples 4.3 and 4.4.

$$q_{cal} = \text{heat capacity of calorimeter} \times \Delta T = C_{cal} \times \Delta T$$

The heat capacity of a calorimeter is commonly called its **calorimeter constant, C_{cal},** and must be determined experimentally for each calorimeter. A calorimeter constant can be determined by running a reaction that produces a known amount of heat in the calorimeter or by mixing two volumes of water at different temperatures, as shown in the following example.

This instant ice pack consists of a bag of solid ammonium nitrate and a bag of water. When the blue bag of water is broken, the ice pack becomes cold as the ammonium nitrate dissolves in the water.

Example
4.5

A 60.0-g sample of water at 84.3°C is added to 50.0 g of water at 23.2°C in a coffee cup calorimeter. Calculate the calorimeter constant if the final temperature of the mixture is 55.7°C.

In order to reach the final temperature, the 60.0 g of water cooled from 84.3°C to 55.7°C as it lost heat. We will call the amount of this heat q_{60}. At the same time, the 50.0 g of water absorbed heat (q_{50}), the calorimeter absorbed heat (q_{cal}), and each increased its temperature from 23.2°C to 55.7°C. We need to determine q_{cal} so that we can calculate C_{cal} ($= q_{cal}/\Delta T$).

Because energy can be neither created nor destroyed, the heat lost by the 60 g of hot water must equal the heat gained by the 50 g of cooler water and by the calorimeter:

$$q_{lost} + q_{gained} = 0$$

so

$$q_{60} + q_{50} + q_{cal} = 0$$

After we calculate q_{60} and q_{50} using the equation $q = cm\Delta T$, we can determine q_{cal}.

$$q_{60} = 4.184 \text{ J g}^{-1} \text{ °C}^{-1} \times 60.0 \text{ g} \times (55.7 - 84.3)\text{°C} = -7180 \text{ J}$$

$$q_{50} = 4.184 \text{ J g}^{-1} \text{ °C}^{-1} \times 50.0 \text{ g} \times (55.7 - 23.2)\text{°C} = 6799 \text{ J}$$

Now we must find q_{cal}.

$$q_{60} + q_{50} + q_{cal} = 0$$

$$q_{cal} = -q_{60} - q_{50}$$

$$= -(-7180 \text{ J}) - 6799 \text{ J} = 381 \text{ J}$$

During a temperature change of 32.5°C, the calorimeter absorbed 381 J. The calorimeter constant, C_{cal} (which is the amount of heat it absorbs when it changes temperature by 1 degree), is

$$C_{cal} = \frac{q_{cal}}{\Delta T} = \frac{381 \text{ J}}{32.5\text{°C}} = 11.7 \text{ J °C}^{-1}$$

The following example is similar to Examples 4.3 and 4.4 except that the heat absorbed by the calorimeter is included in the calculation.

Example
4.6

A 7.45-g sample of solid LiOH dissolved in 120.00 g of water contained in the calorimeter described in Example 4.5. How much heat was produced by the dissolution if the temperature increased from 23.25°C to 34.91°C? The specific heat of the solution produced is 4.20 J g^{-1} °C^{-1}.

As the LiOH dissolves, it produces heat that is absorbed by the solution and the calorimeter. This heat increases their temperatures from 23.25°C to 34.91°C. The total amount of heat produced is the sum of the heat absorbed by the solution and the heat absorbed by the calorimeter. From the specific heat of the solution and its mass

Example 4.6 continued (127.45 g), we can determine how much heat was absorbed by the solution. From the calorimeter constant determined in Example 4.5 (11.7 J °C^{-1}), we can determine how much heat was absorbed by the calorimeter.

$$q_{\text{reaction}} + q_{\text{soln}} + q_{\text{cal}} = 0$$

$$
\begin{aligned}
q_{\text{reaction}} &= -q_{\text{soln}} - q_{\text{cal}} = -cm\,\Delta T - C_{\text{cal}}\,\Delta T \\
&= -cm(T_{\text{final}} - T_{\text{initial}}) - C_{\text{cal}}(T_{\text{final}} - T_{\text{initial}}) \\
&= -[4.20 \text{ J g}^{-1}\,°C^{-1} \times 127.45 \text{ g} \times (34.91 - 23.25)°C] \\
&\quad - [11.7 \text{ J °C}^{-1} \times (34.91 - 23.25)°C] \\
&= -6241 \text{ J} - 136 \text{ J} \\
&= -6.38 \times 10^3 \text{ J} \quad (3 \text{ significant figures justified by the data})
\end{aligned}
$$

A total of 6380 J was produced by the dissolution.

Not all calorimeters trap the heat of a reaction in a solution. If a reaction were run in the steel container of the calorimeter shown in Fig. 4.4, the heat of the reaction would be trapped in the container and in the water surrounding the container. Such calorimeters are used to measure the heats of reactions involving gases. A modification of such a calorimeter was used to measure the heat produced by a living person. A man lived for four days inside a small room surrounded by water. From the increase in water temperature, it was found that the heat produced by his metabolism was about 2400 nutritional Calories per day.

❹.3 Thermochemistry and Thermodynamics

Thermochemistry is a branch of **chemical thermodynamics,** the chemical science that deals with the relationships between heat and other forms of energy known as work. Although we will concentrate on thermochemistry in this chapter and will postpone our broader consideration of thermodynamics until Chapter 19, we do need to consider some thermodynamic ideas that are widely used.

Substances act as reservoirs of energy; energy can be added to them or removed from them. The molecules in liquids and gases move around, and because of this motion they have kinetic energy (Section 1.2). They can store added energy by increasing the speed of their molecular motion, thus increasing the total amount of kinetic energy present in the substance. When energy is removed, the total amount of kinetic energy is reduced. Adding or removing energy can also change the amount of other kinds of energy in a substance, such as that associated with the vibrations and rotations of molecules and with the forces that hold molecules together. The total of all possible kinds of energy present in a substance is called the **internal energy.** We will be interested in the changes in internal energy in a variety of substances.

The substance (or substances) we choose to study is called a **system.** Everything else is called the **surroundings.** As a system undergoes a change, its internal energy can change, and energy can be transferred from the system to the surroundings or from the surroundings to the system.

Thermometer →

Ignition wires
to start reaction

Motor-driven
stirrer

Insulated
outer container

Water

Oxygen
inlet

O_2 atmosphere

Sample

Steel reaction vessel
("bomb")

Figure 4.4

A bomb calorimeter of the type used to measure heat produced or absorbed by reactions involving one or more gases. The gases are contained in the pressure-proof bomb, and the reaction is set off by brief electric heating of a fuse wire in the bomb. The heat produced by the reaction is absorbed by the surroundings: the bomb, the stirrer, the thermometer, and the water. The amount of heat can be determined if the heat capacity of the surroundings has been determined.

As an example of a system let us consider 1 gram of liquid water at 0°C in a container open to the atmosphere (Fig. 4.5). The water is the system. The container and the atmosphere are part of the surroundings. When this system loses 334 joules of heat to the surroundings, it changes to ice at 0°C.

The law of conservation of energy (Section 1.3) tells us that energy can be neither created nor destroyed. Because this system lost energy to the surroundings as heat during the change, the total energy in the system is less after the change than it was before. Loss of heat is one way for a system to reduce its internal energy.

The system also loses energy for a second, less obvious reason. As water freezes, it expands and pushes back the atmosphere. Pushing back the atmosphere is work, just like pumping air into a bicycle tire is work. It requires energy to do work; as the system freezes, it uses some of its internal (stored) energy to do the work of pushing back the atmosphere.

As a second example of a system we can take 1 mole of carbon atoms, 4 moles of hydrogen atoms, and 4 moles of oxygen atoms combined to make 1 mole of methane, CH_4, and 2 moles of oxygen molecules, O_2. Under 1 atmosphere of pressure and at 25°C, this system would have a volume of about 73 liters. If the methane and oxygen in our system combine, the components rearrange themselves to give 1 mole of carbon dioxide gas, CO_2, and 2 moles of liquid water, H_2O, under 1 atmosphere of pressure and at 25°C.

$$CH_4(g) + 2O_2(g) \longrightarrow CO_2(g) + 2H_2O(l)$$

In addition, the system gives up 890,000 joules of heat to the surroundings, reducing its internal energy by 890,000 joules.

The volume of the system after the methane burns is about 24.4 liters. The surroundings must do work on the system to push it from 73 liters to this smaller volume. Some of the energy present in the surroundings is used to do the work, and because this energy cannot disappear (remember the law of conservation of energy, Section 1.3), it appears in the system. This adds to the total energy present in the system. So, although the system loses 890,000 joules of energy to the surroundings as heat when the methane burns, the change in internal energy of the system is less than this. The surroundings do about 4900 joules of work on the system to compress it, and the energy added by this work compensates, to a small extent, for the energy lost as heat.

We will consider how to determine the amount of work involved in a change when we discuss chemical thermodynamics more fully in Chapter 19. For now, you need only

H_2O (l) H_2O (s)

2 mL   2 mL

1 mL   1 mL

(a)   (b)

Figure 4.5

When a system (a) consisting of 1 g of liquid water at 0°C changes to (b) 1 gram of ice at 0°C, 334 J are given up to the surroundings, and the system also does work on the surroundings as it expands.

A burning magnesium ribbon. The heat released when one mole of Mg burns in air is ΔH for the reaction.

recognize that work occurs when a system pushes back the surroundings against a restraining pressure or when the surroundings compress the system against a pressure. Energy is transferred into a system when it absorbs heat from the surroundings or when the surroundings do work on the system. Energy is transferred out of a system when heat is lost from the system or when the system does work on the surroundings.

④.4 Enthalpy Changes

When a change occurs under a constant pressure, and the only work done is due to expansion or contraction of the system under this constant pressure, the heat lost or absorbed by the system during the change is called the **enthalpy change** of the reaction and given the symbol ΔH. The heat of a reaction measured in a coffee cup calorimeter is directly proportional to the enthalpy change of the reaction, because the reaction occurs at the essentially constant pressure of the atmosphere. The heat produced by a reaction measured in a bomb calorimeter is not directly proportional to ΔH, because the sealed bomb prevents the work due to volume changes.

The value of the enthalpy change of a reaction is shown as a ΔH value following the equation for the reaction. The ΔH value indicates the amount of heat associated with the reaction of the number of moles of reactants shown in the chemical equation. The equation

$$H_2(g) + \tfrac{1}{2}O_2(g) \longrightarrow H_2O(l) \qquad \Delta H = -285 \text{ kJ}$$

indicates that when 1 mole of hydrogen gas and $\frac{1}{2}$ mole of oxygen gas at some temperature and pressure change to 1 mole of liquid water at the same temperature and pressure, 285 kJ of heat are given up to the surroundings. The negative value of the enthalpy change, ΔH, indicates an exothermic reaction; a positive value of ΔH would indicate an endothermic reaction. Sometimes the amount of heat is written as though it were a reactant or a product. For a reaction such as this one with a negative ΔH, we could write the heat given off as a product.

$$H_2(g) + \tfrac{1}{2}O_2(g) \longrightarrow H_2O(l) + 285,000 \text{ J}$$

For a reaction with a positive ΔH, we could write the heat that is absorbed as a reactant. The combination reaction of nitrogen with oxygen is such a reaction. It could be written

$$N_2(g) + O_2(g) + 180,500 \text{ J} \longrightarrow 2NO(g)$$

or

$$N_2(g) + O_2(g) \longrightarrow 2NO(g) \qquad \Delta H = +180.5 \text{ kJ}$$

Example 4.7

When 0.0500 mol of HCl(*aq*) reacts with 0.0500 mol of NaOH(*aq*) to form 0.0500 mol of NaCl(*aq*), 2870 J of heat are produced ($q = -2870$ J, Example 4.3). What is ΔH, the enthalpy change for the acid–base reaction

$$HCl(aq) + NaOH(aq) \longrightarrow NaCl(aq) + H_2O(l)$$

run under the conditions described in Example 4.3?

ΔH for the reaction is the heat produced when 1 mol of HCl(*aq*) reacts with 1 mol of NaOH(*aq*) at constant pressure. For the reaction of 0.0500-mol amounts, $q = -2870$ J. The heat resulting from the reaction of 1-mol quantities is 20.0 times greater,

20.0 × −2870 J or −57,400 J (−57.4 kJ). Thus the enthalpy change for the reaction is −57.4 kJ, which we write

$$\text{HCl}(aq) + \text{NaOH}(aq) \longrightarrow \text{NaCl}(aq) + \text{H}_2\text{O}(l) \qquad \Delta H = -57.4 \text{ kJ}$$

The National Institute of Standards and Technology has been particularly active in measuring and tabulating enthalpy changes. Data are reported for specific sets of conditions called **standard states.** Since 1981 the Institute has used a standard state of 298.15 K (25°C) and a pressure of 100 kilopascals (100 kPa, 0.987 atm). Another common standard state, the one used by the Institute before 1981, is 298.15 K and 1 atmosphere of pressure. Because ΔH of a reaction changes very little with such small changes in pressure, ΔH values (except for the most precisely measured values) are the same under both sets of standard conditions. We will use the standard state of 298.15 K and 1 atmosphere and will use the symbol ΔH°_{298} to indicate an enthalpy change for these conditions. (The symbol ΔH is used to indicate an enthalpy change for a reaction where the conditions are not specified.) The enthalpy change of a reaction also depends on the state of the reactants and products (solid, liquid, or gas), so these must also be specified.

The values of many different kinds of enthalpy changes have been determined. Four of the most common kinds of changes are enthalpy of combustion, enthalpy of fusion, enthalpy of vaporization, and standard molar enthalpy of formation.

1. **Enthalpy of Combustion.** An **enthalpy of combustion,** or **heat of combustion,** is the enthalpy change (the amount of heat produced at constant pressure) for the combustion (combination with oxygen) of 1 mole of a substance under standard state conditions. Enthalpies of combustion for several substances have been measured and are listed in Table 4.1. Hydrogen, carbon (as coal or charcoal), methane, acetylene, methanol, and isooctane (a component of gasoline) are used as fuels.

The importance of the phases of the reactants and products in the value of the enthalpy change is illustrated by the table. When liquid water, $\text{H}_2\text{O}(l)$, is formed by combustion of 1 mole of hydrogen, 286 kilocalories of heat are produced. When water vapor, $\text{H}_2\text{O}(g)$, is formed from 1 mol of hydrogen, only 242 kilocalories are produced.

Table 4.1	Enthalpy of Combustion for One Mole of a Substance Under Standard State Conditions	

Substance	Combustion Reaction	Enthalpy of Combustion, ΔH°_{298} (kJ mol^{-1})
Carbon	$\text{C}(s) + \frac{1}{2}\text{O}_2(g) \longrightarrow \text{CO}(g)$	−111
	$\text{C}(s) + \text{O}_2(g) \longrightarrow \text{CO}_2(g)$	−394
Hydrogen	$\text{H}_2(g) + \frac{1}{2}\text{O}_2(g) \longrightarrow \text{H}_2\text{O}(g)$	−242
	$\text{H}_2(g) + \frac{1}{2}\text{O}_2(g) \longrightarrow \text{H}_2\text{O}(l)$	−286
Magnesium	$\text{Mg}(s) + \frac{1}{2}\text{O}_2(g) \longrightarrow \text{MgO}(s)$	−602
Sulfur	$\text{S}(s) + \text{O}_2(g) \longrightarrow \text{SO}_2(g)$	−297
Carbon monoxide	$\text{CO}(g) + \frac{1}{2}\text{O}_2(g) \longrightarrow \text{CO}_2(g)$	−283
Methane	$\text{CH}_4(g) + 2\text{O}_2(g) \longrightarrow \text{CO}_2(g) + 2\text{H}_2\text{O}(g)$	−802
Acetylene	$\text{C}_2\text{H}_2(g) + \frac{5}{2}\text{O}_2(g) \longrightarrow 2\text{CO}_2(g) + \text{H}_2\text{O}(g)$	−1256
Methanol	$\text{CH}_3\text{OH}(l) + \frac{3}{2}\text{O}_2(g) \longrightarrow \text{CO}_2(g) + 2\text{H}_2\text{O}(g)$	−638
Isooctane	$\text{C}_8\text{H}_{18}(l) + \frac{25}{2}\text{O}_2(g) \longrightarrow 8\text{CO}_2(g) + 9\text{H}_2\text{O}(g)$	−5460

Example 4.8

As the photograph shows, the combustion of gasoline is an exothermic process. Assume that the enthalpy of combustion of gasoline is the same as that of isooctane and calculate the amount of heat produced by the combustion of 1.0 L. The density of isooctane is 0.692 g/mL.

We need to determine how much heat (in kilojoules) can be produced by burning 1.0 L of isooctane under standard state conditions. The enthalpy of combustion of isooctane (Table 4.1) is -5460 kJ mol^{-1}; burning 1 mol of isooctane under standard conditions produces 5460 kJ of heat. If we determine how many moles of isooctane are contained in 1.0 L of isooctane and multiply that by the amount of heat produced by combustion of 1 mol of isooctane, we have answered our question. The number of moles can be determined from the molecular mass of isooctane, 114, and the mass of isooctane in 1.0 L. The mass can be determined from the volume and density of isooctane.

$$\text{Mass } C_8H_{18} = 1.0 \text{ L} \times \frac{1000 \text{ mL}}{1 \text{ L}} \times \frac{0.692 \text{ g}}{1 \text{ mL}} = 692 \text{ g } C_8H_{18}$$

$$\text{Mol } C_8H_{18} = 692 \text{ g } C_8H_{18} \times \frac{1 \text{ mol } C_8H_{18}}{114 \text{ g } C_8H_{18}} = 6.07 \text{ mol } C_8H_{18}$$

$$6.07 \text{ mol } C_8H_{18} \times \frac{-5460 \text{ kJ}}{1 \text{ mol } C_8H_{18}} = -33,000 \text{ kJ}$$

Combustion of 1.0 L of isooctane produces 33,000 kJ of heat.

The uncontrolled combustion of gasoline.

2. Enthalpy of Fusion. When heat is added to a crystalline solid, its temperature increases until it reaches the temperature at which the solid will melt. At this point any additional heat causes the solid to begin to melt (fuse). As more heat is added, the temperature remains constant until all of the solid has melted (Fig. 4.6). After that the temperature rises again. The amount of heat required to change a given quantity of a substance from the solid state to the liquid state at a constant temperature is called the **enthalpy of fusion,** or **heat of fusion,** of the substance and is given the symbol ΔH_{fus}. To convert 1 mole (18 grams) of ice at 0°C to liquid water at 0°C requires addition of 6.01 kilojoules of heat to the ice. Thus the enthalpy of fusion of ice is 6.01 kilojoules per mole at 0°C.

$$H_2O(s) \longrightarrow H_2O(l) \qquad \Delta H_{\text{fus}} = 6.01 \text{ kJ mol}^{-1}$$

Note that fusion (melting) is an endothermic process.

Freezing is an exothermic process. When a substance freezes, it *loses* a quantity of heat that is equal to the amount it must gain to melt. To convert 1 mole (18 grams) of liquid water at 0°C to ice at 0°C requires the loss of 6.01 kilojoules of heat from the water. Thus the enthalpy change for freezing of water is -6.01 kilojoules per mole at 0°C.

$$H_2O(l) \longrightarrow H_2O(s) \qquad \Delta H = -\Delta H_{\text{fus}} = -6.01 \text{ kJ mol}^{-1}$$

Note that as heat is removed from water at 0°C and the water changes to ice, its temperature does not change until all of the liquid has frozen. Only at this point does the temperature fall as additional heat is removed.

3. Enthalpy of Vaporization. Heat is required for a liquid to evaporate. When a liquid in an insulated container evaporates, the liquid cools because the heat comes from

(a)   (b)

(c)   (d)

Figure 4.6
(a) A beaker of ice that has just been removed from a freezer; the digital thermometer shows its temperature is −18.3°C. (b) The same beaker after it has absorbed enough heat from the air to warm to 0°C and then to melt a small amount of the ice. (c) After the ice has absorbed more heat, its temperature is still 0°C. The heat caused the ice to change from a solid to a liquid without changing its temperature. (d) Only after all the ice has melted will the heat absorbed cause the temperature to increase.

the liquid itself. The cooling effect due to the evaporation of water is very evident to a swimmer emerging from the water. Some of the water on the swimmer's skin evaporates and leaves behind cooler water, which causes the skin to feel cold.

For the temperature of a liquid to remain constant as it evaporates, the liquid must absorb heat to offset the cooling due to the evaporation. The heat that must be supplied to keep the temperature constant as a given amount of liquid evaporates is called the **enthalpy of vaporization,** or **heat of vaporization,** of the substance and is given the symbol ΔH_{vap}. It requires 44.01 kilojoules of heat to evaporate 1 mole of water at 25°C; thus the enthalpy of vaporization of water is 44.01 kilojoules per mole at 25°C.

$$H_2O(l) \longrightarrow H_2O(g) \qquad \Delta H_{vap} \text{ (at 25°C)} = 44.01 \text{ kJ mol}^{-1}$$

At higher temperatures, less heat is required per mole of liquid evaporated. At its boiling point (100°C), the heat required to convert 1 mole of liquid water to vapor is 40.67 kilojoules (ΔH_{vap} at 100°C = 40.67 kJ mol^{-1}). Thus as water boils at 100°C, for every mole of water that evaporates, 40.67 kilojoules of heat must be added to the liquid. This added heat converts the liquid water to the vapor, but it does not increase the temperature of the liquid water that remains (Fig. 4.7).

One mechanism for the removal of excess heat from the body is evaporation of the water in sweat. In a hot, dry climate as much as 1.5 L of water (1500 g) per day may be lost through such evaporation. Although sweat is not pure water, we can get an *approximate* value of the amount of heat removed by evaporation by assuming that it is. Calculate the amount of heat required to evaporate this much water at $T = 37°C$ (body temperature); $\Delta H_{vap} = 43.46$ kJ mol^{-1} at 37°C.

**Example
4.9**

Example 4.9 continued To evaporate 1 mol of water at 37°C requires 43.46 kJ. So we must determine the number of moles of water in 1500 g and then determine the amount of heat necessary to vaporize this much water.

$$1500 \text{ g H}_2\text{O} \times \frac{1 \text{ mol H}_2\text{O}}{18 \text{ g H}_2\text{O}} = 83.3 \text{ mol H}_2\text{O}$$

$$83.3 \text{ mol H}_2\text{O} \times \frac{43.46 \text{ kJ}}{1 \text{ mol H}_2\text{O}} = 3.6 \times 10^3 \text{ kJ}$$

Thus 3600 kJ of heat are removed by the evaporation of 1.5 L of water.

The quantity of heat evolved as a gas condenses to a liquid equals that absorbed during evaporation. At 100°C, for water,

$$H_2O(l) \longrightarrow H_2O(g) \quad \Delta H = \Delta H_{vap} = 40.67 \text{ kJ mol}^{-1}$$

$$H_2O(g) \longrightarrow H_2O(l) \quad \Delta H = -\Delta H_{vap} = -40.67 \text{ kJ mol}^{-1}$$

The enthalpy changes associated with evaporation and condensation of a liquid are used to cool a refrigerator. Heat is removed from the refrigerated compartment when a liquid refrigerant (usually a Freon such as CCl_2F_2) absorbs the energy needed to change it from a liquid to a gas. The gas is then circulated through a compressor outside the refrigerated compartment and condensed back to a liquid by compression. The heat lost during reliquefaction is lost to the room through the cooling coils on the back of the refrigerator, and the liquid is recycled through the refrigerated compartment where it is allowed to evaporate, repeating the cycle.

4. Standard Molar Enthalpy of Formation. Probably the most useful tabulation of enthalpy changes is for a combination reaction in which *1 mole* of a pure substance is formed from the free elements in their most stable states under standard state conditions. This enthalpy change is referred to as the **standard molar enthalpy of formation** of the substance formed and is designated by ΔH_f°. (Note the subscript letter f and the superscript °; together they identify an enthalpy of *formation under standard state conditions*.) The standard molar enthalpy of formation of $CO_2(g)$ is -394 kilojoules per mole, which is the enthalpy change for the reaction

$$C(s) + O_2(g) \longrightarrow CO_2(g) \quad \Delta H_f^\circ = \Delta H_{298}^\circ = -394 \text{ kJ mol}^{-1}$$

Figure 4.7

(a) The water is being heated by the hot plate below the beaker. The digital thermometer shows that it has absorbed enough heat to increase its temperature from room temperature to 79.3°C. (b) The same beaker after it has absorbed enough heat to warm to 100°C and then begin to boil. (c) Even after enough heat has been added to boil away most of the water, the temperature is still 100°C. The heat converted the water from a liquid to a gas without changing its temperature.

(a)

(b)

(c)

starting with the reactants at a pressure of 1 atmosphere and 25°C with the carbon present as graphite (the most stable form of carbon under this set of standard conditions) and ending with the product, CO_2, also at 1 atmosphere and a temperature of 25°C. For nitrogen dioxide, NO_2, ΔH_f° is 33.2 kilojoules per mole; that is, ΔH_f° is equal to ΔH_{298}° for the *endothermic* reaction

$$\tfrac{1}{2}N_2(g) + O_2(g) \longrightarrow NO_2(g) \qquad \Delta H_f^\circ = \Delta H_{298}^\circ = +33.2 \text{ kJ mol}^{-1}$$

The reaction of $\tfrac{1}{2}$ mole of N_2 and 1 mole of O_2 is correct in this case because the standard molar enthalpy of formation refers to 1 mole of product.

By convention, the standard molar enthalpy of formation of an element in its most stable form is equal to zero (see Table 4.2).

Table 4.2	Standard Molar Enthalpies of Formation[a]
Substance	ΔH_f° (kJ mol^{-1})
Carbon	
C(s, *graphite*)	0
C(g)	716.68
CO(g)	−111
CO$_2$(g)	−394
CH$_4$(g)	−74.8
CH$_3$OH(l)	−238.7
CH$_3$OH(g)	−200.7
Chlorine	
Cl$_2$(g)	0
Cl(g)	121.7
Hydrogen	
H$_2$(g)	0
H$_2$O(g)	−241.8
H$_2$O(l)	−285.83
HCl(g)	−92.31
H$_2$S(g)	−20.6
Nitrogen	
N$_2$(g)	0
NO(g)	90.25
NO$_2$(g)	33.2
NH$_3$(g)	−46.11
Oxygen	
O$_2$(g)	0
Phosphorus	
P(s)	0
P$_4$O$_{10}$(s)	−2984
H$_3$PO$_4$(l)	−1267

[a]See Appendix I for additional values.

Standard molar enthalpies of formation of some common substances are given in Table 4.2 and in Appendix I. The unit of heat in these tables is kilojoules, but many older tables have calories (1 cal = 4.184 J) and kilocalories (the nutritional Calories). If you have occasion to use other tables, be sure to check the units.

Example 4.10

Ozone, $O_3(g)$, forms from oxygen, $O_2(g)$, by an endothermic process. Assuming that both the reactants and the products of the reaction are in their standard states, determine the standard molar enthalpy of formation, ΔH_f°, of ozone from the following information.

$$3O_2(g) \longrightarrow 2O_3(g) \qquad \Delta H_{298}^\circ = 286 \text{ kJ}$$

ΔH_f° is the enthalpy change for the formation of one mole of a substance in its standard state from the elements in their standard states. Thus ΔH_f° for $O_3(g)$ is the enthalpy change for the reaction

$$\tfrac{3}{2}O_2(g) \longrightarrow O_3(g)$$

Because 286 kJ of heat are absorbed when 2 mol of $O_3(g)$ are formed, to form 1 mol of $O_3(g)$ will require half as much heat, or 143 kJ. Thus the enthalpy change is 143 kJ, and

$$\Delta H_f^\circ = 143 \text{ kJ mol}^{-1}$$

Example 4.11

Hydrogen gas, H_2, reacts explosively with gaseous chlorine, Cl_2, to form hydrogen chloride, HCl, which is also a gas. What is the enthalpy change for the combination reaction of 1 mol of $H_2(g)$ with 1 mol of $Cl_2(g)$ if both the reactants and products are at standard state conditions?

$$H_2(g) + Cl_2(g) \longrightarrow 2HCl(g)$$

Because the standard molar enthalpies of formation of $H_2(g)$ and $Cl_2(g)$ are 0 (Table 4.2), these are the most stable states of the elements under standard state conditions. A pure substance, HCl(g), is being formed under standard state conditions from elements in their most stable states under these conditions, so ΔH_{298}° must be proportional to the standard molar enthalpy of formation of HCl(g). In this example, 2 mol of HCl(g) are being formed; therefore,

$$\Delta H_{298}^\circ = 2 \ \Delta H_f^\circ$$

From Table 4.2, $\qquad \Delta H_f^\circ = -92.31 \text{ kJ mol}^{-1}$

Therefore, $\qquad \Delta H_{298}^\circ = 2 \text{ mol HCl} \times (-92.31 \text{ kJ mol}^{-1}) = -184.6 \text{ kJ}$

Thus the reaction evolves 184.6 kJ of heat.

$$H_2(g) + Cl_2(g) \longrightarrow 2HCl(g) \qquad \Delta H_{298}^\circ = -184.6 \text{ kJ}$$

Note the difference in units between ΔH (as well as ΔH_{298}°) and ΔH_f°. The enthalpy change for a reaction, ΔH (or ΔH_{298}°), gives the amount of heat produced by the reaction as it is written and has units of kilojoules or, more rarely, joules. The magnitudes of ΔH and ΔH_{298}° change as the amounts of reactant change. For example, combustion of 1 mole of CO(g) produces 283 kilojoules ($\Delta H = -283$ kJ), whereas combustion of 2 moles of CO(g) produces 566 kilojoules ($\Delta H = -566$ kJ). The standard molar enthalpy of formation of a compound, ΔH_f°, identifies the enthalpy change associated with formation of 1 mole of the compound and has units of kilojoules per mole (kJ mol^{-1}).

4.5 Hess's Law

Some chemical changes can occur in two or more steps. For example, carbon can react with oxygen to form carbon dioxide in a two-step process. If carbon is burned in a limited amount of oxygen, carbon monoxide, CO, is formed.

$$C(s) + \tfrac{1}{2}O_2(g) \longrightarrow CO(g)$$

Carbon monoxide will burn in additional oxygen and form carbon dioxide, CO_2.

$$CO(g) + \tfrac{1}{2}O_2(g) \longrightarrow CO_2(g)$$

The equation describing the overall change of C to CO_2 is the sum of these two chemical changes:

Step 1 $\qquad\qquad\qquad C(s) + \tfrac{1}{2}O_2(g) \longrightarrow CO(g)$

Step 2 $\qquad\qquad\qquad CO(g) + \tfrac{1}{2}O_2(g) \longrightarrow CO_2(g)$

Sum $\qquad\quad C(s) + \tfrac{1}{2}O_2 + \cancel{CO(g)} + \tfrac{1}{2}O_2(g) \longrightarrow \cancel{CO(g)} + CO_2(g)$

Because the CO produced in Step 1 is consumed in Step 2, the net change is

$$C(s) + O_2(g) \longrightarrow CO_2(g)$$

If a chemical reaction can be written as a sum of steps, the enthalpy change of the reaction is equal to the sum of the enthalpy changes of the steps. From the experimental enthalpies of combustion (Table 4.1),

$$C(s) + \tfrac{1}{2}O_2(g) \longrightarrow CO(g) \qquad \Delta H_{298}^\circ = -111 \text{ kJ}$$

$$CO(g) + \tfrac{1}{2}O_2(g) \longrightarrow CO_2(g) \qquad \Delta H_{298}^\circ = -283 \text{ kJ}$$

$$C(s) + O_2(g) \longrightarrow CO_2(g) \qquad \Delta H_{298}^\circ = -394 \text{ kJ}$$

You can see that ΔH for the bottom reaction is the sum of the ΔH values for the two reactions above it. This is an example of the principle stated by **Hess's law: If a process can be written as the sum of several stepwise processes, the enthalpy change of the total process equals the sum of the enthalpy changes of the various steps.**

Hess's law lets us use standard molar enthalpies of formation to calculate enthalpy changes of other reactions. However, before we use this law, let us look briefly at two important features of ΔH for a reaction.

1. ΔH for a reaction in one direction is equal in magnitude and opposite in sign to ΔH for the reaction in the reverse direction. This statement tells us that if we know that ΔH for the reaction

$$H_2O(s) \longrightarrow H_2O(l)$$

is 6.0 kilojoules, then ΔH for the reverse reaction,

$$H_2O(l) \longrightarrow H_2O(s)$$

is simply the negative of that for the forward reaction, or -6.0 kilojoules.

2. ΔH is directly proportional to the quantities of reactants or products. This statement indicates that if the enthalpy of fusion of 1 mole of water is 6.0 kilojoules,

$$H_2O(s) \longrightarrow H_2O(l) \qquad \Delta H = 6.0 \text{ kJ}$$

then the enthalpy of fusion of 2 moles of water is twice as great,

$$2H_2O(s) \longrightarrow 2H_2O(l) \qquad \Delta H = 12 \text{ kJ}$$

Example 4.12

The standard molar enthalpy of formation of $FeCl_2(s)$ is -341.8 kJ mol^{-1}. $FeCl_3(s)$ forms when 1 mol of $FeCl_2(s)$ reacts with $\frac{1}{2}$ mol of $Cl_2(g)$ under standard state conditions; the enthalpy change of the reaction, ΔH°_{298}, is -57.7 kJ. What is the standard molar enthalpy of formation, ΔH°_f, of $FeCl_3(s)$?

The magnitude of the standard molar enthalpy of formation of $FeCl_3(s)$ is equal to ΔH°_{298} for the reaction that forms 1 mol of $FeCl_3(s)$ from the elements under standard state conditions:

$$Fe(s) + \tfrac{3}{2}Cl_2(g) \longrightarrow FeCl_3(s)$$

This combination reaction can be written as the sum of two others.

Step 1 $Fe(s) + Cl_2(g) \longrightarrow FeCl_2(s)$

Step 2 $FeCl_2(s) + \tfrac{1}{2}Cl_2(g) \longrightarrow FeCl_3(s)$

Sum $\overline{\qquad Fe(s) + \tfrac{3}{2}Cl_2(g) \longrightarrow FeCl_3(s)}$

Because 1 mol of $FeCl_2(s)$ is produced by Step 1, the magnitude of ΔH°_{298} for this step is equal to the magnitude of the standard molar enthalpy of formation of $FeCl_2(s)$. ΔH°_{298} for Step 2 is given in the problem. The sum of the enthalpy changes of these two steps is equal to the magnitude of ΔH°_f for $FeCl_3(s)$.

$$Fe(s) + Cl_2(g) \longrightarrow FeCl_2(s) \qquad \Delta H^\circ_{298} = -341.8 \text{ kJ}$$

$$FeCl_2(s) + \tfrac{1}{2}Cl_2(g) \longrightarrow FeCl_3(s) \qquad \Delta H^\circ_{298} = -57.7 \text{ kJ}$$

$$\overline{Fe(s) + \tfrac{3}{2}Cl_2(g) \longrightarrow FeCl_3(s) \qquad \Delta H^\circ_{298} = -399.5 \text{ kJ}}$$

Under standard state conditions, the enthalpy change of the reaction that forms 1 mol of $FeCl_3(s)$ from the elements in their most stable states is -399.5 kJ. Therefore, the standard molar enthalpy of formation of $FeCl_3(s)$ is -399.5 kJ/mol.

Hess's law can be used to determine the enthalpy change, under standard state conditions, of any reaction if the standard molar enthalpies of formation of the reactants and products are available. The procedures used are (1) decompositions of the reactants into their component elements, for which the enthalpy changes are proportional to the negative of the enthalpies of formation of the reactants, followed by (2) recombinations of the elements to give the products, for which the enthalpy changes are proportional to the enthalpies of formation of the products. This is one reason why a table of enthalpies of formation is so useful. The following examples illustrate the process.

Phosphoric acid for use in cola soft drinks and other food products is prepared by the reaction of phosphorus(V) oxide, P_4O_{10}, with water.

$$P_4O_{10}(s) + 6H_2O(l) \longrightarrow 4H_3PO_4(l)$$

How much heat is produced by the reaction of exactly 1 mol of $P_4O_{10}(s)$ with liquid water at constant pressure under standard state conditions?

Example 4.13

The amount of heat, q, produced by a reaction at constant pressure under standard conditions is equal to the standard enthalpy change, ΔH°_{298}, for the reaction. The reaction of $P_4O_{10}(s)$ with water can be written as the sum of three steps, two of which involve decomposition of P_4O_{10} and H_2O to their component elements, and the third of which involves formation of H_3PO_4 from these elements. Obtaining the standard molar enthalpies of formation of $P_4O_{10}(s)$, $H_2O(l)$, and $H_3PO_4(l)$ (-2984, -285.83, and -1267 kJ mol^{-1}, respectively) from Table 4.2, we have all of the information necessary to determine ΔH°_{298}.

The reaction of water with P_4O_{10} is exothermic. When a drop of water is added to solid P_4O_{10}, steam is produced by the heat released.

Step 1

$$P_4O_{10}(s) \longrightarrow 4P(s) + 5O_2(g) \qquad \Delta H^\circ_1 = -\left(1 \text{ mol } P_4O_{10}(s) \times \frac{-2984 \text{ kJ}}{1 \text{ mol } P_4O_{10}(s)}\right)$$

$$= -(-2984 \text{ kJ}) = 2984 \text{ kJ}$$

Step 2

$$6H_2O(l) \longrightarrow 6H_2(g) + 3O_2(g) \qquad \Delta H^\circ_2 = -\left(6 \text{ mol } H_2O(l) \times \frac{-285.83 \text{ kJ}}{1 \text{ mol } H_2O(l)}\right)$$

$$= -(-1715.0 \text{ kJ}) = 1715.0 \text{ kJ}$$

Step 3

$$6H_2(g) + 8O_2(g) + 4P(s) \longrightarrow 4H_3PO_4(l)$$

$$\Delta H^\circ_3 = 4 \text{ mol } H_3PO_4(l) \times \frac{-1267 \text{ kJ}}{1 \text{ mol } H_3PO_4(l)}$$

$$= -5068 \text{ kJ}$$

Sum

$$P_4O_{10}(s) + 6H_2O(l) \longrightarrow 4H_3PO_4(l) \qquad \Delta H^\circ_{298} = \Delta H^\circ_1 + \Delta H^\circ_2 + \Delta H^\circ_3$$

$$= (2984 + 1715 - 5068) \text{ kJ}$$

$$= -369 \text{ kJ}$$

The reaction produces 369 kJ of heat.

The next example shows how to use standard molar enthalpies of formation to calculate an enthalpy of combustion.

Example
4.14

Calculate the enthalpy of combustion of methane according to the following reaction.

$$CH_4(g) + 2O_2(g) \longrightarrow CO_2(g) + 2H_2O(l)$$

This combustion reaction can be written as the sum of three steps: (1) decomposition of CH_4 to $C(s)$ and $H_2(g)$, (2) reaction of H_2 and O_2 to form H_2O, and (3) reaction of C and O_2 to form CO_2. The enthalpy changes of these steps are proportional to the standard molar enthalpies of formation found in Appendix I.

Step 1 $\qquad CH_4(g) \longrightarrow C(s) + 2H_2(g) \qquad \Delta H_1^\circ = -\Delta H_{f_{CH_4(g)}}^\circ$

Step 2 $\qquad 2H_2(g) + O_2(g) \longrightarrow 2H_2O(l) \qquad \Delta H_2^\circ = 2\Delta H_{f_{H_2O(l)}}^\circ$

Step 3 $\qquad C(s) + O_2(g) \longrightarrow CO_2(g) \qquad \Delta H_3^\circ = \Delta H_{f_{CO_2(g)}}^\circ$

Sum $\qquad CH_4(g) + 2O_2(g) \longrightarrow CO_2(g) + 2H_2O(l) \qquad \Delta H_{298}^\circ = \Delta H_1^\circ + \Delta H_2^\circ + \Delta H_3^\circ$

$\Delta H_{298}^\circ = \Delta H_1^\circ + \Delta H_2^\circ + \Delta H_3^\circ$

$$= -\left(1 \text{ mol } CH_4(g) \times \frac{-74.81 \text{ kJ}}{1 \text{ mol } CH_4(g)}\right) + \left(2 \text{ mol } H_2O(l) \times \frac{-285.83 \text{ kJ}}{1 \text{ mol } H_2O(l)}\right)$$

$$+ \left(1 \text{ mol } CO_2(g) \times \frac{-393.51 \text{ kJ}}{1 \text{ mol } CO_2(g)}\right)$$

$$= -890.36 \text{ kJ}$$

The combustion of natural gas, CH_4, in a Bunsen burner is an exothermic reaction.

The combustion of 1 mol of methane produces 890.36 kJ of heat when the water produced is a liquid. (The value of -802 kJ given in Table 4.1 for the enthalpy of combustion of methane is for the formation of *gaseous* water.)

The enthalpy changes associated with phase changes can also be calculated by using Hess's law. For example, evaporation is a phase change that can be described by the general chemical equation

$$\text{Liquid} \longrightarrow \text{Gas}$$

The enthalpy of vaporization of the liquid is equal to the enthalpy change of the process and can be determined by applying Hess's law.

Example
4.15

Using the data in Table 4.2, determine the enthalpy of vaporization of methanol, CH_3OH, under standard state conditions.

The enthalpy of vaporization of methanol is the enthalpy change of the process described by the equation

$$CH_3OH(l) \longrightarrow CH_3OH(g)$$

The enthalpy change of this process can be determined under standard state conditions from the standard molar enthalpies of formation of liquid CH_3OH, -238.7 kJ mol^{-1}, and of gaseous CH_3OH, -200.7 kJ mol^{-1}, using Hess's law.

$$CH_3OH(l) \longrightarrow C(s) + \tfrac{1}{2}O_2(g) + 2H_2(g) \qquad \Delta H^\circ_{298} = 238.7 \text{ kJ}$$

$$C(s) + \tfrac{1}{2}O_2(g) + 2H_2(g) \longrightarrow CH_3OH(g) \qquad \Delta H^\circ_{298} = -200.7 \text{ kJ}$$

$$CH_3OH(l) \longrightarrow CH_3OH(g) \qquad \Delta H^\circ_{298} = 238.7 + (-200.7) \text{ kJ}$$
$$= 38.0 \text{ kJ}$$

The enthalpy change for the evaporation of 1 mol of $CH_3OH(l)$ is 38.0 kJ; hence the enthalpy of vaporization is 38.0 kJ mol^{-1}.

We will consider another form of Hess's law in Chapter 19, when we explore the subject of thermodynamics more fully.

4.6 Fuel and Food

The most common chemical reaction used to produce heat is **combustion,** the rapid combination of a fuel with oxygen, which is normally accompanied by a flame. Combustion is usually started by heating a fuel in oxygen or air, but after the reaction has begun it provides the heat necessary to keep itself going.

The major fuels in our society are fossil fuels, all of which are being depleted much more rapidly than they are being formed. Fossil fuels form very slowly from the remains of plants and animals. They consist primarily of **hydrocarbons,** compounds composed only of hydrogen and carbon. **Natural gas** is composed of low-molecular-mass hydrocarbons, principally methane (CH_4), with small amounts of ethane (C_2H_6), propane (C_3H_8), and butane (C_4H_{10}). These hydrocarbons are almost odorless, so small amounts of foul-smelling compounds called mercaptans are added to the gas as an aid in detecting leaks. Some natural gas contains hydrogen sulfide, a contaminant that is removed before the gas is sold for commercial or residential use. **Petroleum,** from which oil and gasoline are produced, is a liquid that varies in its composition, depending on the location of the wells from which it is pumped. It is a mixture that contains hundreds of different compounds, primarily hydrocarbons ranging from methane to compounds containing 50 carbon atoms per molecule. **Coal** is a solid fuel composed mainly of hydrocarbons with high molecular masses. Compounds containing oxygen, nitrogen, and sulfur are also found in petroleum and coal.

In many parts of the world, wood and dried animal dung are used as residential fuels for cooking and heating.

A synthetic fuel of great interest is hydrogen, H_2, one of the fuels used in the space shuttle (Fig. 4.8). When hydrogen burns, it forms water, a compound with no negative environmental impact. Free hydrogen does not occur naturally. It is a by-product of refining petroleum, and it can also be prepared from water by an endothermic reaction that requires energy.

$$2H_2O(l) \longrightarrow 2H_2(g) + O_2(g) \qquad \Delta H^\circ_{298} = +572 \text{ kJ}$$

As long as this energy must be obtained by combustion of fossil fuels, or as long as hydrogen is obtained from fossil fuels, it is unlikely to become a common fuel. However, if nuclear or solar energy technology becomes suitable for the production of hydrogen, this element could serve as a convenient source of energy.

Figure 4.8

The large central fuel tank of the space shuttle contains liquid hydrogen and liquid oxygen, which are burned in the engines at the rear of the space craft, giving the pale blue flame and invisible water vapor. A mixture of aluminum powder and ammonium perchlorate is the principal ingredient in the boosters. The large clouds of smoke contain aluminum oxide and aluminum chloride.

The amount of heat that a fuel can produce can be determined from its enthalpy of combustion (Section 4.4) or by use of Hess's law (Section 4.5, Example 4.14).

Example 4.16

Which will produce more heat, combustion of 1.0 g of hydrogen, H_2, or combustion of 1.0 g of methane, CH_4, assuming that the water produced is in the gas phase? Enthalpies of formation can be found in Table 4.2.

At first glance it might appear that methane is the choice; the enthalpy of combustion of methane is -802 kJ mol^{-1}, and that of H_2 is -242 kJ mol^{-1}. However, we need to divide these values by the number of grams in 1 mol of each of the fuels in order to find the enthalpy of combustion per gram.

$$\text{For } H_2: \qquad \frac{-242 \text{ kJ}}{1 \text{ mol}} \times \frac{1 \text{ mol}}{2.0159 \text{ g}} = \frac{-120 \text{ kJ}}{1 \text{ g}}$$

$$\text{For } CH_4: \qquad \frac{-802 \text{ kJ}}{1 \text{ mol}} \times \frac{1 \text{ mol}}{16.043 \text{ g}} = \frac{-50.0 \text{ kJ}}{1 \text{ g}}$$

Hydrogen provides 120 kJ of heat per gram of fuel; methane, 50.0 kJ per gram.

Food is the body's fuel. In addition, it provides the nutrients necessary to maintain the physiological functions of the body. Each day, a normally active, healthy adult requires about 130 kJ of energy from food for each kilogram of body weight. This corresponds to about 14 kilocalories or 14 Calories per pound of body weight. (Remember that the Calorie used in nutrition is what chemists call a kilocalorie; 1 Calorie = 1 kcal = 4.184 kJ.)

Most of the energy used by our bodies comes from carbohydrates. These are broken down in the stomach to glucose (blood sugar), which is transported to cells by the blood. In the cells glucose reacts with O_2 in a series of steps, eventually producing carbon dioxide, liquid water, and energy.

$$C_6H_{12}O_6(s) + 6O_2(g) \longrightarrow 6CO_2(g) + 6H_2O(l) \qquad \Delta H^{\circ}_{298} = -2870 \text{ kJ}$$

The amount of heat that can be produced in the body is the same as the amount that would be produced in a calorimeter burning the same amount of glucose under constant pressure. The average enthalpy of combustion per gram of carbohydrate is -17 kJ (-4 kcal g^{-1}), assuming liquid water is the product of the oxidation.

Fats also produce carbon dioxide and water when metabolized in the body. Palmitic acid, a typical fat, reacts as follows:

$$C_{15}H_{31}CO_2H(s) + 23O_2(g) \longrightarrow 16CO_2(g) + 16H_2O(l) \qquad \Delta H^{\circ}_{298} = -9977 \text{ kJ}$$

Fats produce significantly more energy per gram than either carbohydrates or proteins; their enthalpies of combustion average -38 kJ per gram (-9.1 kcal g^{-1}). This high enthalpy of combustion per gram makes fats ideal for storage of energy. Excess energy from overeating is stored by production of fat.

Proteins are not generally oxidized in the body; instead, their components are used to build body proteins. However, in cases where proteins are used to provide energy for the body, they produce about -17 kJ per gram (-4 kcal g^{-1}).

NUTRITION INFORMATION
PER SERVING
SERVING SIZE: 2 OZ (57 GRAMS) DRY
SERVINGS PER PACKAGE (8 OZ):   4
CALORIES   210
PROTEIN   7 GRAMS
CARBOHYDRATE   43 GRAMS
FAT   1 GRAM
CHOLESTEROL*   0 MG (0 MG/100 G)
SODIUM   0 MILLIGRAMS**

Figure 4.9
The Calorie content on this label is determined from the masses of carbohydrate, fat, and protein in a serving.

The Calorie content in a serving of a food (Fig. 4.9) is the sum of the Calories contained in the carbohydrates, fats, and proteins present in the serving.

For Review

Summary

Thermochemistry is the determination and study of the heat absorbed or given off during chemical or physical changes. **Heat, q,** is the form of energy that gives a substance its temperature or that can cause it to melt or to evaporate. Heat moves spontaneously from a hotter object to a cooler object. Heat, whether measured in units of **calories** or **joules,** is measured in a **calorimeter,** usually by determining the temperature change of water or of a solution of known **specific heat.**

As a system loses heat by an **exothermic** process, its **internal energy** is decreased. Heat is added to a system by an **endothermic** process, which increases the internal energy of the system. When a system does **work,** the internal energy of the system is decreased. When work is done on a system, its internal energy increases.

If a chemical change is carried out at constant pressure and the only work done is due to expansion or contraction, q for the change is called the **enthalpy change** and is denoted by the symbol ΔH, or ΔH°_{298} if the reaction occurs under standard state conditions. Examples of enthalpy changes include **enthalpy of combustion, enthalpy of fusion, enthalpy of vaporization,** and **standard molar enthalpy of formation.** The standard molar enthalpy of formation, ΔH°_f, is the enthalpy change accompanying the formation of 1 mol of a substance from the elements in their most stable states at 298.15 K and 1 atm (a **standard state**). If the enthalpies of formation are available for the reactants and products of a reaction, its enthalpy change can be calculated by using **Hess's law:** If a process can be written as the sum of several stepwise processes, the enthalpy change of the total process equals the sum of the enthalpy changes of the various steps. ΔH for a reaction in one direction is equal in magnitude, but opposite in sign, to ΔH for the reaction in the opposite direction, and ΔH is directly proportional to the quantity of reactants.

Heat is produced from fuels by combustion reactions. Common fuels include the fossil fuels—natural gas, petroleum, and coal. Food is the fuel used by the body.

Key Terms and Concepts

calorie (4.1)
calorimetry (4.2)
chemical thermodynamics (4.3)
combustion (4.6)
endothermic reaction (4.1)
enthalpy change, ΔH (4.4)
enthalpy change at standard state
    conditions, $\Delta H°_{298}$ (4.4)
enthalpy of combustion (4.4)
enthalpy of fusion (4.4)

enthalpy of vaporization (4.4)
exothermic reaction (4.1)
food (4.6)
fuel (4.6)
heat (4.1)
heat capacity (4.1)
hydrocarbon (4.6)
internal energy (4.3)
joule (4.1)

measurement of heat (4.1)
nutritional Calorie (4.1)
specific heat (4.1)
standard molar enthalpy of
    formation, $\Delta H°_f$ (4.4)
standard state (4.4)
surroundings (4.3)
system (4.3)
work (4.3)

Exercises

Answers for selected even-numbered exercises marked by red numbers appear at the end of the book. The worked-out solutions to all even-numbered exercises appear in the *Solutions Guide*.

1. As a bathtub of hot water cools to room temperature, it can warm up a bathroom. When a cup of coffee cools from the same temperature, the warming of the same room is not readily detectable. Explain the difference.

2. If its heat capacity is known, what other property of an object must we know in order to calculate its specific heat?

3. If the temperature of the 800 g of water in Fig. 4.2 increases by 45°C, how much heat in joules was added to the water? How much heat in calories?

4. (a) How much would the temperature of the water shown in Fig. 4.2 increase if 29.0 kJ of heat were added?
   (b) How much would the temperature of the water shown in Fig. 4.2 increase if 14.5 kcal of heat were added?
   (c) How much would the temperature of the water shown in Fig. 4.2 increase if 12 nutritional Calories of heat were added?

5. How much heat, in joules and calories, must be added to a 500-g iron skillet with a specific heat of 0.451 J g^{-1} °C^{-1} to increase its temperature from 25°C to 250°C?

6. (a) What is the heat capacity of a 1.05-kg aluminum kettle? The specific heat of aluminum is 0.88 J g^{-1} °C^{-1}.
   (b) How much heat is required to increase the temperature of this kettle from 23.0°C to 100.0°C?
   (c) How much heat is required to heat the filled kettle from 23.0°C to 99.0°C if it contains 1.25 L of water with a density of 0.997 g mL^{-1} and a specific heat of 4.184 J g^{-1} °C^{-1}?

7. A 25.3-g piece of zinc at 96.68°C was added to 50.0 g of water at 21.68°C. The final temperature of the zinc and water was 25.00°C. What is the specific heat of zinc?

8. Calculate the specific heat of water in the units Calories per pound per °F (1 Calorie is the nutritional Calorie = 1000 calories). The specific heat of water is 4.184 J g^{-1} °C^{-1}.

9. How many milliliters of water at 23°C with a density of 1.00 g mL^{-1} must be mixed with 180 mL of coffee at 85°C to cool the drink to 60°C? Assume that coffee and water have the same density and the same specific heat.

10. (a) What is the final temperature when a 45-g aluminum spoon (specific heat 0.88 J g^{-1} °C^{-1}) at 24°C is placed in 180 mL (180 g) of coffee at 85°C and the temperature of the two become equal? Assume that coffee has the same specific heat as water.
   (b) The first time one of the authors solved this problem, he got the answer 88°C. Besides reworking the problem, how else could he recognize that this is an incorrect answer?

Calorimetry

11. Would the amount of heat produced by the reaction in Example 4.3 appear greater, smaller, or the same if the experimenter used a calorimeter that was a poorer insulator than a coffee cup calorimeter? Explain your answer.

12. Would the amount of heat absorbed by the reaction in Example 4.4 appear greater, smaller, or the same if the experimenter used a calorimeter that was a poorer insulator than a

coffee cup calorimeter and if room temperature were 27°C? Explain your answer.

13. If the 1.00 g of $KClO_3$ in Example 4.4 was dissolved in 101 g of water under the same conditions, how much would the temperature change?

14. The following questions refer to the calorimeter described in Example 4.5.
   (a) Would the calorimeter constant for the calorimeter be larger, be smaller, or not change if the final temperature were 56.2°C instead of 55.7°C? (A calculation is not needed to answer this question.)
   (b) Calculate the calorimeter constant if the final temperature were 56.2°C.
   (c) What would the final temperature be if the calorimeter constant were zero?

15. If 504 J of heat is added to 40.0 g of water at 24.3°C in a coffee cup calorimeter, what is the resulting temperature? (Assume $C_{cal} = 0$.)

16. A 70.0-g sample of metal at 22.0°C is placed in 100.0 g of water at 80.0°C in a coffee cup calorimeter ($C_{cal} = 0$) and the metal and water come to the same temperature at 75.6°C. How much heat did the metal pick up from the water? What is the specific heat of the metal?

17. A 70.0-g piece of metal at 80.0°C was placed in 100 g of water at 22.0°C in the same calorimeter used in Problem 16. The temperature stopped changing at 26.4°C. Use the specific heats and determine whether the metals used in this Exercise and in Exercise 16 might be the same or must be different.

18. When a 1.5-g sample of KCl was added to 150 g of water in a coffee cup calorimeter (Fig. 4.3), the temperature decreased by 1.05°C. The specific heat of the resulting solution is 4.18 J g^{-1}.
   (a) Is the dissolution of KCl endothermic or exothermic?
   (b) How much heat is involved in the dissolution of the 1.5-g sample of KCl?

19. When 100 g of 0.200 M NaCl(aq) and 100 g of 0.200 M $AgNO_3(aq)$, both at 21.91°C, are mixed in a coffee cup calorimeter, the temperature increases to 23.48°C as solid AgCl forms.
   (a) Is the formation of AgCl an exothermic or an endothermic process?
   (b) How much heat is produced or absorbed if the specific heat of the products is 4.20 J g^{-1}°C^{-1}?

20. When 1.0 g of acetylene is burned in oxygen in a bomb calorimeter, the temperature of the calorimeter and its contents increases by 0.44°C. If the heat capacity of the calorimeter and its contents is 11.1 kJ °C^{-1}, what is q for this combustion?

21. A sample of 1.0 g of fructose, $C_6H_{12}O_6$, a sugar commonly found in fruits, was burned in oxygen in a bomb calorimeter (Fig. 4.4), and the temperature increased from 26.74°C to 27.49°C. If the specific heat of the calorimeter and its contents is 20.7 kJ °C^{-1}, what is q for the combustion?

22. A 45.0-g piece of metal at 98°C is placed in 100 mL of water initially at 21°C. The final temperature of the metal and the water is 24°C. Is the metal copper or aluminum? (See Section 4.1 for useful data.)

23. The reaction of 50 mL of acid and 50 mL of base described in Example 4.3 increased the temperature of the solution by 6.87°C. How much would the temperature have increased if 100 mL of the acid and 100 mL of the base had been used in the same calorimeter, starting at the same temperature of 22°C?

Enthalpy Changes

24. How does the heat measured in Example 4.3 for the reaction

$$HCl(aq) + NaOH(aq) \longrightarrow NaCl(aq) + H_2O(l)$$

differ from the enthalpy change for the reaction?

25. How does the heat measured in Example 4.4 for the reaction

$$KClO_3(s) \longrightarrow KClO_3(aq)$$

differ from the enthalpy change for the reaction?

26. Which of the enthalpies of combustion in Table 4.1 are not molar enthalpies of formation?

27. Does $\Delta H^\circ_{f_{SO_2(g)}}$ differ from ΔH°_{298} for the reaction $S_8(s) + 8O_2(g) \longrightarrow 8SO_2(g)$? If so, how?

28. How much heat is produced by burning 2.00 mol of isooctane?

29. How much heat is produced by combustion of 125 g of acetylene?

30. How many moles of methane must be burned to produce 100 kJ of heat?

31. What mass of methanol must be burned to produce 638 kJ of heat?

32. How much heat is required to convert 124 g of ice at 0°C to liquid water at the same temperature?

33. How much heat is released when 25 g of steam at 100°C is converted to liquid water at the same temperature?

34. How much heat is required to evaporate 100 g of liquid ammonia, NH_3, if its enthalpy of vaporization is 4.80 kJ mol^{-1}?

35. In 1774 Joseph Priestley prepared oxygen by heating red mercury(II) oxide with sunlight focused through a lens. How much heat was required to decompose 2.0 g of solid HgO to liquid Hg and gaseous O_2? (Assume standard state conditions.)

36. Calculate the molar enthalpy of solution (ΔH for the dissolution) of KCl under the conditions described in Exercise 18.

37. Use the data in Appendix I to determine the amount of heat produced or absorbed by each of the following reactions, which are run under standard state conditions.
   (a) 2.00 mol of liquid benzene, $C_6H_6(l)$, forms from the elements.
   (b) 14.0 g of $CO_2(g)$ forms from the elements.

(c) 1.0 mol of $Mn(s)$ and 1.0 mol of $O_2(g)$ form $MnO_2(s)$.

(d) 1.0 mol of $O_2(g)$ and 1.0 mol of $N_2(g)$ form $NO(g)$.

(e) 2.57 mol of $Cu(s)$ reacts with enough $S(s)$ to form $Cu_2S(s)$.

(f) 5.05 g of iron burns in oxygen and form $Fe_3O_4(s)$.

38. Using the data in Appendix I, determine the enthalpy of combustion of phosphorus when it burns and forms P_4O_{10}.

39. Some refrigerators use the Freon CF_2Cl_2, called dichlorodifluoromethane, as the refrigerant. How much heat is absorbed by the conversion of 1.00 kg of this Freon from a liquid to a gas? The enthalpy of vaporization is 17.4 kJ mol^{-1}.

40. What mass of dichlorodifluoromethane (Exercise 39) must evaporate to absorb enough heat to convert an ice tray of water (550 g of water) at 0°C to ice at 0°C?

41. How much heat is required to convert 2.0 mol of ice at 0°C to steam at 100°C? Assume that the specific heat of liquid water (4.184 J g^{-1} °C^{-1}) does not change between 0°C and 100°C.

42. What mass of hydrogen must be burned [$2H_2(g) + O_2(g) \longrightarrow 2H_2O(l)$] to provide enough heat to convert 1.0 mol of ice at 0°C to liquid water at the same temperature?

Hess's Law

43. The enthalpy of vaporization of ethanol, C_2H_5OH, is 52.3 kJ mol^{-1}. Does the heat of combustion of 1 mol of liquid ethanol produce more heat, less heat, or the same amount of heat as the combustion of gaseous ethanol? *Hint:* Consider the series of steps $C_2H_5OH(l) \longrightarrow C_2H_5OH(g) \longrightarrow$ products.

44. (a) Calculate ΔH for the process

$$N_2(g) + 2O_2(g) \longrightarrow 2NO_2(g)$$

from the following information:

$$N_2(g) + O_2(g) \longrightarrow 2NO(g) \qquad \Delta H = 180.5 \text{ kJ}$$

$$2NO(g) + O_2(g) \longrightarrow 2NO_2(g) \qquad \Delta H = -114.1 \text{ kJ}$$

(b) Is this the enthalpy of formation of $NO_2(g)$?

45. Calculate the standard molar enthalpy of formation of $N_2H_4(g)$ [ΔH°_{298} for the process $N_2(g) + 2H_2(g) \longrightarrow N_2H_4(g)$] from the following information:

$$N_2(g) + 2H_2(g) \longrightarrow N_2H_4(l) \qquad \Delta H^\circ_{298} = 50.6 \text{ kJ}$$

$$N_2H_4(l) \longrightarrow N_2H_4(g) \qquad \Delta H^\circ_{298} = 44.8 \text{ kJ}$$

46. Calculate ΔH for the process

$$Mn(s) + O_2(s) \longrightarrow MnO_2(s)$$

from the following information:

$$2Mn(s) + O_2(g) \longrightarrow 2MnO(s) \qquad \Delta H = -770.4 \text{ kJ}$$

$$2MnO(s) + O_2(g) \longrightarrow 2MnO_2(s) \qquad \Delta H = -269.7 \text{ kJ}$$

47. Calculate the enthalpy of formation of $SO_3(g)$ from the following information:

$$S(s) + O_2(g) \longrightarrow SO_2(g) \qquad \Delta H = -296.8 \text{ kJ}$$

$$2SO_2(g) + O_2(g) \longrightarrow 2SO_3(g) \qquad \Delta H = -197.8 \text{ kJ}$$

48. Calculate ΔH°_{298} for the process

$$Zn(s) + S(s) + 2O_2(g) \longrightarrow ZnSO_4(s)$$

from the following information:

$$Zn(s) + S(s) \longrightarrow ZnS(s) \qquad \Delta H^\circ_{298} = -206.0 \text{ kJ}$$

$$ZnS(s) + 2O_2(g) \longrightarrow ZnSO_4(s) \qquad \Delta H^\circ_{298} = -776.8 \text{ kJ}$$

49. Calculate the standard molar enthalpy of formation of $Co_3O_4(s)$ from the following information:

$$Co(s) + \tfrac{1}{2}O_2(g) \longrightarrow CoO(s) \qquad \Delta H^\circ_{298} = -237.9 \text{ kJ}$$

$$3CoO(s) + \tfrac{1}{2}O_2(g) \longrightarrow Co_3O_4(s) \qquad \Delta H^\circ_{298} = -177.5 \text{ kJ}$$

50. Calculate the enthalpy of vaporization under standard state conditions of each of the following, using the data in Appendix I.

(a) $I_2(s)$ (c) $C_2H_5OH(l)$

(b) $CHCl_3(l)$ (d) $C_2H_5Cl(l)$

51. (a) Calculate the molar enthalpy of combustion of propane, $C_3H_8(g)$, for the formation of $H_2O(l)$ and $CO_2(g)$. The standard molar enthalpy of formation of propane is -104 kJ mol^{-1}.

(b) Calculate the molar enthalpy of combustion of butane, $C_4H_{10}(g)$, for the formation of $H_2O(l)$ and $CO_2(g)$. The standard molar enthalpy of formation of butane is -126 kJ mol^{-1}.

(c) Both propane and butane are used as gaseous fuels. Which one has the higher enthalpy of combustion per gram?

Food and Fuel

52. From the data in Table 4.1, determine which of the following produces the greatest amount of heat per gram when burned under standard conditions: $C(s)$, $CH_4(g)$, or $CH_3OH(l)$.

53. The value for enthalpy of combustion of hard coal averages -35 kJ g^{-1}, that of gasoline, $-33,800$ kJ L^{-1}. How many kilograms of hard coal provide the same amount of heat as is available from 1.0 L of gasoline?

54. Essentially pure ethanol, C_2H_5OH, is used as a fuel for motor vehicles, particularly in Brazil.

(a) Write the balanced equation for the combustion of ethanol to $CO_2(g)$ and $H_2O(g)$, and, using the data in Appendix I, calculate the enthalpy of combustion of 1 mol of ethanol.

(b) The density of ethanol is 0.7893 g mL^{-1}. Calculate the enthalpy of combustion of exactly 1 mL of ethanol.

(c) Assuming that the mileage an automobile gets is directly proportional to the enthalpy of combustion of the fuel, calculate how many times farther an automobile could be expected to go on 1 gal of gasoline than on 1 gal of ethanol. Assume that gasoline has the enthalpy of combustion and the density of *n*-octane, C_8H_{18} ($\Delta H_f^\circ = -208.4$ kJ mol^{-1}; density $= 0.7025$ g mL^{-1}).

55. A teaspoon of the carbohydrate sucrose (common sugar) is reputed to contain 16 nutritional Calories (16 kcal). What is the mass of one teaspoon of sucrose?

56. What is the maximum mass of carbohydrate in a 12-oz can of Diet Coke that contains less than 1 (nutritional) Calorie per can?

57. What mass of fat, in grams and ounces, must be produced in the body to store an extra 100 nutritional Calories?

58. The oxidation of the sugar glucose, $C_6H_{12}O_6$, is described by the equation

$$C_6H_{12}O_6(s) + 6O_2(g) \longrightarrow 6CO_2(g) + 6H_2O(l)$$
$$\Delta H = -2816 \text{ kJ}$$

Metabolism of glucose gives the same products, although the glucose reacts with oxygen in a series of steps in the body.
(a) How much heat in kilojoules is produced by the metabolism of 1.0 g of glucose?
(b) How many nutritional Calories (1 cal = 4.184 J; 1 nutritional Cal = 1000 cal) are produced by the metabolism of 1.0 g of glucose?

Additional Exercises

59. How does the nitrogen in air differ from a sample of nitrogen at standard state conditions?

60. How could the accuracy of the enthalpy change calculated in Example 4.7 from the data of Example 4.3 be improved by changing the experiment described in Example 4.3?

61. The gas burned in most Bunsen burners is essentially pure methane. Why is the heat produced by combustion of 1 mol of methane in a Bunsen burner not exactly equal to the enthalpy of combustion of methane listed in Table 4.1?

62. In hot, dry climates water is cooled by allowing some of it to evaporate slowly. How much water must evaporate to cool 1.0 L (1.0 kg) from 39°C to 21°C? Assume that the enthalpy of vaporization of water is constant between 21° and 39° and is equal to the value at 25°C.

63. Assume the solutions have densities of 1.0 g ml^{-1}, and calculate the approximate value of ΔH for the reaction

$$NaCl(aq) + AgNO_3(aq) \longrightarrow AgCl(s)$$

using the data given in Exercise 19.

64. (a) When 1.418 g of iron reacted with chlorine, 3.220 g of an iron chloride and 8.58 kJ of heat were produced. Write the balanced equation for the reaction and determine ΔH for the change.

(b) Was the reaction run under standard state conditions?

65. Assume that the combustion of fructose described in Exercise 21 was carried out at constant pressure and is described by the equation

$$C_6H_{12}O_6(s) + 6O_2(g) \longrightarrow 6CO_2(g) + 6H_2O(l)$$

Calculate the enthalpy of combustion of fructose under these conditions.

66. A sample of 0.562 g of carbon in the form of graphite is burned in oxygen in a bomb calorimeter (Fig. 4.4). The temperature of the calorimeter increases from 26.74°C to 27.63°C. If the specific heat of the calorimeter and its contents is 20.7 kJ °C^{-1}, how much heat was released by this reaction?

67. The reaction of graphite with oxygen is described by the equation

$$C(s, graphite) + O_2(g) \longrightarrow CO_2(g)$$

Assume that the reaction was run at constant pressure, and calculate the molar enthalpy of formation of $CO_2(g)$ from the data given in Exercise 66. What conditions would be required for this to be a standard molar enthalpy of formation?

68. Water gas, a mixture of H_2 and CO, is an important industrial fuel produced by the reaction of steam with red-hot coke, which is essentially pure carbon.

$$C(s) + H_2O(g) \longrightarrow CO(g) + H_2(g)$$

(a) Assuming that coke has the same enthalpy of formation as graphite, calculate ΔH_{298}° for this reaction.
(b) Methanol, a liquid fuel that could possibly replace gasoline, can be prepared from water gas and additional hydrogen at high temperature and pressure in the presence of a suitable catalyst.

$$2H_2(g) + CO(g) \longrightarrow CH_3OH(g)$$

Under the conditions of the reaction, methanol forms as a gas. Calculate ΔH_{298}° for this reaction and for the condensation of gaseous methanol to liquid methanol.
(c) Calculate the enthalpy of combustion of 1 mol of liquid methanol to $H_2O(g)$ and $CO_2(g)$.

69. (a) Using the data in Appendix I, calculate the standard enthalpy change for each of the following reactions:
(1) $N_2(g) + O_2(g) \longrightarrow 2NO(g)$
(2) $Fe_2O_3(s) + 3H_2(g) \longrightarrow 2Fe(s) + 3H_2O(l)$
(3) $2LiOH(s) + CO_2(g) \longrightarrow Li_2CO_3(s) + H_2O(g)$
(4) $CH_4(g) + N_2(g) \longrightarrow HCN(g) + NH_3(g)$
(5) $CS_2(g) + 3Cl_2(g) \longrightarrow CCl_4(g) + S_2Cl_2(g)$
(b) Which of these reactions are exothermic?

70. The white pigment TiO_2 is prepared by the hydrolysis of titanium tetrachloride, $TiCl_4$, in the gas phase.

$$TiCl_4(g) + 2H_2O(g) \longrightarrow TiO_2(s) + 4HCl(g)$$

How much heat is evolved in the production of exactly 1 mol of $TiO_2(s)$ under standard state conditions?

Structure of the Atom

Light from excited krypton atoms is separated into a line spectrum.

As John Dalton examined the experimental observations that led to his theory that matter was composed of atoms, he found no evidence that atoms were composed of smaller particles. Thus Dalton assumed that atoms were simple indivisible bodies. However, a series of discoveries beginning in the latter part of the nineteenth century showed that atoms are complex systems composed of protons, neutrons, and electrons. The properties of these particles were summarized in Section 2.3.

Of the many different experiments that have contributed to our ideas about the structure of atoms, a few have been particularly important in the development of these ideas. In this chapter, we will examine some of the key experiments. We saw in Chapter 2 that observed regularities in chemical behavior, as shown by the periodic table (Section 2.4), provide additional evidence supporting our view of the structure of the atom.

The chemical behavior of atoms and molecules is primarily determined by the arrangement of their electrons. Thus our study of the structure of atoms is an important step in developing a model of matter that helps us to understand why substances exhibit particular kinds of chemical properties and to recall these properties systematically.

⑤.1 Electrons

Much of our knowledge about the structure of atoms was derived from experiments involving the passage of electricity through different gases at low pressures. The apparatus used for experiments of this type, called a **discharge tube** or a **Crookes tube,** was developed by Sir William Crookes (1832–1919). Crookes passed an electric current through a gas-filled glass tube with electrodes sealed into both ends [Fig. 5.1(a)]. As gas

Figure 5.1

Two types of discharge tubes. (a) In the absence of a charge on the plates, electrons flow from the cathode to the anode (black path). When the plates are changed, the electron stream curves toward the positive plate (red path). (b) A shadow being cast by an object in a stream of electrons. The tube glows where there is no shadow. (c) A photograph of the tube illustrated in (b).

(a)

(b)

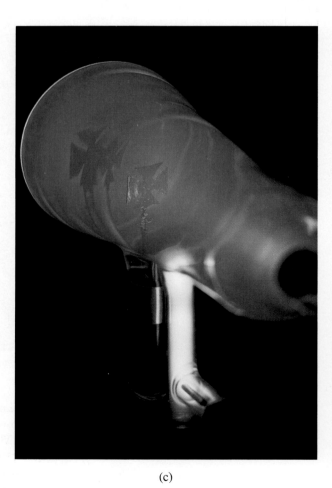

(c)

was pumped out of the tube, a pressure was reached at which the remaining gas glowed. With more pumping, the gas ceased to glow. However, close observation revealed that the glass at one end of the tube was glowing. Crookes suggested that this glow was produced by negative particles, which he called **cathode rays,** passing from the negative electrode (cathode) and moving toward the positive electrode (anode). Those particles that missed the anode hit the glass and made it glow.

Cathode rays were shown to have the following characteristics:

1. They travel from the cathode in straight lines, as indicated by the fact that an object placed in their path casts a sharp shadow on the end of the tube [Fig. 5.1(b)].
2. They cause a piece of metal foil to become hot by striking it for a period of time.
3. They are deflected by magnetic and electric fields [Fig. 5.1(a)], and the direction of the deflection is the same as that shown by negatively charged particles passing through such fields (a charged object attracts an object of opposite charge, whereas objects having charges of the same sign repel each other).

These characteristics are best explained by assuming that cathode rays are streams of small negatively charged particles (electrons).

In 1897 the English physicist Sir J. J. Thomson measured the deflection of cathode-ray particles in both a magnetic field and an electric field. From the strengths of the fields, he determined the ratio of the charge, e, to the mass, m, of the cathode-ray particles. He found e/m to be identical for all of these particles, no matter what metal the electrodes were made of or what kind of gas was in the tube. The charge was measured by the American physicist R. A. Millikan in 1909 (Fig. 5.2). From the values of e/m and e, he found the mass of the electron to be 1/1837 of that of the hydrogen atom, or 0.00055 amu. This quantitative observation that all electrons are identical, regardless of their source, along with the observation that they can be liberated from any kind of atom, proves quite conclusively that electrons are parts of all types of matter.

Electrons are emitted by some metals when the metals are heated to high temperatures. This process is called **thermal emission** and is the source of electrons in X-ray tubes and cathode-ray tubes such as television picture tubes. Electrons are also emitted from metals, most readily from active metals such as cesium, sodium, and potassium, when they are exposed to light (Fig. 5.3). The production of this type of emission results from what is known as the **photoelectric effect.** It is the basis of the electric eye, or photoelectric cell, used in some automatic door openers and automatic cameras.

Figure 5.2

The apparatus used by Millikan. A fine drop of oil drifts from the top of the apparatus through the hole in the top plate into the region between the two plates. The X rays cause the drop to pick up a negative charge, and the drop is attracted toward the positive plate. At one particular voltage, the electrical and gravitational forces are balanced, and the drop remains stationary. From the charge on the plates and the mass of the drop, Millikan calculated the charge on the drop.

Figure 5.3

A photoelectric cell in an electric circuit. Light striking the active metal electrode causes electrons to be emitted and current to flow. The photoelectric effect is used in some elevator doors and doors to markets. A person passing through a light beam interrupts the beam, thereby operating a circuit to open the door. Another application of the photoelectric effect is in automatic cameras.

5.2 Protons

In 1886 Eugen Goldstein, a German physicist, using a Crookes tube with holes in the cathode, observed that another kind of ray originated near the anode and passed through the holes in the cathode. Three years later, Wilhelm Wien showed these rays to be positively charged particles. Their charge-to-mass ratio was found to be much smaller than that for electrons, and it varied with the kind of gas in the tube. Because the ratio varied, it followed that either the charge varied or the mass varied or both. Actually, both vary. Later measurements showed the charge on each particle to be a positive charge, equal either to that on the electron or to some whole-number multiple of that charge, but opposite in sign. The mass of the positive particle was found to be least when hydrogen was used as the gas in the discharge tube. From the values of e and e/m for the positive particles when hydrogen was used, the value of m was calculated as 1.0073 amu. These particles (protons) are one of the basic units of the structure of all atoms.

The formation of positively charged particles (ions) from the molecules of gas in a Crookes tube is caused by the loss of electrons from the molecules when they are struck by high-speed cathode rays. Because any neutral atom or molecule can be made to form positive ions by the loss of one or more electrons, every atom or molecule must contain one or more positive units (or protons). The simplest atom is that of hydrogen—it contains one proton and one electron.

5.3 Neutrons

The existence of the neutron, a particle with a mass close to that of the proton but with no charge, had been postulated for more than ten years before the English physicist James Chadwick detected this third basic unit of the atom in 1932. He showed that uncharged particles (neutrons) are emitted when atoms of beryllium (and other elements) are bombarded with high-velocity helium nuclei (alpha particles). Neutrons were determined to have a mass of 1.0087 amu. They are unstable outside of an atom and slowly disintegrate to form a proton and an electron.

The properties of the basic particles present in an atom are summarized in Table 2.2 of Chapter 2.

5.4 Radioactivity and Atomic Structure

In 1896 additional evidence that atoms are complex rather than indivisible came with the discovery of radioactivity by the French physicist Antoine Becquerel. **Radioactivity** is the spontaneous decomposition of atoms of certain elements, such as radon and uranium, into other elements, with the simultaneous production of emissions, or rays. Three types of rays were characterized by passing them through an electric field (Fig. 5.4):

1. One type of ray curves toward the negative part of the electric field and so must consist of positively charged particles. These are called **alpha (α) particles,** which have a mass of approximately 4 amu and a charge of +2. Alpha particles are helium ions—helium atoms that have lost two electrons each and hence are helium nuclei.

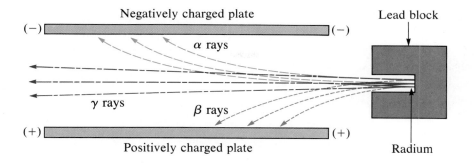

Figure 5.4
The effect of an electric field on radiation from the radioactive substance radium. Beta (β) rays (red paths) are electrons. Alpha (α) rays (blue paths) are nuclei of helium atoms. Gamma (γ) rays (black paths) are similar to X rays.

2. The second type of ray curves toward the positive part of the field, with a deflection much greater than that of the alpha particles. This behavior indicates that these particles, called **beta (β) particles,** are negatively charged and have much less mass than alpha particles. Beta particles have been shown to be electrons.

3. The third type of ray is not deflected at all when it passes through the electric field, indicating that the particles are neither negatively nor positively charged. These rays are similar to X rays but have higher energies than X rays (and higher energies than α particles and β particles as well). These high-energy particles are called **gamma (γ) rays.**

Several other types of rays (radiation) are also known and will be discussed in Chapter 24.

Early experimenters used particles from radioactive materials to investigate the structure of atoms. For example, proof that atoms contain protons was obtained in England by Ernest Rutherford in 1919. Using high-velocity α particles from radium as projectiles, he bombarded atoms such as nitrogen and aluminum and found that protons were ejected from the atoms as a result of these collisions. These experiments indicated quite definitely that the proton is a unit of the atom.

5.5 The Nuclear Atom

Although the experiments we have described indicated that atoms can be characterized as assemblies of electrons, protons, and neutrons, they gave no clue as to how these particles are arranged. The first insight into the architecture of atoms resulted from α-particle scattering experiments by Ernest Rutherford.

When Rutherford projected a beam of α particles from a radioactive source onto very thin gold foil (Fig. 5.5), he found that most of the particles passed through the foil without deflection. However, a few were diverted from their paths, and a very few were deflected back toward their source. From the results of a series of such experiments, Rutherford concluded that (1) the volume occupied by an atom must be largely empty space, because most of the α particles pass through the foil undeflected, and (2) each atom must contain a heavy, positively charged body (the nucleus) because of the abrupt change in path of a few α particles. A fast-moving, positively charged α particle can change path only when it hits or closely approaches another body (the nucleus) with a highly concentrated, positive charge.

Rutherford proposed that an atom consists of a very small, positively charged **nucleus,** in which most of the mass of the atom is concentrated, surrounded by the elec-

Figure 5.5

The scattering of α particles by a gold atom. The α particles, with a 2+ charge, are deflected back toward their source only when they collide with the much heavier, positively charged gold nucleus, with a 79+ charge. (Recall that particles with a charge of like sign repel one another.) Because the nucleus is very small compared to the size of an atom, very few α particles collide with the nucleus. A few other α particles pass close to the gold nucleus and are deflected by the repulsion, but most (shown in blue) pass through the relatively large region occupied by electrons, which are too light to deflect the rapidly moving α particles. If the nucleus were drawn to scale in this figure, it would be invisible.

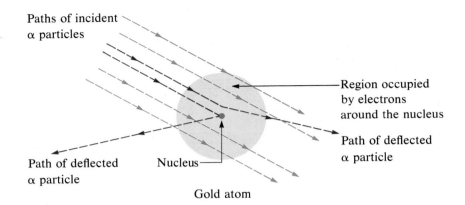

Paths of incident α particles

Region occupied by electrons around the nucleus

Path of deflected α particle

Path of deflected α particle

Nucleus

Gold atom

trons necessary to produce an electrically neutral atom (Fig. 5.5). Rutherford's nuclear theory of the atom, proposed in 1911, is the model we still use.

From this same series of experiments, Rutherford found that, for many of the lighter elements, the number of positive charges in the nucleus (and thus the number of protons in the nucleus) is approximately equal to half of the atomic mass of the element. In 1913 another English physicist, Henry Moseley, reported a method for determining the number of protons in the nucleus of any atom, and hence the number of positive charges in the nucleus. The number of protons in the nucleus is called the **atomic number** of the element. A neutral atom contains the same number of protons as electrons, so the atomic number represents the number of electrons *for a neutral atom* as well (Section 2.3).

Moseley measured the X rays produced by various elements. A modern X-ray tube (Fig. 5.6) is a modified cathode-ray tube in which electrons are produced by thermal emission from a filament heated by an electric current. When a solid target is placed in the beam of electrons, very penetrating rays called X rays are produced by the elements in the target. Using a series of different elements as targets, Moseley showed that the energy of the X rays produced by an element depends on its atomic number. This fact was used to determine the atomic numbers of the heavier elements.

Figure 5.6

In an X-ray tube, electrons striking a target such as tungsten cause the production of X rays. In Moseley's experiment, various elements were used as targets.

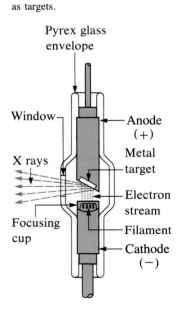

Pyrex glass envelope

Window

X rays

Focusing cup

Anode (+)

Metal target

Electron stream

Filament

Cathode (−)

⑤.6 Isotopes

At about the same time that Moseley was carrying out his experiments, A. J. Dempster and F. W. Aston, working separately, showed that some elements consist of atoms with different masses; such atoms are referred to as isotopes and differ from each other only in the number of neutrons within the nucleus. As mentioned in Section 3.3, isotopes are identified with the atomic number as a subscript and the mass number (the sum of the number of protons and neutrons in the nucleus) as a superscript, both to the left of the symbol for the element. Both Dempster and Aston used early versions of a **mass spectrometer** for their work. In the mass spectrometer (Fig. 5.7), gaseous atoms or molecules are bombarded by high-energy electrons, which knock off electrons to produce positively charged ions. These ions are then directed through a magnetic or electric field, which deflects their paths to an extent dependent on their mass-to-charge ratios (m/e). Ions of any mass-to-charge ratio can be made to strike the detector by varying the field. Because most of the ions are singly charged ($e = 1$), the separation is primarily on the

Figure 5.7

A diagram of a mass spectrometer. Ions leave the ionization chamber and move into the magnetic field. Light ions experience a large deflection and collide with the inner wall of the tube. Heavy ions experience less deflection and collide with the other wall. Only those ions with a specific value of m/e pass through the field into the detector.

basis of mass. Taking into account the magnetic field and other characteristics of the instrument, the mass of each fragment can be determined.

A mass spectrum is determined by varying the magnetic or electric field so that the ions with progressively higher masses strike the detector and then plotting the relative intensities (proportional to the numbers of ions of particular masses), as indicated by the detector, against their mass-to-charge ratios. A mass spectrum illustrating the three isotopes of magnesium is shown in Fig. 5.8. A natural mixture of magnesium consists of approximately 79% $^{24}_{12}Mg$, 10% $^{25}_{12}Mg$, and 11% $^{26}_{12}Mg$. The compositions of naturally occurring elements with atomic numbers 1 through 10 are given in Table 3.1 (Section 3.3).

⑤.7 The Bohr Model of the Atom

Rutherford's nuclear model of the atom, with its very small, high-mass nucleus surrounded by lightweight electrons, accounted nicely for the properties of the atom as revealed by the discharge-tube experiments of Crookes and others, by the α-particle scattering experiments, and by the varying masses of the elements resulting from the presence of isotopes. However, one serious problem remained. According to the physical principles known at the time, such an atom should not be stable. Because there is an attractive force between the positively charged nucleus and the negatively charged electrons, the electrons would be expected to fall into the nucleus. If it were assumed that the electrons moved around the nucleus in circular orbits, centrifugal force acting on the electrons could counterbalance the force of attraction, and the electrons would stay in their orbits. However, according to classical physics, an electron moving in such a circular orbit would radiate energy continuously; continuously losing energy, it should move in smaller and smaller orbits and finally fall into the nucleus.

In 1913 Niels Bohr, a Danish scientist, proposed a solution to the problem by suggesting a new theory for the behavior of matter. He proposed that the energy of an electron in an atom cannot vary continuously but is instead **quantized;** that is, it is restricted to discrete, or individual, values. The success of this theory in explaining the spectra of the hydrogen atom (Section 5.8) and of hydrogenlike ions (which contain only one electron moving about a nucleus) led to its general acceptance.

The **Bohr model of a hydrogen atom** or a hydrogenlike ion assumed that the single electron moved about the nucleus in a circular orbit and that the centrifugal force due to this motion counterbalanced the electrostatic attraction between the nucleus and the

Figure 5.8

The mass spectrum of magnesium, showing the three peaks due to the three naturally occurring isotopes of magnesium.

electron. The energy of the electron was *assumed* to be restricted to certain values, each of which corresponds to an orbit with a different radius. Each of these orbits could be characterized by an integer, n. Bohr showed that the energy of an electron in one of these orbits is given by the equation

$$E = \frac{-kZ^2}{n^2}$$

where k is a constant, Z is the atomic number (the number of units of positive charge on the nucleus), and n is the integer characteristic of the orbit ($n = 1, 2, 3, 4, \ldots$). For a hydrogen atom $Z = 1$ and $k = 2.179 \times 10^{-18}$ J, which gives the energy in joules. Other units of energy commonly used include electron-volts (1 eV $= 1.602 \times 10^{-19}$ J) and ergs (1 erg $= 10^{-7}$ J). In electron-volts, $k = 13.595$ eV.

Example 5.1

A spark promotes the electron in a hydrogen atom into an orbit with $n = 2$. What is the energy, in joules, of an electron with $n = 2$?

The energy of the electron is given by the equation

$$E = \frac{-kZ^2}{n^2}$$

The atomic number, Z, of hydrogen is 1; $k = 2.179 \times 10^{-18}$ J; and the electron is characterized by an n value of 2. Thus

$$E = \frac{-2.179 \times 10^{-18} \text{ J} \times 1^2}{2^2} = -5.448 \times 10^{-19} \text{ J}$$

The distance of the electron from the nucleus is also related to the value of n.

$$\text{Radius of orbit} = \frac{n^2 a_0}{Z}$$

where a_0 is the radius of the orbit in the hydrogen atom for which $n = 1$ (0.529 Å, where 1 Å $= 10^{-10}$ m or 100 pm). According to this model, the closest an electron in a hydrogen atom can get to the nucleus is 0.529 Å (in an orbit with $n = 1$). Thus the electron cannot fall into the nucleus. Because we must add energy to an electron to move it into an orbit with a larger n value, as the electron moves away from the nucleus its energy becomes higher (Table 5.1), reaching zero at an infinite distance ($n = \infty$) where the nucleus no longer can have any attraction for the electron. As the electron moves closer to the nucleus, it loses energy, and its energy becomes lower (more negative).

Thus the Bohr model of the hydrogen atom (and of hydrogenlike ions with only one electron) postulates a single electron that moves in circular orbits about the nucleus (Fig. 5.9). The electron usually moves in the orbit for which $n = 1$, the orbit in which it has the lowest energy. When the electron is in this lowest-energy orbit, the atom is said to be in its **ground state.** If the atom picks up energy from an outside source, it changes to an **excited state** as the electron moves to one of the higher-energy orbits.

Table 5.1		Calculated Energies and Radii for a Hydrogen Atom		
n	Shell	Energy, eV	Distance from Nucleus, Å	Distance from Nucleus, pm
1	K	−13.595	0.529	52.9
2	L	− 3.399	2.116	211.6
3	M	− 1.511	4.761	476.1
4	N	− 0.850	8.464	846.4
5	O	− 0.544	13.225	1322.5
∞	—	0	∞	∞

The notion of the electron moving in a *circular* planetary orbit was not the most important concept of the Bohr model. Indeed, that part of the model is not correct. What was revolutionary was the idea that the electron is restricted to discrete energies that are identified by n.

The integer n is called a **quantum number.** The properties of an electron in a Bohr atom are often identified by giving its quantum number. If we know the quantum number of the electron in a hydrogen atom, we can easily evaluate the energy of the electron or the size of the orbit that it occupies. For example, an electron with the quantum number $n = 1$ resides in the first orbit, with an energy of −13.595 eV and a distance of 0.529 Å from the nucleus.

Instead of quantum numbers, letters are occasionally used to distinguish electrons (Table 5.1). When we speak of a K electron, we mean an electron with $n = 1$. An L electron is an electron with $n = 2$; an M electron, with $n = 3$; etc. In Section 5.10, we will see that there are in fact three additional quantum numbers that also describe various properties of an electron.

5.8 Atomic Spectra and Atomic Structure

The Bohr model of the hydrogen atom would be merely an interesting intellectual curiosity if it could not be checked against experimental data. In fact, it explains the spectrum of hydrogen atoms very well, and this observation tends to substantiate the new assumption in the model. Before we look at the agreement of the model with experiment, however, a brief introduction to light and to spectra is required.

Visible light is one form of **electromagnetic radiation.** (Radio waves, ultraviolet light, X rays, and γ rays are other examples.) All forms of electromagnetic radiation exhibit wavelike behavior. They all can be characterized by a wavelength, λ (Fig. 5.10), and a frequency, ν. The frequency is the rate at which equivalent points on a wave pass a given point in a specified period of time. The product $\lambda\nu$ is equal to the speed, c, with which all forms of electromagnetic radiation, including light, move (2.998×10^8 m/s, or m s^{-1}, in a vacuum), so the wavelength and frequency are inversely proportional ($\nu = c/\lambda$, Fig. 5.11). Different forms of electromagnetic radiation have different wavelengths and frequencies, but they all move with the same speed in a vacuum.

$n = 6$ $\qquad$ $r = 36a_0$

$n = 5$ $\qquad$ $r = 25a_0$

$n = 4$ $\qquad$ $r = 16a_0$

$n = 3$ $\qquad$ $r = 9a_0$

Nucleus

$n = 2$ $\qquad$ $r = 4a_0$

$n = 1$

$r = a_0 = 0.529$ Å

Figure 5.9

A sketch of the hypothetical circular orbits of the Bohr model of the hydrogen atom, drawn to scale. If the nucleus were drawn to scale, it would be invisible.

Figure 5.10

Characteristics of a wave. The distance between identical points, such as consecutive peaks, on the wave is the wavelength, λ (lambda). The number of times per second that identical points on the wave pass a given point is the frequency, ν (nu).

Figure 5.11

The various portions of the electromagnetic spectrum in order of decreasing frequency and increasing wavelength. Wavelength and frequency are inversely proportional. Only the wavelengths in the visible region can be seen by the human eye.

Electromagnetic radiation also has properties associated with particles called **photons.** The light emitted when one electron moves from an orbit with a larger n value to one with a smaller n value is a photon. The energy of a photon may be determined from the expression

$$E = h\nu = \frac{hc}{\lambda}$$

where h is Planck's constant (6.626×10^{-34} J s), c is the velocity, λ is the wavelength, and ν is the frequency of the radiation.

Example 5.2

An experimental iodine laser emits light with a wavelength of 1.315 μm. What is the frequency of this light, and what is the energy per photon?

As we have noted, frequency, ν, is inversely proportional to wavelength, λ.

$$\nu = \frac{c}{\lambda}$$

Because 1 μm $= 10^{-6}$ m, the wavelength given, 1.315 μm, equals 1.315×10^{-6} m. Hence,

$$\nu = \frac{2.998 \times 10^8 \text{ m s}^{-1}}{1.315 \times 10^{-6} \text{ m}}$$

$$= 2.280 \times 10^{14} \text{ s}^{-1}$$

The relationship of the energy of a photon to its wavelength is

$$E = h\frac{c}{\lambda}$$

$$= \frac{(6.626 \times 10^{-34} \text{ J s}) \times (2.998 \times 10^8 \text{ m s}^{-1})}{1.315 \times 10^{-6} \text{ m}} = 1.511 \times 10^{-19} \text{ J}$$

Thus the frequency of the laser light is 2.280×10^{14} s^{-1} (s^{-1} is read "per second") with an energy of 1.511×10^{-19} J per photon. The same value of E is found using the relationship $E = h\nu$.

Sir Isaac Newton separated sunlight into its component colors (a spectrum) by passing it through a glass prism and showing that it contains all wavelengths (and thus all energies) of visible light. Sunlight gives a continuous **spectrum** (Fig. 5.12) such as the one we see in the rainbow and in the "rainbows" sometimes produced when a cut-glass object sits in a sunny window. Sunlight also contains ultraviolet light (very short wavelengths) and infrared light (long wavelengths), which can be detected and recorded with instruments but are invisible to the human eye. Incandescent solids such as the filament in a light bulb also give continuous spectra. However, when an electric current is passed through a gas at low pressure, the gas gives off light that shows a spectrum made up of a number of bright lines (a **line spectrum**) when passed through a prism (Figs. 5.12 and 5.13). Each of these lines corresponds to a single wavelength of light, so the light emitted by such a gas consists of light of discrete energies.

When a tube containing hydrogen at low pressure is subjected to an electric discharge, light of a blue-pink hue is produced. Passage of this light through a prism produces a line spectrum, indicating that it is composed of light of several discrete energies. J. R. Rydberg, in the late nineteenth century, measured the frequencies of the lines in the visible spectrum and found that they could be related by an equation that gives the energies, in joules, of the photons in each line:

$$E = h\nu = 2.179 \times 10^{-18} \left(\frac{1}{n_1^2} - \frac{1}{n_2^2} \right)$$

where n_1 and n_2 are integers, with n_1 smaller than n_2. This equation is empirical; that is, it is derived from observation rather than from theory.

Bohr suggested that a hydrogen atom radiates energy as light when its electron suddenly changes from a higher-energy orbit to one that has a lower energy (Fig. 5.14). Because of conservation of energy, the energy lost by an electron when it moves to a lower-energy orbit must appear somewhere; it usually appears as light. When a hydrogen atom is excited with an electric discharge, the electron gains energy and moves to an orbit of higher energy (and higher n). As the atom relaxes, the electron moves from this higher-energy level to one in which its energy is lower and emits a photon with an energy equal to the difference in energy between the two orbits. According to Bohr's theory (Section 5.7), the electron in a hydrogen atom ($Z = 1$) can have only those *discrete* energies, E_n, permitted by the equation

$$E_n \text{ (in joules)} = \frac{-k}{n^2} = \frac{-2.179 \times 10^{-18}}{n^2}$$

When the electron in a hydrogen atom falls from a higher-energy outer orbit characterized by n_2 to a lower-energy inner orbit characterized by n_1 (n_1 is less than n_2), the difference in energy is the absolute value of the difference in energy between the two orbits, $E_{n_1} - E_{n_2}$. This is the energy E emitted as a photon, or

$$E \text{ (in joules)} = |E_{n_1} - E_{n_2}| = 2.179 \times 10^{-18} \left(\frac{1}{n_1^2} - \frac{1}{n_2^2} \right)$$

Figure 5.12

Sunlight passing through a prism is separated into its component colors, resulting in a continuous spectrum.

Figure 5.13

A comparison of the continuous spectrum of white light (spectrum 1) and the line spectra of the light from excited sodium, hydrogen, calcium, and mercury atoms.

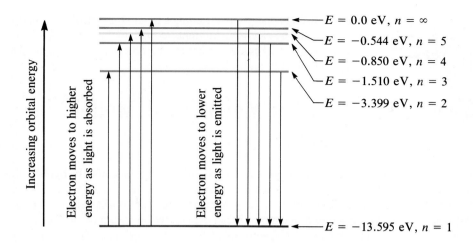

This theoretical expression is exactly the same as the one Rydberg found. The agreement of the two equations—one experimental, one theoretical—provides powerful and indispensable evidence for the validity of the Bohr concept of atomic structure involving discrete energy levels for electrons.

What is the energy (in joules) and the wavelength (in meters) of the photon radiated when an electron, previously excited by an input of energy, moves from the orbit with $n = 4$ to the orbit with $n = 2$ in a hydrogen atom?

Example 5.3

In this case the electron starts out with $n = 4$, so $n_2 = 4$. It finishes with $n = 2$, so $n_1 = 2$. The difference in energy between these two states is given by the expression

$$E = |E_{n_1} - E_{n_2}| = 2.179 \times 10^{-18} \left(\frac{1}{n_1^2} - \frac{1}{n_2^2} \right) \text{ J}$$

$$= 2.179 \times 10^{-18} \left(\frac{1}{2^2} - \frac{1}{4^2} \right) \text{ J}$$

$$= 2.179 \times 10^{-18} \left(\frac{1}{4} - \frac{1}{16} \right) \text{ J}$$

$$= 4.086 \times 10^{-19} \text{ J}$$

The energy of the photon emitted is equal to the difference in energy between the two orbits, 4.086×10^{-19} J. The wavelength of a photon with this energy is found from the expression $E = hc/\lambda$. Rearrangement gives

$$\lambda = \frac{hc}{E}$$

$$= \frac{(6.626 \times 10^{-34} \text{ J s}) \times (2.998 \times 10^8 \text{ m s}^{-1})}{4.086 \times 10^{-19} \text{ J}}$$

$$= 4.862 \times 10^{-7} \text{ m (or 486.2 nm, or 4862 Å)}$$

This frequency corresponds to blue light (Fig. 5.13).

Even though the idea of discrete energy levels applies to all atoms, Bohr's equation works only for atoms or ions with one electron. Attempts to explain the spectra and other physical properties of more complicated atoms require the use of a more complex model, the quantum-mechanical model of the atom.

⑤.9 The Quantum-Mechanical Model of the Atom

It is now known that the laws of ordinary mechanics do not adequately explain the properties of small particles such as electrons. As a consequence, Bohr's theory of an electron moving in a circular orbit about a nucleus must be considered only a first approximation of the structure of the atom. It can explain the spectrum of an atom or ion with a single electron, but not the spectra of atoms with more than one electron. In addition, it fails to provide a satisfactory picture of chemical bonding. Thus the Bohr model has been supplanted by the more mathematical theories of quantum mechanics, which are based on the wavelike nature of the electron.

The **quantum-mechanical model of the hydrogen atom** consists of one proton (as a nucleus) and one electron moving about the proton. Larger atoms have several electrons moving about a positive nucleus. Although the electrons are known to move about the nucleus, the exact path they take cannot be determined. The German physicist Werner Heisenberg expressed this in a form that has come to be known as the **Heisenberg uncertainty principle: It is impossible to determine accurately both the momentum and the position of a particle simultaneously.** (The momentum is the mass of the particle multiplied by its velocity.) The more accurately we measure the momentum of a moving electron (or any other particle), the less accurately we can determine its position (and conversely). An experiment designed to measure the exact position of an electron will alter its momentum, and an experiment designed to measure the exact momentum of an electron will unavoidably change its position. If position and momentum are measured at the same time, the values are inexact for one or the other or both. Although we cannot pinpoint an electron's position or path, we *can* calculate the *probability* of finding an electron at a given location within an atom.

In spite of the limitations described by the uncertainty principle, the behavior of electrons can be determined in a useful way by using the mathematical tools of quantum mechanics. Both the energy of an electron in an atom and the region of space in which it may be found can be determined.

The results of a quantum-mechanical treatment of the problem developed by an Austrian physicist, Erwin Schrödinger, show that the electron may be visualized as being in rapid motion within one of several regions of space located around the nucleus. Each of these regions is called an **orbital** or an **atomic orbital.** Although the electron may be located anywhere within an orbital at any instant in time, it spends most of its time in certain high-probability regions. For example, in an isolated hydrogen atom in its ground state, the single electron effectively occupies all the space within about 1 Å of the nucleus. This gives the hydrogen atom a spherical shape. Within this spherical orbital the electron has the greatest probability of being approximately 0.529 Å from the nucleus. Note that a Bohr orbit and a quantum-mechanical orbital are very different. An orbit is a circular path; an orbital is a three-dimensional region of space.

Some chemists describe the occupancy of an orbital in terms of **electron density.** The electron density is high in those regions of the orbital where the probability of finding an electron is relatively high, and it is low in those regions of the orbital where that probability is low.

Each electron in an atom can be described by a mathematical expression called a **wave function,** which is given the symbol ψ. The shape of an orbital that the electron occupies, the energy of the electron in the orbital (sometimes called the energy of the orbital), and the probability of finding the electron in some region within the orbital can be determined from ψ. For example, the square of the wave function, ψ^2, is a measure of the probability of finding the electron at a given point at distance r from the nucleus; and $4\pi r^2 \psi^2$ (the radial probability density) is a measure of the probability of finding the electron within the volume of a thin spherical shell (somewhat like a layer of an onion) of radius r and thickness dr (where dr is a very small fraction of r).

Figure 5.15 illustrates the electron density in the occupied orbital of a hydrogen atom in the ground state. The electron occupies the orbital in which it will have the lowest possible energy (the lowest-energy orbital). The probability of finding the electron in a thin shell very close to the nucleus is practically zero, but it increases rapidly just beyond the nucleus and becomes highest in a thin shell at a distance of 0.529 Å from the nucleus. The probability then decreases rapidly as the distance of the thin shell from the nucleus increases and becomes exceedingly small at a distance greater than about 1 Å. Most of the time, but not always, the electron is located within a sphere with a radius of 1 Å; that is, the probability of finding the electron inside this sphere is high. Figure 5.16 shows a plot of the probability of finding the electron in a thin shell as a function of r, the distance of the shell from the nucleus, for three of the orbitals in a hydrogen atom.

Figure 5.15

Electron density for an electron of lowest possible energy in a hydrogen atom.

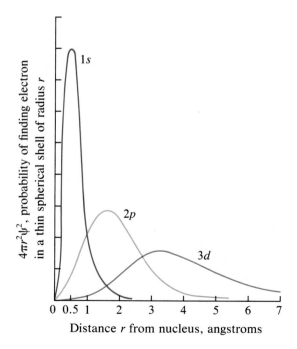

Figure 5.16

The probability of finding the electron at a given distance r from the nucleus for three of the lowest-energy orbitals in a hydrogen atom. The energy of an electron in these orbitals increases as n increases. Note the overlapping of orbitals.

⑤.10 Results of the Quantum-Mechanical Model of the Atom

The general results of the quantum-mechanical model of the atom can be summarized in seven statements.

    1. The location of an electron cannot be determined exactly. All that can be identified is the region, or volume, of space where there is a relatively high probability of finding the electron—that is, the orbital occupied by the electron.

    2. Orbitals are characterized by n, **the principal quantum number,** which may take on any integral value: $n = 1, 2, 3, 4, 5, \ldots$. As n increases, the orbitals extend farther from the nucleus, and the average position of an electron in these orbitals becomes farther from the nucleus (Fig. 5.16). The energies of the orbitals increase as the value of n increases. For values of n greater than 1, there are several different orbitals with the same value of n. A **shell** contains orbitals with the same value of n. Shells may be identified by either the values of n or, though not so often used as the values of n, by the letters K, L, M, N, O, $\ldots$, respectively (an $n = 2$ shell may be called an L shell, for example).

Shell	K	L	M	N	O	P	Q
n	1	2	3	4	5	6	7

    3. Orbitals with the same value of n may have different shapes. The different shapes of orbitals are distinguished by a second quantum number, l, called the **azimuthal, or subsidiary, quantum number.** In atoms with two or more electrons, electrons with different l values (electrons that occupy differently shaped orbitals) have different energies. An electron with $l = 0$ occupies a spherical orbital [Fig. 5.17(a)]. Such an orbital is called an s orbital, and the electron occupying it is called an s electron. An electron with $l = 1$ occupies a dumbbell-shaped region of space [Figs. 5.17(b) and 5.18] and is called a p electron; a d electron, with $l = 2$, occupies a volume of space usually drawn with four lobes [Figs. 5.17(c) and 5.19]; and an f electron, with $l = 3$, occupies a rather complex-looking volume of space usually shown with eight lobes (Figs. 5.17(d) and 5.20). Letters corresponding to the values of l continue alphabetically following f. Although l values higher than 3 are possible, electrons with l greater than 3 are not found unless they have been excited by absorption of energy by an atom.

l	0	1	2	3	4	5	6
Letter designation	s	p	d	f	g	h	i

    In an atom with two or more electrons, the energies of electrons in the orbitals within a given shell increase in the following order:

$$s \text{ electrons} < p \text{ electrons} < d \text{ electrons} < f \text{ electrons}$$

$$\underrightarrow{\text{Increasing energy}}$$

    The mathematics of quantum mechanics tells us that there are limits on the values that l can have: An electron for which the principal quantum number has a value of n can

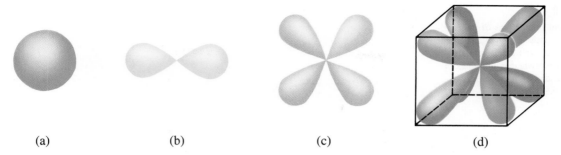

(a) (b) (c) (d)

Figure 5.17

Shapes of the orbitals for (a) an *s* subshell, (b) a *p* subshell, (c) a *d* subshell, and (d) an *f* subshell. To improve the perspective, the *f* orbital is shown within a cube, with lobes of different colors.

have an integral *l* value ranging from 0 to $(n - 1)$. These limits have been verified experimentally from the spectra of atoms.

Shell	*n* Value	Possible *l* Values	Types of Orbitals
K	1	0,	1*s*
L	2	0, 1	2*s*, 2*p*
M	3	0, 1, 2	3*s*, 3*p*, 3*d*
N	4	0, 1, 2, 3	4*s*, 4*p*, 4*d*, 4*f*
O	5	0, 1, 2, 3, 4	5*s*, 5*p*, 5*d*, 5*f*, 5*g*

Thus an electron in a K shell, for which $n = 1$, can have an *l* value of only zero. An electron in a shell with $n = 3$ can have an *l* value of zero (an *s* electron), an *l* value of 1 (a *p* electron), or an *l* value of 2 (a *d* electron), but it cannot have an *l* value higher than 2.

4. For *l* values larger than zero, orbitals with the same value of *l* in any given shell have the same shape and the same energy but differ in their orientation. There are $(2l + 1)$ orbitals with the same *l* quantum number that differ only in their orientation about the nucleus. Each orientation is characterized by a third quantum number, ***m***, the **magnetic quantum number,** which may have any integral value from $-l$ through zero to $+l$. A sphere may have only one orientation in space, and thus there is only one type of spherical, or *s*, orbital. This orbital is characterized by an *l* value of zero; hence *m* here can be only zero. There are three possible values of *m* $(-1, 0, +1)$ for an orbital with $l = 1$ (a *p* orbital) and thus three possible orientations. Figure 5.18 shows how the dumbbell shape of a *p* orbital can be oriented in three ways along the *x*, *y*, and *z* axes of an *xyz* coordinate system. The three *p* orbitals are designated p_x, p_y, and p_z, as shown in the figure, to indicate their directional character. Figure 5.19 shows five orientations of

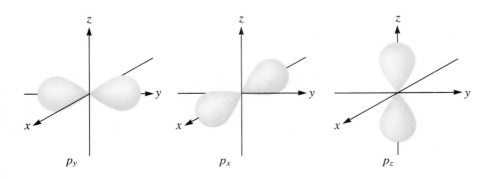

p_y p_x p_z

Figure 5.18

The different orientations of the three equivalent atomic *p* orbitals.

Figure 5.19

The different orientations of the five equivalent atomic d orbitals. The lobes of the d_{z^2} and $d_{x^2-y^2}$ orbitals lie along the axes, whereas the lobes of the d_{xz}, d_{yz}, and d_{xy} orbitals lie between the axes.

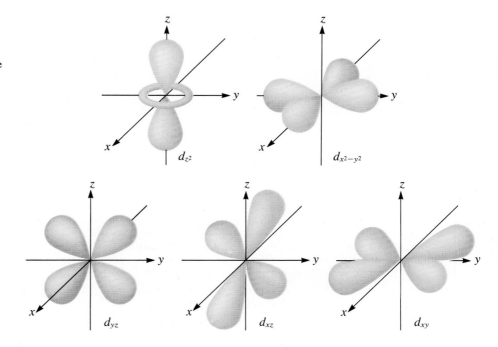

the d orbitals ($l = 2$; $m = -2, -1, 0, +1, +2$). Figure 5.20 shows seven orientations of the f orbitals ($l = 3$; $m = -3, -2, -1, 0, +1, +2, +3$). There is no general agreement on how best to represent the seven f orbitals. Figure 5.20 shows one way.

Degenerate orbitals are orbitals with the same energy. In a free atom, the p orbitals in the same shell have the same energy and are thus referred to as degenerate. Likewise, the five d orbitals in a given shell are degenerate, as are the seven f orbitals. Each set of degenerate orbitals—that is, orbitals with the same l value in a given shell—is referred to as a **subshell.**

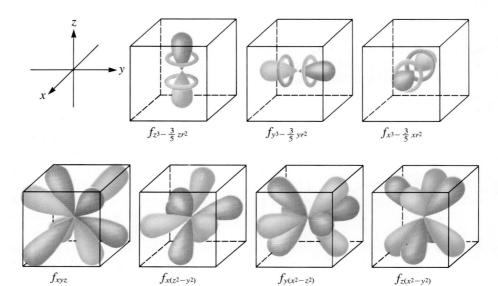

Figure 5.20

The different orientations of the seven equivalent atomic f orbitals. To improve the perspective, each of the seven orbitals is shown within a cube, with lobes of different colors. Only one f orbital is shown in each cube.

Example 5.4

Indicate the number of subshells, the number of orbitals in each subshell, and the values of n, l, and m for the orbitals in the N shell of an atom.

The N shell is the shell with $n = 4$, so it contains subshells with $l = 0, 1, 2$, and 3. Hence there are four subshells.

For the subshell with $l = 0$ (the s subshell), m can be equal only to zero. Thus there is only one $4s$ orbital. For $l = 1$ (the p subshell), $m = -1, 0$, or $+1$, so we find three $4p$ orbitals; for $l = 2$ (the d subshell), $m = -2, -1, 0, +1$, or $+2$, giving five $4d$ orbitals; and for $l = 3$ (the f subshell), $m = -3, -2, -1, 0, +1, +2$, or $+3$, giving seven $4f$ orbitals.

There are 16 orbitals, with the values of n, l, and m indicated above, in the 4 subshells of the N shell of an atom.

5. Electrons have a fourth quantum number, s, the **spin quantum number.** Electrons behave as though each were spinning about its own axis. The spin quantum number specifies the direction of spin of an electron about *its own axis*. The spin can be either counterclockwise or clockwise and is designated arbitrarily by either $s = +\frac{1}{2}$ or $s = -\frac{1}{2}$. Electrons with the same spin quantum number are said to have **parallel spins.**

For every possible combination of n, l, and m, there can be two electrons differing only in the direction of spin about their own axes. Each orbital can contain a maximum of two electrons that have identical n, l, and m values but differ in their s values.

6. The energy of an electron in an atom is limited to discrete values. The mathematics is far more complicated than in the Bohr model, but the energy can be determined from the wave function that describes the behavior of the electron.

7. The maximum number of electrons that may be found in a shell with a principal quantum number of n is $2n^2$. Because each atomic orbital can hold a maximum of two electrons, the number of atomic orbitals in a shell is given by n^2. Table 5.2 summarizes all of the allowed combinations of quantum numbers that may describe an electron in the first five shells of an atom.

5.11 Orbital Energies and Atomic Structure

The energies of atomic orbitals increase as the principal quantum number, n, increases. If an atom contains two or more electrons, the energies of the orbitals increase within a shell as the azimuthal quantum number, l, increases. Although the relative energies of certain orbitals vary from atom to atom, the increasing order of energy is roughly that shown in Fig. 5.21. The energy of an electron in an orbital is indicated by the vertical coordinate in the figure, the orbital with electrons of lowest energy being the $1s$ orbital at the bottom of the diagram. Orbitals that have about the same energy are indicated by the braces at the right of the figure. For atomic numbers greater than 20, the relative energies of the orbitals may differ slightly from the order shown. The actual energies of the electrons in these orbitals vary from atom to atom. For example, the energies of the electrons in $1s$ orbitals become lower and lower as the atomic numbers of the atoms increase.

The arrangement of electrons in the orbitals of an atom (that is, the **electron configuration** of the atom) is described by a number that designates the number of the principal shell, a letter that designates the subshell, and a superscript that designates the number of electrons in that particular subshell. For example, the notation $2p^4$ (read "two-p-four") indicates four electrons in the p subshell of the shell for which $n = 2$; the notation $3d^8$ ("three-d-eight") indicates eight electrons in the d subshell of the shell for which $n = 3$.

In general, electrons fill orbitals from the bottom to the top of Fig. 5.21, in order from lowest to higher energy levels. Each set of orbitals is filled before electrons occupy the next set immediately above. Figure 5.22 gives this order in a format that is easy to remember.

It is possible to predict the electron configuration of an atom in its ground state by using the following guidelines:

1. Electrons in an atom occupy the lowest possible energy levels, or orbitals. The first electron that is placed in a set of atomic orbitals goes into the $1s$ orbital. When the $1s$ orbital is filled, the next electron goes into the $2s$ orbital, and so on. The order of orbital energies is given in Figs. 5.21 and 5.22.

2. The maximum number of electrons in an orbital is limited to two, according to the **Pauli exclusion principle: No two electrons in the same atom can have the same**

Table 5.2   Summary of Allowed Values for Each Quantum Number

Shell	n	l	m	s	Maximum Number of Electrons in Subshell	Maximum Number of Electrons in Shell
K	1	0 (s) 0	0 0	$+\frac{1}{2}$ $-\frac{1}{2}$	$\left.\begin{matrix}1\\1\end{matrix}\right\}2$	2
L	2	0 (s) 1 (p) 1 1	0 −1 0 +1	$+\frac{1}{2}, -\frac{1}{2}$ $+\frac{1}{2}, -\frac{1}{2}$ $+\frac{1}{2}, -\frac{1}{2}$ $+\frac{1}{2}, -\frac{1}{2}$	$\left.\begin{matrix}2\\2\\2\\2\end{matrix}\right\}6$	8
M	3	0 (s) 1 (p) 2 (d)	0 −1, 0, +1 −2, −1, 0, +1, +2	$+\frac{1}{2}, -\frac{1}{2}$ $\pm\frac{1}{2}$ for each value of m $\pm\frac{1}{2}$ for each value of m	2 6 10	18
N	4	0 (s) 1 (p) 2 (d) 3 (f)	0 −1, 0, +1 −2, −1, 0, +1, +2 −3, −2, −1, 0, +1, +2, +3	$\pm\frac{1}{2}$ for each value of m $\pm\frac{1}{2}$ for each value of m $\pm\frac{1}{2}$ for each value of m $\pm\frac{1}{2}$ for each value of m	2 6 10 14	32
O	5	0 (s) 1 (p) 2 (d) 3 (f) 4 (g)	0 −1, 0, +1 −2, −1, 0, +1, +2 −3, −2, −1, 0, +1, +2, +3 −4, −3, −2, −1, 0, +1, +2, +3, +4	$\pm\frac{1}{2}$ for each value of m $\pm\frac{1}{2}$ for each value of m $\pm\frac{1}{2}$ for each value of m $\pm\frac{1}{2}$ for each value of m $\pm\frac{1}{2}$ for each value of m	2 6 10 14 18[a]	50[a]

[a]The total number of 50 electrons for the O shell, including the 18 electrons for the g subshell, is the number of electrons theoretically possible. No element presently known contains more than 32 electrons in the O shell.

Subshell electron capacity

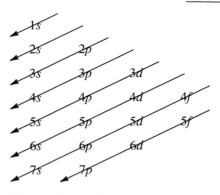

Figure 5.22

Order of occupancy of atomic orbitals. The orbitals fill in order, in the direction of each arrow in turn, going down the arrows from top to bottom.

Figure 5.21

Generalized energy-level diagram for atomic orbitals in an atom with two or more electrons (not to scale). Orbitals of about the same energy are indicated by braces.

set of four quantum numbers. Thus a $1s$ orbital is filled when it contains two electrons: one with $n = 1$, $l = 0$, $m = 0$, and $s = +\frac{1}{2}$; the other with $n = 1$, $l = 0$, $m = 0$, and $s = -\frac{1}{2}$. No other combination of quantum numbers is possible for an electron in the $1s$ orbital (Table 5.2), so a third electron must occupy the $2s$ orbital. The $2s$ orbital, in turn, is filled when it contains two electrons, so the fifth electron is forced into one of the three $2p$ orbitals, and so on.

3. Subshells containing more than one orbital are filled as described by **Hund's rule: Every orbital in a subshell is singly occupied (filled) with one electron before any one orbital is doubly occupied, and all electrons in singly occupied orbitals have the same spin;** that is, their spin quantum numbers are the same. For example, a $3p^2$ electron configuration has one unpaired electron in each of two different $3p$ orbitals. Both electrons have the same spin and the same spin quantum number. A d^6 electron configuration has a pair of electrons that have different spins in one d orbital and four unpaired electrons that have the same spin in the remaining four d orbitals.

🖎.12 The Aufbau Process

In order to illustrate the systematic variations in the electronic structures of the various elements, chemists ''build'' them in atomic order. Beginning with hydrogen, they add one proton to the nucleus and one electron to the proper subshell at a time until they have described the electron configurations of all the elements. This process is called the **aufbau process,** from the German word *aufbau* (building up). Each added electron occupies the subshell of lowest energy available, according to the rules given in Section 5.11. Electrons enter higher-energy subshells only after lower-energy subshells have been filled to capacity.

A single hydrogen atom consists of one proton and one electron. The single electron is found in the $1s$ orbital around the proton. The electron configuration of a hydrogen atom is customarily represented as $1s^1$ (read "one-s-one").

After hydrogen, the next simplest atom is that of the noble gas helium, which has an atomic number of 2 and an atomic mass of approximately 4 amu. The helium atom contains two protons and two neutrons in its nucleus and two electrons in the $1s$ orbital, which is completely filled by these two electrons. The electron configuration of helium is therefore $1s^2$ (read "one-s-two"). Note that in this atom the shell of lowest energy, the K shell ($n = 1$), is completely filled.

The atom next in complexity is lithium, with an atomic number of 3, an atomic mass of approximately 7 amu, and three protons, four neutrons, and three electrons. Two electrons fill the $1s$ orbital, so the remaining electron must occupy the orbital of next lowest energy, the $2s$ orbital. Thus the electron configuration of lithium is $1s^2 2s^1$.

An atom of the metal beryllium, with an atomic number of 4 and an atomic mass of approximately 9 amu, contains four protons and five neutrons in the nucleus, and four electrons. The fourth electron fills the $2s$ orbital, making the electron configuration $1s^2 2s^2$.

An atom of boron (atomic number = 5) contains five electrons: two in the K shell ($n = 1$), which is filled, and three in the L shell ($n = 2$). Because the s subshell in the L shell can contain only two electrons, the fifth electron must occupy the higher-energy $2p$ subshell. The electron configuration of boron, therefore, is $1s^2 2s^2 2p^1$.

Carbon (atomic number = 6) has six electrons. Four of them fill the $1s$ and $2s$ subshells. The remaining two electrons occupy the $2p$ subshell, giving a $1s^2 2s^2 2p^2$ configuration. To describe the distribution of the electrons in the $2p$ subshell, we use Hund's rule. These electrons occupy different $2p$ orbitals but have the same spin and hence the same spin quantum number.

Nitrogen (atomic number = 7) has a $1s^2 2s^2 2p^3$ configuration, with one electron in each of the three $2p$ orbitals, in accordance with Hund's rule. These three electrons have parallel spins. Oxygen atoms (atomic number = 8) have the configuration $1s^2 2s^2 2p^4$, with a pair of electrons in one of the $2p$ orbitals and a single electron in each of the other two. The two unpaired electrons in separate $2p$ orbitals have the same spin. The paired electrons that are in the third $2p$ orbital have opposite spins. Fluorine atoms (atomic number = 9) have the configuration $1s^2 2s^2 2p^5$, with only one $2p$ orbital containing an unpaired electron. All of the electrons in the neon atom (atomic number = 10) are paired, with the configuration $1s^2 2s^2 2p^6$. Both the K and L shells of the noble gas neon are filled (two electrons in the K shell and eight in the L shell).

The sodium atom (atomic number = 11) has eleven electrons, one more than the neon atom. This electron must go into the lowest-energy subshell available, the $3s$ orbital, giving a $1s^2 2s^2 2p^6 3s^1$ configuration. We can abbreviate this as [Ne]$3s^1$. The symbol [Ne] represents the configuration of the two filled shells in Ne (neon), $1s^2 2s^2 2p^6$, which are identical to the two filled inner shells in a sodium atom. Similarly, the configuration of lithium may be represented as [He]$2s^1$, where [He] represents the configuration of the helium atom, which is identical to that of the filled inner shell of lithium. Writing the configurations in this way emphasizes the similarity of the configurations of lithium and sodium. Both atoms have only one electron in an s subshell outside a filled set of inner shells.

The magnesium atom (atomic number = 12), with its 12 electrons in a [Ne]$3s^2$ configuration, is analogous to beryllium, [He]$2s^2$. Both atoms have a filled s subshell outside their filled inner shells. Aluminum (atomic number = 13), with 13 electrons and the electron configuration $[Ne]3s^23p^1$, is analogous to boron, $[He]2s^22p^1$. The electron configurations of silicon (14 electrons), phosphorus (15 electrons), sulfur (16 electrons), chlorine (17 electrons), and argon (18 electrons) are analogous in the compositions of their outer shells to carbon, nitrogen, oxygen, fluorine, and neon, respectively. See Table 5.3 for the configurations of these elements. The table lists the lowest-energy, or ground-state, electron configurations for atoms of each of the known elements.

Table 5.3   Electron Configurations of the Elements

Atomic Number	Symbol	Electron Configuration	Atomic Number	Symbol	Electron Configuration	Atomic Number	Symbol	Electron Configuration
1	H	$1s^1$				73	Ta	$[Xe]6s^24f^{14}5d^3$
2	He	$1s^2$	37	Rb	$[Kr]5s^1$	74	W	$[Xe]6s^24f^{14}5d^4$
			38	Sr	$[Kr]5s^2$	75	Re	$[Xe]6s^24f^{14}5d^5$
3	Li	$1s^22s^1 = [He]2s^1$	39	Y	$[Kr]5s^24d^1$	76	Os	$[Xe]6s^24f^{14}5d^6$
4	Be	$[He]2s^2$	40	Zr	$[Kr]5s^24d^2$	77	Ir	$[Xe]6s^24f^{14}5d^7$
5	B	$[He]2s^22p^1$	41	Nb	$[Kr]5s^14d^4$	78	Pt	$[Xe]6s^14f^{14}5d^9$
6	C	$[He]2s^22p^2$	42	Mo	$[Kr]5s^14d^5$	79	Au	$[Xe]6s^14f^{14}5d^{10}$
7	N	$[He]2s^22p^3$	43	Tc	$[Kr]5s^14d^6$	80	Hg	$[Xe]6s^24f^{14}5d^{10}$
8	O	$[He]2s^22p^4$	44	Ru	$[Kr]5s^14d^7$	81	Tl	$[Xe]6s^24f^{14}5d^{10}6p^1$
9	F	$[He]2s^22p^5$	45	Rh	$[Kr]5s^14d^8$	82	Pb	$[Xe]6s^24f^{14}5d^{10}6p^2$
10	Ne	$[He]2s^22p^6$	46	Pd	$[Kr]4d^{10}$	83	Bi	$[Xe]6s^24f^{14}5d^{10}6p^3$
			47	Ag	$[Kr]5s^14d^{10}$	84	Po	$[Xe]6s^24f^{14}5d^{10}6p^4$
11	Na	$[Ne]3s^1$	48	Cd	$[Kr]5s^24d^{10}$	85	At	$[Xe]6s^24f^{14}5d^{10}6p^5$
12	Mg	$[Ne]3s^2$	49	In	$[Kr]5s^24d^{10}5p^1$	86	Rn	$[Xe]6s^24f^{14}5d^{10}6p^6$
13	Al	$[Ne]3s^23p^1$	50	Sn	$[Kr]5s^24d^{10}5p^2$			
14	Si	$[Ne]3s^23p^2$	51	Sb	$[Kr]5s^24d^{10}5p^3$	87	Fr	$[Rn]7s^1$
15	P	$[Ne]3s^23p^3$	52	Te	$[Kr]5s^24d^{10}5p^4$	88	Ra	$[Rn]7s^2$
16	S	$[Ne]3s^23p^4$	53	I	$[Kr]5s^24d^{10}5p^5$	89	Ac	$[Rn]7s^26d^1$
17	Cl	$[Ne]3s^23p^5$	54	Xe	$[Kr]5s^24d^{10}5p^6$	90	Th	$[Rn]7s^26d^2$
18	Ar	$[Ne]3s^23p^6$				91	Pa	$[Rn]7s^25f^26d^1$
			55	Cs	$[Xe]6s^1$	92	U	$[Rn]7s^25f^36d^1$
19	K	$[Ar]4s^1$	56	Ba	$[Xe]6s^2$	93	Np	$[Rn]7s^25f^46d^1$
20	Ca	$[Ar]4s^2$	57	La	$[Xe]6s^25d^1$	94	Pu	$[Rn]7s^25f^6$
21	Sc	$[Ar]4s^23d^1$	58	Ce	$[Xe]6s^24f^2$	95	Am	$[Rn]7s^25f^7$
22	Ti	$[Ar]4s^23d^2$	59	Pr	$[Xe]6s^24f^3$	96	Cm	$[Rn]7s^25f^76d^1$
23	V	$[Ar]4s^23d^3$	60	Nd	$[Xe]6s^24f^4$	97	Bk	$[Rn]7s^25f^86d^1$
24	Cr	$[Ar]4s^13d^5$	61	Pm	$[Xe]6s^24f^5$	98	Cf	$[Rn]7s^25f^{10}$
25	Mn	$[Ar]4s^23d^5$	62	Sm	$[Xe]6s^24f^6$	99	Es	$[Rn]7s^25f^{11}$
26	Fe	$[Ar]4s^23d^6$	63	Eu	$[Xe]6s^24f^7$	100	Fm	$[Rn]7s^25f^{12}$
27	Co	$[Ar]4s^23d^7$	64	Gd	$[Xe]6s^24f^75d^1$	101	Md	$[Rn]7s^25f^{13}$
28	Ni	$[Ar]4s^23d^8$	65	Tb	$[Xe]6s^24f^9$	102	No	$[Rn]7s^25f^{14}$
29	Cu	$[Ar]4s^13d^{10}$	66	Dy	$[Xe]6s^24f^{10}$	103	Lr	$[Rn]7s^25f^{14}6d^1$
30	Zn	$[Ar]4s^23d^{10}$	67	Ho	$[Xe]6s^24f^{11}$	104	Unq	$[Rn]7s^25f^{14}6d^2$
31	Ga	$[Ar]4s^23d^{10}4p^1$	68	Er	$[Xe]6s^24f^{12}$	105	Unp	$[Rn]7s^25f^{14}6d^3$
32	Ge	$[Ar]4s^23d^{10}4p^2$	69	Tm	$[Xe]6s^24f^{13}$	106	Unh	$[Rn]7s^25f^{14}6d^4$
33	As	$[Ar]4s^23d^{10}4p^3$	70	Yb	$[Xe]6s^24f^{14}$	107	Uns	$[Rn]7s^25f^{14}6d^5$
34	Se	$[Ar]4s^23d^{10}4p^4$	71	Lu	$[Xe]6s^24f^{14}5d^1$	108	Uno	$[Rn]7s^25f^{14}6d^6$
35	Br	$[Ar]4s^23d^{10}4p^5$	72	Hf	$[Xe]6s^24f^{14}5d^2$	109	Une	$[Rn]7s^25f^{14}6d^7$
36	Kr	$[Ar]4s^23d^{10}4p^6$						

Potassium (atomic number = 19) and calcium (atomic number = 20) have one and two electrons, respectively, in the N shell ($n = 4$). Hence potassium corresponds to lithium and sodium in outer shell configuration, whereas calcium corresponds to beryllium and magnesium.

Beginning with scandium (atomic number = 21; see Table 5.3), additional electrons are added successively to the $3d$ subshell after two electrons have already occupied the $4s$ subshell. After the $3d$ subshell is filled to its capacity with 10 electrons, the $4p$ subshell fills. Note that for three series of elements, scandium (Sc) through copper (Cu), yttrium (Y) through silver (Ag), and lutetium (Lu) through gold (Au), a total of ten d electrons are successively added to the $(n - 1)$ shell next to the outer n shell to bring that $(n - 1)$ shell from 8 to 18 electrons. For two series, lanthanum (La) through lutetium (Lu) and actinium (Ac) through lawrencium (Lr), 14 f electrons are successively added to the third shell from the outside [the $(n - 2)$ shell] to bring that shell from 18 to 32 electrons.

Example 5.5

Gaseous cesium (Cs) atoms have been used in an experimental laser. These atoms emit light when their outermost electron is excited to a $7p$ orbital and then falls back into the $6s$ orbital. Without reference to Table 5.3, write the electron configurations of cesium (a) in its ground state and (b) when the outermost electron is excited to a p orbital.

From the order of filling presented in Fig. 5.22, when Cs is in its ground state we can fill the orbitals in the following order with 55 electrons:

$$1s^2 2s^2 2p^6 3s^2 3p^6 4s^2 3d^{10} 4p^6 5s^2 4d^{10} 5p^6 6s^1$$

However, note that many chemists write the orbitals in increasing order of the quantum numbers:

$$1s^2 2s^2 2p^6 3s^2 3p^6 3d^{10} 4s^2 4p^6 4d^{10} 5s^2 5p^6 6s^1$$

Either notation is acceptable. Because Cs contains one more electron than Xe, these configurations can both be abbreviated as $[Xe]6s^1$.

The outermost Cs electron is the electron in the $6s$ orbital. When this electron is excited to a higher-energy p orbital, the configuration changes to $[Xe]7p^1$. It should be noted that this configuration is not the ground-state configuration, the stable configuration. It cannot be predicted from the rules presented in Section 5.11. It occurs only when sufficient energy is put into the atomic system to move the electron from the ground-state $6s$ orbital out to the higher-energy $7p$ orbital.

Students are sometimes troubled by exceptions to the order for the filling of orbitals that is shown in Fig. 5.22. For instance, the electron configurations of chromium (atomic number = 24), copper (atomic number = 29), and lanthanum (atomic number = 57), among others, are not those the figure would lead us to expect. In general, such exceptions involve subshells with very similar energies, and small effects lead to changes in the order of filling.

Half-filled and completely filled subshells represent conditions of preferred stability. This stability is such that an electron shifts from the $4s$ into the $3d$ orbital in order to gain the extra stability of a half-filled $3d$ subshell (in chromium) or a filled $3d$ subshell (in copper).

In other atoms, certain combinations of repulsions between electrons lead to minor exceptions in the expected order of filling, because the magnitude of the repulsions is greater than the small differences in energy between subshells. From Fig. 5.22, we would expect the electron configuration of lanthanum (atomic number = 57) to be [Xe]$6s^2 4f^1$. Instead, as shown in Table 5.3, La has no $4f$ electron but has one $5d$ electron: [Xe]$6s^2 5d^1$. This exception reflects the fact that the $4f$ and $5d$ subshells have very similar energies (see Fig. 5.21) and that electrons change from one subshell to the other easily. A close inspection of Table 5.3 will disclose several such exceptions.

If we remember that exceptions in the expected order of filling of orbitals result from the similar energies of various subshells, our ability to predict the electron configurations for elements on the basis of the expected order of addition of electrons is sufficient for most purposes.

In Section 2.4, we mentioned how the periodic recurrence of similar electron configurations led to the formulation of the periodic law and to construction of the periodic table, a subject that will be discussed in more detail in Chapter 6.

For Review

Summary

A number of experiments have shown that atoms are composed of protons, neutrons, and electrons. **Protons** are relatively heavy particles with a charge of $+1$ and a mass of 1.0073 atomic mass units. **Neutrons** are relatively heavy particles with no charge and a mass of 1.0087 atomic mass units, very close to that of protons. **Electrons** are light particles with a mass of 0.00055 atomic mass units (1/1837 of that of a hydrogen atom) and a charge of -1. Rutherford's α-particle scattering experiments showed that the atom contains a small, massive, positively charged **nucleus** surrounded by electrons.

Bohr described the hydrogen atom in terms of an electron moving in a circular orbit about a nucleus. In order to account for the stability of the hydrogen atom, he postulated that the electron was restricted to certain discrete energies characterized by a **quantum number, n,** which could have only integer values ($n = 1, 2, 3, \ldots$). Thus the energy of the electron was assumed to be **quantized.** From this model we can calculate the energy E of an electron in a hydrogenlike system:

$$E = \frac{-kZ^2}{n^2}$$

where k is a constant and Z is the atomic number. The radius of the orbit can also be calculated as follows:

$$r = \frac{n^2 a_0}{Z}$$

where a_0 is the radius of the orbit in the hydrogen atom for which $n = 1$. Bohr suggested that an atom emits energy, in the form of a photon, only when an electron falls from a higher-energy orbit to a lower-energy orbit. Because the Bohr model accounted for the line spectra produced by samples of hydrogen gas in a discharge tube, his postulation of quantized energies for the electrons in atoms was widely accepted.

Light and other forms of electromagnetic radiation move through a vacuum with a speed, c, of 2.998×10^8 m s^{-1}. This radiation shows wavelike behavior, which can be characterized by a frequency, ν, and a wavelength, λ, such that $c = \lambda \nu$. Electromagnetic radiation also has the properties of particles called **photons.** The energy of a photon is related to the frequency of the radiation: $E = h\nu$, where h is Planck's constant.

The line spectrum of hydrogen is obtained by passing the light from a discharge tube through a prism. From a measurement of the wavelength of each line, the energy of each can be determined. These energies correspond to the values predicted when an electron in a hydrogen atom falls from a higher-energy to a lower-energy state.

Atoms with two or more electrons cannot be described satisfactorily by the Bohr model, and it has been replaced by the **quantum-mechanical model.** This model identifies the behavior of an electron in terms of a **wave function, ψ,** which identifies the **orbital,** or region of space, occupied by the electron. It is possible to calculate the energy of the electron from ψ or to determine the probability of finding the electron in a given location in the orbital. The distribution of an electron within an orbital may be described in terms of **electron density.**

An orbital is characterized by three quantum numbers. The **principal quantum number, n,** may be any positive integer. The energy of the orbital and its average distance from the nucleus are related to n. The **azimuthal quantum number, l,** can have any integral value from 0 to $(n - 1)$. The shape of the orbital is indicated by l, and within a multielectron atom, the energies of orbitals with the same value of n increase as l increases. The **magnetic quantum number, m,** with values ranging from $-l$ to $+l$, describes the orientation of an orbital. A fourth quantum number, the **spin quantum number, s** ($s = \pm\frac{1}{2}$), describes the spin of an electron about its own axis. Orbitals with the same value of n occupy the same **shell.** Orbitals with the same values of n and l occupy the same **subshell.**

n	Shell	Subshells
1	K	$1s$ ($l = 0$)
2	L	$2s$ ($l = 0$), $2p$ ($l = 1$)
3	M	$3s$ ($l = 0$), $3p$ ($l = 1$), $3d$ ($l = 2$)
4	N	$4s$ ($l = 0$), $4p$ ($l = 1$), $4d$ ($l = 2$), $4f$ ($l = 3$)

There are $(2l + 1)$ orbitals in the l subshell of any shell.

By adding electrons one by one to atomic orbitals in the order $1s$, $2s$, $2p$, $3s$, $3p$, $4s$, $3d$, $4p$, etc., and following both the **Pauli exclusion principle** (no two electrons can have the same set of four quantum numbers) and **Hund's rule** (whenever possible, electrons remain unpaired in degenerate orbitals), we can predict the **electron configurations** of most atoms.

The process of "building up" atoms in order of atomic number by adding one proton to the nucleus and one electron to the proper subshell at a time, until the electron configurations of all the elements have been described, is referred to as the **aufbau process.**

Key Terms and Concepts

alpha particles (5.4)
atomic number (5.5)
aufbau process (5.12)
azimuthal quantum number, l (5.10)
beta particles (5.4)
Bohr model of the atom (5.7)
cathode rays (5.1)

degenerate orbitals (5.10)
electron configuration (5.12)
electron density (5.9)
electrons (5.1)
excited state (5.7)
gamma rays (5.4)
ground state (5.7)

Heisenberg uncertainty principle (5.9)
Hund's rule (5.11)
ions (5.2)
isotopes (5.6)
magnetic quantum number, m (5.10)
mass number (5.6)

neutrons (5.3)
nucleus (5.5)
orbital (5.9)
Pauli exclusion principle (5.11)
photoelectric effect (5.1)
photons (5.8)

principal quantum number, n (5.10)
protons (5.2)
quantized (5.7)
quantum-mechanical model of the
    atom (5.9)
radioactivity (5.4)

shell (5.10)
spectrum (5.8)
spin quantum number, s (5.10)
subshell (5.10)
wave function (5.9)

Exercises

Answers for selected even-numbered exercises marked by red numbers appear at the end of the book. The worked-out solutions to all even-numbered exercises appear in the *Solutions Guide*.

Atomic Structure

1. How are cathode rays and β particles similar? How do they differ?
2. How are positive rays and α particles similar? How do they differ?
3. In what way is the lightest hydrogen nucleus unique?
4. What is the evidence that the cathode rays in a discharge tube are negatively charged particles? What is their source?
5. Using the data in Table 3.1, sketch the mass spectrum expected for a sample of neon atoms.
6. Describe and interpret the experiment that shows that an atom contains a small, positively charged nucleus of relatively large mass.

The Bohr Model of the Atom

7. What does it mean to say that the energies of the electrons in hydrogen atoms are quantized?
8. How are the Bohr model and the Rutherford model of the atom similar? How do they differ?
9. What is the lowest possible energy, in electron-volts (eV), for an electron in a He^+ ion?
10. Figure 5.14 gives the energies of an electron in a hydrogen atom for values of n from 1 to 5. What is the energy, in electron-volts, of an electron with $n = 7$ in a hydrogen atom?
11. Calculate the radius of each of the following ions, using the Bohr model.
    (a) Li^{2+} ion
    (b) Be^{3+} ion
    (c) He^+ ion
12. Excited H atoms with electrons in very high-energy levels have been detected. What is the radius (in centimeters) of a H atom with an electron characterized by an n value of 98? How many times larger is that than the radius of the H atom in its ground state?
13. Which is larger, a hydrogen atom with an electron in an orbit with $n = 3$ or a Li^{2+} ion with an electron in an orbit with $n = 4$?

Orbital Energies and Spectra

14. (a) From the data given in Fig. 5.14, calculate the energy, in electron-volts, required to ionize a hydrogen atom. Calculate the energy in joules per atom.
    (b) Using the Bohr model, calculate the energy, in electron-volts, required to ionize a hydrogen atom. Calculate the energy in joules per atom.
15. (a) From the data given in Fig. 5.14, determine the energy, in electron-volts, of the photon emitted when an electron in an excited hydrogen atom moves from an orbit with $n = 5$ to one with $n = 1$.
    (b) From the data given in Fig. 5.14, determine the energy, in electron-volts, of the photon required to move an electron in a hydrogen atom from an orbit with $n = 1$ to one with $n = 5$.
    (c) Using the Bohr model, calculate the energy, in electron-volts, of the photon emitted when an electron in an excited hydrogen atom moves from an orbit with $n = 5$ to one with $n = 1$.
    (d) Using the Bohr model, calculate the energy, in electron-volts, of the photon required to move an electron in a hydrogen atom from an orbit with $n = 1$ to one with $n = 5$.
16. Using the Bohr model, calculate the energy, in electron-volts and joules, of the light emitted by a transition from the $n = 3$ (M) to the $n = 1$ (K) shell in He^+.
17. Consider a collection of hydrogen atoms with electrons randomly distributed in the $n = 1, 2, 3, 4,$ and 5 shells. How many different wavelengths of light are emitted by these atoms as the electrons fall into the lower-energy states?
18. Calculate the lowest and highest energies, in electron-volts, of the light produced by the transitions described in Exercise 17.
19. Calculate the frequencies and wavelengths of the light produced by the two transitions described in Exercise 18.
20. When heated, lithium atoms emit photons of red light with a wavelength of 6708 Å. What is the energy in joules and the frequency of this light?
21. FM-104, an FM radio station, broadcasts at a frequency of 1.039×10^8 s^{-1} (103.9 megahertz). What is the wavelength of these radio waves, in meters?
22. (a) Light that looks blue has a wavelength of 4800 Å. Determine the wavelength in meters, and check whether

this statement about color agrees with the information given in Fig. 5.11.

(b) What is the frequency of this light?

(c) What is the energy of a photon of this blue light?

(d) Does a photon of this blue light have enough energy to excite the electron in a hydrogen atom from the $n = 1$ shell to the $n = 2$ shell?

23. X rays are produced when the electron stream in an X-ray tube knocks an electron out of a low-lying shell of an atom in the target, and an electron from a higher shell falls into the lower-lying shell. The X ray is the photon given off as the electron falls into the lower shell. The most intense X rays produced by an X-ray tube with a copper target have wavelengths of 1.542 Å and 1.392 Å. These X rays are produced when an electron from the L or M shell falls into the K shell of a copper atom. Calculate, in electron-volts, the energy separation of the K, L, and M shells in copper.

The Quantum-Mechanical Model of the Atom

24. What information about an electron in an atom is available from the wave function that describes the electron?

25. How do electron shells, subshells, and orbitals differ?

26. Discuss the following: electron density and atomic orbital.

27. How are the Bohr model and the quantum-mechanical model of the atom similar? How do they differ?

28. What are the four quantum numbers used to describe an electron in the quantum-mechanical model of an atom? What does each describe?

29. Identify the subshell in which electrons with the following quantum numbers are found.

(a) $n = 3$, $l = 1$ (d) $n = 6$, $l = 2$

(b) $n = 2$, $l = 0$ (e) $n = 7$, $l = 1$

(c) $n = 5$, $l = 3$

30. What type of orbital is occupied by an electron with the quantum numbers $n = 3$, $l = 2$? How many degenerate orbitals of this type are found in a multielectron atom?

31. (a) What are the quantum numbers that describe the electron in the $2s$ orbital of a lithium atom?

(b) Excitation of the electron can promote it to energy levels described by other sets of quantum numbers. Which of the following sets of quantum numbers cannot exist in an excited lithium atom (or any other atom)?

(i) $n = 2$, $l = 1$, $m = -1$, $s = +\frac{3}{2}$

(ii) $n = 3$, $l = 2$, $m = 0$, $s = +\frac{1}{2}$

(iii) $n = 3$, $l = 3$, $m = -2$, $s = -\frac{1}{2}$

(iv) $n = 4$, $l = 1$, $m = -2$, $s = +\frac{1}{2}$

(v) $n = 27$, $l = 14$, $m = -8$, $s = -\frac{1}{2}$

32. Write the quantum numbers of the seven electrons in a nitrogen atom. For example, the quantum numbers for one of the $2s$ electrons are $n = 2$, $l = 0$, $m = 0$, $s = +\frac{1}{2}$.

33. Which of the following orbitals are degenerate in an atom with two or more electrons? $3d_{xy}$, $4s$, $4p_z$, $4d_{xy}$, $4p_x$

34. Consider the atomic orbitals (i), (ii), and (iii) shown here in outline.

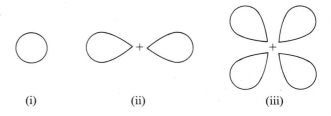

(i)   (ii)   (iii)

(a) What is the maximum number of electrons that can be contained in atomic orbital (iii)?

(b) How many orbitals with the same value of l as orbital (i) can be found in the shell $n = 4$? How many with the same value as orbital (ii)? How many with the same value as orbital (iii)?

(c) What is the smallest n value possible for an electron in an orbital of type (iii)? Of type (ii)? Of type (i)?

(d) What l values characterize each of these three orbitals?

(e) Arrange these orbitals in order of increasing energy in the M shell. Is this order different in other shells?

Electron Configurations

35. Using complete subshell notation ($1s^2 2s^2 2p^6$, etc.), predict the electron configuration of each of the following atoms, without referring to Table 5.3 except to check your answers. (a) $^{23}_{11}$Na, (b) $^{28}_{14}$Si, (c) $^{31}_{15}$P, (d) $^{59}_{27}$Co, (e) $^{65}_{30}$Zn, (f) $^{84}_{36}$Kr, (g) $^{75}_{33}$As, (h) $^{89}_{39}$Y, (i) $^{152}_{63}$Eu, (j) $^{175}_{71}$Lu

36. Using complete subshell notation ($1s^2 2s^2 2p^6$, etc.), predict the electron configuration of each of the following ions or atoms: (a) Na^+, (b) Ne, (c) F^-, (d) O^{2-}, (e) N^{3-}, (f) Mg^{2+}, (g) Al^{3+}

37. Identify the atoms for which the electron configurations are given below, without referring to Table 5.3 except to check your answers.

(a) $1s^2 2s^2 2p^4$ (d) $[Kr]5s^2 4d^{10} 5p^6$

(b) $[Xe]6s^2 5d^1$ (e) $1s^2 2s^2 2p^6 3s^2 3p^6 4s^2 3d^6$

(c) $[Ar]4s^2 3d^5$ (f) $[Rn]7s^2 5f^2 6d^1$

38. The $4s$ orbitals fill before the $3d$ orbitals when building up electronic structures by the aufbau process. However, electrons are lost from the $4s$ orbital before they are lost from the $3d$ orbitals when transition elements are ionized. The ionization of copper ($[Ar]3d^{10}4s^1$) gives Cu^+ ($[Ar]3d^{10}$), for example. The electron configurations of a number of transition metal ions are given below; identify the transition metals.

(a) M^{3+}, $[Ar]3d^3$ (d) M^{3+}, $[Ar]3d^2$

(b) M^{2+}, $[Ar]3d^2$ (e) M^{3+}, $[Kr]4d^6$

(c) M^{3+}, $[Ar]3d^4$ (f) M^{2+}, $[Kr]4d^9$

39. Using subshell notation ($1s^2 2s^2 2p^6$, etc.), predict the electron configurations of the following ions: (a) V^{4+}, (b) Co^{3+},

(c) Cr^{2+}, (d) Pb^{2+}, (e) Ag^+. Read the introduction to Exercise 38 before attempting this exercise.

40. Which of the following sets of quantum numbers describes the most easily removed electron in a boron atom in its ground state? Which of the electrons described is most difficult to remove?
    (a) $n = 1$, $l = 0$, $m = 0$, $s = -\frac{1}{2}$
    (b) $n = 2$, $l = 1$, $m = 0$, $s = -\frac{1}{2}$
    (c) $n = 2$, $l = 0$, $m = 0$, $s = \frac{1}{2}$
    (d) $n = 3$, $l = 1$, $m = 1$, $s = -\frac{1}{2}$
    (e) $n = 4$, $l = 1$, $m = 1$, $s = \frac{1}{2}$

41. $N^+(g)$ can be produced from $N(g)$ by removing one electron from any of the occupied orbitals of the nitrogen atom. Several of these processes are
    (a) $1s^2 2s^2 2p^3 \longrightarrow 1s^1 2s^2 2p^3$
    (b) $1s^2 2s^2 2p^3 \longrightarrow 1s^2 2s^1 2p^3$
    (c) $1s^2 2s^2 2p^3 \longrightarrow 1s^2 2s^2 2p^2$
    The energy of which of these processes corresponds to the energy required to remove the most easily removed electron? Which process will require the most energy?

42. Which of the following electron configurations describe an atom in its ground state and which describe an atom in an excited state?
    (a) $[He]2s^1$ (d) $[Ar]4s^2 3d^9 4p^3$
    (b) $[Ar]5s^1 4d^3$ (e) $[Kr]6s^2 6p^1$
    (c) $[Ar]4s^2 3d^{10} 4p^4$ (f) $[Xe]6s^2 4f^{14} 5d^{10} 6p^2$

Additional Exercises

43. How would the results of the Rutherford α-particle scattering experiment differ if the atom were only twice as large as its nucleus?

44. (a) Are the charges on the nuclei of atoms quantized?
    (b) Are the masses of individual atoms quantized?
    (c) Is the atomic mass of an element that is a mixture of isotopes quantized?

45. Using the Bohr model, determine the energy, in electron-volts, of an electron with $n = 2$ in an excited Li^{2+} ion. What is the radius of the circular orbit?

46. In Chapter 1, the meter was defined as 1,650,763.73 times the wavelength of a certain Kr line. What is the frequency of this radiation (to four significant figures)?

47. Draw an energy-level diagram like that in Fig. 5.21, showing the energies of the atomic orbitals in a hydrogen atom.

48. Figure 5.16 shows the radial probability density of three of the lowest-energy orbitals in a hydrogen atom. Which other orbitals are degenerate with each of these three?

49. The bright yellow light emitted by a sodium vapor lamp, or by heated compounds containing sodium, has wavelengths of 5896 and 5890 Å. These lines result from the relaxation of electrons from one or the other of two closely spaced energy levels to a common lower level. What is the energy separation, in electron-volts, of the two closely spaced levels?

50. The energy required to remove an electron from a Si^{3+} ion is 45.08 eV. To remove an electron from an Al^{3+} ion requires 120.2 eV. Explain the large difference.

51. Assume that, in another universe, the values of the quantum number m are limited to zero or positive integers up to the value of l for a particular subshell; thus for $l = 2$, m could be 0, 1, or 2. Describe the electron configuration of nitrogen (at. no. = 7) and the configuration of fluorine (at. no. = 9) if, with this restriction, all other quantum numbers behaved as described in this chapter. How many unpaired electrons would these atoms contain?

52. Write the electron configuration of each of the following elements, using complete subshell notation: Al, Ar, Kr, Ca, Co, La, Sb, Pb.

53. Sketch the shape of an orbital with $n = 4$, $l = 1$; of an orbital with $n = 4$, $l = 0$.

54. The value of one of the quantum numbers describing the electron that is lost when a copper atom forms a Cu^+ ion cannot be predicted. Which quantum number is it? (Read the introduction to Exercise 38 before attempting this exercise.)

55. What are the n and l values of the electrons lost when a cobalt atom forms a Co^{3+} ion? (Read the introduction to Exercise 38 before attempting this exercise.)

6 Chemical and Physical Properties of the Elements and the Periodic Table

The reaction of potassium with water.

The periodic table is very helpful in correlating both the chemical and physical properties of the elements. In this chapter, we will see how the repeating outer electron configurations have much to do with the properties of elements and can be utilized in the classification of the elements in the periodic table (Section 2.4). For example, the alkali metals (Group IA) all have s^1 outer shell electron configurations, the alkaline earth metals (Group IIA) have s^2 outer shell configurations, and the halogens (Group VIIA) have s^2p^5 outer shell configurations.

Some Elements
of the
Periodic Table

Group IA: Potassium

Group IB: Gold

Group VA: Bismuth

Group IIB: Mercury

Group IIA: Calcium

Group VIIIA: Neon

Group VIA: Sulfur

Group VIIA: Chlorine

Group IVA: Tin

Group IVA: Carbon (in the form of diamond)

Group IIIA: Gallium

6.1 Summary of the Arrangement of Elements in the Periodic Table

As noted in Section 2.4 (Fig. 2.4), the periodic table consists of 7 horizontal rows of elements (periods, or series) and 32 vertical columns of elements (groups or families).

The **first short period** of the table contains the elements hydrogen (H) and helium (He). The **second short period** contains eight elements, beginning with lithium (Li) and ending with neon (Ne). The **third short period** also contains eight elements, beginning with sodium (Na) and ending with argon (Ar).

The **fourth period** is the first of two long periods, each of which contains 18 elements. The fourth period includes the elements from potassium (K) through krypton (Kr). Within this period are the elements from scandium (Sc) through copper (Cu), which are known as the **first transition series.** The **fifth period** begins with rubidium (Rb) and ends with xenon (Xe). Within this period are the elements yttrium (Y) through silver (Ag), which make up the **second transition series.**

The **sixth period,** beginning with cesium (Cs) and ending with radon (Rn), contains 32 elements. The **third transition series,** made up of lanthanum (La) and the elements hafnium (Hf) through gold (Au), is included in the sixth period. The third transition series is split; between lanthanum and hafnium is a series of 14 elements, cerium (Ce) through lutetium (Lu), called the **first inner transition series,** the **lanthanide series,** or the **rare earth elements.** Lanthanum behaves very much like the elements cerium through lutetium. Hence lanthanum is often included in the lanthanide series, even though in terms of electronic structure it is more properly considered to be the first element of the third transition series.

The **seventh period** extends from francium (Fr) through element number 118. However, no elements after element 109 have been characterized. The known elements in this period include a part of the **fourth transition series** (actinium and elements 104 through 109). The unreported elements 110 and 111 would also be members of this series. The elements between actinium (Ac) and element 104, namely the elements thorium (Th) through lawrencium (Lr), make up a second inner transition series referred to as the **actinide series.** Actinium is sometimes included with the actinide series because of its similarity in properties to those elements.

The discoverer of a new element traditionally names the element. However, until the name is recognized by the International Union of Pure and Applied Chemistry (IUPAC), the recommended name of the new element is based on the Latin words for its atomic number. These names are also used for elements, such as element 110, that have not yet been prepared or discovered. An international dispute about credit for the discovery of element 104 led to this new set of systematic names for the heavier elements. In 1964 Soviet scientists reported element 104, which they named kurchatovium, after the leader of their nuclear research program. Five years later, physicists at the University of California suggested that, in fact, *they* had first prepared element 104. They named it rutherfordium, after the British scientist. Neither name was formally adopted, although each is used in its country of origin. In 1979 IUPAC recommended using the name unnilquadium (abbreviated Unq) for element 104 until the question of the original discoverer could be settled. In addition, that body recommended unnilpentium (Unp) for element 105, unnilhexium (Unh) for element 106, unnilseptium (Uns) for element 107, unniloctium (Uno) for element 108, and unnilennium (Une) for element 109. These names are based on the following Latin words for the atomic numbers: *nil* = 0, *un* = 1, *bi* = 2, *tri* = 3, *quad* = 4, *pent* = 5, *hex* = 6, *sept* = 7, *oct* = 8, and *enn* = 9.

6.2 Electron Configuration and the Periodic Table

When arranged in order of increasing atomic number, elements with similar chemical properties occur periodically. Figure 6.1 shows the electron configurations of the elements with atomic numbers 1 through 18, inclusive, arranged as these atoms are arranged in the periodic table. Note the periodic recurrence of similar electron configurations in the outer shells of these elements—that is, the periodicity with respect to the number of **valence electrons** (electrons in the outermost shell).

Elements in any one group have the same number of electrons in their outermost shell: lithium and sodium have only one, beryllium and magnesium have two, fluorine and chlorine have seven electrons in the **valence shell**—the outermost shell, which contains the valence electrons. The similarity in chemical properties among elements of the same group occurs because they have the same numbers of valence electrons, and the number of electrons in the valence shell of an atom determines its chemical properties. **It is the loss, gain, or sharing of valence electrons that determines how elements react.** Thus the periodic table is simply an arrangement of atoms that puts elements with the same number of valence electrons in the same group. This arrangement is emphasized in Fig. 6.2, which shows in periodic table form the electron configuration of the last subshell to be filled by the aufbau process (see also Table 5.3).

It is convenient to classify the elements in the periodic table into four categories according to their atomic structures.

1. Noble Gases. Elements in which the s and p orbitals in the outer shell are completely filled. The noble gases are the members of Group VIIIA (shown in red in Fig. 6.2).

2. Representative Elements. Elements in which the last electron added enters an s or a p orbital in the outermost shell but in which this shell is incomplete. The outermost shell for these elements is the valence shell. The representative elements are those in Groups IA, IIA, IIB, IIIA, IVA, VA, VIA, and VIIA of the periodic table (shown in yellow).

3. Transition Elements. Elements in which the second shell, counting from the outside, is building from 8 to 18 electrons as its d orbitals fill. The outermost s subshell, the ns subshell, and the d subshell of the next shell in, the $(n - 1)d$ subshell, contain the valence electrons in these elements. Thus the $(n - 1)d$ and ns subshells are the valence shells in the transition elements. There are four transition series (shown in green).

(a) First transition series: scandium (Sc) through copper (Cu); $3d$ subshell filling.

(b) Second transition series: yttrium (Y) through silver (Ag); $4d$ subshell filling.

Figure 6.1

The electron configurations of the first 18 elements, arranged in the format of the periodic table.

IA							VIIIA
H $1s^1$	IIA	IIIA	IVA	VA	VIA	VIIA	**He** $1s^2$
Li [He]$2s^1$	**Be** [He]$2s^2$	**B** [He]$2s^22p^1$	**C** [He]$2s^22p^2$	**N** [He]$2s^22p^3$	**O** [He]$2s^22p^4$	**F** [He]$2s^22p^5$	**Ne** [He]$2s^22p^6$
Na [Ne]$3s^1$	**Mg** [Ne]$3s^2$	**Al** [Ne]$3s^23p^1$	**Si** [Ne]$3s^23p^2$	**P** [Ne]$3s^23p^3$	**S** [Ne]$3s^23p^4$	**Cl** [Ne]$3s^23p^5$	**Ar** [Ne]$3s^23p^6$

Figure 6.2

The order of occupancy of atomic orbitals in the periodic table.

(c) Third transition series: lanthanum (La), plus hafnium (Hf) through gold (Au); 5d subshell filling.

(d) Fourth transition series (incomplete): actinium (Ac), plus elements 104 through 109; 6d subshell filling. (If elements 110 and 111 are discovered, this will complete the series.)

Zinc, cadmium, and mercury are sometimes considered transition elements. The aufbau process predicts that they should be transition elements, but they are in fact representative elements by the foregoing definitions. The second electron shell from the outside fills with 18 electrons one element earlier than would normally be predicted in each of the transition element series. This occurs because one of the two *s* electrons already in the outer electron shell is pulled down into the *d* orbital of the next-to-outer shell for Cu, Ag, and Au. The *s* electron in the outer shell is then replaced in Zn, Cd, and Hg, respectively, when the next electron is added.

4. Inner Transition Elements. Elements in which the third shell, counting in from the outside, is building from 18 to 32 electrons as its *f* orbitals fill. The valence shells of the inner transition elements consist of the $(n - 2)f$, $(n - 1)d$, and ns subshells. There are two inner transition series (shown in blue).

   (a) First inner transition series: cerium (Ce) through lutetium (Lu); $4f$ subshell filling.

   (b) Second inner transition series: thorium (Th) through lawrencium (Lr); $5f$ subshell filling.

(Lanthanum and actinium, because of their similarities to the other members of the series, are sometimes included as the first elements of the first and second inner transition series, respectively.)

6.3 Variation of Properties Within Periods and Groups

Elements within a group have identical numbers and generally identical distributions of electrons in their valence shells. Thus we expect them to exhibit very similar chemical behavior. Across a period, we might expect a smoothly varying change in chemical behavior, because each element differs from the preceding element by one electron. However, sometimes the similarities or differences within a group or across a period are not as regular as we might expect. This is because the loss, gain, or sharing of valence electrons depends on several factors, including (1) the number of valence electrons, (2) the magnitude of the nuclear charge and the total number of electrons surrounding the nucleus, (3) the number of filled shells lying between the nucleus and the valence shell, and (4) the distances of the electrons in the various shells from each other and from the nucleus.

   Examples of these four effects on the periodic variation of some physical properties will be considered in the following discussion.

   1. Variation in Covalent Radii. There are several ways to define the radii of atoms and thus to determine their relative sizes. We will use the **covalent radius,** which is defined as half the distance between the nuclei of two identical atoms when they are joined by a single covalent bond (Section 2.6). In general, from left to right across a period of the periodic table, each element has a smaller covalent radius than that of the one preceding it [Table 6.1 and Fig. 6.3 (also shown in the table inside the back cover)].

Table 6.1		Covalent Radii of Third Period Elements	
Atom	Covalent Radius, Å	Nuclear Charge	Electron Configuration
Na	1.86	+11	$[Ne]3s^1$
Mg	1.60	+12	$[Ne]3s^2$
Al	1.43	+13	$[Ne]3s^23p^1$
Si	1.17	+14	$[Ne]3s^23p^2$
P	1.10	+15	$[Ne]3s^23p^3$
S	1.04	+16	$[Ne]3s^23p^4$
Cl	0.99	+17	$[Ne]3s^23p^5$

Figure 6.3

Covalent and ionic radii of the elements. Covalent radii are in red; ionic radii are in blue. Numerical values of radii are in angstrom units (Å). The metals are shaded in green and the nonmetals in yellow.

This change in size can be attributed to the increasing nuclear charge across the period, with the added electrons going into partially occupied shells. Each element in the periodic table has one more electron and one more proton, giving a nuclear charge that is one higher than the preceding element. Within a period, however, the number of shells is constant. In general, within a given period, the larger nuclear charge results in a larger force of electrostatic attraction between the nucleus and the electrons, because the additional electrons are in the same shell. This causes the decrease in covalent radii across the period.

Our values for covalent radii are based on interatomic distances between two identical atoms held together by chemical bonds.

Proceeding down a group of the periodic table, succeeding elements have larger covalent radii as a result of greater numbers of electron shells (Table 6.2), a factor that more than offsets the effect of the larger nuclear charge of each succeeding element. To be more specific, the increasing nuclear charge might lead us to expect that electrons would be held more tightly and pulled closer to the nucleus. However, the total number of shells increases down a group, and shells with larger principal quantum numbers have

Table 6.2		Covalent Radii of the Halogen Group Elements	
Atom	Covalent Radius, Å	Nuclear Charge	Number of Electrons in Each Shell
F	0.64	+ 9	2, 7
Cl	0.99	+17	2, 8, 7
Br	1.14	+35	2, 8, 18, 7
I	1.33	+53	2, 8, 18, 18, 7
At	1.4	+85	2, 8, 18, 32, 18, 7

larger radii. The larger size of the shells, coupled with repulsions between the increasing numbers of electrons, overcome the increased nuclear attraction so that the atoms increase in size down a group.

2. **Variation in Ionic Radii.** As shown in Fig. 6.3 and the table inside the back cover, the radius of a positive ion is less than the covalent radius of its parent atom. A positive ion forms when one or more than one electron is removed from an atom. Usually, the representative elements form positive ions by losing all of their valence electrons. The loss of all electrons from the outermost shell results in a smaller radius, because the remaining electrons occupy shells with smaller principal quantum numbers (and smaller radii). In fact, even the radii of these remaining filled electron shells decrease (relative to their size in the neutral atom) because of the decrease in the total number of electron–electron repulsions within the atom. The decreasing repulsions give rise to a greater average attraction of the nucleus per remaining electron, an effect spoken of as an increase in the *effective* nuclear charge. Thus the covalent radius of a sodium atom ($1s^2 2s^2 2p^6 3s^1$) is 1.86 Å, whereas the ionic radius of a sodium ion ($1s^2 2s^2 2p^6$) is 0.95 Å. Proceeding down the groups of the periodic table, we find that positive ions of succeeding elements have larger radii, corresponding to greater numbers of shells.

A simple negative ion is formed by the addition of one or more than one electron to the valence shell of an atom. This results in a greater force of repulsion among the electrons and a decrease in the effective nuclear charge per electron. Both effects cause the radius of a negative ion to be greater than that of the parent atom. For example, a chlorine atom ($[Ne]3s^2 3p^5$) has a covalent radius of 0.99 Å, whereas the ionic radius of a chloride ion ($[Ne]3s^2 3p^6$) is 1.81 Å. For succeeding elements proceeding down the groups, negative ions have more electron shells and larger radii. (These effects are apparent in Fig. 6.3 and in the table inside the back cover.)

Ions and atoms that have the same electron configuration, such as those in the series N^{3-}, O^{2-}, F^-, Ne, Na^+, Mg^{2+}, and Al^{3+}, and those in the series P^{3-}, S^{2-}, Cl^-, Ar, K^+, Ca^{2+}, and Sc^{3+}, are termed **isoelectronic species.** The greater the nuclear charge, the smaller the radius in a series of isoelectronic ions and atoms. This trend is illustrated in Table 6.3.

As we will see later, many properties of ions can be explained in terms of their sizes and charges.

3. **Variation in Ionization Energies.** The amount of energy required to remove *the most loosely bound* electron from a gaseous atom is called its **first ionization energy.** This change may be represented for any element X by the equation

$$X(g) + energy \longrightarrow X^+(g) + e^-$$

Table 6.3	Radii of Two Sets of Isoelectronic Ions and Atoms						
Species:	N^{3-}	O^{2-}	F^-	Ne	Na^+	Mg^{2+}	Al^{3+}
Nuclear charge:	+7	+8	+9	+10	+11	+12	+13
Radius, Å:	1.71	1.40	1.36	1.12	0.95	0.65	0.50
Electron configuration: $1s^2 2s^2 2p^6$							
Species:	P^{3-}	S^{2-}	Cl^-	Ar	K^+	Ca^{2+}	Sc^{3+}
Nuclear charge:	+15	+16	+17	+18	+19	+20	+21
Radius, Å:	2.12	1.84	1.81	1.54	1.33	0.99	0.81
Electron configuration: $1s^2 2s^2 2p^6 3s^2 3p^6$							

The energy required to remove the second most loosely bound electron is called the **second ionization energy;** to remove the third, the **third ionization energy;** and so on. First ionization energies increase in an irregular way from left to right across a period (Table 6.4). This overall increase can be attributed to the fact that the electrons lost come from the same shell, while the nuclear charge increases.

Figure 6.4 shows the relationship between the first ionization energies and the atomic numbers of several elements. The values of the first ionization energies are provided in Table 6.4. Note that the ionization energy of boron is less than that of beryllium. This is explained by differences in the attraction of the positive nucleus for electrons in different subshells. On the average, an s electron is attracted to the nucleus more than a p electron in the same principal shell. This means that an s electron is harder to remove from an atom than a p electron in the same shell. The electron removed during the ionization of beryllium ([He]$2s^2$) is an s electron, whereas the electron removed

---

Table 6.4 **First Ionization Energies of Some of the Elements, in Kilojoules per Mole**

1 H 1310																	2 He 2370
3 Li 520	4 Be 900											5 B 800	6 C 1090	7 N 1400	8 O 1310	9 F 1680	10 Ne 2080
11 Na 490	12 Mg 730											13 Al 580	14 Si 780	15 P 1060	16 S 1000	17 Cl 1250	18 Ar 1520
19 K 420	20 Ca 590	21 Sc 630	22 Ti 660	23 V 650	24 Cr 660	25 Mn 710	26 Fe 760	27 Co 760	28 Ni 730	29 Cu 740	30 Zn 910	31 Ga 580	32 Ge 780	33 As 960	34 Se 950	35 Br 1140	36 Kr 1350
37 Rb 400	38 Sr 550	39 Y 620	40 Zr 660	41 Nb 670	42 Mo 680	43 Tc 700	44 Ru 710	45 Rh 720	46 Pd 800	47 Ag 730	48 Cd 870	49 In 560	50 Sn 700	51 Sb 830	52 Te 870	53 I 1010	54 Xe 1170
55 Cs 380	56 Ba 500	[57-71] *	72 Hf 700	73 Ta 760	74 W 770	75 Re 760	76 Os 840	77 Ir 890	78 Pt 870	79 Au 890	80 Hg 1000	81 Tl 590	82 Pb 710	83 Bi 800	84 Po 810	85 At ...	86 Rn 1030
87 Fr ...	88 Ra 510	[89-103] †	104 Unq ...	105 Unp ...	106 Unh ...	107 Uns ...	108 Uno ...	109 Une ...									

*Lanthanide series	57 La 540	58 Ce 670	59 Pr 560	60 Nd 610	61 Pm ...	62 Sm 540	63 Eu 550	64 Gd 600	65 Tb 650	66 Dy 660	67 Ho ...	68 Er ...	69 Tm ...	70 Yb 600	71 Lu 480
†Actinide series	89 Ac 670	90 Th ...	91 Pa ...	92 U 400	93 Np ...	94 Pu ...	95 Am ...	96 Cm ...	97 Bk ...	98 Cf ...	99 Es ...	100 Fm ...	101 Md ...	102 No ...	103 Lr ...

Figure 6.4

A graphic illustration of the periodic relationships between first ionization energy and atomic number for some of the elements.

during the ionization of boron ($[He]2s^2 2p^1$) is a p electron; this results in a smaller first ionization energy for boron, even though its nuclear charge is greater by one unit. The two additional nuclear charges in carbon are sufficient to make its first ionization energy larger than that of beryllium. The first ionization energy for oxygen is slightly less than that for nitrogen because of the repulsion between the two electrons occupying the same $2p$ orbital in the oxygen atom. Because these two electrons occupy the same region of space, their repulsion overcomes the additional nuclear charge of the oxygen nucleus. Analogous changes occur in succeeding periods.

The attractive force exerted on the valence electrons by the positively charged nucleus is partially counterbalanced by the repulsive forces between electrons in inner shells and the valence electrons. An electron being removed from an atom is thus shielded from the nucleus by these inner shells. This shielding and the increasing distance of the outer electron from the nucleus provide an explanation of the fact that, proceeding down the groups, succeeding elements generally have smaller first ionization energies. As a rule, the elements in a group have the same outer electron configuration and the same number of valence electrons.

4. Variation in Electron Affinities. The **electron affinity** is a measure of the energy exchanged when an electron is added to a gaseous atom to form a negative ion. A negative value for electron affinity indicates that energy is given up by the system to the surroundings when an electron is added to an atom. The change is expressed for any element X by the equation

$$X(g) + e^- \longrightarrow X^-(g) + energy$$

A positive value for electron affinity indicates that energy must be added to the system to force the electron onto the atom, as represented in the equation

$$Energy + X(g) + e^- \longrightarrow X^-(g)$$

Elements to the left within a period of the periodic table have little tendency to form negative ions; as we go from left to right within a period, elements have an increasing tendency to form negative ions. Hence across a period from left to right, electron affinities tend to become more negative (Table 6.5). However, exceptions are found

Table 6.5			Electron Affinities of Some Elements, in Kilojoules per Mole				
IA							VIIIA
H							**He**
−72	IIA	IIIA	IVA	VA	VIA	VIIA	+20[a]
Li	**Be**	**B**	**C**	**N**	**O**	**F**	**Ne**
−60	+240[a]	−23	−123	0	−141	−322	+30
Na	**Mg**	**Al**	**Si**	**P**	**S**	**Cl**	**Ar**
−53	+230[a]	−44	−120	−74	−201	−348	+35[a]
K	**Ca**	**Ga**	**Ge**	**As**	**Se**	**Br**	**Kr**
−48	+150[a]	−40[a]	−116	−77	−195	−324	+40[a]
Rb	**Sr**	**In**	**Sn**	**Sb**	**Te**	**I**	**Xe**
−46	+160[a]	−40[a]	−121	−101	−190	−295	+40[a]
Cs	**Ba**	**Tl**	**Pb**	**Bi**	**Po**	**At**	**Rn**
−45	+50[a]	−50	−101	−101	−170[a]	−270[a]	+40[a]

[a]Calculated value.

among the elements of Group IIA, Group VA, and Group VIIIA. These groups have filled *ns* subshells, half-filled *np* subshells, and all subshells filled, respectively. The completely filled or half-filled subshells represent relatively stable configurations.

❻.4 Chemical Behavior and the Periodic Table

Much of the behavior of an element can be predicted from its position in the periodic table. As an example, consider the use that Mendeleev made of his periodic table in predicting the properties of unknown elements. Mendeleev's table included only 62 elements, the number known at that time. It also contained six places that he left vacant so that known elements of similar chemical properties would fall in the same group. Mendeleev predicted the properties of the elements that would fit these gaps from the known chemical behavior of their neighbors in the periodic table. The elements are scandium (Sc), gallium (Ga), germanium (Ge), technetium (Tc), rhenium (Re), and polonium (Po), and they all have properties similar to those predicted by Mendeleev.

A comparison of the properties predicted by Mendeleev for germanium, which he called eka-silicon, and those determined experimentally for the element after it was isolated is given in Table 6.6. You can see that the properties are very similar to those of germanium and are intermediate between those of silicon and tin, the neighbors of germanium in Group IVA.

You can apply the same principles Mendeleev used to predict the properties of elements to correlate and recall their behavior. The periodic table provides a powerful framework for showing patterns in the chemical behavior of the elements.

Table 6.6	Predicted Properties for Eka-silicon and Observed Properties of Silicon, Tin, and Germanium			
	Silicon	Predicted for Eka-silicon	Germanium	Tin
Atomic mass	28	72	72.59	118
Density (g/cm^3)	2.3	5.5	5.3	7.3
Color	Gray nonmetal	Gray metal	Gray metal	White metal
Oxidation number with oxygen	+4	+4	+4	+4
Reaction with acid	No reaction	Very slow reaction	Slow reaction with conc. acid	Slow reaction
Formula of chloride	$SiCl_4$	$EkCl_4$	$GeCl_4$	$SnCl_4$

❻.5 Metals, Nonmetals, and Semi-metals

The elements may be divided into three broad groups: metals, nonmetals, and semi-metals. A pure **metal** is generally a good conductor of heat and electricity. It shows a metallic luster and is malleable (can be pounded into sheets) and ductile (can be bent or drawn into wires). A pure **nonmetal** is generally a poor conductor. It normally shows no metallic luster and is brittle and nonductile in the solid state. Some elements, called **semi-metals** or **metalloids,** cannot be satisfactorily classified as either metals or non-metals, for they possess some of the properties of each. The semi-metal silicon, for example, exhibits a bright metallic luster, but it is not a good conductor and it is brittle. Figure 6.5 shows the metal aluminum, the nonmetal sulfur, and the semi-metal silicon.

The distribution of metals, semi-metals, and nonmetals in the periodic table is shown in Fig. 6.6. Metals comprise 78 percent of the 109 elements.

Figure 6.5

Aluminum, a metal (left); silicon, a semi-metal (right); and sulfur, a non-metal (top).

If you are familiar with the general properties of metals and nonmetals, you can reasonably predict a great deal of the chemical behavior of an element simply from its position in the periodic table. The general properties of metals and nonmetals are outlined in Table 6.7. Semi-metals may exhibit either metallic or nonmetallic behavior, depending on the conditions under which they react.

As an example of metallic behavior, consider the behavior of sodium and its compounds. Sodium (Na) is clearly identifiable as a metal; it lies in Group IA at the left of the periodic table. It readily loses its one valence electron when it reduces nonmetals, giving ionic compounds containing the Na^+ ion and the anion formed by the nonmetal.

$$2Na(s) + H_2(g) \longrightarrow 2NaH(s) \qquad (Na^+ \text{ and } H^-)$$

$$2Na(s) + F_2(g) \longrightarrow 2NaF(s) \qquad (Na^+ \text{ and } F^-)$$

$$16Na(s) + S_8(s) \longrightarrow 8Na_2S(s) \qquad (Na^+ \text{ and } S^{2-})$$

$$12Na(s) + P_4(s) \longrightarrow 4Na_3P(s) \qquad (Na^+ \text{ and } P^{3-})$$

Sodium oxide, Na_2O, is a soluble ionic oxide that reacts with water giving sodium hydroxide, a base.

$$Na_2O(s) + H_2O(l) \longrightarrow 2Na^+(aq) + 2OH^-(aq)$$

Figure 6.6

Metals, semi-metals, and nonmetals in the periodic table. The metals are shaded in red, the semi-metals in blue, and the nonmetals in green.

Table 6.7	Properties of Metals and Nonmetals	

Metals	Nonmetals
1. Reduce elemental nonmetals (except noble gases)	1. Oxidize elemental metals and often oxidize other nonmetals that have less ability to attract electrons
2. Form oxides that may react with water to give hydroxides	2. Form oxides that may react with water to give acids
3. Form basic hydroxides	3. Form acidic hydroxyl compounds (oxyacids)
4. React with O_2, F_2, H_2, and other nonmetals, usually giving ionic compounds	4. React with O_2, F_2, H_2, and other nonmetals, giving covalent compounds
5. Form binary metal hydrides that, if soluble, are strong bases	5. Form binary hydrides that may be acidic
6. React with other metals, giving metallic compounds	6. React with metals, often giving ionic compounds
7. Have one to five electrons in outermost shell, usually not more than three	7. Usually have four to eight electrons in outermost shell
8. Readily form cations by loss of electrons	8. Readily form anions by accepting electrons to fill outermost shell (except noble gases)

The hydride of sodium, NaH, is an ionic compound containing H^- ions. The hydride ion, H^-, is a very strong base and accepts hydrogen ion from water to form the metal hydroxide and H_2 in 100% yield.

$$NaH(s) + H_2O(l) \longrightarrow NaOH(aq) + H_2(g)$$

As an example of nonmetallic behavior, consider the behavior of chlorine and its compounds. Chlorine, which lies toward the upper right in the periodic table in Group VIIA, readily gains one electron and thus may be readily identified as a nonmetal. Because chlorine is a nonmetal, we expect it to oxidize metals and to form ionic compounds that contain chloride ion. This ion forms when a chlorine atom picks up one electron and fills its valence shell. Ionic metal chlorides are formed when chlorine oxidizes metals lying to the left of it in the periodic table.

$$2Li(s) + Cl_2(g) \longrightarrow 2LiCl(s) \qquad (Li^+ \text{ and } Cl^-)$$

$$Ca(s) + Cl_2(g) \longrightarrow CaCl_2(s) \qquad (Ca^{2+} \text{ and } Cl^-)$$

$$Mn(s) + Cl_2(g) \longrightarrow MnCl_2(s) \qquad (Mn^{2+} \text{ and } Cl^-)$$

As a nonmetal, chlorine is also expected to oxidize other nonmetals that have less ability to attract electrons (hydrogen and the nonmetals lying to the left and below chlorine in the periodic table) to form covalent molecules. This behavior is in fact observed; for example, the products in the following reactions are covalent:

$$H_2(g) + Cl_2(g) \longrightarrow 2HCl(g)$$

$$P_4(s) + 10Cl_2(g) \longrightarrow 4PCl_5(s)$$

$$Si(s) + 2Cl_2(g) \longrightarrow SiCl_4(l)$$

As is expected for a compound of hydrogen and a halogen, HCl acts as an acid in aqueous solution and is in fact a strong acid in the presence of suitable bases; for example, it donates hydrogen ions to water to form H_3O^+ and Cl^-, and to NH_3 to form NH_4^+ and Cl^-, in 100% yield.

$$HCl(g) + H_2O(l) \longrightarrow H_3O^+(aq) + Cl^-(aq)$$

$$HCl(g) + NH_3(aq) \longrightarrow NH_4^+(aq) + Cl^-(aq)$$

A covalent oxide of chlorine, Cl_2O_7, reacts with water to give the acid $HClO_4$.

$$Cl_2O_7 + H_2O \longrightarrow 2HClO_4$$

Written in ionic form, this reaction is as follows:

$$Cl_2O_7(l) + 3H_2O(l) \longrightarrow 2H_3O^+(aq) + 2ClO_4^-(aq)$$

Perchloric acid, $HClO_4$, contains three oxygen atoms and one hydroxyl group (OH group) covalently bonded to the chlorine.

$$O-\overset{\overset{\displaystyle O}{|}}{\underset{\underset{\displaystyle O}{|}}{Cl}}-O-H$$

Thus $HClO_4$ may be regarded as a hydroxide of the nonmetal, chlorine. Such molecules are more commonly called **oxyacids.** Other common oxyacids that contain hydroxide groups include nitric acid, which can be expressed by either the formula HNO_3 or the formula $HONO_2$; sulfuric acid, H_2SO_4 or $(HO)_2SO_2$; and phosphoric acid, H_3PO_4 or $(HO)_3PO$.

Nomenclature of Ternary Compounds

This is an appropriate time to expand our knowledge of nomenclature (see Section 2.8) by discussing the naming of the oxyacids, such as $HClO_4$ and HNO_3, and their salts. Chlorine, nitrogen, sulfur, phosphorus, and several other elements form oxyacids (ternary compounds with hydrogen and oxygen) that usually differ from each other in oxygen content. The most common acid of a series usually bears the name of the acid-forming element, ending with the suffix -ic, as in chloric acid ($HClO_3$), sulfuric acid (H_2SO_4), nitric acid (HNO_3), and phosphoric acid (H_3PO_4). If the "central" element (Cl, S, etc.) of a related acid has a higher oxidation number than it does in the most common form, the suffix -ic is retained and the prefix per- is added. The name perchloric acid for $HClO_4$ illustrates this rule. If the "central" element has a lower oxidation number than it does in the most common acid, the suffix -ic is replaced with the suffix -ous. Examples are chlorous acid ($HClO_2$), sulfurous acid (H_2SO_3), nitrous acid (HNO_2), and phosphorous acid (H_3PO_3). If the same central element in two acids has lower oxidation numbers than it does in its -ous acid, the acid having the lower of the two oxidation numbers is named by adding the prefix hypo- and retaining the ending -ous. Thus HClO is hypochlorous acid, and H_3PO_2 is hypophosphorous acid.

Metal salts of the oxyacids (compounds in which a metal replaces the hydrogen of the acid) are named by identifying the metal and then the negative acid ion. For these salts the ending -ic of the oxyacid name is changed to -ate, and the ending -ous is changed to -ite. The salts of perchloric acid are perchlorates, those of sulfuric acid are sulfates, those of nitrous acid are nitrites, and those of hypophosphorous acid are hypophosphites. This system of naming applies to all inorganic oxyacids and their salts. The names of the oxyacids for chlorine and their corresponding sodium salts are given in Table 6.8.

Oxyacids that contain more than one replaceable hydrogen atom can form anions that contain hydrogen; H_2SO_4 gives HSO_4^- (hydrogen sulfate), and H_3PO_4 gives

Table 6.8	Names of Oxyacids of Chlorine and the Corresponding Sodium Salts	
Cl Oxidation Number	Acids	Salts
+1	HClO, hypochlorous acid	NaClO, sodium hypochlorite
+3	$HClO_2$, chlorous acid	$NaClO_2$, sodium chlorite
+5	$HClO_3$, chloric acid	$NaClO_3$, sodium chlorate
+7	$HClO_4$, perchloric acid	$NaClO_4$, sodium perchlorate

$H_2PO_4^-$ (dihydrogen phosphate) and HPO_4^{2-} (hydrogen phosphate). Metal salts of these ions are named like other salts of oxyacids; KH_2PO_4, for example, is potassium dihydrogen phosphate.

The system of nomenclature for a class of compounds known as coordination compounds will be described in Chapter 26.

6.6 Variation in Metallic and Nonmetallic Behavior of the Representative Elements

Elements that easily lose electrons exhibit metallic behavior. The elements with only one or two electrons in the valence shell and the heavier elements lying at the bottoms of the groups of the periodic table generally lose electrons most readily. Atoms of nonmetals fill their valence shells either by sharing electrons with other nonmetals or by using electrons transferred from metal atoms. These are the atoms that lie in the upper right-hand portion of the table. Sodium, the active metal at the left end of the third period, enters into chemical combinations by the loss of its single valence electron (see Section 7.2). An atom of chlorine, a typical nonmetal toward the right end of the third period, combines by adding one electron to its valence shell of seven electrons, either by gaining an electron from a metal or by sharing an electron with a nonmetal.

Proceeding across the third period from sodium to chlorine, we encounter five other elements. In general, going across a period, valence electrons are lost with increasing difficulty. Thus the chemical behavior becomes decreasingly metallic and increasingly nonmetallic as we go from left to right. The changeover from metallic to nonmetallic behavior is gradual, but it can be said to occur between aluminum and silicon in this period. Both aluminum and silicon, however, may exhibit metallic or nonmetallic properties under the appropriate conditions.

The variation in the properties of the oxides and hydrides of the representative elements across the third period demonstrates this gradual changeover (Table 6.9). Sodium, magnesium, and aluminum are shiny metals that conduct heat and electricity well. Silicon is a semi-metal. It has a luster characteristic of a metal, but it is a semiconductor (a poor conductor of electricity). Phosphorus, sulfur, and chlorine are dull in appearance and are nonconducting elements. The chemical behavior of these elements also reflects the gradual change in chemical properties across the period. *This variation in behavior*

Table 6.9		**Periodic Variation of the Properties of Oxides and Hydrides of the Elements of the Third Period**				
Group IA	Group IIA	Group IIIA	Group IVA	Group VA	Group VIA	Group VIIA
Reaction of Oxides with Water and the Acid/Base Character of Hydroxides						
Na_2O gives NaOH (strong base)	MgO gives $Mg(OH)_2$ (weak base)	Al_2O_3 N.R.*	SiO_2 N.R.*	P_4O_{10} gives H_3PO_4 (weak acid)	SO_3 gives H_2SO_4 (strong acid)	Cl_2O_7 gives $HClO_4$ (strong acid)
Bonding in Oxides						
Na_2O ionic	MgO ionic	Al_2O_3 ionic	SiO_2 covalent	P_4O_{10} covalent	SO_3 covalent	Cl_2O_7 covalent
Hydrides						
NaH ionic (strong base)	MgH_2 ionic (strong base)	AlH_3 covalent (moderate base)	SiH_4 covalent (very weak acid)	PH_3 covalent (very weak acid)	H_2S covalent (weak acid)	HCl covalent (strong acid)

*Nonreacting

illustrates the fact that the *properties characteristic of metallic behavior become less pronounced and the properties characteristic of nonmetallic character become more pronounced from left to right across a period of representative elements.* For example, base strength, ionic character, and strength as a reducing agent decrease, whereas acid strength, covalent character, and strength as an oxidizing agent increase.

Because atoms at the top of a group lose electrons less easily than those at the bottom of the group, *the metallic character of the elements increases and the nonmetallic character decreases as we go down a group of representative elements.* For example, bismuth, at the bottom of Group VA, is a metallic element; antimony is a semi-metal; and nitrogen, phosphorus, and arsenic, at the top of the group, are nonmetals (Fig. 6.7). Elemental fluorine, at the top of Group VIIA, is a stronger oxidizing agent than elemen-

Figure 6.7

The solid elements of Group VA. From left to right, phosphorus and arsenic (nonmetals), antimony (a semi-metal), and bismuth (a metal). Nitrogen, the lightest member of the group, is a colorless gas and is a nonmetal. White phosphorus, which is shown in the figure, is so reactive in air that it must be stored under water.

tal iodine, near the bottom of the group. Iodine has sufficient metallic character to possess a metallic luster.

The behavior of an element also varies with its oxidation number (see Section 2.7). *The metallic behavior of an element decreases and its nonmetallic behavior increases as the positive oxidation number of the element in its compounds increases.* For instance, in perchloric acid, $HClO_4$ ($HOClO_3$), the oxidation number of chlorine is $+7$; in hypochlorous acid, $HOCl$, chlorine has an oxidation number of $+1$. Perchloric acid is a very strong acid (a characteristic of a compound of an element with pronounced nonmetallic behavior), whereas hypochlorous acid is a weak acid (less pronounced nonmetallic behavior). Thallium(III) chloride, $TlCl_3$, is a covalent compound (a characteristic of a nonmetal chloride) whereas thallium(I) chloride, $TlCl$, is ionic (a characteristic of a metal chloride). The chlorides of tin(IV) and lead(IV), $SnCl_4$ and $PbCl_4$, are liquids containing tetrahedral covalent molecules. The chlorides of tin(II) and lead(II), $SnCl_2$ and $PbCl_2$, are solids with much more ionic character in their bonds than the chlorides of tin(IV) and lead(IV). Thus, in addition to the position of an element in the periodic table, we must consider its oxidation number when predicting the behavior of its compounds.

For Review

Summary

In the periodic table, the elements are arranged in order of increasing atomic number. Elements with similar electron configurations (and, consequently, similar chemical behavior) are found in the same **group,** or **family. Valence electrons** in the outermost s and p orbitals are responsible for the chemical behavior of the **representative elements:** Group IA (the alkali metals, s^1), Group IIA (the alkaline earth metals, s^2), Group IIIA (s^2p^1), Group IVA (s^2p^2), Group VA (s^2p^3), Group VIA (the chalcogens, s^2p^4), Group VIIA (the halogens, s^2p^5), and Group IIB (s^2). **Transition metals** may have valence electrons in the outer shell and the next shell in from the outer shell, the ns and $(n-1)d$ orbitals, respectively. The **inner transition metals** may have valence electrons in three shells: the ns, $(n-1)d$, and $(n-2)f$ orbitals.

The chemical properties of elements and many of their physical properties (such as **atomic radii, ionic radii, ionization energies,** and **electron affinities**) vary in a periodic way with the nature of the valence electrons involved. A gradual change from metallic to nonmetallic behavior occurs for successive elements across each period of the periodic table. Metallic behavior increases from top to bottom in each group. The **semimetals** are intermediate in character between the metals and the nonmetals; they exhibit some metallic and some nonmetallic behavior.

Key Terms and Concepts

actinide series (6.1)

covalent radius (6.3)

electron affinity (6.3)

electron configuration (6.2)

first ionization energy (6.3)

group, or family, of elements (6.1)

inner transition element (6.2)

ionic radius (6.3)

ionization energy (6.3)

isoelectronic species (6.3)

lanthanide series (6.1)

metal (6.5)

metalloid (6.5)

noble gas (6.2)

nomenclature of oxyacids (6.5)

nonmetal (6.5)

oxyacid (6.5)

periodic table (6.1)

period of elements (6.1)

representative element (6.2)

second ionization energy (6.3)

semi-metal (6.5)

third ionization energy (6.3)

transition element (6.2)

valence electron (6.2)

valence shell (6.2)

Exercises

The Periodic Table

1. State the periodic law. How is the periodic table correlated with electronic structure?
2. Describe the noble gases, representative elements, inner transition elements, and transition elements in terms of filling of s, p, d, and f subshells.
3. In terms of electron configuration, explain why there are 2 elements in the first period of the periodic table, 8 elements in the second and third periods, 18 elements in the fourth and fifth periods, and 32 elements in the sixth period.
4. In terms of the electron configuration of the H atom, explain why H could be included in either Group IA or Group VIIA of the periodic table.
5. Which groups of elements in the periodic table have the following electron configurations in their valence shells? (n represents the principal quantum number.)
   (a) ns^2
   (b) ns^2np^2
   (c) ns^2np^4
   (d) $ns^2(n-1)d^4$
   (e) $ns^2(n-1)d^1(n-2)f^{14}$
6. Most representative metals that form positive ions in chemical compounds do so by losing all of their valence electrons. Which group of representative elements in the periodic table forms tripositive ions, M^{3+}?
7. Representative nonmetals that form negative ions in chemical compounds do so by filling their valence shells with electrons. Which group in the periodic table forms dinegative ions, X^{2-}?
8. The formula for silicon chloride is $SiCl_4$. What is the chemical formula for the chlorides of C and Ge, two other members of Group IVA?

Periodic Properties

9. Distinguish between ionization energy and electron affinity.
10. (a) Can a metal have an ionization energy? An electron affinity? Explain your answers.
    (b) Can a nonmetal have an ionization energy? An electron affinity? Explain your answers.
11. Why is the radius of an atom larger than the radius of a positive ion formed from it?
12. Why is the radius of an atom smaller than the radius of a negative ion formed from it?
13. Explain the decreasing radii for the atoms Li, Be, B, and C.
14. Explain the increasing radii of the atoms Cl, S, and P.
15. Explain the decreasing radii of the isoelectronic ions Na^+, Mg^{2+}, and Al^{3+}.
16. Explain the increasing radii of the isoelectronic ions F^-, O^{2-}, and N^{3-}.
17. Arrange each of the atoms or ions in the following groupings in order of increasing size, on the basis of their location in the periodic table:
    (a) Ba, Mg, Pb, Ca, Sr
    (b) Al, Na, Mg, P, Cl
    (c) Br^-, Ca^{2+}, K^+, Se^{2-}
    (d) As^{3-}, Ca^{2+}, Cl^-, K^+
    (e) Al^{3+}, F^-, Na^+, Mg^{2+}, O^{2-}
18. State which member of each of the following pairs has the higher ionization energy: (a) Na or Mg? (b) O or F? (c) O or S? (d) Sr or Ba? (e) P or O? (f) Be or Na? (g) Ar or K? Explain why in each case.

Additional Exercises

19. The ion X^- has three unpaired electrons. If X is a representative element, to which group does it belong?
20. A gaseous ion, X^+ has three unpaired electrons in its most stable state. If X is a representative element, to which group of the periodic table does it belong?
21. The gaseous ion X^{2+} has no unpaired electrons in its most stable state. If X is a representative element, it could be a member of one of two possible groups. Which groups are they?
22. Write a periodic table for the first 14 elements in another universe if the quantum numbers of these elements behave as described in Exercise 51 of Chapter 5.
23. What electron configuration represents the largest neutral atom in the following? The smallest neutral atom?
    (a) $1s^2 2s^2$
    (b) $1s^2 2s^2 2p^6 3s^2$
    (c) $1s^2 2s^2 2p^6 3s^2 3p^6 4s^2$
    (d) $1s^2 2s^2 2p^6 3s^2 3p^6 4s^2 3d^{10}$
24. Identify two different atoms that lose electrons with the quantum numbers $n = 3$, $l = 0$, $m = 0$, $s = +\frac{1}{2}$ during the first ionization of each.
25. Each of the following electron configurations is found in a negative ion. Arrange them in increasing order of their size. The atomic number is given for each.
    (a) ($Z = 7$) [Ne]
    (b) ($Z = 8$) [Ne]
    (c) ($Z = 9$) [Ne]
    (d) ($Z = 34$) [Kr]
    (e) ($Z = 35$) [Kr]
26. Which of the following electron configurations represents the largest positive ion with a charge of +1? The smallest positive ion with a charge of +1?
    (a) $1s^2$
    (b) $1s^2 2s^2 2p^6$
    (c) $1s^2 2s^2 2p^6 3s^2 3p^6$
    (d) $1s^2 2s^2 2p^6 3s^2 3p^6 3d^{10}$

Chemical Bonding: General Concepts

Covalent bonds hold atoms in a regular array in a zeolite.

Although it is important to understand the electronic structures of atoms, most chemists do not deal with isolated atoms. They usually study groups of two or more atoms and the attractive forces, called **chemical bonds,** that hold atoms together. When elements react and form a compound, chemical bonds form between atoms in the compound. When compounds undergo chemical reactions, the bonds between atoms are rearranged. When the atoms separate, the bonds are destroyed and the compounds no longer exist.

In this chapter we will examine two types of chemical bonds and determine how to predict their formation by considering the electronic structures of the atoms involved.

We will see that the forces that hold atoms together are electrical in nature and that the formation of chemical bonds between atoms involves changes in their electronic structures. We will also discover that energy changes accompany the formation or rearrangement of chemical bonds in chemical reactions.

7.1 Ionic Bonds: Chemical Bonding by Electron Transfer

Ionic compounds (Section 2.6) are stabilized by **ionic bonds.** These bonds are electrostatic attractions between ions that are formed by the transfer of electrons between atoms. Ionic bonds usually form when a metal combines with a nonmetal.

Ionic compounds are electrically neutral, because the total number of positive charges on the positive ions and the total number of negative charges on the negative ions are equal. The formula of an ionic compound represents the simplest ratio of the numbers of ions necessary to give the same number of positive and negative charges. For example, the formula of potassium oxide, K_2O, indicates that this ionic compound contains twice as many potassium ions (K^+ ions) as oxide ions (O^{2-} ions).

Sodium chloride, an ionic compound, consists of a regular arrangement of equal numbers of Na^+ ions and Cl^- ions (Fig. 7.1). This arrangement arises because each ion pulls the maximum possible number of oppositely charged ions about itself. In this case each sodium ion is surrounded by six chloride ions, and each chloride ion is surrounded by six sodium ions. The force that holds these ions together in the solid is the strong electrostatic attraction between ions of opposite charge. It requires 769 kilojoules of energy to convert 1 mole of solid sodium chloride to separated gaseous Na^+ and Cl^- ions.

$$NaCl(s) \longrightarrow Na^+(g) + Cl^-(g) \qquad \Delta H = 769 \text{ kJ}$$

Electron-dot formulas, or **Lewis symbols,** are often used to describe valence electron configurations of atoms and monatomic ions. These symbols consist of the symbol for the element and one dot for each valence electron present. When two dots are written adjacent to each other, as in Ca : , they represent a pair of electrons in the same orbital. Examples are given in Table 7.1.

A positive ion (**cation**) found in an ionic compound forms when a neutral atom loses one or more of the electrons in its valence shell (the outer shell; Section 6.2). For example, when a sodium atom loses its one valence electron, it has one more proton than electrons. Thus it is left with a positive charge of +1 and forms a sodium ion. When a calcium atom loses its two valence electrons, a calcium ion with a charge of +2 results.

$$Na \cdot \longrightarrow Na^+ + e^- \qquad Ca : \longrightarrow Ca^{2+} + 2e^-$$

| Sodium atom | Sodium cation | Calcium atom | Calcium cation |

The atoms of most metallic elements readily form cations. These atoms, which have relatively low ionization energies (Section 6.3), tend to be those lying to the left in a period or those lying toward the bottom of a group in the periodic table.

A negative ion (**anion**) found in an ionic compound forms when a neutral atom picks up one or more electrons and fills its outer s and p orbitals. For example, when a

Figure 7.1

The arrangement of sodium and chloride ions in a crystal of sodium chloride (common table salt). The smaller red spheres represent sodium ions, the larger green ones, chloride ions. The upper structure is an "expanded" view that shows the geometry more clearly.

Cl⁻   Na⁺

Table 7.1	Lewis Symbols for the Atoms of the Third Period	
Atom	Electron Configuration	Lewis Symbol
Sodium	$[Ne]3s^1$	Na·
Magnesium	$[Ne]3s^2$	Mg:
Aluminum	$[Ne]3s^23p^1$	·Al:
Silicon	$[Ne]3s^23p^2$	·Si·
Phosphorus	$[Ne]3s^23p^3$	·P·
Sulfur	$[Ne]3s^23p^4$	:S·
Chlorine	$[Ne]3s^23p^5$	:Cl·
Argon	$[Ne]3s^23p^6$	:Ar:

chlorine atom picks up one electron to fill its *s* and *p* orbitals, it contains one more electron than protons. Thus it acquires a negative charge of −1 and forms a chloride ion. When a sulfur atom picks up two electrons, a sulfide ion with a charge of −2 results.

$$:Cl· + e^- \longrightarrow :Cl:^- \qquad :S· + 2e^- \longrightarrow :S:^{2-}$$

| Chlorine atom | Chloride anion | Sulfur atom | Sulfide anion |

The atoms of the nonmetallic elements readily form anions. These atoms have relatively high electron affinities (Section 6.3) and lie in the upper right-hand portion of the periodic table. Nonmetal atoms are only a few electrons short of having filled outer *s* and *p* orbitals and can pick up electrons lost by metal atoms, thereby filling these orbitals. Nonmetals such as F, Cl, Br, O, and S form negative ions.

When metals combine with nonmetals, electrons are transferred from the metals to the nonmetals, and ionic compounds are formed. The use of Lewis symbols to show the transfer of electrons during formation of ionic compounds is illustrated by the following examples:

Metal	Nonmetal	Ionic Compound	
Na·	+ :Cl·	$\longrightarrow$	$Na^+[:Cl:^-]$	(1)

Sodium atom   Chlorine atom   Sodium chloride (sodium ion and chloride ion)

| Mg: | + :O· | $\longrightarrow$ | $Mg^{2+}[:O:^{2-}]$ | (2) |

Magnesium atom   Oxygen atom   Magnesium oxide (magnesium ion and oxide ion)

| Ca: | + 2 :F· | $\longrightarrow$ | $Ca^{2+}[:F:^-]_2$ | (3) |

Calcium atom   Fluorine atoms   Calcium fluoride (calcium ion and two fluoride ions)

7.2   The Electronic Structures of Ions

With a few exceptions, representative elements, Groups IA through VIIA and IIB (Section 6.2), tend to lose all valence electrons when forming cations, making it easy to remember the charges on the positive ions. The charge is equal to the group number of the element forming the ion, because the group number is the same as the number of electrons in the outermost shell of a representative element. Members of Group IA have ionic charges of $+1$; members of Groups IIA and IIB, $+2$; etc. The exceptions to this rule involve elements toward the bottom of the groups: Hg_2^{2+}, Tl^+, Sn^{2+}, Pb^{2+}, and Bi^{3+} form, whereas the expected ions are Hg^{2+}, Tl^{3+}, Sn^{4+}, Pb^{4+}, and Bi^{5+}.

The positive ion produced by the loss of all valence electrons from a representative metal will have either a **noble gas electron configuration** (the same electron configuration as a noble gas), in which the valence shell in the ion has the configuration ns^2np^6 ($1s^2$ for cations of the second period), or a **pseudo-noble gas electron configuration,** in which the outermost shell has the configuration $ns^2np^6nd^{10}$. An example of the latter is the zinc ion, Zn^{2+}, with the electron configuration $1s^22s^22p^63s^23p^63d^{10}$.

Example 7.1

Write the electron configurations, and indicate the charges of the ions formed from the elements K, Ca, Ga, and Cd.

As members of Groups IA, IIA, IIIA, and IIB, respectively, these elements form the ions K^+, Ca^{2+}, Ga^{3+}, and Cd^{2+} by the loss of all of the valence electrons from the atoms. Noble gas electron configurations for K^+ and Ca^{2+} and pseudo-noble gas electron configurations for Ga^{3+} and Cd^{2+} result, as shown in the following table:

Atom		Ion	
K	$1s^22s^22p^63s^23p^64s^1$	K^+	$1s^22s^22p^63s^23p^6$
Ca	$1s^22s^22p^63s^23p^64s^2$	Ca^{2+}	$1s^22s^22p^63s^23p^6$
Ga	$1s^22s^22p^63s^23p^63d^{10}4s^24p^1$	Ga^{3+}	$1s^22s^22p^63s^23p^63d^{10}$
Cd	$1s^22s^22p^63s^23p^63d^{10}4s^24p^64d^{10}5s^2$	Cd^{2+}	$1s^22s^22p^63s^23p^63d^{10}4s^24p^64d^{10}$

Transition and inner transition metal elements behave differently from representative elements. Most transition metal cations have $+2$ or $+3$ charges resulting from the loss of their outermost s electrons (or electron), sometimes followed by the loss of one or two d electrons from the next-to-outermost shell. For example, copper ($1s^22s^22p^63s^23p^63d^{10}4s^1$) forms the ions Cu^+ ($1s^22s^22p^63s^23p^63d^{10}$) and Cu^{2+} ($1s^22s^22p^63s^23p^63d^9$). Although the d orbitals of the transition elements are the last to fill when building up electron configurations by the aufbau principle, the outermost s electrons are the first to be lost when these atoms ionize. When the inner transition metals form ions, they usually have a $+3$ charge resulting from the loss of their outermost s electrons and a d or f electron.

Monatomic negative ions form when a neutral atom picks up enough electrons to fill its outer s and p orbitals completely. Thus it is simple to determine the charge on such an ion; the charge is equal to the number of electrons necessary to fill the s and p orbitals of the parent atom. Oxygen, for example, has the electron configuration $1s^22s^22p^4$, whereas the oxygen anion (oxide ion) has the noble gas electron configuration

$1s^2 2s^2 2p^6$. The two additional electrons required to fill the valence orbitals give the oxide ion the charge of -2.

Example 7.2

Phosphorus is a member of Group VA. A neutral phosphorus atom has the electron configuration $1s^2 2s^2 2p^6 3s^2 3p^3$, or $[Ne]3s^2 3p^3$. A phosphorus atom requires three additional electrons to fill its $3p$ orbitals, so the charge of the phosphorus anion is -3. The electron configuration of P^{3-} is $[Ne]3s^2 3p^6$.

The electronic differences between an atom and its ion give them very different physical and chemical properties. Sodium *atoms* form sodium metal, a soft, silvery-white metal that burns vigorously in air and reacts rapidly with water. Chlorine *atoms* form chlorine gas, Cl_2, a yellow gas that is extremely corrosive to most metals and very poisonous to animals and plants. The vigorous reaction between sodium and chlorine forms the compound sodium chloride, common table salt, which contains *ions* of sodium and chlorine. The ions exhibit properties entirely different from those of the elements sodium and chlorine. Chlorine is poisonous, but sodium chloride is essential to life; sodium atoms react vigorously with water, but sodium chloride is stable in water.

Sodium is a soft metal.

❼.3 Covalent Bonds: Chemical Bonding by Electron Sharing

The bonds between atoms in covalent compounds (Section 2.6) are **covalent bonds.** These are bonds that form when electrons are shared between atoms—that is, when the electrons occupy orbitals of both atoms involved in the bond. Electrons are shared and covalent bonds are formed when both atoms involved in the bond have about the same tendency to give up or to pick up electrons. Nonmetal atoms frequently form covalent bonds with each other.

The hydrogen molecule, H_2, contains a covalent bond between two hydrogen atoms. As two hydrogen atoms approach each other during formation of a molecule, their $1s$ orbitals begin to overlap. The electron in the $1s$ orbital on each atom can then spill over into the $1s$ orbital on the other and can occupy the space around both atoms (Fig. 7.2). The electrons are shared by both atoms and are simultaneously attracted by the nuclei of both. This attraction provides the force that holds the molecule together. The resulting bond is very strong; a large amount of energy—436 kJ—must be added to break the bonds in 1 mole of hydrogen molecules and to release the hydrogen atoms.

$$H_2(g) \longrightarrow 2H(g) \qquad \Delta H = 436 \text{ kJ}$$

Conversely, the same amount of energy is released when 1 mole of H_2 molecules forms from 2 moles of H atoms.

$$2H(g) \longrightarrow H_2(g) \qquad \Delta H = -436 \text{ kJ}$$

In most cases, when atoms form covalent bonds they share enough electrons to assume noble gas electron configurations. Each electron in the bond in a hydrogen

Chlorine is a pale yellow gas.

Crystals of salt, sodium chloride.

(a)

(b)

Figure 7.2

(a) The 1s orbitals on two hydrogen atoms. (b) Electron density in the overlapping 1s orbitals in a hydrogen molecule. The plus signs indicate the location of the hydrogen nuclei.

molecule spends an equal amount of time near each nucleus, so the 1s orbital of each hydrogen atom in the molecule is occupied by both electrons. In effect, each atom has the electronic structure of a helium atom.

The sharing of one pair of electrons by two atoms in a molecule of chlorine gives each atom the electronic structure of an atom of the noble gas argon, because a free atom of chlorine has one less electron than an atom of argon.

$$:\ddot{Cl}\cdot + :\ddot{Cl}\cdot \longrightarrow :\ddot{Cl}:\ddot{Cl}:$$

| Chlorine atoms | Chlorine molecule |

Lewis structures utilize Lewis symbols (Section 7.1) to show electrons in molecules and ions. The Lewis structure shown above for Cl_2 indicates that each Cl atom has three pairs of electrons that are not used in bonding (called **unshared pairs, or lone pairs**) and one shared pair of electrons (written between the atoms). A dash is sometimes used to indicate a shared pair of electrons.

$$H—H \qquad :\ddot{Cl}—\ddot{Cl}:$$

A single shared pair of electrons is called a **single bond.**

The bonding in the other halogen molecules (F_2, Br_2, I_2, and At_2) is like that in the chlorine molecule: one single bond between atoms and three unshared pairs of electrons per atom. Like the chlorine atoms in Cl_2, each atom in these molecules has a filled valence shell and thus the electronic structure of a noble gas.

The number of covalent bonds (shared electron pairs) that an atom can form can often be predicted from the number of electrons needed to fill its outer s and p orbitals. Each atom of a Group IVA element has four electrons in its outer shell and can accept four more electrons to achieve a noble gas electron configuration. These four electrons can be gained by forming four covalent bonds, as illustrated for carbon in CCl_4 (carbon tetrachloride) and silicon in SiH_4 (silane).

Carbon tetrachloride   Silane

Note that the Lewis structure of a molecule in general does not indicate its three-dimensional shape. As will be discussed in Chapter 8, carbon tetrachloride and silane are not flat molecules.

Nitrogen and the other elements of Group VA need three additional electrons to achieve a noble gas configuration. These three electrons can be gained by formation of three single covalent bonds, as in NH_3 (ammonia). Oxygen and the other atoms in Group VIA need two additional electrons to fill their outer s and p orbitals; thus they can form two single covalent bonds. The elements in Group VIIA, such as fluorine, need to form only one single covalent bond in order to fill their outer s and p orbitals.

Ammonia   Water   Hydrogen fluoride

A pair of atoms may share more than one pair of electrons. For example, a **double bond** is formed when two pairs of electrons are shared between two atoms, as between the carbon and oxygen atoms in CH_2O (formaldehyde) and between the two carbon atoms in C_2H_4 (ethylene).

$$\overset{\text{H}}{\underset{\text{H}}{>}}C::\overset{\cdot\cdot}{O}: \quad \text{or} \quad \overset{\text{H}}{\underset{\text{H}}{>}}C=\overset{\cdot\cdot}{O}: \qquad \overset{\text{H}}{\underset{\text{H}}{>}}C::C\overset{\text{H}}{\underset{\text{H}}{<}} \quad \text{or} \quad \overset{\text{H}}{\underset{\text{H}}{>}}C=C\overset{\text{H}}{\underset{\text{H}}{<}}$$

Formaldehyde   Ethylene

A **triple bond** is formed when three electron pairs are shared by two atoms, as in CO (carbon monoxide) and N_2 (nitrogen molecule).

$$:C:::O: \quad \text{or} \quad :C\equiv O: \qquad :N:::N: \quad \text{or} \quad :N\equiv N:$$

Carbon monoxide   Nitrogen molecule

Under normal conditions, the ability to form double or triple bonds is limited almost exclusively to bonds between carbon, nitrogen, and oxygen atoms. For example, the element nitrogen forms the N_2 molecule, which contains a triple bond, whereas the element phosphorus (also in Group VA) forms the P_4 molecule, which contains only single bonds (Fig. 7.3). Phosphorus, sulfur, and selenium sometimes form double bonds with carbon, nitrogen, and oxygen.

The atoms in polyatomic ions, such as OH^-, NO_3^-, and NH_4^+ (Section 2.5), are held together by covalent bonds. Thus compounds containing polyatomic ions are stabilized by both covalent bonds and ionic bonds. For example, potassium nitrate, KNO_3, contains the K^+ cation and the polyatomic NO_3^- anion. Potassium nitrate has ionic bonds resulting from the electrostatic attraction between the ions K^+ and NO_3^- and covalent bonds between the nitrogen and oxygen atoms in NO_3^-.

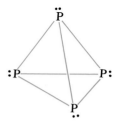

Figure 7.3

The Lewis structure of the P_4 molecule.

7.4 Covalently Bonded Atoms Without a Noble Gas Configuration

Elements in the second row of the periodic table have only four orbitals in their valence shell (Section 5.10). Thus they never form compounds in which they have more than eight electrons in their valence shell. However, atoms in which the outermost electron shell is one where $n = 3$ or greater have more than four valence orbitals and can share more than four pairs of electrons with other atoms. For example, the phosphorus atom in PCl_5 shares five pairs of electrons, and sulfur shares six electron pairs in the SF_6 molecule. In some molecules, such as IF_5 and XeF_4, the number of electrons in the outer shell of the central atom exceeds eight, even though some of its electron pairs are not shared.

$$\overset{\text{Cl}}{\underset{\text{Cl}}{\text{Cl}-\text{P}}}\overset{\text{Cl}}{\underset{\text{Cl}}{}} \qquad \overset{\text{F}}{\underset{\text{F}}{\text{F}-\text{S}-\text{F}}}\overset{\text{F}}{\underset{\text{F}}{}} \qquad \overset{\text{F}}{\underset{\text{F}}{\text{F}-\text{I}-\text{F}}}\overset{\text{F}}{\underset{}{}} \qquad \overset{\text{F}}{\underset{\text{F}}{\text{F}-\text{Xe}-\text{F}}}$$

(The three unshared pairs usually drawn on each Cl and F atom in these Lewis structures have been omitted for clarity.)

A few molecules contain atoms that do not have the noble gas configuration because they have fewer than eight electrons in their valence shell. For example, boron shares electron pairs with three chlorine atoms in BCl_3 (boron trichloride).

$$\overset{..}{B} \cdot + 3 : \overset{..}{\underset{..}{Cl}} \cdot \longrightarrow : \overset{..}{\underset{..}{Cl}} - B \overset{\overset{\displaystyle \cdot \overset{..}{Cl} \cdot}{\diagup}}{\underset{\underset{\displaystyle \cdot \overset{..}{\underset{..}{Cl}} \cdot}{\diagdown}}{}}$$

Boron trichloride

In this molecule, each chlorine atom has filled outer *s* and *p* orbitals. However, boron, with only six electrons in its outer shell, does not; one of its orbitals is vacant.

An atom like the boron atom in BCl_3, which does not have filled outer *s* and *p* orbitals, is very reactive. It readily combines with a molecule containing an atom with an unshared pair of electrons. For example, NH_3 reacts with BCl_3 because the unshared pair on nitrogen can be shared with the boron atom.

$$: \overset{..}{\underset{..}{Cl}} - B \overset{\overset{\displaystyle \cdot \overset{..}{Cl} \cdot}{\diagup}}{\underset{\underset{\displaystyle \cdot \overset{..}{\underset{..}{Cl}} \cdot}{\diagdown}}{}} \quad + \quad \overset{\displaystyle H}{\underset{\displaystyle H}{: N - H}} \quad \longrightarrow \quad : \overset{\overset{\displaystyle : \overset{..}{Cl} :}{|}}{\underset{\underset{\displaystyle : \overset{..}{\underset{..}{Cl}} :}{|}}{Cl}} - B \overset{\overset{\displaystyle H}{|}}{\underset{\underset{\displaystyle H}{|}}{- N - H}}$$

A bond formed when one of the atoms provides both bonding electrons (like the B—N bond in Cl_3BNH_3) is called a **coordinate covalent, or dative, bond.** Coordinate covalent bonds form when a water molecule combines with a hydrogen ion to form a hydronium ion or when an ammonia molecule combines with a hydrogen ion to form an ammonium ion.

$$\overset{\displaystyle H - \overset{..}{O} :}{\underset{\displaystyle H}{|}} \; + \; H^+ \; \longrightarrow \; \left[\overset{\displaystyle H - \overset{..}{O} - H}{\underset{\displaystyle H}{|}} \right]^+ \qquad \overset{\displaystyle H - \overset{\overset{\displaystyle H}{|}}{N} :}{\underset{\displaystyle H}{|}} \; + \; H^+ \; \longrightarrow \; \left[\overset{\displaystyle H - \overset{\overset{\displaystyle H}{|}}{N} - H}{\underset{\displaystyle H}{|}} \right]^+$$

Water molecule   Hydronium ion, H_3O^+ Ammonia molecule   Ammonium ion, NH_4^+

The difference between the coordinate covalent bond and the normal covalent bond is in the mode of formation—that is, whether each atom contributes one electron or one atom contributes both. Once established, equivalent covalent bonds are indistinguishable from one another, because electrons are identical regardless of their source. All of the O—H bonds in H_3O^+ are the same, as are all of the N—H bonds in NH_4^+.

❼.5 Polar Covalent Bonds: Electronegativity

H   Cl

+   +

Figure 7.4

Electron density of the bonding electrons in the HCl molecule. The electron density is greater about the chlorine nucleus. The plus sign on the right indicates the location of the chlorine nucleus in the molecule.

A covalent bond results when electrons are shared between two atoms. If the atoms are identical, as in Cl_2 or H_2, then the electrons are shared equally. The bonding electrons spend the same amount of time on both of the atoms in the bond. On the other hand, if the atoms in a bond are different, the bonding electrons need not be shared equally and a polar covalent bond can result. A **polar covalent bond** is a bond that has a positively charged end and a negatively charged end. In a polar covalent bond, the bonding electrons spend more time near one atom than near the other. For example, the electrons in the H—Cl bond in a hydrogen chloride molecule spend more time near the chlorine atom than near the hydrogen atom. Thus in a HCl molecule, the chlorine atom is somewhat negative and the hydrogen atom somewhat positive. Figure 7.4 shows the distribution of electrons in the H—Cl bond. Compare this figure with Fig. 7.2, which shows the distribution of electrons in the nonpolar bond in H_2.

If a molecule contains polar bonds, it may possess a dipole moment; that is, the entire molecule may have a positive end and a negative end. We will discuss molecules that have a dipole moment in Chapter 8, after discussing the structures of molecules.

Electronegativity is a measure of the attraction of an atom for the electrons in a chemical bond. The more strongly an atom attracts the electrons in its bonds, the larger its electronegativity. We will use a modified version of the set of electronegativity values proposed by Linus Pauling* (Table 7.2). Because the electronegativity of an atom can vary slightly with the bonds it forms, the values in the table are averages.

In general, electronegativity increases from left to right across a period in the periodic table and decreases down a group. Thus the nonmetals, which lie in the upper right of the table, tend to have the highest electronegativities, with fluorine the most electronegative. Metals tend to be the least electronegative elements, and the Group IA metals have the lowest electronegativities.

The absolute value of the difference in electronegativity of two bonded atoms provides a rough measure of the polarity to be expected in the bond. When the difference is

Table 7.2	Pauling's Values of Electronegativities of the Elements																
															Nonmetals		
																H 2.1	He ...
H 2.1																	
Li 1.0	Be 1.5					Metals						B 2.0	C 2.5	N 3.0	O 3.5	F 4.1	Ne ...
Na 1.0	Mg 1.2				Transition metals							Al 1.5	Si 1.7	P 2.1	S 2.4	Cl 2.8	Ar ...
K 0.9	Ca 1.0	Sc 1.2	Ti 1.3	V 1.4	Cr 1.6	Mn 1.6	Fe 1.6	Co 1.7	Ni 1.8	Cu 1.8	Zn 1.7	Ga 1.8	Ge 2.0	As 2.2	Se 2.5	Br 2.7	Kr ...
Rb 0.9	Sr 1.0	Y 1.1	Zr 1.2	Nb 1.2	Mo 1.3	Tc 1.4	Ru 1.4	Rh 1.4	Pd 1.4	Ag 1.4	Cd 1.5	In 1.5	Sn 1.7	Sb 1.8	Te 2.0	I 2.2	Xe ...
Cs 0.9	Ba 1.0	La-Lu 1.1-1.2	Hf 1.2	Ta 1.3	W 1.4	Re 1.5	Os 1.5	Ir 1.6	Pt 1.4	Au 1.4	Hg 1.4	Tl 1.4	Pb 1.6	Bi 1.7	Po 1.8	At 2.1	Rn ...
Fr 0.9	Ra 1.0	Ac-Lr 1.1-	Unq ...	Unp ...	Unh ...	Uns ...	Uno ...	Une ...									

*Linus Pauling is regarded by many as the preeminent chemist of the twentieth century. His work has ranged from physical chemistry to molecular biology. He has made significant contributions to the way chemists understand chemical bonds and molecular structure. Pauling received the Nobel Prize in chemistry in 1954 for his work on the structure of proteins, and he was awarded the Nobel Peace Prize in 1962.

small or zero, the bond is nonpolar. When it is large, the bond is polar or ionic. The absolute values of the electronegativity differences between the atoms in the bonds H—H, H—Cl, and Na$^+$Cl$^-$ are 0, 0.7, and 1.8; the bonds are nonpolar, polar, and ionic, respectively.

It would be very helpful if there were a single value of the differences between electronegativities above which bonds were ionic. Unfortunately, this is not the case. For example, the covalent bond in IF$_5$ has an electronegativity difference of 1.9, and the covalent bond in NH$_3$ a difference of 0.9. The ionic bond in NaCl has an electronegativity difference of 1.8, and that in CsI a difference of 1.3. The best guide to the covalent or ionic character of a bond is the types of atoms involved: Bonds between two nonmetals are generally covalent; bonds between a metal and a nonmetal are often ionic.

Electrons in a polar covalent bond spend more time in the vicinity of the more electronegative atom; thus the more electronegative atom is the one with the partial negative charge. The more electronegative this atom, the more time the bonding electrons spend near it, and the larger its partial negative charge.

Example 7.3

Using the electronegativity values in Table 7.2, arrange the following covalent bonds in order of increasing polarity and identify the negatively charged atom in each: C—H, C—Cl, C—O, N—H, O—H, Be—H.

The polarity of these bonds increases as the absolute value of the electronegativity difference between the atoms increases. The atom with the partial negative charge is the more electronegative of the two in the bond. The following list shows these bonds in order of increasing polarity.

Bond	Electronegativity Difference	Negative Atom
C—Cl	0.3	Cl
C—H	0.4	C
Be—H	0.6	H
N—H	0.9	N
C—O	1.0	O
O—H	1.4	O

⑦.6 Writing Lewis Structures

Sometimes we can write the Lewis structure for a molecule or ion by pairing up the unpaired electrons on the reactant atoms involved.

$$H \cdot + : \overset{..}{Br} \cdot \longrightarrow H : \overset{..}{Br} :$$

$$2H \cdot + : \overset{..}{S} \cdot \longrightarrow H : \overset{..}{S} : \\ \qquad\qquad\qquad\quad H$$

$$\cdot \overset{..}{N} \cdot + \cdot \overset{..}{N} \cdot \longrightarrow : N :: : N :$$

In other cases when a molecule or ion is more complicated, it is helpful to follow the general procedure outlined below. Let us determine the Lewis structures of NH$_4$$^+$, PO$_2F_2$$^-$, and CO as examples in following this procedure.

Step 1. Draw a skeleton structure of the molecule or ion, showing the arrangement of atoms, and connect each atom to another with a single (one electron pair) bond.

$$\begin{array}{ccc} \text{H} & \text{F} & \\ | & | & \\ \text{H---N---H}^+ & \text{F---P---O}^- & \text{C---O} \\ | & | & \\ \text{H} & \text{O} & \end{array}$$

When several arrangements of atoms are possible, as for $PO_2F_2^-$, we must use experimental evidence to choose the correct one. As a rule, however, the less electronegative element is the central atom (for example, P in $PO_2F_2^-$ and PCl_5, S in SF_6, and Cl in ClO_4^-), with the exception that hydrogen cannot be a central atom.

Step 2. Determine the total number of valence (outer shell) electrons in the molecule or ion.

(a) For a *molecule,* this is equal to the sum of the number of valence electrons on each atom.

   CO: Number of valence electrons = 4 (C atom) + 6 (O atom) = 10

(b) For a *positive ion,* such as NH_4^+, this is equal to the sum of the number of valence electrons on the atoms in the ion minus the number of positive charges on the ion (one electron is lost for each single positive charge).

   NH_4^+:   Number of valence electrons = 5 (N atom) + 1 (H atom)
   + 1 (H atom) + 1 (H atom)
   + 1 (H atom) − 1 (positive charge) = 8

(c) For a *negative ion,* such as $PO_2F_2^-$, this is equal to the sum of the number of valence electrons on the atoms in the ion plus the number of negative charges on the ion (one electron is gained for each single negative charge).

   $PO_2F_2^-$:   Number of valence electrons = 5 (P atom) + 6 (O atom)
   + 6 (O atom) + 7 (F atom) + 7
   (F atom) + 1 (negative charge) = 32

Step 3. Deduct the 2 valence electrons for each bond written in Step 1. Distribute the remaining electrons as unshared pairs, so that each atom (except hydrogen) has 8 electrons if possible. If there are too few electrons to give each atom 8 electrons, convert single bonds to multiple bonds, where possible. Remember, the ability to form multiple bonds is limited almost exclusively to bonds between carbon, nitrogen, and oxygen, although phosphorus, sulfur, and selenium sometimes form double bonds with carbon, nitrogen, and oxygen. Thus some elements may have fewer than 8 electrons in their valence shells when they function as central atoms. For example, see the Lewis formula for BCl_3 in Section 7.4.

   In the NH_4^+ ion, the 8 valence electrons are distributed as 4 electron pairs in 4 single bonds; no electrons are left to form unshared pairs. In the $PO_2F_2^-$ ion, 8 of the 32 valence electrons are distributed as 4 electron pairs in 4 single bonds, leaving 24 electrons to be distributed as 3 unshared pairs around each of the fluorine and oxygen atoms. In the CO molecule, 2 of the 10 valence electrons are used in the single bond in the skeleton structure, leaving 8 to be distributed. These remaining 8 electrons could be distributed as 4 unshared pairs, but this would leave at least 1 atom with fewer than 8 electrons. Filled valence shells about the carbon and oxygen atoms can be obtained only if the 10 electrons are distributed in 3 electron pairs in a triple bond, 1 unshared pair on the carbon atom, and 1 unshared pair on the oxygen atom.

$$
\begin{array}{ccc}
\text{H} & :\!\ddot{\text{F}}\!: & \\
| & | & \\
\text{H}\!-\!\text{N}\!-\!\text{H}^+ & :\!\ddot{\text{F}}\!-\!\text{P}\!-\!\ddot{\text{O}}\!:^- & :\text{C}\!\equiv\!\text{O}: \\
| & | & \\
\text{H} & :\!\ddot{\text{O}}\!: &
\end{array}
$$

In those molecules in which there are too many electrons to have only 8 electrons around each atom, the central atom may have more than 8 electrons in its valence shell (see, for example, the Lewis formulas of PCl_5, SF_6, IF_5, and XeF_4 in Section 7.4). However, note that the outer atoms contain a maximum of 8 electrons in their valence shells.

Although heavier atoms can contain more than 8 electrons, a Lewis formula with more than 2 electrons for a hydrogen atom or 8 electrons for an atom of the second period is incorrect and should be reexamined. Hydrogen has only 1 valence orbital and can have only 2 electrons in this orbital. The elements of the second period have only 4 valence orbitals and these can accommodate only 8 electrons.

Example 7.4

Jupiter's atmosphere contains small amounts of the compounds methane, CH_4, acetylene, HCCH, and phosphine, PH_3. What are the Lewis structures of these molecules?

Because hydrogen cannot be a central atom, the skeleton structure (Step 1) of CH_4 must be

$$
\begin{array}{c}
\text{H} \\
| \\
\text{H}\!-\!\text{C}\!-\!\text{H} \\
| \\
\text{H}
\end{array}
$$

CH_4 contains 8 valence electrons, 4 from the carbon atom and 1 from each of 4 hydrogen atoms (Step 2). All of the valence electrons are used in writing single bonds in the skeleton structure. None remain to be distributed, so the Lewis structure is the skeleton structure.

The molecule HCCH has the skeleton structure

$$\text{H}\!-\!\text{C}\!-\!\text{C}\!-\!\text{H}$$

The molecule contains 10 valence electrons, 6 of which are used in the single bonds in the skeleton structure, leaving 4 electrons to be distributed. The attempts to distribute these electrons as unshared pairs, as illustrated below, do not give the carbon atoms 8 electrons each.

$$\text{H}\!-\!\ddot{\text{C}}\!-\!\ddot{\text{C}}\!-\!\text{H} \qquad \text{H}\!-\!\ddot{\text{C}}\!-\!\text{C}\!-\!\text{H}$$

6 electrons per C   4 electrons / 8 electrons

$$\text{H}\!-\!\ddot{\text{C}}\!=\!\text{C}\!-\!\text{H}$$

6 electrons / 8 electrons

Only with a triple bond will both carbon atoms have eight electrons.

$$\text{H}\!-\!\text{C}\!\equiv\!\text{C}\!-\!\text{H}$$

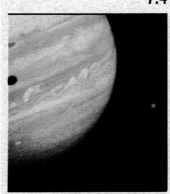

The atmosphere of Jupiter contains small amounts of CH_4, C_2H_2, and PH_3.

The skeleton structure of PH_3 is

$$
\begin{array}{c}
H \\
| \\
P-H \\
| \\
H
\end{array}
$$

Six of the 8 valence electrons in the molecule (5 from the phosphorus atom, 3 from the 3 hydrogen atoms) are used to form single P—H bonds in the skeleton structure. The 2 remaining electrons must appear as an unshared pair on the phosphorus atom in order to give it 8 electrons.

$$
\begin{array}{c}
H \\
| \\
:P-H \\
| \\
H
\end{array}
$$

Write the Lewis structure of the compound ClF_3.

Chlorine is the central atom in this molecule because it is the less electronegative element. The skeleton structure (Step 1) is

$$
\begin{array}{c}
F \\
| \\
Cl-F \\
| \\
F
\end{array}
$$

Example 7.5

ClF_3 contains 28 valence electrons, 7 from the chlorine atom and 21 from the 3 fluorine atoms. Of these, 6 are used in the single bonds, leaving 22 to be placed as unshared pairs. Three unshared pairs can be placed on each fluorine atom, leaving 2 pairs of electrons. Because the valence shell of chlorine has an n value greater than 2 ($n = 3$), it can hold the 2 remaining electron pairs. The Lewis structure is

$$
\begin{array}{c}
:\!F\!: \\
| \\
:\!Cl\!-\!F\!: \\
| \\
:\!F\!:
\end{array}
$$

❼.7 Formal Charge

A concept called formal charge can be used to help us predict the arrangement of the atoms in a molecule and draw the most reasonable Lewis structures for a molecule. The **formal charge** of an atom in a molecule is the *hypothetical* charge we obtain when we assign the electrons shown in the Lewis structure of the molecule as follows:

1. Half of the electrons in a bond are assigned to each atom in the bond.
2. Both electrons of an unshared pair are assigned to the atom to which the unshared pair belongs.

The formal charge of an atom in the molecule equals the number of valence electrons in the free atom less the number of electrons assigned to the atom in the molecule by these two rules. One easy way to check the calculation of formal charges is to add them up: The sum of the formal charges in a molecule should be zero; the sum of the formal charges in an ion should equal the charge on the ion.

It is very important to note that the formal charge calculated for an atom is not the charge on the atom in the molecule. Formal charge is only a useful bookkeeping procedure.

As examples of calculating formal charge, let us determine the formal charges in the molecules C_2H_2 and ClF_3, the Lewis structures that we determined in the preceding two examples.

Example 7.6

What is the formal charge on each atom in C_2H_2 and ClF_3?

The Lewis structures of these molecules are

$$H—C\equiv C—H \qquad \ddot{\underset{..}{F}}—\underset{\underset{..}{\overset{..}{F}}}{\overset{..}{Cl}}—\ddot{\underset{..}{F}}$$

The formal charges are calculated as follows:

	H Atom in C_2H_2	C Atom in C_2H_2	Cl Atom in ClF_3	F Atom in ClF_3
Bonding electrons assigned	1	4	3	1
Nonbonding electrons assigned	0	0	4	6
Total electrons assigned	1	4	7	7
Electrons in isolated atom	1	4	7	7
Formal charge	$1 - 1 = 0$	$4 - 4 = 0$	$7 - 7 = 0$	$7 - 7 = 0$

The following four rules involving formal charge are helpful in deciding between two or more possible Lewis structures for a molecule or ion:

1. A Lewis structure in which all formal charges in a molecule are zero is preferable to one in which some formal charges are not zero.
2. If Lewis structures must have nonzero formal charges, the one with the lowest number of nonzero formal charges is preferable, and a Lewis structure with no more than one large formal charge (-2, $+2$, etc.) is preferable to one with several.
3. Lewis structures should have adjacent formal charges of zero or of opposite sign.
4. When we must choose among several Lewis structures with similar distributions of formal charges, the structure with the negative formal charges on the more electronegative atoms is preferable.

Examining the formal charges in the Lewis structures of the three possible arrangements of the atoms in the thiocyanate ion, NCS^-, will illustrate how the idea of formal charge can help us predict the correct skeleton structure for a Lewis structure. The three possible arrangements are NCS^-, CSN^-, and CNS^-. The possible Lewis structures and the formal charges for each arrangement are

$$[: \overset{..}{N}=C=\overset{..}{S}:]^- \qquad [: \overset{..}{C}=N=\overset{..}{S}:]^- \qquad [: \overset{..}{C}=\overset{..}{S}=\overset{..}{N}:]^-$$

Formal charge $\quad -1 \quad 0 \quad 0 \qquad\qquad -2 \ +1 \quad 0 \qquad\qquad -2 \ +2 \ -1$

The first arrangement of atoms is preferred because it has the lowest number of atoms with nonzero formal charges (Rule 2). Note that the sum of the formal charges in each case is equal to the charge on the ion (-1).

Formal charge gives us some insight into why chlorine atoms do not form double bonds in BCl_3. Consider the following two Lewis structures for BCl_3 (the formal charges are written beside the atoms).

$$\begin{array}{ccc} 0 & : \overset{..}{Cl}: & \\ & | & \\ 0 \quad B & — & \overset{..}{Cl}: \quad 0 \\ & | & \\ 0 & : \overset{..}{Cl}: & \end{array} \qquad\qquad \begin{array}{ccc} 0 & : \overset{..}{Cl}: & \\ & | & \\ -1 \quad B & = & \overset{..}{Cl}: \quad +1 \\ & | & \\ 0 & : \overset{..}{Cl}: & \end{array}$$

In the Lewis structure with the double bond, the boron atom has a formal charge of -1 and the chlorine atom a formal charge of $+1$. This distribution of formal charge is unsatisfactory, because the negative formal charge is on the least electronegative atom (Rule 4) and the structure has a larger number of atoms with nonzero formal charge (Rule 1).

7.8 Resonance

Sometimes two or more Lewis structures can have the same arrangement of atoms but different arrangements of electrons. For example, both Lewis structures of SO_2, sulfur dioxide, have the atoms in the same positions but have some electrons in different positions.

A double bond between two atoms is stronger and shorter than a single bond between the same two atoms. However, experiments show that both sulfur–oxygen bonds in SO_2 have the same length and are identical in all other properties. Because it is not possible to write a single Lewis structure for sulfur dioxide in which both bonds are equivalent, we must apply the concept of **resonance:** If two or more Lewis structures with the same arrangement of atoms can be written for a molecule or ion, the actual distribution of electrons is an *average* of that shown by the various Lewis structures. The actual distribution of electrons in each of the sulfur–oxygen bonds in SO_2 is an average of a double bond and a single bond. The individual Lewis structures are called **resonance forms.** The actual electronic structure of the molecule (the average of the resonance forms) is called a **resonance hybrid** of the individual resonance forms. A double-headed arrow is used between Lewis structures to indicate that they are resonance forms and that *the distribution of electrons is an average of the individual resonance forms.*

It must be emphasized that a molecule described as a resonance hybrid *never* possesses an electronic structure described by a single resonance form. The actual electronic structure is *always* an average of that shown by all resonance forms. A simple analogy to a resonance hybrid is the mule, which is the hybrid offspring of a male donkey and a female horse. Just as the characteristics of a mule are fixed, so the properties of a resonance hybrid are fixed. The mule is not a donkey part of the time and a horse part of the time. It is always a mule. Correspondingly, a molecule with an electronic structure described by a resonance hybrid does not exhibit one electronic structure part of the time and another electronic structure the rest of the time. Instead, the material is always in the form of the intermediate resonance hybrid, which cannot be written with a single Lewis structure.

The distribution of electrons in N_2O, nitrous oxide, provides a second example of resonance.

$$: \overset{..}{N} = N = \overset{..}{O} : \quad \longleftrightarrow \quad : N \equiv N - \overset{..}{\underset{..}{O}} :$$

Because the electron distribution in N_2O is an average of these two resonance forms, the distribution of electrons in the bond between the two nitrogen atoms may be seen to be greater than that in a double bond but less than that in a triple bond. The distribution of electrons in the bond between nitrogen and oxygen in the resonance hybrid is between that in a single bond and that in a double bond.

🅐.9 The Strengths of Covalent Bonds

Stable molecules exist because strong covalent bonds hold the atoms together; energy must be added to break the bonds and separate the atoms. The strength of a covalent bond between two atoms is measured by the energy required to break it—that is, the energy necessary to separate the bonded atoms. The stronger a bond, the more energy is required to break it.

The energy required to break a covalent bond in a gaseous substance is called the **bond energy** of the bond. The bond energy for a diatomic molecule, D_{X-Y}, is defined as the standard enthalpy change for the endothermic reaction.

$$XY(g) \longrightarrow X(g) + Y(g) \qquad D_{X-Y} = \Delta H^{\circ}_{298}$$

For example, the bond energy of the H—H bond, D_{H-H}, is 436 kilojoules per mole of H—H bonds broken:

$$H_2(g) \longrightarrow 2H(g) \qquad D_{H-H} = \Delta H^{\circ}_{298} = 436 \text{ kJ}$$

Bond energies for common diatomic molecules range from 946 kilojoules per mole for N_2 (triple bond) to 150 kilojoules per mole for I_2 (single bond), and from 569 kilojoules per mole for HF to 295 kilojoules per mole for HI.

Molecules with three or more atoms have two or more bonds. The sum of all of the bond energies in such a molecule is equal to the standard enthalpy change for the endothermic reaction that breaks all the bonds in the molecule. For example, the sum of the four C—H bond energies in CH_4, 1660 kilojoules, is equal to the standard enthalpy change of the reaction

$$\overset{\displaystyle H}{\underset{\displaystyle H}{H - \overset{|}{\underset{|}{C}} - H}}(g) \longrightarrow C(g) + 4H(g) \qquad \Delta H^{\circ}_{298} = 1660 \text{ kJ}$$

The *average* C—H bond energy, D_{C-H}, is $1660/4 = 415$ kilojoules per mole because there are four moles of C—H bonds broken in the reaction.

The strength of a bond between two atoms increases as the number of electron pairs in the bond increases. Thus triple bonds are stronger than double bonds between the same two atoms and double bonds are stronger than single bonds between the same two atoms. Average bond energies for some common bonds appear in Table 7.3.

Tabulated enthalpy changes (Appendix I) can be used to obtain bond energies.

Use the data in Appendix I to evaluate the bond energy of a Cl—Cl bond.

Example 7.7

The energy of a mole of single bonds between chlorine atoms, D_{Cl-Cl}, is equal to the standard enthalpy change of the reaction

$$Cl_2(g) \longrightarrow 2Cl(g) \qquad D_{Cl-Cl} = \Delta H^\circ_{298}$$

This is the reaction for the formation of 2 mol of Cl atoms. Referring to Appendix I, we find that the enthalpy of formation of 1 mol of chlorine atoms, $\Delta H^\circ_{f_{Cl(g)}}$, is 121.68 kJ. The enthalpy of formation of 2 mol of Cl atoms is 2×121.68 kJ $= 243.36$ kJ; hence $D_{Cl-Cl} = 243.36$ kJ, and 243.36 kJ are required to break the Cl—Cl bonds in one mol of Cl_2 molecules. The rounded value is given in Table 7.3.

Evaluate the bond energy of the C≡O bond in CO(g) from the data in Appendix I.

Example 7.8

The energy of 1 mol of C≡O bonds, $D_{C≡O}$, is equal to the standard enthalpy of the reaction

$$CO(g) \longrightarrow C(g) + O(g) \qquad D_{C≡O} = \Delta H^\circ_{298}$$

This reaction can be written as three steps, each of which involves an enthalpy of formation (Hess's law, Section 4.5),

$$
\begin{array}{ll}
CO(g) \longrightarrow C(s) + \tfrac{1}{2}O_2(g) & \Delta H^\circ_1 = -\Delta H^\circ_{f_{CO(g)}} \\
C(s) \longrightarrow C(g) & \Delta H^\circ_2 = \Delta H^\circ_{f_{C(g)}} \\
\tfrac{1}{2}O_2(g) \longrightarrow O(g) & \Delta H^\circ_3 = \Delta H^\circ_{f_{O(g)}} \\
\hline
CO(g) \longrightarrow C(g) + O(g) & \Delta H^\circ_{298} = \Delta H^\circ_1 + \Delta H^\circ_2 + \Delta H^\circ_3
\end{array}
$$

$$
\begin{aligned}
D_{C≡O} = \Delta H^\circ_{298} &= -\Delta H^\circ_{f_{CO(g)}} + \Delta H^\circ_{f_{C(g)}} + \Delta H^\circ_{f_{O(g)}} \\
&= -1 \text{ mol } CO(g) \times (-110.5 \text{ kJ mol}^{-1}) + 1 \text{ mol } C(g) \times \\
&\quad (716.68 \text{ kJ mol}^{-1}) + 1 \text{ mol } O(g) \times (249.2 \text{ kJ mol}^{-1}) \\
&= 1076.4 \text{ kJ}
\end{aligned}
$$

Thus 1076.4 kJ are required to break the C≡O bond in CO(g). The rounded value is reported in Table 7.3.

A knowledge of bond energies is helpful in understanding exothermic and endothermic reactions. An exothermic reaction (ΔH negative, heat produced) results when the bonds in the products are stronger than the bonds in the reactants. An endothermic reaction (ΔH positive, heat absorbed) results when the bonds in the products are weaker than those in the reactants.

Consider the following reaction:

$$H_2(g) + Cl_2(g) \longrightarrow 2HCl(g)$$

Table 7.3					Some Average Bond Energies (kJ mol^{-1})						

					Single Bonds						
H	C	N	O	F	Si	P	S	Cl	Br	I	
436	415	390	464	569	395	320	340	432	370	295	H
	345	290	350	439	360	265	260	330	275	240	C
		160	200	270	—	210	—	200	245	—	N
			140	185	370	350	—	205	—	200	O
				160	540	489	285	255	235	—	F
					230	215	225	359	290	215	Si
						215	230	330	270	215	P
							215	250	215	—	S
								243	220	210	Cl
									190	180	Br
										150	I

					Multiple Bonds				
C=C,	611	C=N,	615	C=O,	741	N=N,	418	O=O,	498
C≡C,	837	C≡N,	891	C≡O,	1080	N≡N,	946		

To form the 2 moles of HCl, 1 mole of H—H bonds and 1 mole of Cl—Cl bonds must be broken. This requires the input of 436 kilojoules + 243 kilojoules = 679 kilojoules (the sum of the bond energies of the H—H and Cl—Cl bonds, respectively). During the reaction, 2 moles of H—Cl bonds are formed (bond energy = 432 kilojoules per mole), releasing 2 × 432 kilojoules = 864 kilojoules. Because the bonds in the products are stronger than those in the reactants by 185 kilojoules (864 kJ − 679 kJ), the reaction releases 185 kilojoules more energy than it consumes. This excess energy is released as heat, so the reaction is exothermic and has a ΔH value of −185 kilojoules.

The following example illustrates how bond energies can be used to estimate enthalpy changes. Chemists seldom calculate ΔH values this way, because standard molar enthalpies of formation give more accurate values. However, if enthalpies of formation are not available, bond energies can be used to get a useful approximation.

Example 7.9

Methanol, CH_3OH, is manufactured by the reaction

$$CO(g) + 2H_2(g) \longrightarrow CH_3OH(g)$$

Calculate the approximate enthalpy change, ΔH, of the reaction from the bond energies in Table 7.3.

The enthalpy change for this reaction is approximately equal to the sum of the enthalpy changes of three reactions, each of which involves bond breaking or bond formation:

$$C\equiv O(g) \longrightarrow C(g) + O(g) \qquad \Delta H = D_{C\equiv O}$$

$$2H—H(g) \longrightarrow 4H(g) \qquad \Delta H = 2D_{H—H}$$

$$C(g) + O(g) + 4H(g) \longrightarrow H—\overset{\displaystyle H}{\underset{\displaystyle H}{C}}—O—H \qquad \Delta H = -3D_{C—H} - D_{C—O} \\ -D_{O—H}$$

$$CO(g) + 2H_2(g) \longrightarrow CH_3OH(g) \qquad \Delta H = D_{C\equiv O} + 2D_{H—H} \\ -3D_{C—H} - D_{C—O} - D_{O—H}$$

In Table 7.3, we find that

$$D_{C\equiv O} = 1080 \text{ kJ mol}^{-1} \qquad D_{H-H} = 436 \text{ kJ mol}^{-1}$$

$$D_{C-H} = 415 \text{ kJ mol}^{-1} \qquad D_{C-O} = 350 \text{ kJ mol}^{-1}$$

$$D_{O-H} = 464 \text{ kJ mol}^{-1}$$

Thus

$$\Delta H = [1080 + (2 \times 436) - (3 \times 415) - 350 - 464] \text{ kJ} = -107 \text{ kJ}$$

7.10 Vibrations of Molecules and Infrared Spectroscopy

The vibrations of the atoms in a molecule can be used to study the types of bonds in the molecule and their strengths. The motion of two atoms connected by a covalent bond is somewhat like that of two croquet balls connected by a spring. If we hold one croquet ball and shake the spring once, the other ball bounces (vibrates) up and down on the spring (Fig. 7.5). Two atoms connected by a covalent bond behave the same way; they vibrate back and forth when energy is added.

Bonded atoms vibrate when they absorb electromagnetic radiation. The energy necessary to cause the vibration is much less than that needed to break the bond (Section 7.9) or to cause electronic transitions (Section 5.8), so the energy of the radiation needed is much lower than the energy of visible light. Vibrations occur when molecules absorb radiation in the infrared region of the electromagnetic spectrum (Fig. 5.11). We cannot see this radiation, but we can feel it; it is the heat radiating from a hot object such as the heating element of an electric heater.

The vibration of atoms differs from that of croquet balls in one important respect. Croquet balls can be made to vibrate by hitting them with just about any energy. On the other hand, bonded atoms begin to vibrate only when they absorb radiation with the same frequency as that of their vibration. For example, the carbon and oxygen atoms in a CO molecule can vibrate with a frequency of 6.424×10^{13} vibrations per second. This vibration is started when a CO molecule absorbs infrared radiation with the same frequency ($6.424 \times 10^{13} \text{ s}^{-1}$), which corresponds to a wavelength (Section 5.8) of 4.666×10^{-6} meters.

The frequency of vibration of a pair of bonded atoms depends on the strength of the bond and on the masses of the bonded atoms. The frequency decreases as the bond becomes weaker or as one or both of the atoms become heavier. For example, the frequency of vibration of the atoms in the CO bond decreases from $6.424 \times 10^{13} \text{ s}^{-1}$ in carbon monoxide through $5.477 \times 10^{13} \text{ s}^{-1}$ in $COCl_2$ to $3.106 \times 10^{13} \text{ s}^{-1}$ in CH_3OH as the CO bond decreases from a triple bond through a double bond to a single bond. The frequency of vibration of the H—H and H—Cl bonds, which have about the same bond energies (Table 7.3), decreases from $12.47 \times 10^{13} \text{ s}^{-1}$ for H_2 to $8.646 \times 10^{13} \text{ s}^{-1}$ for HCl as a lighter H atom is replaced with a heavier Cl atom. Thus the vibrational frequency of a pair of bonded atoms can serve as a guide to the type of bond between them, and we can use it to follow changes in bonds during a chemical reaction.

Many of the vibrations of atoms in molecules can be detected by their absorption of infrared radiation in an instrument called an infrared spectrometer (Fig. 7.6). In such a

Figure 7.5

When two croquet balls connected by a spring are given a single shake, they continue to vibrate.

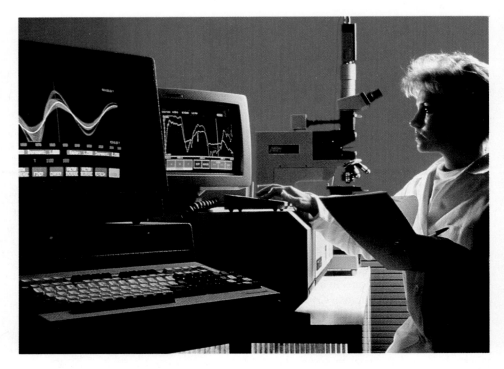

spectrometer, radiation of varying wavelengths is passed through a sample, and the spectrometer measures and graphs the amount of radiation that passes through (see Fig. 7.7 for the details of its operation). If a vibration is excited by a particular wavelength, then the amount of radiation of that wavelength that the sample transmits is reduced, and a peak appears in the spectrum (the graph of the percent of radiation transmitted plotted against the frequency that is passed by the prism). An infrared spectrum of aspirin (acetylsalicylic acid) is shown in Fig. 7.8. The units of frequency along the horizontal axis of the spectrum are not vibrations per second (which are very large units) but are wave numbers with units of cm^{-1}. Wave numbers are directly proportional to the vibrational frequency; they are obtained by dividing the frequency by the speed of light. For example, the vibrational frequency of a CO molecule is 6.424×10^{13} s^{-1}, which corresponds to 2143 cm^{-1} (6.424×10^{13} $s^{-1}/2.999 \times 10^{10}$ $cm \cdot s^{-1}$).

Infrared spectra are much more complicated than we might expect from the number of types of bonds in a molecule. This is because there are several types of vibrations, each with a different frequency, which are combinations of stretching motions and of bending motions of the bonds. Because of this complexity, infrared spectra are commonly used to identify compounds, like fingerprints are used to identify people. The

Figure 7.7

A schematic diagram of an infrared spectrometer. As the frequency of the incident infrared radiation from the source is varied by turning of the prism, the intensity of the transmitted radiation is measured by the detector and intensity is plotted against frequency.

Figure 7.8
The infrared spectrum of aspirin.

Figure 7.9
The infrared spectrum of
acetaminophen.

spectrum of the pain reliever shown in Fig. 7.9, for example, is clearly not the same as the spectrum of aspirin (Fig. 7.8). This pain reliever is not aspirin but acetaminophen, the active ingredient of Tylenol.

The following example illustrates how an infrared measurement can detect changes in a chemical reaction.

Why does the absorption at 1640 cm^{-1} in the infrared spectrum of H_2C=CHCl disappear and a new carbon–carbon absorption appear at 1468 cm^{-1} when H_2C=CHCl reacts with Cl_2 to form H_2ClC—$CHCl_2$?

**Example
7.10**

Writing the Lewis structures of the reactants and products with the C—C bonds in color illustrates the changes that occur in the bonds during the reaction.

$$\begin{array}{c} H \\ \diagdown \\ \diagup \\ H \end{array} C = C \begin{array}{c} H \\ \diagup \\ \diagdown \\ Cl \end{array} + Cl-Cl \longrightarrow \begin{array}{c} H \\ | \\ H-C \\ | \\ Cl \end{array} \begin{array}{c} H \\ | \\ C-Cl \\ | \\ Cl \end{array}$$

The change in the spectrum is due to the disappearance of the carbon–carbon double bond and to the formation of a carbon–carbon single bond. (New peaks also appear as a result of the formation of additional C—Cl bonds and other effects.)

❼.11 Oxidation Numbers

In Section 7.7 we examined the idea of formal charge, one way to assign hypothetical charges to atoms in covalent molecules. In Section 2.7, we introduced the concept of oxidation number, another way to assign charges to atoms. In this section we shall discuss the theoretical basis for the rules used to assign oxidation numbers, but before you read this section you should review Section 2.7.

A formal charge is assigned by distributing the electrons in a covalent bond evenly between the atoms in the bond. An **oxidation number** is assigned as the charge that an atom would have if all the electrons in each bond were located on the more electronegative atom in the bond. The oxidation number of an atom equals the number of valence electrons in the free atom less the number of electrons on the atom after the bonding electrons are assigned to the more electronegative atom. The only time we assign electrons equally when calculating oxidation number is when the two atoms in the bond are the same. In *covalent compounds,* calculating the oxidation number is an arbitrary way of assigning charge, because the electrons are actually shared. In *binary ionic compounds* the bonding electrons are already on the more electronegative atom, because ionic bonds result from electron transfer. Thus the oxidation number of a monatomic ion is equal to the charge on the ion.

As examples of calculating oxidation numbers, let us determine the oxidation numbers of the atoms in the molecules C_2H_2 and ClF_3, the formal charges of which we determined in Example 7.6.

Example 7.11

What is the oxidation number of each atom in C_2H_2 and ClF_3?

The Lewis structures of these molecules are

$$H-C\equiv C-H \qquad \begin{matrix} :\ddot{F}: \\ | \\ :\ddot{C}l-\ddot{F}: \\ | \\ :\ddot{F}: \end{matrix}$$

If we assign the electrons in each C—H and Cl—F bond to the more electronegative atom and distribute the electrons in the C—C bond equally, we can write the following *hypothetical* ionic structures:

$$H^{+1} \quad :\dot{C}:^{-1} \quad :\dot{C}:^{-1} \quad H^{+1} \qquad \begin{matrix} :\ddot{F}:^{-1} \\ \\ Cl^{+3}:\ddot{F}:^{-1} \\ \\ :\ddot{F}:^{-1} \end{matrix}$$

The oxidation numbers are equal to the hypothetical ionic charges. The oxidation number for the H atom is $+1$; for C, -1; for F, -1; and for Cl, $+3$.

The following nine rules for determining the average oxidation number of an atom include those introduced in Section 2.7 and several other useful rules. In particular, the situations in which oxygen can have an oxidation number other than -2 and the identification of oxidation numbers of the nonmetals are considered. These rules follow from the definition of oxidation number.

1. The oxidation number of an atom of any element in its elemental form is considered to be zero (Section 2.7).
2. The oxidation number of a monatomic ion is considered to be equal to the charge on the ion (Section 2.7).
3. The oxidation number of fluorine in a compound is always assigned as -1.
4. The elements of Group IA (except hydrogen) are assigned the oxidation number $+1$ in compounds (Section 2.7).
5. The elements of Group IIA are assigned the oxidation number $+2$ in compounds (Section 2.7).
6. The elements of Group VIIA are assigned the oxidation number -1 when they are combined in compounds with less electronegative elements. Chlorine has an oxidation number of -1 in $NaCl$, CCl_4, PCl_3, and HCl, for example.
7. Oxygen usually is assigned the oxidation number -2 (Section 2.7), but there are three exceptions:
   (a) In compounds with fluorine, oxygen has a positive oxidation number (fluorine is more electronegative than oxygen). For example, oxygen has an oxidation number of $+2$ in OF_2.
   (b) In peroxides (compounds that contain an O—O single bond), oxygen has an oxidation number of -1. An example is hydrogen peroxide, H_2O_2; H—O̤—O̤—H is its Lewis structure.
   (c) In superoxides (compounds containing O_2^-), oxygen has an oxidation number of $-\frac{1}{2}$. An example is KO_2.
8. Hydrogen is assigned the oxidation number -1 in compounds with less electronegative elements and the oxidation number $+1$ in compounds with more electronegative elements. (Section 2.7 states this rule in terms of metals and nonmetals.)
9. The sum of the oxidation numbers of all the atoms in a compound is zero. The sum of the oxidation numbers of all the atoms in an ion is equal to the charge on the ion (Section 2.7).

If we know the oxidation numbers for all but one kind of atom in a compound, we can calculate that unknown oxidation number.

Hydrogen peroxide contains oxygen with an oxidation number of -1.

Example 7.12

Calculate the oxidation number of sulfur in Na_2SO_4, Na_2SO_3, and H_2S.

In Na_2SO_4 the oxidation number for sulfur can be calculated from the oxidation numbers for sodium and oxygen. The two sodium atoms, each with an oxidation number of $+1$ (Group IA, Rule 4), total $+2$; the four oxygen atoms, each with an oxidation number of -2 (Rule 7), total -8. For the sum of the oxidation numbers to be zero, sulfur must have an oxidation number of $+6$. A similar calculation shows the oxidation number of sulfur in Na_2SO_3 to be $+4$.

In H_2S, hydrogen is bonded to a more electronegative element, so it will have an oxidation number of $+1$ (Rule 8). For the sum of the oxidation numbers of all three atoms to be zero, sulfur must have an oxidation number of -2.

As this example shows, an element may have more than one oxidation number, depending on the compound in which it is found. In some compounds, the presence of two or more atoms of the same element with different oxidation numbers gives the average oxidation number a fractional value.

Example 7.13

Calculate the average oxidation number of iron in the mineral lodestone, a magnetic oxide with the formula Fe_3O_4.

In Fe_3O_4 (lodestone), oxygen is combined with a less electronegative element and is assigned an oxidation number of -2. The four oxygen atoms would contribute a total of -8. For the sum of the oxidation numbers in the compound to be zero, the oxidation numbers of the three iron atoms must total $+8$. Hence the average oxidation number for iron in lodestone is $+\frac{8}{3}$ or $+2\frac{2}{3}$. (One formula unit of Fe_3O_4 contains 1 Fe^{2+} ion and 2 Fe^{3+} ions.)

Lodestone, Fe_3O_4, is the magnetic oxide of iron.

7.12 Using Oxidation Numbers to Write Formulas

The formula of a compound may be written using the oxidation numbers of the atoms involved, because the sum of the oxidation numbers of the atoms in the compound must equal zero (Rule 9 in Section 7.11).

Example 7.14

Write the formula for magnesium chloride, using the oxidation numbers of its constituent elements.

Magnesium is a member of Group IIA and so has an oxidation number of $+2$. Chlorine, a member of Group VIIA, is combined with a less electronegative element and so has an oxidation number of -1.

The formula of magnesium chloride cannot be MgCl, because $+2$ and -1 do not add up to 0. For the sum of the oxidation numbers to be zero for the compound, the atoms must be in a ratio of 1 magnesium ion to 2 chloride ions, or $MgCl_2$.

Example 7.15

Write the formula for aluminum oxide.

Aluminum, the less electronegative element, is a member of Group IIIA and so will lose three electrons, giving Al^{3+} with an oxidation number of $+3$. Oxygen, a member of Group VIA, needs two electrons to fill its valence shell, giving the ion O^{2-} with an oxidation number of -2. Because $+3$ plus -2 does not give 0, AlO is not the correct formula for aluminum oxide. Inspection reveals that 2 atoms of aluminum would give a total of 6 units of positive oxidation number, that 3 atoms of oxygen would give 6 units of negative oxidation number, and that the algebraic sum of the oxidation numbers would be 0. The correct simplest formula for aluminum oxide is therefore Al_2O_3.

Oxidation numbers also help us write the formulas of compounds that contain polyatomic ions. We can write the formula of an ionic compound by using the charges of the ions involved, because the sum of the charges of the ions in the compound must equal zero (Section 7.1). Oxidation numbers can be used to determine some of these charges.

Write the formula for iron(III) perchlorate.

The charge on a monatomic ion is equal to its oxidation number. Thus the iron ion is Fe^{3+}. The perchlorate ion, ClO_4^-, has a charge of -1. But with charges of $+3$ for the iron ion and -1 for the perchlorate ion, the formula $Fe(ClO_4)$ cannot be correct. However, if we use 3 perchlorate ions and 1 iron ion, the sum of the positive and negative charges becomes 0; the correct formula is $Fe(ClO_4)_3$.

Example
7.16

A solution of iron(III) perchlorate contains Fe^{3+} and ClO_4^- ions.

7 .13 Periodic Variation of Oxidation Numbers

As we found in Section 7.12, if we know the oxidation numbers of the elements in a compound, we can write the formula of the compound. Thus knowing the oxidation numbers possible for an element can help us predict its reaction products.

Some regularities in the oxidation numbers commonly observed for the representative elements are related to their positions in the periodic table, as shown in Table 7.4. This array of numbers may look formidable at first, but there are many regularities that will simplify your recall of them. Refer to the table as you study the regularities that follow:

1. The maximum positive oxidation number found in any group of representative elements is equal to the number of the group. The maximum possible positive oxidation number increases from $+1$ for the alkali metals (Group IA) to $+7$ for all of the halogens (Group VIIA) except fluorine, which is assigned the oxidation number -1 in its compounds. With the exception of thallium at the bottom of Group IIIA and mercury at the bottom of Group IIB, the maximum positive oxidation number is the only common oxidation number displayed by the metallic elements of Groups IA, IIA, IIB, and IIIA.
2. Metallic elements usually exhibit only positive oxidation numbers.
3. The most negative oxidation number of a group of representative elements is equal to the group number minus 8. For example, for the elements in Group VA, the most negative possible oxidation number is $5 - 8 = -3$. This corresponds to the number of electrons that would have to be gained to provide an outer shell of 8 electrons for the elements.
4. Negative oxidation numbers are commonly limited to nonmetals and semi-metals and are observed only when these elements are combined with a less electronegative element.
5. Elements commonly exhibit positive oxidation numbers only when combined with more electronegative elements.
6. With the exception of carbon, nitrogen, oxygen, and mercury, each representative element that exhibits multiple oxidation numbers in its compounds commonly has oxidation numbers that are either all even or all odd.

Before we proceed, a word of caution about the word *common* in *common oxidation numbers:* The common oxidation numbers of an element are those observed in a majority of its compounds. In some cases, as with the elements in Groups IA and IIA, this

Table 7.4		Commonly Observed Oxidation Numbers for Atoms of the Representative Elements When in Compounds						
1 IA	2 IIA	12 IIB	13 IIIA	14 IVA	15 VA	16 VIA	17 VIIA	18 VIIIA
H +1 −1							H +1 −1	He
Li +1	Be +2		B +3	C +4 to −4	N +5 to −3	O −1 −2	F −1	Ne
Na +1	Mg +2		Al +3	Si +4	P +5 +3 −3	S +6 +4 −2	Cl +7 +5 +3 +1 −1	Ar
K +1	Ca +2	Zn +2	Ga +3	Ge +4	As +5 +3 −3	Se +6 +4 −2	Br +7 +5 +3 +1 −1	Kr +4 +2
Rb +1	Sr +2	Cd +2	In +3	Sn +4 +2	Sb +5 +3 −3	Te +6 +4 −2	I +7 +5 +3 +1 −1	Xe +8 +6 +4 +2
Cs +1	Ba +2	Hg +2 +1	Tl +3 +1	Pb +4 +2	Bi +5 +3	Po +2	At	Rn
Fr +1	Ra +2							

may be nearly all of the known compounds of the element. Of all the thousands of known sodium compounds, for example, there are only a very few, very reactive compounds in which sodium has been shown to exhibit an oxidation number of −1. For other elements, however, the minority may be relatively large. Although boron has an oxidation number of +3 in the majority of its compounds, in one series of compounds it has an oxidation number of +2, and in another it exhibits nonintegral oxidation numbers. Because most compounds discussed in this text involve elements with their common oxidation numbers, memorizing these common oxidation numbers now will make studying the compounds much simpler later on.

❼.14 Prediction of Reaction Products

In this section we will examine some of the general guidelines that can be helpful in answering the question ''What products, if any, are likely to result from the reaction of two or more substances?'' These guidelines are based on the metallic or nonmetallic behavior of the representative elements involved (Section 6.5), the common oxidation states that they are likely to exhibit (Section 7.13), and the similarities of the compounds involved to those types already discussed (Sections 2.10 and 2.12). We will consider only those reactions that occur at room temperature in water and those that occur when the pure substances are heated. Although different conditions may result in different products, these guidelines will serve as a foundation for our consideration of chemical reactions in subsequent chapters. The following four examples illustrate the approach:

Predict the product of the reaction that occurs when elemental gallium (Ga) and sulfur (S_8) are warmed together.

Example 7.17

First consider what we know about gallium and sulfur from their respective positions in the periodic table. Gallium is located in Group IIIA and thus should exhibit metallic behavior, forming compounds in which it exhibits a positive oxidation number. Because it is a member of Group IIIA, the expected oxidation number is $+3$. Sulfur is a member of Group VIA and thus should exhibit nonmetallic behavior. The common oxidation numbers of sulfur are $+6$ (its maximum positive oxidation number, equal to the group number), $+4$, and -2 (its most negative oxidation number, equal to the group number minus 8). In this instance sulfur will combine with the less electronegative gallium, thus it should exhibit the negative oxidation number -2. As a metal, gallium can act as a reducing agent; as a nonmetal, sulfur can act as an oxidizing agent (Section 6.5). Thus we can expect an oxidation–reduction reaction between gallium and sulfur, yielding a product containing gallium with an oxidation number of $+3$ and sulfur with an oxidation number of -2. This leads us to formulate the product (Section 7.12) as Ga_2S_3.

The predicted chemical reaction is therefore

$$16Ga + 3S_8 \longrightarrow 8Ga_2S_3$$

This is indeed the product of the reaction of gallium with sulfur.

Gallium (III) sulfide is produced when gallium metal reacts with sulfur. The white product looks neither like silvery gallium metal (p. 159) nor yellow sulfur (p. 47).

As a general approach to predicting the products of a reaction, examine the reactants to determine whether they are analogous to compounds or elements whose behavior you know. If analogies are not obvious, try the following five-point analysis of the system.

1. Identify each element in the reactants as a metal or a nonmetal from its position in the periodic table, and find its oxidation number (Section 7.11) as well as the oxidation numbers it commonly exhibits in its compounds (Section 7.13).

2. Consider the possibility of an oxidation–reduction reaction (Section 2.11, part 4). The following general considerations are helpful:

(a) An elemental metal will be oxidized by an elemental nonmetal and will thereby reduce the nonmetal.

$$Mg + Cl_2 \longrightarrow MgCl_2 \qquad (1)$$

(b) A less electronegative metal (a more active metal) in its elemental form will often reduce the ion of a more electronegative metal.

$$Mg + SnCl_2 \longrightarrow MgCl_2 + Sn \qquad (2)$$

(c) A more electronegative nonmetal in its elemental form will oxidize a less electronegative nonmetal.

$$S + O_2 \longrightarrow SO_2 \qquad (3)$$

$$2SO_2 + O_2 \longrightarrow 2SO_3 \qquad (4)$$

(d) The metals of Group IA and calcium, strontium, and barium of Group IIA are active enough to reduce the hydrogen in water or acids to hydrogen gas.

$$2Na + 2H_2O \longrightarrow 2NaOH + H_2 \qquad (5)$$

$$Ba + 2HCl \longrightarrow BaCl_2 + H_2 \qquad (6)$$

The other representative metals, with the exception of bismuth and lead (the least metallic representative metals), will only reduce hydrogens in acids.

$$2Al + 3H_2SO_4 \longrightarrow Al_2(SO_4)_3 + 3H_2 \qquad (7)$$

3. Consider the possibility of an acid–base reaction (Section 2.11, Part 5). Remember that the oxides and hydroxides of nonmetals are generally acidic and that the oxides and hydroxides of metals are generally basic (Section 6.5). Thus, we might find acid–base reactions involving familiar types of acids and bases:

$$2HCl + Sr(OH)_2 \longrightarrow SrCl_2 + 2H_2O \qquad (8)$$

acidic oxides with bases:

$$SO_3 + Ca(OH)_2 \longrightarrow CaSO_4 + H_2O \qquad (9)$$

or acids with basic oxides:

$$6HCl + Al_2O_3 \longrightarrow 2AlCl_3 + 3H_2O \qquad (10)$$

4. Consider the possibility of a metathesis reaction (Section 2.11, Part 3). Metathesis reactions between ionic compounds generally occur when one product is a solid, a gas, a weak electrolyte, or a nonelectrolyte.

5. Consider whether the products of the reaction may react with each other or with the solvent (if any).

The next examples illustrate some specific applications of these ideas.

Example 7.18 Write the balanced chemical equation for the reaction of elemental calcium with iodine.

Calcium is a member of Group IIA and is a metal. Iodine is a member of Group VIIA and is a nonmetal. A metal can react with a nonmetal in an oxidation–reduction reaction. Iodine will be reduced to its only available negative oxidation number (-1; it is a member of Group VIIA), whereas calcium will be oxidized to the only oxidation number it exhibits in compounds ($+2$). With these oxidation numbers, the product must be CaI_2. The equation is

$$Ca + I_2 \longrightarrow CaI_2$$

Write a balanced chemical equation for the reaction that occurs when tin(II) oxide is added to hydrochloric acid, a solution of HCl in water.

Example
7.19

HCl is an acid, so look for an acid–base reaction. Tin is a member of Group IVA. It is located near the bottom of the group and has a low oxidation state in SnO, so it should exhibit metallic properties. The oxides of metals are basic; hence we can expect an acid–base reaction between SnO and HCl to produce a salt and water.

$$SnO + 2HCl \longrightarrow SnCl_2 + H_2O$$

What are the two possible products of the reaction of phosphorus, P_4, with chlorine, Cl_2?

Example
7.20

Both phosphorus (Group VA) and chlorine (Group VIIA) are nonmetals. Phosphorus has common oxidation numbers of +5, +3, and −3; chlorine, +7, +5, +3, +1, and −1. Chlorine lies to the right of phosphorus in the third period, so it is more electronegative than phosphorus; thus we recognize that it can oxidize phosphorus. Because phosphorus is oxidized, it will exhibit a positive oxidation number—probably +3 or +5 because these are the common positive oxidation numbers exhibited by a member of Group VA. Chlorine will exhibit a negative oxidation number because it is combined with a less electronegative element. The only negative oxidation number chlorine has is −1. Thus P_4 and Cl_2 could react to give two compounds. In one, phosphorus has an oxidation number of +3 and chlorine has an oxidation number of −1. In the other, phosphorus has an oxidation number of +5 and chlorine has an oxidation number of −1. Thus the two compounds are PCl_3 and PCl_5, respectively.

   Note that either phosphorus(III) chloride or phosphorus(V) chloride can in fact be formed by the appropriate choice of reaction conditions. One mole of P_4 will react with 6 mol of Cl_2 to give 4 mol of PCl_3. If the amount of Cl_2 is increased to 10 mol of Cl_2 per mole of P_4, then 4 mol of PCl_5 are produced. Hence an excess of Cl_2 favors the formation of PCl_5, and an excess of P_4 favors the formation of PCl_3.

$$P_4 + 6Cl_2 \longrightarrow 4PCl_3$$

$$P_4 + 10Cl_2 \longrightarrow 4PCl_5$$

For Review

Summary

When atoms react, their electronic structures change and chemical bonds form. An **ionic bond** is created when electrons are transferred from one atom to another. The resulting compound consists of a regular three-dimensional arrangement of **ions** held together by the strong electrostatic attractions between ions of opposite charge. The charges of ions of the representative metals may be determined readily because, with few exceptions, the electronic structures of these ions have a **noble gas configuration** or a **pseudo-noble gas configuration**.

   Covalent bonds result when electrons are shared as electron pairs between atoms, and the electrons are attracted by the nuclei of both atoms. When only one atom furnishes both electrons of an electron-pair bond, the bond is called a **coordinate covalent**

bond. A **single bond** results when one pair of electrons is shared between two atoms. The sharing of two or three pairs of electrons between two atoms gives a **double bond** or a **triple bond,** respectively. The distribution of electrons in bonds and **unshared pairs** in a molecule can be indicated with a **Lewis structure.** Most Lewis structures can be written by inspection or by starting with a skeleton structure consisting of single bonds and then distributing the remaining electrons as unshared pairs or in multiple bonds to give all atoms a noble gas configuration, if possible. In some instances, a central atom may have an empty valence orbital, or if it is an atom for which n is greater than or equal to 3 for the valence shell, it may have more than 8 electrons in its valence shell. The **formal charges** of the atoms in a Lewis structure are a hypothetical guide to determining the correct Lewis structure.

If two or more Lewis structures with identical arrangements of atoms but different distributions of electrons can be written, the actual distribution of electrons is an average of the distribution indicated by the individual Lewis structures. The actual electron distribution is called a **resonance hybrid** of the individual Lewis structures (which are called **resonance forms**).

The strength of a covalent bond is measured by its **bond energy,** the enthalpy change required to break that particular bond in a mole of molecules. The frequency of the vibration of bonded atoms is proportional to their bond energy; the stronger the bond between two atoms, the higher their vibrational frequency. The vibrational frequency can be measured via infrared spectroscopy.

Although pairs of electrons are often shared between different kinds of atoms, they need not be shared equally. The electrons may spend more time near one atom than near the other in **polar covalent bonds.** The ability of an atom to attract a pair of electrons in a chemical bond is called its **electronegativity.** The greater the difference in electronegativity between two atoms in a covalent bond, the more polar the bond.

The **oxidation number** of an atom in a compound is the charge the atom would have if the compound were ionic. The electronegativities of the elements figure prominently in determining oxidation numbers. We can write the chemical formulas of compounds by using the oxidation numbers of the atoms in the compound.

Elemental metals generally react with elemental nonmetals in such a way that the metal is oxidized and the nonmetal reduced. The resulting oxidation states can often be predicted from the positions of the elements in the periodic table. Most representative metals have a single common positive oxidation state in their compounds, and nonmetals have a single common characteristic negative oxidation state when they form monatomic anions. The reactivity of unfamiliar species can be predicted by comparing them with analogous compounds whose behavior is known or by considering the metallic or nonmetallic character of the elements involved, using the analysis discussed in this chapter.

Key Terms and Concepts

anion (7.1)	ion (7.1)	polar covalent bond (7.5)
bond energy (7.9)	ionic bond (7.1)	pseudo-noble gas electron
cation (7.1)	ionic compound (7.1)	configuration (7.2)
coordinate covalent bond (7.4)	Lewis structure (7.3)	resonance form (7.8)
covalent bond (7.3)	Lewis symbol (7.1)	resonance hybrid (7.8)
double bond (7.3)	noble gas electron configuration	single bond (7.3)
electronegativity (7.5)	(7.2)	triple bond (7.3)
formal charge (7.7)	oxidation number (7.11)	unshared pairs (7.3)

Exercises

Answers for selected even-numbered exercises marked by red numbers appear at the end of the book. The worked-out solutions to all even-numbered exercises appear in the *Solutions Guide*.

Ions and Ionic Bonding

1. How does a cation form from a neutral atom?
2. How does an anion form from a neutral atom?
3. Which of the following atoms would be expected to form negative ions in binary ionic compounds, and which would be expected to form positive ions? P, I, Mg, Cl, In, Cs, N, O, S, Pb, Co.
4. Predict the charge on the monatomic ions formed from the following atoms in binary ionic compounds: P, I, Mg, Cl, Al, K, N, O, S, Ca, Cs.
5. Write the electron configuration of each of the following ions, and identify each as having (a) a noble gas electron configuration, (b) a pseudo-noble gas electron configuration, or (c) neither: As^{3-}, Br^-, Ca^{2+}, Cd^{2+}, F^-, Ga^{3+}, Li^+, N^{3-}, Sn^{2+}, Co^{2+}.
6. Write the Lewis symbols for the monatomic ions formed from the following elements, the elements that form the greatest concentration of monatomic ions in seawater: Cl, Na, Mg, Ca, K, Br, Sr, F.
7. Write the electron configuration and the Lewis symbol for each of the following atoms and for the monatomic ion found in binary ionic compounds containing the element: Al, Br, Sr, Li, As, S.
8. Write the formula of each of the following ionic compounds, using Lewis symbols: MgS, Al_2O_3, $GaCl_3$, K_2O, Li_3N, KF.
9. Write the symbol for the ion and the Lewis symbol of the ion formed from the atoms with the following electron configurations:
   (a) $1s^2 2s^2 2p^1$
   (b) $1s^2 2s^2 2p^5$
   (c) $1s^2 2s^2 2p^6 3s^2$
   (d) $1s^2 2s^2 2p^6 3s^2 3p^6 4s^2 3d^{10}$
   (e) $1s^2 2s^2 2p^6 3s^2 3p^6 4s^2 3d^{10} 4p^4$
   (f) $1s^2 2s^2 2p^6 3s^2 3p^6 4s^2 3d^{10} 4p^1$
10. M and X in the compounds listed below represent elements in the third period of the periodic table. Write the formula of each compound, using the chemical symbols of each element.
    (a) $[M^{3+}][X^{3-}]$
    (b) $[M^{2+}][X^-]_2$
    (c) $[M^+]_3[X^{3-}]$
    (d) $[M^{3+}]_2[X^{2-}]_3$
11. Is it possible to divide the atoms that form positive ions from those that form negative ions by using the values of their electronegativities? If so, what is the approximate value of electronegativity above which atoms form negative ions?
12. Why is it incorrect to speak of the molecular mass of NaCl?

Covalent Bonding

13. What characteristics of the bonded atoms may be used to identify a covalent bond? An ionic bond?
14. How does a covalent bond differ from an ionic bond?

15. Correct the following statement: "The bonds in solid $SnCl_2$ are ionic; the bond in an HCl molecule is covalent. Thus all valence electrons in $SnCl_2$ are located on the Cl^- ions and all valence electrons in an HCl molecule are shared between the H and Cl atoms."
16. Predict which of the following compounds are ionic and which are covalent on the basis of the location of their constituent atoms in the periodic table: F_2CO, VO_2, NCl_3, $FeBr_2$, K_2O, NO, $MgCl_2$, HBr, CaO, IBr, CO_2.
17. How are single, double, and triple bonds similar? How do they differ?
18. Write Lewis structures for the following: H_2, HBr, PCl_3, SF_2, $SiCl_4$, H_3O^+, NH_4^+, BF_4^-.
19. Write Lewis structures for the following: O_2, H_2CO, CS_2, ClNO, H_2CCH_2, HNNH, H_2CNH, NO^-.
20. Write Lewis structures for the following: N_2, CO, CN^-, NO^+, HCCH, HCN, C_2^{2-}.
21. Write Lewis structures for the following: BCl_3, ClF_3, PCl_5, SeF_6, XeF_4, PCl_6^-, $SeCl_3^+$, Cl_2BBCl_2 (contains a B—B bond).
22. Write the Lewis structure for the diatomic molecule P_2, which is found in high-temperature phosphorus vapor.
23. Methanol, H_3COH, is used as the fuel in some race cars; ethanol is used extensively as motor fuel in Brazil. Both produce CO_2 and H_2O when they burn. Write the chemical equations for these reactions, using Lewis structures instead of chemical formulas.

Methanol   Ethanol

24. The skeleton structures of several biologically important molecules are given below. Complete the Lewis structures of these molecules.
    (a) The amino acid cysteine

    (b) Urea

    (c) Pyruvic acid

(d) Uracil

$$\text{Uracil structure}$$

(e) Carbonic acid

$$H-O-\overset{\overset{\displaystyle O}{\|}}{C}-O-H$$

25. Write the Lewis structure for sulfuric acid, H_2SO_4, which has two oxygen atoms and two OH groups bonded to the sulfur.

26. The atmosphere of Titan, the largest moon of Saturn, contains methane (CH_4) and traces of ethylene (C_2H_4), ethane (C_2H_6), hydrogen cyanide (HCN), propyne (H_3CCCH), and diacetylene (HCCCCH). Write the Lewis structures of these molecules.

Resonance

27. Why are the following two Lewis structures *not* resonance forms of N_2O?

$$:N\!=\!\!N\!=\!\!O: \quad \text{and} \quad :N\!\equiv\!\!O\!-\!\ddot{N}:$$

28. Which of the following represent resonance forms of the same species?

(a) $:N\!\equiv\!C\!-\!\ddot{O}:^- \quad$ and $\quad :\!N\!=\!C\!=\!\ddot{O}:^-$

(b)

$$\text{structure}$$ and $$\text{structure}$$

(c)

$$\text{cyclobutadiene structures}$$ and

(d) $:N\!=\!C\!=\!\ddot{S}:^- \quad$ and $\quad :N\!=\!S\!=\!C:^-$

29. Draw resonance forms that describe the distribution of electrons in the following:
(a) selenium dioxide, OSeO
(b) nitrate ion, NO_3^-
(c) nitric acid, $HONO_2$
(d) benzene

$$\text{benzene structure}$$

(e) the formate ion

$$\left[H\!-\!C \overset{\displaystyle O}{\underset{\displaystyle O}{}} \right]^-$$

30. Write the resonance forms of ozone, O_3, the component of the upper atmosphere that protects the earth from ultraviolet radiation.

31. In terms of the bonds present, explain why acetic acid contains two distinct types of carbon–oxygen bonds, whereas the acetate ion formed by loss of a hydrogen ion from acetic acid, contains only one type of carbon–oxygen bond.

$$\text{Acetic acid} \qquad \text{Acetate ion}$$

Acetic acid   Acetate ion

32. Write the resonance forms of the nitrite ion, NO_2^-, and show that this ion is isoelectronic with ozone, O_3.

Formal Charge

33. Calculate the formal charge of hydrogen in the molecules H_2, BeH_2, and H_2O.

34. Determine the formal charge of each element indicated.
(a) Cl in HCl
(b) C in CF_4
(c) N in NH_3
(d) P in PCl_3, the PCl_5 molecule in gaseous PCl_5, and the PCl_4^+ and PCl_6^- ions in solid PCl_5

35. Determine the formal charge of each element indicated.
(a) O in H_3O^+ (c) O and Cl in ClO_3^-
(b) O and S in SO_4^{2-} (d) O in O_2^{2-}

36. Calculate the formal charge of each element in the following compounds and ions: F_2CO, NO^-, BF_4^-, $ClNO$, H_2CCH_2, ClF_5, SeF_6.

37. Keeping in mind that it is necessary to average the properties of each resonance form in order to describe the properties of a molecule or ion that must be described with resonance forms, determine the formal charge on each atom in the following compounds or ions: O_3, SO_2, NO_2^-, NO_3^-, $HONO_2$.

38. Based on formal charge considerations, which of the following would be expected to be the correct arrangement of atoms in nitrosyl chloride, $:\ddot{C}l\!-\!\ddot{N}\!=\!\ddot{O}:$ or $:\ddot{C}l\!-\!\ddot{O}\!=\!\ddot{N}:$?

39. Based on formal charge considerations, which of the following would be expected to be the correct arrangement of atoms in nitrogen(I) oxide, $:N\!=\!N\!=\!\ddot{O}:$ or $:N\!=\!\ddot{O}\!=\!\ddot{N}:$?

Electronegativity and Polar Bonds

40. What is meant by the electronegativity of an element?
41. Without referring to a table of electronegativities, arrange

the atoms in each of the following series in order of increasing electronegativity:

(a) C, F, N, O   (d) Al, Na, O, P

(b) Br, Cl, F, I   (e) Ba, N, O, P

(c) F, O, P, S

42. What is a polar covalent bond?

43. What property of a covalent bond depends on the electronegativities of the atoms involved in the bond?

44. What features of a covalent bond would lead you to expect that the bond is polar?

45. Write the Lewis structure of a molecule that contains a polar single bond. A polar double bond. A polar triple bond.

46. Write the Lewis structure of a molecule that contains a nonpolar single bond. A nonpolar double bond. A nonpolar triple bond.

47. Identify the more polar bond in each of the following pairs of bonds:

(a) HF or HCl   (e) CH or NH

(b) NO or CO   (f) SO or PO

(c) SH or OH   (g) CN or NN

(d) PCl or SCl

48. Which of the following molecules or ions contain polar bonds? O_3, S_8, O_2^{2-}, NO_3^-, CO_2, H_2S, BH_4^-.

Bond Energies

49. How does the bond energy of $HCl(g)$ differ from the standard molar enthalpy of formation of $HCl(g)$? How can the standard molar enthalpy of formation of $HCl(g)$ be used in determining the bond energy?

50. Which bond in each of the following pairs of bonds is the strongest?

(a) C—C or C=C   (d) H—F or H—Cl

(b) C—N or C=N   (e) C—H or O—H

(c) C=O or C≡O   (f) C—N or C—O

51. Using the data in Appendix I, calculate the bond energies of the halogens F_2, Cl_2, and Br_2, and arrange these molecules in decreasing order of bond strength.

52. Using the data in Appendix I, calculate the bond energies of N_2, O_2, and NO. All are gases in their most stable form at standard state conditions.

53. Using the data in Appendix I, calculate the bond energy of the carbon–sulfur double bond in CS_2.

54. Using the data in Appendix I, determine which bond is stronger, the S—F bond in $SF_4(g)$ or in $SF_6(g)$.

55. Using the data in Appendix I, determine which bond is stronger, the P—Cl bond in $PCl_3(g)$ or in $PCl_5(g)$.

56. (a) Using the bond energies given in Table 7.3, determine the approximate enthalpy change for the formation of ethylene from ethane.

$$C_2H_6(g) \longrightarrow C_2H_4(g) + H_2(g)$$

(b) Compare this with the standard state enthalpy change.

57. Using the bond energies in Table 7.3, determine the approximate enthalpy change for each of the following reactions:

(a) $H_2(g) + Cl_2(g) \longrightarrow 2HCl(g)$

(b) $Cl_2(g) + 3F_2(g) \longrightarrow 2ClF_3(g)$

(c) $CH_4(g) + Br_2(g) \longrightarrow CH_3Br(g) + HBr(g)$

(d) $H_2C{=}CH_2(g) + H_2(g) \longrightarrow H_3CCH_3(g)$

(e) $2C_2H_6(g) + 7O_2(g) \longrightarrow 4CO_2(g) + 6H_2O(g)$

(f) $C_2H_4(g) + 3O_2(g) \longrightarrow 2CO_2(g) + 2H_2O(g)$

58. The enthalpy of formation of $AsF_5(g)$ has been determined to be -16.46 kJ g^{-1} of arsenic using the reaction $2As(s) + 5F_2(g) \longrightarrow 2AsF_5(g)$. Using this information and the data in Appendix I, calculate the As—F single bond energy in AsF_5.

Infrared Spectroscopy

59. The vibrational frequency of an NO molecule is 5.624×10^{13} vibrations per second. What is the wavelength of the infrared radiation that excites this vibration? What is the frequency in units of cm^{-1}?

60. The vibrational frequency of a CN^- ion is 6.236×10^{13} vibrations per second. What is the wavelength of the infrared radiation that excites this vibration? What is the frequency in units of cm^{-1}?

61. The vibrational frequency of a carbon–carbon double bond is about 5×10^{13} vibrations per second.

(a) What is the approximate vibrational frequency of a carbon–carbon single bond: 4×10^{13} s^{-1}, 5×10^{13} s^{-1}, or 6×10^{13} s^{-1}?

(b) What is the approximate vibrational frequency of a carbon–carbon triple bond: 4×10^{13} s^{-1}, 5×10^{13} s^{-1}, or 6×10^{13} s^{-1}?

62. The vibrational frequency of the NO^- ion is 4.58×10^{13} s^{-1}. What is the approximate vibrational frequency of the NO^+ ion: 3.50×10^{13} s^{-1}, 4.58×10^{13} s^{-1}, or 6.65×10^{13} s^{-1}?

63. Why do the carbon–oxygen stretching frequencies in the infrared spectrum of acetic acid differ from those in the infrared spectrum of the acetate ion? (See Exercise 31 for information about the structures of these species.)

64. Complete the Lewis structures and predict which of the following three molecules will exhibit the highest carbon–nitrogen stretching frequency.

Oxidation Number

65. Using the definition of oxidation number given at the beginning of Section 7.11, explain why fluorine always has an oxidation number of -1 in compounds and of 0 in F_2.

66. Using the definition of oxidation number given at the begin-

ning of Section 7.11, explain why oxygen has an oxidation number of -1 in hydrogen peroxide, H_2O_2.

67. Using the definition of oxidation number given at the beginning of Section 7.11, explain why hydrogen has an oxidation number of $+1$ in compounds with more electronegative elements.

68. What are the most common oxidation numbers of the following elements in their compounds? F, Li, Mg, Cs, O, Al, Ca.

69. Bromine forms binary compounds with each of the following elements: K, Co, F, Cl, I, Zn, Ca, O, C, P. In which of the compounds will bromine have a positive oxidation number?

70. Determine the oxidation number of each element indicated.
    (a) Cl in HCl
    (b) C in CF_4
    (c) N in NH_3
    (d) P in PCl_3 and PCl_5
    (e) O in H_3O^+
    (f) S in SO_4^{2-}
    (g) Cl in ClO_3^-
    (h) O in O_2^{2-}

71. Determine the oxidation number of each of the elements in the following compounds: F_2CO, K_2O, NO, $MgCl_2$, HBr, NO_3^-, NH_4^+, BF_4^-, ClNO, H_2CCH_2, HNNH, ClF_3, Cl_2BBCl_2.

72. Determine the oxidation number of nitrogen in each of the following compounds: $LiNH_2$, ClNO, NH_4Cl, N_2H_2, HNO_2, HNO_3, NaN_3, KNO_3, $Al(NO_2)_3$.

73. Determine the oxidation number of Co in each of the following compounds: CoO, Co_2O_3, CoF_3, $KCoO_2$, $CaCoCl_4$, $MgCo_2O_4$, $K_5Co(CN)_6$ (CN is an ion with a charge of -1), $Co_2(CO)_8$ (the oxidation numbers of C and O are the same as in the compound CO).

74. Compounds in which lead has an oxidation number of $+4$ generally undergo decomposition reactions (decompose) when they are heated. Which of the following compounds are likely to decompose upon heating? PbO, $PbCl_4$, PbS_2, $PbBr_2$, K_2PbCl_6.

75. The method used to calculate oxidation number in Example 7.11 gives the oxidation number of each atom in a compound; the method illustrated in Example 7.12 gives the average oxidation number of each type of atom in a compound. Determine the oxidation number of each sulfur atom, and the average oxidation number of sulfur, in HSSSSSH.

76. Determine the average oxidation number of sulfur, and the oxidation number of each sulfur atom, in the ion $S_2O_3^{2-}$.

$$:\overset{\displaystyle ..}{\underset{\displaystyle ..}{O}}:$$
$$:\overset{..}{\underset{..}{S}}-\overset{..}{\underset{..}{S}}-\overset{..}{\underset{..}{O}}:^{2-}$$
$$:\overset{\displaystyle ..}{\underset{\displaystyle ..}{O}}:$$

(See Exercise 75 for additional information.)

77. Determine the average oxidation number of carbon and the oxidation number of each carbon atom in acetic acid. See Exercise 75 for additional information and Exercise 31 for the skeleton structure of acetic acid.

78. Explain why the maximum oxidation number of an atom of Group IIA is equal to the number of electrons in its valence shell.

79. Which of the following elements exhibit a positive oxidation number when combined with phosphorus? Mg, F, Al, O, Na, Cl, Fe.

80. With which elements does sulfur form a binary compound in which it has a positive oxidation number?

81. From their positions in the periodic table and without referring to Table 7.4, predict the common oxidation numbers of the following elements in their compounds: Al, Cl, Ca, Cs, As, S, Ge, H.

Formulas of Compounds

82. Why must a sample of sodium oxide, Na_2O, contain two sodium ions for each oxide ion?

83. Write the formula of a binary compound (a compound containing only two elements) for each of the following elements such that the element has the indicated oxidation number.
    (a) Ca, $+2$
    (b) N, -3
    (c) N, $+3$
    (d) S, -2
    (e) Cl, $+1$
    (f) Br, $+5$
    (g) P, $+3$
    (h) Pb, $+2$

Prediction of Reaction Products

84. Complete and balance the equations for the following oxidation–reduction reactions. In some cases the correct answer may depend on the relative amounts of reactants used, as illustrated in Example 7.20.
    (a) $Mg + O_2 \longrightarrow$
    (b) $Al + Cl_2 \longrightarrow$
    (c) $K + S_8 \longrightarrow$
    (d) $Mg + N_2 \longrightarrow$
    (e) $P_4O_6 + O_2 \longrightarrow$
    (f) $Ca + HBr \longrightarrow$
    (g) $Cs(s) + H_2O(l) \longrightarrow$
    (h) $Li + HI \longrightarrow$
    (i) $Sr + CH_3CO_2H \longrightarrow$
    (j) $Al(s) + SnCl_4(g) \longrightarrow$
    (k) $Mg(s) + PbO(s) \longrightarrow$

85. When heated to 700–800°C, diamonds, which are pure carbon, are oxidized by atmospheric oxygen (they burn!). Write the balanced equation for this reaction.

86. Military lasers use the very intense light produced when fluorine combines explosively with hydrogen. What is the balanced equation for this reaction?

87. Dow Chemical Company for many years prepared bromine from the sodium bromide, NaBr, in Michigan brine by treating the brine with chlorine gas. Write a balanced equation for this process.

88. Complete and balance the equations for the following acid–base reactions. If the reactions are run in water as a solvent,

write the reactants and products as solvated ions. In some cases the correct answer may depend on the relative amounts of reactants used.

(a) $HBr(g) + In_2O_3(s) \longrightarrow$

(b) $Mg(OH)_2(s) + HClO_4(aq) \longrightarrow$

(c) $Al(OH)_3(s) + HNO_3(aq) \longrightarrow$

(d) $Li_2O(s) + CH_3CO_2H(l) \longrightarrow$

(e) $SrO(s) + H_2SO_4(l) \longrightarrow$

89. Write a balanced equation for the reaction that occurs when milk of magnesia, $Mg(OH)_2$, is used as an antacid to relieve excess stomach acid. Stomach acid is hydrochloric acid. Other antacids contain aluminum hydroxide, $Al(OH)_3$. Write the balanced equation that describes its action.

Additional Exercises

90. What is the difference between the hypothetical distributions of electrons used to calculate oxidation number and used to calculate formal charge?

91. In what class of substances are the formal charges and the oxidation numbers of the atoms always equal?

92. Compare the oxidation number and formal charge of hydrogen in the molecules H_2, BeH_2, and H_2O.

93. X may indicate a different representative element in each of the following Lewis formulas. To which group does X belong in each case?

(a) $:\overset{:\ddot{F}:}{\underset{:\ddot{F}:}{X}}-\ddot{F}:$

(b) $:\ddot{X}-\ddot{F}:$

(c) $:\ddot{Cl}-\overset{:\ddot{Cl}:}{\underset{:\ddot{Cl}:}{X}}-\ddot{Cl}:$

(d) $:\ddot{O}-\overset{:\ddot{O}:^-}{\underset{:\ddot{O}:}{X}}-\ddot{O}:$

(e) $:\ddot{O}-\overset{:\ddot{F}:}{\underset{:\ddot{F}:}{X}}-\ddot{O}:$

(f) $\overset{X=\ddot{O}:}{.\ddot{Cl}.}$

(g) $:\ddot{I}-X-\ddot{I}:$

(h) $X^{2+}(Cl^-)_2$

(i) $X^+(Cl^-)$

(j) $:\ddot{X}-\overset{.}{\ddot{X}}-\ddot{X}:^-$

94. The number of covalent bonds between two atoms is called bond order. Bond order may be an integer, as with $:N\equiv N:$ (bond order = 3), or a fraction, as with SO_2 (bond order = $1\frac{1}{2}$ because of the resonance $O=S-O \longleftrightarrow O-S=O$). Arrange the molecules and ions in each of the following groups in increasing bond order for the bond indicated. Unshared pairs have been omitted for clarity.

(a) C—O bond order: $C\equiv O$; $O=C=O$; $CH_3-O-O-CH_3$; HCO_2^-

(b) N—N bond order: $CH_3-N=N-CH_3$; N_2; H_2N-NH_2; N_2O

$(N=N=O \longleftrightarrow N\equiv N-O)$

(c) C—N bond order: H_3C-NH_2; CH_3CONH^-

$H_2C=NH$; $H_3C-C\equiv N$

(d) C—C bond order: H_3C-CH_3; $HC\equiv CH$; $H_2C=CH_2$; C_6H_6

95. Arrange the following ion and molecules in increasing order of their C—O bond order (see Exercise 94): CO; CO_3^{2-} (C is the central atom); H_2CO (C is the central atom); CH_3OH (with a CO bond, three CH bonds, and one OH bond).

96. Why is the bond order (Exercise 94) of a bond between H and another atom never greater than 1?

97. As the bond order (Exercise 94) between two atoms of the same type increases, the distance between the two atoms, the bond distance, decreases. How would you expect the bond distance in NO_2^- to compare to that in NO_3^-?

98. A compound with a molecular mass of about 45 contains 52.2% C, 13.1% H, and 34.7% O. Write two possible Lewis structures for this compound.

99. Which of the following represents the molecular structure of hydroxylamine?

$$H-\overset{H}{\underset{H}{\overset{|}{N}}}-\ddot{O}: \qquad H-\overset{H}{\underset{|}{N}}-\ddot{O}-H$$

(a)   (b)

(*Hint:* Using bond energies, determine whether the conversion of structure (a) to structure (b) is endothermic or exothermic.)

100. Does a calculation of formal charge lead to the correct structure for hydroxylamine (Exercise 99)?

101. Write the Lewis structure, name, and chemical formula of the compound that contains 19.7% nitrogen and 80.3% fluorine. Then determine the formal charge and oxidation number of the atoms in this compound.

102. Determine the oxidation numbers of the elements in a compound that contains 32.9% Na, 12.9% Al, and 54.3% F.

103. Write the simplest formula of a compound of potassium, cobalt(II), and chlorine that contains potassium and cobalt in the ratio 2:1.

104. Determine the percent composition of potassium dihydrogen phosphate to three significant figures.

105. Write the formulas of the following compounds: sodium fluoride, calcium sulfide, potassium oxide, magnesium chloride, hydrogen bromide, aluminum nitride, aluminum chloride.

106. Write the formulas of the following compounds: lithium nitrate, calcium perchlorate, potassium sulfate, calcium hydroxide, ammonium sulfate, aluminum phosphate, ammonium phosphate.

107. Write the formulas of the following compounds: iron(II) sulfate, lead(II) bromide, mercury(II) sulfide, manganese(II) nitrate, chromium(III) phosphate, copper(I) oxide, tin(IV) fluoride, vanadium(IV) chloride, chromium(II) perchlorate.

108. Complete and balance the following equations. In some cases the answer may depend on the relative amounts of reactants used.

(a) $Ca(OH)_2(s) + HCl(g) \longrightarrow$

(b) $Sr(OH)_2 + HNO_3 \longrightarrow$

(c) $Ca + S_8 \longrightarrow$

(d) $Cs + P_4 \longrightarrow$

(e) $In + SnSO_4 \longrightarrow$

(f) $Si + F_2 \longrightarrow$

(g) $K(s) + H_2O(l) \longrightarrow$

(h) $H_2 + Br_2 \longrightarrow$

(i) $P + F_2 \longrightarrow$

(j) $Sb + S_8 \longrightarrow$

(k) $Al(s) + HClO_4(aq) \longrightarrow$

109. What is the hydroxide ion concentration in a solution formed by dissolution of 1.00 g of calcium metal in enough water to form 250 mL of the solution?

Molecular Structure, Valence Bond Theory, and Hybridization

*Computer-generated model of DNA showing trigonal
pyramidal, trigonal planar, and bent geometries.*

The properties of molecules often reflect the spatial distribution of their atoms. For
example, humans can digest starch from wheat and corn, but not the cellulose that
forms the bodies of these plants. Starch and cellulose have the same chemical
formula and are practically identical except for small differences in the three-
dimensional arrangement of their atoms. This arrangement plays a very important role in
the chemical behavior of starch and cellulose, as well as in other molecules. In this
chapter we will examine how to predict the three-dimensional arrangement of atoms in
a molecule—the molecular structure of the molecule.

The orbitals in an atom that is part of a molecule behave differently than in the free atom. For example, the atomic orbitals on a free carbon atom are different from those on a carbon atom in a CO_2 molecule or a CH_4 molecule. Once we are able to predict the molecular structure about an atom, we can describe the changes in its atomic orbitals. The concept of hybridization is used to describe these changes, and we will also discuss this concept. Finally, valence bond theory can be used to describe the bonding in a molecule in terms of overlap between the orbitals on the atoms in that molecule.

Figure 8.1

Bond distances and angles in the formaldehyde molecule, H_2CO (1 Å=100 pm = 10^{-10} m).

Figure 8.2

The linear structure of the $HgCl_2$ molecule. The bonds are on opposite sides of the Hg atom.

Valence Shell Electron-Pair Repulsion Theory

8.1 Predicting Molecular Structures

The three-dimensional arrangement of the atoms in a molecule is called its **molecular structure.** The structure of a molecule is described in terms of its bond distances and bond angles (Fig. 8.1). A **bond distance** is the distance between the nuclei of two bonded atoms along a straight line joining the nuclei. Bond distances are measured in picometers (1 pm = 10^{-12} m) or in angstrom units (1 Å=100 pm = 10^{-10} m). A **bond angle** is the angle between any two bonds that include a common atom.

We can predict approximate bond angles around a central atom in a molecule from the number of bonds and unshared electron pairs on the central atom by using the **valence shell electron-pair repulsion theory (VSEPR theory).** The electrons in the valence shell of a central atom in a molecule form regions of high electron density either as bonding pairs of electrons, located primarily between bonded atoms, or as unshared pairs occupying regions of space shaped rather like those occupied by the bonding pairs. The electrostatic repulsion of these electrons is reduced to a minimum when the various regions of high electron density assume positions as far from each other as possible. For example, in a molecule such as $HgCl_2$ with two bonds and no unshared pairs on the central atom, the bonds are as far apart as possible, and the electrostatic repulsion between these regions of high electron density is reduced to a minimum when they are on opposite sides of the central atom. The bond angle is 180° (Fig. 8.2). This and other geometries that minimize the repulsions among regions of high electron density (bonds and/or unshared pairs) are illustrated in Table 8.1. *Two regions of electron density around a central atom in a molecule form a linear structure; three regions form a trigonal planar structure; four regions, a tetrahedral structure; five regions, a trigonal bipyramidal structure; and six regions, an octahedral structure.* If the regions of high electron density are not identical, the bond angles may differ by several degrees from the ideal values given in Table 8.1. Nevertheless, the structures given are usually good approximations for the distribution of electron density around a central atom.

A small distortion of a structure from that predicted in Table 8.1 may be attributed to differences in the repulsions between the various regions of high electron density. In effect, an unshared pair of electrons occupies a region of space that is larger than that occupied by the electrons in a triple bond, which is larger than that for a double bond, which, in turn, is larger than that for a single bond; that is, unshared pair > triple bond > double bond > single bond. In formaldehyde, H_2CO, the regions of high electron density consist of two single bonds and one double bond, and the bond angles differ

Table 8.1   Arrangement of Unshared Pairs and Bonds as a Result of Electron-Pair Repulsions

Two regions of high electron density (bonds and/or unshared pairs)	180° M	**Linear.** 180° angle.
Three regions of high electron density (bonds and/or unshared pairs)	120° M	**Trigonal planar.** All angles 120°.
Four regions of high electron density (bonds and/or unshared pairs)	109.5° M	**Tetrahedral.** All angles 109.5°.
Five regions of high electron density (bonds and/or unshared pairs)	90° M 120°	**Trigonal bipyramidal.** Angles of 90° or 120°. An attached atom may be equatorial (in the plane of the triangle) or axial (above or below the plane of the triangle).
Six regions of high electron density (bonds and/or unshared pairs)	90° M	**Octahedral.** All angles 90°.

Figure 8.3

(a) Regions occupied by the unshared pair (shown in red) and bonds (black) in NH_3 and (b) the resulting trigonal pyramidal molecular structure. (c) Lone pair/bonded pair repulsion is stronger than bonded pair/bonded pair repulsion.

by about 3° (Fig. 8.1). The larger double bond occupies the larger space, so the smaller single bonds are pushed together as indicated by the smaller H—C—H bond angle.

Even though the arrangement of unshared pairs and bonds in a molecule may correspond to one of the arrangements in Table 8.1, its molecular structure may look different. The presence of an unshared pair affects the structure of the molecule, but the unshared pair is undetectable by most experimental techniques used to determine structure. Consequently, the molecular structure is described as though the unshared pair were not there. The NH_3 molecule, for example, has a tetrahedral arrangement of regions of electron density [Fig. 8.3(a)]. However, one of these regions is an unshared pair and is not observed when the molecular structure is determined experimentally. The molecular structure (the arrangement of atoms only) is a trigonal pyramid [Fig. 8.3(b)] with the nitrogen atom at the apex and three hydrogen atoms forming the base. The

Table 8.2	Molecular Structures Based on the Valence Shell Electron-Pair Repulsion Theory

Regions of High Electron Density (bonds and unshared pairs)	Molecular Structures and Examples (chemical bonds are indicated in black, unshared pairs in red)
Three: trigonal planar arrangement of bonds and/or unshared pairs	3 Bonds — 0 Unshared pairs — Trigonal planar — CO_3^{2-}, BF_3, NO_3^- • 2 Bonds — 1 Unshared pair — Angular (about 120°) — NO_2^-, ClNO
Four: tetrahedral arrangement of bonds and/or unshared pairs	4 Bonds — 0 Unshared pairs — Tetrahedral — NH_4^+, CH_4 • 3 Bonds — 1 Unshared pair — Trigonal pyramidal — H_3O^+, PCl_3, NH_3 • 2 Bonds — 2 Unshared pairs — Angular (about 109.5°) — NH_2^-, H_2O
Five: trigonal bipyramidal arrangement of bonds and/or unshared pairs	5 Bonds — 0 Unshared pairs — Trigonal bipyramidal — PF_5, $SnCl_5^-$ • 4 Bonds — 1 Unshared pair — Seesaw — SF_4, ClF_4^+ • 3 Bonds — 2 Unshared pairs — T-shaped — ICl_3, ClF_3 • 2 Bonds — 3 Unshared pairs — Linear — I_3^-, ClF_2^-
Six: octahedral arrangement of bonds and/or unshared pairs	6 Bonds — 0 Unshared pairs — Octahedral — PCl_6^-, SF_6, IF_6^+ • 5 Bonds — 1 Unshared pair — Square pyramidal — IF_5, XeF_5^+ • 4 Bonds — 2 Unshared pairs — Square planar — ICl_4^-, XeF_4

H—N—H bond angle in NH_3 is smaller than the 109.5° angle in a regular tetrahedron (Table 8.1) because of the larger size of the unshared pair of electrons relative to the single bonds [Fig. 8.3(c)]. Table 8.2 illustrates the structures that are observed for various combinations of unshared pairs and bonds.

For several of the examples in Table 8.2, a different arrangement of the locations of unshared pairs and bonds would give a different molecular structure. For example, the molecular structure of ClF_3 is T-shaped, as shown in Fig. 8.4(a). However, two other possible arrangements for the three bonds and two unshared pairs can also be written [Figs. 8.4(b) and (c)]. The stable structure [Fig. 8.4(a)] is the one that puts the unshared pairs as far apart as possible in locations with as much room as possible and thus minimizes electron-pair repulsions. In trigonal bipyramidal arrangements (such as that of ClF_3), the positions with the most room are those in the triangular plane of the molecule, because some electrons in these positions are 120° apart.

8.2 Rules for Predicting Molecular Structures

To use the VSEPR theory to predict molecular structures, we apply the following five-point procedure:

1. Write the Lewis structure of the molecule as described in Section 7.6.
2. Count the regions of high electron density (unshared pairs and chemical bonds) around the central atom in the Lewis structure. A single, double, or triple bond counts as one region of high electron density. An unpaired electron counts as an unshared pair.
3. Identify the most stable arrangement of the regions of high electron density as linear, trigonal planar, tetrahedral, trigonal bipyramidal, or octahedral (Table 8.1).
4. If more than one arrangement of unshared pairs and chemical bonds is possible, choose the one that will minimize unshared-pair repulsions. In trigonal bipyramidal arrangements, repulsion is minimized when every unshared pair is in the plane of the triangle. In an octahedral arrangement with two unshared pairs, repulsion is minimized when the unshared pairs are on opposite sides of the central atom.
5. Identify the molecular structure (the arrangement of atoms) from the locations of the atoms at the ends of the bonds (Table 8.2).

The following examples illustrate the use of VSEPR theory to predict the structure of molecules or ions that have no unshared pairs of electrons.

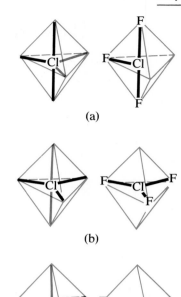

Figure 8.4

Possible arrangements of two unshared pairs (shown in red) and three bonds (black) in ClF_3, and also the resulting molecular structures showing only the positions of the atoms without the unshared pairs. Part (a) shows the stable T-shaped arrangement.

Predict the molecular structure of a gaseous $BeCl_2$ molecule.

The Lewis structure of $BeCl_2$ is

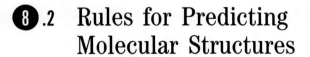

The central beryllium atom has no unshared pairs but is bonded to two atoms. There are therefore two regions of high electron density around it. Two regions of high electron density arrange themselves on opposite sides of the central atom with a bond angle of 180° (Table 8.1). $BeCl_2$ should be a linear molecule.

Example 8.1

Example 8.2

Predict the molecular structure of BCl_3.

The Lewis structure of BCl_3 is

$$:\overset{..}{\underset{..}{Cl}}-\overset{\overset{\displaystyle :\overset{..}{\underset{..}{Cl}}:}{|}}{B}-\overset{..}{\underset{..}{Cl}}:$$

BCl_3 contains three bonds, and there are no unshared pairs on boron. The arrangement of three regions of high electron density will be trigonal planar (Table 8.1). The bonds in BCl_3 should lie in a plane with 120° angles between them, a trigonal planar arrangement (Fig. 8.5).

(a)

(b)

(c)

Figure 8.5

(a) Trigonal planar arrangement of three bonds in BCl_3, (b) the resulting trigonal planar molecular structure, and (c) a model of BCl_3.

Example 8.3

Predict the molecular structure of NH_4^+.

The Lewis structure of NH_4^+ is

$$H-\overset{\overset{\displaystyle H}{|}}{\underset{\underset{\displaystyle H}{|}}{N}}-H^+$$

NH_4^+ contains four bonds from the nitrogen atom to hydrogen atoms. Four regions of high electron density arrange themselves so that they point at the corners of a tetrahedron with the central atom in the middle (Table 8.1). The hydrogen atoms located at the ends of the bonds are located at the corners of a tetrahedron. The molecular structure of NH_4^+ (Fig. 8.6) is tetrahedral.

(a)

(b)

(c)

Figure 8.6

(a) Tetrahedral arrangement of four bonds in NH_4^+, (b) the resulting tetrahedral molecular structure, and (c) a model of the NH_4^+ ion.

The effect of unshared pairs of electrons on molecular structure is illustrated in the following examples.

Predict the molecular structure of H_2O.

The Lewis structure of H_2O,

Example 8.4

$$\text{H}$$
$$|$$
$$:\overset{..}{\underset{..}{O}}\!-\!\text{H}$$

indicates that there are four regions of high electron density around the oxygen atom—two unshared pairs and two chemical bonds. These four regions are arranged in a tetrahedral fashion [Fig. 8.7(a)], as indicated in Table 8.1. However, the arrangement of the atoms themselves (the molecular structure) in H_2O is angular with a bond angle of approximately 109.5° [Table 8.2 and Fig. 8.7(b)].

(a)   (b)

Figure 8.7

(a) Tetrahedral arrangement of two unshared pairs (shown in red) and two bonds (black) in H_2O and (b) the resulting bent molecular structure.

Predict the molecular structure of SF_4.

The Lewis structure of SF_4,

Example 8.5

indicates five regions of high electron density around the sulfur atom—one unshared pair and four chemical bonds. These five regions are directed toward the corners of a trigonal bipyramid (Table 8.1). In order to minimize unshared pair–bond pair repulsions, the unshared pair occupies one of the locations in the plane of the triangle. The molecular structure (Fig. 8.8) is that of a seesaw (Table 8.2).

(a)   (b)

Figure 8.8

(a) Trigonal bipyramidal arrangement of one unshared pair (shown in red) and four bonds (black) in SF_4 and (b) the resulting seesaw-shaped molecular structure.

Example 8.6 Predict the molecular structure of IF_4^-.

The Lewis structure of IF_4^-,

indicates six regions of high electron density around the iodine atom—two unshared pairs and four bonds. These six regions adopt an octahedral arrangement. The two possible arrangements of unshared pairs and bonds are illustrated in Figs. 8.9(a) and 8.9(b). To minimize repulsions, the unshared pairs should be on opposite sides of the central atom, so the structure in Fig. 8.9(a) is the more stable of the two. The five atoms are all in the same plane and have a square planar configuration.

Figure 8.9

(a), (b) Possible octahedral arrangements of two unshared pairs (shown in red) and four bonds (black) in IF_4^- and (c) the stable square planar molecular structure.

(a)

(b)

(c)

Finally, we can see that VSEPR theory can be used even when all of the atoms around a central atom are not identical.

Example 8.7 Predict the molecular structure of ClO_2F.

The least electronegative element, chlorine, is the central element, as shown in this Lewis structure:

$$: \overset{..}{\underset{..}{O}} : $$
$$: Cl — \overset{..}{\underset{..}{F}} :$$
$$: \overset{..}{\underset{..}{O}} :$$

The four regions of high electron density are arranged tetrahedrally. The atoms are arranged to give a trigonal pyramidal structure, as shown in Fig. 8.10.

Figure 8.10

(a) Tetrahedral arrangement of one unshared pair (shown in red) and three bonds (black) in ClO_2F and (b) the resulting trigonal pyramidal molecular structure.

(a)

(b)

The predictions of valence shell electron-pair theory have been verified in a variety of ways—for example, by structure determination via X-ray diffraction (Section 11.21), dipole moment measurements (Section 8.3), and infrared spectroscopy (Section 7.10). Infrared spectroscopy can be used because the infrared spectrum of a molecule or ion depends in part on its geometry. Molecules with the same number of atoms, but with different structures, generally have different numbers or different intensities of absorptions in their infrared spectra.

Example 8.8

Why does the infrared spectrum of an SO_3 molecule, which has three absorptions, differ from that of the SO_3^{2-} ion, which has four absorptions?

The different numbers of absorptions could result from different structures of SO_3 and SO_3^{2-}. We can check to see whether this is a possible explanation by deriving the structures from VSEPR theory. The Lewis structures are

SO_3^{2-}

$$:\overset{..}{O}-\overset{..}{\underset{|}{S}}-\overset{..}{O}:^{2-}$$
$$:\overset{..}{O}:$$

SO_3

$$:\overset{..}{O}=\overset{..}{S}-\overset{..}{O}: \longleftrightarrow :\overset{..}{O}-\overset{..}{S}=\overset{..}{O}: \longleftrightarrow :\overset{..}{O}-\overset{..}{S}-\overset{..}{O}:$$

The four regions of electron density about S in SO_3^{2-}, one of which is an unshared pair, indicate a trigonal pyramidal structure for this ion. The three regions about S in SO_3 indicate that this molecule should be trigonal planar. The different structures are responsible for the different numbers of absorptions in the infrared spectra of these species.

8.3 Polar Molecules

Polar bonds, which have a positive end and a negative end, were described in Section 7.5. If a molecule has a positive end and a negative end, it is also **polar** and possesses a **dipole. Polar molecules** contain polar covalent bonds. In a molecule of hydrogen chloride, for example, the hydrogen atom is at the positively charged end of the molecule, and the chlorine atom is at the negatively charged end. Polar molecules tend to align when placed in an electric field, with the positive end of the molecule oriented toward the negative plate and the negative end toward the positive plate (Fig. 8.11). Polar molecules are attracted to an electrically charged object; nonpolar molecules are not (Fig. 8.12).

Polar molecules randomly oriented in the absence of an electric field

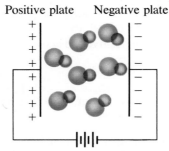

Positive plate   Negative plate

Polar molecules tending to line up in an electric field

Figure 8.11

Polar molecules, such as hydrogen chloride, tend to align in an electric field, with their positive ends oriented toward the negative plate and their negative ends toward the positive plate.

Figure 8.12

The stream of water (left) is deflected toward the electrically charged rod because the polar water molecules, H_2O, are attracted by the charge. The nonpolar carbon tetrachloride molecules, CCl_4, are not attracted, so a stream of carbon tetrachloride (right) is unaffected.

Molecules that contain two or more polar bonds may or may not be polar. If the bonds in a molecule are arranged such that their dipoles cancel, then the molecule is nonpolar. This is the situation in CO_2; each of the bonds is polar, but the molecule as a whole is nonpolar. The CO_2 molecule is linear with the polar C=O bonds on opposite sides of the C atom. The bond polarities cancel because they are pointed in opposite directions.

Negative end of bond ⟶ $^-O{=}^+C^+{=}O^-$ ⟵ Negative end of bond
Positive end of bond ⤴ ⤴ Positive end of bond

Although it may not be so obvious, the bond dipoles also cancel in trigonal planar, tetrahedral, trigonal bipyramidal, and octahedral molecules, if all of the polar bonds are identical, and nonpolar molecules are observed.

If two or more identical polar bonds in a molecule are arranged such that their dipoles do not cancel, then the molecule is polar. Examples include H_2S and NH_3. An H atom is at the positive end and the N or S atom is at the negative end of the polar bonds in these molecules.

Negative end of molecule   S⟨H H   Positive end of molecule   Negative end of molecule   N(H)(H)—H   Positive end of molecule

Molecules of this type contain unshared electron pairs that prevent the bonds from adopting an arrangement that cancels the bond dipoles.

Sometimes a molecule is polar because it contains two or more different types of polar bonds. Chloromethane, CH_3Cl, is one example. Although the polar C—Cl and C—H bonds are arranged in a tetrahedral geometry, the C—Cl bond has a dipole that is different from that of the C—H bonds, and the dipoles do not completely cancel.

The experiment illustrated in Fig. 8.12 indicates that water molecules are polar and carbon tetrachloride molecules are not. Explain the difference.

**Example
8.9**

As shown in Table 7.2, the electronegativities of oxygen (3.5) and hydrogen (2.1) are different, so an O—H bond is polar. Similarly, the electronegativities of carbon (2.5) and chlorine (2.8) indicate that the C—Cl bond is polar. Both molecules contain polar bonds, so the difference in their properties must reflect a difference in their structures. The Lewis structures of these molecules are

$$\begin{array}{ccc} \text{H} & & :\overset{..}{\text{Cl}}: \\ | & & | \\ :\overset{..}{\text{O}}\text{—H} & \quad :\overset{..}{\text{Cl}}\text{—}\overset{|}{\text{C}}\text{—}\overset{..}{\text{Cl}}: \\ & & | \\ & & :\overset{..}{\text{Cl}}: \end{array}$$

From the Lewis structures we can tell that H_2O is a bent molecule (Fig. 8.7) and CCl_4 is a tetrahedral molecule. As in H_2S, the dipoles of the bonds in H_2O do not cancel, but the bond dipoles in the tetrahedral CCl_4 molecule do cancel.

Valence Bond Theory and Hybridization of Atomic Orbitals

Lewis structures and VSEPR theory are usually satisfactory for identifying how electrons are distributed in a molecule and for predicting molecular geometries. However, a more thorough understanding of bonding requires us to use one of the models of bonding that is based on quantum mechanics. As described in Section 7.3, a covalent bond forms when one or more pairs of electrons are shared by two atoms and are simultaneously attracted by the nuclei of both. In the remainder of this chapter, we will discuss valence bond theory and hybridization, one way to explain how two atoms share electrons.

❽.4   Valence Bond Theory

Valence bond theory describes covalent bonding in terms of pairing of electrons in overlapping atomic orbitals. Orbitals **overlap** when a portion of one orbital and a portion of a second occupy the same region of space. According to valence bond theory, a covalent bond results when an atomic orbital on one atom overlaps an atomic orbital on a second atom and an electron pair occupies both orbitals. Because of the overlap, the electrons are simultaneously attracted to both nuclei, and this attraction leads to bonding. The strength of a covalent bond depends on the amount of overlap of the atomic

Figure 8.13

The sum of the energies of the electrons in two hydrogen atoms as a function of the distance between the atoms. At a distance of 0.74 Å, the H—H bond distance, the energy is at a minimum of -436 kJ per mole of H_2 molecules, the bond energy of the H—H bond.

Figure 8.14

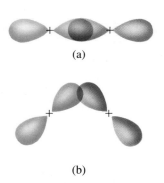

The overlap of p orbitals of two different atoms in two different orientations with an identical distance between the two nuclei. The overlap (shown in purple) is greatest when the orbitals are directed end-to-end (a). Any other arrangement (b) results in less overlap. The plus signs indicate the locations of the nuclei.

orbitals involved. The strongest bond results when two bonded atoms are arranged such that the orbitals forming the bond have the maximum possible overlap.

Overlap increases as atoms approach each other. However, there is an optimum distance between two bonded nuclei in any bond. Figure 8.13 illustrates how the sum of the energies of two hydrogen atoms changes as they approach each other. When the atoms are far apart there is no overlap, and we say the sum of the energies is zero. As the atoms move together their orbitals begin to overlap, and each electron begins to feel the attraction of the nucleus on the other atom. In addition, the electrons begin to repel each other, as do the nuclei. While the atoms are still widely separated, the attractions are stronger than the repulsions and the energy of the system decreases. As the atoms move closer together the overlap increases, so the attraction of the nuclei for the electrons continues to increase (as do the repulsions among electrons and between the nuclei). At some specific distance between the atoms, which varies from bond to bond, the energy reaches its lowest value; this specific distance corresponds to the bond distance between the two atoms (Section 8.1). The bond is stable because the attractive and repulsive forces are balanced. If the distance between the nuclei were to decrease further, the repulsions would become larger than the attractions, and the energy of the system would increase rapidly. The difference between the energy of the two separated atoms and the energy when the atoms are at the bond distance equals the bond energy (Section 7.9).

In addition to the distance between two orbitals, their orientation (other than for two s orbitals, which are spherical) also affects their overlap. The maximum overlap is obtained when orbitals are oriented such that they overlap end-to-end. Figure 8.14 illustrates this for two p orbitals; the overlap is greater when the orbitals overlap end-to-end rather than at an angle.

The overlap of two s orbitals (as in H_2), the overlap of an s orbital and a p orbital (as in HCl), and the end-to-end overlap of two p orbitals (as in Cl_2) produces a **sigma bond** **(σ bond),** as illustrated in Fig. 8.15. A sigma bond is a covalent bond in which the electron density is concentrated in the region along the internuclear axis. That is, a line between the nuclei would pass through the center of the overlap region. Single bonds, as described by the valence bond theory, are sigma bonds.

A **pi bond (π bond)** is a covalent bond that results from the side-by-side overlap of

(a)   (b)   (c)

Figure 8.15

Sigma bonds form from the overlap (a) of two *s* orbitals, (b) of an *s* orbital and a *p* orbital, and (c) of two *p* orbitals. The plus signs indicate the locations of the nuclei.

two *p* orbitals, as illustrated in Fig. 8.16. In a pi bond the regions of orbital overlap lie above and below the internuclear axis. Double bonds, such as that found in O_2, consist of a sigma bond and a pi bond. Triple bonds, such as that in N_2, consist of a sigma bond and two pi bonds.

$$H-\overset{..}{\underset{..}{Cl}}:\qquad :\overset{..}{O}=\overset{..}{O}:\qquad :N\equiv N:$$

One sigma bond   One sigma bond   One sigma bond
                        and one pi bond   and two pi bonds

The overlap in a pi bond is less than that in a sigma bond, so pi bonds are generally weaker than sigma bonds. This is the reason why a double bond between two atoms generally is not twice as strong as a single bond between the corresponding atoms (see Section 7.9).

8.5 Hybridization of Atomic Orbitals

Thinking in terms of overlapping atomic orbitals is one way to explain how chemical bonds form. However, it may not be obvious how some molecular structures maximize orbital overlap in order for the most stable bonds to form. For example, consider the water molecule, a bent molecule with a tetrahedral bond angle (Fig. 8.7). Because an oxygen atom has two unpaired electrons (one in each of two $2p$ orbitals), we might expect the two O—H bonds to form from the overlap of these two $2p$ orbitals with the $1s$ orbitals of the hydrogen atoms. If this were the case, the bond angle would be 90°, as shown in Fig. 8.17, because *p* orbitals are perpendicular to each other (Section 5.10, Fig. 5.18). Experimental evidence shows that the bond angle is not 90° but 104.5°; thus it is not appropriate to describe the bonding in H_2O as resulting from the overlap of the *p* orbitals with hydrogen *s* orbitals.

Quantum-mechanical calculations explain why the observed bond angles in H_2O differ from those predicted by the overlap of the $1s$ orbital of the H atoms with *p* orbitals of the O atom. These calculations lead to the important conclusion that the arrangement of the orbitals in an atom in a molecule is not the same as the arrangement of the orbitals in an isolated (unbonded) atom.

The valence orbitals in an isolated oxygen atom are those described in Chapter 5: the $2s$ and the three $2p$ orbitals. The valence orbitals in an oxygen atom in a water molecule differ; they consist of four equivalent orbitals that point approximately toward the corners of a tetrahedron (Fig. 8.18). Consequently, the overlap of the O and H orbitals should result in a tetrahedral bond angle. The observed angle of 104.5° is experimental evidence that quantum-mechanical calculation gives a useful explanation. (We shall see how the orbitals on the O atom can be described when we consider sp^3 hybridization in Section 8.8.)

We can describe the nature of the valence orbitals in a bonded atom by using the concept of **hybridization,** the mixing of the atomic orbitals of an isolated atom to generate a new set of atomic orbitals, called **hybrid orbitals.** Hybrid orbitals are new types of atomic orbitals that result when two or more orbitals of an isolated atom mix.

Figure 8.16

Pi bonds form from the side-by-side overlap of two *p* orbitals. The plus signs indicate the locations of the nuclei.

Figure 8.17

The hypothetical overlap of two of the $2p$ orbitals on an O atom (one shown in red and the other in blue) with the $1s$ orbitals of two H atoms (shown in yellow) produces a bond angle of 90°. The plus signs indicate the locations of the nuclei.

(a)

(b)

Figure 8.18

(a) The four valence orbitals of the O atom in H_2O are directed toward the corners of a tetrahedron. (b) Two of the hybrid orbitals overlap with the $1s$ orbitals of H atoms and form the O—H bonds in H_2O. The other two valence orbitals contain the unshared electron pairs present in an H_2O molecule.

They are used to describe the orbitals in bonded atoms. The following six ideas are important in understanding hybridization:

1. Hybrid orbitals are not used in isolated atoms. They are used only to explain covalent bonding.
2. Hybrid orbitals have shapes and orientations that are very different from those of the atomic orbitals in isolated atoms.
3. All orbitals in a set of hybrid orbitals are equivalent and form identical bonds (when the bonds are to a set of identical atoms).
4. The number of hybrid orbitals in a bonded atom is equal to the number of valence orbitals that are used to form the hybrid orbitals.
5. The type of hybrid orbital on a bonded atom depends on the geometry of its unshared electron pairs and the atoms bonded to it.
6. Sigma bonds in polyatomic molecules usually involve the overlap of hybrid orbitals. Pi bonds result from the overlap of unhybridized orbitals.

In the remainder of this chapter, we shall discuss the common types of hybrid orbitals.

8.6 *sp* Hybridization

The beryllium atom in a gaseous $BeCl_2$ molecule (Example 8.1) is an example of a middle atom with no unshared pairs of electrons in a linear set of three atoms. The four valence orbitals in such a *bonded* atom consist of two hybrid orbitals and two *p* orbitals that are not involved in the hybridization. The hybrid orbitals are called *sp* **hybrid orbitals** because they result from the hybridization of the $2s$ orbital and one of the $2p$ orbitals of the atom. *sp* **hybridization** produces two *sp* hybrid orbitals that lie in a linear geometry (Fig. 8.19). In the linear $BeCl_2$ molecule, these hybrid orbitals overlap with orbitals of the chlorine atoms to form two identical sigma bonds. The orbitals and electron distribution in an isolated beryllium atom and in the bonded Be atom can be illustrated as follows. Each orbital is represented by a circle and each electron by an arrow; arrows pointing in opposite directions designate electrons of opposite spin. The red arrows are electrons from the chlorine atoms in the Be—Cl bonds.

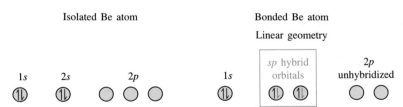

When atomic orbitals hybridize, the electrons in these orbitals may be redistributed in the hybridized orbitals. When a Be atom hybridizes, the electrons redistribute such that

Figure 8.19

Hybridization of an *s* orbital (red) and a *p* orbital of the same atom (blue) to produce two *sp* hybrid orbitals (purple).

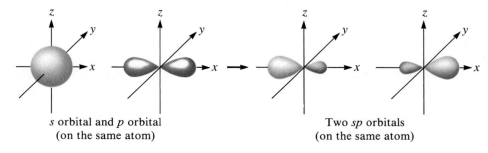

s orbital and *p* orbital (on the same atom)　　　　Two *sp* orbitals (on the same atom) there is one electron per hybrid orbital. Each of these electrons pairs with the unpaired electron on a chlorine atom when a hybrid orbital and a chlorine orbital overlap during the formation of the Be—Cl bonds.

Other atoms that exhibit *sp* hybridization include the mercury atom in the linear $HgCl_2$ molecule, the zinc atom in $Zn(CH_3)_2$, which contains a linear C—Zn—C arrangement, and the carbon atoms in HCCH (acetylene, Section 8.11).

8.7 *sp²* Hybridization

The valence orbitals of an atom surrounded by a trigonal planar arrangement of unshared pairs and bonding pairs consist of a set of three **sp^2 hybrid orbitals** and one unhybridized *p* orbital. This arrangement results from **sp^2 hybridization,** the mixing of one *s* orbital and two *p* orbitals that produces three identical hybrid orbitals. Each of these three hybrid orbitals points toward a different corner of an equilateral triangle (Fig. 8.20).

The structure of BF_3 suggests sp^2 hybridization for boron in this compound. The molecule is trigonal planar, and the boron atom is involved in three bonds to fluorine atoms (Fig. 8.21).

The orbitals and electron distribution in an isolated boron atom and in the bonded atom can be illustrated as follows. (The red arrows represent the electrons from the F atoms in the B—F bonds.)

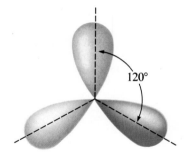

Figure 8.20

The shape and trigonal planar orientation of the three sp^2 hybrid orbitals. Although the three hybrid orbitals are shown in different colors for clarity, they are identical.

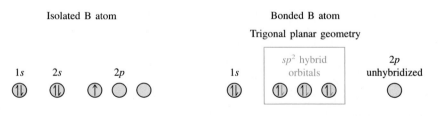

Note that the three valence electrons of the boron atom are redistributed in the three hybrid orbitals and that each boron electron pairs with a fluorine electron when B—F bonds form.

Other atoms that exhibit sp^2 hybridization include the boron atom in BCl_3 (Fig. 8.5), the nitrogen atom in NO_3^- and ClNO, the sulfur atom in SO_2, and the carbon atom in H_2CCH_2 and H_2CO.

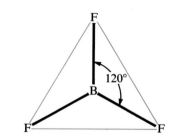

Figure 8.21

The trigonal planar structure of BF_3.

8.8 *sp³* Hybridization

The valence orbitals of an atom surrounded by a tetrahedral arrangement of unshared pairs and bonding pairs consist of a set of four **sp^3 hybrid orbitals.** The hybrids result from **sp^3 hybridization,** the mixing of the *s* orbital and all three *p* orbitals that produces four identical hybrid orbitals. Each of these hybrid orbitals points toward a different corner of a tetrahedron [Fig. 8.18(a)].

A molecule of methane, CH_4, consists of a carbon atom surrounded by four hydrogen atoms at the corners of a tetrahedron. This indicates that the carbon atom in methane exhibits sp^3 hybridization. The orbitals and electron distribution in an isolated carbon atom and in the bonded atom can be illustrated as follows. (The red arrows represent the electrons from the H atoms in the C—H bonds.) Note that the four valence electrons of

Figure 8.22

The methane molecule. (a) Diagram showing the overlap of the four tetrahedral sp^3 hybrid orbitals (yellow) with four s orbitals (red) of four hydrogen atoms. (b) The overall outline of the four bonds (orange) in methane.

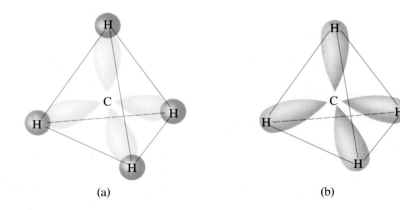

(a)   (b)

the carbon atom are redistributed in the hybrid orbitals and that each pairs with a hydrogen electron when the C—H bonds form.

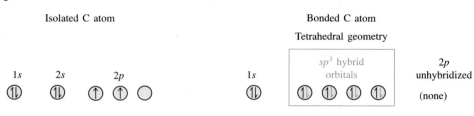

Isolated C atom   Bonded C atom

Tetrahedral geometry

$1s$ $2s$ $2p$ $1s$ sp^3 hybrid orbitals $2p$ unhybridized

(none)

In a methane molecule the $1s$ orbital of each of the four hydrogen atoms overlaps with one of the four sp^3 orbitals of the carbon atom to form an sp^3–s sigma (σ) bond. This results in the formation of four very strong equivalent covalent bonds between one carbon atom and four hydrogen atoms to produce the methane molecule, CH_4 (Fig. 8.22).

The structure of ethane, C_2H_6, is similar to that of methane in that each carbon in ethane has four neighboring atoms arranged at the corners of a tetrahedron—three H atoms and one C atom (Fig. 8.23). In ethane an sp^3 orbital of one carbon atom overlaps end-to-end with an sp^3 orbital of a second carbon atom to form a σ bond. Each of the other three sp^3 hybrid orbitals of each carbon atom overlaps with an s orbital of a hydrogen atom to form additional σ bonds. The structure and overall outline of the bonding orbitals of ethane are shown in Fig. 8.23. Ethane is made up of two tetrahedra with one corner in common.

An sp^3 hybrid orbital can also hold an unshared pair of electrons. For example, the nitrogen atom in ammonia [Fig. 8.3(a)] is surrounded by three bonding pairs of electrons and an unshared pair, all directed to the corners of a tetrahedron. Thus the nitrogen atom may be regarded as being sp^3 hybridized with one hybrid orbital occupied by the unshared pair (represented by the pair of black arrows).

(a)

(b)

Figure 8.23

The ethane molecule. (a) The overlap diagram for the ethane molecule. (b) The overall outline of the seven bonds (orange) in ethane.

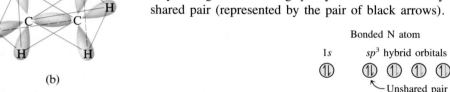

Bonded N atom

$1s$ sp^3 hybrid orbitals

Unshared pair

The molecular structure of water (Fig. 8.7) is consistent with a tetrahedral arrangement of two unshared pairs and two bonding pairs of electrons [Fig. 8.18(b)]. Thus we say that the oxygen atom is sp^3 hybridized, with two of the hybrid orbitals occupied by unshared pairs and two by bonding pairs.

Any atom with a tetrahedral arrangement of unshared pairs and bonding pairs may be regarded as being sp^3 hybridized. But note that hybridization can occur *only* when the atomic orbitals involved have very similar energies. It is possible to hybridize $2s$ and $2p$ orbitals, or $3s$ and $3p$ orbitals, for example, but not $2s$ and $3p$ orbitals.

8.9 Other Types of Hybridization

An atom with either a trigonal bipyramidal or an octahedral arrangement of bonding electron pairs and unshared pairs cannot form hybrid orbitals using only its four s and p valence orbitals. To accommodate five pairs of electrons in a trigonal bipyramidal arrangement, an atom must hybridize five atomic orbitals—the s orbital, the three p orbitals, and one of the d orbitals in its valence shell (or shells)—giving five sp^3d **hybrid orbitals.** With an octahedral arrangement of six electron pairs, an atom hybridizes six atomic orbitals—the s orbital, the three p orbitals, and two of the d orbitals in its valence shell—giving six sp^3d^2 **hybrid orbitals.**

In a molecule of phosphorus(V) chloride, PCl_5 (Fig. 8.24), there are five P—Cl bonds (and thus five pairs of valence electrons around the phosphorus atom) directed toward the corners of a trigonal bipyramid. To form a set of sp^3d hybrid orbitals, the s orbital, the three p orbitals, and one of the d orbitals must be hybridized.

Figure 8.24

Structure of phosphorus(V) chloride, PCl_5; sp^3d hybridization.

Other atoms that exhibit sp^3d hybridization include the sulfur atom in SF_4 (Fig. 8.8) and the chlorine atom in ClF_3 [Fig. 8.4(a)] and in ClF_4^+.

The sulfur atom in sulfur(VI) fluoride, SF_6, exhibits sp^3d^2 hybridization. A molecule of sulfur(VI) fluoride has six fluorine atoms surrounding a single sulfur atom (Fig. 8.25). To bond six fluorine atoms, the sulfur atom undergoes hybridization such that the s orbital, the three p orbitals, and two of the d orbitals form six equivalent sp^3d^2 hybrid orbitals, each one directed toward a different corner of an octahedron.

Figure 8.25

The octahedral structure of SF_6; sp^3d^2 hybridization.

Other atoms that exhibit sp^3d^2 hybridization include the phosphorus atom in PCl_6^-, the iodine atom in IF_6^+, IF_5, ICl_4^- (Table 8.2), and IF_4^- [Fig. 8.9(a)], and the xenon atom in XeF_4.

8.10 Assignment of Hybrid Orbitals to Bonded Atoms

The geometrical arrangements characteristic of the various sets of hybrid orbitals are shown in Table 8.3. To find the hybridization of a central atom, we first determine the geometry of its regions of high electron density and then assign the set of hybridized orbitals from Table 8.3 that corresponds to this arrangement.

Example 8.10

What is the hybridization of the nitrogen atom in the ammonium ion, NH_4^+?

As described in Example 8.3, the nitrogen atom in NH_4^+ has a tetrahedral arrangement of regions of high electron density. This corresponds to sp^3 hybridization of nitrogen (Table 8.3).

Example 8.11

Urea, $NH_2C(O)NH_2$, is sometimes used as a source of nitrogen in fertilizers. What is the hybridization of the nitrogen and carbon atoms in urea?

The Lewis structure of urea is

$$\begin{array}{ccccc} H & & O & & H \\ | & & \| & & | \\ H-N-&C&-N-H \\ \cdot\cdot & & & & \cdot\cdot \end{array}$$

The nitrogen atoms are surrounded by four regions of high electron density, which arrange themselves in a tetrahedral geometry (Table 8.1). The hybridization in a tetrahedral arrangement is sp^3 (Table 8.3). This is the hybridization of the nitrogen atoms in urea.

The carbon atom is surrounded by three regions of electron density, positioned in a trigonal planar arrangement (Table 8.1). The hybridization in a trigonal planar arrangement is sp^2 (Table 8.3), which is the hybridization of the carbon atom in urea.

Table 8.3   **Hybrid Orbitals**

180°
sp—Linear

120°
sp^2—Trigonal planar

109.5°
sp^3—Tetrahedral

90°
120°
sp^3d—Trigonal bipyramidal

90°
90°
sp^3d^2—Octahedral

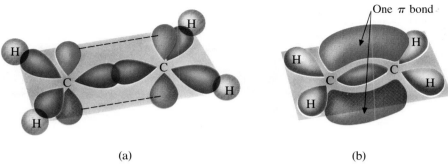

(a)   (b)

Figure 8.26

The ethylene molecule. (a) The overlap diagram of three sp^2 hybrid orbitals (blue) on carbon atoms and four s orbitals (red) from four hydrogen atoms. There are four C—H σ bonds and a carbon–carbon double bond involving one C—C σ bond and one C—C π bond. The dashed lines, each connecting two lobes, indicate the side-by-side overlap of the two unhybridized p orbitals (green). The sp^2 hybrid orbitals lie in a plane with the unhybridized p orbitals extending above and below the plane and perpendicular to it. (b) The overall outline of the bonds in ethylene. The two portions of the π bond (shown in green), resulting from the side-by-side overlap of the unhybridized p orbitals, are above and below the plane. Carbon–hydrogen bonds are shown in purple.

8.11 Hybridization Involving Double and Triple Bonds

If we apply the VSEPR theory (Section 8.1) to the Lewis structure of ethylene, C_2H_4,

$$\begin{array}{c}\text{H}\\ \diagdown\end{array}\text{C}=\text{C}\begin{array}{c}\text{H}\\ \diagup\end{array}$$
$$\begin{array}{c}\text{H}\end{array}\diagup\qquad\diagdown\begin{array}{c}\text{H}\end{array}$$

each carbon atom should be surrounded by one carbon atom and two hydrogen atoms, forming a trigonal planar array. Thus the sigma (σ) bonds from each carbon atom should be formed using a set of sp^2 hybrid orbitals directed toward the corners of a triangle. These orbitals form the C—H single bonds and the σ bond in the C=C double bond (Fig. 8.26). The pi (π) bond in the C=C bond, which gives it a bond order of 2, results from the $2p$ orbital that is not involved in the sp^2 hybridization.

Only two $2p$ orbitals hybridize with the $2s$ orbital, so one $2p$ orbital is left unhybridized. As shown in Fig. 8.27, the unhybridized p orbital (shown in green) is perpendicular to the plane of the sp^2 orbitals. Thus when two sp^2 hybridized carbon atoms come together, one sp^2 orbital on each of them can overlap to form a σ bond, while the unhybridized $2p$ orbitals can overlap in a side-by-side fashion. This overlap results in a π bond (Section 8.4). The two carbon atoms of ethylene are thus bound together by two kinds of bonds—one σ and one π—giving a double bond.

Note that in an ethylene molecule, the four hydrogen atoms and the two carbon atoms are all in the same plane. If the two planes of sp^2 hybrid orbitals are tilted, the π bond is weakened because the p orbitals that form it cannot overlap effectively if they are not parallel. A planar configuration for the ethylene molecule is the most stable form.

As we have seen for $BeCl_2$, if just one $2p$ orbital hybridizes with a $2s$ orbital, two sp hybrid orbitals result. This arrangement leaves two $2p$ orbitals unhybridized (Fig. 8.28). When sp hybrid orbitals of two carbon atoms combine, they overlap end-to-end to form

Figure 8.27

Diagram illustrating the three trigonal sp^2 hybrid orbitals of the carbon atom, which lie in the same plane, and the one unhybridized p orbital (shown in green), which is perpendicular to the plane.

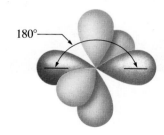

Figure 8.28

Diagram of the two linear sp hybrid orbitals of the carbon atom, which lie in a straight line, and the two unhybridized p orbitals (shown in green).

Figure 8.29

The acetylene molecule. (a) The overlap diagram of two *sp* hybrid carbon atoms and two *s* orbitals from two hydrogen atoms. There are two C—H σ bonds and a carbon–carbon triple bond involving one C—C σ bond and two C—C π bonds. The dashed lines, each connecting two lobes, indicate the side-by-side overlap of the four unhybridized *p* orbitals. The *sp* hybrid orbitals are shown in blue, and the unhybridized *p* orbitals are shown in green. (b) The overall outline of the bonds in acetylene. The two portions of the π bonds (in green) are positioned with one above and below the line of the σ bonds and the other behind and in front of the line of the σ bonds.

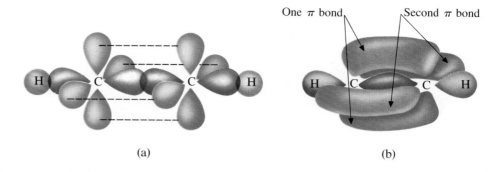

(a)   (b)

a σ bond (Fig. 8.29). The remaining *sp* orbital on each carbon may be used to bond with another atom such as hydrogen, forming a linear molecule such as acetylene, H—C≡C—H. In addition to this, as indicated in Fig. 8.29, the two sets of unhybridized *p* orbitals are positioned such that they overlap side-by-side and hence form two π bonds. The two carbon atoms of acetylene are thus bound together by one σ bond and two π bonds, giving a triple bond.

8.12 Nuclear Magnetic Resonance

Nuclear magnetic resonance (NMR) is a technique that can be used to determine the structure of many molecules and ions and the hybridization of various atoms within them. The technique measures the small magnetic fields produced by certain types of atomic nuclei.

Electrons behave as though they spin around their own axes, with spin quantum numbers of $+\frac{1}{2}$ and $-\frac{1}{2}$ (Section 5.10). This spin causes them to behave like tiny bar magnets. Nuclei of certain atoms also appear to spin on their own axes, and they too behave like very small bar magnets. For example, the nuclei of hydrogen (a proton), fluorine, and phosphorus atoms all have a spin and behave like bar magnets.

When a nucleus with a spin is placed in a magnetic field, it aligns itself with the field (a lower-energy condition) or against the field (a higher-energy condition). Energy is required to change the nucleus from alignment with the field to the higher-energy condition of alignment against the field. The energy a nucleus absorbs as it realigns itself in a magnetic field can be detected on an instrument called an NMR spectrometer. This energy forms the basis for NMR spectroscopy.

In an NMR spectrometer (Fig. 8.30), a solution of a sample is suspended in a magnetic field and the energy necessary to change the alignment of the nuclei in the field is provided as electromagnetic radiation in the radiofrequency range (Section 5.8). The frequency of the radiation is varied, and the nuclei change their orientation in the field when the energy of the radiation is equal to the difference in energy between the two orientations of the nucleus. The absorption of the radiofrequency energy as the nuclei change orientation is detected by the spectrometer and plotted (Fig. 8.31). An NMR spectrum plots the energies of the transitions of the nuclei relative to a sample with a standard energy.

The amount of energy necessary to change the alignment of a nucleus in an applied magnetic field depends on the strength of the magnetic field at the nucleus. The strength

Figure 8.30

A nuclear magnetic resonance spectrometer. The sample is suspended in a magnetic field produced by the superconducting magnet in the background on the right. The console on the left contains the electronics for detecting and plotting the spectrum shown on the monitor.

Figure 8.31

The NMR spectrum of the hydrogen atoms in ethanol. The peaks in this spectrum indicate absorption of radiofrequency radiation as the hydrogen nuclei change their orientation in the magnetic field.

of the magnetic field at the nucleus depends on (1) the strength of the applied field, (2) the presence of additional magnetic fields due to neighboring nuclei with magnetic moments, and (3) the electron density around the nucleus. The electrons around a nucleus shield it from the full effects of the applied magnetic field. Thus the data in an NMR spectrum provide information about the number and kinds of neighboring nuclei around an atom with a nucleus that has a magnetic moment (the structure around the atom) and the electron density around the nucleus (the atom's hybridization or the hybridization of its neighbors).

We will not concern ourselves with the details of interpreting an NMR spectrum, but as an example of the kinds of information available, let us consider the spectrum of the hydrogen nuclei in ethanol, which has the formula C_2H_6O. This molecule could have either of two structures:

$$\text{Structure I} \qquad \text{Structure II}$$

The NMR spectrum of ethanol (Fig. 8.31) shows three groups of peaks. The peaks labeled A and B are due to hydrogen atoms bonded to carbon atoms with sp^3 hybridization. Peak C results from a hydrogen atom bonded to an oxygen atom. This information alone is enough to identify the structure of ethyl alcohol as Structure II, because Structure I does not have an oxygen–hydrogen bond. The number of peaks in the spectrum are related in a somewhat complex way to the number of hydrogen atoms bonded to each carbon or oxygen atom in the molecule. The spectrum indicates that three hydrogen atoms are bonded to a carbon atom with sp^3 hybridization, two hydrogen atoms are bonded to a second carbon atom with sp^3 hybridization, and one hydrogen atom is bonded to the oxygen atom. This is also an indication that the structure of ethanol must be Structure II.

For Review

Summary

The **molecular structure,** or three-dimensional arrangement of the atoms in a molecule or ion, is described in terms of **bond distances** and **bond angles.** We can predict approximate bond angles by using the **valence shell electron-pair repulsion (VSEPR) theory.** According to this theory, regions of high electron density (either bonding pairs or unshared pairs) located about a central atom repel each other, and the most stable arrangement is reached when they are as far away from each other as possible. For two regions of high electron density, the most stable arrangement is a **linear structure;** for three, a **trigonal planar structure;** for four, a **tetrahedral structure;** for five, a **trigonal bipyramidal structure;** and for six, an **octahedral structure.** Because an unshared pair of electrons is undetectable by the techniques used to determine molecular structure, the expected arrangement of the regions of high electron density and the actual molecular structure may appear different. In ammonia, three bonding pairs and one unshared pair are in a tetrahedral arrangement, but the nitrogen and hydrogen atoms form a trigonal pyramid. Other geometries are illustrated in Table 8.2. **Nuclear magnetic resonance, NMR,** is a technique that can be used to determine the structure of many molecules and ions.

Valence bond theory describes bonding as resulting from the presence of a pair of electrons in two overlapping orbitals. Two orbitals on different atoms **overlap** when they occupy the same region of space. A bond results from the simultaneous attraction of the electrons to both of the bonded nuclei.

The orbitals a central atom uses to form bonds with other atoms may be described as **hybrid orbitals,** combinations of some or all of its valence atomic orbitals. These hybrid orbitals may form **sigma (σ) bonds** directed toward other atoms of the molecule, or they may contain unshared pairs. The type of hybridization around a central atom can be determined from the geometry of the regions of high electron density about it. Two such regions imply sp hybridization; three, sp^2 hybridization; four, sp^3 hybridization; five, sp^3d hybridization; and six, sp^3d^2 hybridization.

Atomic orbitals that are not used in hybridization are available to form **pi (π) bonds.** The carbon atoms in ethylene, C_2H_4, are sp^2 hybridized, and the remaining p orbital on each is used to form a π bond, resulting in a double bond. The carbon atoms in acetylene, HCCH, are sp hybridized, and the two remaining p orbitals on each are used to form two π bonds, resulting in a triple bond.

Key Terms and Concepts

bond angle (8.1)
bond distance (8.1)
double bond (8.11)
hybrid orbitals (8.5)
hybridization (8.5, 8.10)
linear structure (8.1)
molecular structure (8.1)
nuclear magnetic resonance (NMR) (8.12)

octahedral structure (8.1)
pi (π) bond (8.4, 8.11)
polar molecules (8.3)
sigma (σ) bond (8.4, 8.11)
tetrahedral structure (8.1)
trigonal bipyramidal structure (8.1)
trigonal planar structure (8.1)

triple bond (8.11)
valence bond theory (8.4)
valence shell electron-pair repulsion (VSEPR) theory (8.1)

Exercises

Answers for selected even-numbered exercises marked by red numbers appear at the end of the book. The worked-out solutions to all even-numbered exercises appear in the *Solutions Guide*.

Molecular Structure

1. How many regions of high electron density are required around an atom to form a linear arrangement of these regions about the atom? A trigonal planar arrangement? A tetrahedral arrangement? A trigonal bipyramidal arrangement? An octahedral arrangement? What are the angles between the regions in each of these arrangements?

2. Predict the structure of each of the following molecules:
   (a) TeF_6 (d) BeH_2
   (b) PF_5 (e) BH_3
   (c) $SiCl_4$

3. Identify the structure of each of the following ions:
   (a) PF_6^- (c) SiF_5^-
   (b) SO_4^{2-} (d) CH_3^+

4. What is the structure of each of the following molecules?
   (a) IF_5 (e) SeF_4
   (b) PF_5 (f) XeF_4
   (c) $BrCl_3$ (g) XeF_2
   (d) PCl_3 (h) SF_2

5. Predict the structure of each of the following ions:
   (a) H_3O^+ (d) ICl_4^-
   (b) CH_3^- (e) $TeCl_4^{2-}$
   (c) $SnCl_3^-$ (f) NH_2^-

6. Identify the structure of each of the following molecules:
   (a) ClNO (N is the central atom)
   (b) CS_2
   (c) Cl_2CO (C is the central atom)
   (d) Cl_2SO (S is the central atom)
   (e) SO_2F_2 (S is the central atom)
   (f) XeO_2F_2 (Xe is the central atom)

7. Predict the structure of each of the following:
   (a) IF_6^+ (f) BrF_5
   (b) PCl_5 (g) SiO_4^{4-}
   (c) SeO_2 (h) $ClSO^+$ (S is the central atom)
   (d) ClF_4^+
   (e) PH_3 (i) ClO_2^-

8. Predict the geometry around the indicated atom or atoms:
   (a) The sulfur atom in sulfuric acid, H_2SO_4 [$(HO)_2SO_2$]
   (b) The chlorine atom in chloric acid, $HClO_3$ [$HOClO_2$]
   (c) The oxygen atoms in hydrogen peroxide, HOOH
   (d) The nitrogen atom in nitric acid, HNO_3 [$HONO_2$]
   (e) The oxygen atom in the OH group in nitric acid, HNO_3 [$HONO_2$]
   (f) The central oxygen atom in the ozone molecule, O_3
   (g) Each of the carbon atoms in propyne, CH_3CCH
   (h) The carbon atom in the Freon CCl_2F_2
   (i) Each of the carbon atoms in allene, $H_2C=C=CH_2$

9. Identify the structures of the molecules and polyatomic ions in the compounds listed in Exercise 93 in Chapter 7.

10. Which of the following molecules that contain only two carbon atoms and several hydrogen atoms would contain the strongest carbon–carbon bond: (a) a molecule in which both C atoms have a tetrahedral molecular structure about them; (b) a molecule in which both C atoms have a trigonal planar structure about them; or (c) a molecule in which both C atoms have a linear structure about them?

Dipole Moments

11. How do polar bonds give polar molecules? How can a molecule containing polar bonds be nonpolar?

12. Which of the molecules listed in Exercise 2 contain dipolar bonds? Which of these molecules have a dipole moment?

13. Which of the molecules listed in Exercise 4 contain dipolar bonds? Which of these molecules have a dipole moment?

14. Which of the molecules listed in Exercise 6 contain dipolar bonds? Which of these molecules have a dipole moment?

15. What is the difference between the molecules listed in Exercise 2 that do not have dipole moments and those listed in Exercise 4 that do?

16. The molecule XF_3 has a dipole moment. Is X boron or phosphorus?

Valence Bond Theory

17. How does valence bond theory differ from the Lewis description of chemical bonding?

18. Use valence bond theory to explain the bonding in H_2, HF, and F_2. Show the overlap of atomic orbitals involved in the bonds.

19. Use valence bond theory to explain the bonding in O_2. Show the overlap of atomic orbitals involved in the bonds in O_2.

20. The bond energy of a C—C single bond averages 415 kJ mol^{-1}; that of a C=C double bond, 611 kJ mol^{-1}. Explain why the double bond is not twice as strong as the single bond.

21. Draw a curve that describes the change in the sum of the energies of H and Cl during the bond formation in HCl. What is the approximate energy at the lowest point on the curve?

22. Why is the concept of hybridization required in valence bond theory?

Hybridization

23. What is a hybrid orbital? Illustrate your answer with the hybrid orbitals that may be formed by carbon.

24. What are the angles between the hybrid orbitals in each of the following sets: sp, sp^2, sp^3, sp^3d, sp^3d^2?

25. Identify the hybridization of each carbon atom in each of the following molecules:

(a) Vinyl chloride, the compound used to make the plastic PVC (polyvinyl chloride), $H_2C\!=\!CHCl$

(b) Carbon tetrafluoride, CF_4

(c) Acetic acid, the compound that gives vinegar its acidic taste,

$$H-\underset{\underset{H}{|}}{\overset{\overset{H}{|}}{C}}-\overset{\overset{O}{\|}}{C}-OH$$

(d) Calcium cyanamide, $Ca^{2+}(NCN^{2-})$, used as a fertilizer and in preparation of the plastic Melmac

26. What is the hybridization of the central atom in each of the following molecules?
(a) TeF_6 (d) BeH_2
(b) PF_5 (e) BH_3
(c) $SiCl_4$

27. Identify the hybridization of the central atom in each of the following ions:
(a) PF_6^- (d) NO_3^-
(b) SO_4^{2-} (e) NO_2^+
(c) SiF_5^- (f) CH_3^+

28. How are the atomic orbitals of the central atoms hybridized in each of the following molecules?
(a) IF_5 (d) SeF_4
(b) BrF_3 (e) XeF_4
(c) PCl_3 (f) XeF_2

29. What hybrid orbitals are found on the central atom in each of the following ions?
(a) H_3O^+ (e) $TeCl_4^{2-}$
(b) CH_3^- (f) NH_2^-
(c) $SnCl_3^-$ (g) NO_2^-
(d) ICl_4^-

30. What hybrid orbitals are found on the central atom in each of the following molecules? Which orbitals form the π bonds?
(a) $ClNO$ (d) Cl_2SO
(b) CS_2 (e) SO_2F_2
(c) Cl_2CO (f) XeO_2F_2

31. Show the distribution of the valence electrons in each of the hybridized atoms in the following molecules (1) before the isolated atom is hybridized and (2) after hybridization and bond formation.
(a) SeF_6 (e) PH_3
(b) PCl_5 (f) BrF_5
(c) SeO_2 (g) $TeCl_4$
(d) CF_4

Additional Exercises

32. Predict the hybridization around the indicated atom or atoms.

(a) The sulfur atom in sulfuric acid, H_2SO_4 $[(HO)_2SO_2]$

(b) The chlorine atom in chloric acid, $HClO_3$ $[HOClO_2]$

(c) The oxygen atoms in hydrogen peroxide, $HOOH$

(d) The nitrogen atom in nitric acid, HNO_3 $[HONO_2]$

(e) The oxygen atom in the OH group in nitric acid, HNO_3 $[HONO_2]$

(f) The central oxygen atom in the ozone molecule, O_3

(g) Each of the carbon atoms in propyne, CH_3CCH

(h) The carbon atom in the Freon CCl_2F_2

(i) Each of the carbon atoms in allene, $H_2C\!=\!C\!=\!CH_2$

33. Formaldehyde, H_2CO, contains a carbon–oxygen double bond. Describe the hybrid orbitals of the carbon atoms that form the σ bonds in this molecule and the atomic orbitals of oxygen and carbon that give the π bond. Note that it is not necessary to hybridize the oxygen atom.

34. Acetonitrile, H_3CCN, contains a carbon–nitrogen triple bond. Describe the hybrid orbitals of the carbon atoms that form the σ bonds in this molecule and the atomic orbitals of nitrogen and carbon that give the π bonds. Note that it is not necessary to hybridize the nitrogen atom.

35. XF_3 has a trigonal planar molecular structure. To which main group of the periodic table does X belong?

36. In the compound $H\!-\!X\!=\!O$, X exhibits sp^2 hybridization. To which main group of the periodic table does X belong?

37. If XCl_3 exhibits a dipole moment, X could be a member of either of two groups in the periodic table. Which ones?

38. Elemental sulfur consists of covalently bonded, puckered rings of eight sulfur atoms, S_8. The S—S—S angles in the ring are $107.9°$. The production of sulfuric acid, $SO_2(OH)_2$, from sulfur involves oxidation of sulfur to SO_2, then oxidation to SO_3, and finally reaction with water to give sulfuric acid. Trace the changes in the hybridization of the sulfur atom during this sequence of reactions.

39. Although the location of the unshared pairs in its hybrid orbitals cannot be observed, the oxygen atom in water is believed to exhibit sp^3 hybridization. Explain.

40. A 0.10-mol sample of a compound contains 0.10 mol of carbon atoms, 0.10 mol of nitrogen atoms, and 0.10 mol of hydrogen atoms. Identify the molecular structure of the compound and the hybridization of the carbon atoms. Describe the bonding in the compound in terms of valence bond theory, and show the overlap of the various orbitals that are used in forming the bonds.

41. One mol of P reacts with 1.5 mol of F_2 to give a compound containing one P atom and several F atoms per molecule. Identify the molecular structure of the compound and the hybridization of the carbon atoms. Describe the bonding in the compound in terms of valence bond theory, and show the overlap of the various orbitals that are used in forming the bonds.

9 Molecular Orbitals

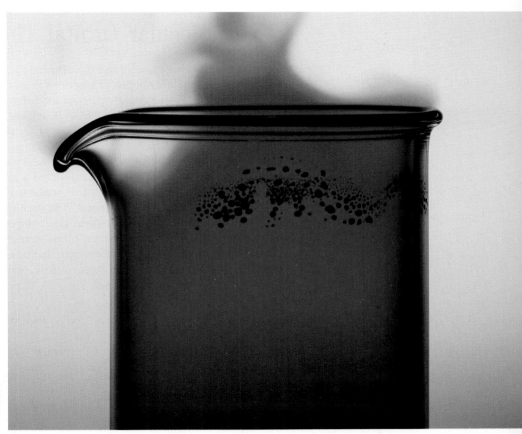

Iodine crystals sublime when heated, forming the characteristic purple iodine vapor.

Why is the iodine vapor in the opening photograph purple? This is because the I_2 molecules in the vapor absorb some colors of light, but not the light that appears purple to most of us. Light is absorbed when a valence electron in the molecule is excited from one energy level to another. This excitation is identical to that occurring when an electron in an individual atom is excited by the absorption of light (Section 5.8).

How can we describe the energies of electrons in molecules? Lewis structures are not appropriate for this. As we saw in Chapter 7, Lewis structures describe bonding in terms of shared and unshared pairs of electrons. They indicate nothing about the energies of the electrons, and, except for noting that shared pairs of electrons spend time between the atoms they connect, Lewis structures indicate little about the distribution of electrons in a molecule. The model of hybridization that we discussed in Chapter 8 also gives us no information about the energy of the electrons in a molecule.

Molecular orbital theory provides a model for describing the distribution of electrons in a molecule and the energies of these electrons. It helps explain why some substances are electrical conductors, some are semiconductors, and some are insulators. Molecular orbital theory also explains the bonding in molecules such as NO and ions such as He_2^+ that are difficult to describe with Lewis structures.

9.1 Molecular Orbital Theory

Molecular orbital theory describes the distribution of electrons in molecules in much the same way that the distribution of electrons in atoms is described using atomic orbitals. Using quantum mechanics, it describes the behavior of an electron in a molecule by a wave function, ψ, which may be used to determine the energy of the electron and the region of space within which it moves. As in an atom, an electron in a molecule is limited to discrete (quantized) energies, and the region of space in which the electron is likely to be found is called an *orbital*. However, because the orbital extends over all of the atoms in the molecule, the orbital is called a **molecular orbital.** Like an atomic orbital, a molecular orbital is full when it contains two electrons (with opposite spin).

Because the types of orbitals found in molecules vary with the molecule, we will first consider molecular orbitals in molecules composed of two identical atoms (H_2 or Cl_2, for example). Such molecules are called **homonuclear diatomic molecules.** The types of molecular orbitals in these diatomic molecules, **sigma (σ) orbitals** and **pi (π) orbitals,** are shown in Fig. 9.1. In three of these orbitals, called σ_s, σ_p, and π_p orbitals (read as "sigma-s," "sigma-p," and "pi-p"), the electrons are more or less between

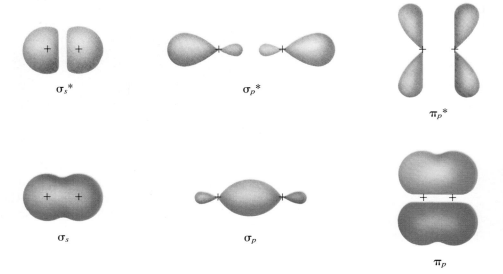

Figure 9.1

Molecular orbitals found in homonuclear diatomic molecules. Bonding molecular orbitals are shown in green, antibonding molecular orbitals in red. The plus signs (+) indicate the locations of nuclei.

the nuclei. Electrons in these orbitals are attracted by both nuclei at the same time and are of lower energy than they would be in the isolated atoms. Thus electrons in these orbitals stabilize the molecule; the orbitals are called **bonding orbitals.** Electrons in the orbitals called $\sigma_s{}^*$, $\sigma_p{}^*$, and $\pi_p{}^*$ (read as "sigma-s-star," "sigma-p-star," and "pi-p-star") are located well away from the region between the two nuclei. Electrons in these latter orbitals are of higher energy than they would be in the isolated atoms, so they destabilize the molecule. The orbitals are called **antibonding orbitals.**

The exact wave functions that describe the behavior of an electron in molecular orbitals are very difficult to determine. Approximate wave functions are generally used instead. One approximation involves using the sum or the difference of the wave functions of the constituent atoms to describe the behavior of the electrons in the molecule. The wave functions of any number of atomic orbitals may be added together, or subtracted from one another, to give the wave function of a molecular orbital. At this stage, however, we will use only one atomic orbital on each of the two atoms of a diatomic molecule to approximate a molecular orbital in the molecule.

In a diatomic molecule, two molecular orbitals result from every two atomic orbitals that combine. The two molecular orbitals can be thought of as being described by the addition or subtraction of the parts of the two atomic orbitals that overlap and share the same region of space. The molecular orbital resulting from the addition of the overlapping parts of two atomic orbitals has a relatively large density between the two nuclei, indicating that electrons occupying such an orbital spend a large amount of time between the nuclei (Fig. 9.2, bottom right). This is a bonding situation, and the molecular orbital is a bonding orbital. A second molecular orbital, arrived at by subtraction of the overlapping parts of the atomic orbitals, has a lower density between the nuclei, indicating that the electrons spend little time between them (Fig. 9.2, top right). Such a situation is unstable, and the molecular orbital is an antibonding orbital.

Figure 9.2 illustrates the two types of molecular orbitals that can be formed from two s atomic orbitals on adjacent atoms: a σ_s (bonding) orbital, formed by addition of the two s orbitals on adjacent atoms, and a $\sigma_s{}^*$ (antibonding) orbital, formed by subtraction of the s orbitals. (The subscript letters designate the type of atomic orbitals added or subtracted to give a molecular orbital.) Electrons fill the lower-energy bonding molecular orbital before the higher-energy antibonding molecular orbital, just as they fill atomic orbitals of lower energy before those of higher energy.

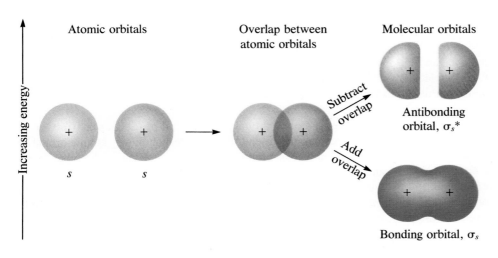

Figure 9.2

A representation of the formation of sigma (σ) molecular orbitals by the combination of two s atomic orbitals. The bonding molecular orbital is shown in green, the antibonding molecular orbital in red. The plus signs (+) indicate the locations of nuclei.

Figure 9.3

A representation of the formation of sigma (σ) and pi (π) molecular orbitals by the combination of p orbitals. Bonding molecular orbitals are shown in green, antibonding molecular orbitals in red. The plus signs ($+$) indicate the locations of nuclei.

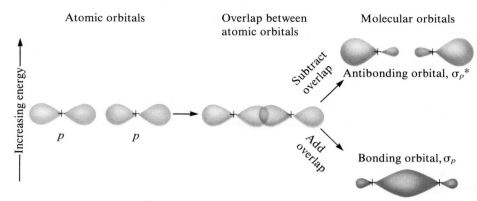

(a) The bonding and antibonding molecular orbitals formed by the end-to-end overlap of two p atomic orbitals.

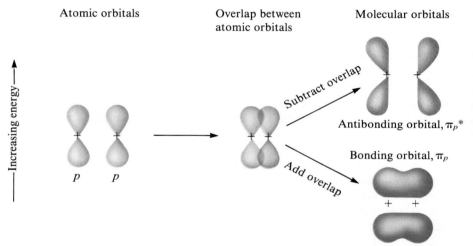

(b) The bonding and antibonding molecular orbitals formed by the side-to-side overlap of two p atomic orbitals.

Figure 9.3 illustrates the four kinds of molecular orbitals that can be formed from end-to-end or side-by-side combinations of two p atomic orbitals on adjacent atoms: σ_p, σ_p^*, π_p, and π_p^*. When combined end-to-end [Fig. 9.3(a)], two p atomic orbitals form two σ molecular orbitals (as is the case with atomic s orbitals). However, when two p atomic orbitals are combined side-by-side [Fig. 9.3(b)], the two resulting molecular orbitals are π orbitals.

Each atom contains three p atomic orbitals: p_x, p_y, and p_z (Section 5.10). One of these, say the p_x orbital, combines end-to-end with a corresponding p_x atomic orbital of another atom to form two σ molecular orbitals, σ_{p_x} and $\sigma_{p_x}^*$. Each of the other two p atomic orbitals, p_y and p_z, combines side-by-side with a corresponding p atomic orbital of another atom, giving rise to two sets of π bonding and π^* antibonding molecular orbitals. The set of π and π^* orbitals from the p_y atomic orbitals is oriented at right angles to the set from the p_z orbitals. It is as if one set of π and π^* molecular orbitals were oriented along the y axis of a set of coordinates and the other set were oriented along the z axis. The notations π_{p_y} and π_{p_z} (read as "pi-p-y" and "pi-p-z") are thus applied to the bonding orbitals, and $\pi_{p_y}^*$ and $\pi_{p_z}^*$ ("pi-p-y star" and "pi-p-z star") to the antibonding orbitals. Except for their orientation, the π_{p_y} and π_{p_z} orbitals are identical and have the same energy; that is, they are **degenerate orbitals.** The $\pi_{p_y}^*$ and $\pi_{p_z}^*$ antibonding orbitals are also identical except for their orientation and are degenerate.

A total of six molecular orbitals results from the combinations of the six p atomic orbitals in two atoms: σ_{p_x} and $\sigma_{p_x}^*$, π_{p_y} and $\pi_{p_y}^*$, and π_{p_z} and $\pi_{p_z}^*$ molecular orbitals.

The difference between bonding as described by valence bond theory (Chapter 8) and as described by molecular orbital theory can be puzzling. Valence bond theory focuses on orbitals that are on individual atoms (atomic orbitals) and the bonds formed by overlap of these orbitals. Molecular orbital theory concentrates on bonding and antibonding molecular orbitals that extend over the entire molecule and on the distribution of valence electrons in these orbitals. The two theories are different ways of describing the same behavior and generally lead to the same predictions about the stability of molecules, the strength of bonds, and chemical reactivity.

⑨.2 Molecular Orbital Energy Diagrams

The relative energy levels of the lower-energy atomic and molecular orbitals of a homonuclear diatomic molecule are typically as shown in Fig. 9.4. Each colored disk represents one atomic or molecular orbital that can hold either one or two electrons. Bonding

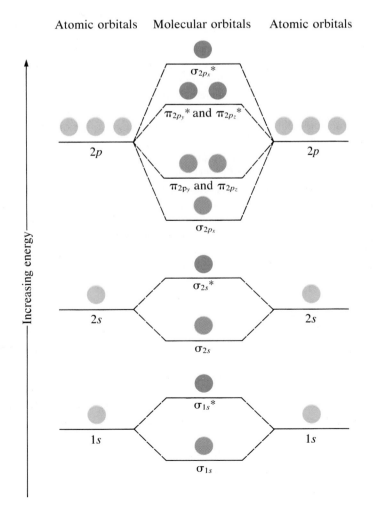

Figure 9.4

Molecular orbital energy diagram for a diatomic molecule containing identical atoms. A colored disk represents an atomic or molecular orbital that can hold one or two electrons. Atomic orbitals are orange, bonding molecular orbitals are green, and antibonding molecular orbitals are red.

and antibonding molecular orbitals are joined by dashed lines to the atomic orbitals that combine to form them.

The distribution of electrons in the molecular orbitals of a homonuclear diatomic molecule can be predicted by filling these molecular orbitals in the same way that atomic orbitals are filled, by the aufbau process (Section 5.12). The number of electrons in each orbital is indicated with a superscript. Thus a molecule containing seven electrons has the molecular electron configuration $(\sigma_{1s})^2(\sigma_{1s}*)^2(\sigma_{2s})^2(\sigma_{2s}*)^1$.

In some cases the energy levels of the σ_p and the two π_p bonding orbitals are reversed; the π_{p_y} and π_{p_z} bonding orbitals are slightly lower in energy than the σ_{p_x} orbital. There is a reason for this. We have assumed in our discussion thus far that s orbitals interact only with s orbitals to form σ_s molecular orbitals and that p orbitals interact only with p orbitals to form σ_p or π_p molecular orbitals. The main interactions do indeed occur between orbitals that are identical in energy, but an s orbital can interact with a p orbital, as shown in Fig. 9.5, if the s and p orbitals are similar in energy. The mixing of s and p orbitals shifts the energies of the molecular orbitals and in some cases even changes the relative positions of their energy levels. Hence the π_{p_y} and π_{p_z} molecular orbitals, which normally have a higher energy than the σ_{p_x} orbital, sometimes have a slightly lower energy than the σ_{p_x} orbital. Such energy shifts are most likely when the energy difference between the s and p orbitals is small.

9 .3 Bond Order

As electrons fill molecular orbitals such as those shown in Fig. 9.4 for a diatomic molecule, some electrons enter bonding molecular orbitals, and others may enter antibonding molecular orbitals. Thus some electrons contribute to the stability of the molecule, whereas others may destabilize it. The net contribution of the electrons to the stability of a molecule can be identified by determining the net order of the bond that results from the filling of the molecular orbitals by electrons.

When using Lewis formulas to describe the distribution of electrons in molecules, we define the order of a bond (bond order) between two atoms as the number of bonding pairs of electrons between the atoms (see Exercise 94, Chapter 7). Bond order is defined differently when the molecular orbital description of the distribution of electrons is used, but the resulting bond order is the same. In the molecular orbital model, the **bond order for a given bond is the net number of pairs of bonding electrons and is equal to half of the difference between the number of bonding electrons and the number of antibonding electrons.**

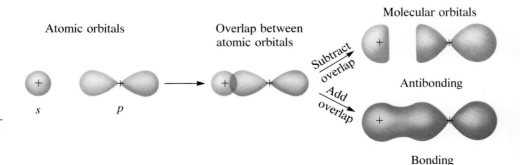

Figure 9.5

A representation of the two molecular orbitals formed by the combination of an s atomic orbital with a p atomic orbital.

The order of a covalent bond is a guide to its strength; a bond between two given atoms becomes stronger as the bond order increases. If the distribution of electrons in the molecular orbitals between two atoms is such that the resulting bond would have a negative bond order or a bond order of zero, a stable bond does not form.

9.4 The Dihydrogen Molecule, H$_2$

A dihydrogen molecule (H$_2$) forms from two hydrogen atoms, each with one electron in a $1s$ atomic orbital. When the atomic orbitals of the two atoms combine, the electrons seek the molecular orbital of lowest energy, the σ_{1s} bonding orbital. Each molecular orbital can hold two electrons, so both electrons are in the σ_{1s} bonding orbital. The electron configuration is $(\sigma_{1s})^2$. This can be represented by a molecular orbital energy diagram (Fig. 9.6) in which one electron in an orbital is indicated by an arrow, ⬆. Two electrons of opposite spin in an orbital are designated ⬆⬇. A dihydrogen molecule, H$_2$, readily forms from two hydrogen atoms, because the energy of a H$_2$ molecule is lower than that of two H atoms. The σ_{1s} orbital that contains both electrons is lower in energy than either of the two $1s$ atomic orbitals.

The order of the bond in a dihydrogen molecule is equal to half of the difference between the number of bonding electrons and the number of antibonding electrons (Section 9.3). A dihydrogen molecule contains two bonding electrons and no antibonding electrons.

$$\text{Bond order in H}_2 = \frac{(2 - 0)}{2} = 1$$

Because the bond order for the hydrogen–hydrogen bond is equal to 1, the bond is a single bond.

9.5 Two Diatomic Helium Species: He$_2^+$ and He$_2$

A helium atom has two electrons, both of which are in its $1s$ orbital (Table 5.3). The helium ion (He$^+$) results from the loss of one of these electrons. When a helium atom and a helium ion combine to give a dihelium ion, He$_2^+$, two of the electrons occupy

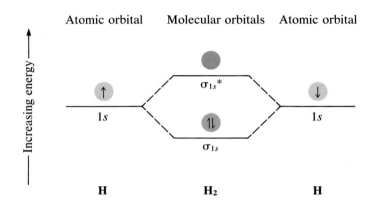

Atomic orbital   Molecular orbitals   Atomic orbital

Increasing energy →

σ_{1s}^*

$1s$ $1s$

σ_{1s}

H   H$_2$ H

Figure 9.6

Molecular orbital energy diagram for the dihydrogen molecule, H$_2$.

Figure 9.7

Molecular orbital energy diagram for
the He_2^+ ion.

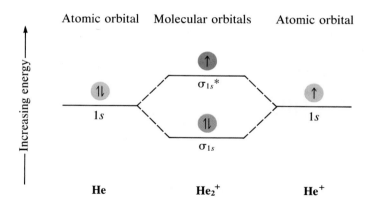

the σ_{1s} bonding orbital. The third electron must go into the molecular orbital that is next lowest in energy, the $\sigma_{1s}*$ antibonding orbital, so He_2^+ has the configuration $(\sigma_{1s})^2(\sigma_{1s}*)^1$. The locations of the electrons are illustrated in the molecular orbital energy-level diagram of Fig. 9.7.

The net energy of a dihelium ion is slightly lower than the sum of the energies of a helium atom and a helium ion, because there are two electrons in the lower-energy molecular orbital and only one in the higher-energy molecular orbital. The lower net energy for the dihelium ion means that a helium atom and a helium ion are likely to combine to form a dihelium ion.

The bond order of the dihelium ion indicates that the bond in the ion is weak. The bond order is $\frac{1}{2}$ [$(2 - 1)/2 = \frac{1}{2}$].

The distribution of electrons and the bonding in the He_2^+ ion are difficult to describe using Lewis structures. This is one of those situations, noted in the introduction to this chapter, wherein a different model is needed to describe a system satisfactorily.

Two helium atoms do not combine to form a dihelium molecule, He_2, with four electrons, because the two electrons in the lower-energy bonding orbital would be balanced by the two electrons in the higher-energy molecular orbital. [The configuration would be $(\sigma_{1s})^2(\sigma_{1s}*)^2$.] The net energy change would be zero, so there is no driving force for helium atoms to form the diatomic molecule. In fact, helium exists as discrete atoms rather than as diatomic molecules.

The bond order in a hypothetical dihelium molecule would be zero [$(2 - 2)/2$]. A bond order of zero indicates that no bond is formed between two atoms.

9.6 The Dilithium Molecule, Li_2

The combination of two lithium atoms to form a dilithium molecule, Li_2, is analogous to the formation of H_2, except that the atomic orbitals involved are the $2s$ orbitals. Each of the two lithium atoms, with an electron configuration $1s^2 2s^1$, has one valence electron. Hence two valence electrons are available to go into the σ_{2s} bonding molecular orbital. (The lower-lying $1s$ electrons in the $1s$ orbital of each atom are not appreciably involved in the bonding.) Because both valence electrons occupy the lower-energy σ_{2s} bonding orbital (Fig. 9.8), Li_2 should be a stable molecule. The molecule is, in fact, present in appreciable concentration in lithium vapor at temperatures near the boiling point of the element.

In general, electrons in inner shells of atoms are not involved in forming molecular orbitals. Because of the relatively high effective nuclear charge experienced by the

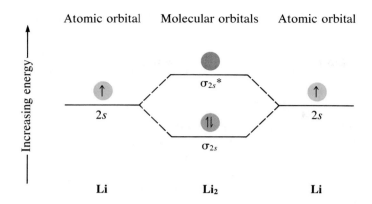

Figure 9.8

Molecular orbital energy diagram for Li_2. Lower-energy electrons in the $1s$ orbital of each atom are not shown.

electrons in inner shells, the inner shells have small radii. Consequently, inner shells of adjacent atoms do not overlap. To indicate that inner shells do not form molecular orbitals, we include letters that stand for them when we write the electron configuration of diatomic molecules. The configuration for Li_2 is KK $(\sigma_{2s})^2$, where the two K's indicate that the $1s$ orbitals (the K shells) on each atom are filled but do not enter into the bonding.

In calculating the bond order for Li_2, we get the same result if we use all the electrons in the molecule [two σ_{1s} electrons, two $\sigma_{1s}*$ electrons, and two σ_{2s} electrons; bond order $= (6 - 4)/2 = 1$] or only the valence electrons [two σ_{2s} electrons; bond order $= (2 - 0)/2 = 1$]. Either way the bond order is calculated to be 1, corresponding to a lithium–lithium single bond.

9.7 The Instability of the Diberyllium Molecule, Be_2

The diatomic molecule of beryllium, Be_2, unlike the diatomic lithium molecule, would not be expected to be particularly stable; two of the four valence electrons would go to the σ_{2s} bonding orbital and the other two to the $\sigma_{2s}*$ antibonding orbital (Fig. 9.9). The electron configuration would be $KK(\sigma_{2s})^2(\sigma_{2s}*)^2$. The net energy change, just as is the case with diatomic helium, is zero, indicating no tendency for beryllium atoms to combine to form the diatomic beryllium molecule. This is in accord with the experimental

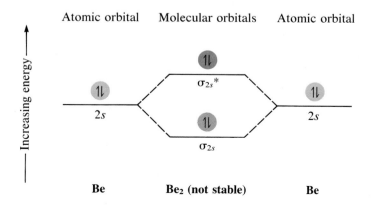

Figure 9.9

Molecular orbital energy diagram for Be_2 (not stable). Lower-energy electrons in the $1s$ orbital of each atom are not shown.

finding that no stable Be_2 molecule is known. The bond order of a hypothetical diberyllium molecule would be zero $[(4 - 4)/2 = 0]$.

9.8 The Diboron Molecule, B_2

The element boron has the electronic structure $1s^2 2s^2 2p^1$. Hence the p orbitals make an important contribution to the bonding of boron. We have noted that combinations of p atomic orbitals give rise to both σ and π molecular orbitals and that the two π_p bonding orbitals are of equal energy (degenerate). The filling of degenerate molecular orbitals is analogous to the filling of degenerate atomic orbitals (Section 5.11). **Whenever two or more molecular orbitals have the same energy, electrons fill all of these orbitals singly with parallel spins before any pairing of electrons takes place within these orbitals.**

We have noted that sometimes the energy of the σ_p orbital is slightly lower than the energies of the two π_p orbitals and that sometimes the reverse is true. Experimental magnetic data for the B_2 molecule tell us that the molecule contains two unpaired electrons. This indicates that *in this particular case* the two π_p orbitals are lower in energy than the σ_p orbital and are filled first, one electron going singly into each. If the σ_p orbital were lower in energy than the two π_p orbitals, the two electrons would be expected to pair within that orbital. Figure 9.10, the molecular orbital energy diagram for diboron, shows the two unpaired electrons. The electron configuration of B_2 is $KK(\sigma_{2s})^2(\sigma_{2s}{}^*)^2(\pi_{2p_y}, \pi_{2p_z})^2$. The four electrons in the σ_{2s} and $\sigma_{2s}{}^*$ orbitals balance

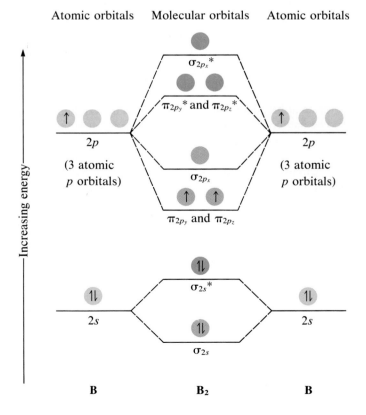

Figure 9.10

Molecular orbital energy diagram for B_2. Lower-energy electrons in the $1s$ orbital of each atom are not shown.

each other in terms of energy and do not make a significant contribution to the stability of the B_2 molecule. However, the two π_p electrons in bonding orbitals stabilize the diboron molecule.

Four electrons in the valence shell of a diboron molecule occupy bonding molecular orbitals, and two occupy antibonding molecular orbitals. Thus the bond order of the boron–boron bond is $(4 - 2)/2 = 1$, indicating a single bond.

❾.9 The Dicarbon Molecule, C_2

The dicarbon molecule, C_2, is similar to diboron, B_2. As in B_2, the π_{2p} orbitals of C_2 have a lower energy than the σ_{2p} orbital. The two additional electrons (one from each atom) fill the π_{2p_y} and π_{2p_z} molecular orbitals, giving the electronic structure $KK(\sigma_{2s})^2(\sigma_{2s}*)^2(\pi_{2p_y}, \pi_{2p_z})^4$. The calculated bond order for the carbon–carbon bond is $(6 - 2)/2 = 2$, indicating a double bond.

❾.10 The Dinitrogen Molecule, N_2

The dinitrogen molecule, N_2, is well known and very stable. Experiment shows that the two $2s$ and three $2p$ electrons from each nitrogen atom are paired in the molecular orbitals of the N_2 molecule and that the π_{2p} orbitals are lower in energy than the σ_{2p} orbital (Fig. 9.11). The electron configuration is $KK(\sigma_{2s})^2(\sigma_{2s}*)^2(\pi_{2p_y}, \pi_{2p_z})^4(\sigma_{2p_x})^2$.

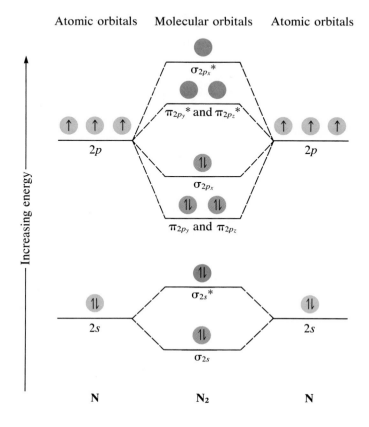

Figure 9.11

Molecular orbital energy diagram for N_2. Lower-energy electrons in the $1s$ orbital of each atom are not shown.

The exceptional stability of the dinitrogen molecule is consistent with the assumption that the three bonding molecular orbitals resulting from the overlap of all $2p$ atomic orbitals are fully occupied with six electrons. This leads to a bond order of $(8 - 2)/2 = 3$, corresponding to a triple bond.

❾.11 The Dioxygen Molecule, O_2

The order of the σ_{2p} and π_{2p} orbitals in the dioxygen molecule differs from that for B_2, C_2, and N_2; the σ_{2p} orbital in oxygen is at a lower energy than the π_{2p} orbitals (Fig. 9.12).

The electron configuration for O_2 [$KK(\sigma_{2s})^2(\sigma_{2s}*)^2(\sigma_{2p_x})^2(\pi_{2p_y}, \pi_{2p_z})^4(\pi_{2p_y}*, \pi_{2p_z}*)^2$] is consistent with the fact that an oxygen molecule has two unpaired electrons. This proved difficult to explain on the basis of valence electron formulas, but molecular orbital theory explains it quite simply. In fact, the unpaired electrons of the oxygen molecule provide one of the strong pieces of evidence supporting the molecular orbital theory.

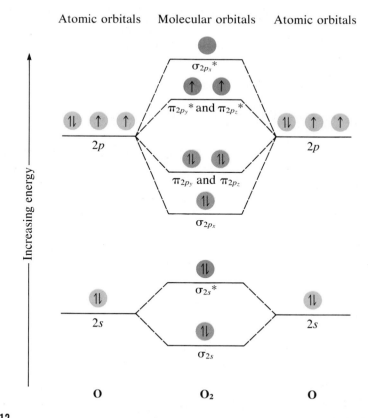

Figure 9.12

Molecular orbital energy diagram for O_2. Lower-energy electrons in the $1s$ orbital of each atom are not shown.

Liquid oxygen is attracted into a magnetic field because O$_2$ molecules contain unpaired electrons. Liquid oxygen can be suspended between the poles of a magnet.

The bond in the dioxygen molecule is weaker than the bond in the dinitrogen molecule; the bond energy of the O=O bond is 498 kilojoules per mole, whereas that of the N≡N bond is 946 kilojoules per mole (Section 7.9). The two electrons in the antibonding orbitals make the bond in the oxygen molecule weaker than the bond in the nitrogen molecule, in which no electrons are in antibonding orbitals.

A dioxygen molecule contains eight bonding electrons in its valence shell (in the σ_{2s}, σ_{2p}, π_{2p_y}, and π_{2p_z} molecular orbitals) and four antibonding electrons (in the σ_{2s}^*, $\pi_{2p_y}^*$, and $\pi_{2p_z}^*$ molecular orbitals). Thus the bond order in the dioxygen molecule is $(8 - 4)/2 = 2$, corresponding to a double bond. The double bond in O$_2$ is not as strong as the triple bond in N$_2$.

9.12 The Difluorine Molecule, F$_2$

The difluorine molecule has no unpaired electrons. Of its ten p electrons six electrons are in bonding orbitals and four are in antibonding orbitals. The electronic structure is KK$(\sigma_{2s})^2$ $(\sigma_{2s}^*)^2(\sigma_{2p_x})^2(\pi_{2p_y}, \pi_{2p_z})^4(\pi_{2p_y}^*, \pi_{2p_z}^*)^4$. Because F$_2$ has two more electrons in antibonding molecular orbitals than O$_2$, the difluorine molecule has a weaker bond than the dioxygen molecule. In fact, the F$_2$ bond is one of the weakest of the covalent bonds; the bond energy is only 160 kilojoules per mole.

The bond order of the difluorine molecule is $(8 - 6)/2 = 1$, corresponding to a single bond.

9.13 The Instability of the Dineon Molecule, Ne$_2$

The Ne$_2$ molecule has no appreciable tendency to form, because it would have the same number of electrons in antibonding orbitals as in bonding orbitals. As with helium, the atoms remain as discrete atoms. A hypothetical Ne$_2$ molecule would have the electron configuration KK$(\sigma_{2s})^2(\sigma_{2s}^*)^2(\sigma_{2p_x})^2(\pi_{2p_y}, \pi_{2p_z})^4(\pi_{2p_y}^*, \pi_{2p_z}^*)^4(\sigma_{2p_x}^*)^2$ and a bond order of zero.

⑨.14 Diatomic Systems with Two Different Elements

Thus far we have considered only molecular orbitals in molecules and ions containing two identical atoms, but molecular orbital theory can be extended to **heteronuclear diatomic species**—diatomic molecules and ions with bonds between atoms of two different elements.

Molecular orbitals of heteronuclear diatomic species are not fundamentally different from those of homonuclear diatomic molecules. Electrons still move over the whole molecule in molecular orbitals that can be approximated by combinations of atomic orbitals from each atom. However, in heteronuclear molecules the equivalent atomic orbitals for each contributing atom do not have the same energy. Orbitals for the more electronegative element are at a lower energy. Figure 9.13 shows a molecular orbital energy diagram for nitric oxide, NO. The energies of the atomic orbitals of oxygen are lower than those of nitrogen because of the greater charge of the oxygen nucleus. Consequently, some molecular orbitals of NO are closer in energy to the energy of the

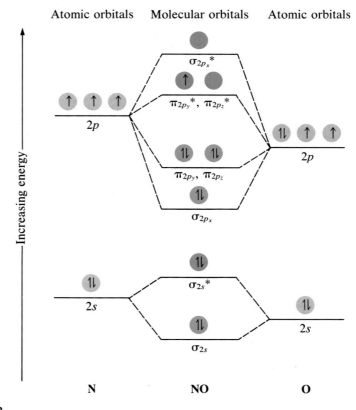

Figure 9.13

Molecular orbital energy diagram for NO. Lower-energy electrons in the $1s$ orbital of each atom are not shown.

oxygen atomic orbitals than to that of the nitrogen atomic orbitals. Other molecular orbitals are closer in energy to the energy of the nitrogen atomic orbitals than to that of the oxygen atomic orbitals.

Unlike the molecular orbitals in a diatomic molecule composed of identical atoms, the molecular orbitals in a heteronuclear diatomic molecule are not symmetrical. The electron density is greater nearer the atom whose atomic orbital is closest to the energy of the molecular orbital. Figure 9.14 illustrates the distribution of electron density in the σ_{2s} and $\sigma_{2s}*$ orbitals of N_2 and NO. In the N_2 molecule, symmetrical σ_{2s} and $\sigma_{2s}*$ orbitals are formed by combination of two $2s$ orbitals that have identical energies. In the NO molecule, unsymmetrical σ_{2s} and $\sigma_{2s}*$ orbitals are formed by combination of the $2s$ orbital of oxygen with the higher-energy $2s$ orbital of nitrogen. The $\sigma_{2s}*$ orbital is closer in energy to the nitrogen $2s$ atomic orbital (Fig. 9.13); hence this antibonding molecular orbital has the greatest electron density near the nitrogen atom. The electron density of the bonding σ_{2s} orbital is greatest near the oxygen atom, because the energy of this molecular orbital is closer to that of the oxygen $2s$ atomic orbital. The pair of electrons in the σ_{2s} molecular orbital spends more time, on the average, closer to the oxygen atom than to the nitrogen atom. The electrons in the $\sigma_{2s}*$ molecular orbital spend more time closer to the nitrogen atom.

In spite of the asymmetry of the orbitals in heteronuclear diatomic molecules, they are filled the same way as the orbitals of homonuclear diatomic molecules. Each molecular orbital still holds only two electrons, and the lowest-energy orbitals are filled first. The electron configuration of NO is $KK(\sigma_{2s})^2(\sigma_{2s}*)^2(\sigma_{2p_x})^2(\pi_{2p_y}, \pi_{2p_z})^4(\pi_{2p_y}*, \pi_{2p_z}*)^1$. Because there are more electrons in bonding molecular orbitals with greater electron density near the oxygen atom than in antibonding orbitals with greater electron density near the nitrogen atom, the bond is polar (Section 7.5).

Molecular orbital energy diagrams like the one for NO can be used to describe the electron distribution in many other heteronuclear diatomic molecules and ions, such as CO, NO^+, CN^-, and NO^-.

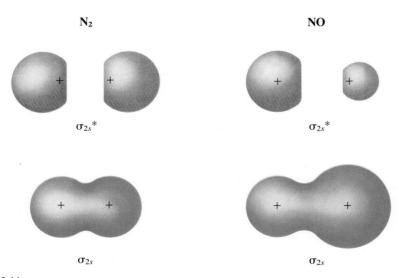

Figure 9.14

Sigma (σ) molecular orbitals found in N_2 and NO. The plus signs (+) indicate the locations of nuclei.

To explain the bonding in a molecule such as HF, it is necessary to introduce the idea that only atomic orbitals that are similar in energy can be combined to give molecular orbitals. If the energies of two atomic orbitals are very different, molecular orbitals do not form from them. In HF the $1s$ orbital of hydrogen has about the same energy as the $2p$ orbitals of fluorine (Fig. 9.15). Thus the molecular orbitals form from the hydrogen $1s$ orbital and the fluorine $2p_x$ orbital (Fig. 9.16). The energy difference between the hydrogen $1s$ orbital and the fluorine $2s$ orbital is too great for these atomic orbitals to combine.

When an s orbital combines with a p orbital, it does so in the head-to-tail fashion shown in Fig. 9.16. In HF this gives the bonding and antibonding orbitals shown in Fig. 9.15. The $2s$, $2p_y$, and $2p_z$ orbitals of the fluorine atom are shown at the same energies as those of the original fluorine atomic orbitals in Fig. 9.15. To a first approximation, the energies of the $2s$, $2p_y$, and $2p_z$ orbitals in the molecule do not differ from their energies in a free fluorine atom, because they do not combine with orbitals of the hydrogen atom. As may be seen in the molecular orbital energy diagram of HF (Fig. 9.15), one bonding and one antibonding orbital are formed. The eight valence electrons are located in the lowest-energy orbitals in the molecule—the $2s$, $2p_y$, and $2p_z$ atomic orbitals on fluorine and the σ bonding orbital. The molecule is stable because the two electrons in the σ orbital have a lower energy in the molecule than in the isolated atoms.

9.15 Metals, Insulators, and Semiconductors

Metals and some compounds (such as ReO_3 and TiS_2) are **electrical conductors;** electrons can move through them with little resistance. Other elements (for example, sulfur and iodine) and most compounds are **insulators;** electrons cannot move through them, so they do not conduct electricity. A few elements and compounds, including silicon and

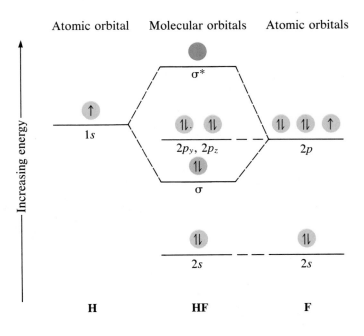

Figure 9.15

Molecular orbital energy diagram for HF. The filled $1s$ orbital of F is not shown.

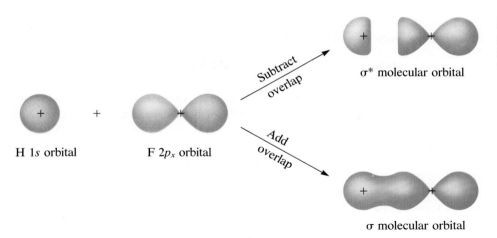

Figure 9.16

Sigma (σ) molecular orbitals found in HF. The plus signs (+) indicate the locations of nuclei.

gallium arsenide (GaAs), are **semiconductors.** They conduct electricity better than insulators but not so well as metals.

The differences in conductivity between metals, insulators, and semiconductors result from differences in their electronic structures. These differences can be described by **band theory,** a type of molecular orbital theory. According to this theory, atomic orbitals of the atoms in a solid combine to yield molecular orbitals that extend throughout the entire solid. As the number of atoms (and thus the number of atomic orbitals) in a molecule increases, the number of molecular orbitals increases (Fig. 9.17). As the number of molecular orbitals, or **energy levels** as they are sometimes called, increases, the difference in energy between them becomes smaller and smaller until there is very little difference in energy between adjacent molecular orbitals. The result is a continuous

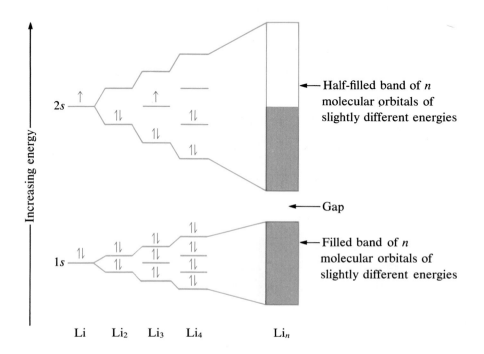

Figure 9.17

Atomic orbitals in a Li atom; molecular orbitals in Li$_2$, Li$_3$, and Li$_4$; and bands in a lithium crystal (Li$_n$).

band of molecular orbitals, or energy levels, that extends through the entire crystal. There is one energy level in the band for each atomic orbital that participates in forming it. Each of the energy levels in the band can contain two electrons. However, only the higher-energy electrons in a band are sufficiently free, or mobile, to cause electrical conductivity.

To gain a better understanding of band theory, consider the case of lithium, the electronic structure of which is $1s^2 2s^1$. A very small crystal of lithium contains about 10^{18} atoms. For this many atoms, the energy difference between energy levels is so small that the levels are essentially continuous, and they constitute a band. In a lithium crystal, one band arises from the $1s$ atomic orbitals and is fully occupied with electrons. However, the second band, arising from the $2s$ atomic orbitals, is only half-filled with electrons (Fig. 9.17). Between the two bands is a **gap**—a range of energy in which no energy levels, or molecular orbitals, are located. No electrons can be found with these energies, because there are no energy levels for them to occupy.

The spacing of the bands in a substance and their filling determine whether the substance is a conductor, a nonconductor (insulator), or a semiconductor (a poor conductor). A substance such as lithium, which contains partially filled bands [Fig. 9.18(a)], exhibits **metallic conduction.** If the bands are completely filled or completely empty and the energy gap between bands is large [Fig. 9.18(b)], the substance is an **insulator.** Diamond is an example of such an insulator. A substance that contains a completely filled band and a completely empty band can behave as a **semiconductor** if the energy gap between the filled and empty bands is so small that electrons from the filled band can be promoted to energy levels in the empty band by thermal energy (heat). Promotion of electrons leaves empty levels called **holes** in the previously filled band. The previously empty band then contains a few electrons that can conduct an electric current [Fig. 9.18(c)]. Because the number of electrons is much smaller than in a metal, the material is a semiconductor, as is silicon and the other semi-metals. Alternatively, electrons can be provided to the empty band by addition of impurities with extra electrons (for example, arsenic with the valence shell $4s^2 4p^3$, as an impurity in silicon, $3s^2 3p^2$). The extra electrons occupy what would be an empty band in the pure material.

Figure 9.18

(a) Partially filled bands are found in metals. (b) Completely filled and completely empty bands separated by a large gap are found in insulators. (c) A completely filled band and a completely empty band separated by a small gap are found in semiconductors at 0 K. When warmed to room temperature, a few electrons are thermally promoted from the previously filled band to the previously empty band, as shown.

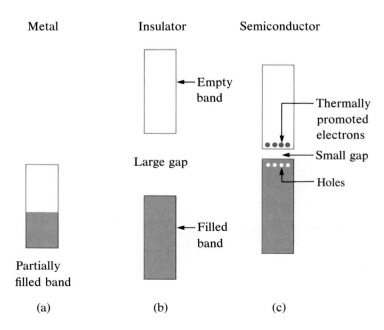

⑨.16 The Solar Cell

An enormous amount of energy is given off by the sun. Earth receives more energy from sunlight in two days than is stored in all known reserves of fossil fuels. The **solar cell** generates electric power from sunlight at the rate of 90 watts per square yard of illuminated surface.

The basic unit of a solar cell is a thin wafer of very pure silicon containing a tiny amount of arsenic. Because arsenic has five valence electrons and silicon has four, replacement of silicon atoms with arsenic atoms creates **n-type silicon** (silicon that contains electrons in what would be an empty band in pure silicon). A thin layer of silicon containing a trace of boron is placed on the surface of the wafer. Boron has only three valence electrons, so replacement of silicon atoms with boron atoms forms **p-type silicon** (silicon that is missing electrons in what would be a filled band in pure silicon). Holes (a few vacant energy levels in an otherwise filled band) thus exist at the surface of the wafer, and a junction, called a p-n junction, exists between the body of the wafer and its thin surface layer. Electrons diffuse through the junction from the wafer to the holes; at the same time holes, or electron vacancies, form in the body of the wafer. This diffusion results in a net positive charge within the body of the wafer, which was neutral prior to the diffusion of electrons (negative charges) out of it, and a net negative charge on the surface layer. Thus an electrostatic potential develops between the two regions, until it is just large enough to prevent any further charge migration. When the diffusion of electrons is just balanced by the electrostatic potential, equilibrium is established between the two forces and hence also between electrons and holes. At equilibrium a net difference in potential exists between the two regions.

In a solar cell one electrical lead is attached to the body of the wafer, and one lead to the surface. When the cell is exposed to sunlight, energy from the sunlight causes electrons to be released from their positions in the lattice near the p-n junction, thereby upsetting the equilibrium between electrons and holes and causing additional electrons to move across the junction into the body of the wafer. By this means, a sufficient force is built up to cause electrons to move through the electrical leads. An electric current is simply a flow of electrons; thus a current flows through the wire. The device is an electric cell with the positive terminal at the p-contact and the negative terminal at the n-contact (Fig. 9.19).

In actual practice a series of such wafers makes up a solar cell. The first practical application of the solar cell was as a power source for eight telephones on a rural line in Georgia in 1955. Such cells are used to power communication devices in satellites and spacecraft, especially those designed to remain in space for long periods. They are also the power source in experimental solar-powered cars (Fig. 9.20).

p-type silicon
surface layer
(boron-treated)

Sunlight

n-type silicon wafer
(arsenic-treated)

Figure 9.19
A solar cell.

Figure 9.20
An experimental solar-powered car.

For Review

Summary

Molecular orbital theory describes the behavior of an electron in a molecule by a wave function, which may be used to determine the energy of the electron and the region of space in the molecule where it is most likely to be found. The electron occupies an orbital that is called a **molecular orbital** because it may extend over all the atoms in the molecule. An electron in a **bonding molecular orbital** stabilizes a molecule. An electron in an **antibonding molecular orbital** makes a molecule less stable. A σ_s molecular orbital is a bonding orbital created by the addition of the overlap of two s orbitals of adjacent atoms. A σ_p molecular orbital is a bonding orbital created by the addition of the end-to-end overlap of p orbitals of adjacent atoms. A π_p molecular orbital is a bonding orbital resulting from the addition of the side-to-side overlap of p orbitals of adjacent atoms. The $\sigma_s{}^*$, $\sigma_p{}^*$, and $\pi_p{}^*$ molecular orbitals are antibonding orbitals resulting from the subtraction of the overlap of atomic orbitals.

One order of increasing energies of the molecular orbitals in a **homonuclear diatomic molecule** is given by the electron configuration $(\sigma_{1s})(\sigma_{1s}{}^*)(\sigma_{2s})(\sigma_{2s}{}^*)(\sigma_{2p_x})(\pi_{2p_y},$ $\pi_{2p_z})(\pi_{2p_y}{}^*, \pi_{2p_z}{}^*)(\sigma_{2p_x}{}^*)$. In some molecules the order of the σ_{2p} and π_{2p} levels is reversed. Electrons fill the orbitals of lowest energy first, and both π_{2p} orbitals (or $\pi_{2p}{}^*$ orbitals) must be occupied by one electron before either will accept two electrons. According to their molecular orbital electron configurations, H_2 and $He_2{}^+$ are stable, whereas He_2, which would contain the same number of bonding and antibonding electrons, is not. Similarly, Li_2, B_2, C_2, N_2, O_2, and F_2 are expected to be stable, whereas Be_2 and Ne_2 are not. Experimental evidence confirms these expectations. **Heteronuclear diatomic species** are similar to homonuclear molecules in the formation and filling of orbitals, but the molecular orbitals are not symmetrically distributed between the two atoms because of the differences in energy between the two types of atomic orbitals. Polar bonds result. The **bond order** of a bond between two atoms equals half the difference between the number of bonding electrons and the number of antibonding electrons it contains.

Molecular orbitals that extend through a solid form **bands** of energy levels. The distribution of electrons in these bands results in **electrical conductors, semiconductors,** or **insulators.**

Key Terms and Concepts

antibonding orbital (9.1)
band theory (9.15)
bond order (9.3)
bonding orbital (9.1)
degenerate orbitals (9.1)
electrical conductor (9.15)

heteronuclear diatomic molecule (9.14)
homonuclear diatomic molecule (9.1)
insulator (9.15)
metal (9.15)
molecular orbital (9.1)

molecular orbital energies (9.2)
overlap (9.1)
pi (π) orbital (9.1)
semiconductor (9.15)
sigma (σ) orbital (9.1)
solar cell (9.16)

Exercises

Molecular Orbitals

1. Why does an electron in a bonding molecular orbital formed from two atomic orbitals have a lower energy than it has in either of the individual atomic orbitals?

2. How do the following differ and how are they similar?
   (a) Molecular orbitals and atomic orbitals
   (b) Bonding orbitals and antibonding orbitals
   (c) σ orbitals and π orbitals

3. Formulate a rule, similar to Hund's rule (Section 5.11), for the filling of molecular orbitals, and give specific examples of its application.

4. Describe the similarities and differences between σ orbitals formed from two s atomic orbitals, from two p atomic orbitals, and from an s and a p atomic orbital.

5. Draw diagrams showing the molecular orbitals that can be formed by combining two s orbitals, by combining two p orbitals, and by combining an s and a p orbital.

6. Describe the similarities and differences between the set of molecular orbitals formed by end-to-end overlap of p orbitals and the set of molecular orbitals formed by side-by-side overlap of p orbitals.

7. Consider the molecular orbitals represented by the following outlines (each plus sign indicates the location of a nucleus).

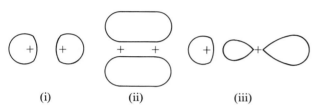

(i)   (ii)   (iii)

(a) Indicate how each of these is formed either by addition or by subtraction of the overlap between s and/or p orbitals.

(b) Which of these is a member of a degenerate pair of molecular orbitals?

Homonuclear Diatomic Molecules

8. Using molecular orbital energy diagrams and the electron occupancy of the molecular orbitals, compare the stability of H_2, HHe, and He_2.

9. Write the molecular orbital electron configurations for the homonuclear diatomic ions X_2^{2+}, where X is one of the elements of the second period of the periodic table. Judging by the bond order of these ions, explain which would not be expected to be stable.

10. The peroxide ion, O_2^{2-}, is found in the ionic compound sodium peroxide, Na_2O_2. Draw the molecular orbital energy diagram of this ion, and write the molecular orbital electron configuration.

11. The acetylide ion, C_2^{2-}, is a component of calcium acetylide. Draw the molecular orbital energy diagram of this ion, and write the molecular orbital electron configuration.

12. Diatomic molecules of sulfur, S_2, are found in the vapor above molten sulfur. Draw a molecular orbital energy diagram for S_2, using only the orbitals in the valence shell of sulfur that are occupied in the free atom. What is the electron configuration of S_2?

13. Draw a molecular orbital energy diagram for the ion S_2^{2-}, using only the orbitals in the valence shell of sulfur that are occupied in the free atom. What is the electron configuration of S_2^{2-}?

14. (a) Determine the bond order of each member of the following groups.

    (i) H_2, H_2^+, H_2^- (iv) F_2, F_2^+, F_2^-
    (ii) O_2, O_2^{2+}, O_2^{2-} (v) N_2, N_2^+, N_2^-
    (iii) Li_2, Be_2^+, Be_2

(b) Which member of each group is predicted by the molecular orbital model to have the strongest bond?

Heteronuclear Diatomic Molecules

15. How does the molecular orbital energy diagram for a homonuclear diatomic molecule such as N_2 or O_2 differ from that of a heteronuclear diatomic molecule such as NO (Fig. 9.13)? How are they similar?

16. How do the molecular orbitals in a homonuclear diatomic molecule such as N_2 or O_2 differ from those in a heteronuclear diatomic molecule such as NO? How are they similar?

17. Under what conditions does an s atomic orbital on one atom combine with a p atomic orbital on a second atom rather than with the s atomic orbital on the second atom?

18. What does the presence of a polar bond in a molecule imply about the shapes of its molecular orbitals?

19. Draw the molecular orbital energy diagrams for CO and NO^+. Show that CO and NO^+ are isoelectronic and have the same bond order. How does the molecular orbital electron configuration of these species compare with that for NO?

20. Draw the molecular orbital energy diagram of BrCl, using only those valence orbitals occupied in the free atoms.

21. Will the unpaired electron in NO spend more time near the nitrogen nucleus or near the oxygen nucleus, or will it spend equal amounts of time near both? Explain your answer.

22. Draw the molecular orbital energy diagram of HCl.

23. (a) Determine the bond order of each member of the following groups.

    (i) NO, NO^+, NO^- (iii) CN, CN^+, CN^-
    (ii) CO, CO^+, CO^- (iv) OF, OF^+, OF^-

(b) Which member of each group is predicted by the molecular orbital model to have the strongest bond?

24. Under what conditions could HF and HF^+ have the same bond order?

Metals, Insulators, and Semiconductors

25. Explain why the partially filled band in lithium metal is exactly half-filled.

26. Explain why a semiconductor no longer conducts when it is cooled to 0 kelvins.

27. How are metals and semiconductors alike at room temperature? How do they differ?

28. How are semiconductors and insulators alike at 0 kelvins? How do they differ at 0 K? How do their similarities and differences change as they warm from 0 K?

29. Which of the following elements would form p-type semi-conductors with silicon? Which would form n-type semi-conductors? Al, As, In, P, Se

30. Explain why some substances that are insulators at room temperature conduct electricity at higher temperatures.

31. The two forms of elemental carbon differ in their electrical properties: Graphite is a semiconductor; diamond is an insulator. How do the band structures of these two substances differ?

32. Which of the following solid materials contain partially filled bands? Mg, S, Cu, NaCl

Additional Exercises

33. Like the ionization energy of an atom (Section 6.3), the ionization energy of a molecule or ion is the energy sufficient to remove the least tightly bound electron from it. Arrange the following molecules and ions in increasing order of first ionization energy.
    (a) NO, NO^+, NO^- (e) F_2, F_2^+, F_2^-
    (b) CO, CO^+, CO^- (f) N_2, N_2^+, N_2^-
    (c) CN, CN^+, CN^- (g) O_2, O_2^-, O_2^{2-}
    (d) OF, OF^+, OF^-

34. Identify the member of each of the following pairs that has the highest first ionization energy in the gas phase.
    (a) H and H_2 (d) C and C_2
    (b) N and N_2 (e) B and B_2
    (c) O and O_2

35. Which member of each group of molecules and ions in Exercise 33 is predicted to have the highest bond stretching frequency?

36. Predict whether each of the following atoms, ions, and molecules contains only paired electrons or contains some unpaired electrons.
    (a) Be   (e) C_2 (i) NO
    (b) Be^+ (f) O   (j) NO^-
    (c) Be_2^{2+} (g) O_2 (k) Ne_2^+
    (d) C   (h) CO (l) Cl_2^+

37. Consider the molecular orbitals represented by the following outlines (each plus sign indicates the location of a nucleus).

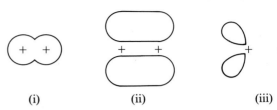

(i)   (ii)   (iii)

(a) What is the maximum number of electrons that can be placed in molecular orbital (i)? In orbital (ii)? In orbital (iii)?

(b) How many orbitals of type (i) are found in the valence shell of F_2? How many orbitals of type (iii)?

(c) What homonuclear diatomic molecule formed by an element in the third period of the periodic table has its two highest-energy electrons in orbitals of type (iii)?

(d) What homonuclear diatomic molecule formed by the elements in the third period of the periodic table has its four highest-energy electrons in orbitals of type (iii)?

38. Identify the homonuclear diatomic molecules or ions that have the following electron configurations:
    (a) X_2^+: $KK(\sigma_{2s})^2(\sigma_{2s}*)^1$
    (b) X_2: $KK(\sigma_{2s})^2(\sigma_{2s}*)^2(\pi_{2p_y}, \pi_{2p_z})^2$
    (c) X_2^-: $KK(\sigma_{2s})^2(\sigma_{2s}*)^2(\pi_{2p_y}, \pi_{2p_z})^1$
    (d) X_2^-: $KK(\sigma_{2s})^2(\sigma_{2s}*)^2(\sigma_{2p_x})^2(\pi_{2p_y}, \pi_{2p_z})^3$

39. Consider the following types of molecular orbitals.

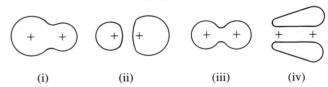

(i)   (ii)   (iii)   (iv)

(a) Which is found in homonuclear diatomic molecules?
(b) Which is found in heteronuclear diatomic molecules?

10

The Gaseous State and the Kinetic-Molecular Theory

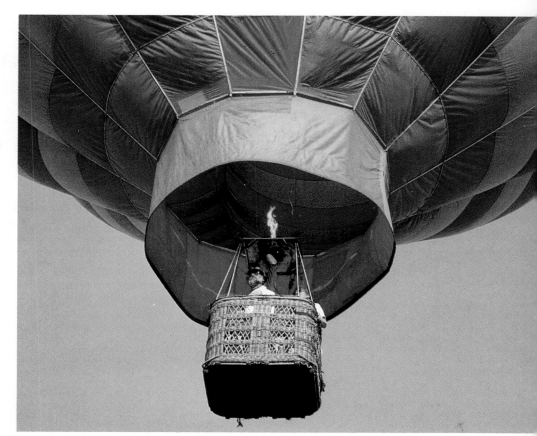

Hotter air is less dense than cooler air, so a hot air balloon floats.

Gases have played an important part in the development of chemistry. The identification of oxygen as a component of air by Priestley and by Lavoisier was crucial to the development of the atomic theory. The belief that water is an element changed when it was prepared by the reaction of the gases oxygen and hydrogen and was thereby shown to be a compound. The densities of gases played an important role in the determination of atomic masses. Conclusions regarding chemical stoichiometry and the molecular nature of matter followed from observations of the volumes of gases that combine in chemical reactions. The variations in the pressure and volume of a gas with temperature led to the discovery of the concept of absolute zero and the development of the kinetic-molecular theory of gas behavior.

In this chapter we will consider how the temperature, pressure, volume, and mass of a sample of gas are related. The equations that describe these relationships are the tools used to describe the quantitative behavior of gases. We will see how to use them to convert physical measurements to moles of gas present, to the molecular mass of a gas, or to the quantities of gases involved in chemical changes. We will also describe the kinetic-molecular model of gases and compare the experimental behavior of gases with the predictions of this theoretical model. Doing so will help us determine whether the assumptions used in the theory to describe the nature of molecules of gases lead to a useful model for the behavior of gases.

The Physical Behavior of Gases

🔟.1 Behavior of Matter in the Gaseous State

Because we are surrounded by an ocean of gas—the atmosphere—many of the properties of gases are familiar to us from our daily activities. We know that squeezing a balloon decreases the volume of the gas inside. In fact, the volume of any gas, unlike that of a solid or a liquid, can be decreased greatly by increasing the pressure upon the gas. Gases can be compressed. The gas in a cylinder, such as that shown in Fig. 10.1, can be compressed by increasing the weight on the piston. The gas confined in the cylinder decreases in volume until it exerts enough pressure to support the greater weight.

Figure 10.1

Gas molecules in a container move closer together as they are subjected to more and more pressure by a moving piston at constant temperature. The number of molecules represented is a minute fraction of the number present in such a volume.

If we heat a gas in a closed container, such as an automobile tire or a can, its pressure increases. Heating a gas in a closed cylinder like the one shown in Fig. 10.1 increases the pressure inside the cylinder, unless the piston moves. Raising the piston increases the volume and allows the gas to expand. This expansion can keep the pressure constant. The ability to expand and fill a container of any size is characteristic of all gases.

Perfume released into the corner of a room can, in time, be detected by its odor all over the room even if the air is still. When a sample of gas is introduced into an evacuated container, it almost instantly fills the container uniformly. These are examples of the diffusion of gases. Diffusion results because the molecules of a gas are in constant high-speed motion. Two gases introduced into the same container mix by diffusion.

⑩.2 The Pressure of a Gas

An astronaut can survive in space because his or her space suit contains oxygen gas (Fig. 10.2). Although it is not obvious because of the shielding over the suit, the flexible portions of the suit bulge rather like a balloon. The gas in the suit is pressing outward against the inside of the suit with a force of about 5 pounds per square inch (5 psi). In space, there is no air or other gas outside the space suit. Thus there is no force on the outside to counterbalance the force on the inside of the suit.

The force a gas exerts on a surface (such as on the inside of the space suit) is used to measure its pressure. The **pressure** of a gas is the force it exerts on a square of known area. In the United States, pressure is often measured in pounds of force on a unit of area equal to one square inch (pounds per square inch, or psi). The pressure unit in the International System of Units (SI) is the **pascal (Pa),** which is the pressure of a force of one newton on an area of one square meter; 1 Pa = 1 newton/m^2. A **newton (N)** is the force that, when applied for 1 second, gives a 1-kilogram mass a speed of 1 meter per second. However, it may be more helpful to think of a newton as the force with which a 0.102-kilogram (3.6-ounce) object presses on a table. Thus a pascal equals the pressure exerted by 0.102 kilogram lying on a square with an edge length of 1 meter. One pascal is a very small pressure; 0.102 kilogram of water would cover a square meter to a depth of only 0.01 centimeter, and this film of water would not exert much pressure. In many cases, it is more convenient to use units of **kilopascals (kPa)** than units of pascals (1 kPa = 1000 Pa).

Pressure is also commonly measured in units of **atmospheres (atm).** One atmosphere of pressure is defined as the average pressure of the air at sea level at a latitude of 45°. One atmosphere is equal to 101.325 kPa.

The pressure exerted by the air (a mixture of gases) may be measured by a simple mercury **barometer** (Fig. 10.3). A barometer can be made by filling an 80-centimeter-long glass tube, closed at one end, with mercury and inverting it in a container of mercury. The mercury in the tube falls until the pressure exerted by the atmosphere upon the surface of the mercury in the container is just sufficient to support the weight of the mercury in the tube. Because the pressure of the atmosphere is proportional to the height of the mercury column (the vertical distance between the surface of the mercury in the tube and that in the open vessel), pressure is sometimes expressed in terms of **millimeters of mercury (mmHg).** A pressure of 1 mmHg is generally referred to as a **torr** after

Figure 10.2

The pressure of oxygen in astronaut Bruce McCandless's space suit is about 5 psi.

Figure 10.3

A mercury barometer. The height h of the mercury column is proportional to the pressure; thus the pressure can be given as the height of the column in millimeters, leading to the pressure unit mmHg.

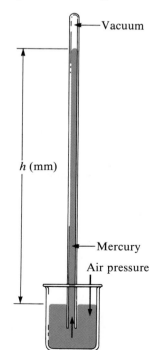

Vacuum

h (mm)

Mercury

Air pressure

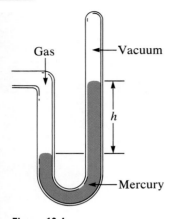

Figure 10.4

Mercury manometer.

Evangelista Torricelli, who invented the barometer in 1643. A column of mercury exactly 1 millimeter high exerts a pressure of exactly 1 torr.

A second type of barometer, a **manometer**, has two arms, one closed and one open to the atmosphere or connected to a container filled with gas (Fig. 10.4). The pressure exerted by the atmosphere or by a gas in a container is proportional to the height of the column of mercury, the distance between the mercury levels in the two arms of the tube (h in the diagram).

One atmosphere of pressure (101.325 kPa) will support a column of mercury 760 millimeters in height. Thus 1 atmosphere of pressure is exactly 760 millimeters of mercury, or 760 torr. The pressure of the atmosphere varies with the distance above sea level and with climatic changes. At higher elevations the pressure is less. The atmospheric pressure at 20,000 feet is only half of that at sea level because about half of the atmosphere is below this elevation.

The conversions among units of pressure are

$$1 \text{ atm} = 760 \text{ mmHg} = 760 \text{ torr} = 101.325 \text{ kPa}$$

Example 10.1

Weather reports in the United States often give barometric pressures in inches of mercury rather than atm or torr (29.92 inches of Hg = 760 torr). Convert a pressure of 29.2 inches of mercury to torr, atmospheres, and kilopascals.

This problem involves conversion of a measurement in one set of units to other sets of units. It is analogous to the conversions described in Section 1.9. The problem gives the relationship between inches of mercury and torr (760 torr/29.92 inches of Hg). First convert the pressure in inches of mercury to torr:

$$29.2 \text{ in Hg} \times \frac{760 \text{ torr}}{29.92 \text{ in Hg}} = 742 \text{ torr}$$

Now convert torr into atmospheres and into kilopascals, using the conversion factors given in this section.

$$742 \text{ torr} \times \frac{1 \text{ atm}}{760 \text{ torr}} = 0.976 \text{ atm}$$

$$742 \text{ torr} \times \frac{101.325 \text{ kPa}}{760 \text{ torr}} = 98.9 \text{ kPa}$$

10.3 Relationship of Volume and Pressure at Constant Temperature: Boyle's Law

The compressibility of a gas can be measured experimentally. These experiments show that when the pressure of a given sample of a gas increases, its volume decreases; when the pressure decreases, its volume increases. The volume of a gas is reduced by half when the pressure of the gas doubles, provided that the temperature of the gas does not change (Fig. 10.5). Conversely, the volume of a gas doubles when its pressure is halved.

Figure 10.5

An illustration of the variation of the pressure of a gas with volume (for a constant quantity of gas at constant temperature). Note that the volume of the gas times its pressure is always the same.

There are at least three ways to describe the change in gas volume as the pressure changes: We can use a table of values, a graph, or a mathematical equation. Figure 10.6 is a graph that shows the relationship of the volume of the sample of gas in Fig. 10.5 to its pressure. This graph shows how the volume of the gas V changes as the pressure P changes at a constant temperature. The volume decreases as the pressure increases, and it increases as the pressure decreases. The graph in Fig. 10.6(a) contains a curved line, so it is difficult to read accurately at low pressures and at low volumes. Generally, it is easier to work with graphs that contain straight lines, and there is another way of graphing the data that yields a straight line. If we plot the inverse of the volume $1/V$ as the pressure changes, a straight line results [Fig. 10.6(b)]. A graph of the inverse of the pressure $1/P$ as the volume changes also gives a straight line. Similar plots are obtained with any sample of gas.

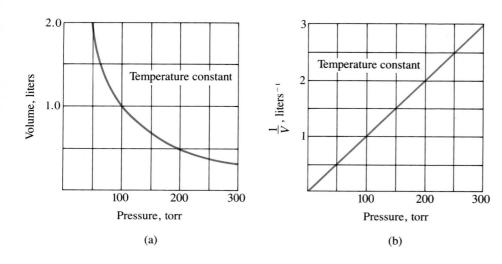

(a)   (b)

Figure 10.6

(a) A graph of the change in the volume of the sample of gas in Fig. 10.5 as its pressure changes at constant temperature. Note how the volume decreases as the pressure increases and, conversely, how the volume increases as the pressure decreases. This graph illustrates an inversely proportional relationship.
(b) A graph of the change in the inverse of the volume $1/V$ of the sample of gas in Fig. 10.5 as the pressure changes at constant temperature.

We can also represent the change in gas volume with a change in pressure by using a mathematical equation. If two variables, such as the volume and the pressure of our sample of gas, give a straight line when one is plotted against the inverse of the other, the two variables are said to be inversely proportional or to exhibit **inverse proportionality;** that is, one variable is proportional to the inverse of the other. The mathematical relationship between the inversely proportional variables volume and pressure can be written

$$V \propto \frac{1}{P}$$

where V is the volume of the gas, P is its pressure, and $\propto$ means "is proportional to." The proportionality may be changed to an equality by including a constant, k, referred to as a *proportionality constant.*

$$V = \text{constant} \times \frac{1}{P} \quad \text{or} \quad V = k \times \frac{1}{P}$$

This equation can be rearranged to give

$$PV = \text{constant} \quad \text{or} \quad PV = k$$

The meaning of this equation is that **the pressure of a given mass of gas times its volume is always equal to the same number (is constant) if the temperature does not change.** When the mass of the gas or the temperature changes, the value of the constant changes. The equation was first used to describe the behavior of gases in 1660 by Robert Boyle, an English physicist and chemist who studied gases. It is summarized in the statement now known as **Boyle's law: The volume of a given mass of gas held at constant temperature is inversely proportional to the pressure under which it is measured.**

The following examples illustrate how the behavior of gases can be described.

Example 10.2 Determine the volume of the sample of gas in Fig. 10.5 when the pressure is 260 torr, using (a) Fig. 10.6(a), (b) Fig. 10.6(b), and (c) Boyle's law.

(a) The curved line in Fig. 10.6(a) indicates the relationship between V and P for the sample of gas. At a pressure of 260 torr, the line indicates that V has a value of about 0.4 L.

(b) The straight line in Fig. 10.6(b) indicates the relationship between $1/V$ and P for the sample of gas. At a pressure of 260 torr, the line indicates that $1/V$ has a value of about 2.6 L^{-1}. Because $1/V = 2.6$ L^{-1},

$$V = \frac{1}{2.6 \text{ L}^{-1}} = 0.38 \text{ L}$$

Note that it is easier to read the value of $1/V$ from the straight line than to read the value of V from the curve in Fig. 10.6(a).

(c) From Boyle's law we know that $PV = \text{constant}$. We can find the constant from any of the three pairs of experimental volume and pressure values shown in Fig. 10.5. Let's use $V = 1.0$ L and $P = 100$ torr.

$$k = PV = 100 \text{ torr} \times 1.0 \text{ L} = 1.0 \times 10^2 \text{ torr L}$$

Using this value of the constant, we can find the volume at 260 torr by rearranging the Boyle's law equation, $PV = k$, to solve for V.

$$V = \frac{k}{P}$$

$$= \frac{1.0 \times 10^2 \text{ torr L}}{260 \text{ torr}} = 0.38 \text{ L}$$

A sample of Freon gas used in an air conditioner has a volume of 325 L and a pressure of 96.3 kPa at 20°C. What will the pressure of the gas be when its volume is 975 L at 20°C?

Example 10.3

First find the constant in Boyle's law, $PV = k$, at the first pressure and volume.

$$k = 96.3 \text{ kPa} \times 325 \text{ L} = 3.130 \times 10^4 \text{ kPa L}$$

Because the product of pressure and volume is always equal to 3.130×10^4 kPa L for this sample of gas at 20°C, we can find the second pressure from the value of k and the second volume.

$$PV = k$$

$$P = \frac{k}{V}$$

$$= \frac{3.130 \times 10^4 \text{ kPa L}}{975 \text{ L}} = 32.1 \text{ kPa}$$

There is a less formal way of solving this problem based on predicting the direction of the change in pressure. At constant temperature, the pressure of a gas decreases as the volume of the gas increases. The new pressure will be determined by the ratio of the two volumes, with the smaller volume as the numerator and the larger volume as the denominator. Multiplying the original pressure by this ratio will give the new (lower) pressure.

$$96.3 \text{ kPa} \times \frac{325 \text{ L}}{975 \text{ L}} = 32.1 \text{ kPa}$$

10.4 Relationship of Volume and Temperature at Constant Pressure: Charles's Law

If a filled balloon is cooled so that the gas inside becomes cold, the balloon contracts (Fig. 10.7). This is an example of the effect of temperature on the volume of a confined gas. Studies of the effect of temperature on the volume of gases conducted by the French physicist S. A. C. Charles in 1787 showed that the change in volume of a confined mass of gas at a constant pressure could be represented by a graph like that in Fig. 10.8. This

Volume decreases as temperature decreases

———————————————————————————————▶

◀———————————————————————————————

Volume increases as temperature increases

Figure 10.7

The effect of temperature on a gas. When a balloon filled at room temperature, $T = 25°C$, is placed in contact with liquid nitrogen, $T = -196°C$, the volume of the gas in the balloon decreases as it cools.

graph shows how the volume V of a gas changes as its temperature T changes, if the pressure does not change. The volume increases as the temperature increases, and it decreases as the temperature decreases. Because the graph of the change of volume as the temperature changes is a straight line, the volume and temperature of the gas are said to be directly proportional, or to exhibit **direct proportionality.**

The mathematical equation that describes the relationship between the volume and temperature of a given mass of gas is known as **Charles's law: The volume of a given mass of gas is directly proportional to its temperature on the Kelvin scale when the pressure is held constant,** or

$$V \propto T$$

Figure 10.8

A graph of the change in the volume of 1 mol of nitrogen gas as the temperature changes at a constant pressure of 1 atm. Note how the volume increases as the temperature increases. This graph illustrates a directly proportional relationship. The line stops at 77 K because nitrogen liquefies at this temperature.

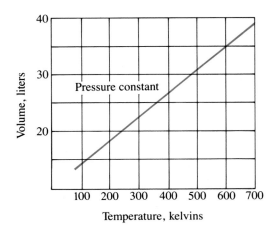

If we use a proportionality constant that depends on the mass of gas and its pressure, we get the equation

$$V = \text{constant} \times T \quad \text{or} \quad V = k \times T$$

Hence

$$\frac{V}{T} = \text{constant} \quad \text{or} \quad \frac{V}{T} = k \tag{1}$$

This constant is different from that in Boyle's law. It does not vary unless the mass of the gas or the pressure changes. Equation (1) means that, **as the Kelvin temperature of a given mass of gas changes with no change in pressure, its volume also changes such that the ratio V/T remains the same.** A decrease in T results in a decrease in V, and an increase in T results in an increase in V.

Charles's law applies to the volume of a gas and *its Kelvin temperature*. In Section 1.14 we saw that the relationship between the Kelvin and Celsius temperature scales is $K = °C + 273.15$. (Remember that temperatures on the Kelvin scale are by convention reported without a degree sign.)

The following examples illustrate the application of Charles's law.

A sample of carbon dioxide, CO_2, occupies 300 mL at 10°C and 750 torr. What volume will the gas have at 30°C and 750 torr? (Following the convention established in Section 1.10, assume all figures are significant.)

Example 10.4

The relationship between volume and temperature requires the use of the Kelvin scale, so we must first convert the Celsius temperatures to the Kelvin scale:

$$10°C + 273.15 = 283 \text{ K}$$
$$30°C + 273.15 = 303 \text{ K}$$

Using the first Kelvin temperature (283 K) and the corresponding volume (300 mL), find the constant in the Charles's law equation.

$$\frac{V}{T} = k$$

$$k = \frac{300 \text{ mL}}{283 \text{ K}} = 1.06 \text{ mL K}^{-1}$$

Now solve for V at the second temperature.

$$V = T \times k$$
$$= 303 \text{ K} \times 1.06 \text{ mL K}^{-1} = 321 \text{ mL}$$

This problem can also be solved in a less formal way based on predicting the direction of the change in volume. From Charles's law, we know that when the temperature of a gas is raised at constant pressure, the gas expands. The final volume can be found by multiplying the initial volume by that ratio of the Kelvin temperatures that gives the larger volume (high temperature on top in the ratio).

$$300 \text{ mL} \times \frac{303 \text{ K}}{283 \text{ K}} = 321 \text{ mL}$$

Example 10.5

Temperature is sometimes measured with a gas thermometer by measuring the change in the volume of the gas as the temperature changes but the pressure remains constant. The hydrogen in a particular hydrogen gas thermometer has a volume of 150.0 cm^3 when immersed in a mixture of ice and water (0.00°C). When immersed in boiling liquid ammonia, the volume of the hydrogen, at the same pressure, is 131.7 cm^3. Find the temperature of boiling ammonia on the Kelvin and Celsius scales.

This problem asks us to find the temperature of a 131.7-cm^3 sample of hydrogen gas that has a volume of 150.0 cm^3 at a temperature of 0.00°C and the same pressure. Because the initial temperature of 0.00°C is 273.15 K, the constant for this sample of hydrogen in the Charles's law equation is

$$k = \frac{V}{T} = \frac{150.0 \text{ cm}^3}{273.15 \text{ K}} = 0.54915 \text{ cm}^3 \text{ K}^{-1}$$

The temperature at which the volume is 131.7 cm^3 can then be determined.

$$\frac{V}{T} = k$$

$$T = \frac{V}{k} = \frac{131.7 \text{ cm}^3}{0.54915 \text{ cm}^3 \text{ K}^{-1}} = 239.8 \text{ K}$$

Subtracting 273.15 from 239.8 K, we find that the temperature of the boiling ammonia on the Celsius scale is −33.3°C.

⑩.5 The Kelvin Temperature Scale

In Section 1.14 we discussed the Kelvin temperature scale. Now, with some knowledge of the effect of temperature on gases, we are ready to examine the basis for the Kelvin scale.

As we have already seen, when a sample of a gas is heated at constant pressure, its volume increases. Likewise, when a gas is cooled at constant pressure, its volume decreases. Graphs of volume and temperature data for several different gases at constant pressure are shown in Fig. 10.9. In this figure, the temperature is in degrees Celsius. The straight lines reflect the direct proportionality between the volume and temperature of each sample. The data stop at those temperatures at which the gases condense. If the straight lines are extrapolated (extended) to the temperatures at which the gases would have a zero volume if they did not condense, the lines all intersect the temperature axis at −273.15°C, regardless of the gas. Below this temperature, gases would theoretically have a negative volume. Negative volumes are impossible, so −273.15°C must be the lowest temperature possible. This temperature, called **absolute zero,** is taken as the zero point of the Kelvin temperature scale. The freezing point of water (0.00°C) is therefore 273.15 kelvins, and the normal boiling point (100.00°C) is 373.15 kelvins.

To lower the temperature of a substance, we remove heat. Absolute zero (0 K) is the temperature reached when all heat has been removed from a substance. Obviously, a substance cannot be cooled any further after all heat has been removed from it.

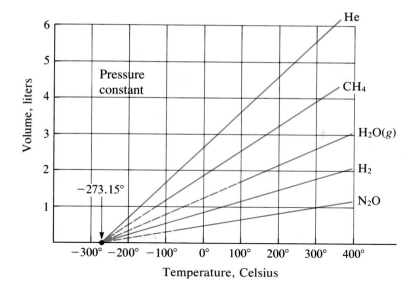

Figure 10.9
Charles's law explains behavior for several gases, each at constant pressure. The volumes of all gases extrapolate to 0 L at −273.15°C. The dashed lines represent the extrapolated portion of each line for temperatures below the temperature at which the gases condense and form liquids.

10.6 Reactions Involving Gases: Gay-Lussac's Law

Gases combine, or react, in definite and simple proportions by volume, provided that the volumes of the reactants and products are measured under the same conditions of temperature and pressure. For example, it has been determined by experiment that one volume of nitrogen will combine with three volumes of hydrogen to give two volumes of ammonia gas.

$$N_2(g) \;+\; 3H_2(g) \;\longrightarrow\; 2NH_3(g)$$

1 volume   3 volumes   2 volumes

The units, of course, must be the same: If the volume of nitrogen is measured in liters, the volumes of hydrogen and ammonia must also be measured in liters. Experimental observations on the volumes of combining gases were summarized by Joseph Louis Gay-Lussac (1788–1850) in **Gay-Lussac's law: The volumes of gases involved in a reaction, at constant temperature and pressure, can be expressed as a ratio of small whole numbers.** It has been shown that the small whole numbers in such a ratio are equal to the coefficients in the balanced equation that describes the reaction.

What volume of $O_2(g)$ measured at 25°C and 760 torr is required to react with 1.0 L of methane [$CH_4(g)$, the principal component of natural gas] measured under the same conditions of temperature and pressure?

Example 10.6

The ratio of the volumes of CH_4 and O_2 will be equal to the ratio of their coefficients in the balanced equation for the reaction.

$$CH_4(g) \;+\; 2O_2(g) \;\longrightarrow\; CO_2(g) \;+\; 2H_2O(g)$$

1 volume   2 volumes   1 volume   2 volumes

Example 10.6 continued

From the equation we see that one volume of CH_4, in this case 1.0 L, will react with two volumes (liters) of O_2.

$$1.0 \text{ L } CH_4 \times \frac{2 \text{ L } O_2}{1 \text{ L } CH_4} = 2.0 \text{ L } O_2$$

A volume of 2.0 L of O_2 will be required to react with 1.0 L of CH_4.

Example 10.7

In a recent year a volume of 683 billion cubic feet of gaseous ammonia, measured at 25°C and 1 atm, was manufactured in the United States. What volume of $H_2(g)$, measured under the same conditions, was required to prepare this amount of ammonia by reaction with N_2?

The ratio of the volumes of H_2 and N_2 will be equal to the ratio of the coefficients in the equation

$$N_2(g) + 3H_2(g) \longrightarrow 2NH_3(g)$$
$$\text{1 volume} \qquad \text{3 volumes} \qquad \text{2 volumes}$$

We see that two volumes of NH_3, in this case in units of billion ft^3, will be formed from three volumes of H_2. Thus

$$683 \text{ billion } ft^3 \ NH_3 \times \frac{3 \text{ billion } ft^3 \ H_2}{2 \text{ billion } ft^3 \ NH_3} = 1.02 \times 10^3 \text{ billion } ft^3 \ H_2$$

The manufacture of 683 billion ft^3 of NH_3 required 1020 billion ft^3 of H_2. (At 25°C and 1 atm this is the volume of a cube with an edge length of approximately 1.9 mi!)

It is important to remember that Gay-Lussac's law applies only to substances in the gaseous state measured at the same temperature and pressure. The volumes of any solids or liquids involved in the reactions cannot be determined using this law.

❿.7 An Explanation of Gay-Lussac's Law: Avogadro's Law

The Italian physicist Amedeo Avogadro advanced an hypothesis in 1811 to account for the behavior of gases. His hypothesis, which has since been experimentally confirmed, is known as **Avogadro's law: Equal volumes of all gases, measured under the same conditions of temperature and pressure, contain the same number of molecules.**

The explanation of Gay-Lussac's law by Avogadro's law may be illustrated by the reaction of the gases hydrogen and oxygen at 200°C to give gaseous water (water vapor), with the reactants and product at the same temperature and pressure. Gay-Lussac's law indicates that two volumes of H_2 and one volume of O_2 will combine to give two volumes of H_2O.

$$2H_2(g) + O_2(g) \longrightarrow 2H_2O(g)$$
$$\text{2 volumes} \qquad \text{1 volume} \qquad \text{2 volumes}$$

Two volumes   One volume   Two volumes

Hydrogen   Oxygen   Water vapor
$2H_2(g)$ + $O_2(g)$ $\longrightarrow$ $2H_2O(g)$

Figure 10.10
Two volumes of hydrogen combine with one volume of oxygen to yield two volumes of water vapor.

According to Avogadro's law, equal volumes of gaseous H_2, O_2, and H_2O contain the same number of molecules. Because two molecules of water are formed from two molecules of hydrogen and one molecule of oxygen, the volume of hydrogen required and the volume of gaseous water produced are both twice as great as the volume of oxygen required. This relationship is illustrated in Fig. 10.10.

10.8   The Ideal Gas Equation

Boyle's law, Charles's law, and Avogadro's law are special cases of one equation, the **ideal gas equation,** that relates pressure, volume, temperature, and number of moles of an **ideal gas** (a gas that follows these gas laws perfectly). Although strictly speaking the ideal gas equation applies only to an ideal gas, under normal conditions of temperature and pressure it also applies very well to real gases because real gases behave very nearly like ideal gases under these conditions. Generally in this text we will approximate the behavior of all gases as ideal.

The ideal gas equation is

$$PV = nRT$$

where P is the pressure of a gas, V is its volume, n is the number of moles of the gas, T is its temperature on the Kelvin scale, and R is a constant called the **gas constant.** The following paragraphs show how the equation reduces to either Boyle's law, Charles's law, or Avogadro's law under the appropriate conditions.

Boyle's law (Section 10.3) states that for a given amount of a gas that exhibits ideal behavior, the product of its volume V and its pressure P is a constant at constant temperature. Because n, R, and T do not change under the conditions for which Boyle's law holds, their product is a constant. Therefore the ideal gas equation, $PV = nRT$, becomes

$$PV = \text{constant}$$

which is the mathematical expression for Boyle's law.

Charles's law (Section 10.4) states that the volume V of a sample of an ideal gas divided by its temperature T on the Kelvin scale is equal to a constant at constant pressure. If we rearrange the ideal gas equation so that the terms that do not vary (n, R, and P) are on the right side and V and T are on the left, we obtain the equation expressing Charles's law.

$$\frac{V}{T} = \frac{nR}{P} = \text{constant}$$

If equal volumes of gases, under the same conditions of temperature and pressure, contain the same number of molecules (Avogadro's law, Section 10.7), then they contain the same number of moles, n, of gas. Thus Avogadro's law may be written in the form of an equation as follows:

$$V = \text{constant} \times n$$

We can rearrange the ideal gas equation to yield this expression by placing the constant quantities R, T, and P together:

$$V = \frac{RT}{P} \times n$$

At constant P and T,

$$V = \text{constant} \times n$$

The numerical value of R in the ideal gas equation can be determined by substituting experimental values for P, V, n, and T in the equation. Exactly 1 mole of any gas that very closely approximates ideal behavior occupies a volume of 22.414 liters at 273.15 K and a pressure of exactly 1 atmosphere. Substituting these values in $PV = nRT$ gives

$$(1 \text{ atm})(22.414 \text{ L}) = (1 \text{ mol})(R)(273.15 \text{ K})$$

$$R = \frac{22.414 \text{ L} \times 1 \text{ atm}}{1 \text{ mol} \times 273.15 \text{ K}}$$

$$= 0.08206 \text{ L atm/mol K}$$

The numerical value for R is different when other units are used for P, V, or T. For example, if we take the pressure in kilopascals, we calculate another value of R as follows:

$$R = \frac{22.414 \text{ L} \times 101.325 \text{ kPa}}{1 \text{ mol} \times 273.15 \text{ K}}$$

$$= 8.314 \text{ L kPa/mol K}$$

The units of pressure, volume, temperature, and amount of gas used in the ideal gas equation must always be the same as the units for R.

The ideal gas equation contains five terms (P, V, n, R, and T). If we know any four of these, we can rearrange the equation and find the fifth. The following examples illustrate some of the ways in which the ideal gas equation can be used to relate P, V, T, and n.

Example 10.8

Calculate the volume occupied by 0.54 mol of N_2 at 15°C and 0.967 atm. Use the value of R with the units of L atm/mol K.

In this problem we are given $n = 0.54$ mol, $T = 15°C$, and $P = 0.967$ atm and told to use 0.08206 L atm/mol K to find V. Thus we must rearrange $PV = nRT$ to solve for V.

$$V = \frac{nRT}{P}$$

Because the equation requires that the temperature be in kelvins, we convert the temperature from °C to K.

$$T = 15°C + 273.15 = 288 \text{ K}$$

Substitution gives

$$V = \frac{nRT}{P} = \frac{(0.54 \text{ mol})(0.08206 \text{ L atm/mol K})(288 \text{ K})}{0.967 \text{ atm}}$$

$$= 13 \text{ L (to two significant figures, as justified by the data)}$$

Note that the units cancel to liters, an appropriate unit for volume. Cancellation of units is a very simple way of checking to see that the units for R are consistent with those for P, V, n, and T.

Methane, CH_4, can be used as fuel for an automobile; however, it is a gas at normal temperatures and pressures, which causes some problems with storage. One gallon of gasoline could be replaced by 655 g of CH_4. What is the volume of this much methane at 25°C and 745 torr? Use the value of R with the units of L atm/mol K.

Example 10.9

As shown in Example 10.8, the volume of an ideal gas may be obtained from the equation

$$V = \frac{nRT}{P}$$

The units of R (liters, atmospheres, moles, and kelvins) require that the pressure be expressed in atmospheres rather than in torr as given in the problem, the amount of gas in moles rather than in grams, and the temperature in K. Once these conversions are completed, the values can be substituted into the equation and the volume calculated.

$$P = 745 \text{ torr} \times \frac{1 \text{ atm}}{760 \text{ torr}} = 0.980 \text{ atm}$$

$$n = 655 \text{ g } CH_4 \times \frac{1 \text{ mol}}{16.04 \text{ g } CH_4} = 40.8 \text{ mol}$$

$$T = 25°C + 273.15 = 298 \text{ K}$$

Now we substitute into the rearranged equation.

$$V = \frac{nRT}{P}$$

$$= \frac{(40.8 \text{ mol})(0.08206 \text{ L atm/mol K})(298 \text{ K})}{0.980 \text{ atm}}$$

$$= 1.02 \times 10^3 \text{ L}$$

During the Second World War, British drivers sometimes used fuel gas for their automobiles because gasoline was rationed. The bag on the top of this car was required to hold the large volume of gas necessary.

Thus it would require 1020 L (269 gal) of gaseous methane at about 1 atm of pressure to replace 1 gal of gasoline. It requires a large container to hold enough methane at 1 atm to replace several gallons of gasoline (see the photograph).

While resting, the average human male consumes 200 mL of O_2 per hour at 25°C and 1.0 atm for each kilogram of mass. How many moles of O_2 are consumed by a 70-kg man while resting for 1 h?

Example 10.10

For the purpose of this problem, let us assume the oxygen consumption per kilogram per hour is good to two significant figures. The volume of O_2 consumed by a resting 70-kg male is then 14,000 mL h^{-1}, or 14 L h^{-1}.

Example 10.10 continued

To solve for moles, rearrange the ideal gas equation, $n = PV/RT$. The pressure and volume are given in atmospheres and liters, so use $R = 0.08206$ L atm/mol K. The temperature is $25°C + 273.15 = 298$ K. These values can now be used to find n.

$$n = \frac{PV}{RT} = \frac{(1.0 \text{ atm})(14 \text{ L})}{(0.08206 \text{ L atm/mol K})(298 \text{ K})} = 0.57 \text{ mol } O_2$$

Example 10.11

What is the pressure in kilopascals in a 35.0-L balloon at 25°C filled with pure hydrogen gas produced by the reaction of 34.11 g of CaH_2 with water?

To use the ideal gas equation, $PV = nRT$, for determining P, we must know V, n, R, and T ($P = nRT/V$). Values for V and T are given; R must be 8.314 L kPa/mol K in order for the pressure units to be kilopascals; and n can be calculated from the mass of CaH_2 and the equation for the reaction.

$$CaH_2 + 2H_2O \longrightarrow Ca(OH)_2 + 2H_2$$

$$34.11 \text{ g CaH}_2 \times \frac{1 \text{ mol CaH}_2}{42.10 \text{ g CaH}_2} = 0.810 \text{ mol CaH}_2$$

$$0.810 \text{ mol CaH}_2 \times \frac{2 \text{ mol H}_2}{1 \text{ mol CaH}_2} = 1.62 \text{ mol H}_2$$

so

$$n = 1.62 \text{ mol}$$

Now we convert T to the Kelvin scale.

$$T = 25°C + 273.15 = 298 \text{ K}$$

Using the ideal gas equation gives

$$P = \frac{nRT}{V} = \frac{(1.62 \text{ mol})(8.314 \text{ L kPa/mol K})(298 \text{ K})}{35.0 \text{ L}} = 115 \text{ kPa}$$

The pressure in the balloon (115 kPa) is about 14% greater than atmospheric pressure (101 kPa).

Example 10.12

What volume of hydrogen at 27°C and 723 torr may be prepared by the reaction of 8.88 g of gallium with an excess of hydrochloric acid?

$$2Ga(s) + 6HCl(aq) \longrightarrow 2GaCl_3(aq) + 3H_2(g)$$

In order to calculate the volume of hydrogen produced, we need to know the number of moles, n, of hydrogen produced. This can be determined from the number of moles of gallium reacting and the chemical equation. The moles of gallium reacting can be determined from the mass of gallium used and its atomic mass. Thus this problem requires the following steps:

Mass of Ga	→	Moles of Ga	→	Moles of H$_2$	→	Volume of H$_2$

$$8.88 \text{ g Ga} \times \frac{1 \text{ mol Ga}}{69.72 \text{ g Ga}} = 0.127 \text{ mol Ga}$$

$$0.127 \text{ mol Ga} \times \frac{3 \text{ mol H}_2}{2 \text{ mol Ga}} = 0.191 \text{ mol H}_2$$

Now we use the ideal gas equation to get the volume of H_2, after converting the temperature to kelvins and the pressure to atmospheres.

$$V = \frac{nRT}{P}$$

$$= \frac{(0.191 \text{ mol } H_2)(0.08206 \text{ L atm/mol K})(300 \text{ K})}{0.951 \text{ atm}}$$

$$= 4.94 \text{ L}$$

10.9 Standard Conditions of Temperature and Pressure

As the foregoing discussion shows, the volume of a given quantity of gas and the quantity (either moles or mass) of a given volume of gas vary with changes in pressure and temperature. In order to simplify comparisons of gases, chemists have adopted a set of **standard conditions of temperature and pressure (STP).** Accordingly, 273.15 K (0°C) and 1 atmosphere (760 torr, or 101.325 kilopascals) are commonly used as standard conditions for reporting properties of gases.

Calculate the volume, in liters, occupied by 1.00 mol of an ideal gas at STP.

For units of R in L atm/mol K, T is exactly 273.15 K and P is exactly 1 atm. Thus

Example 10.13

$$V = \frac{nRT}{P}$$

$$= \frac{(1.00 \text{ mol})(0.08206 \text{ L atm/mol K})(273.15 \text{ K})}{1.00 \text{ atm}}$$

$$= 22.4 \text{ L}$$

Note that the units cancel to liters, an appropriate unit for volume.

The volume of one mole of any gas at 0°C and 1 atmosphere pressure is 22.4 L and is referred to as the **molar volume** (see Fig. 10.11).

28.2 cm, or 11.1 in

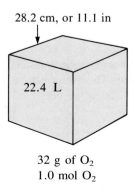

22.4 L

32 g of O_2
1.0 mol O_2

22.4 L

2.0 g of H_2
1.0 mol H_2

22.4 L

17 g of NH_3
1.0 mol NH_3

Figure 10.11

A mole of any gas occupies a volume of approximately 22.4 L at 0°C and 1 atm of pressure. A cube with an edge length of 28.2 cm, or 11.1 in., contains 22.4 L.

We can convert the volume of a gas at any temperature and pressure to its volume at standard conditions or at any other temperature and pressure by using either the ideal gas equation or a combination of Boyle's and Charles's laws.

Example 10.14

A sample of ammonia is found to occupy 250 mL under laboratory conditions of 27°C and 740 torr. Find the volume at standard conditions of 0°C and 760 torr. (All figures in the data are significant.)

1. Using the Ideal Gas Equation. Put all constant terms in the equation on the right side and all variable terms on the left. In this example the moles of ammonia and R do not vary, so

$$\frac{PV}{T} = nR = \text{constant}$$

Now evaluate the constant term, nR, at the initial conditions (250 mL, 27°C + 273.15 = 300 K, and 740 torr).

$$\frac{740 \text{ torr} \times 250 \text{ mL}}{300 \text{ K}} = nR = 616.7 \text{ mL torr/K}$$

Next calculate the volume at standard conditions (0°C = 273.15 K, 760 torr = 1 atm). Because the amount of ammonia does not change, nR remains constant:

$$\frac{PV}{T} = \text{constant} = nR$$

Rearranging the equation gives

$$V = nR \times \frac{T}{P}$$

$$= 616.7 \text{ mL torr/K} \times \frac{273.15 \text{ K}}{760 \text{ torr}}$$

$$= 222 \text{ mL}$$

Note that the units cancel to leave mL, a correct unit for volume.

2. Using a Combination of Boyle's and Charles's Laws. First convert the Celsius temperatures to the Kelvin scale: 27°C = 300 K, and 0°C = 273.15 K. A decrease in temperature from 300 K to 273.15 K alone will cause a decrease in the volume of ammonia. Therefore multiply the original volume by a fraction made up of the two temperatures and having a value of less than 1 to correct for the temperature change:

$$250 \text{ mL} \times \frac{273.15 \text{ K}}{300 \text{ K}}$$

The increase in pressure from 740 torr to 760 torr alone will also decrease the volume, so multiply by a fraction with the smaller pressure in the numerator. This factor can be included in the same expression with the temperature factor to obtain the corrected volume:

$$250 \text{ mL} \times \frac{273.15 \text{ K}}{300 \text{ K}} \times \frac{740 \text{ torr}}{760 \text{ torr}} = 222 \text{ mL}$$

10.10 Densities and Molar Masses of Gases

In previous sections of this chapter we saw how the ideal gas equation relates the pressure, volume, temperature, and moles of a gas. In this section we shall see how to use the ideal gas equation with other equations to find other properties of a gas. We do not intend to provide more equations to be memorized, but to show how additional information about a gas can be determined by combining relationships that we have seen up to this point.

The ideal gas equation ($PV = nRT$) and the equation $m = n \times M$ (Section 3.4), which relates m (the mass of a sample), n (the number of moles in the sample), and M (its molar mass) can be used to determine two other properties of a gas: density and molar mass.

Density of a Gas

The density d of a gas is the mass of one liter of the gas. Thus if we can determine the mass of some volume of a gas, we can determine its density: $d = m/V$. The ideal gas equation can be used to determine the number of moles of a gas in some convenient volume (such as one liter), and the relationship $m = n \times M$ can then be used to determine the mass of the gas.

Example 10.15

What is the density of ethane gas, C_2H_6, at a pressure of 183.4 kPa and a temperature of 25°C?

The density of ethane under these conditions is the mass of exactly 1 L of C_2H_6. The number of moles of ethane in 1 L can be determined from the ideal gas equation, and the mass of the gas in 1 L can be determined from the number of moles and the molar mass of ethane.

$$n = \frac{PV}{RT}$$

$$= \frac{183.4 \text{ kPa} \times 1 \text{ L}}{8.314 \text{ L kPa/mol K} \times 298 \text{ K}} = 0.0740 \text{ mol}$$

$$m = n \times M$$

$$= 0.0740 \text{ mol } C_2H_6 \times \frac{30.1 \text{ g } C_2H_6}{1 \text{ mol } C_2H_6} = 2.23 \text{ g } C_2H_6$$

$$d = \frac{m}{V} = \frac{2.23 \text{ g}}{1 \text{ L}} = 2.23 \text{ g/L}$$

Note that we must specify both the temperature and the pressure of a gas when reporting its density, because the number of moles of a gas (and thus the mass of the gas) in a liter changes with temperature or pressure. Gas densities are often reported at STP.

Many chemists prefer to derive a mathematical equation that can be used to calculate the property of interest before substituting numbers into the calculation. The following example shows how the equations $PV = nRT$, $m = n \times M$, and $d = m/V$ can be combined to derive an equation for calculating the density of a gas.

Example 10.16

Derive an equation that can be used to calculate the density of a gas from its molar mass, pressure, and temperature.

The density of a gas is calculated from the equation

$$d = \frac{m}{V}$$

Introduce the molar mass M of the gas into this equation, using the equation $m = nM$ and substituting nM for m. Thus

$$d = \frac{nM}{V}$$

Introduce the pressure and temperature of the gas by rearranging the ideal gas equation to $V = nRT/P$ and then substituting this for the volume of the gas.

$$d = \frac{nM}{nRT/P}$$

Rearranging this equation and canceling the common terms gives

$$d = \frac{PM}{RT}$$

an equation that can be used to calculate the density of a gas from its molar mass, pressure, and temperature.

Molar Mass of a Gas

If we know the mass m of a sample of a compound and the number of moles n in the sample, we have two of the three quantities in the equation $m = n \times M$. Thus we can rearrange the equation to find M, the molar mass of the compound. If we measure the mass of a sample of a gas at a known volume, temperature, and pressure, then we can determine the number of moles of gas by using the ideal gas equation and then can determine the molar mass of the gas.

Example 10.17

A sample of phosphorus that weighs 3.243×10^{-2} g exerts a pressure of 31.89 kPa in a 56.0-mL bulb at 550°C. What are the molar mass and molecular formula of phosphorus vapor?

We can find the molar mass of phosphorus vapor by rearranging the equation $m = n \times M$ to solve for M. The mass of phosphorus vapor is given in the problem; so we need to find the moles of vapor by using the ideal gas equation.

$$n = \frac{PV}{RT} = \frac{31.89 \text{ kPa} \times 0.0560 \text{ L}}{8.314 \text{ L kPa/mol K} \times 823 \text{ K}}$$

$$= 2.61 \times 10^{-4} \text{ mol}$$

The molar mass can now be determined from the mass of the gas and the number of moles.

$$M = \frac{m}{n}$$

$$= \frac{3.243 \times 10^{-2} \text{ g}}{2.61 \times 10^{-4} \text{ mol}}$$

$$= 124 \text{ g/mol}$$

Because the molar mass of phosphorus vapor is 124 g/mol, the mass of a single molecule is 124 amu. The mass of a single phosphorus atom is 31 amu, thus there must be 124/31, or 4, phosphorus atoms in a molecule of phosphorus vapor, and the molecular formula is therefore P_4. The P_4 molecule is a tetrahedron (Fig. 10.12).

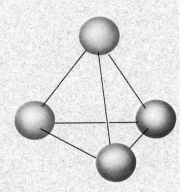

Figure 10.12

The molecular structure of gaseous phosphorus, P_4.

10.11 The Pressure of a Mixture of Gases: Dalton's Law

In the absence of a chemical reaction between the components of a mixture of gases, the individual gases do not affect one another's pressures, and each individual gas exerts the same pressure before and after it is mixed with other gases. The pressure exerted by each gas is called the **partial pressure** of that gas, and the total pressure of the mixture of gases is the sum of the partial pressures of all the gases present. This is **Dalton's law of partial pressures,** which may be stated as follows: **The total pressure of a mixture of ideal gases is equal to the sum of the partial pressures of the component gases.**

$$P_T = P_A + P_B + P_C + \cdots$$

In this equation P_T is the total pressure of a mixture of gases, P_A is the pressure of gas A; P_B is the pressure of gas B; etc. Thus if nitrogen gas is at a pressure of 1 atmosphere in a 1-liter flask, and oxygen gas is at a pressure of 1 atmosphere in a second 1-liter flask, transfer of the oxygen into the flask with the nitrogen gives a mixture with a total pressure of 2 atmospheres (provided the temperature does not change).

What is the total pressure in atmospheres in a 10.0-L vessel containing 2.50×10^{-3} mol of H_2, 1.00×10^{-3} mol of He, and 3.00×10^{-4} mol of Ne at 35°C? **Example 10.18**

The total pressure in the 10.0-L vessel is the sum of the partial pressures of the gases, because they do not react with each other.

$$P_T = P_{H_2} + P_{He} + P_{Ne}$$

Example
10.18
continued

The partial pressure of each gas can be determined from the ideal gas equation, using $P = nRT/V$.

$$P_{H_2} = \frac{(2.50 \times 10^{-3}\ \text{mol})(0.08206\ \text{L atm/mol K})(308\ \text{K})}{10.0\ \text{L}} = 6.32 \times 10^{-3}\ \text{atm}$$

$$P_{He} = \frac{(1.00 \times 10^{-3}\ \text{mol})(0.08206\ \text{L atm/mol K})(308\ \text{K})}{10.0\ \text{L}} = 2.53 \times 10^{-3}\ \text{atm}$$

$$P_{Ne} = \frac{(3.00 \times 10^{-4}\ \text{mol})(0.08206\ \text{L atm/mol K})(308\ \text{K})}{10.0\ \text{L}} = 7.58 \times 10^{-4}\ \text{atm}$$

$$P_T = (0.00632 + 0.00253 + 0.00076)\ \text{atm} = 9.61 \times 10^{-3}\ \text{atm}$$

Pressure of gas
and water vapor
is 760 torr

Atmosphere =
760 torr

Figure 10.13

Method by which the pressure on a confined mixture of gases can be made equal to the atmospheric pressure. The level of water inside and that outside the vessel are made the same. In the diagram a typical atmospheric pressure of 760 torr is indicated. The actual pressure depends on the atmospheric pressure.

The pressure of a sample of a gas that does not react with water can be measured by collecting the gas in a container over water and making its pressure equal to air pressure (which can be measured by a barometer). This is easily accomplished by adjusting the water level (Fig. 10.13) so that it is the same both inside and outside the container. The gas is then at atmospheric pressure.

However, another factor must be considered when determining pressure by this method. There is always gaseous water (water vapor) above a sample of water. When a gas is collected over water, it soon becomes saturated with water vapor. The total pressure of the mixture equals the sum of the partial pressures of the gas and the water vapor, according to Dalton's law. The pressure of the pure gas is therefore equal to the total pressure minus the pressure of the water vapor.

The pressure of the water vapor above a sample of water in a closed container like that in Fig. 10.13 depends on the temperature, as shown in Fig. 10.14 and Table 10.1. At 23°C, the vapor pressure of water is 21.1 torr (Table 10.1). Thus at 23°C, the total

Figure 10.14

A graph of water vapor pressure as a function of temperature.

Table 10.1		Vapor Pressure of Ice and Water at Various Temperatures			
Temperature, °C	Pressure, torr	Temperature, °C	Pressure, torr	Temperature, °C	Pressure, torr
−10	1.95	12	10.5	27	26.7
−5	3.0	13	11.2	28	28.3
−2	3.9	14	12.0	29	30.0
−1	4.2	15	12.8	30	31.8
0	4.6	16	13.6	35	42.2
1	4.9	17	14.5	40	55.3
2	5.3	18	15.5	50	92.5
3	5.7	19	16.5	60	149.4
4	6.1	20	17.5	70	233.7
5	6.5	21	18.7	80	355.1
6	7.0	22	19.8	90	525.8
7	7.5	23	21.1	95	633.9
8	8.0	24	22.4	99	733.2
9	8.6	25	23.8	100.0	760.0
10	9.2	26	25.2	101.0	787.6
11	9.8				

pressure of 760 torr in the bottle in Fig. 10.13 would consist of 21 torr due to water vapor and 739 torr due to the other gases. At 29°C, water has a vapor pressure of 30 torr. At 29°C, then, the bottle would contain water vapor at 30 torr and the other gases at 730 torr.

Example 10.19

If 0.200 L of argon is collected over water at a temperature of 26°C and a pressure of 750 torr in a system like that shown in Fig. 10.13, what is the partial pressure of argon?

According to Dalton's law, the total pressure in the bottle (750 torr) is the sum of the partial pressure of argon and the partial pressure of gaseous water.

$$P_T = P_{Ar} + P_{H_2O}$$

Rearranging this equation to solve for the pressure of argon gives

$$P_{Ar} = P_T - P_{H_2O}$$

The pressure of water vapor above a sample of liquid water at 26°C is 25.2 torr (Table 10.1), so

$$P_{Ar} = 750 \text{ torr} - 25.2 \text{ torr} = 725 \text{ torr}$$

Example 10.20

A 1.34-g sample of solid calcium carbide, CaC_2, was allowed to react with water. The acetylene, C_2H_2, produced by the reaction

$$CaC_2(s) + 2H_2O(l) \longrightarrow C_2H_2(g) + Ca(OH)_2(s)$$

Example 10.20 continued

Figure 10.15

Acetylene from the reaction of CaC_2 with water is collected over water.

CaC$_2$ and water

C$_2$H$_2$ plus water vapor

was collected over water in a system like that shown in Fig. 10.15. If 471 mL of acetylene gas was collected at a temperature of 23°C and a pressure of 743 torr, what was the percent yield of the reaction?

To determine the percent yield (Section 3.11), we need the actual yield and the theoretical yield. We determine the theoretical yield as follows:

$$1.34 \text{ g CaC}_2 \times \frac{1 \text{ mol CaC}_2}{64.1 \text{ g CaC}_2} = 2.09 \times 10^{-2} \text{ mol CaC}_2$$

$$2.09 \times 10^{-2} \text{ mol CaC}_2 \times \frac{1 \text{ mol C}_2\text{H}_2}{1 \text{ mol CaC}_2} = 2.09 \times 10^{-2} \text{ mol C}_2\text{H}_2$$

To determine the actual yield, we need to calculate the moles of C_2H_2 produced. This is available from the ideal gas equation, $PV = nRT$, and the data in the problem. However, the pressure in the equation must be the pressure of $C_2H_2(g)$, not the pressure of a mixture of $H_2O(g)$ and $C_2H_2(g)$. So we use Dalton's law to get that partial pressure. The vapor pressure of water at 23°C is 21.1 torr (Table 10.1). Therefore,

$$P_{C_2H_2} = P_T - P_{H_2O}$$
$$= 743 \text{ torr} - 21.1 \text{ torr} = 722 \text{ torr (or 0.950 atm)}$$

Using the ideal gas equation with P in atmospheres, T in kelvins, and V in liters, we find n, the moles of C_2H_2 produced.

$$n = \frac{PV}{RT}$$

$$= \frac{0.950 \text{ atm} \times 0.471 \text{ L}}{0.08206 \text{ L atm/mol K} \times 296 \text{ K}} = 1.84 \times 10^{-2} \text{ mol}$$

Now we calculate the percent yield.

$$\text{Percent yield} = \frac{\text{actual yield}}{\text{theoretical yield}} \times 100$$

$$= \frac{1.84 \times 10^{-2} \text{ mol}}{2.09 \times 10^{-2} \text{ mol}} \times 100 = 88.0\%$$

🔟.12 Diffusion of Gases: Graham's Law

When a sample of gas is set free from one part of a closed container, it very quickly diffuses throughout the container (see Fig. 10.16).

If a mixture of gases is placed in a container with porous walls, diffusion of the gases through the walls occurs. The lighter gases diffuse through the small openings of the porous walls more rapidly than the heavier ones. In 1832 Thomas Graham studied the rates of diffusion of different gases and formulated **Graham's law: The rates of diffusion of gases are inversely proportional to the square roots of their densities (or their molar masses).**

$$\frac{\text{Rate of diffusion of gas A}}{\text{Rate of diffusion of gas B}} = \frac{\sqrt{\text{density B}}}{\sqrt{\text{density A}}} = \frac{\sqrt{\text{mol. mass B}}}{\sqrt{\text{mol. mass A}}}$$

Calculate the ratio of the rate of diffusion of hydrogen to the rate of diffusion of oxygen.

Example 10.21

Using densities. The density of hydrogen is 0.0899 g/L, and that of oxygen is 1.43 g/L.

$$\frac{\text{Rate of diffusion of hydrogen}}{\text{Rate of diffusion of oxygen}} = \frac{\sqrt{1.43 \text{ g/L}}}{\sqrt{0.0899 \text{ g/L}}} = \frac{1.20}{0.300} = \frac{4}{1}$$

Using molar masses.

$$\frac{\text{Rate of diffusion of hydrogen}}{\text{Rate of diffusion of oxygen}} = \frac{\sqrt{32}}{\sqrt{2}} = \frac{\sqrt{16}}{\sqrt{1}} = \frac{4}{1}$$

Hydrogen diffuses four times as rapidly as oxygen.

Rates of diffusion depend on the speeds of the molecules—the faster the molecules move, the faster they diffuse. Molecules of smaller mass move with faster speeds than molecules of larger mass; thus the former diffuse more rapidly. Differences in diffusion

Stopcock closed	Stopcock just opened	Some time after stopcock opened
(a)	(b)	(c)

Figure 10.16

Two gases, H_2 and O_2, separated by a stopcock intermingle when the stopcock is opened; they mix by diffusing together. The rapid motion of the molecules and the relatively large spaces between them explain why diffusion occurs. Note that H_2, the lighter of the two gases, diffuses faster than O_2. Thus the instant the stopcock is opened (b), more H_2 molecules move to the O_2 side than O_2 molecules move to the H_2 side. After some time has passed (c), the slower-moving O_2 molecules and the faster-moving H_2 molecules have both distributed themselves evenly on either side of the vessel.

rates of gaseous substances are used in the separation of light isotopes from heavy ones. Diffusion through a porous barrier from a region of higher pressure to one of lower pressure has been used for the large-scale separation of gaseous $^{235}_{92}UF_6$ from $^{238}_{92}UF_6$ at the atomic energy installation in Oak Ridge, Tennessee. It is said that for separation to be complete, a given volume of UF_6 must be diffused some two million times.

The Molecular Behavior of Gases

⑩.13 The Kinetic-Molecular Theory

Bernoulli in 1738, Poule in 1851, and Kronig in 1856 suggested that properties of gases such as compressibility, expansibility, and diffusibility could be explained by assuming that gases consist of continuously moving molecules. During the latter half of the nineteenth century, Clausius, Maxwell, Boltzmann, and others developed this hypothesis into the detailed **kinetic-molecular theory** of gases. This theory consists of the following seven assumptions about the nature of the molecules of an ideal gas.

1. Gases are composed of molecules that are in continuous, completely random motion in all directions. The molecules move in straight lines and change direction only when they collide with other molecules or with the walls of a container.
2. The pressure of a gas in a container results from the bombardment of the walls of the container by the gas molecules.
3. At a given temperature, the pressure in a container does not change with time. Thus the collisions among molecules and between molecules and walls must be elastic; that is, the collisions involve no loss of energy due to friction.
4. At relatively low pressures the average distance between gas molecules is large compared to the size of the molecules.
5. At relatively low pressures the attractive forces between gas molecules, which depend on the separation of the molecules, are of no significance and can be ignored because the molecules are relatively widely separated.
6. Because the molecules are small compared to the distances between them, they may be considered to have no volume.
7. The average kinetic energy of the molecules (the energy due to their motion) is proportional to the temperature of the gas on the Kelvin scale and is the same for all gases at the same temperature.

As we will show in the next section, the assumptions of the kinetic-molecular theory explain the gas laws.

⑩.14 Relationship of the Behavior of Gases to the Kinetic-Molecular Theory

The test of the kinetic-molecular theory is its ability to describe the behavior of a gas quantitatively. We shall show that the various gas laws can be derived from the assumptions of the theory; this has led chemists to believe that the assumptions of the theory accurately represent the properties of gas molecules.

1. Boyle's Law. The pressure exerted by a gas in a container is caused by the bombardment of the walls of the container by rapidly moving molecules of the gas. The pressure varies directly with the number of molecules hitting the walls per unit of time. Reducing the volume of a given mass of gas by half doubles the number of molecules per unit of volume. The number of impacts per unit of time on the same area of wall surface is also doubled: This doubles the pressure. These results are in accordance with Boyle's law relating volume and pressure.

2. Charles's Law. At constant volume, an increase in temperature increases the pressure of a gas. This increase in pressure reflects the increase in average speed and kinetic energy of the molecules as the temperature is raised. An increase in the average speed results in more frequent and harder impacts on the walls of the container—that is, it results in greater pressure.

In order for the pressure to remain constant with the increasing temperature, the volume must increase so that each molecule travels farther, on the average, before hitting a wall. The smaller number of molecules striking any wall at a given time exactly offsets the greater force with which each molecule hits, making it possible for the pressure to remain constant.

3. Dalton's Law. Because of the relatively large distance between the molecules of a gas, the molecules of one component of a mixture of gases bombard the walls of the container with the same frequency in the presence of other kinds of molecules as in their absence. The total pressure of a mixture of gases equals the sum of the partial pressures of the individual gases.

4. Graham's Law. The fact that the molecules of a gas are in rapid motion and the fact that the spaces between the molecules are relatively large explain the phenomenon of diffusion. Gas molecules can move past each other easily.

The rate of diffusion depends on the mass of the molecules of a gas because, at the same temperature, molecules of all gases have the same average kinetic energy. The kinetic energy, KE, of a moving body, in joules, is equal to $\frac{1}{2}mu^2$, where m is its mass in kilograms and u is its speed in meters per second. The average kinetic energy, KE_{avg}, of the molecules of a gas consisting of one type of molecule is equal to $\frac{1}{2}m(u^2)_{avg}$, where $(u^2)_{avg}$ is the average of the squares of the speeds of the molecules. Thus at a given temperature, lighter molecules, such as hydrogen, must move at higher speeds than heavier molecules, such as oxygen, because both have the same average kinetic energy (Fig. 10.17).

Figure 10.17

Distributions of the molecular speeds of different gases. The lighter gases move with faster average speeds.

For two different gases at the same temperature,

$$\text{Average kinetic energy for first gas} = \tfrac{1}{2}m_1(u_1{}^2)_{\text{avg}}$$
$$\text{Average kinetic energy for second gas} = \tfrac{1}{2}m_2(u_2{}^2)_{\text{avg}}$$

where m_1 and m_2 are the masses of individual molecules of the two gases and $(u_1{}^2)_{\text{avg}}$ and $(u_2{}^2)_{\text{avg}}$ are the averages of the squares of their speeds.

According to the kinetic-molecular theory, the kinetic energies of the two gases are equal. Hence

$$\tfrac{1}{2}m_1(u_1{}^2)_{\text{avg}} = \tfrac{1}{2}m_2(u_2{}^2)_{\text{avg}}$$

Dividing both sides of the equation by $\tfrac{1}{2}$ gives

$$m_1(u_1{}^2)_{\text{avg}} = m_2(u_2{}^2)_{\text{avg}}$$

Rearranging and taking square roots gives

$$\frac{(u_1)_{\text{rms}}}{(u_2)_{\text{rms}}} = \frac{\sqrt{m_2}}{\sqrt{m_1}}$$

where $(u_1)_{\text{rms}}$ and $(u_2)_{\text{rms}}$ are the root-mean-square speeds of the respective molecules—that is, the square roots of the averages of the squares of the speeds:

$$(u_1)_{\text{rms}} = \sqrt{(u_1{}^2)_{\text{avg}}} \qquad (u_2)_{\text{rms}} = \sqrt{(u_2{}^2)_{\text{avg}}}$$

The rate at which a gas diffuses, R, is proportional to u_{rms}, the root-mean-square speed of its molecules. The molar masses, M_1 and M_2, of two gases are proportional to the masses of the individual molecules. Thus

$$\frac{R_1}{R_2} = \frac{\sqrt{M_2}}{\sqrt{M_1}}$$

This equation states that the ratio of the rates of diffusion of two gases, held at the same temperature and pressure, equals the inverse ratio of the square roots of their molar masses.

Hydrogen is the lightest gas and therefore diffuses the most rapidly. The root-mean-square speed of its molecules at room temperature is about 1 mile per second; that of oxygen molecules is about $\tfrac{1}{4}$ mile per second. Collisions between molecules make diffusion rates much lower than would be expected from such speeds. A molecule in hydrogen gas at standard conditions has about 11 billion collisions per second. Hydrogen molecules travel about 1.7×10^{-5} centimeter between collisions and, on the average, collide about 60,000 times in traveling between two points 1 centimeter apart.

🔟.15 The Distribution of Molecular Velocities

The individual molecules of a gas travel at different speeds. Because of the enormous number of collisions, the speeds of the molecules vary from practically zero to thousands of meters per second. The exchange of energy accompanying each collision can change the speed of a given molecule over a wide range. However, because a large number of molecules is involved, the distribution of the molecular speeds of the total number of molecules is constant.

The distribution of molecular speeds is shown in Fig. 10.18. The vertical axis represents the number of molecules, and the horizontal axis represents the molecular speed, u. The most probable speed is α, and the root-mean-square speed of the molecules is u_{rms}. The graph indicates that very few molecules move at very low or very high speeds. The number of molecules with intermediate speeds increases rapidly up to a maximum and then drops off rapidly.

At the higher temperature the whole curve is shifted to higher speeds. Thus at a higher temperature, more molecules have higher speeds and fewer molecules have lower speeds. This is in accordance with expectations based on kinetic-molecular theory.

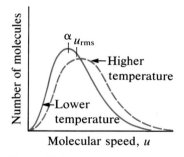

Figure 10.18

Molecular speed plotted against number of molecules of a gas at different temperatures.

10.16 Derivation of the Ideal Gas Equation from Kinetic-Molecular Theory

The mathematical expression of the ideal gas equation, $PV = nRT$, can be derived from the kinetic-molecular theory of gases. Consider N molecules, each having a mass m, confined within a cubical container as shown in Fig. 10.19, with an edge length of l centimeters. Although the molecules are moving in all possible directions, we may assume that $\frac{1}{3}$ of the molecules ($\frac{1}{3}N$) are moving in the direction of the x axis, $\frac{1}{3}$ in the direction of the y axis, and $\frac{1}{3}$ in the direction of the z axis. This assumption is valid because the motion of the molecules is entirely random and no particular direction is preferred.

Initially, let us assume that all molecules are moving with the same speed and consider the collisions of molecules with wall A (Fig. 10.19). A molecule, on the average, travels $2l$ centimeters between two consecutive collisions with wall A as it moves back and forth across the container. If the speed of the molecule is u centimeters per second, it will collide $u/2l$ times per second with wall A. The collisions are perfectly elastic, so the molecule will rebound with a speed of $-u$, having lost no kinetic energy as a result of the collision. Because momentum is defined as the product of mass and speed, the average momentum before a collision is mu and after a collision is $-mu$. Thus the average change in momentum per molecule per collision is $2mu$. There are $u/2l$ collisions per second, making the average change in momentum per molecule per second

$$2mu \times \frac{u}{2l} = \frac{mu^2}{l}$$

The total change in momentum per second for the $N/3$ molecules that can collide with wall A is

$$\frac{N}{3} \times \frac{mu^2}{l}$$

This is the average force on wall A, because force is equal to change of momentum per second. Pressure is force per unit area. Because the area of A is l^2, the pressure P on A is

$$P = \frac{\text{force}}{\text{area}} = \frac{1}{l^2} \times \frac{N}{3} \times \frac{mu^2}{l} = \frac{N}{3} \times \frac{mu^2}{l^3}$$

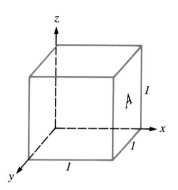

Figure 10.19

Drawing illustrating the container used in the derivation of the ideal gas equation from the kinetic-molecular theory.

However, l^3 is equal to the volume V of the cubical container; thus we have

$$P = \frac{N}{3} \times \frac{mu^2}{V}$$

or

$$PV = \tfrac{1}{3}Nmu^2$$

Actually, molecules move with different speeds, so we must use the average of the squares of their speeds. Thus

$$PV = \tfrac{1}{3}Nm(u^2)_{avg}$$

This is the fundamental equation of the kinetic-molecular theory of gases. It describes the behavior of an ideal gas exactly, and it is a very good approximation for the behavior of real gases at ordinary pressures.

The equation also may be written as follows:

$$PV = \tfrac{2}{3}N[\tfrac{1}{2}m(u^2)_{avg}]$$

The term in the set of brackets, $\tfrac{1}{2}m(u^2)_{avg}$, is the expression for the average kinetic energy of the gas, KE_{avg} (Section 10.14, Part 4). Thus

$$PV = \tfrac{2}{3}N(KE_{avg})$$

The average kinetic energy of the molecules, KE_{avg}, is directly proportional to the Kelvin temperature, T.

$$KE_{avg} = kT$$

The number of molecules, N, is proportional to the number of moles of molecules, n.

$$N = k'n$$

Substituting the expressions for KE_{avg} and N in the equation for PV gives

$$PV = \tfrac{2}{3}(k'n)(kT) = n(\tfrac{2}{3}k'k)T$$

The expression $\tfrac{2}{3}k'k$ is the constant (being made up entirely of constants) that we write as R and call the gas constant. Therefore,

$$PV = nRT$$

Thus, from the assumptions of the kinetic-molecular theory (Section 10.13), we can derive the ideal gas equation. Because this equation describes the behavior of gases very well, the assumptions used in its derivation are strongly supported.

⑩.17 Deviations from Ideal Gas Behavior

When a gas at ordinary temperature and pressure is compressed, the volume is reduced as the molecules are crowded closer together. This reduction in volume is really a reduction in the amount of empty space between the molecules. At high pressures the molecules are crowded so close together that the actual volume of the molecules—the molecular volume—is a relatively large fraction of the total volume, including the empty space between molecules. Because the molecules themselves cannot be compressed, only a fraction of the entire volume is affected by a further increase in pressure. Thus at very high pressures the whole volume is not inversely proportional to the pressure, as predicted by Boyle's law. However, even at moderately high pressures, most of the volume is empty space and is not occupied by molecules.

The molecules in a real gas at relatively low pressures have practically no attraction for one another because they are far apart. Thus they behave almost like molecules of ideal gases. However, as the molecules are crowded closer together at high pressures, the force of attraction between the molecules increases. This attraction has the same effect as an increase in external pressure. Consequently, when external pressure is applied to a volume of gas, especially at low temperatures, there is a slightly greater decrease in volume than should be achieved by the pressure alone. This slightly greater decrease in volume caused by intermolecular attraction is more pronounced at low temperatures because the molecules move more slowly, their kinetic energy is smaller relative to the attractive forces, and they fly apart less easily after collisions with one another.

In 1879 van der Waals expressed the deviations of real gases from the ideal gas laws quantitatively in what is now known as the **van der Waals equation:**

$$\left(P + \frac{n^2a}{V^2}\right)(V - nb) = nRT$$

The constant a represents the attraction between molecules, and van der Waals assumed that this force varies inversely as the square of the total volume of the gas. (See Sections 11.2 and 11.3 for a discussion of the nature of the van der Waals force.) Because this force augments the pressure and thus tends to make the volume smaller, it is added to the term P.

The term b in the equation represents the total volume of the molecules themselves and is subtracted from V, the total volume of the gas. When V is large, both nb and n^2a/V^2 are negligible, and the van der Waals equation reduces to the simple gas equation, $PV = nRT$.

At low pressures the correction for intermolecular attraction, a, is more important than the one for molecular volume, b. At high pressures and small volumes, the correction for the volume of the molecules becomes important, because the molecules themselves are incompressible and constitute an appreciable fraction of the total volume. At some intermediate pressure the two corrections cancel one another, and the gas appears to follow the relationship given by $PV = nRT$ over a small range of pressures.

Strictly speaking, then, the ideal gas equation applies exactly only to gases whose molecules do not attract one another and do not occupy an appreciable part of the whole volume. Because no real gases have these properties, we speak of such hypothetical gases as *ideal* gases. Under ordinary conditions, however, the deviations from the gas laws are so slight that they may be disregarded.

For Review

Summary

A gas takes the shape and volume of its container. Gases are readily compressible and capable of infinite expansion. The pressure of a gas may be expressed (in terms of force per unit area) in the SI units of **pascals** or **kilopascals.** Other units used for pressure include **torr** and **atmospheres** (1 atm = 760 torr = 101.325 kPa).

The behavior of gases can be described by a number of laws based on experimental observations of their properties. For example, the volume of a given quantity of a gas is inversely proportional to the pressure of the gas, provided that the temperature does not change **(Boyle's law)**. The volume of a given quantity of a gas is directly proportional to its temperature on the Kelvin scale, provided that the pressure does not change **(Charles's law)**. Gases react in simple proportions by volume **(Gay-Lussac's law)**, because under the same conditions of temperature and pressure, equal volumes of all gases contain the same number of molecules **(Avogadro's law)**. The rates of diffusion of gases are inversely proportional to the square roots of their densities or to the square roots of their molar masses **(Graham's law)**. In a mixture of gases the total pressure is equal to the sum of the partial pressures of the gases present. The **partial pressure** of a gas is the pressure that the gas would exert if it were the only gas present. The volumes and densities of gases are often reported under **standard conditions of temperature and pressure (STP)**: 0°C and 1 atmosphere.

The equations describing Boyle's law, Charles's law, and Avogadro's law are special cases of the **ideal gas equation,** $PV = nRT$, where P is the pressure of the gas, V is its volume, n is the number of moles of the gas, and T is its Kelvin temperature. R is the **gas constant.** The value we use for the gas constant when applying the equation depends on the units used for P and V.

The ideal gas equation has been derived for a gas that obeys the assumptions of the **kinetic-molecular theory** of gases. This theory assumes that gases consist of molecules of negligible volume, which are widely separated with no attraction between them. The molecules move randomly and change direction only when they collide with one another or with the walls of the container. These collisions are elastic. The pressure of a gas results from the bombardment of the walls of the container by its molecules. The average kinetic energy of the molecules is proportional to the temperature of the gas and is the same for all gases at a given temperature.

All molecules of a gas are not moving at the same speed at the same instant of time. Some move relatively slowly, others relatively rapidly. The speeds are distributed over a wide range. The average of the squares of the molecular speeds, $(u^2)_{avg}$, is directly proportional to the temperature of the gas on the Kelvin scale and inversely proportional to the masses of the individual molecules. Heating a gas increases both the value of $(u^2)_{avg}$ and the number of molecules moving at higher speeds. As shown by Graham's law, heavier molecules diffuse more slowly than lighter ones. Heavier molecules move more slowly, on the average.

The molecules in a real gas (in contrast to those in an ideal gas) possess a finite volume and attract each other slightly. At relatively low pressures the molecular volume can be neglected. At temperatures well above the temperature at which the gas liquefies, the attractions between molecules can be neglected. Under these conditions the ideal gas equation is a good approximation for the behavior of a real gas. However, at lower temperatures, higher pressures, or both, corrections for molecular volume and molecular attractions are required. The **van der Waals equation** can be used to describe the behavior of real gases under these conditions.

Key Terms and Concepts

absolute zero (10.5)
Avogadro's law (10.7)
barometer (10.2)
Boyle's law (10.3, 10.14)
Charles's law (10.4, 10.14)

Dalton's law (10.11, 10.14)
diffusion (10.1, 10.12, 10.14)
direct proportionality (10.4)
gas constant (10.8, 10.16)
Gay-Lussac's law (10.6, 10.7)

Graham's law (10.12, 10.14)
kinetic energy (10.14)
kinetic-molecular theory (10.13)
ideal gas (10.8, 10.13)
ideal gas equation (10.8, 10.16)

Exercises

Answers for selected even-numbered exercises marked by red numbers appear at the end of the book. The worked-out solutions to all even-numbered exercises appear in the *Solutions Guide*.

Pressure

1. Is the pressure of the gas in the hot air balloon shown at the opening of this chapter greater than, less than, or equal to that of the atmosphere outside the balloon?
2. What is the height of the mercury column shown in Fig. 10.3 when the air pressure is 95.3 kPa?
3. What is the height of the mercury in the manometer shown in Fig. 10.4 when the gas pressure is 0.0100 atm?
4. A typical barometric pressure in Kansas City is 740 torr. What is this pressure in atmospheres, in millimeters of mercury, and in kilopascals?
5. Canadian tire gauges are marked in units of kilopascals. What reading on such a gauge corresponds to 25.0 lb/in²? (1 atm = 14.7 lb/in²)
6. A medical laboratory catalog describes the pressure in a cylinder of a gas as 14.82 MPa. What is the pressure of this gas in atmospheres and in torr? (1 MPa = 10⁶ Pa)
7. Arrange the following gases in order of increasing pressure: H_2 at 250 torr, N_2 at 1.4 atm, O_2 at 98 kPa.
8. A biochemist adds carbon dioxide, CO_2, to an evacuated bulb like the one shown and stops when the difference in the heights h of the mercury columns is 3.56 cm. What is the pressure of CO_2 in the bulb in atmospheres? In kilopascals?

The Gas Laws

9. Using Boyle's law, set up a mathematical equation relating the initial volume, V_1, and the final volume, V_2, of a given quantity of an ideal gas at constant temperature as the pressure changes from the initial pressure, P_1, to the final pressure, P_2.
10. Determine the pressure of the gas in the container shown in Fig. 10.5 when its volume is 0.66 L (a) using Boyle's law and (b) using a graph of $1/P$ against V prepared from the data in the figure.
11. The volume of a sample of carbon monoxide, CO, is 405 mL at 10.0 atm and 467 K. What volume will it occupy at 4.29 atm and 467 K?
12. The volume of a sample of acetylene, C_2H_2, is 1.86 L at 831 torr and 27°C. What volume will it occupy at 27°C and 477 torr?
13. A sample of oxygen, O_2, occupies 32.2 mL at 0°C and 917 torr. What volume will it occupy at 0°C and 760 torr?
14. When filled with air, a typical 13.2-L scuba tank has a pressure of 153 atm. How many liters of air at 0.950 atm will such a scuba tank provide, assuming no change in temperature?
15. A cylinder of oxygen for medical use contains 35.4 L of oxygen at a pressure of 149.6 atm. What is the volume of this oxygen, in liters, at 1.00 atm of pressure and the same temperature?
16. Using Charles's law, set up a mathematical equation relating the initial volume V_1 and temperature T_1 of a given quantity of an ideal gas at constant pressure to some other volume V_2 and temperature T_2.
17. Determine the volume of 1 mol of N_2 gas at 500 K and 1 atm, using Fig. 10.8.
18. What is the volume of a sample of ethane at 467 K and 1.1 atm if it occupies 405 mL at 298 K and 1.1 atm?
19. What is the volume of a sample of carbon monoxide, CO, at 3°C and 744 torr if it occupies 13.3 L at 55°C and 744 torr?
20. The gas in a 1.00-L bottle at 25°C can be put into a 1-qt (0.946-L) bottle at the same pressure if the temperature is reduced. What temperature is required?
21. A 2.50-L volume of hydrogen measured at the normal boiling point of nitrogen, −196°C, is warmed to the normal boiling point of water, 100°C. Calculate the new volume of the gas, assuming ideal behavior and no change in pressure.
22. A gas occupies 275 mL at 67°C and 380 Pa. What final

temperature would be required to decrease the pressure to 305 Pa if the volume were held constant?

23. A high-altitude balloon is filled with 1.41×10^4 L of hydrogen at a temperature of 21°C and a pressure of 745 torr. What is the volume of the balloon at a height of 20 km, where the temperature is −48°C and the pressure is 63.1 torr?

24. If the CO_2 in the bulb in Exercise 8 is warmed from 21.2°C to 35.2°C, what will be the height h of the mercury column? Ignore the change in volume that is due to the motion of the mercury; in other words, assume that the volume remains constant.

25. A spray can is used until it is empty except for the propellant gas, which has a pressure of 1.1 atm at 23°C. If the can is thrown into a fire ($T = 475°C$), what will be the pressure in the hot can?

The Ideal Gas Equation

26. In addition to the data found in Fig. 10.9, what data do we need to find the mass of the sample of He used to determine the line for He in the figure?

27. Assume the pressure is 0.917 atm, and determine how many moles of CH_4 are contained in the sample of gas used to gather data for Fig. 10.9.

28. Assume the pressure is 0.917 atm, and determine how many grams of N_2O are contained in the sample of gas used to gather data for Fig. 10.9.

29. How would Fig. 10.6(a) change if the number of moles of gas in the sample used to determine the curve were doubled?

30. How would Figure 10.6(b) change if the number of moles of gas in the sample used to determine the curve were reduced by half?

31. How many moles of hydrogen sulfide, H_2S, are contained in a 327.2-mL bulb at 48.1°C if the pressure is 149.3 kPa?

32. How many moles of chlorine gas, Cl_2, are contained in a 10.3-L tank at 21.2°C if the pressure is 633 torr?

33. How many moles of oxygen gas, O_2, are contained in a cylinder of medical oxygen with a volume of 35.4 L, a pressure of 149 atm, and a temperature of 19.5°C?

34. A small cylinder of helium for use in chemistry lectures has a volume of 334 mL. How many moles of helium are contained in such a cylinder at a pressure of 154 atm and a temperature of 23°C?

35. Say the gas in Fig. 10.5 is carbon dioxide. What is the mass of gas in the container if the temperature is 23°C?

36. What is the temperature of a 0.274-g sample of methane, CH_4, confined in a 300.0-mL bulb at a pressure of 198.7 kPa?

37. What is the volume of a bulb that contains 8.17 g of neon at 13°C and a pressure of 8.73 atm?

38. Assume that 1.000 lb (453.6 g) of dry ice (solid CO_2) is placed in an evacuated 2.00-L bottle. What is the pressure in the bottle, in atmospheres, at a temperature of 45°C after all the $CO_2(s)$ has been converted to gas?

39. How many grams of gas are present in each of the following cases?
    (a) 0.100 L of NO at 703 torr and 62°C
    (b) 8.75 L of CH_4 at 278.3 kPa and 843 K
    (c) 73.3 mL of I_2 at 0.462 atm and 125°C
    (d) 4341 L of BF_3 at 2.22 atm and 788 K
    (e) 221 mL of Ne at 0.23 torr and −54°C

40. Calculate the volume in liters of each of the following quantities of gas at STP.
    (a) 6.72 g of C_2H_2 (d) 0.720 mol of BF_3
    (b) 0.588 g of NH_3 (e) 13.5 mol of SO_2
    (c) 1.47 kg of C_2H_6 (f) 0.027 mol of PH_3

41. (a) What mass of nitrosyl chloride, NOCl, occupies a volume of 0.250 L at a temperature of 325 K and a pressure of 113.0 kPa?
    (b) What is the density of NOCl under these conditions?

42. Calculate the density of fluorine gas, F_2, at STP and at 30.0°C and 725 torr.

43. Calculate the density of Freon 12, CF_2Cl_2, at 30.0°C and 0.954 atm.

44. Calculate the density of nitrogen, N_2, at a temperature of 273 K and a pressure of 101.3 kPa.

45. (a) What is the concentration of the atmosphere in molecules per milliliter at STP?
    (b) At a height of 150 km (about 94 mi), the atmospheric pressure is about 3.0×10^{-6} torr and the temperature is 420 K. What is the concentration of the atmosphere in molecules per milliliter at 150 km?

Dalton's Law of Partial Pressures

46. If all three of the gases in Fig. 10.11 were placed together in a 22.4-L container at 0°C, what would the pressure be if no reaction occurred?

47. A cylinder of a gas used for calibration of blood gas analyzers in medical laboratories contains 5.0% CO_2, 12.0% O_2, and the remainder N_2 at a total pressure of 146 atm. What is the partial pressure of each component of this gas? (The percentages given indicate the percent of the total pressure that is due to each component.)

48. Most mixtures of hydrogen gas with oxygen gas are explosive. However, a mixture that contains less than 3.0% O_2 is not. If enough O_2 is added to a cylinder of H_2 at 33.2 atm to bring the total pressure to 34.5 atm, is the mixture explosive?

49. A 5.73-L flask at 25°C contains 0.0388 mol of N_2, 0.147 mol of CO, and 0.0803 mol of H_2. What is the pressure in the flask in atmospheres, in torr, and in kilopascals?

50. A mixture of 0.200 g of H_2, 1.00 g of N_2, and 0.820 g of Ar is stored in a closed container at STP. Find the volume of the container, assuming that the gases exhibit ideal behavior.

51. A sample of carbon monoxide was collected over water at a

total pressure of 764 torr and a temperature of 23°C. What is the pressure of the carbon monoxide? (See Table 10.1 for the vapor pressure of water.)

52. A sample of oxygen collected over water at a temperature of 29.0°C and a pressure of 764 torr has a volume of 0.560 L. What volume would the dry oxygen have under the same conditions of temperature and pressure?

53. The volume of a sample of a gas collected over water at 32.0°C and 752 torr is 627 mL. What will the volume of the gas be when it is dried and measured at STP?

54. A 265-mL sample of gaseous nitric oxide, NO, was collected over mercury at 19°C and 714.0 torr. If the same sample of nitric oxide were collected over water at 19°C and 714.0 torr, what would its volume be? (The vapor pressure of mercury is negligible.)

55. Which is denser at the same temperature and pressure, dry air or air saturated with water vapor? Explain.

Combining Volumes; Molecular Masses; Applied Stoichiometry

56. What volume of O_2 at STP is required to oxidize 14.0 L of CO at STP to CO_2? What volume of CO_2 is produced at STP?

57. Methanol (sometimes called wood alcohol), CH_3OH, is produced industrially by the following reaction:

$$CO(g) + 2H_2(g) \xrightarrow[\text{300°C, 300 atm}]{\text{Copper catalyst}} CH_3OH(g)$$

Assuming that the gases behave as ideal gases, find the ratio of the total volume of the reactants to the final volume.

58. Calculate the volume of oxygen required to burn 4.00 L of propane gas, C_3H_8, to produce carbon dioxide and water, if the volumes of both the propane and the oxygen are measured under the same conditions of temperature and pressure.

59. A 2.50-L sample of a colorless gas at STP decomposed to give 2.50 L of N_2 and 1.25 L of O_2 at STP. What is the colorless gas?

60. An acetylene tank for an oxyacetylene welding torch provides 9340 L of acetylene gas, C_2H_2, at STP. How many tanks of oxygen, each providing 7.00×10^3 L of O_2 at STP, will be required to burn the acetylene?

$$2C_2H_2 + 5O_2 \longrightarrow 4CO_2 + 2H_2O$$

61. How could you show by experiment that the molecular formula of acetylene is C_2H_2, not CH?

62. What is the molar mass of methylamine if 0.157 g of methylamine gas occupies 125 mL with a pressure of 99.5 kPa at 22°C?

63. In 1894 one of the noble gases of Group VIIIA was first isolated by allowing a large volume of air to react with magnesium so that only the noble gas, contaminated with traces

of other noble gases, remained. A 32-mL sample of this gas weighs 0.054 g at 9°C and 748 torr. Determine the apparent atomic mass of this monatomic gas. (The traces of other gases are negligible.) Which noble gas is it?

64. A sample of an oxide of nitrogen isolated from the exhaust of an automobile was found to weigh 0.571 g and to occupy 1.00 L at 356 torr and 27°C. Calculate the molar mass of this oxide, and determine whether it was NO, NO_2, or N_2O_5.

65. The density of a certain gaseous fluoride of phosphorus is 3.93 g/L at STP. Calculate the molar mass of this fluoride, and determine its molecular formula.

66. Cyclopropane, a gas containing only carbon and hydrogen, is often used as an anesthetic for major surgery. Taking into account that 0.45 L of cyclopropane at 120°C and 0.72 atm reacts with O_2 to give 1.35 L of CO_2 and 1.35 L of $H_2O(g)$ at the same temperature and pressure, determine the molecular formula of cyclopropane.

67. Joseph Priestley first prepared pure oxygen by heating mercuric oxide, HgO.

$$2HgO(s) \xrightarrow{\triangle} 2Hg(l) + O_2(g)$$

What volume of O_2 at 15°C and 0.980 atm is produced by the decomposition of 2.36 g of HgO?

68. Cavendish prepared hydrogen in 1766 by the rather quaint method of passing steam through a red-hot gun barrel.

$$4H_2O(g) + 3Fe(s) \xrightarrow{\triangle} Fe_3O_4(s) + 4H_2(g)$$

What volume of H_2 at a pressure of 783 torr and a temperature of 21°C can be prepared from the reaction of 10.0 g of H_2O?

69. Hydrogen gas will reduce Fe_3O_4 in the reverse of the reaction shown in Exercise 68.
   (a) What volume of H_2 at 195 atm and 35°C is required to reduce 1.00 metric ton of Fe_3O_4 to Fe? (1 metric ton = 1000 kg)
   (b) If the reduction is run at 500°C and 1.0 atm, what volume of water vapor is produced?

70. Gaseous hydrogen chloride, $HCl(g)$, is prepared commercially by the reaction of NaCl with H_2SO_4 (Section 2.12, Part 1). What mass of NaCl is required to prepare enough $HCl(g)$ to fill a 35.4-L cylinder to a pressure of 125 atm at 0°C?

71. If the oxygen consumed by a resting human male (Section 10.8, Example 10.10) is used to produce energy via the oxidation of glucose,

$$C_6H_{12}O_6 + 6O_2 \longrightarrow 6CO_2 + 6H_2O$$

what is the mass of glucose required per hour for a resting 70-kg male?

72. Sulfur dioxide is an intermediate in the preparation of sulfuric acid (Section 2.12). What volume of SO_2 at 343°C and 1.21 atm is produced by the combustion of 1.00 kg of sulfur?

73. What volume of oxygen at 423.0 K and a pressure of 127.4 kPa is produced by the decomposition of 129.7 g of BaO_2 to BaO and O_2?

74. In a laboratory experiment, $KClO_3$ is decomposed by heating to give KCl and O_2. What mass of $KClO_3$ must be decomposed to give 638 mL of O_2 at a temperature of 18°C and a pressure of 752 torr?

75. In a laboratory determination, a 0.1009-g sample of a compound containing boron and chlorine gave 0.3544 g of silver chloride upon reaction with silver nitrate. A 0.06237-g sample of the compound exerted a pressure of 6.52 kPa at 27°C in a volume of 147 mL. What is the molecular formula of the compound?

76. As 1 g of the radioactive element radium decays over 1 year, it produces 1.16×10^{18} alpha particles (helium nuclei). Each alpha particle becomes an atom of helium gas. What volume of helium gas at a pressure of 56.0 kPa and a temperature of 25°C is produced?

Kinetic-Molecular Theory; Graham's Law

77. Using the postulates of the kinetic-molecular theory, explain why a gas uniformly fills a container of any shape.

78. Show how Boyle's law, Charles's law, and Dalton's law follow from the assumptions of the kinetic-molecular theory.

79. Describe what happens to the average kinetic energy of ideal gas molecules when the conditions are changed as follows:
    (a) The pressure of the gas is increased by decreasing the volume at constant temperature.
    (b) The pressure of the gas is increased by increasing the temperature at constant volume.
    (c) The average velocity of the molecules is increased by a factor of 2.

80. Can the speed of a given molecule in a gas double at constant temperature? Explain your answer.

81. What is the ratio of the kinetic energy of a helium atom to that of a hydrogen molecule in a mixture of two gases? What is the ratio of the root-mean-square speeds, u_{rms}, of the two gases?

82. A 1-L sample of CO initially at STP is heated to 546°C, and its volume is increased to 2 L.
    (a) What effect do these changes have on the number of collisions of the molecules of the gas per unit area of the container wall?
    (b) What is the effect on the average kinetic energy of the molecules?
    (c) What is the effect on the root-mean-square speed of the molecules?

83. The root-mean-square speed of H_2 molecules at 25°C is about 1.6 km/s. What is the root-mean-square speed of a CH_4 molecule at 25°C?

84. Show that the ratio of the rate of diffusion of Gas 1 to the rate of diffusion of Gas 2, R_1/R_2, is the same at 0°C and 100°C.

85. Heavy water, D_2O (mol. mass = 20.03), can be separated from ordinary water, H_2O (mol. mass = 18.01), as a result of the difference in the relative rates of diffusion of the molecules in the gas phase. Calculate the relative rates of diffusion of H_2O and D_2O.

86. Which of the following gases diffuse more slowly than oxygen? F_2, Ne, N_2O, C_2H_2, NO, Cl_2, H_2S

87. Calculate the relative rate of diffusion of HF compared to that of HCl and the relative rate of diffusion of O_2 compared to that of O_3.

88. A gas of unknown identity diffuses at the rate of 83.3 mL s^{-1} in a diffusion apparatus in which carbon dioxide diffuses at the rate of 102 mL s^{-1}. Calculate the molecular mass of the unknown gas.

89. (a) When two cotton plugs, one moistened with ammonia and the other with hydrochloric acid, are simultaneously inserted into opposite ends of a glass tube 87.0 cm long, a white ring of NH_4Cl forms where gaseous NH_3 and gaseous HCl first come into contact.

$$NH_3(g) + HCl(g) \longrightarrow NH_4Cl(s)$$

At what distance from the ammonia-moistened plug does this occur?

(b) A student is trying to identify an amine that is one of three possible compounds: CH_3NH_2, $(CH_3)_2NH$, or $(CH_3)_3N$. In this case, a white ring due to the amine hydrochloride forms at a distance of 41.2 cm from the amine-moistened plug. What is the correct formula for the amine?

Nonideal Behavior of Gases

90. Graphs showing the behavior of several different gases follow. Which of these gases exhibit behavior significantly different from that expected for ideal gases?

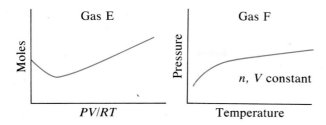

91. Describe the factors responsible for the deviation of the behavior of real gases from that of an ideal gas.
92. Under which of the following sets of conditions does a real gas behave most like an ideal gas, and for which conditions is a real gas expected to deviate from ideal behavior? Explain.
    (a) High pressure, small volume
    (b) High temperature, low pressure
    (c) Low temperature, high pressure
93. For which of the following gases should the correction for the molecular volume be largest? CO, CO_2, H_2, He, NH_3, SF_6

Additional Exercises

94. For 1 mol of H_2 showing ideal gas behavior, draw labeled graphs of:
    (a) the variation of P with V at $T = 273$ K
    (b) the variation of V with T at $P = 1.00$ atm
    (c) the variation of P with T at $V = 22.4$ L
    (d) the variation of the average velocity of the gas molecules with T
    (e) the variation of $1/P$ with V at $T = 273$ K
95. Figure 10.10 shows a greatly magnified view of a sample of gas that contains 8 molecules of hydrogen gas. What is the volume of a container that contains 8 hydrogen molecules at a pressure found in one of the best vacuum chambers on earth, 1.0×10^{-10} torr?
96. What is the temperature of the water if the partial pressure of the gas contained in the bottle shown in Fig. 10.13 is 730 torr?
97. A liter of methane gas, CH_4, at STP contains more atoms of hydrogen than does a liter of pure hydrogen gas, H_2, at STP. Using Avogadro's law as a starting point, explain why.
98. A commercial mercury vapor analyzer can detect, in air, concentrations of gaseous Hg atoms (which are poisonous) as low as 2×10^{-3} mg/m³ of air (1 m³ = 1000 L). What is the partial pressure of gaseous mercury if the atmospheric pressure is 755 torr at 21°C?
99. (a) What is the total volume of the $CO_2(g)$ and $H_2O(g)$ at 600°C and 735 torr produced by the combustion of 1.00 L of $C_3H_8(g)$ measured at STP?
    (b) What is the partial pressure of CO_2 in the product gases?
100. Butene, an important petrochemical used in the production of synthetic rubber, is composed of carbon and hydrogen. A 0.0124-g sample of this compound produces 0.0390 g of CO_2 and 0.0159 g of H_2O when burned in an oxygen atmosphere. If the volume of a 0.125-g gaseous sample of the compound at 735 torr and 45°C is 60.2 mL, what is the molecular formula of the compound?
101. Ethanol, C_2H_5OH, is produced industrially from ethylene, C_2H_4, by the following sequence of reactions:

$$3C_2H_4 + 2H_2SO_4 \longrightarrow C_2H_5HSO_4 + (C_2H_5)_2SO_4$$

$$C_2H_5HSO_4 + (C_2H_5)_2SO_4 + 3H_2O \longrightarrow$$
$$3C_2H_5OH + 2H_2SO_4$$

What volume of ethylene at STP is required to produce 1.000 metric ton (1000 kg) of ethanol if the overall yield of ethanol is 90.1%?
102. Thin films of amorphous silicon for electronic applications are prepared by decomposing silane gas, SiH_4, on a hot surface at low pressures.

$$SiH_4(g) \xrightarrow{\triangle} Si(s) + 2H_2(g)$$

What volume of SiH_4 at 130 Pa and 800 K is required to produce a 10.0-cm-by-10.0-cm film that is 200 Å thick? (1 Å = 10^{-8} cm.) The density of amorphous silicon is 1.9 g/cm³.
103. One molecule of hemoglobin will combine with four molecules of oxygen. If 1.0 g of hemoglobin combines with 1.53 mL of oxygen at body temperature (37°C) and a pressure of 743 torr, what is the molar mass of hemoglobin?
104. Ethanol, C_2H_5OH, is often produced by the fermentation of sugars. For example, the preparation of ethanol from the sugar glucose is represented by the equation

$$C_6H_{12}O_6(aq) \xrightarrow{\text{Yeast}} 2C_2H_5OH(aq) + 2CO_2(g)$$

What volume of CO_2 at STP is produced by the fermentation of 125 g of glucose if the reaction has a yield of 97.5%?
105. One method of analyzing amino acids is the van Slyke method. The characteristic amino groups (—NH_2) in protein material are allowed to react with nitrous acid, HNO_2, to form N_2 gas. From the volume of the gas, the amount of amino acid can be determined. A 0.0604-g sample of a biological sample containing glycine, $CH_2(NH_2)COOH$, was analyzed by the van Slyke method and yielded 3.70 mL of N_2 collected over water at a pressure of 735 torr and 29°C. What was the percentage of glycine in the sample?

$$CH_2(NH_2)COOH + HNO_2 \longrightarrow$$
$$CH_2(OH)COOH + H_2O + N_2$$

106. Natural gas often contains hydrogen sulfide, H_2S, a gas that is itself a pollutant and that produces another pollutant, sulfur dioxide, upon combustion. Hydrogen sulfide is removed from raw natural gas by the reaction

$$HOC_2H_4NH_2 + H_2S \longrightarrow (HOC_2H_4NH_3)HS$$

How much ethanolamine, $HOC_2H_4NH_2$, is required to remove the H_2S from 1.00×10^3 ft³ of natural gas at STP if the partial pressure of H_2S is 233 Pa? (1 ft³ = 28.3 L)

107. One step in the production of sulfuric acid (Section 2.12) involves oxidation of $SO_2(g)$ to $SO_3(g)$, using air at 400°C with vanadium(V) oxide as a catalyst. Assuming that air is 21% oxygen by volume, determine what volume of air at 19°C and 754 torr is required to produce enough SO_3 to give 1.00 metric ton of sulfuric acid, H_2SO_4. (1 metric ton = 1000 kg)

108. A sample of a compound of xenon and fluorine was confined in a bulb with a pressure of 18 torr. Hydrogen was added to the bulb until the pressure was 72 torr. Passage of an electric spark through the mixture produced Xe and HF. After the HF was removed by reaction with solid KOH, the final pressure of xenon and unreacted hydrogen in the bulb was 54 torr. What is the empirical formula of the xenon fluoride in the original sample? (*Note:* Xenon fluorides contain only one xenon atom per molecule.)

109. A 0.250-L bottle contains 75.0 mL of a 3.0% by mass solution of hydrogen peroxide. How much will the pressure (in torr) in the bottle increase if the H_2O_2 decomposes to $H_2O(l)$ and $O_2(g)$ at 34°C? Assume that the density of the solution is 1.00 g/cm^3 and that the volume of the liquid does not change during the decomposition.

110. The pressure in a sample of hydrogen collected above water in a 425-mL bottle at 35°C is 763 torr. Find the volume of the sample when the temperature falls to 23°C, assuming its pressure does not change.

11 Intermolecular Forces, Liquids, and Solids

Molten lava solidifies when it flows into the ocean and cools.

A gaseous substance occupies a much larger volume than the same mass of the substance as a solid or a liquid. For example, 44 grams of dry ice (1 mole of solid CO_2) has a volume of 26 milliliters, a volume about the size of a golf ball. The volume of 44 grams of liquid CO_2 is only 40 milliliters. If 44 grams of dry ice is placed in an empty balloon at 25°C and 1 atmosphere and is allowed to warm and form a gas, the balloon expands to a volume of about 25,000 milliliters, the volume of a beachball with a diameter of about 14 inches. This is an increase of almost 1000 times from the volume of the solid to the volume of the gas. Because of their small volumes relative to the volume of the gas phase, liquids and solids are often called **condensed phases.**

Liquids and solids are familiar forms of matter that exhibit many differing properties. We know that liquids flow and assume the shape of any container into which they are poured. We also know that solids are rigid. Many liquids evaporate; most solids do not. However, in spite of the apparent differences in their behavior, many of the properties of both liquids and solids are similar. For example, solids and liquids are both essentially incompressible; we cannot change the volume of a sample of ice or liquid water by pressing on it. Both solid and liquid CO_2 occupy a much smaller volume than gaseous CO_2. Both can be used for refrigeration: When either liquid or solid CO_2 is converted to a gas, heat is absorbed and the surroundings are cooled.

The similarities and differences in the behavior of liquids and solids can be explained in terms of the same kinetic-molecular theory that we used to describe the properties of gases (Section 10.13). In this chapter we will explore their behavior and examine how the kinetic-molecular theory can help us to understand these properties. The forces that cause molecules to form liquids or solids will be examined as well as the regularities in structure that result when atoms, molecules, or ions arrange themselves into crystalline materials.

⓫.1 Kinetic-Molecular Theory: Liquids and Solids

When we studied gases, we saw that their molecules are in constant motion and that, in general, the empty space between the molecules is large compared to the sizes of the molecules themselves (Section 10.13). As a consequence of their motion, gas molecules possess a kinetic energy that overcomes the forces of attraction between them. However, as a gas is cooled, the average speed and kinetic energy of the molecules decrease. When the gas is cooled sufficiently, intermolecular attractions prevent the molecules from moving apart, the gas condenses, and the molecules come into constant contact. This condensation produces either a liquid or a solid. You have probably seen liquid water form on a cold glass or soft drink can as the water vapor in the air is cooled by the cold glass or can. The frost that forms in a freezer and during some winter nights (Fig. 11.1) results when water vapor comes in contact with a very cold surface and is converted directly to solid water without going through the liquid phase.

Increased pressure also brings the molecules of a gas closer together such that the attractions between the molecules become strong relative to their kinetic energy. Gases can be liquefied by compression if the temperature is not too high. Carbon dioxide is a gas at room temperature and 1 atmosphere, but it generally is a liquid in CO_2 fire extinguishers because the pressure is greater than about 65 atmospheres. At this pressure, gaseous carbon dioxide condenses to a liquid at room temperature.

Although the molecules in a liquid are in contact, they still move about. Thus a liquid can change its shape, take the shape of its container, evaporate, and diffuse. However, because of the much shorter distances that molecules in a liquid can move before they collide with other molecules, they diffuse much more slowly than in gases. Liquids are relatively incompressible, because an increase in pressure can only slightly reduce the distance between the closely packed molecules. Thus the volume of a liquid decreases very little with increased pressure.

It is difficult to describe the arrangement of molecules in a liquid because it changes from moment to moment as the molecules move. We can only say that the molecules that make up a liquid are relatively closely packed in a random arrangement.

Figure 11.1

Frost forms when water vapor in the air is cooled and is converted directly to ice.

When the temperature of a liquid becomes sufficiently low, or the pressure on the liquid becomes sufficiently high, the molecules of the liquid no longer have enough kinetic energy to move past each other, and a solid is formed. Solids are rigid. They cannot expand like gases or be poured like liquids because the molecules cannot change position easily.

The molecules in a solid are not still. Although most molecules in a solid do not move about, they do vibrate. Diffusion takes place to a very limited extent in the solid state, and some solids even evaporate. You may have seen dry ice (solid carbon dioxide) evaporate without melting. You can smell moth balls and solid room deodorants, because these solids slowly evaporate and the gaseous molecules can be detected by their odor. As the temperature of a solid is lowered, the motion of the molecules gradually decreases to a minimum at 0 kelvin (absolute zero).

The evaporation of liquids and solids can be explained in terms of the kinetic-molecular theory. In a liquid, just as in a gas, the molecules move randomly—some slowly, many at intermediate rates, and some very rapidly. A few rapidly moving molecules near the surface of the liquid may possess enough kinetic energy to overcome the attraction of their neighbors and escape—that is, evaporate—into the gas above the liquid (Fig. 11.2), becoming molecules in the gas phase. Although the molecules in a solid do not move through the solid, they do vibrate—some gently, many with intermediate energy, and some wildly. A few wildly vibrating molecules on the surface of some solids may possess enough energy to overcome the attraction of their neighbors and escape into the gas phase.

A comparison of gases, liquids, and crystalline solids based on the kinetic-molecular model of the behavior of their molecules is presented in Fig. 11.3.

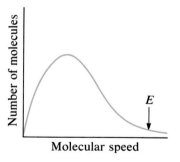

Figure 11.2

Distribution of molecular speeds in a liquid. Molecules with speeds greater than E possess sufficient kinetic energy to escape from the surface of the liquid into the gas phase.

Forces Between Molecules

Under appropriate conditions, the attractions between all gas molecules can cause them to form liquids or solids. The strengths of these attractive forces vary widely, though usually the *inter*molecular forces between small molecules are weak compared to the *intra*molecular forces that bond atoms together within a molecule. For example, to overcome the intermolecular forces in a mole of liquid HCl and convert it to gaseous HCl requires only about 17 kilojoules. However, to break a mole of the bonds between

Gas — Widely separated, disordered molecules in continuous motion.

Cool or increase pressure / Heat or decrease pressure

Liquid — Closely spaced, disordered molecules in continuous motion.

Cool / Heat

Crystalline solid — Ordered molecules in contact and in relatively fixed positions.

Figure 11.3

The arrangement of molecules in a gas, a liquid, and a crystalline solid. The density of the gaseous molecules is exaggerated for the purpose of illustration.

Figure 11.4

Two arrangements of polar molecules
that allow an attraction between the
negative end of one molecule and the
positive end of another.

(a)   (b)

the hydrogen and chlorine atoms in hydrogen chloride requires about 25 times more energy, or 430 kilojoules.

The attractive forces between molecules, which are collectively called **van der Waals forces,** are electrical in nature and result from the attraction of charges of opposite sign. In the next sections we shall consider the various intermolecular forces that form liquids or solids.

⓫.2 Dipole–Dipole and Ion–Dipole Attractions

One type of van der Waals force is a **dipole–dipole attraction,** an attractive force that results from the electrostatic attraction of the positive end of one polar molecule (Section 8.3) for the negative end of another (Fig. 11.4). The ICl molecule is a polar molecule with a dipole. The more electronegative chlorine atom bears a partial negative charge, whereas the less electronegative iodine atom bears a partial positive charge. The dipole–dipole attraction of the positive end of one ICl molecule for the negative end of another causes ICl molecules to attract each other.

The effect of the dipole–dipole attraction in ICl is apparent when we compare the properties of ICl molecules to nonpolar Br_2 molecules. ICl is a solid at $0°C$, Br_2 is a liquid. Both ICl and Br_2 have the same number of atoms and approximately the same molecular mass. At $0°C$, in the gas phase, both molecules would have approximately the same kinetic energy. However, the dipole–dipole attractions between ICl molecules are sufficient to cause them to form a solid, whereas the intermolecular attraction between nonpolar Br_2 molecules are not.

Molecules with a dipole are attracted to ions as well as to other polar molecules. The electrostatic attraction between an ion and a molecule with a dipole is called an **ion–dipole attraction.** The stability of $CaCl_2 \cdot 6H_2O$ is due in part to the ion–dipole attraction of the positive calcium ion for the negative ends of the water molecules. Ion–dipole attractions also play an important role in the dissolution of ionic compounds in polar solvents (Section 12.8).

⓫.3 Dispersion Forces

A third component of the van der Waals attractions is called the **London dispersion force** (after Fritz London, who in 1928 first explained it). Dispersion forces cause nonpolar substances such as Br_2, the other halogens, and the noble gases to condense to liquids and to freeze into solids when the temperature is lowered sufficiently.

Because of the constant motion of its electrons, an atom can develop a temporary dipole moment. A second atom, in turn, can be distorted by the appearance of the dipole

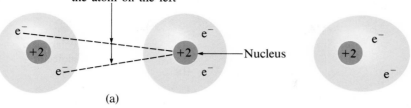

Attractive forces will distort
the atom on the left

Nucleus

(a)

(b)

Figure 11.5

A representation of the formation of
the temporary dipoles that give rise
to dispersion forces. The temporary
dipole in the atom on the right in
(a) produces a dipole in the atom on
the left. The attraction of the two
resulting dipoles (b) produces the attractive force.

in the first atom. Its nucleus is attracted toward the negative end of the first atom (Fig.
11.5). Thus a negative end on the second atom is formed away from the negative end of
the first atom, and the two rapidly fluctuating, temporary dipoles attract each other.
Dispersion forces are the result of these attractions. If the two atoms are located in
different molecules, the two molecules are attracted to each other.

Dispersion forces between molecules are present when any two molecules are close
together. The forces between the atoms are weak, however, and become significant only
when the atoms are almost touching. Although the principal forces that stabilize a liquid
or solid may be due to dipole–dipole or other attractive forces, dispersion forces always
play some role in their stability.

Larger and heavier atoms and molecules exhibit stronger dispersion forces than
smaller and lighter atoms and molecules. F_2 and Cl_2 are gases at room temperature, Br_2
is a liquid, and I_2 is a solid. In this group the attractive forces become stronger as the
atoms and molecules involved become larger (from F_2 to I_2). The effect of size is readily
explained by London's theory. In a larger atom the valence electrons are, on the average, farther from the nuclei than in a smaller atom. Thus they are less tightly held and
can more easily form the temporary dipoles that produce the attraction.

The shapes of molecules also affect the magnitudes of the dispersion forces between
them. For example, *n*-pentane [Fig. 11.6(a)] is a liquid at room temperature, whereas
*neo*pentane [Fig. 11.6(b)] is a gas. Thus the dispersion forces in *n*-pentane are larger

(a)

(b)

Figure 11.6

The ball-and-stick molecular models
and Lewis structures of (a) *n*-pentane
and (b) *neo*pentane.

Figure 11.7

(a) The spherical charge distribution in a krypton atom and the distortion caused (b) by an ion and (c) by a polar molecule.

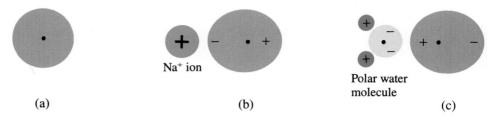

Na⁺ ion

Polar water molecule

(a)   (b)   (c)

than those in *neo*pentane, even though both compounds are composed of molecules with the same chemical formula, C_5H_{12}. The *neo*pentane molecule is shaped in such a way that the valence electrons in the carbon–carbon bonds are well inside the molecule. The *n*-pentane molecule is shaped in such a way that the valence electrons in the carbon–carbon bonds are closer to the surface of the molecule. Thus any dispersion forces that involve electrons participating in carbon–carbon bonds must act over a longer distance with *neo*pentane, and this results in weaker overall attractive forces.

Dipoles can also be induced in atoms or nonpolar molecules by ions or by other molecules with dipoles (Fig. 11.7). Such induced dipoles give rise to **ion-induced dipole attractions** and **dipole-induced dipole attractions,** respectively.

⓫.4 Hydrogen Bonding

Nitrosyl fluoride (ONF, molecular mass 49 amu) is a gas at room temperature. Water (H_2O, molecular mass 18 amu) is a liquid, even though it has a lower molecular mass. This difference between the two compounds cannot be attributed to dispersion forces; both molecules have about the same shape, and ONF is the heavier and larger molecule. Nor can it be attributed to differences in the dipole moments of the molecules; both molecules have the same dipole moment. The large difference between the boiling points of these two molecules is due to a special kind of dipole–dipole attraction called **hydrogen bonding.**

Hydrogen bonds can form whenever hydrogen is bonded to one of the more electronegative elements, such as fluorine, oxygen, nitrogen, or chlorine (Section 7.5). The large difference in electronegativity between hydrogen (2.1) and the second element (4.1 for fluorine, 3.5 for oxygen, 3.0 for nitrogen, 2.8 for chlorine) leads to a highly polar covalent bond in which the hydrogen bears a large partial positive charge and the second element bears a large partial negative charge. The electrostatic attraction between the partially positive hydrogen atom in one molecule and the partially negative atom in another molecule gives rise to the strong dipole–dipole attraction called a **hydrogen bond.** Stronger than other dipole–dipole attractions and London forces, hydrogen bonds are about 5 to 10% as strong as ordinary covalent bonds. Examples of hydrogen bonds include $HF \cdots HF$, $H_2O \cdots HOH$, $H_3N \cdots HNH_2$, $H_3N \cdots HOH$, and $H_2O \cdots HOCH_3$. Figure 11.8 illustrates the two hydrogen bonds about a water molecule in liquid water.

Because hydrogen bonds are relatively strong, they can have a pronounced effect on the properties of condensed phases. For example, we generally expect the amount of energy necessary to overcome intramolecular attractive forces to decrease with decreasing molecular mass (Section 11.3). An example appears in Fig. 11.9, which shows the enthalpies of vaporization (Section 4.4) of a series of compounds. With the exception of H_2O, HF, and NH_3, the hydrides and the noble gases shown in Fig. 11.9 exhibit this trend. The compounds H_2O, HF, and NH_3 deviate because they possess appreciable hydrogen bonding. Energy is required to break these hydrogen bonds in order to convert these substances to gases. Hence they have abnormally large enthalpies of vaporization.

——— Covalent bond

- - - - Hydrogen bond

Figure 11.8

A distorted tetrahedral arrangement of covalent bonds (solid red lines) and hydrogen bonds (broken black lines) about an oxygen atom in liquid or solid water. Two hydrogen atoms participate in covalent bonds, and two participate in hydrogen bonds to the oxygen. Each bond from a hydrogen atom and away from the tetrahedron leads to an oxygen atom of another water molecule.

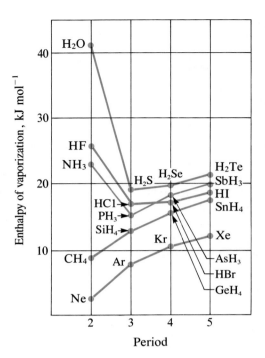

Figure 11.9

The enthalpies of vaporization of several binary hydrides and noble gases. Each line connects compounds of elements in a given group of the periodic table. Note that for elements of the same group, the enthalpy values decrease with decreasing mass, except for HF, H_2O, and NH_3. These three compounds are believed to possess extensive hydrogen bonding.

Properties of Liquids and Solids

⓫.5 Evaporation of Liquids and Solids

The level of water present in an open vessel drops upon standing because of **evaporation,** the change of condensed matter to a gas. Some liquids, such as ether, alcohol, and gasoline, evaporate more rapidly than water under the same conditions. Others evaporate more slowly. Motor oil and ethylene glycol (antifreeze) evaporate so slowly that they seem not to evaporate at all.

Some solids evaporate too. Chemists refer to this direct conversion from the solid phase to the gas phase (without passing through the liquid phase) as **sublimation.** Over a period of time, an ice cube in a freezer becomes smaller as it sublimes. Snow sublimes at temperatures below its melting point. When solid iodine is heated, the solid sublimes and a beautiful purple vapor forms (see photograph on page 237). Evaporation and sublimation were explained in terms of the kinetic-molecular theory in Section 11.1.

When a solid or a liquid is in a closed container, molecules that evaporate cannot escape. Eventually, some strike the surface of the solid or liquid and move back into it. This change from the vapor back to a condensed state is called **condensation.** When the rate of condensation becomes equal to the rate of evaporation, the vapor in the container is in **equilibrium** with the solid or liquid. At equilibrium, neither the amount of the condensed phase nor the amount of the vapor in the container changes. However, some molecules from the vapor condense at the same time that an equal number of molecules from the solid or liquid evaporate; the equilibrium is a **dynamic equilibrium.**

Freeze-dried food is obtained when a water-containing food is cooled to freeze the water, which is then removed as a vapor by decreasing the pressure.

Figure 11.10

A closed vessel at 25°C containing only liquid water and water vapor. The vapor pressure is proportional to the difference in height, h, of the mercury in the two columns of the manometer.

Figure 11.11

The vapor pressures of four common liquids at various temperatures. The intersection of a curve with the dashed line at 760 torr, when projected down to the temperature axis, indicates the normal boiling point of that substance. (The normal boiling point of ethyl ether is 34.6°C; of ethyl alcohol, 78.4°C; of water, 100°C; of ethylene glycol, 198°C, which is off this scale.)

$$\text{Liquid (or solid)} \underset{\text{Condensation}}{\overset{\text{Evaporation}}{\rightleftharpoons}} \text{Vapor}$$

The pressure exerted by the vapor in equilibrium with a solid or a liquid at a given temperature is called the **vapor pressure** of the condensed phase. Neither the area of the surface of the solid or liquid in contact with the vapor nor the size of the vessel have any effect on the vapor pressure. Vapor pressure is commonly measured by introducing a solid or a liquid into a closed container and measuring, with a manometer, the increase in pressure that is due to the vapor in equilibrium with the condensed phase (see Section 10.2 and Fig. 11.10).

The vapor pressure of a liquid or a solid depends on the kind of molecules in it. The vapor pressures of the four liquids shown in Fig. 11.11 differ because the attractive forces between the molecules in each liquid differ. Ethyl ether has the smallest (and most easily overcome) intermolecular forces, as is evident from its higher vapor pressure at every temperature shown. The very low vapor pressure of ethylene glycol (too low even to be shown on the graph at room temperature, about 25°C) is a reflection of the strong forces between its molecules.

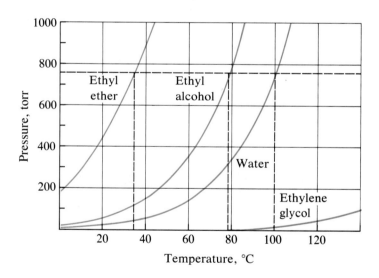

The vapor pressures of all liquids increase as their temperatures increase, because the rates of motion of their molecules increase with increasing temperature. At a higher temperature, more molecules move rapidly enough to escape from the liquid, as shown in Fig. 11.12. The escape of more molecules per unit of time and the greater speed of each molecule that escapes both contribute to the higher vapor pressure.

As one might expect, the vapor pressures of solids behave analogously to those of liquids. Those solids in which the intermolecular forces are weak exhibit measurable vapor pressures at room temperature. The vapor pressures of solids increase with increasing temperature. For example, the vapor pressure of solid iodine is 0.2 torr at 20° and 90 torr at 114°, its melting point.

At the beginning of this section we discussed sublimation, the direct conversion from the solid to the gas phase. The *combined* processes of a solid passing directly into the gas phase without melting and the gas recondensing directly into the solid also is called *sublimation*. Many substances, such as iodine, can be purified by sublimation (Fig. 11.13) if the impurities have low vapor pressures.

Figure 11.12

Distribution of molecular speeds in a liquid at two temperatures. At the higher temperature, more molecules have the necessary speed, E, to escape from the liquid into the gas phase.

⑪.6 Boiling of Liquids

As a liquid is heated, the kinetic energy of its molecules increases. Thus its vapor pressure increases until the vapor pressure equals the pressure of the gas above it; at this point the liquid begins to boil. When a liquid boils, bubbles of vaporized liquid form within it and then rise to the surface, where they burst and release the vapor.

When additional heat is added to a boiling liquid, the temperature of the remaining liquid stays constant. The heat converts some of the liquid to the gas phase rather than raising the temperature of the liquid. The amount of heat needed to convert a given amount of a boiling liquid to vapor is the enthalpy of vaporization (Section 4.4) of the liquid at its boiling temperature.

The **normal boiling point** of a liquid is the temperature at which its vapor pressure equals one atmosphere (760 torr, Fig. 11.11). A liquid boils at temperatures higher than its normal boiling point when the external pressure is greater than one atmosphere; conversely, the boiling point is lowered by decreasing the pressure (Fig. 11.14). For example, at high altitudes where the atmospheric pressure is less than 760 torr, water boils at temperatures below its normal boiling point of 100°C. Food in boiling water cooks more slowly at high altitudes than at sea level, because the temperature of boiling water is lower at the higher altitude.

Figure 11.13

The crystals of iodine at the top of the test tube resulted from sublimation of the iodine in the bottom of the tube.

From the graph presented in Fig. 11.11, determine the boiling point of water contained in a bell jar such as that shown in Fig. 11.14(b) at a pressure of 510 torr. (This is a common atmospheric pressure in Leadville, Colorado, at elevation 10,200 feet.)

Example 11.1

The graph of the vapor pressure of water versus temperature indicates that the vapor pressure of water is 510 torr at about 90°C. Thus at about 90°C, the vapor pressure of water is equal to that of the atmosphere in the bell jar and the water will boil.

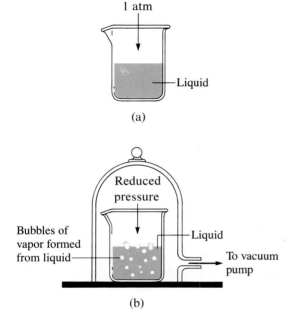

(a)

1 atm

Liquid

Reduced pressure

Bubbles of vapor formed from liquid

Liquid

To vacuum pump

(b)

Figure 11.14

A liquid such as ethyl alcohol that (a) does not boil at room temperature under 1 atmosphere of pressure (b) may boil at that same temperature when we reduce the pressure by placing the liquid in a bell jar and pumping out the air.

Liquid air boils when exposed to room temperature because the intermolecular forces are very weak.

Table 11.1   Molecular Mass and Boiling Points

Substance	He	Ne	Ar	Kr	Xe	Rn
Molecular mass, amu	4.0	20.18	39.95	83.8	131.3	222
Boiling point, °C	−268.9	−245.9	−185.7	−152.9	−107.1	−61.8

Substance	H_2	F_2	Cl_2	Br_2	I_2
Molecular mass, amu	2.016	38.0	70.91	159.8	253.8
Boiling point, °C	−252.7	−187	−34.6	58.8	184.4

Boiling points increase as the forces of attraction between molecules increase. The trend of increases in intermolecular attraction with increasing size (Section 11.3) is reflected in the boiling points of the substances shown in Table 11.1.

⓫.7 Distillation

Dissolved materials in a liquid may make it unsuitable for particular purposes. For example, hard water (water containing dissolved minerals) should not be used in automobile batteries or steam irons because it shortens their lives.

Water and other liquids may be separated from some impurities by a process known as **distillation** (Fig. 11.15). The impure liquid is boiled, and the vapor is condensed in another part of the apparatus. Dissolved matter that does not evaporate stays in the flask. Distillation takes advantage of the facts that (1) heating a liquid speeds up its rate of evaporation (an endothermic change) and (2) cooling a vapor favors its condensation (an exothermic change). The distillation of two or more substances from a mixture is described more fully in Section 12.16.

Figure 11.15

Laboratory distillation apparatus. When impure water is distilled with this apparatus, nonvolatile substances remain in the distilling flask (the flask that is heated). The water is vaporized, condensed in a water-cooled condenser, and finally collected as distillate in the receiving flask.

⓫.8 Melting of Solids

As heat is added to a crystalline solid, the average energy of its molecules or ions increases. At some point, this energy becomes large enough to overcome some of the forces holding the molecules or ions in their fixed positions, and the solid begins to melt. If heating is continued, all of the solid melts, but the temperature of the mixture of solid and liquid does not increase as long as any solid remains. (Any heat that is added to a melting solid converts a portion of the solid to a liquid rather than raising the temperature of the solid.) After all of the solid has melted, additional heat will then increase the temperature of the liquid until it begins to boil (Fig. 11.16; see also Figs. 4.6 and 4.7).

If, during melting, heating is stopped and no heat is allowed to escape, the solid and liquid phases remain in equilibrium. The changes from solid to liquid and liquid to solid continue, but the rate of melting is equal to the rate of freezing, and the quantities of solid and liquid remain constant. The temperature at which the solid and liquid phases of a given substance are in equilibrium is called the **melting point** of the solid or the **freezing point** of the liquid. With the notable exception of water, most substances expand when they melt and contract when they freeze.

The amount of heat needed to melt a given amount of solid is the enthalpy of fusion of the solid (Section 4.4). The enthalpy of fusion and the melting point of a crystalline solid are determined by the strength of the attractive forces between the units present in the crystal. Molecules with weak attractive forces form crystals with low melting points. Crystals consisting of particles with stronger attractive forces melt at higher temperatures.

Quartz, SiO_2

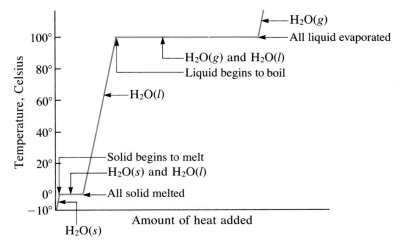

Figure 11.16

Heating curve for water. When ice is heated, the temperature increases until the melting point is reached (red line). The temperature then remains constant until all of the ice is melted (blue line), then it increases again (red line). When the water begins to boil, the temperature again remains constant (blue line) until all of the water has vaporized. The temperature then increases again (red line).

Figure 11.17

A sample of liquid water and water vapor (a) at 25°C, (b) at 100°C, and (c) at 374°C. At the critical temperature, 374°C, the boundary between liquid and vapor disappears.

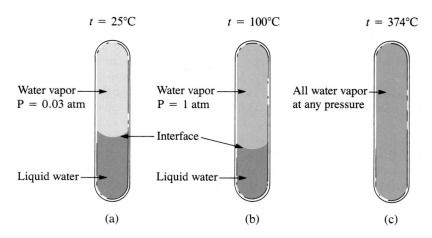

$t = 25°C$ $t = 100°C$ $t = 374°C$

Water vapor
P = 0.03 atm

Water vapor
P = 1 atm

All water vapor
at any pressure

Interface

Liquid water   Liquid water

(a)   (b)   (c)

11.9 Critical Temperature and Pressure

At 25°C a sample of water sealed in an evacuated tube exists as liquid water and water vapor with a pressure of 23.8 torr (Table 10.1). There is a clear boundary between the two phases [Fig. 11.17(a)]. As the temperature is increased, the pressure of the vapor increases. At 100°C, for example, the pressure is 760 torr, but liquid water and the vapor are present and the boundary between them is still distinct [Fig. 11.17(b)]. However, at a temperature of 374°C, the boundary disappears [Fig. 11.17(c)], and all of the water in the tube is physically identical. It is no longer possible to distinguish liquid and vapor. The temperature above which it is no longer possible to distinguish a liquid from its vapor is called the **critical temperature**. Above this temperature, a gas cannot be liquefied *no matter how much pressure is applied*. The pressure required to liquefy a gas at its critical temperature is called the **critical pressure**. The critical temperatures and critical pressures of some common substances are given in Table 11.2.

Example 11.2

If a CO_2 fire extinguisher is shaken on a cool day (say 18°C), liquid CO_2 can be heard sloshing around in the cylinder. However, the same cylinder appears to contain no liquid on a hot summer day (say 35°C). Explain these observations.

On the cool day, the temperature of the CO_2 is below the critical temperature of CO_2, 304 K or 31°C (Table 11.2), so liquid CO_2 is present in the cylinder. On the hot day, the temperature of the CO_2 is greater than its critical temperature of 31°C, so no liquid CO_2 exists.

Above the critical temperature, the average kinetic energy of the molecules in a substance is sufficient to overcome their mutually attractive forces. Therefore, they will not cling together and form a liquid, no matter how great the pressure. When the temperature is decreased, the average kinetic energy of the molecules falls. At the critical temperature, the intermolecular forces are just large enough—relative to the average kinetic energy—to liquefy the gas, provided the pressure is equal to or greater than the critical pressure. The pressure helps the intermolecular forces bring the molecules close enough together to liquefy. Below the critical temperature, the pressure required for liquefaction decreases with decreasing temperature until it reaches 1 atmosphere at the normal boiling temperature. Substances with strong intermolecular attractions, such as

Table 11.2	Critical Temperatures and Pressures of Some Common Substances	
	Critical Temperature, K	Critical Pressure, atm
Hydrogen	33.24	12.8
Nitrogen	126.0	33.5
Oxygen	154.3	49.7
Carbon dioxide	304.2	73.0
Ammonia	405.5	111.5
Sulfur dioxide	430.3	77.7
Water	647.1	217.7

water and ammonia, have high critical temperatures; substances with weak intermolecular attractions, such as hydrogen and nitrogen, have low critical temperatures.

⓫.10 Phase Diagrams

When water at 80°C is confined in a syringe with a pressure of 760 torr on the plunger, only liquid water is found to be present [Fig. 11.18(a)]. As heat is added, the temperature of the water increases, but as long as the pressure is held at 760 torr, only liquid water will be present. When the temperature reaches 100°C, adding more heat produces water vapor, provided the pressure remains at 760 torr [Fig. 11.18(b)]. With the further addition of heat, the temperature remains constant at 100°C until all of the liquid water changes to vapor. If the addition of heat is stopped and no heat is allowed to escape

760 torr

760 torr

Water vapor (100°)

Liquid water (80°)

Liquid water (100°)

$t = 80°C$

$t = 100°C$

(a)

(b)

Figure 11.18

Syringes containing water at 760 torr. (a) At 80°C and 760 torr, only liquid water is contained in the syringe. (b) When the water is warmed to 100°C and then a little additional heat is added, the syringe contains both liquid water and water vapor at 100°C and 760 torr.

Realgar, AsS

Figure 11.19

(a) Phase diagram for water. (b) An expanded portion between −20°C and 10°C, showing that the equilibrium of solid and gas phases varies with temperature.

while both liquid water and water vapor are present, the mixture remains at equilibrium.

When heat is removed from water vapor at 110°C and a constant pressure of 760 torr, the vapor cools until it reaches 100°C, at which point liquid water begins to form. If more heat is removed, the temperature does not change until all of the vapor condenses. Thus 100°C and 760 torr is found to be one point at which liquid water and water vapor are at equilibrium. At a lower pressure of 600 torr, the equilibrium between liquid and vapor is found at 94°C. At 380 torr, the equilibrium is found at 80°C.

Water in a syringe at 10°C and a pressure of 380 torr cools as heat is removed. When the temperature reaches 0.005°C, further loss of heat results in formation of ice with no change in temperature until all of the liquid is frozen. Ice and liquid water are in equilibrium at 0.005°C at a pressure of 380 torr. At 760 torr, the equilibrium between ice and water occurs at 0°C.

All of the information concerning the temperatures and pressures at which the various phases of a substance are in equilibrium can be summarized in its **phase diagram,** a diagram showing the pressures and temperatures at which gaseous, liquid, and solid phases of a substance can exist. Such a diagram is constructed by plotting points that represent the pressures and temperatures at which two different phases of a substance are in equilibrium. A part of the phase diagram for water is given in Fig. 11.19(a). Figure 11.19(b) shows an expanded portion of Fig. 11.19(a).

The red line *BC* in the phase diagram of water [(Fig. 11.19(a)] is a plot of the vapor pressure of water versus temperature. It shows the combinations of temperature and pressure at which liquid water and water vapor are in equilibrium. This diagram shows that when the pressure is 760 torr, the liquid and vapor are at equilibrium only when the temperature is 100°C, as we saw in the experiment with the syringes. The figure also indicates that the equilibrium occurs at 94°C when the pressure is 600 torr and at 80°C when the pressure is 380 torr.

If the figure were large enough, line *BC* would be seen to terminate at a temperature of 374°C and a pressure of 165,500 torr (217.7 atmospheres), the critical temperature

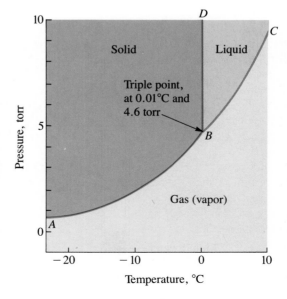

(a)

(b)

and pressure of water. Beyond the critical temperature, liquid and gaseous water cannot be in equilibrium because liquid water cannot exist above the critical temperature.

The blue line *AB* in Fig. 11.19 is a plot of the vapor pressure of ice versus temperature; at any combination of temperature and pressure on this line, ice and water vapor are in equilibrium. The purple line *BD* in Fig. 11.19 shows the temperature at which ice and liquid water are in equilibrium as the pressure changes.

For each value of pressure and temperature falling within the portion of the phase diagram [Fig. 11.19(a)] labeled "Solid" (760 torr and −10°C, for example), water exists only as a solid (ice). Similarly, for values of pressure and temperature within the portion labeled "Liquid" (760 torr and 80°C, for example), water exists only as a liquid. For any combination of pressure and temperature in the region labeled "Gas" (760 torr and 110°C, for example), water exists only in the gaseous state. At −5°C and 760 torr, the point on the diagram is in the region indicating that only solid water is stable. Moving across the diagram horizontally at a constant pressure of 760 torr, we see that as the temperature increases, water becomes a liquid at 0°C, which is its *normal melting temperature*. At this temperature and pressure, both solid and liquid water can exist in equilibrium. Water is stable only as a liquid at a pressure of 760 torr for temperatures between 0°C and 100°C. It changes to a gas at 100°C, its *normal boiling temperature,* at which liquid water at 760 torr and water vapor at 760 torr can exist at equilibrium. At temperatures above 100°C at 760 torr, water is stable only as a gas.

The almost vertical purple line *BD* in Fig. 11.19 shows us that as the pressure increases, the melting temperature remains almost constant (it actually decreases very slightly). On the other hand, the diagram indicates clearly that the boiling temperature increases markedly with an increase in pressure. Representative vapor pressures for water are given in Table 10.1.

The lines that separate the various regions in Fig. 11.19 represent points at which an equilibrium exists between two phases. One point exists where all three phases are in equilibrium. This point, referred to as the **triple point,** occurs at point *B* in Fig. 11.19, where the three lines intersect. At the pressure and temperature of the triple point [4.6 torr and 0.01°C (273.16 K)], all three states are in equilibrium with each other.

Aquamarine, $Be_3Al_2Si_6O_{18}$

11.11 Cohesive Forces and Adhesive Forces

All of the various intermolecular forces holding a liquid together are called **cohesive forces.** The types of cohesive forces within a liquid, the size and shape of its molecules, and its temperature determine how easily it flows. The **viscosity** of a liquid is a measure of its resistance to flow. Water, gasoline, and other liquids that flow freely have a low viscosity. Syrup, honey, and other liquids that do not flow freely have a high viscosity. The more complex the molecules in a liquid and the stronger the intermolecular forces between them, the more difficult it is for them to move past each other and the greater the viscosity of the liquid. As the temperature increases, the molecules move more rapidly and their kinetic energies are better able to overcome the cohesive forces that hold them together. Thus the viscosity of the liquid decreases. Viscosity is measured by either measuring the rate at which a metal ball falls through a liquid (the ball falls more slowly through a more viscous liquid) or measuring the rate at which a liquid flows through a narrow tube (more viscous liquids flow more slowly).

The molecules within a liquid are attracted equally in all directions by the cohesive forces within the liquid. However, the molecules on the surface of a liquid are attracted

Honey is a viscous liquid.

Surface

Figure 11.20

Attractive forces experienced by a molecule at the surface and by a molecule in the bulk of a liquid.

Surface tension keeps this insect afloat.

only into the liquid and to either side (Fig. 11.20). This unbalanced molecular attraction tends to pull the surface molecules back into the liquid such that the minimum number of molecules possible are on the surface. The surface area is reduced to a minimum. A small drop of liquid tends to assume a spherical shape because in a sphere the ratio of surface area to volume is at a minimum. **Surface tension** is the force that causes the surface of a liquid to contract. The surface of a liquid acts as though it were a stretched membrane. A steel needle carefully placed on water will float. Some insects, even though they are denser than water, move on its surface because they are supported by the surface tension.

The forces of attraction between a liquid and a surface are **adhesive forces.** Water does not wet some surfaces, such as waxed surfaces and polyethylene, for example, because the adhesive forces between water and these surfaces are weak. Thus water forms drops on these surfaces, because the cohesive forces within the drops are greater than the adhesive forces between the water and the plastic. Water wets glass and increases its surface area as it spreads out on the glass, because the adhesive force between water and glass is greater than the cohesive forces within the water. **Capillary action** occurs when one end of a small-diameter tube is immersed in a liquid that wets the tube. The liquid creeps up the sides of the tube until the weight of the liquid and the adhesive forces are in balance. The smaller the diameter of the tube, the higher the liquid climbs. It is partly by capillary action that water and dissolved nutrients are brought from the soil up through the roots and into a plant.

When water is confined in a glass tube, its **meniscus** (surface) has a concave shape, because the water wets the glass and creeps up the side of the tube. On the other hand, the meniscus of mercury confined in a tube is convex, because mercury does not wet glass and the cohesive forces in the mercury tend to draw it into a drop.

Are the adhesive forces between the surface and the drops of water greater or less than the cohesive forces within the drops?

Note the difference between the shape of the meniscus of water and that of the meniscus of mercury in these glass containers.

The Structures of Crystalline Solids

⑪.12 Types of Solids

When most liquids are cooled, they eventually freeze. Their molecules or ions assume ordered positions and form crystalline solids. A **crystalline solid** is a homogeneous solid in which the atoms, ions, or molecules are arranged in a definite repeating pattern [Fig. 11.21(a)]. Although some solids (such as diamonds and the individual grains in sugar, sand, and table salt) are single crystals, most common crystalline solids are aggregates of many small crystals. Common examples of the latter are sandstone, chunks of ice, granite, and metal objects.

Many liquids such as molten glass, molten plastics, and molten butter, which consist of large molecules that cannot move readily into ordered positions, do not form crystalline solids when cooled. Instead, as the temperature is lowered, their large molecules move more and more slowly and finally stop in random positions before they can move into an ordered arrangement. The resulting materials are called **amorphous solids** or **glasses** [Fig. 11.21(b)]. Amorphous solids lack an ordered internal structure. Common examples of amorphous solids include candle wax, butter, glass, and plastics such as those in polyethylene bags, compact disks, and recording tape.

There are several different types of crystalline solids. **Ionic solids,** such as sodium chloride and potassium nitrate, are composed of positive and negative ions. **Molecular solids,** such as ice and sucrose (table sugar), are composed of neutral molecules. The structures of ice, a molecular solid, and of sodium chloride, an ionic solid, are shown in Fig. 11.22.

(a)

(b)

• Boron   ◦ Oxygen

Figure 11.21

(a) A two-dimensional illustration of the ordered arrangement of atoms in a crystal of boric oxide. (b) An illustration showing the disorder in amorphous boric oxide.

(a)

◦ Oxygen

• Hydrogen

— Covalent bonds

-- Hydrogen bonds

(b)

● Na⁺

● Cl⁻

Figure 11.22

(a) The arrangement of water molecules in ice, a molecular solid, showing each oxygen atom (yellow) with four hydrogen atoms (brown) as nearest neighbors, two attached by covalent bonds (red) and two by hydrogen bonds (purple). The oxygen atoms at the corners of a prism are also at the corners of adjoining prisms; this is only a portion of a continuous array. (b) The structure of sodium chloride, an ionic solid, consists of sodium ions (red) and chloride ions (green).

C

O   Si

C   Si

(a)   (b)   (c)

Figure 11.23

A covalent crystal contains a three-dimensional network of covalent bonds,
as illustrated by the structures of (a) diamond, (b) silicon dioxide,
and (c) silicon carbide. Lines between atoms indicate covalent bonds.

Figure 11.24

Ionic metal oxides are used to line
this crucible. They do not melt when
in contact with molten iron because
they have very high melting temperatures.

Crystals of some other solids may be regarded as giant molecules. These include
crystals of metals such as copper, aluminum, and iron; crystals of diamond, silicon, and
some other nonmetals; and crystals of some covalent compounds such as silicon dioxide
(sand) and silicon carbide (carborundum, the abrasive on sandpaper). The atoms in all of
these solids are held together by a three-dimensional network of covalent bonds, and it
is not possible to identify individual molecules in them. Solids composed of metal atoms
are called **metallic solids,** and the other solids that can be regarded as giant molecules
are called **covalent solids.** The structures of metallic solids are discussed in Section
11.14. Structures of some covalent solids are shown in Fig. 11.23.

The strengths of the attractive forces between the units present in different crystals
vary widely, as indicated by the melting points of the crystals. Small symmetrical molecules, such as H_2, N_2, O_2, and F_2, have weak attractive forces and form molecular
crystals with very low melting points (below $-200°C$). Molecular crystals consisting of
larger, nonpolar molecules have stronger attractive forces and melt at higher temperatures, whereas molecular crystals composed of asymmetrical molecules with permanent
dipole moments melt at still higher temperatures; examples include ice (mp $0°C$) and
table sugar (mp $185°C$). Diamond is a covalent crystal in which carbon atoms are held
together by strong covalent bonds [Fig. 11.23(a)]; the melting point of diamond is very
high (above $3500°C$). The atoms in crystals of metals are bonded together by electrons in
bands (Section 9.15). The melting points of the metals vary widely. Mercury is a liquid
at room temperature, and the alkali metals melt below $200°C$. Several post-transition
metals also have low melting points, whereas the transition metals melt at temperatures
above $1000°C$. The electrostatic forces of attraction between the ions in ionic solids can
be quite strong; thus many ionic crystals also have high melting points (as high as
$3000°C$; Fig. 11.24).

A crystalline solid has a sharp melting temperature because the forces holding its
atoms, ions, or molecules together are all of the same strength. Thus the attractions
between the units that make up the crystal all have the same strength and all require the
same amount of energy to be broken. The gradual softening of an amorphous material,
so different from the sharp melting of a crystalline solid, results from the structural
nonequivalence of the molecules in the amorphous solid. Some forces are weaker than
others, and when an amorphous material is heated, the weakest intermolecular attractions break first. As the temperature is increased further, the stronger attractions are
broken. Thus amorphous materials soften over a range of temperatures.

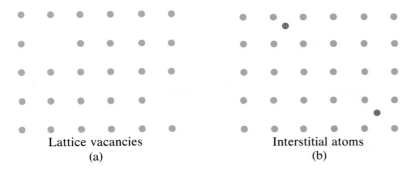

Figure 11.25

Representations of two types of crystal defects.

Lattice vacancies
(a)

Interstitial atoms
(b)

⑪.13 Crystal Defects

In a crystalline solid the atoms, ions, or molecules are arranged in a definite repeating pattern, but occasional defects may occur in the pattern. Several types of defects are known. It is common for some positions that should contain atoms or ions to be vacant [Fig. 11.25(a)]. Less commonly, some atoms or ions in a crystal may occupy positions, called **interstitial sites,** that are located between the regular positions for atoms [Fig. 11.25(b)]. Certain distortions occur in some impure crystals, as for example when the cations, anions, or molecules of the impurity are too large to fit into the regular positions without distorting the structure. Minute amounts of impurities are sometimes added to a crystal to cause imperfections in the structure so that the electrical conductivity (see Section 9.15) or some other physical properties of the crystal will change. This has practical applications in the manufacture of semiconductors and computer chips.

⑪.14 The Structures of Metals

A pure metal is a crystalline solid in which the metal atoms are packed closely together in a repeating array, or pattern. In most metals the atoms pack together as though they were spheres. When spheres of equal size are packed together as closely as possible in a plane, they arrange themselves as shown in Fig. 11.26(a), each sphere in contact with six others. This arrangement, called **closest packing,** can extend indefinitely in a single layer. Crystals of many metals can be described as stacks of such closest packed layers.

Two types of stacking of closest packed layers are observed in simple metallic crystalline structures. In both types a second layer (B) is placed on the first layer (A) so that each sphere in the second layer is in contact with three spheres in the first layer, as shown in Fig. 11.26(b). A third layer can be positioned in one of two ways.

Spherical pills arrange themselves in a closest packed array.

Figure 11.26

(a) A portion of a layer of closest packed spheres in the same plane. Each sphere touches 6 others. (b) Spheres in two closest packed layers. Each sphere in layer B (the blue layer) touches 3 spheres in layer A (the yellow layer). In an actual crystal many more than two planes would exist. Each sphere contacts 6 spheres in its own layer, 3 spheres in the layer below, and 3 spheres in the layer above; each sphere touches a total of 12 other spheres.

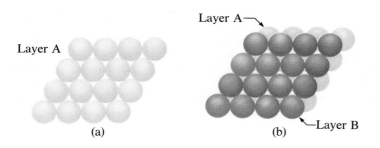

Layer A

Layer A

Layer B

(a)

(b)

Figure 11.27

Figure 11.27

A portion of two types of crystal structures in which spheres are packed as compactly as possible. The lower diagrams show the structures expanded for clarification. Note that the first and third layers have identical orientations in (a). The first and third layers have different orientations in (b). In both structures, each sphere is surrounded by 12 others in an infinite extension of the structure and is said to have a coordination number of 12.

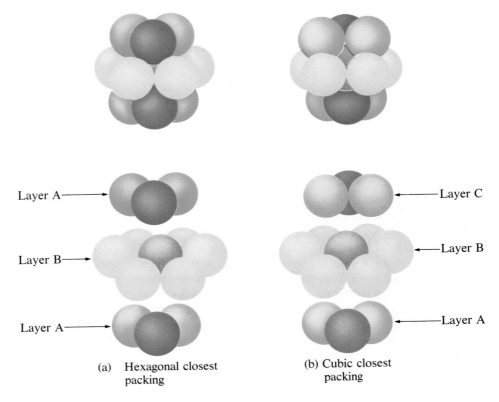

Layer A

Layer B

Layer A

Layer C

Layer B

Layer A

(a)   Hexagonal closest packing

(b) Cubic closest packing

In one positioning, each sphere in the third layer lies directly above a sphere in the first layer [Fig. 11.27(a)]. The third layer is also type A. The stacking continues with type B and type A close packed layers alternating (ABABAB···). This arrangement is called **hexagonal closest packing.** Metals that crystallize this way have a **hexagonal closest packed structure.** Examples include Be, Cd, Co, Li, Mg, Na, and Zn. (Those elements or compounds that crystallize with the same structure have **isomorphous structures.**)

In the second positioning, the third layer is located such that its spheres are not directly above those in either layer A or layer B [Fig. 11.27(b)]. This layer is type C. The stacking continues with alternating layers of type A, type B, and type C (ABCABC···), an arrangement called **cubic closest packing.** Metals that crystallize this way have a **cubic closest packed,** or **face-centered cubic, structure.** Examples include Ag, Al, Ca, Cu, Ni, Pb, and Pt.

In crystals of metals with either hexagonal closest packing or cubic closest packing, each atom touches 12 equidistant neighbors, 6 in its own plane and 3 in each adjacent plane. This gives each atom a coordination number of 12. The **coordination number** of an atom or ion is the number of neighbors touching it. About two-thirds of all metals crystallize in closest packed arrays with coordination numbers of 12.

Most of the remaining metals crystallize in a **body-centered cubic structure,** which contains planes of spheres that are *not* closest packed. Each sphere in a plane is surrounded by four nearest neighbors [Fig. 11.28(a)], rather than the six in closest packed planes. The spheres in such a plane *do not touch.* The structure consists of repeating layers of these planes. The second layer is stacked on top of the first such that a sphere in the second layer *touches* four spheres in the first layer [Fig. 11.28(b)]. The spheres of the third layer are positioned directly above the spheres of the first layer (Fig.

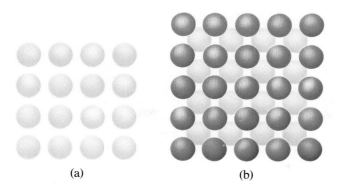

(a)　　　　　　　　(b)

Figure 11.28

(a) A portion of a plane of spheres found in a body-centered cubic structure. Note that the spheres do not touch. (b) Spheres in two layers of a body-centered cubic structure. Each sphere in one layer touches four spheres in the adjacent layer but none in its own layer.

11.29); those of the fourth, above the second; etc. Any atom in this structure touches four atoms in the layer above it and four atoms in the layer below it. An atom in a body-centered cubic structure thus has a coordination number of 8. Isomorphous metals exhibiting a body-centered cubic structure include Ba, Cr, Mo, W, and Fe at room temperature.

Polonium (Po) crystallizes in the **simple cubic structure,** which is rare for metals. It contains planes in which each sphere *touches* its four nearest neighbors [Fig. 11.30(a)]. Thus the structure is not closest packed. The planes are stacked directly above each other such that an atom in the second layer touches only one atom in the first layer [Fig. 11.30(b)]. The coordination number of a polonium atom in a simple cubic array is 6: an atom touches four other atoms in its own layer, one atom in the layer above, and one atom in the layer below.

⓫.15 The Structures of Ionic Crystals

Ionic crystals consist of two or more different kinds of ions that usually have different sizes. The packing of these ions into a crystal structure is more complex than the packing of metal atoms that are the same size and kind.

Most monatomic ions behave as charged spheres; their attraction for ions of opposite charge is the same in every direction. Consequently, stable structures result (1) when ions of one charge are surrounded by as many ions as possible of the opposite charge and (2) when the cations and anions are in contact with each other. The structures are determined by two factors: the relative sizes of the ions and the relative numbers of positive and negative ions required to maintain the electrical neutrality of the crystal as a whole.

In simple ionic structures the anions, which are normally larger than the cations, are usually arranged in a closest packed array. The spaces remaining between the anions,

(a)

(b)

Figure 11.29

(a) A portion of a body-centered cubic structure, showing parts of three layers. (b) An expanded view of a body-centered cubic structure with the layers separated. In an infinite extension of this structure, each sphere touches four spheres in the layer above it and four spheres in the layer below and is said to have a coordination number of 8.

(a)　　　　　　　　(b)

Figure 11.30

(a) A portion of a plane of spheres found in a simple cubic structure. Note that the spheres are in contact. (b) A portion of a simple cubic structure, showing two of the planes.

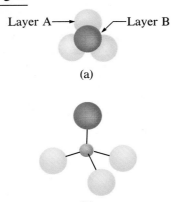

(a)

(b)

Figure 11.31

(a) Spheres in two adjacent closest packed layers that form a tetrahedral hole. (b) A cation (smaller sphere) located in a tetrahedral hole surrounded by four anions (larger spheres) from a different perspective. The structure has been expanded to show the geometrical relationships.

Figure 11.33

A cation in the cubic hole in a simple cubic array of anions.

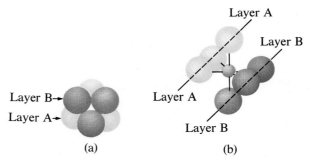

(a)   (b)

Figure 11.32

(a) Spheres in two adjacent closest packed layers that form an octahedral hole. (b) A cation (red sphere) located in an octahedral hole surrounded by six anions (larger spheres) from a different perspective. The structure has been expanded to show the geometrical relationships.

called **holes** or **interstices,** are occupied by the smaller cations. Figures 11.31 and 11.32 illustrate the two most common types of holes. The smaller of these is found between three spheres in one plane and one sphere in an adjacent plane [Fig. 11.31(a)]. The four spheres that bound this hole are arranged at the corners of a tetrahedron [Fig. 11.31(b)]; the hole is called a **tetrahedral hole.** The larger type of hole is found at the center of six spheres (three in one layer and three in an adjacent layer) located at the corners of an octahedron (Fig. 11.32). Such a hole is called an **octahedral hole.**

Depending on the relative sizes of the cations and anions, the cations of an ionic compound can occupy tetrahedral or octahedral holes. As we will discuss in Section 11.16, relatively small cations occupy tetrahedral holes, and larger cations occupy octahedral holes. If the cations are too large to fit into the octahedral holes, the packing of the anions may change to give a more open structure, such as a simple cubic array (Fig. 11.30). The larger cations can then occupy the larger cubic holes made possible by the more open spacing (Fig. 11.33).

In either a hexagonal closest packed or a cubic closest packed array of anions, there are two tetrahedral holes for each anion in the array. The isomorphous compounds Li_2O, Na_2O, Li_2S, Na_2S, and Li_2Se, among others, crystallize with a cubic closest packed array of anions with the relatively small cations in tetrahedral holes. The ratio of tetrahedral holes to anions is 2 to 1; thus all of these holes must be filled by cations, because the cation-to-anion ratio is 2 to 1 in these compounds. A compound that crystallizes in a closest packed array of anions with cations in the tetrahedral holes can have a maximum cation-to-anion ratio of 2 to 1; all of the tetrahedral holes are filled at this ratio. Compounds with a ratio of less than 2 to 1 may also crystallize in a closest packed array of anions with cations in the tetrahederal holes, if the ionic sizes fit. In these compounds, however, some of the tetrahedral holes remain vacant.

Example 11.3

Zinc sulfide crystallizes with zinc ions occupying $\frac{1}{2}$ of the tetrahedral holes in a closest packed array of sulfide ions. What is the formula of zinc sulfide?

Because there are 2 tetrahedral holes per anion (sulfide ion) and $\frac{1}{2}$ of these are occupied by zinc ions, there must be $\frac{1}{2} \times 2$, or 1, zinc ion per sulfide ion. Thus the formula is ZnS.

The ratio of octahedral holes to anions in either a hexagonal or a cubic closest packed structure is 1 to 1. Thus compounds with cations in octahedral holes in a closest packed array of anions can have a maximum cation-to-anion ratio of 1 to 1. In NiO, MnS, NaCl, and KH, for example, all of the octahedral holes are filled. Ratios of less than 1 to 1 are observed when some of the octahedral holes remain empty.

Example 11.4

In a simple cubic array of anions (Fig. 11.33), there is one cubic hole that can be occupied by a cation for each anion in the array. In CsCl, and in other compounds with the same structure, all of the cubic holes are occupied. Half of the cubic holes are occupied in SrH_2, UO_2, $SrCl_2$, and CaF_2.

Different types of ionic compounds can crystallize in the same structure when the relative sizes of their ions and their stoichiometries (the two principal features that determine structure) are similar.

11.16 The Radius Ratio Rule

The structure of an ionic compound is largely the result of stoichiometry and of simple geometric and electrostatic relationships that depend on the relative sizes of the cation and anion. A relatively large cation can touch a large number of anions and so occupies a cubic or an octahedral hole, whereas a relatively small cation can touch only a few anions and so occupies a tetrahedral hole.

Consider a cation, M^+, with a coordination number of 6. As shown in Fig. 11.34(a), the M^+ ion touches four X^- ions in a plane. In addition, although they are not shown in the figure, there is an X^- ion above the M^+ ion and touching it and another below and touching it. Note that the M^+ ion is large enough to expand the array of X^- ions so that the X^- ions are not in contact with one another. As long as the expansion is not great enough to allow still another anion to touch the cation, this is a stable situation; the cation–anion contacts are maintained. Figure 11.34(b) illustrates what happens when the size of the M^+ ion is decreased somewhat. Here the X^- ions touch each other, as do the M^+ and X^- ions. If the size of M^+ is further decreased, it becomes impossible to get a structure with a coordination number of 6. The anions touch [Fig. 11.34(c)], but there is no contact between the M^+ and X^- ions—this is an unstable structure. In this case a more stable structure would be formed with only four anions about the cation. The limiting condition for the formation of a structure with a coordination number of 6 is illustrated in Fig. 11.34(b): The X^- ions touch one another, and the M^+ and X^- ions touch. This occurs when the sizes of the ions are such that the **radius ratio** (the radius of the positive ion, r^+, divided by the radius of the negative ion, r^-) is equal to 0.414.

There is a minimum radius ratio (r^+/r^-) for each coordination number. Below this value an ionic structure having that coordination number is generally not stable. Table 11.3 lists the approximate limiting values for the radius ratios for ionic compounds.

(a)

(b)

(c)

Figure 11.34

Packing of anions (green spheres) around cations of varying size (red spheres). Decreasing size of cations is illustrated successively in (a), (b), and (c).

Table 11.3	Limiting Values for the Radius Ratio for Ionic Compounds[a]	
Coordination Number	Type of Hole Occupied	Approximate Limiting Values of r^+/r^-
8	Cubic	Above 0.732
6	Octahedral	0.414 to 0.732
4	Tetrahedral	0.225 to 0.414

[a]r^+ is radius of cation; r^- is radius of anion.

Example 11.5 Predict the coordination number of Cs^+ ($r^+ = 1.69$ Å) and of Na^+ ($r^+ = 0.95$ Å) in CsCl and NaCl, respectively. The radius of a chloride ion is 1.81 Å.

For CsCl:

$$\frac{r^+}{r^-} = \frac{1.69 \text{ Å}}{1.81 \text{ Å}} = 0.934$$

The radius ratio is greater than 0.732 (Table 11.3), which indicates that a coordination number of 8 is likely for Cs^+ in CsCl.

For NaCl:

$$\frac{r^+}{r^-} = \frac{0.95 \text{ Å}}{1.81 \text{ Å}} = 0.52$$

This radius ratio is between 0.414 and 0.732 and so indicates that a coordination number of 6 is likely for Na^+ in NaCl (Table 11.3).

The radius ratio rule is only a guide to the type of structure that may form. It applies strictly only to ionic crystals and in some cases fails with them. In compounds in which the bonds are covalent, the rule may not hold. In spite of its limitations, however, the radius ratio rule is a useful guide for predicting many structures. It also underlines one of the most significant features responsible for the structures of ionic solids: the relative sizes of the cations and anions.

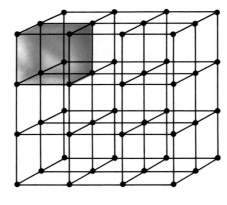

Figure 11.35

A portion of a simple cubic space lattice. One unit cell is shaded in blue.

⓫.17 Crystal Systems

The atoms in a crystal are arranged in a definite repeating pattern, so any one point in the crystal matches many other points having identical environments. The collection of all of the points within the crystal that have identical environments is called a **space lattice.** A simple three-dimensional cubic space lattice is shown in Fig. 11.35. (The atoms around the points have been omitted so that you can see the lattice.) Figure 11.36 illustrates a portion of the structure of sodium chloride. This structure will be described more fully later in this section, but for now let us consider only the space lattice associated with it. There are an infinite number of ways to construct a space lattice in the sodium chloride structure. The points of one possible space lattice are located at the centers of the sodium ions, as shown in Fig. 11.36(a). Alternatively, points with identical environments could be located at the centers of chloride ions [Fig. 11.36(b)] or between sodium and chloride ions [Fig. 11.36(c)]. In each case the resulting space lattice is the same; only the locations of the points of the lattice differ.

That part of a space lattice that will generate the entire lattice if repeated in three dimensions is called a **unit cell.** The cube shaded in Fig. 11.35 is a unit cell for the simple cubic space lattice. The cubes outlined in Fig. 11.36 illustrate three ways in which unit cells may be selected for the sodium chloride structure. The structure of a crystal is specified by describing the size and shape of the unit cell and indicating the arrangement of its contents. The crystal can be built up by repeating the unit cell in three dimensions.

Thus far we have considered only unit cells shaped like a cube, but there are others. In general, a unit cell is a parallelepiped for which the size and shape are defined by the lengths of three axes (a, b, and c) and the angles (α, β, and γ) between them (Fig. 11.37). The axes are defined as being the lengths between points in the space lattice. Consequently, **unit cell axes join points with identical environments.** It can be shown that unit cells must have one of the seven shapes indicated in Table 11.4.

Variations in the number and location of lattice points in these seven unit cells give rise to 14 types of space lattices, shown in Fig. 11.38. In some of these, points with identical surroundings (lattice points) are found only at the corners of the unit cell. In others the points of the lattice occur both at the corners and in the centers of some or all of the faces of the unit cell. In still others the points of the lattice are found both at the corners and in the center of the unit cell.

Students sometimes have trouble reconciling the number of points or atoms given as the number per unit cell with the diagram of the unit cell. Some of the points or atoms shown in a diagram of a unit cell may be shared by other unit cells and therefore not lie

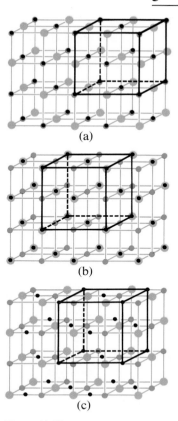

(a)

(b)

(c)

Figure 11.36

A portion of the structure of NaCl, showing three positions for a space lattice. Small red spheres represent Na^+, large green spheres Cl^-. (a) Lattice points in the center of the Na^+ ions. (b) Lattice points in the center of the Cl^- ions. (c) Lattice points with a chloride ion to the left and a sodium ion to the right. Black lines connect points that define a unit cell in each lattice. The unit cell of NaCl is usually described as seen in (a) or (b). Note that this structure has been expanded for clarity; the ions touch in the actual structure.

Table 11.4	Unit Cells of the Seven Crystal Systems	
System	Axes	Angles
Cubic	$a = b = c$	$\alpha = \beta = \gamma = 90°$
Tetragonal	$a = b \neq c$	$\alpha = \beta = \gamma = 90°$
Orthorhombic	$a \neq b \neq c$	$\alpha = \beta = \gamma = 90°$
Monoclinic	$a \neq b \neq c$	$\alpha = \gamma = 90°; \beta \neq 90°$
Triclinic	$a \neq b \neq c$	$\alpha \neq \beta \neq \gamma \neq 90°$
Hexagonal	$a = b \neq c$	$\alpha = \beta = 90°; \gamma = 120°$
Rhombohedral	$a = b = c$	$\alpha = \beta = \gamma \neq 90°$

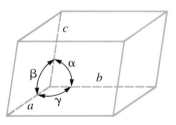

Figure 11.37

A unit cell.

Figure 11.38

Unit cells of the 14 types of space lattices.

Simple cubic   Body-centered cubic   Face-centered cubic   Tetragonal   Body-centered tetragonal

Orthorhombic   End-centered orthorhombic   Body-centered orthorhombic   Face-centered orthorhombic

Hexagonal   Rhombohedral   Monoclinic   End-centered monoclinic   Triclinic

Simple

(a)

Body-centered

(b)

Face-centered

(c)

Figure 11.39

Cubic unit cells showing, in the upper figures, the locations of lattice points and, in the lower figures, metal atoms located on the lattice points.

completely within the unit cell shown. In order to determine the number of lattice points or of atoms in a unit cell, use the following four rules:

1. A point or atom lying completely within a unit cell belongs to that unit cell only, and we therefore count it as 1 when totaling the number of points or atoms in the unit cell.

2. A point or atom lying on a face of a unit cell is shared equally by two unit cells, and we therefore count it as $\frac{1}{2}$ when totaling the number of points or atoms in a unit cell.

3. A point or atom lying on an edge is shared by four unit cells and is therefore counted as $\frac{1}{4}$.

4. A point or atom lying at a corner is shared by eight unit cells and is therefore counted as $\frac{1}{8}$.

Now let us look more closely at the contents of some cubic unit cells. The lattice points associated with the space lattice of each of the three cubic unit cells are indicated in Fig. 11.39. There is 1 lattice point ($8 \times \frac{1}{8}$) in the unit cell of the simple cubic lattice [Fig. 11.39(a)]. Because a unit cell containing one lattice point is called a **primitive cell,** the simple cubic lattice is sometimes called a **primitive cubic lattice.** The second cell [Fig. 11.39(b)] has 2 lattice points, 1 at the corners ($8 \times \frac{1}{8}$) and 1 in the center of the cube. This is called a **body-centered cubic unit cell.** Such a cell has points with identical surroundings at the corners and at its center. The third cell [Fig. 11.39(c)] has 4 lattice points (points with identical environments), 1 at the corners $(8 \times \frac{1}{8})$ and 3 from the 6 face centers $(6 \times \frac{1}{2})$. This is called a **face-centered cubic unit cell.**

The structure of polonium (Section 11.14) may be described as consisting of a simple cubic space lattice with an atom located at each of the lattice points [Fig. 11.39(a)]. The length of the unit cell edge is 3.36 Å. Because the polonium atoms touch along the edges of the cell and CsCl is *not* a body-centered structure, the shortest distance between the centers of polonium atoms is 3.36 Å, and the radius of each polonium atom is thus 1.68 Å. (Remember that the distance between two atoms is measured between their nuclei.)

A metal with a body-centered cubic structure consists of a space lattice composed of body-centered cubic unit cells [Fig. 11.39(b)]. One metal atom is located on each lattice point, so there are two identical metal atoms (atoms with identical environments) in the unit cell. The atoms touch along the diagonal of the cubic unit cell.

A metal with a cubic closest packed structure may be described as consisting of a space lattice made up of face-centered cubic unit cells [Fig. 11.39(c)]. One metal atom is located on each lattice point, so there are four equivalent metal atoms in each unit cell. The structure in Fig. 11.39(c) is the same as that in Fig. 11.27(b), but the perspective is different. Note that the atoms touch along the diagonals of the faces of the cell.

Ionic compounds can also crystallize with cubic unit cells; CsCl, NaCl, and one form of ZnS (zinc blende) crystallize with cubic space lattices. Another form of ZnS (wurtzite) crystallizes with a hexagonal space lattice. The assumption of two or more crystal structures by the same substance is called **polymorphism.**

The structure of CsCl is simple cubic. Chloride ions are located on the lattice points at the corners of the cell, and the cesium ion is located at the center of the cell (Fig. 11.40). The cesium ion and the chloride ion touch along the diagonal of the cubic cell. There are one cesium ion and one chloride ion per unit cell, giving the 1-to-1 stoichiometry required by the formula for cesium chloride. There is no lattice point in the center of the cell and CsCl is *not* a body-centered structure because a cesium ion is not identical to a chloride ion.

Sodium chloride crystallizes with a face-centered cubic unit cell (Fig. 11.40). Chloride ions are located on the lattice points of a face-centered cubic unit cell. Sodium ions are located in the octahedral holes in the middle of the cell edges and in the center of the cell. The sodium and chloride ions touch each other. The unit cell contains four sodium

Figure 11.40

The unit cells of some ionic compounds of the general formula MX. The red spheres represent positive ions (cations), and the green or yellow spheres represent negative ions (anions). These structures have been expanded to show the geometrical relationships. In the crystal the cations and anions touch.

Cesium chloride
CsCl

● Cs$^+$

● Cl$^-$

Sodium chloride
NaCl

● Na$^+$

● Cl$^-$

Zinc blende
ZnS

● Zn^{2+}

● S^{2-}

= Ca^{2+}

= F^-

Figure 11.41

The unit cell of CaF_2. The red spheres represent calcium ions, Ca^{2+}, and the yellow-green spheres fluoride ions, F^-. Note the face-centered cubic array of Ca^{2+} and the simple cubic array of F^-. This structure has been expanded to show the geometrical relationships. In the crystal the cations and anions touch.

ions and four chloride ions, giving the 1-to-1 stoichiometry required by the formula, NaCl.

The cubic form of zinc sulfide, zinc blende, also crystallizes in a face-centered cubic unit cell (Fig. 11.40). This structure contains sulfide ions on the lattice points of a face-centered cubic lattice. (The arrangement of sulfide ions is identical to the arrangement of chloride ions in sodium chloride.) Zinc ions are located in alternating tetrahedral holes—that is, in one half of the tetrahedral holes. There are four zinc ions and four sulfide ions in the unit cell, making the unit cell neutral in net charge.

A calcium fluoride unit cell is also a face-centered cubic unit cell (Fig. 11.41), but in this case the cations are located on the lattice points; equivalent calcium ions are located on the lattice points of a face-centered cubic lattice. All of the tetrahedral sites in the face-centered cubic array of calcium ions are occupied by fluoride ions. There are four calcium ions and eight fluoride ions in a unit cell, giving a calcium-to-fluorine ratio of 1-to-2, as required by the formula of calcium fluoride, CaF_2. Close examination of Fig. 11.41 will reveal the simple cubic array of fluoride ions with calcium ions in one half of the cubic holes. The structure cannot be described in terms of a space lattice of points on the fluoride ions, because the fluoride ions do not all have identical environments. The orientation of the four calcium ions about the fluoride ions differs.

11.18 Calculation of Ionic Radii

If we know the edge length of a unit cell and the positions of the constituent ions, we can calculate ionic radii for the ions in the crystal lattice if we make certain assumptions about individual ionic shapes and interionic contacts. The following examples illustrate the method and assumptions for cubic structures.

Example 11.6

The edge length of the unit cell of LiCl (NaCl-like structure, face-centered cubic) is 5.14 Å. Assuming anion–anion contact, calculate the ionic radius for the chloride ion.

The NaCl structure (Fig. 11.40) contains a right triangle involving two chloride ions and one sodium ion. In the isomorphous LiCl structure, the lithium ion is so small that all ions in the structure touch, as shown in Fig. 11.34(b).

Because a, the distance between the center of a chloride ion and the center of a lithium ion, is $\frac{1}{2}$ of the edge length of the cubic unit cell,

$$a = \frac{5.14 \text{ Å}}{2}$$

Similarly, b is the distance between the center of a chloride ion and the center of a lithium ion and hence is also $\frac{1}{2}$ of the edge length of the cubic unit cell.

$$b = \frac{5.14 \text{ Å}}{2}$$

By the Pythagorean theorem, c, the distance between the centers of two chloride ions, can be calculated.

$$c^2 = a^2 + b^2$$
$$= \left(\frac{5.14}{2}\right)^2 + \left(\frac{5.14}{2}\right)^2 = 13.21$$

$$c = \sqrt{13.21} = 3.63 \text{ Å}$$

Because the anions are assumed to touch each other, c is twice the radius of one chloride ion. Hence the radius of the chloride ion is $\frac{1}{2}c$.

$$r_{Cl^-} = \tfrac{1}{2}c = \tfrac{1}{2} \times 3.63 \text{ Å} = 1.81 \text{ Å}$$

Example 11.7

The edge length of the unit cell of KCl (NaCl-like structure, face-centered cubic) is 6.28 Å. Assuming anion–cation contact, calculate the ionic radius for the potassium ion.

Inspection of the structure in Fig. 11.40 shows that the distance between the center of a potassium ion and the center of a chloride ion is $\frac{1}{2}$ of the edge length of the cubic unit cell for KCl, or

$$\tfrac{1}{2} \times 6.28 \text{ Å} = 3.14 \text{ Å}$$

Assuming anion–cation contact, 3.14 Å is the sum of the ionic radii for K^+ and Cl^-.

$$r_{K^+} + r_{Cl^-} = 3.14 \text{ Å}$$

In Example 11.6, r_{Cl^-} was calculated as 1.81 Å. Therefore

$$r_{K^+} = 3.14 \text{ Å} - 1.81 \text{ Å} = 1.33 \text{ Å}$$

Note that the chloride ions do not touch in solid potassium chloride.

It is important to realize that values for ionic radii calculated from the edge lengths of unit cells depend on numerous specific assumptions, such as a perfect spherical shape for ions, which are approximations at best. Hence such calculated values are themselves approximate, and comparisons cannot be pushed too far. Nevertheless, this method has proved useful for calculating ionic radii from experimental measurements such as X-ray crystallographic determinations.

11.19 The Lattice Energies of Ionic Crystals

The **lattice energy, U,** of an ionic compound may be defined as the energy required to separate the ions in a mole of the compound by infinite distances. For the ionic solid MX, the lattice energy is the enthalpy change of the *endothermic* process

$$MX(s) \longrightarrow M^{n+}(g) + X^{n-}(g) \qquad U = \Delta H^{\circ}_{298}$$

The same amount of energy is released when a mole of an ionic compound is formed by bringing positive and negative ions together from infinite distances. Lattice energies can be calculated from basic principles, or they can be measured experimentally.

The calculation of lattice energies is based primarily on the work of Born, Lande, and Mayer. They derived the following equation to express the lattice energy, U, of an ionic crystal:

$$U = \frac{C(Z^+ Z^-)}{R_0}$$

C is a constant that depends on the type of crystal structure and the electronic structures of the ions; Z^+ and Z^- are the charges on the ions; and R_0 is the interionic distance (the sum of the radii of the positive and negative ions). For a given structure the principal factors determining the lattice energy are Z^+, Z^-, and R_0. The lattice energy increases rapidly with the charges on the ions. When all other parameters are kept constant, doubling the charge on both cation and anion quadruples the lattice energy. For example, the lattice energy of LiF (Li^+ and F^-; $Z^+ = 1$, $Z^- = -1$) is 1023 kilojoules per mole, whereas that of MgO (Mg^{2+} and O^{2-}; $Z^+ = 2$, $Z^- = -2$) is 3900 kilojoules per mole (R_0 is nearly the same for both compounds).

The lattice energy also increases rapidly with decreasing interionic distance in the crystal lattice, which may result from decreases in the cation radius, the anion radius, or both. Some crystals that exhibit a large difference in interionic distances and lattice energies are lithium fluoride and rubidium chloride (table at left).

	Interionic Distance, R_0	Lattice Energy, U
LiF	2.008 Å	1023 kJ mol^{-1}
RbCl	3.28 Å	680 kJ mol^{-1}

The large lattice energies of many ionic compounds result from strong electrostatic forces between the ions in the crystal. These strong interionic forces are also responsible for the relatively large heats of fusion, sublimation, and vaporization and for the high melting and boiling temperatures of these compounds, compared to most molecular compounds. These forces must be overcome in order to vaporize a crystal to separated gaseous ions, for example. The same strong forces are responsible for the fact that ionic crystals are generally hard, dense, rigid, and nonvolatile. Some covalent substances, such as diamond and silicon carbide, also have similar properties. In such cases the very strong forces in the crystal are due to strong covalent bonds, which extend in three dimensions throughout the crystal (Fig. 11.23), rather than to the weaker London forces usually found in molecular compounds.

11.20 The Born–Haber Cycle

The lattice energies of only a few ionic crystals have been measured, because it is not possible to measure most lattice energies directly. However, a cyclic process can be used to calculate the lattice energy from other quantities. This **Born–Haber cycle** is a cycle that involves ΔH_f°, the enthalpy of formation of the compound (Section 4.4); I, the ionization energy of the metal (Section 6.3, Part 3); $E.A.$, the electron affinity of the nonmetal (Section 6.3, Part 4); ΔH_s°, the enthalpy of sublimation of the metal; D, the bond dissociation energy of the nonmetal (Section 7.9); and U, the lattice energy of the compound. The Born–Haber cycle for sodium chloride analyzes the formation of $NaCl(s)$ from $Na(s)$ and $\frac{1}{2} Cl_2(g)$ as a step-by-step process that may be expressed diagrammatically as follows, with the overall change in color and the individual steps in black.

$$
\begin{array}{ccc}
Na^+(g) + Cl^-(g) & & \\
\uparrow I \quad\quad \downarrow {-E.A.} & \searrow {-U} & \\
Na(g) + Cl(g) & & \\
\uparrow \Delta H_s^\circ \quad \uparrow \frac{1}{2}D & & \\
Na(s) + \frac{1}{2}Cl_2(g) & \xrightarrow{\Delta H_f^\circ} & NaCl(s)
\end{array}
$$

This diagram indicates hypothetical steps in the formation of sodium chloride from 1 mole of sodium metal and $\frac{1}{2}$ mole of chlorine gas. First we assume that the sodium metal

Rhombic sulfur, S_8

is vaporized and the bonds in the diatomic chlorine molecules are broken. Then the sodium atoms are ionized, and the electrons from them are transferred to the chlorine atoms to form chloride ions. The gaseous sodium ions and chloride ions thus formed come together to give solid sodium chloride. The enthalpy change in this step is the negative of the lattice energy, which is the amount of energy required to produce 1 mole of gaseous sodium ions and 1 mole of gaseous chloride ions from 1 mole of solid sodium chloride. The total energy evolved in this hypothetical preparation of sodium chloride is equal to the experimentally determined enthalpy of formation, ΔH_f°, of the compound from its elements. Hess's law (Section 4.5) can be used to show the relationship between the enthalpies of the individual steps and the enthalpy of formation as follows:

1. Enthalpy of sublimation of Na(s)

$$Na(s) \longrightarrow Na(g) \qquad\qquad \Delta H = \Delta H_s^\circ \quad = 109 \text{ kJ}$$

2. One-half of the bond energy of Cl_2

$$\tfrac{1}{2}Cl_2(g) \longrightarrow Cl(g) \qquad\qquad \Delta H = \tfrac{1}{2}D \quad = 122 \text{ kJ}$$

3. Ionization energy of Na(g)

$$Na(g) \longrightarrow Na^+(g) + e^- \qquad\qquad \Delta H = I \qquad = 496 \text{ kJ}$$

4. Negative of the electron affinity of Cl

$$Cl(g) + e^- \longrightarrow Cl^-(g) \qquad\qquad \Delta H = -E.A. = -368 \text{ kJ}$$

5. Negative of the lattice energy of NaCl(s)

$$Na^+(g) + Cl^-(g) \longrightarrow NaCl(s) \qquad\qquad \Delta H = -U \quad = ?$$

6. Enthalpy of formation of NaCl(s), Appendix I: add Steps 1–5

$$Na(s) + \tfrac{1}{2}Cl_2(g) \longrightarrow NaCl(s) \qquad\qquad \Delta H = \Delta H_f^\circ \quad = -411 \text{ kJ}$$

$$\Delta H_f^\circ = \Delta H_s^\circ + \tfrac{1}{2}D + I + (-E.A.) + (-U)$$

The value of ΔH_f° is accurately known for many substances. If the other thermochemical values are available, we can solve for the lattice energy, U, by rearranging the equation for ΔH_f° as follows:

$$U = -\Delta H_f^\circ + \Delta H_s^\circ + \tfrac{1}{2}D + I - E.A.$$

For sodium chloride, using the above data, the lattice energy is

$$U = (411 + 109 + 122 + 496 - 368) \text{ kJ} = 770 \text{ kJ}$$

The Born–Haber cycle may be used to calculate any one of the quantities in the equation for lattice energy, provided that all the others are known. Usually ΔH_f°, ΔH_s°, I, and D are known. The direct measurement of electron affinities is rather difficult, and accurate values of electron affinity have been determined only for the halogens. For halogen compounds, then, the Born–Haber cycle can be used to calculate lattice energies, which are found to agree well with those obtained by other means. Having verified that the cycle gives satisfactory calculated values, chemists use it to calculate electron affinities that cannot be measured directly using values of U calculated by the method of Born, Lande, and Mayer (Section 11.19).

🔟.21 X-Ray Diffraction

The size of the unit cell and the arrangement of atoms in a crystal can be determined experimentally from measurements of the **diffraction** of X rays by the crystal. X rays are electromagnetic radiation with wavelengths (Section 5.8) about as long as the distance between neighboring atoms in crystals (about 2 Å).

There is a simple mathematical relationship among the wavelength λ of the X rays, the distance between the planes in the crystal, and the angle of diffraction (reflection). When a beam of monochromatic X rays strikes two planes of a crystal at an angle θ, it is reflected (Fig. 11.42). The rays from the lower plane travel farther than those from the upper plane by a distance equal to the sum of the distances BC and CD. If this distance is equal to 1, 2, 3, or any other integral number of wavelengths (such that $n\lambda = BC + CD$), the two beams emerging from the crystal will be in phase and will reinforce each other. From the right triangle ABC of Fig. 11.42,

$$\sin BAC = \frac{BC}{AC}$$

Rearranging gives

$$BC = AC \sin BAC$$

The distance AC is the distance between the crystal planes, which we will call d. Angle BAC is equal to θ. Then

$$BC = d \sin \theta$$

But the difference in the path lengths of the two beams is equal to $BC + CD$. Because $BC = CD$, the total difference in path length is $2BC$. X rays will be reflected, provided that, as indicated previously,

$$n\lambda = BC + CD = 2BC$$

Hence

$$n\lambda = 2d \sin \theta$$

which is called the **Bragg equation** after W. H. Bragg, the English physicist who showed that the diffraction of X rays can be interpreted as though a crystal were a stack of planes.

If the X rays strike the crystal at any angle other than θ, the extra distance $BC + CD$ will not be equal to an integral number of wavelengths, and there will be interference of the reflected rays. This will destroy the intensity of the reflected rays.

Selenite, $CaSeO_4 \cdot 2H_2O$

Figure 11.42

Diffraction of a monochromatic beam of X rays by planes of atoms in a crystal.

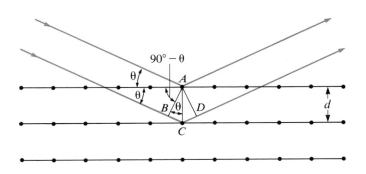

The reflection corresponding to $n = 1$ is called the first-order reflection; that corresponding to $n = 2$ is the second-order reflection; and so forth. Each successive order has a larger angle.

By rotating a crystal and varying the angle θ at which the X-ray beam strikes it, we can determine the values of θ at which diffraction occurs by looking for the maximum diffracted intensities. If the wavelength of the X rays is known, the spacing d of the planes within the crystal can be determined from these values. On the other hand, if the X rays strike planes for which d is known, their wavelength can be determined by measuring the angles.

For Review

Summary

The physical properties of condensed matter (liquids and solids) can be explained in terms of the kinetic-molecular theory, which we used in Chapter 10 to explain the physical properties of gases. In a liquid, the intermolecular attractive forces hold the molecules in contact, although they still have sufficient kinetic energy to move past each other (**diffuse**). Because the molecules are in contact, liquids are essentially incompressible. The speeds of the molecules in a liquid vary, so some molecules have enough kinetic energy to escape from the liquid, leading to **evaporation.** The pressure of a vapor in dynamic equilibrium with a liquid is called the **vapor pressure** of the liquid. The vapor pressure of a liquid increases with increasing temperature, and the **boiling point** of the liquid is reached when its vapor pressure equals the external pressure on the liquid. The **normal boiling point** of a liquid is the temperature at which its vapor pressure is equal to 1 atmosphere.

When the temperature of a liquid becomes sufficiently low, or the pressure on the liquid sufficiently high, the molecules can no longer move past each other and a rigid solid forms. Many solids are **crystalline;** that is, they are composed of a repeating pattern of atoms, molecules, or ions. Others are **amorphous solids,** in which the disordered arrangement of molecules found in a liquid is retained. Crystalline solids melt at that specific temperature at which enough energy has been added for the kinetic energy of their molecules just to overcome the intermolecular attractive forces holding the molecules in their fixed positions in the crystal. The temperature at which a solid and its liquid are in equilibrium is called the **melting point** of the solid or the **freezing point** of the liquid. Amorphous solids do not have sharp melting points but rather soften over a range of temperature. Some solids exhibit a measurable vapor pressure and will **sublime.**

The conditions under which a solid and a liquid, a liquid and a gas, or a solid and a vapor are in equilibrium are described by a **phase diagram.** At the **triple point,** all three phases are in equilibrium.

Intermolecular attractive forces, collectively referred to as **van der Waals forces,** are responsible for the behavior of liquids and solids and are electrostatic in nature. **Dipole–dipole attractions** result from the electrostatic attraction of the negative end of one dipolar molecule for the positive end of another. **Ion–dipole attractions** result from the electrostatic attraction of an ion for a dipolar molecule. The temporary dipole that results from the motion of the electrons in an atom can induce a dipole in an adjacent atom and give rise to the **London dispersion force.** London forces increase with increasing molecular size. Forces between molecules also result from **ion-induced dipole attractions** and **dipole-induced dipole attractions.** **Hydrogen bonding** is a special

X-ray diffraction photograph of a grain of salt, a single crystal of sodium chloride. When the crystal was rotated in a beam of X rays, the X rays diffracted from many different sets of planes in the crystal. The spacing of the spots (the locations where the diffracted beams struck the film) indicates the size of the unit cell of the crystal. The intensity (brightness) of each spot depends on the location of the atoms in the unit cell. It is possible to determine the location of the atoms in the unit cell from the relative intensities of the spots.

type of dipole–dipole attraction that results when hydrogen is bonded between two very electronegative elements such as F, O, N, or Cl.

The various intermolecular forces are responsible for the critical temperature and critical pressure of a substance. The **critical temperature** of a substance is that temperature above which the substance cannot be liquefied, no matter how much pressure is applied. The **critical pressure** is the pressure required to liquefy a gas at its critical temperature.

The structures of crystalline metals and simple ionic compounds can be described in terms of packing of spheres. Metal atoms can pack in **hexagonal closest packed structures, cubic closest packed structures, body-centered structures,** and **simple cubic structures.** The anions in simple ionic structures commonly adopt one of these structures, and the cations occupy the spaces remaining between the anions. Small cations usually occupy **tetrahedral holes** in a closest packed array of anions. Larger cations usually occupy **octahedral holes.** Still larger cations can occupy **cubic holes** in a simple cubic array of anions. The **radius ratio rule** serves as a guide to the **coordination number** of the cation. The structure of a solid can be described by indicating the size and shape of a **unit cell** and the contents of the cell. The dimensions of a unit cell can be determined by a study of the **diffraction** of X rays from a crystal.

The energy required to separate the ions in a mole of an ionic compound by an infinite distance is called the **lattice energy** of the compound. The lattice energy is proportional to the product of the charges on the ions and inversely proportional to the distance between their centers. Lattice energies can be calculated, or they can be determined by using Hess's law in a **Born–Haber cycle.**

Key Terms and Concepts

adhesive force (11.11)
amorphous solid (11.12)
body-centered cubic structure (11.14)
body-centered cubic unit cell (11.17)
boiling point (11.6)
Born–Haber cycle (11.20)
Bragg equation (11.21)
cohesive force (11.11)
condensation (11.5)
coordination number (11.14)
covalent solid (11.12)
critical pressure (11.9)
critical temperature (11.9)
crystal defects (11.13)
crystalline solid (11.12)
cubic closest packed structure (11.14)
dipole–dipole attraction (11.2)
dipole-induced dipole attraction (11.3)

distillation (11.7)
dynamic equilibrium (11.5)
evaporation (11.5)
face-centered cubic structure (11.14)
face-centered cubic unit cell (11.17)
freezing point (11.8)
glass (11.12)
hexagonal closest packed structure (11.14)
hydrogen bond (11.4)
intermolecular forces (11.2)
interstitial sites (11.13)
ion–dipole attraction (11.2)
ionic radius (11.16, 11.18)
ionic solid (11.12)
ion-induced dipole attraction (11.3)
isomorphous structures (11.14)
lattice energy (11.19, 11.20)
London dispersion force (11.3)

melting point (11.8)
metallic solid (11.12)
molecular solid (11.12)
normal boiling point (11.6)
octahedral hole (11.15)
phase diagram (11.10)
radius ratio (11.16)
simple cubic structure (11.14)
space lattice (11.17)
sublimation (11.5)
surface tension (11.11)
tetrahedral hole (11.15)
triple point (11.10)
unit cell (11.17)
van der Waals force (11.2)
vapor pressure (11.5)
viscosity (11.11)
X-ray diffraction (11.21)

Exercises

Answers for selected even-numbered exercises marked by red numbers appear at the end of the book. The worked-out solutions to all even-numbered exercises appear in the *Solutions Guide.*

Kinetic-Molecular Theory and the Condensed State

1. The density of liquid NH_3 is 0.64 g/mL; the density of gaseous NH_3 at STP is 0.0007 g/mL. Explain the difference between the densities of these two phases.

2. In what ways are liquids similar to solids? In what ways are liquids similar to gases?

3. The types of intermolecular forces in a substance are identical whether it is a solid, a liquid, or a gas. Why, then, does a substance change phase from a gas to a liquid or to a solid?

4. Describe how the motions of the molecules change as a substance changes from a solid to a liquid and from a liquid to a gas.

5. Explain why liquids assume the shape of any container into which they are poured, whereas solids are rigid and retain their shape.

6. How does an increase in pressure lead to liquefaction of a gas?

7. How does a decrease in temperature lead to liquefaction of a gas?

8. Ethyl chloride (b.p. = 13°C) is used as a local anesthetic. When the liquid is sprayed on the skin, it cools the skin enough to freeze and numb it. Explain the cooling effect of liquid ethyl chloride.

9. The density of liquid ethyl chloride, C_2H_5Cl, is 0.903 g/mL at its boiling temperature of 13°C. What is the density of gaseous ethyl chloride, in grams per milliliter, at the same temperature and a pressure of 1 atm? (*Hint:* Use the ideal gas equation, Section 10.8.)

10. Why does iodine sublime more rapidly at 110°C than at 25°C?

Attractive Forces in Liquids and Solids

11. What evidence indicates that all neutral atoms and molecules exert attractive forces on each other?

12. Define the following and give an example of each: (a) dispersion force, (b) dipole–dipole attraction, (c) ion–dipole attraction, (d) dipole-induced dipole attraction, (e) ion-induced dipole attraction.

13. Why do the boiling points of the noble gases increase in the order He < Ne < Ar < Kr < Xe?

14. Why do the molar enthalpies of vaporization of the following liquids increase in the order CH_4 < C_2H_6 < C_3H_8, even though all three liquids are stabilized by the same dispersion forces (forces between the hydrogen atoms on the outside of the molecules)?

15. Why do the enthalpies of vaporization of the following liquids increase in the order CH_4 < NH_3 < H_2O, even though all three liquids have approximately the same molecular mass?

16. Identify and describe the most important interatomic or intermolecular force responsible for forming each of the following solids: Cu, O_2, NO, HF, Si, $CaCl_2$.

17. Identify the two most important forces that cause the following to crystallize:
    (a) CH_3CH_2OH (c) CH_3CH_2Cl
    (b) NH_4F, an ionic solid   (d) $Xe \cdot (H_2O)_7$

18. Explain why a hydrogen bond between two water molecules is weaker than a hydrogen bond between two hydrogen fluoride molecules.

19. Silane (SiH_4), phosphine (PH_3), and hydrogen sulfide (H_2S) melt at −185°C, −133°C, and −85°C, respectively. What does this suggest about the polar character and intermolecular attractions in the three compounds?

20. The enthalpy of vaporization of $CS_2(l)$ is 119 J/g. Would you expect the enthalpy of vaporization of $CO_2(l)$ to be 226 J/g, 119 J/g, or 27 J/g? Explain your answer.

21. The melting point of $O_2(s)$ is −218°C. Would you expect the melting point of $N_2(s)$ to be −210°C, −218°C, or −228°C? Explain your answer.

22. The melting point of $H_2O(s)$ is 0°C. Would you expect the melting point of $H_2S(s)$ to be −85°C, 0°C, or 185°C? Explain your answer.

23. Which member of each of the following pairs has the higher vapor pressure at a given temperature?
    (a) $Br_2(s)$ or $I_2(s)$ (c) $LiCl(l)$ or $MgS(l)$
    (b) $HBr(s)$ or $Kr(s)$ (d) $CaCl_2(s)$ or $Cl_2(s)$

24. The hydrogen bonds in liquid hydrogen fluoride, HF, are stronger than those in liquid water, yet the molar enthalpy of vaporization of liquid hydrogen fluoride is less than that of water. Explain.

Melting, Evaporation, and Boiling

25. What feature characterizes as dynamic the equilibrium between a liquid and its vapor in a closed container?

26. Why does spilled gasoline evaporate more rapidly on a hot day than on a cold day?

27. Explain why the vapor pressure of a liquid increases as its temperature increases.

28. How does the boiling of a liquid differ from its evaporation?

29. When is the boiling point of a liquid equal to its normal boiling point?

30. What is the approximate boiling point of water in Denver when the atmospheric pressure is 625 torr? See Fig. 11.11 for data.

31. The liquid C_4H_{10} in a butane lighter has a boiling point of −1°C; the octane (C_8H_{18}) in gasoline has a boiling point of 125°C. Explain why the boiling point of $C_4H_{10}(l)$ is lower than that of $C_8H_{18}(l)$, even though the intermolecular forces are of the same type in both liquids.

32. (a) Look up the boiling points of HF, HCl, HBr, and HI in a handbook and explain why they vary as they do.
    (b) Look up the boiling points of Ne, Ar, Kr, and Xe in a handbook and explain why they vary as they do.
    (c) Neon and HF have approximately the same molecular masses. Explain why their boiling points differ.

(d) Compare the change in the boiling points of Ne, Ar, Kr, and Xe with the change of the boiling points of HF, HCl, HBr, and HI and explain the difference between the changes with increasing atomic or molecular mass.

33. How do we know that some solids such as ice and naphthalene have vapor pressures sufficient to evaporate?

34. What is the relationship between the intermolecular forces in a solid and its melting temperature?

35. A syringe like that shown in Fig. 11.18(a) at a temperature of 20°C is filled with liquid ether in such a way that there is no space for any vapor.
    (a) In one experiment the temperature is kept constant and the plunger is withdrawn somewhat, forming a volume that can be occupied by vapor. What is the approximate pressure of the vapor produced?
    (b) If the system were insulated and no heat could enter or leave, would the temperature of the liquid increase, decrease, or remain constant as the plunger was withdrawn? Explain.

36. Arrange each of the following sets of compounds in order of increasing boiling temperature:
    (a) HCl, H_2S, SiH_4 (c) CH_4, C_2H_6, C_3H_8
    (b) F_2, Cl_2, Br_2, I_2 (d) N_2, NO, CaO

Phase Diagrams, Critical Temperature, and Critical Pressure

37. Is it possible to liquefy oxygen at room temperature (about 25°C)? Is it possible to liquefy ammonia at room temperature? Explain your answers.

38. Draw a rough graph that shows how the pressure changes inside a cylinder of carbon dioxide, which contains $CO_2(l)$ and $CO_2(g)$ at a pressure of 65 atmospheres, as gaseous carbon dioxide is released from the cylinder at constant temperature. Draw a similar graph for the pressure change as $O_2(g)$ is released from a cylinder of oxygen gas at 25°C.

39. What is the triple point of a substance?

40. From the phase diagram for water [Fig. 11.19(a)], determine the physical state of water at:
    (a) −10°C and 400 torr   (e) 80°C and 50 torr
    (b) 25°C and 700 torr   (f) −10°C and 2 torr
    (c) 50°C and 300 torr   (g) 50°C and 2 torr
    (d) 90°C and 300 torr

41. What phase changes can water undergo as the temperature changes if the pressure is held at 2 torr? If the pressure is held at 400 torr?

42. What phase changes can water undergo as the pressure changes if the temperature is held at 0.005°C? If the temperature is held at 40°C? At −40°C?

43. If one continues beyond point C on the line BC in Fig. 11.19(a), at what temperature and pressure does the line end?

44. Using the phase diagram for water (Fig. 11.19), determine the following:
    (a) The approximate pressure at which water changes from a gas to a liquid at 60°C. At 20°C.
    (b) The approximate temperature at which water converts from a solid to a liquid at 300 torr. From a liquid to a gas.
    (c) The freezing point of water at 5 torr.

45. From the accompanying phase diagram for carbon dioxide, determine the physical state of CO_2 at:
    (a) −30°C and 20 atm   (e) 20°C and 15 atm
    (b) −60°C and 10 atm   (f) −10°C and 25 atm
    (c) −60°C and 1 atm   (g) 20°C and 20 atm
    (d) 0°C and 1 atm

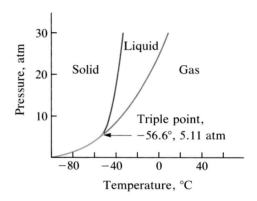

46. What phase changes can carbon dioxide undergo as the temperature changes if the pressure is held at 20 atmospheres? If the pressure is held at 2 atmospheres? (See Exercise 45 for the phase diagram of carbon dioxide.)

47. What phase changes can carbon dioxide undergo as the pressure changes if the temperature is held at −60°C? If the temperature is held at −40°C? At 40°C? (See Exercise 45 for the phase diagram of carbon dioxide.)

48. If one continues along the line dividing the liquid phase from the gas phase in the phase diagram for carbon dioxide (Exercise 45), at what temperature and pressure does the line end?

49. Dry ice, $CO_2(s)$, does not melt at atmospheric pressure. It sublimes at a temperature of −78°C. What is the lowest pressure at which $CO_2(s)$ will melt to give $CO_2(l)$? At approximately what temperature will this occur? (See Exercise 45 for the phase diagram for CO_2.)

Properties of Solids

50. What types of liquids form amorphous solids?

51. Explain why a sample of amorphous boric oxide, (B_2O_3, Fig. 11.21) could be considered a form of a liquid even though it looks like a solid, is rigid, and shatters when struck with a hammer.

52. Explain why ice, which is a crystalline solid, has a melting temperature of 0°C, whereas butter, which is an amorphous solid, softens over a range of temperatures.

53. Identify the type of crystalline solid (metallic, covalent ionic, or molecular) formed by each of the following substances:

    (a) SiO_2 (e) KCl   (i) Cu
    (b) CO   (f) C (diamond) (j) $BaSO_4$
    (c) NH_3 (g) NH_4F (k) Polyethylene
    (d) C_2H_5OH (h) Elemental sulfur   (Section 2.12)

54. What is the coordination number of a chromium atom in the body-centered cubic structure of chromium?

55. Cobalt metal crystallizes in a hexagonal closest packed structure. What is the coordination number of a cobalt atom?

56. Describe the crystal structure of aluminum, which crystallizes with four equivalent metal atoms in a cubic unit cell.

57. Describe the crystal structure of iron, which crystallizes with two equivalent metal atoms in a cubic unit cell.

58. The free space in a metal may be found by subtracting the volume of the atoms in a unit cell from the volume of the cell. Calculate the percentage of free space in each of the three cubic lattices if all atoms in each are of equal size and touch their nearest neighbors. Which of these structures represents the most efficient packing? That is, which packs with the least amount of unused space?

59. Tungsten crystallizes in a body-centered cubic unit cell with an edge length of 3.165 Å.
    (a) What is the atomic radius of tungsten in this structure?
    (b) Calculate the density of tungsten.

60. Lead (atomic radius = 1.75 Å) crystallizes in a face-centered cubic unit cell with the nearest neighbors in contact.
    (a) Calculate the edge length of the unit cell.
    (b) Calculate the density of lead.

61. Silver crystallizes in a face-centered cubic unit cell with a silver atom on each lattice point. If the edge length of the unit cell is 4.050 Å, what is the atomic radius of silver? Calculate the density of silver.

62. What is the formula of rutile, a mineral that may be described as a closest packed array of oxide ions with titanium atoms in $\frac{1}{2}$ of the octahedral holes? Explain your answer.

63. Cadmium sulfide, sometimes used as a yellow pigment by artists, crystallizes with cadmium occupying $\frac{1}{2}$ of the tetrahedral holes in a closest packed array of sulfide ions. What is the formula of cadmium sulfide? Explain your answer.

64. Although it is a covalent compound, silicon carbide can be described as a cubic closest packed array of silicon atoms, with carbon atoms in $\frac{1}{2}$ of the tetrahedral holes. What is the coordination number of carbon in silicon carbide? What is the hybridization of the silicon and carbon atoms? Explain your answer.

65. A compound of thallium and iodine crystallizes in a simple cubic array of iodide ions with thallium ions in all of the cubic holes. What is the formula of this iodide? Explain your answer.

66. The magnetic oxide of cobalt used on recording tapes crystallizes with cobalt atoms occupying $\frac{1}{8}$ of the tetrahedral holes and $\frac{1}{2}$ of the octahedral holes in a closest packed array of oxide ions. What is the empirical formula? Explain your answer.

67. A compound containing zinc, aluminum, and sulfur crystallizes with a closest packed array of sulfide ions. Zinc ions are found in $\frac{1}{8}$ of the tetrahedral holes, and aluminum ions in $\frac{1}{2}$ of the octahedral holes. What is the empirical formula of the compound? Explain your answer.

68. Why are compounds that are isomorphous with ZnS generally not observed when the radius ratio for the compound is greater than 0.42?

69. Explain why the chemically similar alkali metal chlorides NaCl and CsCl have different structures, whereas the chemically different NaCl and MnS have the same structure.

70. Each of the following compounds crystallizes in a structure matching that of NaCl, CsCl, ZnS, or CaF_2. From the radius ratio, predict which structure is formed by each. Show your work.

    (a) ZnSe   (e) SrSe   (i) TlBr
    (b) BaF_2 (f) SrF_2 (j) CaS
    (c) NaF   (g) CoO   (k) BeO
    (d) AlAs   (h) CsBr

71. Rubidium iodide crystallizes with a cubic unit cell that contains iodide ions at the corners and a rubidium ion in the center. What is the formula of the compound? Explain your answer.

72. A cubic unit cell contains manganese ions at the corners and fluoride ions at the center of each edge.
    (a) What is the empirical formula of this compound? Explain your answer.
    (b) What is the coordination number of the Mn^{3+} ion?
    (c) Calculate the edge length of the unit cell if the radius of a Mn^{3+} ion is 0.65 Å.
    (d) Calculate the density of the compound.

73. A cubic unit cell contains a cobalt ion in the center of the cell, lanthanum(III) (La^{3+}) ions at the corners of the cell, and oxide ions in the center of each face. What is the empirical formula of this compound? What is the oxidation number of the cobalt ion? Explain your answer.

74. Thallium(I) iodide crystallizes with the same structure as CsCl. The edge length of the unit cell of TlI is 4.20 Å. Calculate the ionic radius of Tl^+. (The ionic radius of I^- may be found on the inside of the back cover.)

75. LiH crystallizes with the same crystal structure as NaCl. The edge length of the cubic unit cell of LiH is 4.08 Å.
    (a) Calculate the ionic radius of H^-. (The ionic radius of Li^+ may be found on the inside of the back cover.)
    (b) Which contains a greater mass of hydrogen, 1.00 cm^3 of liquid H_2 (density 0.0899 g/cm^3) or 1.00 cm^3 of LiH?

76. The unit cell edge length of CaF_2 is 5.46295 Å. The density of CaF_2 is 3.1805 g/cm^3. From these data and the atomic masses of calcium and fluorine, calculate Avogadro's number.

77. The lattice energy of KF is 794 kJ mol^{-1}, and the interionic distance is 2.69 Å. The Sr–O distance in SrO, which has the same structure as KF, is 2.53 Å. Is the lattice energy of SrO about 745, 844, 2987, 3176, or 3375 kJ mol^{-1}? Explain your answer.

78. The lattice energy of LiF is 1023 kJ mol^{-1}, and the Li–F distance is 2.008 Å. NaF crystallizes in the same structure as LiF but with a Na–F distance of 2.31 Å. Which of the following values most closely approximates the lattice energy of NaF: 510, 890, 1023, 1175, or 4090 kJ mol^{-1}? Explain your choice.

79. What is the spacing between crystal planes that diffract X rays with a wavelength of 1.541 Å at an angle θ of 15.55° (first-order reflection)?

80. What X-ray wavelength would give a second-order reflection ($n = 2$) with an angle θ of 10.40° from planes with a spacing of 4.00 Å?

81. Gold crystallizes in a face-centered cubic unit cell. The second-order reflection ($n = 2$) of X rays for the planes that make up the tops and bottoms of the unit cells is at $\theta = 22.20°$. The wavelength of the X rays is 1.54 Å. What is the density of metallic gold?

Additional Exercises

82. Most reactions in a chemical laboratory are run in the gaseous or liquid state. If molecules have to come in contact in order to react, explain why a mixture of solid reagents does not, in general, react very rapidly.

83. What is the height, in millimeters, of the mercury column in Fig. 11.10? See Section 10.11 for useful information.

84. Eighteen grams of liquid water occupies 18.8 mL at 100°C. Determine what volume 18 g of water vapor occupies at 100°C, assuming that water vapor behaves like an ideal gas.

85. What is the noble gas used in the example illustrated in Fig. 11.5?

86. Which member of each of the following pairs has the stronger attractive forces? Verify your answers by using enthalpies of vaporization (Section 4.4 and Appendix I).
    (a) $Al(s)$ or $I_2(s)$
    (b) $CHCl_3(l)$ or $CCl_4(l)$
    (c) $CH_3OH(l)$ or $C_2H_5OH(l)$
    (d) $C_2H_5Cl(l)$ or $C_2H_5OH(l)$

87. Explain why some molecules in a solid may have enough energy to sublime away from the solid, even though the solid does not contain enough energy to melt.

88. How much energy is released when 250 g of steam at 135°C is converted to ice at −20°C? The specific heat of steam is

2.00 J/g K; that of liquid water is 4.18 J/g K; that of ice is 2.04 J/g K.

89. How much energy is required to convert 135.0 g of ice at −8.0°C to steam at 225°C? (See Exercise 88 for additional information.)

90. By referring to Fig. 11.11, determine the approximate boiling point of ethyl ether at 400 torr, of ethyl alcohol at 0.25 atm, and of water at 55 kPa. At what temperature is the vapor pressure of ethyl alcohol equal to the vapor pressure of ethyl ether at 20°C?

91. Is work done on a gas or by the gas when it condenses to a liquid?

92. The melting points of NaCl, KCl, and RbCl decrease with increasing atomic number of the alkali metal. Suggest an explanation.

93. How much heat must be removed to condense 2.00 L of $HCN(g)$ at 25°C and 1 atmosphere to a liquid under the same conditions? The enthalpy of vaporization of $HCN(l)$ is 26 kJ mol^{-1}.

94. The enthalpy of vaporization of water is larger than its enthalpy of fusion. Explain why.

95. (a) To break each hydrogen bond in ice requires 3.5×10^{-20} J. The measured enthalpy of fusion of ice is 6.01 kJ mol^{-1}. Essentially all of the energy involved in the enthalpy of fusion goes to break hydrogen bonds. What percentage of the hydrogen bonds is broken when ice is converted to liquid water?
    (b) How much additional heat would be required, per mole, to break the remaining hydrogen bonds?

96. Which of the following elements reacts with sulfur to form a solid in which the sulfur atoms form a closest packed array with all of the octahedral holes occupied: Li, Na, Be, Ca, Al, O_2?

97. The carbon atoms in the unit cell of diamond occupy the same positions as both the zinc and sulfur atoms in cubic zinc sulfide. How many carbon atoms are found in the unit cell of diamond? The bonds between the carbon atoms are covalent. What is the hybridization of a carbon atom in diamond?

98. The density of diamond is 3.51 g/cm^3. Calculate the length of the unit cell edge of diamond. (The structure of diamond is described in Exercise 97 and shown in Fig. 11.23.)

99. When an electron in an excited molybdenum atom falls from the L to the K shell, an X ray is emitted. These X rays are diffracted at an angle of 7.75° by planes with a separation of 2.64 Å. What is the difference in energy between the K shell and the L shell in molybdenum?

100. What is the percent by mass of cobalt in a compound that contains cobalt and fluorine if the structure can be described as a closest packed array of fluoride atoms with cobalt in $\frac{1}{3}$ of the octahedral holes? What is the oxidation number of cobalt?

Solutions; Colloids

continued

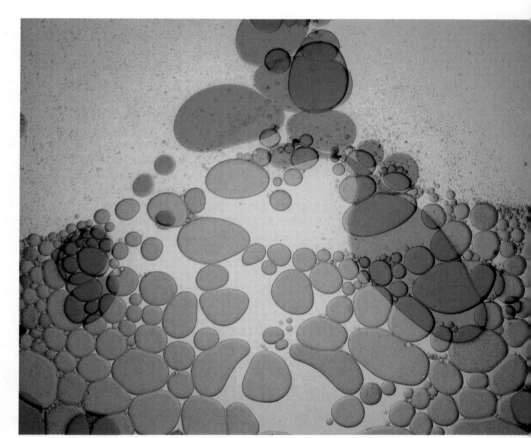

Immiscible liquids of different colors and densities produce fascinating patterns.

Solutions are crucial to the processes that sustain life and to many other processes that involve chemical reactions. When food is digested, for example, the nutrients must go into solution before they can pass through the walls of the intestine into the blood. There, they are carried throughout the body in solution. The dissolution of substances from the air and the earth is important in converting rocks to soil, in altering the fertility of the soil, and in changing the form of the earth's surface. Many minerals are the result of reactions that have taken place in solution.

Most chemical reactions take place in solution. In a gaseous or liquid solution, molecules and ions can move freely, come into contact with each other, and react. In solids, molecules and ions cannot move freely; chemical reactions between solids, if they occur at all, are generally very slow.

In this chapter we will consider the nature of solutions. We will examine factors that determine whether a solution will form and the properties of any solution that results. In addition, we will discuss colloids—systems that resemble solutions but consist of dispersions of particles that are somewhat larger than ordinary molecules or ions.

12.1 The Nature of Solutions

When sugar is stirred with enough water, the sugar dissolves and a solution of sugar in water is formed. The solution consists of the **solute** (the substance that dissolves—in this case, sugar) and the **solvent** (the substance in which a solute dissolves—in this case, water). The molecules of sugar are uniformly distributed among the molecules of water; that is, the solution is a **homogeneous mixture** of solute and solvent molecules. The molecules of sugar diffuse continuously through the water, and although sugar molecules are heavier than water molecules, the sugar does not settle out upon standing.

When potassium dichromate, $K_2Cr_2O_7$, dissolves in water (Fig. 12.1), the potassium ions and dichromate ions from the crystalline solid become uniformly distributed throughout the water. This solution is a homogeneous mixture of water molecules, potassium ions, and dichromate ions. The solute particles (ions in this case) diffuse through the water just as molecular solutes do; they do not settle out upon standing.

A solution with a small proportion of solute to solvent is **dilute;** one with a large proportion of solute to solvent is **concentrated** (Fig. 12.1). A solution is **unsaturated** when more solute will dissolve in it; it is **saturated** when no more solute will dissolve. If excess solute and a saturated solution are in contact, the dissolved solute is in equilib-

Figure 12.1

Two solutions and a sample of solid potassium dichromate, $K_2Cr_2O_7$. The solution on the left was prepared by dissolving 1.0 g of $K_2Cr_2O_7$, the solution on the right by dissolving 10.0 g of $K_2Cr_2O_7$. Note that both solutions are homogeneous; you can tell by the color that the orange $Cr_2O_7^{2-}$ ion is uniformly distributed. The more intense color of the solution on the right shows that it contains more of the $Cr_2O_7^{2-}$ ion than the solution on the left and is the more concentrated solution.

rium with the excess solute. The **solubility** of a solute is the quantity that will dissolve in a given amount of solvent to produce a saturated solution. Because solutions can have different concentrations, it is evident that the composition of a solution may vary within certain limits. Thus a solution is not a compound; a compound always has the same composition.

All solutions—whether they contain dissolved molecules or dissolved ions— exhibit some similar properties: (1) homogeneity, (2) absence of settling, (3) the molecular or ionic state of subdivision of the components, and (4) a composition that can be varied continuously within limits.

When solid sugar is added to a saturated solution of sugar, it falls to the bottom and no more seems to dissolve. Actually, molecules of sugar continue to leave the solid and dissolve, but at the same time, molecules of sugar in solution collide with the solid and take up positions on the crystal. When enough molecules return to the solid that the process of crystallization counterbalances that of dissolution, a state of equilibrium exists.

If a saturated solution is prepared at an elevated temperature and undissolved solute is removed, the solution can sometimes be cooled without crystallization of solute. When the cool solution contains more solute than it would if the dissolved solute were in equilibrium with undissolved solute, it is a **supersaturated solution.** Such solutions are unstable, and the excess dissolved solute may crystallize spontaneously. Alternatively, agitation of the solution or the addition of a seed crystal of the solute may start crystallization of the excess solute. After crystallization is complete, a saturated solution, in equilibrium with the crystals of solute, remains. Some syrups are supersaturated solutions of sugar in water.

Water is used so often as a solvent that the word *solution* has come to imply a water solution to many people. **Aqueous solutions** have water as the solvent. However, almost any gas, liquid, or solid can act as a solvent for other gases, liquids, or solids. Many alloys are solid solutions of one metal dissolved in another; for example, nickel coins contain nickel dissolved in copper. Air is a gaseous solution, a homogeneous mixture of gases. Oxygen (a gas), alcohol (a liquid), and sugar (a solid) all dissolve in water (a liquid) to form liquid solutions.

Although it is easy to identify the solute and solvent in most cases (as when 1 gram of sugar is dissolved in 100 milliliters of water), sometimes the identification is difficult. For example, it is not possible to distinguish solute from solvent in a solution of equal amounts of ethanol and water. In such cases, the choice is arbitrary.

12.2 Solutions of Gases in Liquids

The amount of gas that dissolves in a liquid depends on the nature of the gas and the liquid solvent. For example, at 0°C and 1 atmosphere, 0.049 liters of oxygen, 1.7 liters of carbon dioxide, 80 liters of sulfur dioxide, or 1180 liters of ammonia will dissolve in 1 liter of water. At 20°C and 1 atmosphere, 0.200 liters of stibine, SbH_3, will dissolve in 1 liter of water, but 25 liters of SbH_3 will dissolve in 1 liter of carbon disulfide.

The pressure of the gas and the temperature also affect the solubility of a gas. The solubility of a gas increases as the pressure of the gas increases. You can see the effect of pressure upon solubility in bottled carbonated beverages. Pressure forces carbon dioxide into solution in the beverage, and the bottle is tightly capped to maintain this pressure. When you open the bottle, the pressure decreases and some of the gas escapes from the solution (Fig. 12.2).

Figure 12.2

When the pressure of the *gaseous* carbon dioxide above this beverage was reduced by opening the bottle, the *dissolved* carbon dioxide escaped from the solution and formed the bubbles shown.

If 1 gram of a gas dissolves in 1 liter of water at 1 atmosphere of pressure, 5 grams will dissolve at 5 atmospheres. This direct proportionality is expressed quantitatively by **Henry's law: The quantity of a gas that dissolves in a definite volume of liquid is directly proportional to the pressure of the gas,** or

$$C_g = kP_g$$

where C_g is the solubility of the gas in the solution, P_g is the pressure of the gas over the solution, and k is a proportionality constant that depends on the identity of the gas and of the solvent.

Example 12.1

The solubility of gaseous O_2 is 0.035 g or 1.1×10^{-3} mol per liter of water at 0°C and 0.50 atm. What is k in Henry's law for this solubility if the solubility is expressed in moles per liter?

According to Henry's law, the solubility C_g of a gas (1.1×10^{-3} mol/L, in this case) is directly proportional to the pressure P_g of the gas. That is, the solubility is equal to a proportionality constant k times the pressure (0.50 atm, in this case).

$$C_g = kP_g$$

Because we know C_g and P_g, we need to rearrange this expression to solve for k.

$$k = \frac{C_g}{P_g}$$

$$= \frac{(1.1 \times 10^{-3} \text{ mol/L})}{0.50 \text{ atm}}$$

$$= 2.2 \times 10^{-3} \text{ mol/L atm}$$

The effect of pressure does not follow Henry's law when a chemical reaction takes place between the gas and the solvent. Thus the solubility of ammonia in water does not increase as rapidly with increasing pressure as predicted by the law, because ammonia, being a base, reacts to some extent with water to form ammonium ions and hydroxide ions.

$$NH_3 + H_2O \rightleftharpoons NH_4^+ + OH^-$$

The solubilities of most gases in water decreases with an increase in temperature, provided that the gas does not react with water (Fig. 12.3). For example, 48.9 milliliters of oxygen dissolve in 1 liter of water at 1 atmosphere and 0°C, but only 31.6 milliliters dissolve at 25°C, 24.6 milliliters at 50°C, and 23.0 milliliters at 100°C. This relationship is not one of inverse proportion, however, and the solubility of a gas in a liquid at a given temperature must be determined experimentally. The decreasing solubility of gases such as oxygen with increasing temperature is a very important factor in thermal pollution of natural waters. A heat discharge that increases the temperature by a few degrees can reduce the solubility of oxygen in the water to a level too low for many forms of aquatic life to survive.

Gases can form supersaturated solutions. If a solution of a gas in a liquid is prepared either at low temperature or under pressure (or both), then as the solution warms or as the gas pressure is reduced, the solution may become supersaturated. For example, a bottle of a carbonated beverage may not liberate the excess dissolved carbon dioxide

Figure 12.3

The small bubbles of air in this glass of water formed when the water warmed and the solubility of its dissolved air decreased.

when the carbon dioxide pressure above the solution is reduced by opening the bottle, but it does if it is shaken or stirred.

Most gases can be expelled from solvents by boiling their solutions in an open container. The gases oxygen, nitrogen, carbon dioxide, and sulfur dioxide, for example, can be removed from water by boiling the solution for a few minutes.

12.3 Solutions of Liquids in Liquids (Miscibility)

Two liquids that mix with each other in all proportions are said to be completely **miscible.** Ethanol, sulfuric acid, and ethylene glycol (antifreeze), for example, are completely miscible with water (Fig. 12.4). Liquids that mix with water in all proportions are usually polar substances (Section 8.3) or substances that form hydrogen bonds (Section 11.4). For such liquids, the dipole–dipole attractions (or hydrogen bonding) of the solute molecules with the solvent molecules are at least as strong as those between molecules in the pure solute or in the pure solvent. Hence the two kinds of molecules mix easily.

Two liquids that do not mix are called **immiscible.** Two layers are formed when two immiscible liquids are poured into the same container. Gasoline, oil, benzene, carbon tetrachloride, and many other nonpolar liquids are immiscible with water (Fig. 12.5).

Figure 12.4
Water and antifreeze (ethylene glycol and yellow dye) are miscible; the yellow mixture of the two is homogeneous.

Figure 12.5
Water and oil are immiscible. Eventually the oil floats to the surface and two separate layers form.

Figure 12.6

Bromine (a deep orange liquid) and water are partially miscible. The top layer in this mixture is a dilute (but saturated) solution of bromine in water; the bottom layer is a dilute (but saturated) solution of water in bromine.

There is no effective attraction between the molecules of such nonpolar liquids and polar water molecules. The only strong attractions in such a mixture are between the water molecules, so they effectively squeeze out the molecules of the nonpolar liquid. Nonpolar liquids may be miscible with each other, however, because there is no appreciable tendency for solvent molecules to attract other solvent molecules and squeeze out solute molecules. The solubility of polar molecules in polar solvents and of nonpolar molecules in nonpolar solvents is an illustration of the old chemical axiom "Like dissolves like."

Two liquids, such as ether and water or bromine and water, that are slightly soluble in each other are said to be partially miscible. Two partially miscible liquids usually form two layers when mixed. Each layer is a saturated solution of one liquid in the other (Fig. 12.6), and a dynamic equilibrium occurs between the two layers. When the partially miscible liquids bromine and water are in contact and at equilibrium, bromine molecules leave the bromine layer and enter the water layer at the same rate at which bromine molecules leave the water layer and return to the bromine layer. Similarly, water molecules leave the water layer and enter the bromine layer at the same rate at which water molecules leave the bromine layer and return to the water layer.

12 .4 The Effect of Temperature on the Solubility of Solids in Liquids

The dependence of solubility on temperature for a number of inorganic substances in water is shown by the solubility curves in Fig. 12.7. Generally, the solubility of a solid increases with increasing temperature, although there are exceptions. A sharp break in a

Figure 12.7

Graph showing the effect of temperature on the maximum solubility of several solid inorganic substances. The break in the red curve occurs at the temperature (32.4°C) at which solid $Na_2SO_4 \cdot 10H_2O$ decomposes to Na_2SO_4 and water.

solubility curve indicates the formation of a new compound with a different solubility. For example, when solid $Na_2SO_4 \cdot 10H_2O$ in equilibrium with a saturated solution is heated to 32.4°C, it forms the anhydrous salt, Na_2SO_4, in equilibrium with a saturated solution. The red curve in Fig. 12.7 shows the effect of increasing temperature on the solubility of $Na_2SO_4 \cdot 10H_2O$ up to 32.4°C (it increases with temperature), and above this point the curve shows the effect on the solubility of anhydrous Na_2SO_4 (it decreases with increasing temperature).

⑫.5 The Solubilities of Common Metal Compounds

Knowledge of the solubilities of metallic compounds is very useful to students and chemists. Memorizing solubilities of individual compounds is unnecessary; it is simpler to learn the following six general rules. (Note that these rules are for simple compounds of the more common metals; there are exceptions for less common metals and complex compounds.)

1. Most nitrates and acetates are soluble in water; silver acetate, chromium(II) acetate, and mercury(I) acetate are slightly soluble; bismuth acetate reacts with water and forms insoluble bismuth oxyacetate, $BiO(CH_3CO_2)$.
2. All chlorides are soluble except those of mercury(I), silver, lead (II), and copper(I); lead(II) chloride is soluble in hot water.
3. All sulfates except those of strontium, barium, and lead(II) are soluble; calcium sulfate and silver sulfate are slightly soluble.
4. Carbonates, phosphates, borates, arsenates, and arsenites are insoluble, except those of the ammonium ion and the alkali metals.
5. The hydroxides of the alkali metals and of barium and strontium are soluble, and other hydroxides are insoluble; calcium hydroxide is slightly soluble.
6. Most sulfides are insoluble. However, the sulfides of the alkali metals are soluble, but they react with water to give solutions of the hydroxide and hydrogen sulfide ion, HS^-; the sulfides of the alkaline earth metals and of aluminum also react to give OH^- and HS^- (or H_2S if the metal hydroxide is insoluble).

⑫.6 Solid Solutions

When a mixture of lithium chloride and sodium chloride is melted, mixed well, and allowed to cool, the resulting crystalline solid contains an array of chloride ions with a random distribution of lithium ions and sodium ions in holes in the array (Fig. 12.8). The crystal is a **solid solution** of LiCl and NaCl. It is homogeneous, just like a liquid solution. Its composition can be varied (from pure LiCl to pure NaCl), and neither NaCl nor LiCl separates out on standing. Solid solutions of ionic compounds result when ions of one type randomly replace other ions of about the same size in a crystal.

Some ionic substances appear to be **nonstoichiometric compounds;** that is, their chemical formulas deviate from ideal ratios or are variable. In other respects, however, these substances resemble compounds; they are not heterogeneous mixtures but are instead homogeneous throughout. These so-called nonstoichiometric compounds are, in fact, solid solutions of two or more compounds. A sample of ruby, for example, with the

Figure 12.8

A portion of the structure of a solid solution of LiCl and NaCl. The chloride ions (large green spheres) form a face-centered cubic array, with the octahedral holes occupied by a random distribution of lithium ions (smaller purple spheres) and sodium ions (larger red spheres).

(a)

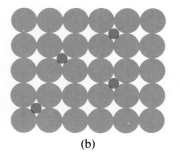

(b)

Figure 12.9

Two-dimensional representations of alloys. (a) A substitutional solid solution in which solute atoms (purple spheres) replace atoms of the solvent crystal (red spheres). (b) An interstitial solid solution in which small solute atoms (blue spheres) occupy holes in the lattice of the solvent crystal (red spheres).

formula $Cr_{0.02}Al_{1.98}O_3$, is a solid solution of Cr_2O_3 in Al_2O_3 with a 1-to-99 ratio of Cr to Al. Some nonstoichiometric compounds are solid solutions containing one ion in two different oxidation states. For example, $TiO_{1.8}$ contains both Ti^{3+} and Ti^{4+} ions and may be considered a solid solution of Ti_2O_3 and TiO_2.

Some **alloys** are solid solutions composed of two or more metals. In such an alloy, atoms of one of the component metals take up positions in the crystal lattice of the other. The solute atoms may randomly replace some of the atoms of the solvent crystal to form a class of solid solutions called **substitutional solid solutions** [Fig. 12.9(a)]. For example, chromium dissolves in nickel to form a solid solution in which the chromium atoms replace nickel atoms in the face-centered cubic structure of nickel. The solubility may be limited (zinc and copper; chromium and nickel) or practically infinite (nickel and copper).

Small atoms (hydrogen, carbon, boron, and nitrogen) may occupy the holes in the lattice of a metal, forming another class of solid solutions called **interstitial solid solutions** [Fig. 12.9(b)]. A solid solution of carbon in iron (austenite) is an example; the iron atoms are on the lattice points of a face-centered cubic lattice, and the carbon atoms occupy the interstitial positions.

Not all alloys are solid solutions. Some are *heterogeneous* mixtures in which the component metals are mutually insoluble and the solid alloy is composed of an intimate mixture of crystals of each metal. For example, tin and lead (in plumber's solder) are insoluble in each other in the solid state. Other alloys, such as Cu_5Zn_8 and Ag_3Al, are actually compounds that form with only one specific stoichiometric composition. In general, the formulas of such intermetallic compounds are not those that would be predicted on the basis of the usual valence rules.

The Process of Dissolution

12.7 The Role of Disorder and Energy Changes in the Formation of Solutions

When ethanol is added to water, a solution forms without the input of energy. That is, the solution forms by a **spontaneous process.** Chemists recognize two factors in such a spontaneous process: (1) changes in energy and (2) changes in the amount of disorder of the components of the solution. In the process of dissolution, the change in disorder results from the mixing of the solute and solvent. The energy changes occur because the intermolecular attractions change from solute–solute and solvent–solvent attractions to a mixture of solute–solvent attractions. First let us consider the formation of a solution in which energy changes are insignificant, so we can concentrate on how changes in disorder contribute to the formation of solutions. Then we will consider the energy change factor as indicated by the enthalpy of solution (Section 4.4).

When the strengths of the intermolecular forces of attraction between the solute and solvent molecules (or ions) are the same as the strengths of the forces between the molecules in the separate components, a solution is formed with no accompanying energy change. Such a solution is called an **ideal solution.** An ideal solution also obeys Raoult's law exactly (Section 12.14). Solutions of ideal gases (or gases such as helium and argon, which closely approach ideal behavior) contain molecules with no significant intermolecular attractions, so these solutions are ideal solutions.

When you open the stopcock between bulbs that contain helium and argon [Fig. 12.10(a)], the gases spontaneously diffuse together and form a solution of helium and argon [Fig. 12.10(b)]. This solution forms because the disorder of the helium and argon molecules increases when they mix. They occupy a volume twice as large as that which each occupied before mixing, and the molecules are randomly distributed among one another.

Other solutions that closely approximate ideal solutions include solutions of pairs of chemically similar substances such as the liquids methanol (CH_3OH) and ethanol (C_2H_5OH) or the liquids chlorobenzene (C_6H_5Cl) and bromobenzene (C_6H_5Br). If the gases shown in Fig. 12.10(a) were replaced with methanol and ethanol (or with chlorobenzene and bromobenzene), the molecules of the liquids would diffuse together spontaneously (although at a much slower rate than the gases), giving solutions with a disorder greater than that of the pure liquids. These examples show that **processes in which the disorder of the system increases tend to occur spontaneously.** Moving molecules become randomly distributed among one another unless something holds them back.

Intermolecular forces of attraction might keep molecules from mixing. These forces are small and negligible in gases, so gases are mutually soluble in all proportions. In liquids and solids, however, the intermolecular attractions are stronger and much more important to their behavior. Sometimes, solute molecules attract each other strongly but attract solvent molecules weakly. The solute molecules thus remain in contact with each other and do not dissolve, even though formation of a solution would increase their disorder. If the solvent molecules attract each other strongly but do not attract the solute molecules, the solvent molecules do not separate to let the solute dissolve. A solution forms only when the attractions between solute and solvent molecules are about equal to the combination of the attractions between solute molecules and those between solvent molecules.

To see why gasoline and water don't mix, let us consider what happens when octane, a typical hydrocarbon in gasoline, is added to water. Water molecules are held in contact by hydrogen bonds (Section 11.4); octane molecules are held in contact by London dispersion forces (Section 11.3). When the two liquids are mixed, the attraction between the octane molecules and the water molecules is not strong enough to overcome the hydrogen bonds between the water molecules. The relatively strong hydrogen bonds keep the water molecules clustered together and no mixing occurs. Eventually, the water and octane separate into two layers again.

On the other hand, if we add methanol to water, a solution forms readily. Water–water, methanol–methanol, and water–methanol hydrogen bonds are of about equal strength. There is no tendency for stronger hydrogen bonding to cause the water molecules or the methanol molecules to cluster together, and a solution forms because of the increase in disorder.

If the solute–solvent attractions are stronger than the solute–solute and solvent–solvent attractions, heat is released (the dissolution process is exothermic) as the stronger attractions form during dissolution. If the solute–solvent attractions are weaker than the solute–solute and solvent–solvent attractions, heat is absorbed (the dissolution

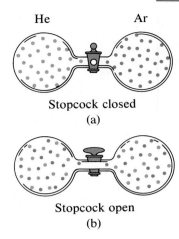

He   Ar

Stopcock closed
(a)

Stopcock open
(b)

Figure 12.10

The spontaneous mixing of helium and argon to give a solution. When the stopcock between samples of the two pure gases (a) is opened, they mix by diffusion to give a solution (b) in which the disorder of the molecules of the two gases is increased.

Figure 12.11

When concentrated sulfuric acid dissolves in water, the solution gets hot, as indicated by the rise in temperature from 24°C to 92°C.

process is endothermic). For example, when 1 mole of sulfuric acid is dissolved in 9 moles of water, the resulting acid–water interactions are stronger than the combination of the acid–acid attractive forces in pure sulfuric acid and the water–water attractive forces in pure water. The solution becomes very hot (Fig. 12.11) because 63.2 kilojoules of heat is produced (the enthalpy of solution is negative). The loss of energy, as heat, when sulfuric acid dissolves in water indicates that the solution contains less energy than the separate components before mixing.

Processes in which the energy content of the system decreases tend to occur spontaneously. Thus both a loss of energy and an increase in disorder favor a spontaneous process such as the formation of a solution. For a solution to form, however, it is not necessary for both the energy change and the change in disorder to favor a spontaneous process. When ammonium nitrate is added to water, it dissolves even though the solution cools as heat is absorbed from the water. In this case the solute–solute and solvent–solvent attractions are larger than the solute–solvent attractions. A solution forms in spite of the endothermic enthalpy of solution, because the increase in disorder is so large that it more than compensates for the increase in the energy content. Ammonium nitrate is used to make instant "ice packs" for treatment of athletic injuries. A thin-walled plastic bag of water is sealed inside a larger bag with NH_4NO_3. When the smaller bag is broken, a cold solution of NH_4NO_3 forms (Chapter 4, page 104), and the cold decreases swelling of the injured area.

12.8 Dissolution of Ionic Compounds

When ionic compounds dissolve in water, the associated ions in the solid separate because water reduces the strong electrostatic forces between them. Let us consider the dissolution of potassium chloride in water. Ion–dipole forces (Section 11.3) attract the hydrogen (positive) end of a polar water molecule to a negative chloride ion at the surface of the solid, and they attract the oxygen (negative) end to a positive potassium ion. The water molecules penetrate between individual K^+ and Cl^- ions at the surface of the crystal and surround them, reducing the strong interionic forces that bind the ions together and letting them move off into solution as hydrated ions (Fig. 12.12). Several water molecules associate with (solvate) each ion in solution. The increase in the dis-

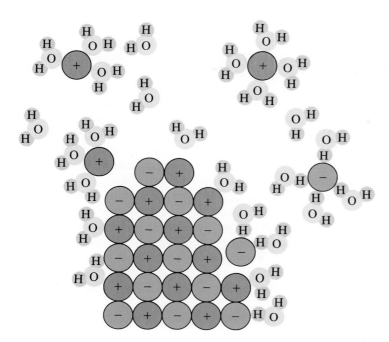

Figure 12.12

The dissolution of potassium chloride in water and the hydration of its ions. Water molecules in front of and behind the ions are not shown. The red positive spheres represent potassium ions; the green negative spheres represent chloride ions.

tance between ions that is due to the layers of water molecules around them reduces the electrostatic attraction between oppositely charged ions. In addition, the layers of water act as insulators, which further reduces the electrostatic attraction. The reduction of the electrostatic attraction permits the independent motion of each hydrated ion in a dilute solution, resulting in an increase in the disorder of the system as the ions change from their ordered positions in the crystal to much more disordered and mobile states in solution. This increased disorder is responsible for the dissolution of many ionic compounds, including potassium chloride, which dissolve with absorption of heat. In other cases, the electrostatic attractions between the ions in a crystal are so large that the increase in disorder cannot compensate for the energy required to separate the ions, and the crystal is insoluble.

Ionic compounds dissolve in polar solvents only when the polar solvent molecules can solvate and insulate the ions. In general, the higher the dielectric constant of a solvent (a measure of a solvent's ability to solvate ions and to reduce the electrostatic attraction between them), the greater the solubility of an ionic compound in it. This phenomenon is strikingly illustrated in Table 12.1. Ionic substances in general do not dissolve appreciably in nonpolar solvents, such as benzene or carbon tetrachloride,

Table 12.1	The Solubility of Sodium Chloride and the Dielectric Constant of the Solvent	
Solvent	Solubility of NaCl (grams per 100 g of solvent, 25°C)	Dielectric Constant of the Solvent
Water, H_2O	36.12	80.0
Methanol, CH_3OH	1.3	33.1
Carbon tetrachloride, CCl_4	0.00	2.2

because the nonpolar solvent molecules are not strongly attracted to ions, and therefore have low dielectric constants.

Ionic compounds are electrolytes (Section 2.10); their solutions conduct electricity. Other substances, such as sugar and alcohol, that form solutions that do not conduct electricity are called nonelectrolytes.

Electrolytes and nonelectrolytes can be classified experimentally with an apparatus consisting of an electrical circuit containing an electric lamp and two electrodes in a beaker (Fig. 12.13). When the beaker is filled with pure water, the lamp does not light because essentially no current flows. When a nonelectrolyte such as sugar is added to the water, the lamp still does not light. If an electrolyte such as potassium chloride is dissolved in the water, however, the lamp glows brightly.

Svante Arrhenius, a Swedish chemist, first successfully explained electrolytic conduction. The current theory of electrolytes embodies most of the postulates of Arrhenius's theory. According to the current theory, when a solution conducts an electric current, positive ions move toward the negative electrode while negative ions move toward the positive electrode. The movement of the ions toward the electrodes of opposite charge accounts for electrolytic conduction. A solution of a nonelectrolyte contains *molecules* of the nonelectrolyte rather than ions, and thus it cannot conduct an electric current.

Pure water is an extremely poor conductor of electricity, indicating very slight ionization (actually only about 2 out of every 1 billion molecules ionize at 25°C). Water ionizes when one molecule of water gives up a proton to another molecule of water, yielding hydronium and hydroxide ions.

$$H_2O + H_2O \rightleftharpoons H_3O^+ + OH^-$$

⑫.9 Dissolution of Molecular Electrolytes

Pure hydrogen chloride consists of covalent HCl molecules and contains no ions. A solution of hydrogen chloride in a nonpolar solvent such as benzene is a nonelectrolyte and so does not contain ions. However, when hydrogen chloride dissolves in water, it is a strong electrolyte (the HCl molecules are 100% ionized, Section 2.10). The water

Figure 12.13

Apparatus for demonstrating the conductivity of solutions. The solution on the left contains the nonelectrolyte sugar and has no conductivity. The solution in the middle contains a small quantity of NaCl (100% ionized—a strong electrolyte) in the water. The solution on the right is a 5% acetic acid solution. The acetic acid is only partially ionized—a weak electrolyte.

molecules play an important part in forming ions, because hydrogen chloride molecules react with water to form hydronium ions (H_3O^+) and chloride ions (Cl^-). As shown by the Lewis formulas, a hydrogen ion (proton) shifts from a polar hydrogen chloride molecule to a lone pair of electrons on the water molecule.

$$H—\overset{..}{\underset{H}{O}}: + (H)—\overset{..}{\underset{..}{C}l}: \longrightarrow H—\overset{..}{\underset{H}{O}}—H^+ + :\overset{..}{\underset{..}{C}l}:^-$$

The hydronium ions and chloride ions conduct the current in the solution. All common strong acids react with water when they dissolve, and all are strong electrolytes.

Many other compounds dissolve in water as hydrated molecules. In many cases these molecules are weak electrolytes (only a small fraction ionizes), so the solutions conduct electricity weakly (Section 2.10). For example, cyanic acid, HOCN, dissolves in water principally as hydrated molecules. Only a small percentage of these dissolved molecules ionize under ordinary conditions.

$$H—\overset{..}{\underset{H}{O}}: + (H)—\overset{..}{\underset{..}{O}}—C{\equiv}N: \rightleftharpoons H—\overset{..}{\underset{H}{O}}—H^+ + :\overset{..}{\underset{..}{O}}—C{\equiv}N:^-$$

The reaction proceeds only to the extent of 6% in a 0.1 M solution of HOCN. Other acids, such as acetic acid (CH_3CO_2H), nitrous acid (HNO_2), and hydrogen cyanide (HCN), are also weak electrolytes, and only a small fraction of their hydrated molecules ionize at any one time.

Some bases are also weak electrolytes; they dissolve to give solutions of hydrated molecules, some of which undergo ionization. For example, a solution of ammonia in water consists primarily of hydrated molecules, $NH_3(aq)$, with small amounts of ammonium ions, $NH_4^+(aq)$, and hydroxide ions, $OH^-(aq)$, which result from the reaction of ammonia with water.

$$H—\overset{H}{\underset{H}{N}}: + (H)—\overset{..}{\underset{H}{O}}: \rightleftharpoons H—\overset{H}{\underset{H}{N}}—H^+ + :\overset{..}{\underset{..}{O}}—H^-$$

The halides and cyanides of cadmium and mercury are also weak electrolytes. When these compounds dissolve, they give solutions of molecules. A small fraction of the metal–chlorine or metal–cyanide bonds break, and the few resulting hydrated ions account for the low conductivities of the solutions.

Expressing Concentration

⑫.10 Percent Composition

To express the concentration of a solute, we can state the mass of solute in a given mass of solvent (for example, 1 gram of NaCl in 100 grams of water), or we can give its composition as **percent by mass.** A 10% NaCl solution by mass may contain 10 grams of NaCl in 100 grams of solution (10 grams of NaCl and 90 grams of water), or it may contain any other ratio of NaCl to solution for which the mass of NaCl is 10% of the total mass, for example, 20 milligrams of NaCl in 200 milligrams of solution, 1.5 grams of NaCl in 15 grams of solution, or 7.4 kilograms of NaCl in 74 kilograms of solution.

$$\% \text{ solute} = \frac{\text{mass of solute}}{\text{mass of solution}} \times 100$$

Example 12.2

A bottle of a certain ceramic tile cleanser, which is essentially a solution of hydrogen chloride, contains 130 g of HCl and 750 g of water. What is the percent by mass of HCl in this cleanser?

The percent by mass of the solute is

$$\% \text{ solute} = \frac{\text{mass solute}}{\text{mass solution}} \times 100$$

$$= \frac{130 \text{ g}}{130 \text{ g} + 750 \text{ g}} \times 100 = 14.8\%$$

When using percent composition by mass in calculations, it is convenient to use grams of solute per 100 grams of solution (g solute/100 g solution), because the number of grams of solute in 100 grams of solution is equal to the percent by mass of solute. To calculate the mass of solute in a given *volume* of solution, given the percent composition by mass, you must know the density of the solution, the mass of 1 milliliter of the solution.

Example 12.3

Concentrated hydrochloric acid, a saturated solution of hydrogen chloride, HCl, in water, is often used in the general chemistry laboratory. It has a density of 1.19 g/mL and contains 37.2% HCl by mass. What mass of HCl is contained in exactly 1 L of this concentrated acid?

This problem requires the following steps.

$$\boxed{\begin{array}{c}\text{Volume} \\ \text{of} \\ \text{solution}\end{array}} \longrightarrow \boxed{\begin{array}{c}\text{Mass} \\ \text{of} \\ \text{solution}\end{array}} \longrightarrow \boxed{\begin{array}{c}\text{Mass} \\ \text{of} \\ \text{HCl}\end{array}}$$

We know that the mass of exactly 1 mL of the concentrated hydrochloric acid solution is 1.19 g. Because 1 L equals 1000 mL,

$$\frac{1.19 \text{ g solution}}{1 \text{ mL}} \times 1000 \text{ mL} = 1190 \text{ g solution}$$

The solution contains 37.2% HCl by mass (37.2 g HCl/100.0 g solution).

$$1190 \text{ g solution} \times \frac{37.2 \text{ g HCl}}{100.0 \text{ g solution}} = 443 \text{ g HCl}$$

A student needs 125 g of HCl to prepare a metal chloride. What volume of concentrated hydrochloric acid that has a density of 1.19 g/mL and contains 37.2% HCl by mass contains 125 g of HCl?

Example

12.4

This problem requires the following steps.

Because the solution contains 37.2% HCl, there is 37.2 g of HCl per 100.0 g of solution, giving the conversion factor 37.2 g HCl/100.0 g solution or 100.0 g solution/37.2 g HCl.

$$125 \text{ g HCl} \times \frac{100.0 \text{ g solution}}{37.2 \text{ g HCl}} = 336 \text{ g solution}$$

The mass of 1 mL of solution is 1.19 g (1 mL/1.19 g).

$$336 \text{ g solution} \times \frac{1 \text{ mL solution}}{1.19 \text{ g solution}} = 282 \text{ mL solution}$$

Thus 282 mL of the concentrated hydrochloric acid contains 125 g of HCl.

⓬.11 Molarity

We have already considered the concept of molarity. In Section 3.8 the **molarity, M,** of a solution was defined as the number of moles of solute in exactly 1 liter of solution. Molarity may be calculated by dividing the moles of solute in a solution by the volume of the solution.

$$\text{Molarity} = \frac{\text{moles of solute}}{\text{liters of solution}}$$

Because 1 mole of any substance contains the same number of molecules as 1 mole of any other substance, equal volumes of 1 M solutions contain the same numbers of molecules of solute. The use of molarity to express the concentration of a solution makes it easy to select a desired number of moles, molecules, or ions of the solute by measuring out the appropriate volume of solution. For example, if 1 mole of sodium hydroxide is needed for a given reaction, we can use 40 grams of solid sodium hydroxide (1 mole), or 1 liter of a 1 M solution of the base, or 2 liters of a 0.5 M solution.

To prepare a solution of known molarity, measure out the required moles of the solute and add enough solvent to give the desired volume of solution. To prepare 1 liter of a 1.00 M solution, you could dissolve 1.00 mole of pure cobalt sulfate (155 g of $CoSO_4$) in enough water to form 1 liter of solution (Fig. 12.14).

Examples of the use of molar concentrations in stoichiometry calculations were presented in Chapter 3. However, here is one more as a reminder.

Figure 12.14

In one method of preparing a 1.00 M solution of cobalt(II) sulfate, 155 g of $CoSO_4$ (1 mol) is added to a flask that is calibrated to hold 1.000 L, and enough water is added to make 1.000 L of solution. The second photograph shows the 1.00 M solution after the solution has been shaken to ensure uniform mixing.

Example 12.5

Concentrated sulfuric acid is a solution that has a density of 1.84 g/mL and contains 98.3% H_2SO_4 by mass. What is the molarity of this acid?

Calculating the moles of H_2SO_4 in 1.00 L of concentrated sulfuric acid requires the following steps:

Volume of solution (1.00 L)	→	Mass of solution	→	Mass of H_2SO_4	→	Moles of H_2SO_4

The mass of 1 mL of solution is 1.84 g; the mass of 1.00 L is given by the equation

$$1000 \text{ mL solution} \times \frac{1.84 \text{ g solution}}{1.00 \text{ mL solution}} = 1.84 \times 10^3 \text{ g solution}$$

There are 98.3 g of H_2SO_4 per 100 g of solution, because the solution is 98.3% H_2SO_4 by mass, so the mass of H_2SO_4 can be calculated.

$$1.84 \times 10^3 \text{ g solution} \times \frac{98.3 \text{ g } H_2SO_4}{100 \text{ g solution}} = 1.81 \times 10^3 \text{ g } H_2SO_4$$

Now we calculate the number of moles of H_2SO_4 in 1.00 L of the solution to obtain the molarity.

$$1.81 \times 10^3 \text{ g } H_2SO_4 \times \frac{1 \text{ mol } H_2SO_4}{98.0 \text{ g } H_2SO_4} = 18.5 \text{ mol } H_2SO_4$$

$$\frac{18.5 \text{ mol } H_2SO_4}{1.00 \text{ L solution}} = 18.5 \text{ M}$$

When a solution is diluted, the volume is increased by adding more solvent. Although the concentration is decreased, the total amount of solute remains constant.

If 0.850 L of a 5.00 M solution of copper nitrate, $Cu(NO_3)_2$, is diluted to a volume of 1.80 L by adding water (see photograph), what is the molarity of the resulting diluted solution?

Example 12.6

Because the number of moles of copper nitrate in the solution does not change on dilution, the problem can be solved by the following steps:

$$\boxed{\text{Volume of concentrated solution}} \longrightarrow \boxed{\text{Moles of } Cu(NO_3)_2} \longrightarrow \boxed{\text{Molarity of diluted solution}}$$

$$0.850 \text{ L solution} \times \frac{5.00 \text{ mol } Cu(NO_3)_2}{1.00 \text{ L solution}} = 4.25 \text{ mol } Cu(NO_3)_2$$

$$\frac{4.25 \text{ mol } Cu(NO_3)_2}{1.80 \text{ L solution}} = 2.36 \text{ M}$$

The solution was diluted from 5.00 M to 2.36 M.

Simple addition of water to a 0.850-L sample of a 5.00 M solution of $Cu(NO_3)_2$ (left) produces 1.80 L of a diluted (2.36 M) solution (right).

How many milliliters of water will be required to dilute 11 mL of a 0.45 M acid solution to a concentration of 0.12 M?

Example 12.7

Again the number of moles of solute does not change. The following steps are necessary to solve this problem.

Example 12.7 continued

We convert the volume to liters and solve for the moles of acid present.

$$11 \text{ mL} \times \frac{1 \text{ L}}{1000 \text{ mL}} = 1.1 \times 10^{-2} \text{ L}$$

$$1.1 \times 10^{-2} \text{ L solution} \times \frac{0.45 \text{ mol acid}}{1.00 \text{ L solution}} = 4.95 \times 10^{-3} \text{ mol acid}$$

Rearrangement of the expression for calculating molarity (molarity = moles/liters) gives the following expression.

$$\text{Liters} = \frac{\text{moles}}{\text{molarity}}$$

$$\text{Liters of dilute solution} = 4.95 \times 10^{-3} \text{ mol acid} \times \frac{1.00 \text{ L solution}}{0.12 \text{ mol acid}}$$

$$= 4.1 \times 10^{-2} \text{ L solution}$$

We convert to milliliters.

$$4.1 \times 10^{-2} \text{ L} \times \frac{1000 \text{ mL}}{1.00 \text{ L}} = 41 \text{ mL solution}$$

The final volume of the solution minus the original volume is equal to the volume of water added in the dilution.

$$41 \text{ mL} - 11 \text{ mL} = 30 \text{ mL}$$

A concentration unit called *normality* is sometimes used to describe the concentrations of acids and bases or of oxidizing and reducing agents. Normality will be described in detail in the chapters dealing with acid–base reactions (Section 16.13) and with electrochemical reactions (Section 20.15).

12.12 Molality

The **molality, m,** of a solution is the number of moles of solute in exactly 1 kilogram of solvent. Molality can be calculated by dividing the moles of solute in a solution by the mass of the solvent in kilograms.

$$\text{Molality} = \frac{\text{moles of solute}}{\text{kilograms of solvent}}$$

Note that *kilograms of solvent* rather than liters of solution are specified. This is the difference between molality and molarity.

Example 12.8

What is the molality of a solution that contains 0.850 g of ammonia, NH_3, in 125 g of water?

After the mass of NH_3 has been converted to moles of NH_3, the molality can be determined by dividing by the kilograms of water, the solvent.

$$0.850 \text{ g NH}_3 \times \frac{1 \text{ mol NH}_3}{17.0 \text{ g NH}_3} = 5.00 \times 10^{-2} \text{ mol NH}_3$$

$$\text{Molality} = \frac{\text{moles of solute}}{\text{kilograms of solvent}} = \frac{\text{mol NH}_3}{\text{kg H}_2\text{O}}$$

$$= \frac{5.00 \times 10^{-2} \text{ mol NH}_3}{0.125 \text{ kg H}_2\text{O}} = 0.400 \text{ mol/kg} = 0.400 \text{ m}$$

Calculate the molality of an aqueous solution of sodium chloride if 0.250 kg of the solution contains 40.0 g of NaCl.

Example 12.9

The mass of solvent is the difference between the mass of the solution, 0.250 kg, and the mass of NaCl in the solution, 0.0400 kg.

$$0.250 \text{ kg} - 0.0400 \text{ kg} = 0.210 \text{ kg}$$

The molality is determined by converting the mass of NaCl to moles of NaCl and dividing by the mass of the solvent, water, in kilograms.

$$40.0 \text{ g NaCl} \times \frac{1 \text{ mol NaCl}}{58.5 \text{ g NaCl}} = 0.684 \text{ mol NaCl}$$

$$\text{Molality of NaCl} = \frac{0.684 \text{ mol NaCl}}{0.210 \text{ kg H}_2\text{O}} = 3.26 \text{ mol/kg} = 3.26 \text{ m}$$

12.13 Mole Fraction

The **mole fraction, X,** of each component in a solution is the number of moles of the individual component divided by the total number of moles of all components present. The mole fraction of substance A in a solution (or other mixture) of substances A, B, C, etc., is expressed as follows:

$$\text{Mole fraction of A} = X_A = \frac{\text{moles A}}{\text{moles A} + \text{moles B} + \text{moles C} + \cdots}$$

The sum of the mole fractions of all components of a mixture always equals 1.

Calculate the mole fraction of each component in a solution containing 42.0 g CH_3OH, 35 g C_2H_5OH, and 50.0 g C_3H_7OH.

Example 12.10

The number of moles of each component is calculated first.

$$42.0 \text{ g CH}_3\text{OH} \times \frac{1 \text{ mol CH}_3\text{OH}}{32.0 \text{ g CH}_3\text{OH}} = 1.31 \text{ mol CH}_3\text{OH}$$

$$35 \text{ g C}_2\text{H}_5\text{OH} \times \frac{1 \text{ mol C}_2\text{H}_5\text{OH}}{46.0 \text{ g C}_2\text{H}_5\text{OH}} = 0.76 \text{ mol C}_2\text{H}_5\text{OH}$$

$$50.0 \text{ g C}_3\text{H}_7\text{OH} \times \frac{1 \text{ mol C}_3\text{H}_7\text{OH}}{60.0 \text{ g C}_3\text{H}_7\text{OH}} = 0.833 \text{ mol C}_3\text{H}_7\text{OH}$$

Example 12.10 continued

The mole fractions are

$$X_{CH_3OH} = \frac{1.31}{1.31 + 0.76 + 0.833} = \frac{1.31}{2.90} = 0.452$$

$$X_{C_2H_5OH} = \frac{0.76}{1.31 + 0.76 + 0.833} = \frac{0.76}{2.90} = 0.26$$

$$X_{C_3H_7OH} = \frac{0.833}{2.90} = 0.287$$

Note, as a check on the work, that the sum of the mole fractions, $0.452 + 0.26 + 0.287$, is 1.00.

Example 12.11

Calculate the mole fraction of solute and solvent for a 3.0 m solution of sodium chloride.

A 3.0 m solution of sodium chloride contains 3.0 mol of NaCl dissolved in exactly 1 kg, or 1000 g, of water. Once we know the number of moles of water, we can calculate the mole fractions.

$$1000 \text{ g H}_2\text{O} \times \frac{1 \text{ mol H}_2\text{O}}{18.0 \text{ g H}_2\text{O}} = 55.6 \text{ mol H}_2\text{O}$$

$$X_{NaCl} = \frac{3.0}{3.0 + 55.6} = 0.051$$

$$X_{H_2O} = \frac{55.6}{3.0 + 55.6} = 0.949$$

Note that the sum of the two mole fractions, $0.051 + 0.949$, is 1.000. Hence we also could have calculated one of these mole fractions by simply taking the difference. For example,

$$X_{H_2O} = 1.000 - X_{NaCl}$$

$$= 1.000 - 0.051 = 0.949$$

Example 12.12

A sulfuric acid solution containing 571.6 g of H_2SO_4 per liter of solution at 20°C has a density of 1.3294 g/mL. Calculate (a) the molarity, (b) the molality, (c) the percent by mass of H_2SO_4, and (d) the mole fractions for the solution.

(a)
$$571.6 \text{ g H}_2\text{SO}_4 \times \frac{1 \text{ mol H}_2\text{SO}_4}{98.08 \text{ g H}_2\text{SO}_4} = 5.828 \text{ mol H}_2\text{SO}_4$$

$$\text{Molarity} = \frac{5.828 \text{ mol H}_2\text{SO}_4}{1.000 \text{ L solution}} = 5.828 \text{ mol/L} = 5.828 \text{ M}$$

(b) Because we know the number of moles of H_2SO_4 in 1 L of solution, to calculate the molality we need to find the mass of water in 1 L of solution. The following steps are required.

The mass of 1 L of solution is given by rearranging the expression for calculating density (density = mass/volume).

$$\text{Density} \times \text{volume} = \text{mass}$$

$$\frac{1.3294 \text{ g}}{1 \text{ mL}} \times 1000 \text{ mL} = 1329.4 \text{ g}$$

Thus 1 L of solution weighs 1329.4 g and contains 571.6 g of H_2SO_4. The mass of water is therefore

$$1329.4 \text{ g} - 571.6 \text{ g} = 757.8 \text{ g (or } 0.7578 \text{ kg)}$$

$$\text{Molality} = \frac{5.828 \text{ mol } H_2SO_4}{0.7578 \text{ kg } H_2O} = 7.691 \text{ mol/kg} = 7.691 \text{ m}$$

(c) The solution contains 571.6 g of H_2SO_4 in 1329.4 g of solution.

$$\text{Percent by mass} = \frac{571.6 \text{ g } H_2SO_4}{1329.4 \text{ g solution}} \times 100 = 43.00\% \text{ } H_2SO_4 \text{ (by mass)}$$

(d) The number of moles of water present in 1 L of the solution is given by

$$757.8 \text{ g } H_2O \times \frac{1 \text{ mol}}{18.02 \text{ g } H_2O} = 42.05 \text{ mol } H_2O$$

$$X_{H_2SO_4} = \frac{\text{mol } H_2SO_4}{\text{mol } H_2SO_4 + \text{mol } H_2O}$$

$$= \frac{5.828}{5.828 + 42.05} = \frac{5.828}{47.88} = 0.1217$$

$$X_{H_2O} = \frac{42.05}{47.88} = 0.8782$$

Note that the sum of the mole fractions, 0.1217 + 0.8782, is 0.9999 (or 1.0000 within the customary uncertainty of 1 in the last significant figure).

Colligative Properties of Solutions

12.14 Lowering of the Vapor Pressure of the Solvent

The freezing temperature of a solution, the vapor pressure of the solvent above a solution, and the boiling temperature of a solution change as the concentration of solute particles changes. Interestingly, however, these changes are independent of the nature (kind, size, and charge) of the solute particles, provided that the solution approximates ideal behavior (Section 12.7). The changes depend only on the *concentration* of solute particles. For example, solutions of 1 mole of solid sugar ($C_{12}H_{22}O_{11}$), 1 mole of liquid ethylene glycol [$C_2H_4(OH)_2$, antifreeze], and 1 mole of gaseous nitrous oxide (N_2O), each dissolved in 1 kilogram of water, begin to freeze at $-1.86°C$. A solution containing 0.5 mole of ammonium ions (NH_4^+) and 0.5 mole of chloride ions (Cl^-), resulting from the dissolution of ammonium chloride in 1 kilogram of water, also freezes at $-1.86°C$; this solution contains a total of 1 mole of dissolved particles. The lowering of the freezing temperature of a solvent that is due to the presence of a solute and the other properties of solutions (the vapor pressure of the solvent and the boiling temperature) that depend only on the concentration of solute species are called **colligative properties.**

When a nonvolatile substance (or one with such a low vapor pressure that we can disregard it) is dissolved, the vapor pressure of the solvent is lowered. For example, the vapor pressure of an aqueous sugar solution at 20°C is less than that of pure water at 20°C.

For an ideal solution, the decrease in vapor pressure is proportional to the ratio of the number of solute molecules to the total number of solute and solvent molecules. The greater the number of solute molecules, the lower the vapor pressure of the solution. These considerations are summed up in **Raoult's law: The vapor pressure of the solvent in an ideal solution, P_{solv}, is equal to the mole fraction of the solvent, X_{solv}, times the vapor pressure of the pure solvent, $P°_{solv}$.**

$$P_{solv} = X_{solv}P°_{solv} \tag{1}$$

The decrease in vapor pressure, ΔP, of an ideal solution, compared to that of the pure solvent, is equal to the mole fraction of solute, X_{solute}, times the vapor pressure of pure solvent, $P°_{solv}$.

$$\Delta P = X_{solute}P°_{solv} \tag{2}$$

As we noted in Section 12.7, solutions of chemically similar pairs of substances often closely approximate ideal behavior. Dilute solutions also tend to exhibit ideal behavior.

Example 12.13

Calculate the vapor pressure of an ideal solution of 92.1 g of glycerin, $C_3H_8O_3$, in 184 g of ethanol, C_2H_5OH, at 40°C. The vapor pressure of pure ethanol at 40°C is 135.3 torr. Glycerin is essentially nonvolatile at this temperature.

We can find the vapor pressure of ethanol from Equation (1), $P_{solv} = X_{solv}P°_{solv}$, but first we need to determine its mole fraction.

$$92.1 \text{ g } C_3H_8O_3 \times \frac{1 \text{ mol } C_3H_8O_3}{92.1 \text{ g } C_3H_8O_3} = 1.00 \text{ mol } C_3H_8O_3$$

$$184 \text{ g } C_2H_5OH \times \frac{1 \text{ mol } C_2H_5OH}{46.0 \text{ g } C_2H_5OH} = 4.00 \text{ mol } C_2H_5OH$$

$$X_{C_2H_5OH} = \frac{4.00}{1.00 + 4.00} = 0.800$$

Now we can calculate the vapor pressure of ethanol in the solution.

$$P_{C_2H_5OH} = X_{C_2H_5OH}P°_{C_2H_5OH} = 0.800 \times 135.5 \text{ torr} = 108 \text{ torr}$$

The vapor pressure of the solvent (ethanol) has been lowered from 135.3 torr to 108 torr by adding glycerin. A change of 27.1 torr can be calculated from Equation (2).

$$\Delta P = X_{solute} P^\circ_{solv} = 0.200 \times 135.3 \text{ torr} = 27.1 \text{ torr}$$

12.15 Elevation of the Boiling Point of the Solvent

A liquid boils when its vapor pressure equals the external pressure on its surface (Section 11.6). Adding a solute lowers the vapor pressure of a liquid, so a higher temperature is needed to increase the vapor pressure to the point where the solution boils. The elevation of the boiling point is the same when solutions of the same concentration are considered; 1 mole of any nonvolatile nonelectrolyte dissolved in 1 kilogram of water raises the boiling point by 0.512°C.

The change in boiling point of a dilute solution, ΔT, from that of the pure solvent is directly proportional to the *molal* concentration of the solute

$$\Delta T = K_b \, m \qquad (1)$$

where m is the molal concentration of the solute in the solvent and K_b is the increase in boiling point for a 1 m solution of a nonvolatile nonelectrolyte. K_b is called the **molal boiling-point elevation constant.** The values of K_b for several solvents are listed in Table 12.2; you can see that the value of K_b varies for each solvent.

The extent to which the vapor pressure of a solvent is lowered and the boiling point is elevated depends on the number of solute particles present in a given amount of solvent, not on the mass or size of the particles. A mole of sodium chloride forms 2 moles of ions in solution and causes nearly twice as great a rise in boiling point as does 1 mole of nonelectrolyte. One mole of sugar contains 6.022×10^{23} particles (as molecules), whereas 1 mole of sodium chloride contains $2 \times 6.022 \times 10^{23}$ particles (as ions). Calcium chloride, $CaCl_2$, which consists of three ions, causes nearly three times as great a rise in boiling point as does sugar. Section 12.22 explains why the elevation is not exactly twice (for NaCl) or exactly three times (for $CaCl_2$) that of the boiling-point elevation for a nonelectrolyte.

Table 12.2 **Boiling Points, Freezing Points, and Molal Boiling-Point Elevation and Freezing-Point Depression Constants for Several Solvents**

Solvent	Boiling Point, °C (760 torr)	K_b(°C/m)	Freezing Point, °C	K_f(°C/m)
Water	100.0	0.512	0	1.86
Acetic acid	118.1	3.07	16.6	3.9
Benzene	80.1	2.53	5.48	5.12
Chloroform	61.26	3.63	−63.5	4.68
Nitrobenzene	210.9	5.24	5.67	8.1

Example 12.14

How much does the boiling point of water change when 1.00 g of glycerin, $C_3H_8O_3$, is dissolved in 47.8 g of water?

Because the change in boiling point is proportional to the molal concentration of glycerin, we first calculate its molal concentration.

$$1.00 \text{ g } C_3H_8O_3 \times \frac{1 \text{ mol } C_3H_8O_3}{92.1 \text{ g } C_3H_8O_3} = 1.09 \times 10^{-2} \text{ mol } C_3H_8O_3$$

$$\frac{1.09 \times 10^{-2} \text{ mol } C_3H_8O_3}{0.0478 \text{ kg } H_2O} = 0.228 \text{ m}$$

The change in boiling point is equal to the molal concentration of the glycerin multiplied by K_b (0.512°C/m for water, Table 12.2).

$$\Delta T = K_b \text{ m} = 0.512°C/m \times 0.228 \text{ m} = 0.117°C$$

Example 12.15

Find the boiling point of a solution of 92.1 g of iodine, I_2, in 800.0 g of chloroform, $CHCl_3$, assuming that the iodine is nonvolatile.

First we calculate the molality of iodine in the solution, because the change in boiling point of a dilute solution is proportional to m.

$$92.1 \text{ g } I_2 \times \frac{1 \text{ mol } I_2}{253.8 \text{ g } I_2} = 0.363 \text{ mol } I_2$$

$$\frac{0.363 \text{ mol } I_2}{0.8000 \text{ kg } CHCl_3} = 0.454 \text{ m}$$

The value of the molal boiling-point elevation constant for chloroform (Table 12.2) is 3.63°C/m. Thus, for a 0.4536 m solution,

$$\Delta T = K_b \text{ m} = 3.63°C/m \times 0.454 \text{ m} = 1.65°C$$

Because the boiling point of chloroform, 61.26°C, is raised by 1.65°C, the boiling point of the solution will be

$$61.26°C + 1.65°C = 62.91°C$$

⑫.16 Distillation of Solutions

In many cases pure solvent may be recovered from a solution by distillation (Section 11.7). If the solute is nonvolatile, an apparatus like the one shown in Fig. 11.15 may be used. Distillation relies on the facts that heating a liquid speeds up its rate of evaporation and increases its vapor pressure, while cooling a vapor favors condensation.

The boiling point of a solution is the temperature at which the total vapor pressure of the mixture is equal to the atmospheric pressure. The total vapor pressure of a solution composed of two volatile substances depends on the concentration and the vapor pressure of each substance and will be one of three types:

1. between the vapor pressures of the pure components,
2. less than the vapor pressure of either pure component, or
3. greater than that of either pure component.

Usually the total vapor pressure, and thus the boiling point, of a mixture of two liquids lies between those of the two components.

When a solution of type 1 is distilled, the vapor produced at the boiling point is richer in the lower-boiling component (the component with the higher vapor pressure) than was the original solution. When this vapor is condensed, the resulting distillate contains more of the lower-boiling component than did the original mixture. This means that the composition of the boiling mixture constantly changes, the amount of the lower-boiling component of the mixture constantly decreases, and the boiling point rises as distillation continues. The vapor (and the distillate) contains more and more of the higher-boiling component and less and less of the lower-boiling component as distillation proceeds. Changing the receiver at intervals yields successive fractions, each one increasingly richer in the less volatile (higher-boiling) component. If this process of **fractional distillation** is repeated several times, relatively pure samples of the two liquids can be obtained.

Fractionating columns have been devised that achieve separation of liquids that would require a great number of simple fractional distillations of the type just described. Crude oil, a complex mixture of hydrocarbons, is separated into its components by fractional distillation on an enormous scale (Fig. 12.15).

The vapor pressure of a solution of nitric acid and water is less than that of either component (a solution of type 2). When a dilute solution is distilled, the first fraction of

Figure 12.15

Fractional distillation of crude oil. Oil heated to about 425°C in the furnace vaporizes when it enters the tower at its base. The vapors rise through bubble caps in a series of trays in the tower. As the vapors gradually cool, fractions of higher, then of lower, boiling points condense to liquids and are drawn off. The fraction of highest boiling point is drawn off at the bottom as a residue. It is heavy fuel oil. In modern refineries these fractions, which still consist of mixtures of hydrocarbons, are further processed.

Gasoline vapors

Condenser

Gas

Gasoline 38°

Kerosene 150°

Heating oil 260°

Lubricating oil 315°–370°

Crude oil vapors

Bubble cap

Liquid

Superheated steam

Residue

Crude oil

Furnace

distillate consists mostly of water, because water has a higher vapor pressure than nitric acid under distillation conditions. As distillation is continued, the solution remaining in the distilling flask becomes richer in nitric acid. When a concentration of 68% HNO_3 by mass is reached, the solution boils at a constant temperature of 120.5°C (at 760 torr). At this temperature, the liquid and the vapor have the same composition, and the liquid distills without any further change in composition.

When a nitric acid solution more concentrated than 68% is distilled, the vapor first formed contains a large amount of HNO_3. The solution that remains in the distilling flask contains a greater percentage of water than at first, and the concentration of the nitric acid in the distilling flask decreases as the distillation is continued. Finally, a concentration of 68% HNO_3 is reached, and the solution again boils at the constant temperature of 120.5°C (at 760 torr). The 68% solution of nitric acid is referred to as a **constant boiling solution.**

Solutions of both type 2 and type 3 produce constant boiling solutions when distilled. A constant boiling solution forms a vapor with the same composition as the solution; thus it distills without a change in concentration. Constant boiling solutions are also called **azeotropic mixtures.** Other common and important substances that form azeotropic mixtures with water are HCl (20.24%, 110°C at 760 torr) and H_2SO_4 (98.3%, 338°C at 760 torr).

⑫.17 Depression of the Freezing Point of the Solvent

Solutions freeze at lower temperatures than pure liquids. We use solutions of antifreezes such as ethylene glycol in automobile radiators because they freeze at lower temperatures than pure water. Sea water freezes at a lower temperature than fresh water.

The freezing point of a solution or of a pure liquid is the temperature at which the solid and liquid are in equilibrium and at which both have the same vapor pressure. For example, pure water and ice have the same vapor pressure at 0°C. When aqueous solutions freeze, the solid that separates is almost always pure ice. Thus the vapor pressure of the ice is not affected by the presence of the solute. However, the water in the solution has a lower vapor pressure than ice at 0°C. If the temperature falls, the vapor pressure of the ice decreases more rapidly than does that of the water in the solution, and at some temperature below 0°C the ice and the water have the same vapor pressure. This is the temperature at which the solution and ice again are in equilibrium; it is the freezing point of the solution.

If ice and an aqueous solution are placed in contact and kept at 0°C (or at some temperature above the freezing point of the solution), the ice melts. This property permits the use of sodium chloride and calcium chloride to melt ice on streets and highways (Fig. 12.16).

One mole of a nonelectrolyte, such as ethylene glycol, when dissolved in 1 kilogram of water, gives a solution that freezes at −1.86°C. In general, the difference, ΔT, between the freezing point of a pure solvent and the freezing point of a solution of a nonelectrolyte dissolved in that solvent is directly proportional to the *molal* concentration of the solute.

$$\Delta T = K_f \, m$$

Figure 12.16
Rock salt (NaCl), calcium chloride, or a mixture of the two is used to melt ice.

The constant K_f, the **molal freezing-point depression constant,** is the change in freezing point for a 1 m solution; it varies for each solvent. Values of K_f for several solvents are listed in Table 12.2.

Example 12.16

What is the freezing point of the solution of 92.1 g of I_2 in 800.0 g of $CHCl_3$ described in Example 12.15?

The molal concentration of I_2 was shown to be 0.454 m. The value of the molal freezing-point depression constant, K_f, in Table 12.2 is 4.68°C/m. Thus for a 0.454 m solution,

$$\Delta T = K_f \, m = 4.68°C/m \times 0.454 \, m = 2.12°C$$

The freezing point of the solution is 2.12° lower than that of pure $CHCl_3$, or

$$\text{Freezing point of solution} = -63.5°C - 2.12°C = -65.6°C$$

A mole of sodium chloride in 1 kilogram of water shows nearly twice the freezing-point depression produced by a molecular compound. Each individual ion produces the same effect on the freezing point as a single molecule does. In Section 12.22 we will consider why the lowering produced by sodium chloride is not exactly twice that produced by a similar amount of a nonelectrolyte.

Example 12.17

Assume that each of the ions in calcium chloride, $CaCl_2$, has the same effect on the freezing-point of water as a nonelectrolyte molecule. Calculate the difference between the freezing point of water and that of a solution of 0.724 g of $CaCl_2$ in 175 g of water.

The difference in freezing points is the freezing-point depression and is proportional to the molal concentration of dissolved species—in this case, Ca^{2+} and Cl^- ions. One mole of $CaCl_2$ contains 3 mol of ions (1 mol of Ca^{2+} ions and 2 mol of Cl^- ions), so

**Example
12.17**
continued

the molality of ions in the solution is three times greater than the molality of $CaCl_2$. The following chain of calculations is one way to determine the difference in freezing points.

$$0.724 \text{ g } CaCl_2 \times \frac{1 \text{ mol } CaCl_2}{111.0 \text{ g } CaCl_2} = 6.52 \times 10^{-3} \text{ mol } CaCl_2$$

$$6.52 \times 10^{-3} \text{ mol } CaCl_2 \times \frac{3 \text{ mol ions}}{1 \text{ mol } CaCl_2} = 1.96 \times 10^{-2} \text{ mol ions}$$

$$\text{Molality of ions} = \frac{1.96 \times 10^{-2} \text{ mol ions}}{0.175 \text{ kg } H_2O} = 0.112 \text{ m}$$

$$\Delta T = K_f \text{ m} = 1.86°C/m \times 0.112 \text{ m} = 0.208°C$$

12.18 Phase Diagram for an Aqueous Solution of a Nonelectrolyte

Figure 12.17 contains a phase diagram (in red) for an aqueous solution of a nonelectrolyte, such as sucrose, $C_{12}H_{22}O_{11}$. The phase diagram for pure water (see Section 11.10) is included as a blue line for comparison. You can see that the freezing point for the solution is lower than that for pure water (the red line, separating solid and liquid states,

Figure 12.17

Phase diagram for a 1 m aqueous solution of a nonelectrolyte (red solid lines) compared to that for pure water (blue dashed lines). The diagram is not to scale in order to show more clearly the differences between the solution and pure water.

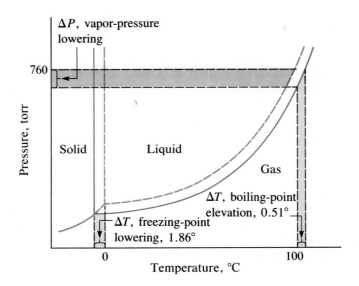

is displaced to the left of the blue one). Correspondingly, the higher boiling point for the solution is shown by the displacement of the solid line separating the liquid and gas states to the right of the dashed one. The decrease in vapor pressure of the solution, at any given temperature, is indicated by the vertical distance (shown in orange) between the dashed line and the solid line. On the diagram, the freezing-point depression and the boiling-point elevation are the horizontal distances (shown in yellow) between the broken line and the solid line near 0°C and near 100°C, respectively, at a pressure of 760 torr.

12.19 Osmosis and Osmotic Pressure of Solutions

Certain membranes (such as cellophane, animal bladders, and some polymer films) that permit a solvent to pass through, but not a solute, are called **semipermeable membranes.** When a solution and its pure solvent are separated by a semipermeable membrane, the pure solvent diffuses through the membrane and dilutes the solution (Fig. 12.18). This process is known as **osmosis.** During osmosis, the volume of the solution increases because solvent molecules move from the pure solvent to the solution.

When osmosis is carried out in an apparatus like that shown in Fig. 12.18, the level of the solution rises until its hydrostatic pressure (which is due to the weight of the column of solution in the tube) is great enough to prevent the further osmosis of solvent molecules into the solution. The pressure required to stop the osmosis from a pure solvent into a solution is called the **osmotic pressure, π,** of the solution. The osmotic pressure of a dilute solution can be calculated from the expression

$$\pi = MRT$$

where M is the molar concentration of the solute, R is the gas constant, and T is the temperature of the solution on the Kelvin scale.

Figure 12.18

Apparatus for demonstrating osmosis. The levels are equal at the start (a), but at equilibrium (b) the level of the sugar solution is higher because of the net transfer of water molecules into it.

What is the osmotic pressure in atmospheres of a 0.30 M solution of glucose in water that is used for intravenous infusion at body temperature, 37°C?

The osmotic pressure, π, in atmospheres can be found using the formula $\pi = MRT$, where T is on the Kelvin scale (310 K) and the value of R includes the unit of atmospheres (0.08206 L atm/mol K).

$$\pi = MRT$$

$$= 0.30 \text{ mol/L} \times 0.08206 \text{ L atm/mol K} \times 310 \text{ K} = 7.6 \text{ atm}$$

Example 12.18

If a solution is placed in an apparatus like the one shown in Fig. 12.19, applying pressure greater than the osmotic pressure of the solution reverses the osmosis and increases the volume of the pure solvent. This technique of **reverse osmosis** is used for desalting sea water. Plants that use this principle produce water for the city of Key West and for other parts of the world.

Pressure

Water | Sugar solution

Semipermeable membrane

Figure 12.19

Application of a pressure greater than the osmotic pressure reverses the osmosis.

The effects of osmosis are particularly evident in biological systems, because cells are surrounded by semipermeable membranes. Carrots and celery that have become limp because they have lost water can be made crisp again by placing them in water. Water moves into the carrot or celery cells by osmosis. A cucumber placed in a concentrated salt solution loses water by osmosis and becomes a pickle. Osmosis can also affect animal cells. Solute concentrations are particularly important when solutions are injected into the body. Solutes in body cell fluids and blood serum give these solutions an osmotic pressure of approximately 7.7 atmospheres. Solutions injected into the body must have the same osmotic pressure as blood serum; that is, they should be **isotonic** with blood serum. If a less concentrated solution, a **hypotonic solution,** is injected in sufficient quantity to dilute the blood serum, water from the diluted serum passes into the blood cells by osmosis, causing the cells to expand and rupture. When a more concentrated solution, a **hypertonic solution,** is injected, the cells lose water to the more concentrated solution, shrivel, and possibly die (see photographs below).

⑫.20 Determination of Molecular Masses

The effect of a solute on the freezing point, boiling point, vapor pressure, and osmotic pressure of a solution can be measured. Changes in these properties are directly proportional to the concentration of solute present, so the molecular mass of the solute can be determined from the change.

Red blood cells swell in a hypotonic solution.

Normal red blood cells in an isotonic solution.

Red blood cells shrivel in a hypertonic solution.

Example
12.19

A solution of 35.7 g of a nonelectrolyte in 220.0 g of chloroform has a boiling point of 64.5°C. What is the molecular mass of this compound?

This problem requires the following steps.

From the boiling point of pure chloroform (61.26°C, Table 12.2), we can calculate ΔT, the increase in boiling temperature.

$$\Delta T = 64.5°C - 61.26°C = 3.2°C$$

From K_b for chloroform (3.63°C/m, Table 12.2), we can calculate the molal concentration of the electrolyte (mol solute/mass solvent) by rearranging the equation $\Delta T = K_b m$.

$$m = \frac{\Delta T}{K_b} = \frac{3.2°C}{3.63°C/m} = 0.88 \ m$$

The number of moles of solute in 0.2200 kg (220.0 g) of solvent is then calculated as follows:

$$\text{Moles of solute} = \frac{0.88 \ \text{mol solute}}{1.00 \ \text{kg solvent}} \times 0.2200 \ \text{kg solvent}$$

$$= 0.19 \ \text{mol solute}$$

We can then calculate the molar mass.

$$\text{Molar mass} = \frac{35.7 \ \text{g}}{0.19 \ \text{mol}} = 180 \ \text{g/mol, or } 1.8 \times 10^2 \ \text{g/mol}$$

A molar mass of 180 g/mol corresponds to a molecular mass of 180 amu. (Note that only two significant figures are justified, because the value of ΔT has only two significant figures.)

Example
12.20

When 4.00 g of a certain nonelectrolyte is dissolved in 55.0 g of benzene, the resulting solution freezes at 2.32°C. Calculate the molecular mass of the nonelectrolyte.

The steps for this problem are

Freezing point of solution	→	ΔT	→	Molal concentration of compound	→	Moles of compound in sample	→	Molecular mass of compound

According to Table 12.2, K_f for benzene is 5.12°C/m and its freezing point is 5.48°C. The freezing point of the solution is 2.32°C, so the 4.00 g of solute has lowered the freezing point from 5.48°C to 2.32°C. Thus $\Delta T = 3.16°C$.

The molality of the solution is

$$m = \frac{\Delta T}{K_f} = \frac{3.16°C}{5.12°C/m} = 0.617 \ m$$

Example 12.20
continued

The number of moles of solute in 0.0550 kg (55.0 g) of solvent is

$$\text{Moles of solute} = \frac{0.617 \text{ mol}}{1.000 \text{ kg solvent}} \times 0.0550 \text{ kg solvent}$$

$$= 0.0339 \text{ mol}$$

The molar mass can then be calculated:

$$\text{Molar mass} = \frac{4.00 \text{ g}}{0.0339 \text{ mol}} = 118 \text{ g/mol}$$

$$\text{Molecular mass} = 118 \text{ amu}$$

Example 12.21

One liter of an aqueous solution containing 20.0 g of hemoglobin has an osmotic pressure of 5.9 torr at 22°C. What is the molecular mass of hemoglobin?

The steps for this problem are

From $\pi = MRT$, we can relate the osmotic pressure to the molar concentration, provided that the pressure is expressed in atmospheres to match the units in R (0.08206 L atm/mol K) and the temperature is expressed on the Kelvin scale ($T = 273 + 22 = 295$ K).

$$\pi = 5.9 \text{ torr} \times \frac{1 \text{ atm}}{760 \text{ torr}} = 7.8 \times 10^{-3} \text{ atm}$$

Rearrangement of $\pi = MRT$ gives $M = \pi/RT$.

$$M = \frac{7.8 \times 10^{-3} \text{ atm}}{(0.08206 \text{ L atm/mol K})(295 \text{ K})} = 3.2 \times 10^{-4} \text{ mol/L} = 3.2 \times 10^{-4} \text{ M}$$

Because the volume of the solution containing the 20.0 g of hemoglobin is 1 L, 20.0 g of hemoglobin is equal to 3.2×10^{-4} mol.

$$\text{Molar mass} = \frac{20.0 \text{ g}}{3.2 \times 10^{-4} \text{ mol}} = 62,000 \text{ g/mol}$$

$$\text{Molecular mass} = 62,000 \text{ amu}$$

⑫.21 The Effect of Electrolytes on Colligative Properties

The effect of nonelectrolytes on the colligative properties of a solution is dependent only on the number, not on the kind, of particles dissolved. For example, 1 mole of any nonelectrolyte dissolved in 1 kilogram of water produces the same lowering of the freezing point as does 1 mole of any other nonelectrolyte, because 1 mole of any non-electrolyte contains 6.022×10^{23} molecules. However, the lowering of the freezing point produced by 1 mole of a strong electrolyte is much greater than that from 1 mole of a nonelectrolyte, because the electrolyte ionizes when it dissolves. When 1 mole of sodium chloride is dissolved in 1 kilogram of water, the solution freezes at $-3.37°C$. The freezing point is lowered 1.81 times as much as for a nonelectrolyte. This illustrates the fact that 1 mole of an electrolyte produces more than 6.022×10^{23} solute particles. Almost all acids, bases, and salts behave this way when dissolved.

⑫.22 Ion Activities

If the ions of sodium chloride were completely separated in aqueous solution, it would lower the freezing point and raise the boiling point of the solvent twice as much as would an equal molal concentration of a nonelectrolyte, because it gives 2 moles of ions per mole of compound. However, 1 mole of sodium chloride lowers the freezing point of water only 1.81 times as much. A similar discrepancy occurs for the boiling-point elevation. Apparently, the ions of sodium chloride (and other strong electrolytes) are not completely separated in solution.

Peter J. W. Debye and Erich Hückel proposed a theory to explain the apparent incomplete ionization of strong electrolytes. They suggested that although interionic attraction in an aqueous solution is very greatly reduced by hydration of the ions and the insulating action of the polar solvent, it is not completely nullified. The residual attractions prevent the ions from behaving as totally independent particles (Fig. 12.20). In some cases a positive and negative ion may actually touch, giving a solvated unit called an **ion pair.** Thus the **activity,** or the effective concentration, of any particular kind of ion is less than that indicated by the actual concentration. This is evident in the colligative properties of the solution and in the amount of electric current conducted by it. Ions become more and more widely separated the more dilute the solution, and the residual

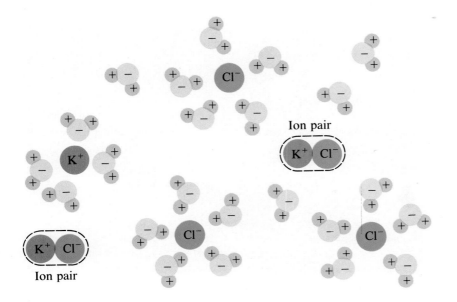

Figure 12.20

Diagrammatic representation of the various species thought to be present in an aqueous solution of potassium chloride.

interionic attractions become less and less. Thus in extremely dilute solutions, the effective concentrations of the ions (their activities) are essentially equal to the actual concentrations.

Colloid Chemistry

Solutions are dispersions of discrete molecules or ions of a solute. We will now consider dispersions of particles that are significantly larger than simple molecules.

⑫.23 Colloids

Solutions are homogeneous mixtures in which no settling occurs and in which the dissolved species are in a molecular or ionic state of subdivision. Suspensions, such as a suspension of sand in water, exhibit different behavior. The suspended particles are visible and settle out after mixing. **Colloids** form heterogeneous mixtures that exhibit an intermediate type of behavior. The particles in a colloid are large enough to scatter light, a phenomenon called the **Tyndall effect.** This can make colloidal mixtures appear cloudy or opaque (Fig. 12.21). However, the particles are so small that they do not settle out upon standing. For example, the mixture obtained when powdered starch is heated with water is not homogeneous, but the particles of insoluble starch do not settle out. Such a system is called a **colloidal dispersion;** the finely divided starch is called the **dispersed phase,** and the water is called the **dispersion medium.**

The term colloid—from the Greek words *kolla,* meaning glue, and *eidos,* meaning like—was first used in 1861 by Thomas Graham to classify substances such as starch and gelatin. We now know that colloidal properties are not limited to this class of substances; any substance can exist in colloidal form. Many colloidal particles are aggre-

Figure 12.21

This searchlight beam is scattered by colloidal-size water droplets when it passes through clouds. Scattering of a beam of light by colloidal dispersion is called the Tyndall effect.

Table 12.3   Colloidal Systems

Dispersed Phase	Dispersion Medium	Examples	Common Name
Solid	Gas	Smoke, dust	Solid aerosol
Solid	Liquid	Starch suspension, some inks, paints, milk of magnesia	Sol
Solid	Solid	Colored gems, some alloys	Solid sol
Liquid	Gas	Clouds, fogs, mists, sprays	Liquid aerosol
Liquid	Liquid	Milk, mayonnaise, butter	Emulsion
Liquid	Solid	Jellies, gels, opal (SiO_2 and H_2O), pearl ($CaCO_3$ and H_2O)	Solid emulsion
Gas	Liquid	Foams, whipped cream, beaten egg whites	Foam
Gas	Solid	Pumice, floating soaps	

gates of hundreds or even thousands of molecules, but others (such as proteins and polymer molecules) consist of a single large molecule. Proteins and synthetic polymer molecules may have molecular masses ranging from a few thousand to many million atomic mass units.

Colloids may be dispersed in a gas, a liquid, or a solid, and the dispersed phase may be a gas, a liquid, or a solid. However, a gas dispersed in another gas is not a colloidal system, because the particles are of molecular dimensions. Examples of colloidal systems are given in Table 12.3.

12.24 Preparation of Colloidal Systems

A colloidal system is prepared by producing particles of colloidal dimensions and distributing these particles through the dispersion medium. Particles of colloidal size are formed by two methods:

1. **Dispersion methods,** that is, the subdivision of larger particles. For example, paint pigments are produced by dispersing large particles via grinding in special mills.
2. **Condensation methods,** that is, growth from smaller units, such as molecules or ions. For example, clouds form when water molecules condense and form very small droplets.

A few solid substances, when brought into contact with water, disperse spontaneously and form colloidal systems. Gelatin, glue, and starch behave in this manner. The particles are already of colloidal size; the water simply disperses them. Some atomizers produce colloidal dispersions. Powdered milk with particles of colloidal size is produced by dehydrating milk spray.

An **emulsion** can be prepared by shaking together two immiscible liquids. Agitation breaks one liquid into droplets of colloidal size, which then disperse throughout the other liquid. The droplets of the dispersed phase, however, tend to coalesce, forming large drops, and separation of the liquids into two layers follows. Therefore, emulsions are usually stabilized by substances called **emulsifying agents.** For example, a little soap will stabilize an emulsion of kerosene in water. Milk is an emulsion of butterfat in water with the protein casein as the emulsifying agent. Mayonnaise is an emulsion of oil in vinegar with egg yolk as the emulsifying agent. Oil spills in the ocean may be difficult to clean up, partly because the oil and water can form an emulsion.

Condensation methods form colloidal particles by aggregation of smaller particles. If the particles grow beyond the colloidal size range, precipitates form and no colloidal system results. Condensation methods often employ chemical reactions. A dark red colloidal suspension of iron(III) hydroxide can be prepared by mixing a concentrated solution of iron(III) chloride with hot water.

$$Fe^{3+} + 3Cl^- + 6H_2O \longrightarrow Fe(OH)_3 + 3H_3O^+ + 3Cl^-$$

A colloidal gold sol results from the reduction of a very dilute solution of gold(III) chloride by a reducing agent such as formaldehyde, tin(II) chloride, or iron(II) sulfate.

$$Au^{3+} + 3e^- \longrightarrow Au$$

Some gold sols prepared by Faraday in 1857 are still intact.

⑫.25 Soaps and Detergents

Soaps are metal salts of fatty acids. Soluble soaps are made by boiling either fats or oils with a strong base, such as sodium hydroxide. Pioneers made soap by boiling fat with a strongly basic solution made by leaching potassium carbonate, K_2CO_3, from wood ashes with hot water. When animal fat is treated with sodium hydroxide, glycerol and sodium salts of fatty acids such as palmitic, oleic, and stearic acid are formed. The sodium salt of stearic acid, sodium stearate, has the formula $C_{17}H_{35}CO_2Na$ and contains a nonpolar hydrocarbon chain, the $-C_{17}H_{35}$ unit, and an ionic carboxylate group, the $-CO_2^-$ unit.

Detergents (soap substitutes) also contain nonpolar hydrocarbon chains, such as $-C_{12}H_{25}$, and an ionic group, such as a sulfate, $-OSO_3^-$, or a sulfonate, $-SO_3^-$. Soaps form insoluble calcium and magnesium compounds in hard water; detergents form water-soluble products—a definite advantage for detergents.

The cleansing action of soaps and detergents can be explained in terms of the structures of the molecules involved.

Hydrocarbon chain   Ionic end

Sodium stearate (soap)

Sodium lauryl sulfate (detergent)

The hydrocarbon end of a soap or detergent molecule is attracted by dirt, oil, or grease particles, and the ionic end is attracted by water (Fig. 12.22). The result is that the molecules at the interface between the dirt particles and the water become oriented in such a way that the dirt particles are suspended as colloidal particles and are readily washed away.

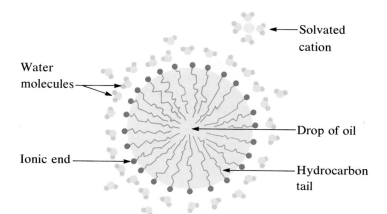

Figure 12.22
Diagrammatic cross section of an emulsified drop of oil in water with soap or detergent as the emulsifier. The negative ions of the emulsifier are oriented at the interface between the oil particle and water. The positive ions are solvated and move independently through the water. The nonpolar hydrocarbon end of the ion is in oil, and the ionic end ($-CO_2^-$ for soap, $-SO_3^-$ for detergent) is in water.

Solvated cation

Water molecules

Ionic end

Drop of oil

Hydrocarbon tail

⑫.26 Brownian Movement

When a colloidal system against a black background in a darkened space is viewed with a microscope at right angles to an intense beam of light, the colloidal particles look like tiny bright flashes of light in irregular rapid, dancing motion (Fig. 12.23). This motion is called **Brownian movement** after the botanist Robert Brown, who first observed it in 1828. He could not explain it, but we now know that the colloidal particles are so small that bombardment by molecules of the dispersion medium makes them move irregularly. Any particle in suspension is bombarded on all sides by the moving molecules of the dispersion medium. Particles larger than colloidal size do not move because bombardment on one side is likely to be counterbalanced by an equal bombardment on the opposite side. For particles of colloidal size, however, the probability of equal and simultaneous bombardments on opposite sides is slight, so they move irregularly. This movement explains why dispersed particles in colloidal systems do not settle, even though they are denser than the dispersion medium. Studies of Brownian movement yielded one of the earliest confirmations of the kinetic-molecular theory.

Figure 12.23
A diagram showing how six particles in suspension might move as a result of unequal bombardment by molecules of the dispersion medium.

⑫.27 Electrical Properties of Colloidal Particles

Dispersed colloidal particles are usually electrically charged. A particle of an iron(III) hydroxide sol, for example, does not contain enough hydroxide ions to compensate exactly for the positive charges on the iron(III) ions. Thus each individual colloidal particle bears a positive charge, and the colloidal dispersion consists of charged colloidal particles and some free hydroxide ions, which keep the dispersion electrically neutral. In an electrolytic cell (Fig. 12.24), the dispersed particles move to the negative electrode, the cathode. Opposite charges attract each other, so this is good evidence that the iron(III) hydroxide particles are positively charged. At the cathode the colloidal particles lose their charge and coagulate as a precipitate. All colloidal particles in any one system have charges of the same sign. This helps to keep them dispersed, because like charges

Coagulated $Fe(OH)_3$

+ charged particles of $Fe(OH)_3$

Figure 12.24
Colloidal iron(III) hydroxide is coagulated in an electrolytic cell.

Figure 12.25

In a Cottrell precipitator, positively and negatively charged particles in smoke are precipitated as they pass over the electrically charged plates.

repel each other. Most metal hydroxide colloids have positive charges, whereas most metal sulfides and metals form negatively charged dispersions.

The carbon and dust particles in smoke are often colloidally dispersed and electrically charged. Frederick Cottrell, an American chemist, developed a process to remove these particles. The charged particles are attracted to highly charged electrodes, where they are neutralized and deposited as dust (Fig. 12.25). The process is also important in the recovery of valuable products from the smoke of smelters, furnaces, and kilns.

12.28 Gels

Under certain conditions, the dispersed phase in a colloidal system coagulates so that the whole mass, including the liquid, sets to an extremely viscous body known as a **gel.** For example, a hot aqueous "solution" of gelatin sets to a gel on cooling. Because the formation of a gel is accompanied by the taking up of water or some other solvent, the gel is said to be hydrated or solvated. Apparently the fibers of the dispersed substance form a complex three-dimensional network, the interstices being filled with the liquid medium or a dilute solution of the dispersed phase.

Pectin, a carbohydrate from fruit juices, is a gel-forming substance important in jelly making. Silica gel, a colloidal dispersion of hydrated silicon dioxide, is formed when dilute hydrochloric acid is added to a dilute solution of sodium silicate. Canned Heat is a gel made by mixing alcohol and a saturated aqueous solution of calcium acetate. The wall of a living cell is colloidal in character, and within the cell is a gel. In fact, all living tissue is colloidal, and life processes depend on the chemistry of colloids.

For Review

Summary

A **solution** forms when one substance, a **solute,** dissolves in a second substance, a **solvent,** giving a homogeneous mixture of atoms, molecules, or ions. The solute may be a solid, a liquid, or a gas. The solvent is usually a liquid, although solutions of gases in other gases and solutions of gases, liquids, and solids in solids are possible. Substances that dissolve and give solutions that contain ions and conduct electricity are called **electrolytes.** Electrolytes may be molecular compounds that react with the solvent to give ions, or they may be ionic compounds. **Nonelectrolytes** are substances that dissolve to give solutions of molecules. These solutions do not conduct electricity.

The extent to which a gas dissolves in a liquid solvent is proportional to the pressure of the gas, provided that the gas does not react with the solvent. Generally, the solubility of a gas decreases with increasing temperature. Polar liquids tend to be soluble (**miscible**) in water, whereas nonpolar liquids tend to be insoluble (**immiscible**) in water. Generally, the solubility of solids in water increases with increasing temperature, but there are exceptions.

Solutions that obey **Raoult's law** exactly—**ideal solutions**—form when the average strength of the intermolecular forces of attraction between the solute and solvent is equal to the average strength of the forces of attraction between pure solute molecules and between pure solvent molecules. Ideal solutions form by a **spontaneous process,** because the disorder of the molecules of solute and solvent increases when the solution forms. An increase in the average strength of the solute–solvent intermolecular attractive forces, compared to those in the pure solute and solvent, also favors spontaneous formation of a solution. The relative strengths of the solute–solute and solvent–solvent attractions compared to the solute–solvent attractions can be measured by the enthalpy of solution of the solute in the solvent. In many cases, the increase in disorder compensates for the decrease in the average strength of the solute–solvent attractions compared to those of the pure components of a solution.

The relative amounts of solute and solvent in a solution can be described quantitatively as the **concentration** of the solution. Units of concentration include **percent composition, molar concentration, molal concentration,** and **mole fraction.**

Properties of a solution that depend only on the concentration of solute particles are called **colligative properties.** They include changes in the vapor pressure, boiling point, and freezing point of the solvent in the solution. The magnitudes of these properties depend only on the total concentration of solute particles in solution, not on the type of particles. The total concentration of solute particles in a solution also affects its **osmotic pressure.** This is the pressure that must be applied to the solution in order to prevent diffusion of molecules of pure solvent through a semipermeable membrane into the solution.

A **colloid** is a suspension of small, insoluble particles, which are usually larger than molecules but small enough not to settle from the dispersion medium. Examples of colloids include smoke, clouds, paints, mayonnaise, and foams.

Key Terms and Concepts

alloy (12.6)
azeotropic mixture (12.16)
boiling-point elevation (12.15)
Brownian motion (12.26)
colligative properties (12.14)
colloid (12.23)
constant boiling solution (12.16)
detergent (12.25)
electrolyte (12.8)
emulsion (12.24)
fractional distillation (12.16)
freezing-point depression (12.17)

gel (12.28)
Henry's law (12.2)
ideal solution (12.7)
ion activity (12.22)
miscibility (12.3)
molality (12.12)
molarity (12.11)
mole fraction (12.13)
nonelectrolyte (12.8)
nonstoichiometric compounds (12.6)
osmosis (12.19)
osmotic pressure (12.19)

percent composition (12.10)
Raoult's law (12.14)
saturated solution (12.1)
soap (12.25)
solid solutions (12.6)
solubility (12.1)
spontaneous process (12.7)
supersaturated solution (12.1)
Tyndall effect (12.23)
unsaturated solution (12.1)
vapor-pressure lowering (12.14)

Exercises

Answers for selected even-numbered exercises marked by red numbers appear at the end of the book. The worked-out solutions to all even-numbered exercises appear in the *Solutions Guide*.

The Nature of Solutions

1. How do solutions differ from compounds? From ordinary mixtures?
2. Show how solutions of (a) carbon dioxide in air, (b) ethanol, C_2H_5OH, in water, and (c) potassium chloride in water exhibit the principal characteristics of solutions.
3. Describe how the solutions shown in Fig. 12.1 and Fig. 12.4 exhibit the principal characteristics of solutions. How do these solutions differ?
4. Why are the majority of chemical reactions most readily carried out in solution?
5. Explain the following terms as applied to solutions: solute, solvent, electrolyte, nonelectrolyte, saturated, supersaturated, unsaturated, concentrated, dilute.
6. Describe the effect on the solubility of a gas of (a) the nature of the gas and its solvent, (b) the pressure on the gas, (c) the temperature, and (d) the reaction of the gas with the solvent.

7. At 0°C, 3.36 g of CO_2 at 1.00 atm dissolves in exactly 1 L of water. At 0°C and 4.00 atm, how many grams of CO_2 dissolve in exactly 1 L of water?

8. In order to prepare supersaturated solutions of most solids, we cool saturated solutions. Supersaturated solutions of gases are prepared by warming saturated solutions. Explain the reasons for the difference in the two procedures.

9. Why is a solution of nitric acid, HNO_3, in water a good conductor of an electric current, even though both pure nitric acid and water are not?

10. Why are solid ionic compounds nonconductors, whereas ionic compounds that are fused (melted) are good conductors?

11. Using the general rules given in Section 12.5, answer the following questions:
    (a) When HCl is added to an unknown solution, a white precipitate forms. What common cations might be present in the solution?
    (b) The addition of a solid metal sulfide to water produces H_2S and an insoluble solid. What common metal sulfides exhibit this behavior?
    (c) When H_2SO_4 is added to a solution, no precipitate forms. What common metal cations are not present in the solution?
    (d) A solution of sodium phosphate was added to a second solution, and no precipitate formed. What common metal cations might be present in the second solution?
    (e) A solution of $Pb(NO_3)_2$ was added to a second solution, and no precipitate formed. What common anions might be present in the second solution?

12. Suppose you are presented with a clear solution of sodium thiosulfate, $Na_2S_2O_3$. How could you determine whether the solution is unsaturated, saturated, or supersaturated?

13. Complete the equation and write the net ionic equation for each of the following precipitation reactions (run in water), using the solubility rules given in Section 12.5 as a guide.
    (a) $Pb(NO_3)_2 + K_2SO_4$ (d) $Pb(NO_3)_2 + NaCl$
    (b) $Na_2S + CoCl_2$ (e) $BaCl_2 + K_2CO_3$
    (c) $MnBr_2 + LiOH$

The Process of Dissolution

14. Which of the following spontaneous processes occurs with an increase in disorder?
    (a) Evaporation of water
    (b) Precipitation of AgCl from solution
    (c) Condensation of water vapor to ice
    (d) Mixing of natural gas [$CH_4(g)$] and air
    (e) Dissolution of KBr in water

15. Indicate the most important types of intermolecular attractions (Sections 11.2–11.4) in each of the following solutions:
    (a) The solutions in Fig. 12.1

    (b) Methanol, CH_3OH, in ethanol, C_2H_5OH
    (c) The solution in Fig. 12.11
    (d) HCl in benzene, C_6H_6
    (e) Carbon tetrachloride, CCl_4, in the Freon CF_2Cl_2
    (f) $O_2(l)$ in $N_2(l)$

16. Heat is released when some solutions form; heat is absorbed when other solutions form. Provide a molecular explanation for the difference between these two types of spontaneous processes.

17. Explain why HBr, a gas, is a nonelectrolyte when dissolved in benzene and an electrolyte when dissolved in water.

18. Explain why the ions Na^+ and Cl^- are strongly solvated in water but not in hexane, a solvent composed of nonpolar molecules.

19. Compare the processes that occur when methanol (CH_3OH), hydrogen chloride (HCl), and sodium hydroxide (NaOH) dissolve in water. Write equations and prepare sketches showing the form in which each of these compounds is present in its respective solution.

20. Solid water (ice) is soluble in ethanol, C_2H_5OH, at −5°C. Compare the process that occurs when ice dissolves in ethanol with the one that occurs when sodium chloride dissolves in water. (See Section 11.12 for a description of the structure of ice.)

21. Explain, in terms of the intermolecular attractions between solute and solvent, why methanol, CH_3OH, is miscible with water in all proportions but only 0.11 g of butanol, $CH_3CH_2CH_2CH_2OH$, dissolves in 100 g of water at 25°C.

22. Suggest an explanation for the observations that ethanol, C_2H_5OH, is completely miscible with water and that ethanethiol, C_2H_5SH, is soluble only to the extent of 1.5 g per 100 mL of water.

Units of Concentration

23. What is the difference between a 1 M solution and a 1 m solution?

24. How did the concentration of CO_2 in the beverage shown in Fig. 12.2 change when the bottle was opened?

25. What are the approximate molar concentrations of the solutions shown in Fig. 12.1? These solutions are contained in 500-mL beakers.

26. There is about 1.0 g of calcium, as Ca^{2+}, in 1.0 L of milk. What is the molarity of Ca^{2+} in milk?

27. Calculate the number of moles and the mass of the solute in each of the following solutions:
    (a) 2.00 L of 18.5 M H_2SO_4, concentrated sulfuric acid
    (b) 100 mL of 3.8×10^{-5} M NaCN, the minimum lethal concentration of sodium cyanide in blood serum
    (c) 500 mL of 0.30 M glucose, $C_6H_{12}O_6$, used for intravenous injection
    (d) 5.50 L of 13.3 M formaldehyde, H_2CO, used to "fix" tissue samples

(e) 325 mL of 1.8×10^{-6} M $FeSO_4$, the minimum concentration of iron sulfate detectable by taste in drinking water

28. Calculate the molarity of each of the following solutions:
    (a) 0.195 g of cholesterol, $C_{27}H_{46}O$, in 0.100 L of serum, the average concentration of cholesterol in human serum
    (b) 4.25 g of NH_3 in 0.500 L of solution, the concentration of NH_3 in household ammonia
    (c) 222.0 g of ethylene glycol, $C_2H_4(OH)_2$, in 393.6 mL of an antifreeze solution
    (d) 595 g of isopropyl alcohol, C_3H_8OH, in 1.00 L of solution, the concentration of isopropyl alcohol in rubbing alcohol
    (e) 0.029 g of I_2 in 0.100 L of solution, the solubility of I_2 in water at 20°C

29. Calculate the molality of each of the following solutions:
    (a) 71.0 g of sodium carbonate (washing soda), Na_2CO_3, in 1.00 kg of water, a saturated solution at 0°C
    (b) 583 g of H_2SO_4 in 1.50 kg of water, the acid solution used in an automobile battery
    (c) 0.86 g of NaCl in 100 g of water, a solution of sodium chloride for intravenous injection
    (d) 46.85 g of codeine, $C_{18}H_{21}NO_3$, in 125.5 g of ethanol, C_2H_5OH
    (e) 0.372 g of histamine, C_5H_9N, in 125 g of chloroform, $CHCl_3$

30. Calculate the mole fractions of solute and solvent in each of the solutions in Exercise 29.

31. What mass of concentrated nitric acid (68.0% HNO_3 by mass) is needed to prepare 400.0 g of a 10.0% solution of HNO_3 by mass?

32. What mass of sulfuric acid solution (95% by mass) is needed to prepare 200.0 g of a 20.0% solution of the acid by mass?

33. What mass of a 4.00% NaOH solution by mass contains 15.0 g of NaOH?

34. What mass of HCl is contained in 45.0 mL of an HCl solution that has a density of 1.19 g/cm³ and contains 37.21% HCl by mass?

35. What mass of solid NaOH (97.0% NaOH by mass) is required to prepare 1.00 L of a 10.0% solution of NaOH by mass? The density of the 10.0% solution is 1.109 g/cm³.

36. The hardness of water (hardness count) is usually expressed as parts per million (by mass) of $CaCO_3$, which is equivalent to milligrams of $CaCO_3$ per liter of water. What is the molar concentration of Ca^{2+} ions in a water sample with a hardness count of 175?

37. The Safe Drinking Water Act sets the maximum permissible amount of cadmium in drinking water at 0.01 mg/L. What is the maximum permissible molar concentration of cadmium in drinking water?

38. The concentration of glucose, $C_6H_{12}O_6$, in normal spinal fluid is 75 mg/100 g. What is the molal concentration?

39. What volume of a 0.20 M K_2SO_4 solution contains 57 g of K_2SO_4?

40. A 0.553 M solution of $NaHCO_3$ has a density of 1.032 g/cm³. What is the molality of the solution?

41. Calculate what volume of a sulfuric acid solution (density = 1.070 g/mL, and containing 10.00% H_2SO_4 by mass) contains 18.50 g of pure H_2SO_4.

42. A 13.0% solution of K_2CO_3 by mass has a density of 1.09 g/cm³. Calculate the molarity of the solution.

43. Equal volumes of 0.050 M $Ca(OH)_2$ and 0.400 M HCl are mixed. Calculate the molarity of each ion present in the final solution.

44. What volume of 0.600 M HCl is required to react completely with 2.50 g of sodium hydrogen carbonate?

$$NaHCO_3 + HCl \longrightarrow NaCl + CO_2 + H_2O$$

45. Calculate the volume of 0.050 M HCl necessary to precipitate the silver contained in 12.0 mL of 0.050 M $AgNO_3$.

$$Ag^+(aq) + Cl^-(aq) \longrightarrow AgCl(s)$$

46. What volume of a 0.33 M solution of hydrobromic acid would be required to neutralize completely 1.00 L of 0.15 M barium hydroxide?

47. To 10.0 mL of a 0.100 M $K_2Cr_2O_7$ solution we add 10.0 mL of a 0.100 M $Pb(NO_3)_2$ solution. What mass of $PbCr_2O_7$ forms?

48. A gaseous solution was found to contain 15% H_2, 10% CO, and 75% CO_2 by mass. What is the mole fraction of each component?

49. A sample of lead glass is prepared by melting together 20.0 g of silica, SiO_2, and 80.0 g of lead(II) oxide, PbO. What is the mole fraction of SiO_2 and of PbO in the glass?

50. Calculate the mole fractions of methanol, CH_3OH, ethanol, C_2H_5OH, and water in a solution that is 40% methanol, 40% ethanol, and 20% water by mass. (Assume the data are good to two significant figures.)

51. Concentrated hydrochloric acid is 37.0% HCl by mass and has a density of 1.19 g/mL. Calculate (a) the molarity, (b) the molality, and (c) the mole fraction of HCl and of H_2O.

52. Calculate (a) the percent composition and (b) the molality of an aqueous solution of $NaNO_3$, if the mole fraction of $NaNO_3$ is 0.20.

Colligative Properties

53. A solution of potassium nitrate (an electrolyte) and a solution of glycerine (a nonelectrolyte) both boil at 100.3°C. What other physical properties of the two solutions are identical?

54. Which evaporates faster under the same conditions, 50 mL of distilled water or 50 mL of sea water?

55. Which of the solutions shown in Fig. 12.1 has the higher

vapor pressure? The lower freezing temperature? The higher boiling temperature?

56. In addition to the information given with the figure, what physical property of the solutions shown in Fig. 12.1 do we need to calculate the vapor pressure, boiling temperature, and freezing temperature?

57. The triple point of air-free water (Section 11.10) is defined as 273.15 K. Why is it important that the water be free of air?

58. Why does 1 mol of sodium chloride depress the freezing point of 1 kg of water almost twice as much as 1 mol of glycerin?

59. Explain what is meant by osmotic pressure. How is the osmotic pressure of a solution related to its concentration?

60. The cell walls of red and white blood cells are semipermeable membranes. The concentration of solute particles in the blood is about 0.6 M. What happens to blood cells that are placed in pure water? In a 1 M sodium chloride solution?

61. A 1 m solution of HCl in benzene has a freezing point of 0.4°C. Is HCl an electrolyte in benzene? Explain.

62. Arrange the following solutions in decreasing order by their freezing points: 0.1 m Na_3PO_4, 0.1 m C_2H_5OH, 0.01 m CO_2, 0.15 m NaCl, and 0.2 m $CaCl_2$.

63. Some mammals, including humans, excrete hypertonic urine in order to conserve water. In humans, some parts of the ducts of the kidney (which contain the urine) pass through a fluid that contains a much more concentrated salt solution than that normally found in the body. Explain how this could help conserve water in the body.

64. A solution of 5.00 g of a compound in 25.00 g of carbon tetrachloride (bp 76.8°C; $K_b = 5.02$°C/m) boils at 81.5°C at 1 atm. What is the molecular mass of the compound?

65. A solution contains 5.00 g of urea, $CO(NH_2)_2$, per 0.100 kg of water. If the vapor pressure of pure water at 25°C is 23.7 torr, what is the vapor pressure of the solution?

66. A 12.0-g sample of a nonelectrolyte is dissolved in 80.0 g of water. The solution freezes at −1.94°C. Calculate the molecular mass of the substance.

67. A sample of an organic compound (nonelectrolyte) weighing 1.350 g lowered the freezing point of 10.0 g of benzene by 3.66°C. Calculate the molecular mass of the organic compound.

68. Calculate the boiling-point elevation of 0.100 kg of water containing 0.010 mol of NaCl, 0.020 mol of Na_2SO_4, and 0.030 mol of $MgCl_2$, assuming complete dissociation of these electrolytes.

69. What is the approximate freezing point of a 0.27 m aqueous solution of sodium bromide? Assume complete dissociation of this electrolyte.

70. How could you prepare a 3.08 m aqueous solution of glycerin, $C_3H_8O_3$? What is the freezing point of this solution?

71. If 26.4 g of the nonelectrolyte dibromobenzene, $C_6H_4Br_2$, is dissolved in 0.250 kg of benzene, what are (a) the freez-

ing point of the solution and (b) the boiling point of the solution at 1 atm?

72. A sample of sulfur weighing 0.210 g was dissolved in 17.8 g of carbon disulfide, CS_2 ($K_b = 2.34$°C/m). If the boiling-point elevation was 0.107°C, what is the formula of a sulfur molecule in carbon disulfide?

73. What is the boiling point, at 1 atm, of a solution containing 140.0 g of sucrose, $C_{12}H_{22}O_{11}$, in 400.0 g of water?

74. Lysozyme is an enzyme that cleaves cell walls. A 0.100-L sample of a solution of lysozyme that contains 0.0750 g of the enzyme exhibits an osmotic pressure of 1.32×10^{-3} atm at 25°C. What is the molecular mass of lysozyme?

75. The osmotic pressure of a solution containing 7.0 g of insulin per liter is 23 torr at 25°C. What is the molecular mass of insulin?

76. The osmotic pressure of human blood is 7.6 atm at 37°C. What mass of glucose, $C_6H_{12}O_6$, is required to make 1.00 L of aqueous solution for intravenous feeding if the solution must have the same osmotic pressure as blood at body temperature, 37°C?

Colloids

77. Distinguish between dispersion methods and condensation methods for preparing colloidal systems.

78. How do colloidal ''solutions'' differ from true solutions with regard to dispersed particle size and homogeneity?

79. Identify the dispersed phase and the dispersion medium in each of the following colloidal systems: starch dispersion, smoke, fog, pearl, whipped cream, floating soap, jelly, milk, and ruby.

80. Explain the cleansing action of soap.

81. How can it be demonstrated that colloidal particles are electrically charged?

82. What is the structure of a gel?

83. Explain the phenomenon of Brownian movement. What is its relationship to the stability of the dispersed particles of a colloidal system?

Additional Exercises

84. Calculate the percent by mass of KBr in a saturated solution of KBr in water at 40°C. See Fig. 12.7 for useful data.

85. What is the concentration of the solution shown in the figure in Example 12.6 if enough water evaporates for the volume of the solution to be 0.50 L?

86. Why does ice melt when placed in an aqueous solution that is kept at 0°C?

87. What is a constant boiling solution? Describe two ways in which to prepare a constant boiling solution of HNO_3.

88. The salt calcium chloride, $CaCl_2$, does not depress the freezing point of water three times as much as the same concentration of a nonelectrolyte does. Explain.

89. The radius of a water molecule, assuming a spherical shape, is approximately 1.40 Å. Assume that water molecules cluster around each metal ion in a solution such that the water molecules essentially touch both the metal ion and each other. On this basis, and assuming that 4, 6, 8, and 12 are the only possible coordination numbers, find the maximum number of water molecules that can hydrate each of the following ions.

(a) Mg^{2+} (radius 0.65 Å)   (c) Rb^+ (1.48 Å)
(b) Al^{3+} (0.50 Å)   (d) Sr^{2+} (1.13 Å)

90. Hydrogen gas dissolves in the metal palladium with hydrogen atoms going into the holes between metal atoms. Determine the molarity, molality, and percent by mass of hydrogen atoms in a solution (density = 10.8 g/cm^3) of 0.94 g of hydrogen gas in 215 g of palladium metal.

91. How many liters of $NH_3(g)$ at 25°C and 1.46 atm are required to prepare 3.00 L of a 2.50 M solution of NH_3?

92. A 1.80-g sample of an acid, H_2X, required 14.00 mL of KOH solution for neutralization of all the hydrogen ions. Exactly 14.2 mL of this same KOH solution was found to neutralize 10.0 mL of 0.750 M H_2SO_4. Calculate the molecular mass of H_2X.

93. A 0.200-L volume of gaseous ammonia measured at 30.0°C and 764 torr was absorbed in 0.100 L of water. How many milliliters of 0.0100 M hydrochloric acid are required in the neutralization of this aqueous ammonia? What is the molarity of the aqueous ammonia solution? (Assume no change in volume when the gaseous ammonia is added to the water.)

94. Calculate the percent by mass and the molality in terms of $CuSO_4$ for a solution prepared by dissolving 11.5 g of $CuSO_4 \cdot 5H_2O$ in 0.100 kg of water. Remember to consider the water released from the hydrate.

95. It is desired to produce 1.000 L of 0.050 M nitric acid by diluting 10.00 M nitric acid. Calculate the volume of the concentrated acid and the volume of water required in the dilution.

96. What is the molarity of H_3PO_4 in a solution that is prepared by dissolving 10.0 g of P_4O_{10} in sufficient water to make 0.500 L of solution?

97. A solution of sodium carbonate having a volume of 0.400 L was prepared from 4.032 g of $Na_2CO_3 \cdot 10H_2O$. Calculate the molarity of this solution.

98. A solution of $Ba(OH)_2$ is 0.1055 M. What volume of 0.211 M nitric acid is required in the neutralization of 15.5 mL of the $Ba(OH)_2$ solution?

99. The sulfate in 50.0 mL of dilute sulfuric acid was precipitated using an excess of barium chloride. The mass of $BaSO_4$ formed was 0.482 g. Calculate the molarity of the sulfuric acid solution.

100. A sample of $HgCl_2$ weighing 9.41 g is dissolved in 32.75 g of ethanol, C_2H_5OH ($K_b = 1.20$°C/m). The boiling-point elevation of the solution is 1.27°C. Is $HgCl_2$ an electrolyte in ethanol? Show your calculations.

101. A salt is known to be an alkali metal fluoride. A quick approximate determination of freezing point indicates that 4 g of the salt dissolved in 100 g of water produces a solution that freezes at about -1.4°C. What is the formula of the salt? Show your calculations.

102. A solution of 0.045 g of an unknown organic compound in 0.550 g of camphor melts at 158.4°C. The melting point of pure camphor is 178.4°C. K_f for camphor is 37.7°C/m. The solute contains 93.46% C and 6.54% H by mass. What is the molecular formula of the solute? Show your calculations.

103. How many liters of HCl gas, measured at 30.0°C and 745 torr, are required to prepare 2.50 L of a 1.60 M solution of hydrochloric acid?

104. The sugar fructose contains 40.0% C, 6.7% H, and 53.3% O by mass. A solution of 11.7 g of fructose in 325 g of ethanol has a boiling point of 78.59°C. The boiling point of ethanol is 78.35°C, and K_b for ethanol is 1.20°C/m. What is the molecular formula of fructose?

105. The vapor pressure of methanol, CH_3OH, is 94 torr at 20°C. The vapor pressure of ethanol, C_2H_5OH, is 44 torr at the same temperature. Calculate the mole fraction of methanol and of ethanol in a solution of 50.0 g of methanol and 50.0 g of ethanol. Ethanol and methanol form a solution that behaves like an ideal solution. Calculate the vapor pressure of methanol and of ethanol above the solution at 20°C. Calculate the mole fraction of methanol and of ethanol in the vapor above the solution.

13 The Active Metals

Coral reefs are composed of calcium carbonate deposited by marine animals.

As we learned in Chapter 6, all the elements in Groups IA, IIA, and IIIA of the periodic table are metals except boron, which is a semi-metal. Twelve of these 16 metals are referred to as the **active metals,** and they exhibit remarkably similar chemical behavior. They are lithium, sodium, potassium, rubidium, cesium, and francium from Group IA; magnesium, calcium, strontium, barium, and radium from Group IIA; and aluminum from Group IIIA (Fig. 13.1).

All of these metals are easily oxidized (Section 2.11); that is, they lose their valence electrons readily. The resulting cations are thus reduced (gain electrons) with great

Figure 13.1

The location of the active metals (shown in yellow) in the periodic table. Nonmetals are shown in green, semi-metals in blue, and the remaining metals in red.

difficulty. Each metal forms many simple, ionic compounds and exhibits only a single positive oxidation number, the numerical value of which, without the positive sign, is the group number of the element. All of these metals react with acids to yield hydrogen gas and ionic salts, and most react with water to form hydrogen gas and the metal hydroxide. They react with most nonmetals to form binary compounds.

Several of the active metals are among the most common of the elements. They do not occur in nature as free elements because of their extreme reactivity (most react with water and oxygen in air). However, their compounds are widely distributed. Large mineral deposits of relatively pure compounds of sodium, potassium, magnesium, calcium, and aluminum are found in many parts of the world. Chlorides of sodium, magnesium, calcium, and potassium are the most abundant compounds in sea water. Potassium compounds are found in all plants. Both sodium and potassium compounds are essential to animal life. Magnesium, calcium, and aluminum ions are found in dolomite ($MgCO_3 \cdot CaCO_3$), limestone ($CaCO_3$), and silicate rocks (silicates are silicon–oxygen poly-atomic anions, such as $Si_2O_6^{4-}$). The chlorophyll in green plants is a magnesium-containing compound. Calcium ion is a component of bones, teeth, and nerve cells. Many compounds of these elements figure prominently in trade, commerce, and chemical industry, and we use them routinely every day.

In this chapter we will examine the kinds of compounds the active metals form and the chemical behavior of these compounds. We begin by examining the behavior of these elements in terms of their positions in the periodic table. We will then see how these very reactive elements can be isolated and consider their more important uses. The formation and uses of some of their more important compounds are also described. Finally, we will use the principles developed in preceding chapters to explain the similarities and differences observed in the behavior of these ionic compounds.

⑬.1   The Activity Series

Before we discuss the chemistry of the active metals, it will be helpful to consider briefly the variable reactivities of metals in general. Certain metals, such as the active metals sodium and potassium, react readily with cold water, displacing hydrogen and forming metal hydroxides. Other metals, such as magnesium and iron, react with water only when heated. Sodium and potassium react much more vigorously with acids than do magnesium and iron. Experimental observations like these are used to arrange the metals in order by their chemical activities and thereby to establish an **activity,** or **electromotive, series.** A brief form of the activity series containing only the common elements is given in Table 13.1. Elements exhibiting more metallic behavior are at the top of the series (Groups IA and IIA). In general, the less the metallic character of an element, the lower it appears in the series.

Potassium is the most reactive of the common metals and therefore heads the activity series. Each succeeding metal in the series is less reactive, and gold, the least reactive

Table 13.1   Activity Series of Common Metals

Oxides reducibility	Metals	React with cold water, liberating hydrogen	React with steam, liberating hydrogen	React with acids, liberating hydrogen	React with oxygen, giving oxides
Oxides are not reduced to the metal by hydrogen	K, Ba, Sr, Ca, Na	React with cold water, liberating hydrogen			
	Mg, Al, Mn, Zn, Cr		React with steam, liberating hydrogen	React with acids, liberating hydrogen	React with oxygen, giving oxides
Oxides are reduced to the metal by hydrogen	Fe, Cd				
	Co, Ni, Sn, Pb				
	H, Sb, As, Bi, Cu				
Oxides are decomposed by heat alone	Hg, Ag, Pd, Pt, Au			Form oxides indirectly	

Figure 13.2

When an iron nail is immersed in a solution of copper sulfate (top), copper (a less active metal than iron) is deposited as the iron reduces the Cu^{2+} ion to metallic copper and is itself oxidized to Fe^{2+} (bottom).

of all, is found at the bottom of the series. In theory, any metal in the series, in its elemental form, will reduce the ion, in water, of any metal below it in the series. For example, the copper ion in an aqueous solution of a copper(II) salt is reduced to copper metal by iron, which is above copper in the series (Fig. 13.2).

$$Fe(s) + Cu^{2+}(aq) \longrightarrow Cu(s) + Fe^{2+}(aq)$$

In a similar manner aqueous silver ions are reduced by metallic copper, and aqueous mercury ions are reduced by both copper and silver. Any metal above hydrogen in the series will liberate hydrogen from aqueous acids (solutions of acids in water); those from cadmium to the top will liberate hydrogen from hot water or steam; and those from sodium to the top will liberate hydrogen even from cold water. The metals below hydrogen do not displace hydrogen from water or from aqueous acids.

The reactivity of the metals toward oxygen decreases down the series, as do the enthalpy of formation and the stability of the compounds formed. It is evident then that the activity series is very useful since it indicates the possibility of a reaction of a given metal with water, acids, salts of other metals, and oxygen. In addition, the series provides some indication of the stability of the compounds formed. It should be noted, however, that the order in which the elements are placed in the series depends somewhat on the conditions under which the activity is observed. A series determined from observations of the activities of the metals with respect to their ions in water will be slightly different from that reflecting the order of activity at high temperatures and in the absence of a solvent. The series shown in Table 13.1 is applicable to reactions in water. The activity series of metals will be discussed in more detail in Chapter 20.

The Elemental Active Metals

⑬.2 Periodic Relationships Among Groups IA, IIA, and IIIA

Even though not all the elements in Groups IIA and IIIA are considered to be active metals, we will consider the periodic relationships of all the elements of Groups IA, IIA, and IIIA (Table 13.2). This will help us view the behavior of the active metals in the context of the entire periodic table.

1. **Group IA, the Alkali Metals.** The alkali metals—lithium, sodium, potassium, rubidium, cesium, and francium—constitute Group IA of the periodic table. The heaviest of these, francium, is a highly radioactive element that occurs in nature in very small quantities. It has been estimated that only 15 grams of francium exists in the top kilometer of the earth's crust; accordingly, it is not well characterized. Although hydrogen is often shown in Group IA (and in Group VIIA, Fig. 13.1), it is a nonmetal and is therefore not considered in this chapter.

The properties of the alkali metals suggest that they are more closely related than the members of any other family of elements in the periodic table. The single electron in the outermost (valence) shell of each is not tightly bound, so these metals have the largest atomic radii (Table 13.2) and the lowest first ionization energies (see Table 6.4) in their

Table 13.2   **Properties of the Elements of Groups IA–IIIA[a]**

	Group IA	Group IIA	Group IIIA
	Lithium	**Beryllium**	**Boron**
Common oxidation number	+1	+2	+3
Atomic radius (Å)	1.52	1.11	0.88
Ionic radius (Å)	0.60	0.31	0.20
Density (g/cm^3)	0.534	1.85	2.34
Melting point (°C)	180	1278	2300
Boiling point (°C)	1326	2970	—
	Sodium	**Magnesium**	**Aluminum**
Common oxidation number	+1	+2	+3
Atomic radius (Å)	1.86	1.60	1.43
Ionic radius (Å)	0.95	0.65	0.50
Density (g/cm^3)	0.968	1.74	2.70
Melting point (°C)	98	651	660
Boiling point (°C)	889	1107	2467
	Potassium	**Calcium**	**Gallium**
Common oxidation number	+1	+2	+3
Atomic radius (Å)	2.31	1.97	1.22
Ionic radius (Å)	1.33	0.99	0.62
Density (g/cm^3)	0.856	1.55	5.91
Melting point (°C)	63.4	850	29.8
Boiling point (°C)	757	1490	2403
	Rubidium	**Strontium**	**Indium**
Common oxidation number	+1	+2	+3
Atomic radius (Å)	2.44	2.15	1.62
Ionic radius (Å)	1.48	1.13	0.81
Density (g/cm^3)	1.532	2.54	7.31
Melting point (°C)	38.8	770	156.6
Boiling point (°C)	679	1384	2000
	Cesium	**Barium**	**Thallium**
Common oxidation number	+1	+2	+1, +3
Atomic radius (Å)	2.62	2.17	1.71
Ionic radius (Å)	1.69	1.35	0.95 (+3)
Density (g/cm^3)	1.87	3.5	11.85
Melting point (°C)	28.7	704	303.5
Boiling point (°C)	690	1638	1457
	Francium	**Radium**	
Common oxidation number	+1	+2	
Atomic radius (Å)	2.7	2.20	
Ionic radius (Å)		1.52	
Density (g/cm^3)		~5	
Melting point (°C)		700	
Boiling point (°C)		<1737	

[a]The active metals appear in red.

Figure 13.3

A sample of lithium on water containing phenolphthalein, which is an acid–base indicator that is pink in basic solution (Fig. 16.3). Lithium floats because it is less dense than water.

Figure 13.4

Potassium for laboratory use is supplied as $\frac{1}{2}$-pound sticks stored under kerosene or mineral oil or in sealed containers to prevent contact with air and water.

respective periods. Thus the valence electron is easily lost, and these metals readily form stable cations with a charge of $+1$. The corresponding difficulty with which these ions are reduced explains why it is hard to isolate the elements. No samples were isolated in a pure state until 1807, when Sir Humphry Davy produced sodium and potassium by the electrolytic reduction of their hydroxides. Of the members of the group that have been extensively studied, the cesium atom is largest and has the lowest first ionization energy. Thus cesium is the most reactive. However, our knowledge of trends in periodic properties suggests that francium, which has a larger radius than cesium, should have a lower first ionization energy and should be even more reactive.

The alkali metals all react vigorously with water to form hydrogen gas and a basic solution of the metal hydroxide (Fig. 13.3). As an example, the reaction of sodium with water is

$$2Na + 2H_2O \longrightarrow 2NaOH + H_2$$

The vigor of the reaction increases with increasing atomic size (from top to bottom) in the group; with the possible exception of lithium, the reaction is explosive. The heat evolved when sodium and potassium react with water may cause the hydrogen produced or the metal to ignite. Rubidium and cesium do ignite in contact with water. *Never touch an alkali metal with your fingers; the heat of the reaction of the metal with the moisture of your skin could cause ignition of the metal.*

The alkali metals react directly with oxygen, sulfur, hydrogen, phosphorus, and the halogens, giving binary ionic compounds containing the $+1$ metal ions. These metals are so reactive with moisture and air (with the oxygen in the air) that they are generally stored under kerosene, under mineral oil, or in sealed containers (Fig. 13.4).

The alkali metals are silvery-white in color, are so soft that they can be cut with a knife (Fig. 13.5), and are excellent conductors of heat and electricity.

2. Group IIA, the Alkaline Earth Metals. The alkaline earth metals—beryllium, magnesium, calcium, strontium, barium, and radium—constitute Group IIA of the periodic table. The heaviest of these, radium, is a radioactive element that occurs in nature in very small quantities; there are only a few kilograms worldwide.

Because of the increasing nuclear charge and the addition of a second electron to the same principal quantum level (see Section 5.10) the atoms of the alkaline earth metals are smaller and have higher first ionization energies (Table 6.4) than those of the corresponding alkali metals within the same period. Because the valence shell electrons are more tightly bound, the alkaline earth metals are not as reactive as the corresponding alkali metals (Fig. 13.6), but they are nevertheless very reactive elements. Their reactivity increases, as expected, with increasing size and decreasing ionization energy. Both valence electrons of the Group IIA elements are involved in chemical reactions, and these elements readily form compounds in which they exhibit the group oxidation number of $+2$. Because of their high reactivity, the alkaline earth metals, like the alkali metals, cannot be readily prepared by ordinary chemical techniques.

The lightest alkaline earth metal, beryllium, forms compounds in which it exhibits predominantly covalent character. Compounds of magnesium often show some covalent character, but the magnesium can be regarded as a $+2$ ion. Calcium, strontium, and barium form ionic compounds. The gradation from covalent to ionic character and the increase in reactivity from beryllium to barium and radium are due to the increasing atomic radius and the resulting lower ionization energy, leading to the increasing ease of loss of the valence electrons in these atoms.

Beryllium does not react with water, even when heated, and it reacts with nitrogen and oxygen in the air only when heated above 600°C; the reaction produces BeO and

Figure 13.5

Sodium is so soft that it can be cut with a knife.

Figure 13.6

A sample of calcium in water containing phenolphthalein (an indicator that is pink in basic solution). The reaction is not as vigorous as that of sodium or of potassium with water.

Be_3N_2. Magnesium reacts slowly with hot water or steam and with oxygen upon warming. The reactivity of magnesium metal at room temperature is often masked because the surface of the metal reacts with air and becomes covered with a tightly adhering layer of magnesium oxycarbonate that protects the metal and prevents additional reaction. Calcium, strontium, and barium react with water and air (Fig. 13.7) at room temperature; barium shows the most vigorous reaction. The products of the reactions with water are hydrogen and the metal hydroxide or, when magnesium reacts with steam, magnesium oxide. These metals react directly with acids, sulfur, phosphorus, the halogens, and, with the exception of beryllium, with hydrogen to yield hydrides. Unlike the salts of the alkali metals, many of the common salts of the alkaline earth metals are insoluble in water. The solubility of the hydroxides increases, but the solubility of the carbonates and sulfates decreases, with increasing atomic number.

    3. Group IIIA. Group IIIA contains the elements boron, aluminum, gallium, indium, and thallium. The increase in metallic character moving down a group of the periodic table, which is only just apparent in Group IIA, is clearly illustrated by the elements of Group IIIA. The lightest element, boron, is semiconducting, and its compounds, which are covalent, display distinctively nonmetallic properties. For example,

(a)   (b)

Figure 13.7

(a) Fresh calcium turnings have a metallic luster until (b) they become dull because the metal surface is covered with calcium oxide from the reaction of the metal with oxygen in the air.

Figure 13.8

Aluminum oxide does not adhere to aluminum foil where it has been treated to produce a very thin film of mercury on its surface. Thus such aluminum foil is not protected by the customary oxide film and ''rusts'' in air, producing white aluminum oxide. Note the white Al_2O_3 that is forming on the surface and falling off.

boron oxide, B_2O_3, is acidic and its hydroxide, $B(OH)_3$, is a weak acid (boric acid, sometimes written H_3BO_3). The remaining elements of the group are metals, but the oxides and hydroxides change character. The oxides and hydroxides of aluminum and gallium exhibit both acidic and basic behavior, illustrative of both nonmetallic and metallic behavior in these two elements; that is, they are **amphoteric** (see Section 2.10). Indium and thallium oxides and hydroxides exhibit only basic behavior, in accordance with the clearly metallic character of these elements.

The Group IIIA elements have a valence shell electron configuration of ns^2np^1 (Table 13.3). Aluminum uses all of its valence electrons when it reacts, giving compounds in which it has an oxidation number of $+3$. Although many of these compounds are covalent, others, such as AlF_3 and Al_2O_3, are ionic. Aqueous solutions of aluminum salts contain the cation $Al^{3+}(aq)$. Gallium, indium, and thallium also form ionic compounds containing the M^{3+} ions. A few compounds with a $+1$ oxidation number are known for gallium and indium, and both the $+1$ and $+3$ oxidation numbers are commonly observed with thallium. In aqueous solution, the $Tl^+(aq)$ ion is the stable simple thallium ion.

The metals of Group IIIA (Al, Ga, In, and Tl) are all reactive. These elements become coated by a hard, thin, tough film of the metal oxide that forms when they are exposed to air and protects them from chemical attack. When the film is broken, these elements react with water and oxygen (Fig. 13.8) giving compounds with oxidation numbers of $+3$ for the metals. Thallium also reacts with water and oxygen but gives thallium(I) derivatives. The metals of Group IIIA all react directly with nonmetals such as sulfur, phosphorus, and the halogens, forming binary compounds.

All of the metals in Groups IA and IIA exhibit only one oxidation number: $+1$ and $+2$, respectively. Group IIIA differs in that gallium, indium, and thallium exhibit not only the oxidation number of $+3$ corresponding to their group number (IIIA) but also an oxidation number (in this case, $+1$) that is 2 less than the group number. This phenomenon is quite general in some other groups of representative elements as well. For example, tin and lead in Group IVA commonly occur in both the $+2$ and the $+4$ oxidation numbers; phosphorus, arsenic, antimony and bismuth in Group VA are found in both the $+3$ and the $+5$ oxidation numbers; and sulfur, selenium, and tellurium in Group VIA occur in both the $+4$ and the $+6$ oxidation numbers.

Within Group IIIA (unlike the elements of Groups IA and IIA, in which reactivity increases down the group), gallium, indium, and thallium are progressively less reactive. The three elements are also less reactive than aluminum.

Table 13.3	Electron Configurations of Group IIIA Metals[a]
Al	$1s^22s^22p^63s^23p^1$
Al^{3+}	$1s^22s^22p^6 \equiv$ [Ne]
Ga	$1s^22s^22p^63s^23p^63d^{10}4s^24p^1$
Ga^{3+}	$1s^22s^22p^63s^23p^63d^{10} \equiv$ [Ar]$3d^{10}$
In	$1s^22s^22p^63s^23p^63d^{10}4s^24p^64d^{10}5s^25p^1$
In^{3+}	$1s^22s^22p^63s^23p^63d^{10}4s^24p^64d^{10} \equiv$ [Kr]$4d^{10}$
Tl	$1s^22s^22p^63s^23p^63d^{10}4s^24p^64d^{10}4f^{14}5s^25p^65d^{10}6s^26p^1$
Tl^{3+}	$1s^22s^22p^63s^23p^63d^{10}4s^24p^64d^{10}4f^{14}5s^25p^65d^{10} \equiv$ [Xe]$4f^{14}5d^{10}$

[a] Valence electrons in the neutral atoms are shown in color.

Aluminum and the metals of Groups IA and IIA form ions that have noble gas electron configurations (Table 13.3). The neutral atoms have their valence electrons outside of a filled inner shell that contains only 8 electrons. The +3 ions of gallium, indium, and thallium have pseudonoble gas electron configurations (see Section 7.2). Their neutral atoms have their valence electrons outside of a filled inner shell that contains 18 electrons. Gallium, indium, and thallium are members of the group of elements that follow the transition metals in their respective periods. The metals of this set are called the **post-transition metals;** we will describe their chemistry when we consider the behavior of all of the post-transition metals in Chapter 28.

🔞.3 Occurrence and Isolation of the Active Metals

As we said in the introduction to this chapter, the active metals are not found as free elements in nature because of their extreme reactivity. Several of the active metals are among the most abundant of the elements (see Section 1.5, Table 1.1). Aluminum is the most abundant metal in the Earth's crust (8.3% by weight). It is approached in abundance only by iron (6.2%) and calcium (4.6%). Compounds of the active metals occur extensively, including simple compounds such as chlorides, oxides or hydroxides, carbonates, sulfates, and nitrates, as well as more complex silicates. The natural abundances of these metals and the more common minerals that contain them are listed in Table 13.4; sources from which the elements are isolated are in boldface type.

Although compounds containing ions of the active metals are abundant, the metals are difficult to isolate. The active metals are easily oxidized, so it is difficult to reduce their ions back to neutral atoms. The largest quantities of the pure metals are prepared by

Table 13.4		The Active Metals, Their Natural Abundances in the Earth's Crust, and Their Sources
Element	Abundance (% by mass)	Minerals and Sources
Lithium	0.0018	**Lepidolite,** spodumene ($LiAlSi_2O_6$)
Sodium	2.63	**Rock salt** (NaCl), **trona** [$Na_2CO_3 \cdot NaHCO_3 \cdot (H_2O)_2$], **Chile saltpeter** ($NaNO_3$)
Potassium	2.40	**Sylvite** (KCl), **carnallite** [$KMgCl_3(H_2O)_6$]
Rubidium	0.0078	**Lepidolite**
Cesium	0.0003	**Pollucite** ($Cs_4Al_4Si_9O_{26}H_2O$)
Francium	trace	
Magnesium	1.93	Magnesite ($MgCO_3$), dolomite ($MgCO_3 \cdot CaCO_3$), epsomite [$MgSO_4(H_2O)_7$], silicates, **sea water, brines**
Calcium	3.39	Dolomite [$(Mg,Ca)CO_3$]; aragonite, marble, and **limestone** ($CaCO_3$); silicates
Strontium	0.02	**Celestite** ($SrSO_4$)
Barium	0.04	**Barite** ($BaSO_4$)
Radium	1×10^{-10}	**Uranium-containing ores**
Aluminum	7.50	**Bauxite** [$AlO(OH)$, $Al(OH)_3$], various silicates and clays, corundum (Al_2O_3)

electrolysis, in which the input of electrical energy forces reduction to occur. Electrolysis is often used to carry out oxidation–reduction reactions of species that are oxidized or reduced with difficulty.

1. **The Preparation of Lithium and Sodium.** The most important method for the production of both lithium and sodium is the electrolysis of the molten chloride. For sodium the reaction involved in the process is

$$2NaCl(l) \xrightarrow[600°C]{\text{Electrolysis}} 2Na(l) + Cl_2(g)$$

The electrolysis is carried out in a cell (Fig. 13.9) that contains molten sodium chloride (melting point 801°C), to which calcium chloride has been added to lower the melting point to 600°C. When a direct current is passed through the cell, of which one type is known as a Downs cell, the sodium ions migrate to the negatively charged cathode, pick up electrons, and are thus reduced to sodium metal. Chloride ions migrate to the positively charged anode, lose electrons, and thus are oxidized to chlorine gas. The overall change is obtained by adding the following reactions, in which e^- represents an electron:

At the cathode:	$2Na^+ + 2e^- \longrightarrow 2Na(l)$
At the anode:	$2Cl^- \longrightarrow Cl_2(g) + 2e^-$
Overall change:	$2Na^+ + 2Cl^- \longrightarrow 2Na(l) + Cl_2(g)$

Separation of the molten sodium and chlorine prevents recombination. The liquid sodium, which is less dense than the molten chlorides, floats to the surface and flows into the collector. The gaseous chlorine is collected in tanks at high pressure. Chlorine, which will be discussed in Chapter 21, is as valuable a product as the sodium.

Metallic lithium is also prepared by electrolysis. A molten mixture of lithium chloride and potassium chloride at about 450°C is used.

2. **The Preparation of Potassium, Rubidium, and Cesium.** Potassium, rubidium, and cesium are produced on a relatively small scale, because they offer few advantages over the less expensive sodium. Although potassium could be produced by the electrolytic reduction of molten KCl, its solubility in the melt and its volatility at the operating temperature of the cell renders the process difficult. Most potassium is produced by the reaction of molten sodium with molten potassium chloride.

$$Na(l) + KCl(l) \longrightarrow K(g) + NaCl(l)$$

The sodium is added to the bottom of a column of molten potassium chloride, and potassium vapor escapes from the top. This vapor is condensed and cast into sticks. Note that the reduction of potassium ions by sodium metal is not predicted from the activity series (Section 13.1), or from our discussion of the reactivity increasing with increasing size in the Group IA elements. Even though potassium is above sodium in the activity series, this reaction proceeds because potassium is more volatile than sodium and distills out of the reaction mixture. As in a metathesis reaction, the production of a gas as a product drives the reaction toward completion.

A similar process using calcium metal and rubidium chloride or cesium chloride is employed to produce metallic rubidium or cesium, respectively.

3. **The Preparation of Magnesium, Calcium, Strontium, and Barium.** Magnesium metal is prepared by the electrolysis of magnesium chloride, which may be obtained from several different sources, including sea water (which contains about 0.54%

Figure 13.9

A section of a Downs cell for the production of sodium and chlorine.

magnesium chloride). Nearly 6 million tons of magnesium as the chloride is contained in each cubic mile of seawater, but almost 800 tons of seawater must be processed to obtain 1 ton of magnesium.

The preparation of magnesium begins with the production of calcium hydroxide by addition of calcium oxide, CaO, to water.

$$CaO + H_2O \longrightarrow Ca(OH)_2$$

The calcium oxide is readily obtained by roasting limestone or oyster shells from shallow waters along the coast. Both limestone and oyster shells are calcium carbonate, $CaCO_3$, which decomposes upon heating to form the oxide.

$$CaCO_3(s) \xrightarrow{\;\Delta\;} CaO(s) + CO_2(g)$$

Addition of calcium hydroxide, $Ca(OH)_2$, to sea water separates magnesium as insoluble magnesium hydroxide, $Mg(OH)_2$.

$$Mg^{2+}(aq) + [2Cl^-(aq)] + Ca(OH)_2(s) \longrightarrow Mg(OH)_2(s) + Ca^{2+}(aq) + [2Cl^-(aq)]$$

After filtration, the magnesium hydroxide is treated with hydrochloric acid to produce a solution of magnesium chloride.

$$Mg(OH)_2(s) + 2H_3O^+(aq) + [2Cl^-(aq)] \longrightarrow Mg^{2+}(aq) + [2Cl^-(aq)] + 4H_2O(l)$$

This solution is evaporated to recover $Mg(H_2O)_6Cl_2$, more commonly written as $MgCl_2 \cdot 6H_2O$. This crystallized salt is then partially dehydrated by heating. A melt of the partially dehydrated magnesium chloride with the composition $MgCl_2 \cdot 1.5H_2O$ $[Mg_2(H_2O)_3Cl_4]$ is electrolyzed. Magnesium ions are reduced to molten magnesium metal at the cathode, and chloride ions are oxidized to chlorine gas at the anode. The chlorine gas that is produced can be either sold or used to manufacture more hydrochloric acid for the process.

$$MgCl_2 \cdot 1.5H_2O(l) \xrightarrow[700°C]{\text{Electrolysis}} Mg(l) + Cl_2(g) + 1.5H_2O(g)$$

The center dot in the formula for partially dehydrated magnesium chloride indicates that the water is present in the solid as **water of hydration**—that is, water that is present as identifiable molecules. These molecules are held in the solid by ion–dipole attractions (see Section 11.2) between the metal ions and the polar water molecules and by hydrogen bonds (see Section 11.4) between the hydrogen of the water molecule and the negatively charged halide anions.

Electrolysis of their molten chlorides is also the most important method for producing calcium, strontium, and barium. However, barium is also produced by the **King process,** the reduction of a mixture of barium oxide and barium peroxide with aluminum. At temperatures of 950–1100°C and at low pressures (10^{-3}–10^{-4} torr), barium distills out of the mixture and is collected on a cold surface.

4. The Preparation of Aluminum. Aluminum is prepared by a process invented in 1886 by Charles M. Hall, who began work on the problem while a student at Oberlin College. The process was discovered independently a month or two later by Paul L. T. Héroult in France.

The first step in the production of aluminum from the mineral bauxite involves purification of the mineral. The reaction of bauxite, AlO(OH), with hot sodium hydroxide forms soluble sodium aluminate, while clay and other impurities remain undissolved.

$$AlO(OH)(s) + NaOH(aq) + H_2O(l) \longrightarrow Na[Al(OH)_4](aq)$$

After the impurities are removed by filtration, aluminum hydroxide is reprecipitated by adding acid to the aluminate.

$$Na[Al(OH)_4](aq) + H_3O^+(aq) \longrightarrow Al(OH)_3(s) + Na^+(aq) + 2H_2O(l)$$

The precipitated aluminum hydroxide is removed by filtration and heated, forming the oxide, Al_2O_3, which is then dissolved in a molten mixture of cryolite, Na_3AlF_6, and calcium fluoride, CaF_2. This solution is electrolyzed in a cell like that shown in Fig. 13.10. Aluminum ions are reduced to the metal at the cathode, and oxygen, carbon monoxide, and carbon dioxide are liberated at the anode.

Aluminum prepared by electrolysis is about 99% pure; the impurities are small amounts of copper, iron, silicon, and aluminum oxide. If aluminum of exceptionally high purity (99.9%) is needed, it may be obtained by the electrolytic **Hoopes process** (Fig. 13.11), which employs a molten bath consisting of three layers. The bottom layer is a molten alloy of copper and impure aluminum, the top layer is pure molten aluminum, and the middle layer (the electrolyte) consists of a molten mixture of the fluorides of barium, aluminum, and sodium with nearly enough aluminum oxide to saturate it. The densities of the layers are such that their separation is maintained during electrolysis. The bottom layer serves as the anode and the top layer serves as the cathode. As electrolysis proceeds, the aluminum in the bottom layer is oxidized and

Figure 13.10

A cell for the production of aluminum.

Cathode
(−)

e

d

c

b

a

Anode
layer (+)

Figure 13.11

The Hoopes electrolytic cell for the purification of aluminum: (a) is the bottom portion of the cell in contact with the anode layer; (b) is an alloy of impure molten aluminum and copper, which acts as the anode and at which the oxidation takes place; (c) is an electrolyte consisting of a mixture of molten fluorides; (d) is the molten layer of pure aluminum at the cathodes; (e) is a funnel arrangement by which impure aluminum can be added to the bottom of the cell.

passes into solution in the electrolyte as Al^{3+}, leaving the impurities behind; they are not oxidized under these conditions. The aluminum ion is reduced at the cathode. During electrolysis, purified aluminum is drawn off from the upper layer, and the impure metal is added to the lower layer.

13.4 Uses of the Active Metals

The alkali metals, unlike magnesium and aluminum, are not suitable for structural applications because of their reactivity and softness. The major utility of these elements stems from their reactivity and low melting points. They serve as starting materials for useful compounds, some of which are discussed in the following sections. Lithium is used as an alloying agent with other metals. Lithium–lead alloys are used in bearings, and lithium–magnesium and lithium–aluminum alloys are used in aviation and aerospace applications because of their lightness and high strength. The major industrial application of lithium is in a compound called lithium stearate, which is employed as a gelling agent and thickener to convert oils into all-purpose lubricating greases that have high water resistance and excellent working properties at both high and low temperatures.

A major earlier use of sodium was as an alloy with lead to produce antiknock lead compounds, primarily tetraethyl lead, for gasoline. This use has declined sharply and is being phased out; unleaded gasoline is required in automobile engines equipped with catalytic converters. Sodium and its alloys with potassium are increasingly being employed as heat exchange liquids in some nuclear reactors (Sections 24.11 and 24.12). Sodium is also used as a reducing agent in the production of other metals (such as potassium, titanium, zirconium, and the heavier alkali metals) from their chlorides or oxides. Lithium and sodium are used as reducing agents in the manufacture of certain organic compounds, including dyes, drugs, and perfumes. Sodium and its compounds impart a yellow color to a flame (Fig. 13.12). The yellow light penetrates fog well, so sodium is sometimes used in street lights. The synthetic rubber industry consumes large amounts of sodium, and the metal is used to prepare compounds such as sodium peroxide and sodium oxide that cannot be made from sodium chloride. Potassium has no major industrial uses for which sodium cannot be substituted, so the commercial uses of potassium are limited.

Magnesium is a silvery-white metal that is malleable and ductile at high temperatures. Though very reactive, it does not undergo extensive reaction with air or water at room temperature, because of the protective oxycarbonate film that forms on its surface (Section 13.2). Magnesium is the lightest of the widely used structural metals; most of

Figure 13.12

Heating sodium or sodium salts causes emission of a bright yellow light. This wire was dipped into a solution of a sodium salt.

the magnesium produced is used in making lightweight alloys, the most important of which are those with aluminum and zinc.

The potent reducing power of hot magnesium is utilized in preparing many metals and nonmetals, such as silicon and boron, from their oxides. Indeed, the affinity of magnesium for oxygen is so great that burning magnesium reacts with carbon dioxide, reducing the carbon of the oxide to elemental carbon.

$$2Mg + CO_2 \longrightarrow 2MgO + C$$

(A CO_2 fire extinguisher cannot be used to put out a magnesium fire.) The brilliant white light emitted by burning magnesium makes it useful in flashbulbs, flares, and fireworks.

Calcium, strontium, and barium are all silvery-white metals that are crystalline, malleable, and ductile. Calcium is harder than lead, strontium is about as hard as lead, and barium is quite soft. Calcium is used as a dehydrating agent for certain organic solvents, as a reducing agent in the production of certain metals, as a scavenger to remove gases in molten metals in metallurgy, as a hardening agent for lead used for covering cables and making storage battery grids and bearings, in steel making when alloyed with silicon, and for many other purposes.

Elemental strontium is not abundant and has no commercial uses. Alloys of barium and nickel are used in spark plugs because of their high thermal emission of electrons. It is interesting that Mg^{2+} and Ca^{2+} are not poisonous but Be^{2+} and Ba^{2+} are very much so.

Freshly cut aluminum has a silvery appearance, but the surface soon becomes oxidized and assumes a duller luster (Fig. 13.13). The tenacious oxide coating protects the metal from further corrosion (Section 13.2). The metal is very light, possesses high tensile strength, and, weight for weight, is twice as good an electrical conductor as copper.

The fact that aluminum is an excellent conductor of heat and is lightweight and corrosion-resistant account for its use in the manufacture of cooking utensils. The most important uses of aluminum are in the construction and transportation industries and in the manufacture of containers for packaging. All of these industries depend on the lightness, toughness, and tensile strength of the metal. About half of the aluminum produced in this country is converted to alloys for special uses. Aluminum is also used in the manufacture of electrical transmission wire, as a paint pigment, and (in the form of foil) as a wrapping material.

Aluminum is one of the best reflectors of heat and light, including ultraviolet light. For this reason it is used as an insulating material and as a mirror in reflecting telescopes.

Figure 13.13

(a) These aluminum turnings have been freshly cut and (b) they will oxidize over a period of time to form a duller film of aluminum oxide, Al_2O_3.

(a)

(b)

When powdered aluminum and iron(III) oxide are mixed and ignited by means of a magnesium fuse, a vigorous and highly exothermic reaction occurs (Fig. 13.14).

$$2Al(s) + Fe_2O_3(s) \longrightarrow 2Fe(s) + Al_2O_3(s) \qquad \Delta H° = -851.4 \text{ kJ}$$

This is known as the **thermite reaction** and is applied in the **Goldschmidt process.** The temperature of the reaction mixture rises to about 3000°C, so the iron and aluminum oxide become liquid. The process is frequently used in welding large pieces of iron or steel. The thermite reaction is used in the reduction of metallic oxides that are not readily reduced by carbon, such as MoO_3 and WO_3, or metallic oxides that do not give pure metals when reduced by carbon, such as MnO_2 and Cr_2O_3. The reaction is also of particular value for the production of carbon-free alloys, such as ferrotitanium.

Compounds of the Active Metals

With few exceptions, the simple compounds of the active metals are ionic. They contain cations of the metals and anions composed of nonmetals. The anions may be monatomic anions such as Cl^-, O^{2-}, and S^{2-} or polyatomic anions such as OH^-, CO_3^{2-}, NO_3^-, and SO_4^{2-}. Much of the chemical behavior of these compounds reflects the chemical behavior of the anion.

Figure 13.14

The thermite reaction, the reaction of aluminum with iron(III) oxide produces a temperature of about 3000°C.

⓫.5 Compounds of the Active Metals with Oxygen: Oxides, Peroxides, and Superoxides

Compounds of the active metals with oxygen fall into three categories: (1) **oxides,** containing oxide ions, O^{2-}; (2) **peroxides,** containing peroxide ions, O_2^{2-}, with single oxygen–oxygen covalent bonds; and (3) **superoxides,** containing superoxide ions, O_2^-, with oxygen–oxygen covalent bonds having bond orders of $1\frac{1}{2}$.

The metals of Group IA form oxides, M_2O; peroxides, M_2O_2; and superoxides, MO_2. The metals of Group IIA form oxides, MO, and peroxides, MO_2. Aluminum forms two oxides, both with the formula Al_2O_3 but having different structures.

1. Preparation of the Oxides, Peroxides, and Superoxides. Oxides of most metals are produced by heating the corresponding hydroxides, nitrates, or carbonates. However, most alkali metal salts containing these anions are extremely stable and do not decompose to the oxides at elevated temperatures. Burning the metals in air is not a satisfactory method for preparation of alkali metal oxides either. When burned in air, lithium forms lithium oxide (contaminated with some lithium peroxide, Li_2O_2); sodium forms sodium peroxide (contaminated with some sodium oxide, Na_2O); and potassium, rubidium, and cesium form superoxides.

All of the alkali metal oxides can be prepared by the reaction of the nitrates or hydroxides with the elemental metal.

$$2MNO_3 + 10M \longrightarrow 6M_2O + N_2 \qquad (M = Li, Na, K, Rb, Cs)$$

$$2MOH + 2M \longrightarrow 2M_2O + H_2 \qquad (M = Li, Na, K, Rb, Cs)$$

Pure Li_2O and Na_2O can be prepared by the reaction of the metal in a closed container with a carefully controlled amount of oxygen.

$$4M + O_2 \longrightarrow 2M_2O \qquad (M = Li, Na)$$

Sodium peroxide is formed when Na or Na_2O is heated in pure oxygen.

$$2Na + O_2 \longrightarrow Na_2O_2$$

$$2Na_2O + O_2 \longrightarrow 2Na_2O_2$$

The peroxides of potassium, rubidium, and cesium can be prepared by heating the metal or its oxide in a carefully controlled amount of oxygen. With an excess of oxygen, the superoxides KO_2, RbO_2, and CsO_2 form.

$$2M + O_2 \longrightarrow M_2O_2 \qquad (2 \text{ mol M per mol } O_2)$$

$$M + O_2 \longrightarrow MO_2 \qquad (1 \text{ mol M per mol } O_2)$$

The stability of the peroxides and superoxides of the alkali metals increases as the size of the cation increases.

The oxides of the alkaline earths are usually prepared by heating the respective carbonates, MCO_3. The hydroxides, $M(OH)_2$, also decompose at elevated temperatures, forming oxides.

$$MCO_3 \xrightarrow{\Delta} MO + CO_2(g) \qquad (M = Mg, Ca, Sr, Ba)$$

$$M(OH)_2 \xrightarrow{\Delta} MO + H_2O(g) \qquad (M = Mg, Ca, Sr, Ba)$$

The stability of the carbonates increases as the size of the cation increases, as does that of the peroxides and the superoxides of the alkali metals. The temperature required to give a carbon dioxide pressure of 1 atmosphere is about 540°C for $MgCO_3$, 900°C for $CaCO_3$, 1290°C for $SrCO_3$, and 1360°C for $BaCO_3$.

Pure samples of the alkaline earth oxides cannot be prepared by burning the metals in air. Magnesium burns vigorously, but the MgO (sometimes called **magnesia**) that is produced is contaminated with magnesium nitride, Mg_3N_2, produced by the reaction of magnesium with the nitrogen of the air. Calcium gives CaO contaminated with calcium peroxide, CaO_2, and calcium nitride, Ca_3N_2. When strontium and barium burn, they form the peroxides, SrO_2 and BaO_2, respectively. Several different modifications of aluminum oxide exist. Heating aluminum hydroxide, $Al(OH)_3$, or aluminum oxyhydroxide, AlO(OH), below 450°C drives off water and produces **gamma-alumina** (γ-alumina), a form of aluminum oxide, Al_2O_3, that reacts with water and dissolves in acids. Above 1000°C the reaction of aluminum with oxygen or loss of water from $Al(OH)_3$ or AlO(OH) produces **alpha-alumina** (α-alumina), a very hard form of Al_2O_3 that does not react with water and is not attacked by acids. Yet another form of Al_2O_3 occurs as the protective oxide on the surface of the metal.

2. Reactions and Uses of the Oxides, Peroxides, and Superoxides. The oxides of the active metals all contain the oxide ion, a very powerful hydrogen ion acceptor.

Name	Formula	Parent Nonmetal Oxide	Reaction
Borate	BO_3^{3-}	B_2O_3	$B_2O_3 + 3O^{2-} \longrightarrow 2BO_3^{3-}$
Carbonate	CO_3^{2-}	CO_2	$CO_2 + O^{2-} \longrightarrow CO_3^{2-}$
Nitrate	NO_3^-	N_2O_5	$N_2O_5 + O^{2-} \longrightarrow 2NO_3^-$
Phosphate	PO_4^{3-}	P_4O_{10}	$P_4O_{10} + 6O^{2-} \longrightarrow 4PO_4^{3-}$
Sulfite	SO_3^{2-}	SO_2	$SO_2 + O^{2-} \longrightarrow SO_3^{2-}$
Sulfate	SO_4^{2-}	SO_3	$SO_3 + O^{2-} \longrightarrow SO_4^{2-}$
Perchlorate	ClO_4^-	Cl_2O_7	$Cl_2O_7 + O^{2-} \longrightarrow 2ClO_4^-$

Table 13.5   Formation of Common Oxyanions

With the exception of the very insoluble α-alumina, these oxides react with water to form hydroxides and with acids to form salts.

$$M_2O + H_2O \longrightarrow 2MOH \qquad (M = Li, Na, K, Rb, Cs)$$

$$MO + H_2O \longrightarrow M(OH)_2 \qquad (M = Mg, Ca, Sr, Ba)$$

$$M_2O + 2HCl \longrightarrow 2MCl + H_2O \qquad (M = Li, Na, K, Rb, Cs)$$

$$MO + 2HNO_3 \longrightarrow M(NO_3)_2 + H_2O \qquad (M = Mg, Ca, Sr, Ba)$$

$$\gamma\text{-}Al_2O_3 + 3H_2SO_4 \longrightarrow Al_2(SO_4)_3 + 3H_2O$$

The oxides of the active metals also react with many nonmetal oxides, forming oxyanions. Examples are given in Table 13.5 above.

When a metal oxide reacts with a nonmetal oxide, a coordinate covalent bond (Section 7.4) is formed. The oxide ion acts as an electron pair donor and the nonmetal oxide acts as an electron pair acceptor. The reaction of sodium oxide with sulfur dioxide is shown as an example.

Figure 13.15

When heated, calcium oxide produces an intense white light.

The oxides of the alkali metals are used in the laboratory as sources of the metal ions and of the oxide ion, but they have little industrial utility. On the other hand, magnesium oxide, calcium oxide, and aluminum oxide do. Magnesium oxide is used widely in making fire brick, crucibles, furnace linings, and thermal insulation, which are all applications that require chemical and thermal stability. Calcium oxide, sometimes called **quicklime** or **lime** in the industrial market, is very reactive, and its principal uses reflect its reactivity. The reaction of calcium oxide with water is vigorous and exothermic; consequently, it is used as a drying agent in applications such as the preparation of anhydrous alcohol and anhydrous ammonia. Calcium oxide is used in the isolation of magnesium from sea water (see Section 13.2). Pure calcium oxide emits an intense white light when heated to a high temperature (Fig. 13.15). Blocks of calcium oxide heated by gas flames were used as stage lights in theaters before electricity was available. This is the source of the phrase "in the limelight."

Alpha-alumina occurs in nature as the mineral **corundum,** a very hard substance used as an abrasive for grinding and polishing. Several precious stones consist of α-Al_2O_3 with metal ion impurities that impart color (Fig. 13.16): ruby [Cr(III) as impurity—red]; sapphire [Fe(II), Fe(III), Ti(IV)—blue]; oriental amethyst [Cr(III), Ti(IV)—violet]; and oriental topaz [Fe(III)—yellow]. Artificial rubies and sapphires are now manufactured by melting aluminum oxide (mp = 2050°C) with small amounts of oxides to produce the desired colors and then cooling the melt in such a way as to produce large crystals. These gems are indistinguishable from natural stones, except for microscopic, rounded air bubbles in the synthetic ones and flattened bubbles in the natural stones. The synthetic gems are used not only as jewelry but also as bearings ("jewels") in some watches and other instruments and as dies through which wires are drawn. Ruby lasers use synthetic ruby crystals. Very finely divided aluminum oxide, called **activated alumina,** is used as a dehydrating agent and a catalyst. A recent development in aluminum technology has been the production of Al_2O_3 fibers that have a diameter about 20 times less than that of a human hair and can be fabricated into a variety of forms, such as blankets, papers, and boards. Fibers of Al_2O_3 can also be used to strengthen metals.

The peroxide ion is a powerful hydrogen ion acceptor; the peroxides of Groups IA and IIA are strong bases. Solutions of these peroxides are basic because of the reaction of the peroxide ion with water, which functions as a weak acid in this case.

(a)　　　　　　　　　(b)

(c)　　　　　　　　　(d)

Figure 13.16

These precious stones contain α-Al_2O_3 with transition metal ion impurities. (a) Ruby. (b) Sapphire. (c) Amethyst. (d) Topaz.

$$O_2^{2-} + H_2O \longrightarrow O_2H^- + OH^-$$

$$O_2H^- + H_2O \rightleftharpoons H_2O_2 + OH^-$$

Peroxides also are strong oxidizing agents. Sodium peroxide is used as an oxidizing and bleaching agent. It bleaches by oxidizing colored compounds to colorless compounds.

Superoxides are also strong oxidizing agents and are used to provide emergency supplies of oxygen. For example, potassium superoxide is used in gas masks for mine safety work. Moisture from the breath reacts with the superoxide to give oxygen for the wearer of the mask to breathe.

$$4KO_2 + 2H_2O \longrightarrow 4KOH + 3O_2$$

When the breath is exhaled through the mask, carbon dioxide is absorbed by the potassium hydroxide.

$$CO_2 + KOH \longrightarrow KHCO_3$$

The wearer needs no air from outside the mask.

13.6 Hydroxides of the Active Metals

1. Preparation of Hydroxides. All of the active metals form ionic **hydroxides.** With the exception of magnesium and aluminum hydroxides, the hydroxides of the active metals can be prepared in the laboratory by reaction of the respective metals with water, a reaction that produces hydrogen and the metal hydroxide (Figs. 13.3 and 13.6). However, these reactions are violent and can be dangerous, so the soluble hydroxides are generally prepared from the reaction of the respective oxide with water.

$$M_2O + H_2O \longrightarrow 2MOH \qquad (M = Li, Na, K, Rb, Cs)$$

$$MO + H_2O \longrightarrow M(OH)_2 \qquad (M = Ca, Sr, Ba)$$

These reactions are very exothermic; equipment in which they occur can get very hot.

The insoluble hydroxides of magnesium and aluminum can be prepared by addition of a solution of a soluble hydroxide, such as sodium hydroxide, to a solution of a magnesium or an aluminum salt such as a chloride, nitrate, or sulfate (Fig. 13.17).

$$Mg(NO_3)_2(aq) + 2NaOH(aq) \longrightarrow Mg(OH)_2(s) + 2NaNO_3(aq)$$

$$Al_2(SO_4)_3(aq) + 6NaOH(aq) \longrightarrow 2Al(OH)_3(s) + 3Na_2SO_4(aq)$$

An excess of hydroxide solution must be avoided in the preparation of aluminum hydroxide, or it will redissolve with the formation of a complex ion. This ion is the **aluminate ion** and is commonly written as $[Al(OH)_4]^-$, but it also contains water molecules bonded to the aluminum ion by coordinate covalent bonds and is better written as $[Al(H_2O)_2(OH)_4]^-$.

$$Al(OH)_3(s) + OH^-(aq) + 2H_2O(l) \longrightarrow [Al(H_2O)_2(OH)_4]^-(aq)$$

2. Reactions and Uses of the Hydroxides. The active metal hydroxides exhibit reactions typical of compounds that contain the strongly basic hydroxide ion. They react with acids in acid–base reactions (see Section 2.11) to form salts and water. They also react with many covalent nonmetal oxides to form oxyanions, of the type shown in Table 13.5.

Figure 13.17

Aluminum hydroxide, $Al(OH)_3$, forms as a white gelatinous precipitate when a solution of NaOH is added to a solution of an aluminum salt, such as $Al(NO_3)_3$.

As we noted in Part 3 of Section 13.2, the oxide and the hydroxide of aluminum exhibit both acidic and basic behavior. This amphoterism is also found for a small number of other metal oxides and hydroxides as the transition from metals that form basic oxides to nonmetals that form acidic oxides occurs in the periodic table. These oxides and hydroxides of amphoteric metals dissolve not only in acidic solutions but also in basic solutions. When aluminum hydroxide dissolves in an acid, the hydroxide ions combine with the hydrogen ions of the acid to form water and the aluminum salt of the acid. In such a reaction, aluminum hydroxide behaves like a base.

$$Al(OH)_3 + 3H_3O^+ \longrightarrow Al^{3+} + 6H_2O$$

When aluminum hydroxide dissolves in base, hydroxide ions and water molecules bind to the aluminum ions, forming the complex ion $[Al(H_2O)_2(OH)_4]^-$ (see Part 1 of this section). Because aluminum hydroxide removes free hydroxide ions from the solution, it is regarded as an acid in this case. Aluminum hydroxide exhibits both acidic and basic behavior, depending on the nature of the other components in the solution.

The alkali metal hydroxides are the most basic of all hydroxides. In addition to their reaction with acids, they readily absorb CO_2 and H_2S to form carbonates (or hydrogen carbonates) and sulfides (or hydrogen sulfides). For this reason they are used for CO_2 absorption in closed systems such as space shuttles and submarines and for the removal of sulfur compounds from petroleum products.

Because they are very soluble, the alkali metal hydroxides form the most concentrated solutions of all of the hydroxides. **Sodium hydroxide**, NaOH, is frequently called **caustic soda** in commerce, and its solutions are sometimes referred to as **lye** or **soda lye**. The large quantities of sodium hydroxide used industrially are prepared from sodium chloride, because it is a less expensive starting material than the oxide. Sodium hydroxide was the ninth-ranked chemical in production in the United States in 1989 (over 11 million tons), and this production was almost entirely by electrolysis of solutions of sodium chloride (Fig. 13.18).

$$[2Na^+(aq)] + 2Cl^-(aq) + 2H_2O(l) \xrightarrow{\text{Electrolysis}} [2Na^+(aq)] + 2OH^-(aq) + H_2(g) + Cl_2(g)$$

During electrolysis the sodium ions are not reduced. Instead, water, which is more easily reduced than sodium ions, is reduced to hydrogen gas and hydroxide ions at the cathode. The hydroxide ions replace the chloride ions that are oxidized to chlorine gas at the anode, and sodium hydroxide accumulates in the solution. After electrolysis the solution

Figure 13.18

A diaphragm cell for the production of sodium hydroxide. Brine, a solution of NaCl, enters the cell at the top and flows through the diaphragm. $Cl_2(g)$ is produced at the anode ($2Cl^- \longrightarrow Cl_2 + 2e^-$). $H_2(g)$ and $OH^-(aq)$ are produced at the cathode ($2H_2O + 2e^- \longrightarrow H_2 + 2OH^-$).

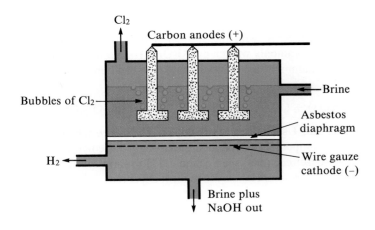

Cl₂
Carbon anodes (+)
Bubbles of Cl₂
Brine
Asbestos diaphragm
H₂
Wire gauze cathode (–)
Brine plus NaOH out

still contains some sodium chloride, but this can be removed relatively easily because it is less soluble than sodium hydroxide in the solution. Upon evaporation of some of the water from the solution, the sodium chloride crystallizes before any solid sodium hydroxide forms, so it can be removed by filtration. Such a process is called **fractional crystallization.**

Sodium hydroxide is an ionic compound that melts and boils without decomposition. It is very soluble in water, giving off a great deal of heat and forming very basic solutions; 40 grams of sodium hydroxide dissolves in only 60 grams of water at 25°C. Sodium hydroxide is employed in the production of other sodium compounds and is used to neutralize acidic solutions during the production of other chemicals such as petrochemicals and polymers.

Potassium hydroxide is manufactured by an electrolytic process similar to that used for sodium hydroxide. It, too, is very soluble in water and forms very alkaline solutions. Potassium hydroxide is more expensive than sodium hydroxide, because potassium chloride is more expensive than sodium chloride. Inasmuch as sodium hydroxide can almost always replace potassium hydroxide as a base, the use of potassium hydroxide is limited to the production of other potassium-containing compounds.

The hydroxides of the active metals of Group IIA show a smooth gradation in properties and a steady increase in solubility as the atomic mass of the metal increases. Magnesium hydroxide, $Mg(OH)_2$, is almost insoluble. An aqueous suspension of magnesium hydroxide is used as the antacid **milk of magnesia.** Calcium hydroxide, $Ca(OH)_2$, and strontium hydroxide, $Sr(OH)_2$, exhibit limited solubility, whereas barium hydroxide, $Ba(OH)_2$, is soluble enough to form saturated solutions approaching those of the alkali metal hydroxides in hydroxide ion concentration.

Calcium hydroxide, $Ca(OH)_2$, known commercially as **slaked lime** or **hydrated lime,** is prepared from calcium oxide by reaction with water (slaking). Because of its activity and cheapness, calcium hydroxide is used more extensively in commercial applications than any other base (Fig. 13.19). Calcium hydroxide has a limited solubility (1.7 grams dissolves in 1 liter of water), but when suspended in water with substances that react with hydroxide ions, it furnishes a ready supply of hydroxide ions because the solid continues to dissolve as hydroxide ions are removed from solution by reaction (Fig. 13.20). A saturated solution of calcium hydroxide is called **limewater;** a suspension, **milk of lime.**

During 1989 over 16 million tons of lime were produced in the United States, making it sixth in industrial production (after sulfuric acid, nitrogen, oxygen, ethylene, and ammonia). The manufacture of at least 150 industrial chemicals requires the use of either calcium hydroxide or calcium oxide. Calcium hydroxide is also used in the construction trades. Mortar is a mixture of slaked lime, sand, and water. It dries and hardens (sets) when exposed to air because it reacts with carbon dioxide to form calcium carbonate.

$$Ca(OH)_2 + CO_2 \longrightarrow CaCO_3 + H_2O$$

The crystals of calcium carbonate bind the particles of sand together.

Aluminum hydroxide is widely used to fix dyes to fabrics. Cloth soaked in a hot solution of aluminum acetate becomes impregnated with aluminum hydroxide. When aluminum hydroxide is precipitated from a solution containing a dye, the precipitate is colored. The aluminum hydroxide adsorbs the dye and holds it fast to the cloth. When used in this way, aluminum hydroxide is called a **mordant.**

Aluminum hydroxide is also used in the purification of water, because its gelatinous character (Fig. 13.17) enables it to carry down any suspended material in the water,

Figure 13.19

Slaked lime, $Ca(OH)_2$, is used to treat acid soil.

Figure 13.20

Slaked lime, $Ca(OH)_2$, is dumped on a lake to neutralize the effects of acid rain.

including most of the bacteria. The aluminum hydroxide for water purification is ordinarily produced by the reaction of aluminum sulfate with lime.

$$2Al^{3+} + 3SO_4{}^{2-} + 3Ca^{2+} + 6OH^- \longrightarrow 2Al(OH)_3(s) + 3CaSO_4(s)$$

13.7 Carbonates and Hydrogen Carbonates of the Active Metals

The active metals of Group IA and IIA form ionic **carbonates**—compounds that contain the carbonate ion, $CO_3{}^{2-}$. The reaction of solutions of carbonates with carbon dioxide yields **hydrogen carbonates**—compounds containing the $HCO_3{}^-$ ion.

1. **Preparation of the Carbonates and Hydrogen Carbonates.** Most solid oxides and hydroxides of the alkali metals and of the alkaline earth metals react with carbon dioxide to form carbonates.

$$M_2O + CO_2 \longrightarrow M_2CO_3 \qquad (M = Li, Na, K, Rb, Cs)$$

$$2MOH + CO_2 \longrightarrow M_2CO_3 + H_2O \qquad (M = Li, Na, K, Rb, Cs)$$

$$MO + CO_2 \longrightarrow MCO_3 \qquad (M = Ca, Sr, Ba)$$

$$M(OH)_2 + CO_2 \longrightarrow MCO_3 + H_2O \qquad (M = Mg, Ca, Sr, Ba)$$

Solid magnesium oxide does not react with carbon dioxide. Aluminum carbonate is unknown.

Alkali metal hydrogen carbonates, $MHCO_3$, form in solution when solutions of the hydroxides are saturated with carbon dioxide; the formation of sodium hydrogen carbonate is represented by the equation

$$[Na^+(aq)] + OH^-(aq) + CO_2(g) \longrightarrow [Na^+(aq)] + HCO_3{}^-(aq)$$

The use of less carbon dioxide or the addition of an equivalent quantity of the hydroxide to a solution of the hydrogen carbonate gives a solution of the carbonate ion; again, the sodium salts are good examples.

$$[2Na^+(aq)] + 2OH^-(aq) + CO_2(g) \longrightarrow [2Na^+(aq)] + CO_3{}^{2-}(aq) + H_2O(l)$$

$$[Na^+(aq)] + HCO_3{}^-(aq) + [Na^+(aq)] + OH^-(aq) \longrightarrow$$
$$[2Na^+(aq)] + CO_3{}^{2-}(aq) + H_2O(l)$$

Lithium carbonate is not very soluble and precipitates from solution more readily than the other alkali metal carbonates.

Alkaline earth carbonates are not soluble; they precipitate when solutions of soluble alkali metal carbonates are added to solutions of soluble alkaline earth metal salts. The following equation uses barium chloride and sodium carbonate as an example.

$$Ba^{2+}(aq) + [2Cl^-(aq)] + [2Na^+(aq)] + CO_3{}^{2-}(aq) \longrightarrow$$
$$BaCO_3(s) + [2Na^+(aq)] + [2Cl^-(aq)]$$

Although insoluble in pure water, the alkaline earth carbonates dissolve readily in water that contains dissolved carbon dioxide because of the formation of hydrogen carbonate salts. The formation of calcium hydrogen carbonate is typical.

$$CaCO_3(s) + CO_2(aq) + H_2O(l) \longrightarrow Ca^{2+}(aq) + 2HCO_3{}^-(aq)$$

Hydrogen carbonates of the alkaline earth metals are stable only in solution; evaporation of the solution produces the carbonates.

Sodium carbonate is prepared industrially in the United States by extraction from the mineral **trona,** $Na_2CO_3 \cdot NaHCO_3 \cdot 2H_2O$. Following recrystallization from water to remove clay and other impurities, trona is roasted to produce Na_2CO_3.

$$2(Na_2CO_3 \cdot NaHCO_3 \cdot 2H_2O) \xrightarrow{\Delta} 3Na_2CO_3 + 5H_2O(g) + CO_2(g)$$

Sodium carbonate is also manufactured by the **Solvay process.** This process is based on the reaction of ammonium hydrogen carbonate with a saturated solution of sodium chloride. Sodium hydrogen carbonate precipitates, because it is only slightly soluble in the reaction medium.

$$Na^+ + [Cl^-] + [NH_4^+] + HCO_3^- \longrightarrow NaHCO_3(s) + [NH_4^+] + [Cl^-]$$

The basic raw materials used in the process are calcium carbonate **(limestone)** and common table salt. The carbon dioxide is generated by heating limestone.

$$CaCO_3 \xrightarrow{\Delta} CaO + CO_2 \tag{1}$$

The ammonia is obtained by treating ammonium chloride, formed as a by-product of the process, with calcium hydroxide.

$$2NH_4^+ + [2Cl^-] + [Ca^{2+}] + 2OH^- \longrightarrow$$
$$2NH_3(g) + 2H_2O + [Ca^{2+}] + [2Cl^-] \tag{2}$$

Calcium hydroxide results from slaking the lime produced during the generation of carbon dioxide [Equation (1)].

$$CaO + H_2O \longrightarrow Ca^{2+} + 2OH^- \tag{3}$$

Aqueous ammonia reacts with the carbon dioxide, yielding ammonium hydrogen carbonate.

$$NH_3 + CO_2 + H_2O \longrightarrow NH_4^+ + HCO_3^- \tag{4}$$

Sodium hydrogen carbonate is also a valued product of the Solvay process; after being freed of ammonium chloride by recrystallization, it is made commercially available. The major portion of the sodium hydrogen carbonate, however, is converted to sodium carbonate by heating.

$$2NaHCO_3 \xrightarrow{\Delta} Na_2CO_3 + H_2O + CO_2 \tag{5}$$

The carbon dioxide from this reaction is used to produce more sodium hydrogen carbonate. The only by-product of the entire process that is not reused in the process is calcium chloride, and this finds commercial use in such applications as the melting of ice and snow on streets and highways and in dust abatement on dirt roads.

When a solution of sodium carbonate is evaporated below 35.2°C, **sodium carbonate 10-hydrate, $Na_2CO_3 \cdot 10H_2O$** (known as **washing soda,** because it was used at one time to wash wool and textiles), crystallizes; above this temperature the monohydrate $Na_2CO_3 \cdot H_2O$ crystallizes. Heating either hydrate produces the anhydrous compound.

2. Reactions and Uses of the Carbonates and Hydrogen Carbonates. Carbonates are moderately strong bases. Aqueous solutions are basic because the carbonate ion accepts a hydrogen ion from water, as shown by the equation

$$CO_3^{2-} + H_2O \rightleftharpoons HCO_3^- + OH^-$$

Figure 13.21

The reaction of an acid and a carbonate salt produces gaseous carbon dioxide.

Figure 13.22

A Missouri limestone quarry beside the Mississippi River.

They react with acids, forming salts of the metal, gaseous carbon dioxide, and water (Fig. 13.21). The reaction of calcium carbonate, the active ingredient of the well-known antacid Tums®, with hydrochloric acid (stomach acid) illustrates the reaction.

$$CaCO_3(s) + 2HCl(aq) \longrightarrow CaCl_2(aq) + CO_2(g) + H_2O(l)$$

Hydrogen carbonates, the major active ingredients in many antacids (for example, Alka-Seltzer®) are also bases, but they are much weaker bases than carbonates.

An interesting use of lithium carbonate stems from the discovery that small doses of orally administered Li_2CO_3 are an effective treatment for manic-depressive psychoses. How Li_2CO_3 works is not well understood, but it is probably related to the effect of the Li^+ ion on the Na^+/K^+ balance and/or the Mg^{+2}/Ca^{+2} balance in the brain.

Sodium carbonate, commonly called **soda ash** or **soda** in the industrial market, is an important chemical. In 1989 it was eleventh among industrial chemicals in the United States, with a production of 9.9 million tons. It is used extensively in the manufacture of glass, other chemicals, soap, paper and pulp, cleansers, and water softeners and in the refining of petroleum.

Sodium hydrogen carbonate, $NaHCO_3$, is commonly called **bicarbonate of soda** or **baking soda.** Baking powders contain a mixture of baking soda and an acid such as potassium hydrogen tartrate or cream of tartar, $KHC_4H_4O_6$, or calcium dihydrogen phosphate, $Ca(H_2PO_4)_2$. As long as the powder is dry, no reaction occurs, but as soon as water is added, the acid reacts with the hydrogen carbonate anion and carbon dioxide is formed.

$$HC_4H_4O_6^- + HCO_3^- \longrightarrow C_4H_4O_6^{2-} + CO_2 + H_2O$$

$$H_2PO_4^- + HCO_3^- \longrightarrow HPO_4^{2-} + CO_2 + H_2O$$

The carbon dioxide is trapped in the dough and expands when warmed, producing the texture characteristic of biscuits and other quickbreads.

The lactic acid of sour milk and buttermilk or the acetic acid in vinegar will also furnish hydrogen ion and thus serve the same purpose as the acidic component of baking powders. Thus it is possible to make dough rise using sour milk, buttermilk, or vinegar with ordinary sodium hydrogen carbonate (baking soda).

It is rarely necessary to manufacture **calcium carbonate** because it is widely distributed as limestone, a mineral second in abundance only to silicate rocks in the earth's crust. Coral reefs such as the one shown in this chapter's opening photograph are composed of calcium carbonate deposited by marine animals. Pearls are concentric layers of calcium carbonate deposited around a foreign particle, such as a grain of sand, that has entered the shell of an oyster.

Limestone is the naturally occurring building stone that is the most widely used in the United States (Fig. 13.22). Most limestone is composed of particles of **calcite,** the low-temperature form of calcium carbonate that results when precipitation occurs below 30°C. Above 30°C calcium carbonate crystallizes in the high-temperature form known as **aragonite.** A single crystal of calcite possesses the property of **birefringence,** or double refraction; when a beam of light enters the crystal, it is broken into two beams (Fig. 13.23).

When water containing carbon dioxide comes into contact with limestone rocks, they dissolve because **calcium hydrogen carbonate** is formed. This reaction is responsible for the formation of caves in beds of limestone rock. If water containing calcium hydrogen carbonate finds its way into a cave where the $Ca(HCO_3)_2$ can liberate carbon dioxide, calcium carbonate may again be deposited.

$$Ca^{2+}(aq) + 2HCO_3^-(aq) \longrightarrow CaCO_3(s) + CO_2(g) + H_2O(l)$$

This deposition gives the beautiful limestone formations that are found in many caves (Fig. 13.24).

When aqueous solutions of calcium hydrogen carbonate are heated, calcium carbonate readily precipitates. This reaction is often responsible for the formation of scale in kettles and boilers and is the basis for one method of removing carbonate hardness from water (see Sections 29.12 and 29.13).

⑬.8 Halides of the Active Metals

The binary compounds of the active metals with the halogens are called **halides**. With the exception of $AlCl_3$, $AlBr_3$, and AlI_3, the active metal halides are ionic compounds.

1. **Preparation of the Halides.** The halides of the active metals form readily when the metals react directly with elemental halogens or with solutions of the hydrogen halides (HF, HCl, HBr, and HI) in water. With the partial exceptions of magnesium and aluminum, the reactions with the active metals occur so readily that they can be extremely violent and dangerous. Reactions other than those that employ the elemental active metals are generally used to prepare the halides, because there is less potential for an accident.

Solutions of the halides of the active metals are prepared in the laboratory by addition of aqueous hydrohalic acids to carbonates, hydroxides, oxides, or other compounds containing basic anions. Sample reactions include

$$Na_2CO_3(s) + 2H_3O^+(aq) + [2F^-(aq)] \longrightarrow$$
$$2Na^+(aq) + [2F^-(aq)] + 3H_2O(l) + CO_2(g)$$

$$Mg(OH)_2(s) + 2H_3O^+(aq) + [2Br^-(aq)] \longrightarrow Mg^{2+}(aq) + [2Br^-(aq)] + 4H_2O(l)$$

$$\gamma\text{-}Al_2O_3(s) + 6H_3O^+(aq) + [6I^-(aq)] \longrightarrow 2Al^{3+}(aq) + [6I^-(aq)] + 9H_2O(l)$$

Evaporation of the water gives anhydrous halides of sodium, potassium, rubidium, and cesium. The other active metals form hydrated halides such as $LiCl \cdot 3H_2O$, $CaCl_2 \cdot 6H_2O$, $BaCl_2 \cdot 8H_2O$, and $AlCl_3 \cdot 6H_2O$. With the exception of magnesium and aluminum halides, the hydrated halides can be converted to anhydrous halides by heating.

Anhydrous halides of magnesium and aluminum cannot be prepared simply by heating the hydrated halides. The hydrated halides decompose upon heating, giving water vapor, the hydrogen halide, and the metal oxide; two typical examples are

$$MgCl_2 \cdot 6H_2O(s) \xrightarrow{\text{Heat}} MgO(s) + 2HCl(g) + 5H_2O(g)$$

$$2(AlBr_3 \cdot 6H_2O)(s) \xrightarrow{\text{Heat}} Al_2O_3(s) + 6HBr(g) + 9H_2O(g)$$

The oxides are formed in these cases because they are stabilized by large lattice energies (Section 11.19) resulting from the small metal ions with charges of +2 and +3. Anhydrous halides of magnesium and aluminum are prepared by heating the metal or the hydrated halide in a stream of the gaseous hydrogen halide, which prevents formation of the oxides.

$$Mg + 2HBr(g) \xrightarrow{\text{Heat}} MgBr_2 + H_2$$

$$AlCl_3 \cdot 6H_2O \xrightarrow[\text{Heat}]{\text{HCl}(g)} AlCl_3 + 6H_2O(g)$$

Figure 13.23

Calcite, or Iceland spar, has the unusual property of birefringence, or double refraction. Notice that the calcite produces two images of the pencil.

Figure 13.24

Stalactites and stalagmites are cave formations of calcium carbonate, as seen in the Luray Caverns, Virginia.

Anhydrous aluminum chloride, bromide, and iodide show some covalent character by virtue of the relatively high charge ($+3$) and small size of the aluminum ion, but the aluminum trihalides exhibit a change in behavior as the halogen family is considered from top to bottom in the periodic table. Aluminum trifluoride differs from the others in that it is much less volatile, is insoluble, and has a much greater enthalpy of formation. X-ray studies show that in solid AlF_3 and $AlCl_3$, each aluminum ion is surrounded by six halide ions in an octahedral array (see Section 11.15). However, unlike AlF_3 (which does not change), $AlCl_3$ changes its structure, either at the sublimation point of 180°C or at the melting point of 192°C, such that its coordination number is 4. Measurement of the density of aluminum chloride vapor shows that it is dimeric in the gas phase, with a formula of Al_2Cl_6. In these molecules each aluminum atom is tetrahedrally surrounded by four chlorine atoms, with two of the chlorine atoms (shown in color) bridging the two aluminum atoms.

$$\begin{array}{ccc} Cl & Cl & Cl \\ & Al \; \; Al & \\ Cl & Cl & Cl \end{array}$$

Aluminum
chloride

Each aluminum atom possesses an octet of electrons. X-ray studies show that there are no discrete Al_2Cl_6 molecules in solid $AlCl_3$. The structure consists of a closest packed array of chloride ions (see Section 11.14), with aluminum ions in the octahedral holes. Thus the aluminum changes its coordination number from 6 to 4 when the solid melts or sublimes. In contrast, $AlBr_3$ and AlI_3 form dimeric Al_2Br_6 and Al_2I_6 units in the crystalline and liquid states as well as in the gaseous states.

2. Reactions and Uses of the Halides. Sodium chloride or **rock salt,** NaCl, the chloride used most extensively in the chemical industry, is one of the most abundant minerals. It occurs in vast underground deposits either as the solid (Fig. 13.25) or as brine, a concentrated aqueous solution of NaCl. Thus most of the salt consumed comes from salt beds or from brine. Sea water is 2.7% sodium chloride, and the highly concentrated waters of the Dead Sea are 27% NaCl.

Sodium chloride is the usual source of sodium or chlorine in almost all other compounds containing these elements. Its most extensive use is in the manufacture of chlo-

Figure 13.25

Salt is mined from beds up to 500 feet thick. This mine is near Cleveland, Ohio.

rine, hydrochloric acid, sodium hydroxide, and sodium carbonate. Sodium chloride is an essential constituent of the foods of animals. It not only makes food more palatable but is also the source of chlorine for the production of hydrochloric acid, a constituent of gastric juice, and a source of sodium, which is one of most important biological ions. Sodium chloride is also a constituent of the blood and is essential for the life processes of the human body.

Potassium (along with sodium) is one of the two most important biological ions. It is a major essential element of plant nutrition and growth, and potassium chloride is the predominant source of potassium in fertilizers. Potassium bromide is used extensively in photography.

Calcium chloride, $CaCl_2$, is obtained from brines and can be prepared in the laboratory as described earlier in this section. Calcium chloride is very soluble in water. The salt crystallizes from water as the hexahydrate, $CaCl_2 \cdot 6H_2O$, which melts at $-55°C$. Thus it is used to melt snow and ice on highways and sidewalks (see Fig. 12.16) and, with water, as a cooling brine in refrigeration plants. Because it absorbs moisture from the air and becomes liquid (that is, it is **deliquescent**), $CaCl_2 \cdot 6H_2O$ is used to control dust on unpaved roads and in coal mines.

Strontium chloride, $SrCl_2$, like other strontium salts, produces a red flame and is used in flares and fireworks (Fig. 13.26). The antiperspirant "aluminum chlorohydrate," $Al_2(OH)_5Cl \cdot 2H_2O$, is an **astringent;** it acts by constricting the openings of sweat glands to reduce the amount of perspiration that escapes. Other aluminum compounds are used as astringents to control bleeding from cuts and scrapes.

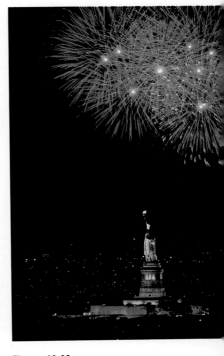

Figure 13.26
The red colors in these fireworks result when strontium salts are heated.

13.9 Hydrides of the Active Metals

With the exception of aluminum, the active metals react with hydrogen at slightly elevated temperatures, giving ionic metal hydrides.

$$2M + H_2 \longrightarrow 2MH \qquad (M = Li, Na, K, Rb, Cs)$$

$$M + H_2 \longrightarrow MH_2 \qquad (M = Mg, Ca, Sr, Ba)$$

Aluminum hydride can be prepared by the metathesis reaction of anhydrous aluminum trichloride with lithium aluminum hydride, $LiAlH_4$, in solution in diethyl ether; aluminum hydride precipitates from the solution.

$$3LiAlH_4 + AlCl_3 \xrightarrow{\text{Ether}} 4AlH_3 + 3LiCl$$

The binary hydrides of the metals of Groups IA and IIA are ionic compounds containing the hydride anion, H^-. They crystallize with structures similar to those of the halides, with the hydride ion in the location normally occupied by the halide ion. For example, sodium hydride, NaH, and potassium hydride, KH, crystallize with the sodium chloride structure (Fig. 13.27). Aluminum hydride is one of the covalent compounds of aluminum.

The hydrides are readily decomposed by water with the liberation of hydrogen. Hydride ions are strong bases, and they readily react with hydrogen ions from H_2O,

$$H^- + H_2O \longrightarrow H_2(g) + OH^-(aq)$$

leaving hydroxide ions in solution. Hydrides are also strong reducing agents, because hydrogen, having an oxidation number of -1, is not particularly stable.

○ H^- ● Na^+

Figure 13.27

The crystal structure of NaH. This is the same structure as that of NaCl (Fig. 11.40, Section 11.17). The smaller spheres (red) represent sodium ions, the larger ones (beige) hydride ions. The upper structure is an "expanded" view that shows the geometry more clearly.

⑬.10 Other Salts of the Active Metals

Thousands of salts of the active metals have been prepared. Generally these are formed from the metals, or from the common compounds that we have just discussed, by one of three general types of reactions: acid–base, oxidation–reduction, or metathesis reactions. Examples of reactions that can be used to form a variety of additional salts of the active metals are described below, as are uses of some of the more interesting compounds.

1. Acid–Base Reactions. The reaction of an acid and a base produces a salt and water. Oxides, hydroxides, and carbonates of the active metals react with solutions of most acids to form solutions of salts. The salts can be isolated by evaporation of the solvent. Like the halides, the solid compounds may contain water of hydration. Sulfuric acid, the leading industrial chemical in world production (see Section 2.12), is used in hundreds of processes. In most of these procedures, it is neutralized by NaOH. The end product is the salt **sodium sulfate,** commonly called **salt cake.**

$$2NaOH + H_2SO_4 \longrightarrow Na_2SO_4 + 2H_2O$$

Salt cake is used extensively in the paper, glass, and detergent industries.

2. Oxidation–Reduction Reactions. Because the active metals are generally very reactive, oxidation–reduction reactions utilizing the metals are difficult to control and are generally restricted to preparation of compounds of magnesium or aluminum. The other metals are sometimes used when it is necessary to prepare a salt of a particularly unreactive substance or to prepare a compound that decomposes in water. Oxidation–reduction reactions involving the anions in compounds of the active metals are common.

Magnesium sulfide and **aluminum sulfide** decompose in water, but they can be prepared by causing the metal to react with sulfur or by heating the metal in a stream of hydrogen sulfide.

$$Mg + H_2S(g) \xrightarrow{\triangle} MgS + H_2(g)$$
$$2Al + 3H_2S(g) \xrightarrow{\triangle} Al_2S_3 + 3H_2(g)$$

Some salts are prepared by oxidation or reduction of the anion in a second salt; for example, sodium sulfide is prepared by reduction of sodium sulfate with carbon.

$$Na_2SO_4 + 2C \xrightarrow{900°C} Na_2S + 2CO_2$$

3. Metathesis Reactions. Insoluble salts can often be prepared by mixing solutions of two soluble compounds. **Barium sulfate** is prepared in this way from the soluble salts barium chloride and sodium sulfate.

$$Ba^{2+}(aq) + [2Cl^-(aq)] + [2Na^+(aq)] + SO_4^{2-}(aq) \longrightarrow$$
$$BaSO_4(s) + [2Na^+(aq)] + [2Cl^-(aq)]$$

Barium sulfate is used in taking X-ray photographs of the intestinal tract (Fig. 13.28) because it is opaque to X rays. Even though Ba^{2+} is poisonous, $BaSO_4$ is so slightly soluble that it is nonpoisonous. **Calcium sulfate** can be prepared by an analogous metathesis reaction. **Anhydrous calcium sulfate** occurs in nature as the mineral **anhydrite,** $CaSO_4$, and as the dihydrate, **gypsum,** $CaSO_4 \cdot 2H_2O$. The latter is found in enormous deposits. Even though it is low in solubility, calcium sulfate is largely responsible for the noncarbonate hardness of ground waters (see Section 29.12).

When gypsum is heated, it loses water, forming the hemihydrate $(CaSO_4)_2 \cdot H_2O$.

$$2(CaSO_4 \cdot 2H_2O) \longrightarrow (CaSO_4)_2 \cdot H_2O + 3H_2O$$

Figure 13.28
The contrast in this X-ray photograph of the large intestine has been enhanced by the patient's ingestion of $BaSO_4$, which absorbs X rays to a much greater extent than do body tissues or bone. The left part of the photograph shows diverticulitis of the colon; the right part shows a normal colon.

The hemihydrate is known as **plaster of paris.** When it is ground to a fine powder and mixed with water, it sets by forming small interlocking crystals of gypsum. The setting results in an increase in volume, so the plaster fits tightly in any mold into which it is poured. Plaster of paris is used extensively as a component of plaster for the interiors of buildings and in the manufacture of statuary, stucco, wallboard, and casts of various kinds.

Gypsum is also used in making Portland cement (see Section 25.17), blackboard crayon (erroneously called chalk), plate glass, terra-cotta, pottery, and orthopedic and dental plasters. Anhydrous calcium sulfate is sold as Drierite®, a drying agent for gases and organic liquids. **Calcium dihydrogen phosphate monohydrate,** $Ca(H_2PO_4)_2 \cdot H_2O$, which is used in baking powders, can be prepared by mixing solutions of calcium nitrate and potassium dihydrogen phosphate.

$$Ca^{2+}(aq) + [2NO_3^-(aq)] + [2K^+(aq)] + 2H_2PO_4^-(aq) + H_2O(l) \longrightarrow$$
$$Ca(H_2PO_4)_2 \cdot H_2O(s) + [2K^+(aq)] + [2NO_3^-(aq)]$$

Other metathesis reactions occur because a volatile product is formed. Both **sodium sulfate,** Na_2SO_4, and **sodium hydrogen sulfate,** $NaHSO_4$, can be prepared from the reaction of sodium chloride and sulfuric acid, because hydrogen chloride is a volatile product.

$$NaCl + H_2SO_4 \longrightarrow NaHSO_4 + HCl(g)$$

$$2NaCl + H_2SO_4 \longrightarrow Na_2SO_4 + 2HCl(g)$$

13.11 Ionic Sizes and the Chemistry of the Active Metals

For the most part, the active metals form compounds in which the metals are present as ions. These elements do not exhibit multiple oxidation states, and they are neither oxidized nor reduced during the vast majority of the reactions involving their compounds. Thus any differences in the chemical behavior of these compounds must be attributable either to the anion present or to the size and charge of the metal ion. Within a group, any differences between compounds with the same anion must be due to differences in ionic sizes of the cations. As examples of the effect of ionic size, we will consider how the behavior of lithium differs from that of the other alkali metals, the solubilities of the active metal sulfates, and the thermal stabilities of the alkaline earth carbonates.

1. **The Behavior of Lithium.** Some distinctive differences between the behavior of lithium compounds and that of compounds of the other alkali metals are related to the relatively small size of the lithium ion. The radius of Li^+ is 0.60 Å; the radii of Na^+, K^+, Rb^+, and Cs^+ ions are 0.95, 1.33, 1.48, and 1.69 Å, respectively. A table of atomic and ionic radii may be found inside the back cover of this book.

The stability of a solid compound is related to its lattice energy (see Section 11.19); compounds with larger lattice energies are more stable than those with smaller lattice energies. As we noted in Section 11.19, the lattice energy U of a solid depends on (1) the charge on the ions, Z^+ and Z^-, and (2) the distance R_0 between the positive ion (the cation) and the negative ion (the anion).

$$U = \frac{C(Z^+Z^-)}{R_0}$$

Thus lattice energies increase with increasing charge on the ions and with decreasing distance between the negative and positive ions (as the cations and/or anions become smaller).

Lithium hydride is stable to about 900°C, whereas sodium hydride decomposes at about 350°C. Lithium hydroxide and lithium carbonate decompose upon heating and form the oxide; the hydroxides and carbonates of the other alkali metals simply melt. Lithium fluoride and lithium carbonate are not soluble; the other fluorides and carbonates are. All of these differences reflect the smaller size of the Li^+ ion and the correspondingly larger lattice energies of lithium compounds, especially those with small anions, compared to the other alkali metals.

The solubilities and thermal stabilities of lithium compounds resemble those of magnesium compounds—behaviors that are reflected in the so-called diagonal relationships described in Section 13.12.

2. **Solubilities of Group IIA Sulfates.** The solubilities of the sulfates of the active metals of Group IIA decrease regularly with increasing atomic number of the metal (Table 13.6). Magnesium sulfate, $MgSO_4$, is soluble; barium sulfate, $BaSO_4$, is insoluble. These differences in solubility can be interpreted as resulting from the change in the size of the metal ions in these compounds.

For an ionic compound to dissolve in water, the crystal lattice must be broken down into its component ions. This requires energy, which is provided during hydration of the

Table 13.6	Molar Solubilities of Alkaline Earth Sulfates	
$MgSO_4$	2.80 mol/L	
$CaSO_4$	1.4×10^{-3} mol/L	
$SrSO_4$	7.6×10^{-5} mol/L	
$BaSO_4$	1.1×10^{-6} mol/L	

ions with the formation of ion–dipole bonds between the ions and water (see Section 12.8). If the energy given up as the hydrated ions form is greater than the lattice energy, the compound should be soluble. If it is less than the lattice energy, the compound should be relatively insoluble. As we proceed in sequence from $MgSO_4$ to $BaSO_4$, the size of the metal ion increases. In turn, the strength of the ion–dipole attractions between the positive ions and water molecules decreases because these attractions, like ion–ion attractions (see Section 11.19), decrease as the distance increases. Thus progressively less energy is given up as the larger ions form ion–dipole attractions. On the other hand, the lattice energies of the sulfates do not change much upon going from magnesium to barium, because the sulfate ion is large relative to the metal ions. In those compounds where the anion is large relative to the size of the cation, changes in the size of the cation have little effect on the lattice energy, because the size of the anion dominates the cation–anion distance. With smaller anions, the cation plays a more significant role. Thus as we proceed from $MgSO_4$ to $BaSO_4$, the energy required to break up the lattice into ions does not change dramatically, but the energy available to break it up (that is, the energy released as a result of the formation of ion–dipole attractions) decreases. The solubility of these compounds reflects these changes in energy.

   3. **Decomposition of the Group IIA Carbonates.** As we noted in Section 13.5, magnesium carbonate decomposes to the metal oxide and carbon dioxide at about 540°C, whereas barium carbonate decomposes at about 1360°C. The intermediate carbonates decompose at intermediate temperatures.

   The increase in decomposition temperature with increasing atomic weight results from the increasing ionic size of the metal ions in these compounds. As in the series of sulfates, and for the same reason, the lattice energies of the Group IIA carbonates do not vary much with the size of the metal ion, because the anion (the carbonate ion in this case) is a relatively large ion. However, the lattice energies of the oxides, which result from the decomposition, are much more sensitive to the changing size of the metal ion. This is because the oxide ion is smaller than the carbonate ion and is about the same size as the cations in these systems. All of these decompositions are endothermic and require heating to proceed. However, the formation of magnesium oxide as a product, with its higher lattice energy, releases more energy to help compensate for the energy necessary to decompose the carbonate than does the formation of barium oxide, with its smaller lattice energy. Thus the decomposition of the carbonates of the lighter metals is less endothermic and requires less heat from outside the system. Therefore, the decomposition reactions proceed at lower temperatures for the carbonates of the lighter alkaline earth metals than for those of the heavier ones.

13.12 Diagonal Relationships

In some respects the properties of the first elements of Groups IA and IIA resemble those of the second elements in the adjacent groups more than those of the heavier members of their own group. This behavior results in the **diagonal relationships** indicated by the arrows.

The diagonal relationships between the properties of these elements result from similarities in their ionic radii and their similar high charge densities. The charge density is simply the charge of an ion divided by its ionic radius. The radius of Li^+, 0.60 Å, is closer to that of Mg^{2+}, 0.65 Å, than to that of Na^+, 0.95 Å. Both Be^{2+} and Al^{3+} are small ions, with radii of 0.31 and 0.50 Å, respectively. The charge density of Be^{2+}, 6.5, is closer to that of Al^{3+}, 6.0, than to that of Mg^{2+}, 3.1.

A comparison of the properties of lithium compounds with compounds of the other alkali metals and of magnesium illustrates the relationship. Lithium is the only alkali metal to form an oxide when it burns in an excess of oxygen, and it forms a nitride, Li_3N, with nitrogen. The other alkali metals do not behave this way. Magnesium burns in oxygen, forming MgO, and reacts with N_2, forming the nitride Mg_3N_2. The fluorides, carbonates, and phosphates of both lithium and magnesium are insoluble, whereas those of the other alkali metals are soluble.

Beryllium resembles aluminum more than the other alkaline earth elements in the amphoteric behavior of its oxide and hydroxide. Like aluminum, and unlike the other alkaline earth elements, it forms covalent halides and hydrides.

For Review

Summary

The **active metals** are the **alkali metals** lithium, sodium, potassium, rubidium, cesium, and francium from Group IA; the **alkaline earth metals** magnesium, calcium, strontium, barium, and radium from Group IIA; and **aluminum** from Group IIIA. These metals exhibit similar chemical behavior. They all react with acids to form hydrogen gas and salts; with water they form hydrogen gas and basic hydroxides, although the reactivity of magnesium and aluminum is masked by inert coatings. Their oxides and hydroxides are basic. They react with most nonmetals. All are easily oxidized, and the resulting ions are reduced with great difficulty. Each of these metals exhibits a single oxidation number in ionic compounds. Several of the active metals are among the most common of the elements.

The atoms of the active metals are relatively large, and the metals have low densities. Lithium, sodium, and potassium float on water as they react vigorously. The lightness and high strength of magnesium and aluminum make them valuable structural materials.

The alkali metals are more alike in their properties than the members of any other group of elements. The single electron in the outermost shell of each is loosely bound and easily lost. These metals readily form stable positive ions with a charge of +1 in ionic compounds that are usually soluble. The alkali metals all react vigorously with water to form hydrogen gas and a basic solution of the metal hydroxide. The reaction is explosive with all Group IA metals except lithium. The metals are so reactive with moisture and air that they must be stored in kerosene, in mineral oil, or in sealed containers.

Each of the two electrons in the outermost shell of each of the alkaline earth metals is more tightly bound than the single electron in the preceding alkali metal, so each alkaline earth atom is smaller than, and not so reactive as, the preceding alkali metal atom. These elements easily form compounds in which the metals exhibit an oxidation number of +2. Compounds of magnesium often show some covalent character, but the magnesium in them can generally be regarded as a +2 ion. Like the alkali metals, the alkaline earth elements are difficult to prepare by chemical methods; the pure elements are isolated by electrochemical techniques.

Aluminum forms both ionic and covalent compounds, in which it has an oxidation number of +3. Its reactive amphoteric oxide and hydroxide react with both acids and bases. Aluminum is also manufactured by an electrochemical process.

Because of their reactivity, none of the active metals are found as free elements in nature. They occur extensively as simple compounds such as chlorides, oxides or hydroxides, carbonates, sulfates, and nitrates and as more complex silicates. Aluminum and calcium are two of the most abundant metals in the Earth's crust. Many of these elements can be prepared by electrolysis reactions.

Compounds of the active metals are widely used in many industrial applications. Compounds of the alkali metals serve as starting materials for other useful compounds. Sodium and potassium compounds are essential to plant and animal life, and the ions of these two elements are important biological ions.

Compounds of the active metals with oxygen fall into the three categories of oxides, peroxides, and superoxides. The oxides are usually produced by heating the corresponding hydroxides, nitrates, or carbonates. Peroxides and superoxides are formed by heating the metal or metal oxide in oxygen. Heating lithium, magnesium, and calcium in air also yields the nitride. The oxides, peroxides, and superoxides of the active metals all dissolve in water to form basic solutions. The hydroxides of the active metals react with acids in acid–base reactions to form salts and water. They also react with many covalent nonmetal oxides to form oxyanions. The hydroxides have many commercial uses. Caustic soda (NaOH), milk of magnesia [$Mg(OH)_2$], and slaked lime [$Ca(OH)_2$] are all important active metal hydroxides.

Carbonates of the alkali and alkaline earth metals are usually prepared by reaction of an oxide or hydroxide with carbon dioxide. Aluminum carbonate is unknown. Active metal carbonates or hydrogen carbonates, are well known in our everyday life. They include limestone ($CaCO_3$), washing soda ($Na_2CO_3 \cdot 10H_2O$), Tums® ($CaCO_3$), Alka-Seltzer® ($NaHCO_3$), and baking soda ($NaHCO_3$).

All of the active metals form halides that, except for $AlCl_3$, $AlBr_3$ and AlI_3, are ionic. The halides can be prepared when the metals react directly with elemental halogens or with solutions of the hydrohalic acids (HX). These reactions occur so readily that they can be violent, and better laboratory preparations involve the addition of aqueous hydrohalic acids to active metal compounds containing such basic anions as hydroxides, oxides, or carbonates. Sodium chloride is one of the most abundant minerals, and it is used extensively in the chemical industry.

Other salts of the active metals can be prepared by acid–base reactions, oxidation–reduction reactions, or metathesis reactions.

The sizes of the active metal cations play an important role in their chemistry. The chemistry of lithium is, in many respects, more similar to that of magnesium than to that of sodium because of the similarities in their ionic radii and charge densities. This is known as the diagonal relationship.

Experimental observations of the reactivities of metals are used to arrange metals in order of their chemical activities in an activity (or electromotive) series. The more metallic (or reactive) elements are at the top of this series and the less metallic elements appear at the bottom of the activity series.

Key Terms and Concepts

acid–base reactions (13.5, 13.10)
activity series (13.1)
alkali metal (13.2)
alkaline earth metal (13.2)
amphoteric compounds (13.2)
carbonates and hydrogen carbonates (13.7)
diagonal relationships (13.12)
electrolysis reactions (13.3)

electron configuration (13.2)
fractional crystallization (13.6)
halides (13.8)
hydrides (13.9)
hydroxides (13.6)
ionic size effects (13.11)
ionization energy (13.2)
metathesis reactions (13.10)
mordant (13.6)

nitrates (13.10)
oxidation–reduction reactions (13.10)
oxides (13.5)
periodic relationships (13.2)
peroxides (13.5)
preparation of pure metals (13.3)
sulfates (13.10)
superoxides (13.5)

Exercises

Answers for selected even-numbered exercises marked by red numbers appear at the end of the book. The worked-out solutions to all even-numbered exercises appear in the *Solutions Guide*.

The Alkali Metals

1. Why does the reactivity of the alkali metals decrease from cesium to lithium?
2. How do the alkali metals differ from the alkaline earth metals in atomic structure and general properties?
3. Is the reaction of rubidium with water more or less vigorous than that of sodium? Than that of magnesium?
4. Why are alkali metals stored under kerosene, under mineral oil, or in sealed containers?
5. Predict the product of burning francium in air.
6. What safety precautions should be taken when handling the alkali metals?
7. By analogy with its reaction with water, suggest a chemical formula for the product of the reaction between potassium metal and $H_2Se(g)$.
8. Write an equation for the preparation of elemental cesium.
9. Why is calcium chloride added to the electrolyte in the electrolysis of molten sodium chloride?
10. Why must the chlorine and sodium resulting from the electrolysis of sodium chloride be kept separate during the production of sodium metal?
11. Outline the chemical reactions involved in the Solvay process for the production of sodium carbonate.
12. Consult a handbook for solubilities, and suggest a reason why potassium hydrogen carbonate cannot be manufactured by the Solvay process.
13. When potassium combines with hydrogen, why should the hydrogen have an oxidation state of -1?
14. When a hydride ion encounters a proton in aqueous solution, a reaction occurs to produce hydrogen gas. Is this an acid-base reaction? If so, identify the acid and the base.

15. Supply a name or formula for each of the following:
    (a) rock salt
    (b) Li_3N
    (c) rubidium superoxide
    (d) caustic soda
    (e) washing soda
    (f) soda ash
    (g) baking soda
16. Physiological saline concentration—that is, the sodium chloride concentration in our bodies—is approximately 0.16 M. Saline solution for contact lenses is prepared to match the physiological concentration. If you purchase 25 mL of contact lens saline solution, how many grams of sodium chloride have you bought?
17. Using equations, describe the reaction of water with potassium, with potassium hydride, and with potassium peroxide.
18. Sodium chloride and strontium chloride are both white solids. How could you distinguish one from the other? (''Taste them'' is not an acceptable answer.)
19. A 25.00-mL sample of CsOH solution is exactly neutralized with 35.27 mL of 0.1062 M HNO_3. What is the concentration of the CsOH solution?
20. Explain why the stoichiometries of binary lithium compounds are similar to those of sodium, whereas their solubilities are more similar to those of the binary compounds of magnesium.
21. What difference between LiCl and LiF makes LiCl soluble in water whereas LiF is insoluble?
22. Give balanced equations for the overall reaction in the electrolysis of lithium chloride and for the reactions occurring at the electrodes.

The Alkaline Earth Metals

23. Supply a name or formula for each of the following:
    (a) quicklime
    (b) slaked lime
    (c) milk of lime
    (d) CaO_2
    (e) magnesia
    (f) milk of magnesia
    (g) SrH_2
    (h) plaster of paris

24. Figure 12.16 depicts calcium chloride being spread on a sidewalk to melt ice. Explain how calcium chloride (or sodium chloride) acts to melt the ice.

25. What weight of Epsom salts ($MgSO_4 \cdot 7H_2O$) can be prepared from 5.0 kg of magnesium?

26. Suppose you discovered a diamond completely encased in limestone. How could you chemically free the diamond without harming it?

27. How many grams of oxygen gas are required to react completely with 3.01×10^{21} atoms of magnesium to yield magnesium oxide?

28. What property or properties of beryllium or its compounds keep(s) it from being classified as an active metal?

29. Account for the differences in size between the alkaline earth metal atoms and their respective 2+ cations (Table 13.2).

30. What weight, in grams, of hydrogen gas is produced by the complete reaction of 10.01 g of calcium with water?

31. Predict the formulas for the nine compounds formed when each species in column 1 reacts with each species in column 2.

1	2
Na	I
Sr	Se
Al	O

32. Magnesium is an active metal; it is burned in the form of ribbons and filaments to provide flashes of brilliant light. Why is it possible to use magnesium in construction and even for the fabrication of cooking grills?

33. A magnesium fire cannot be extinguished by either water or carbon dioxide. Explain why this is so. How would you extinguish such a fire?

34. Select:
    (a) the most metallic of the elements Na, Be, and Ba
    (b) the most soluble of the compounds Li_2CO_3, Na_2CO_3, and $CaCO_3$
    (c) the most covalent of the compounds NaCl, $CaCl_2$, and $BeCl_2$
    (d) the lowest first ionization energy among the elements Rb, Mg, and Ba
    (e) the smallest among Al, Al^+, and Al^{3+}
    (f) the largest among Cs^+, Ba^{2+}, and Xe

35. How is metallic calcium produced commercially?

36. Write a balanced chemical equation describing the dehydrating action of calcium metal.

37. Solely on the basis of the lattice energy of the product, should we expect potassium or calcium to be more reactive with oxygen?

38. Write a balanced equation for the reaction of strontium with each of the following: oxygen, hydrogen bromide, hydrogen, nitrogen, phosphorus, and water.

39. The reaction of quicklime (CaO) with water produces slaked lime [$Ca(OH)_2$], which is widely used in the construction industry to make mortar and plaster. The reaction of quicklime and water is highly exothermic.

$$CaO(s) + H_2O(l) \longrightarrow Ca(OH)_2(s) \quad \Delta H = -350 \text{ kJ/mol}$$

    (a) What is the enthalpy of reaction per gram of quicklime that reacts?
    (b) How much heat, in kilojoules, is associated with the production of 1 ton of slaked lime?

40. A sample of $MgSO_4 \cdot xH_2O$ weighing 5.018 g is heated until the water of hydration is completely driven off. The resulting anhydrous $MgSO_4$ weighs 2.449 g. What is the formula of the hydrated compound?

41. When $MgNH_4PO_4$ is heated to 1000°C, it is converted to $Mg_2P_2O_7$. A 1.203-g sample containing magnesium yielded 0.5275 g of $Mg_2P_2O_7$ after precipitation of $MgNH_4PO_4$ and heating. What percent by mass of magnesium was present in the original sample?

42. The barium ion is poisonous. Why, then, is it safe for patients to take barium sulfate internally when photographs of the intestinal tract are needed?

Group IIIA

43. Give three examples of how beryllium chemically resembles aluminum.

44. Illustrate the amphoteric nature of aluminum hydroxide by citing suitable equations.

45. Why can aluminum, which is an active metal, be used so successfully as a structural metal?

46. Why is it impossible to prepare anhydrous aluminum chloride by heating the hexahydrate to drive off all the water? How can it be prepared?

47. What is the Goldschmidt process?

48. The elements sodium, aluminum, and chlorine belong to the same period.
    (a) Which has the greatest electronegativity?
    (b) Which of the atoms is smallest?
    (c) Write the Lewis structure for the covalent compound formed between aluminum and fluorine.
    (d) Will the oxide of each element be acidic, basic, or amphoteric?

49. How does $B(OH)_3$ differ from $Al(OH)_3$ in its chemical properties?

50. Contrast the properties of aluminum and gallium and their compounds.

51. Describe the production of metallic aluminum by electrolytic reduction.

52. Write balanced chemical equations for the following reactions.

(a) Gaseous hydrogen fluoride is bubbled through a suspension of bauxite in molten sodium fluoride.
(b) Metallic aluminum is burned in air.
(c) Aluminum is heated in an atmosphere of chlorine.
(d) Aluminum is heated in hydrogen sulfide gas.
(e) Aluminum hydroxide is added to a solution of nitric acid.

Additional Exercises

53. Write balanced chemical equations for the following reactions.
    (a) Sodium oxide is added to water.
    (b) Sodium peroxide is added to water.
    (c) Sodium peroxide is added to an aqueous solution of HBr.
    (d) Cesium carbonate is added to an excess of an aqueous solution of HF.
    (e) Rubidium superoxide is added to water.
    (f) An electric current is passed through a sample of molten $CaBr_2$.
    (g) α-Alumina is added to an aqueous solution of $HClO_4$.
    (h) Hydrogen bromide gas is passed over a sample of calcium hydride.
    (i) Sulfur dioxide gas is passed over barium oxide.
    (j) Potassium peroxide is warmed (very carefully) with potassium hydride.
    (k) Barium and barium hydroxide are heated together.
    (l) Aluminum is heated with calcium oxide in a vacuum.
    (m) A solution of sodium carbonate is added to a solution of barium nitrate.
    (n) A solution of sodium carbonate is added to a solution of magnesium nitrate.
    (o) Titanium metal is produced from the reaction of titanium tetrachloride with elemental sodium.

54. (a) A current of 1000 A flowing for 96.5 s contains 1 mol of electrons. How long will it take to produce 100 kg of sodium metal when a current of 50,000 A is passed through a Downs cell like that shown in Fig. 13.9 if the yield of sodium is 100% of the theoretical yield?
    (b) What volume of chlorine at 25°C and 1.00 atm is produced?

55. A current of 1000 A flowing for 96.5 s contains 1 mol of electrons. What mass of magnesium is produced when 100,000 A is passed through a $MgCl_2$ melt for 1.00 h if the yield of magnesium is 85% of the theoretical yield?

56. Which of the following is the most basic: $LiOH$, $P(OH)_3$, $Sr(OH)_2$, $CsOH$, or $As(OH)_3$?

57. Peroxides, like oxides, are basic. What volume of 0.250 M H_2SO_4 solution is required to neutralize a solution containing 5.00 g of CaO_2?

58. (a) Write the electron configuration for the isoelectronic 10-electron ions Na^+, Mg^{2+}, and Al^{3+}.
    (b) Write the electron configurations for the ions K^+, Ca^{2+}, and Ga^{3+}, and indicate how the configuration of Ga^{3+} differs from that of the other two ions.

59. Determine the oxidation number of oxygen in lithium oxide, in sodium peroxide, and in cesium superoxide.

60. What volume of oxygen at 25°C and 1.00 atm pressure is required to prepare 1.00 kg of potassium peroxide? To prepare 1.00 kg of potassium superoxide?

61. Under typical conditions of temperature and pressure, an average resting male requires 0.20 L of O_2 per hour per kilogram of body mass. What mass of KO_2 is required to provide a 1.00-h supply of oxygen at 0°C and 1.00 atm to an average 100-kg resting male?

62. Calculate the density of vapor above a sample of aluminum trichloride at 171°C. The vapor pressure of $AlCl_3$ at 171°C is 400 torr.

14 Chemical Kinetics

A lizard warms itself, thereby speeding up its metabolism.

Whenever we plan to run a chemical reaction, we should ask at least two questions. One is ''Will the reaction produce the desired products in useful quantities?'' We can answer this question through the use of equilibrium and thermodynamic calculations, as discussed in the next chapter and in Chapters 17–19, or we can use qualitative considerations, such as the fact that the reaction of an acid with a base yields a salt or the fact that an active metal generally reacts with a nonmetal. The second question is ''Will the reaction proceed rapidly enough to be useful?'' A reaction that takes 50 years to produce a product is about as useless as one that never gives a product at all!

This chapter considers the second question—that is, the rate at which a chemical reaction yields products **(chemical kinetics).** We shall examine factors that influence the rates of chemical reactions, the mechanisms by which reactions proceed, and the quantitative techniques used to determine and to describe the rate at which reactions occur. How to determine whether a reaction will give the desired products in useful quantities will be discussed in subsequent chapters.

🕎.1 The Rate of Reaction

The quantitative measure of the rate at which a chemical process gives products is called its **rate of reaction.** Rates of reaction, like all rates, involve production or consumption during some unit of time. For example, the rate of production of a well is measured in gallons *per minute*. The rate of an electric generating plant's use of coal is measured in tons *per hour*. **The rate of a chemical reaction is measured by the decrease in concentration of a reactant or the increase in concentration of a product in a unit of time.** For example, when hydrogen peroxide is dissolved in water, it slowly decomposes according to the following equation:

$$2H_2O_2(aq) \longrightarrow 2H_2O(l) + O_2(g)$$

The change in concentration with time at 40°C of a solution that is initially 1 M in hydrogen peroxide is shown in Fig. 14.1 and in Table 14.1.

From these data, which must be found experimentally, we can determine the rate at which the hydrogen peroxide decomposes.

$$\text{Rate} = -\frac{\text{change in concentration of reactant}}{\text{time interval}}$$

$$= -\frac{[H_2O_2]_{t_2} - [H_2O_2]_{t_1}}{t_2 - t_1} = -\frac{\Delta[H_2O_2]}{\Delta t}$$

In these equations, brackets are used to indicate molar concentrations. As in Chapter 4, the symbol delta (Δ) indicates "the change in." Thus $[H_2O_2]_{t_1}$ represents the molar concentration of hydrogen peroxide at some time t_1; $[H_2O_2]_{t_2}$ represents the molar concentration of hydrogen peroxide at a later time t_2; and $\Delta[H_2O_2]$ represents the change in molar concentration of hydrogen peroxide during the time interval Δt (that is, $t_2 - t_1$). The minus sign preceding the expression is used to convert the rate of disappearance of hydrogen peroxide to a positive rate for the reaction. Reaction rates are positive.

Figure 14.1

The decomposition of H_2O_2 ($2H_2O_2 \longrightarrow 2H_2O + O_2$) at 40°C. The intensity of the color represents the concentration of H_2O_2 at the indicated time after the reaction begins. Note that H_2O_2 is actually colorless; the color indicated here is symbolic of the decreasing concentration of H_2O_2 with time.

1.000 M	0.500 M	0.250 M	0.125 M	0.0625 M
0 s	2.16×10^4 s	4.32×10^4 s	6.48×10^4 s	8.64×10^4 s
(0 h)	(6 h)	(12 h)	(18 h)	(24 h)

Table 14.1		Variation in the Rate of Decomposition of $H_2O_2(aq)$ at 40°C			
Time, seconds	$[H_2O_2]$, mol L^{-1}	$\Delta[H_2O_2]$, mol L^{-1}	Δt, seconds	Rate, mol L^{-1} s^{-1}
0	1.000	−0.500	2.16×10^4	2.31×10^{-5}
2.16×10^4	0.500	−0.250	2.16×10^4	1.16×10^{-5}
4.32×10^4	0.250	−0.125	2.16×10^4	0.579×10^{-5}
6.48×10^4	0.125	−0.062	2.16×10^4	0.29×10^{-5}
8.64×10^4	0.0625			

Example 14.1

Calculate the average rate of decomposition of a 1.000 M solution of hydrogen peroxide at 40°C for the period of the reaction from 0 to 21,600 s, using the data in Table 14.1.

In Table 14.1 we find that for the period of the reaction from 0 to 21,600 s,

$$t_1 = 0 \text{ s}, \ [H_2O_2]_{t_1} = 1.000 \text{ mol } L^{-1}$$

and

$$t_2 = 21,600 \text{ s}, \ [H_2O_2]_{t_2} = 0.500 \text{ mol } L^{-1}$$

Thus

$$\Delta t = t_2 - t_1 = 21,600 \text{ s} - 0 \text{ s} = 21,600 \text{ s}$$

$$\Delta[H_2O_2] = [H_2O_2]_{t_2} - [H_2O_2]_{t_1}$$

$$= 0.500 \text{ mol } L^{-1} - 1.000 \text{ mol } L^{-1}$$

$$= -0.500 \text{ mol } L^{-1}$$

$$\text{Rate} = -\left(\frac{\Delta[H_2O_2]}{\Delta t}\right) = -\left(\frac{-0.500 \text{ mol } L^{-1}}{21,600 \text{ s}}\right)$$

$$= 2.31 \times 10^{-5} \text{ mol } L^{-1} \text{ s}^{-1}$$

The unit mol/L (moles per liter, or molarity) can be written mol L^{-1}, because $1/X = X^{-1}$ according to the mathematical rules for exponents. The unit s^{-1} (per second) is equivalent to 1/s.

The reaction rates present in Table 14.1 are averages of the rates during all 21,600-second intervals. The rate of decomposition of hydrogen peroxide is faster at the beginning of the decomposition ($t = 0$ seconds) than it is at 21,600 seconds. The average rate of decomposition between 0 and 21,600 seconds is 2.31×10^{-5} mol L^{-1} s^{-1}. When we calculate the rate for the time interval from 0 to 86,400 seconds, we find a lower average rate of 1.09×10^{-5} mol L^{-1} s^{-1}.

A graph plotting the concentration of hydrogen peroxide against time can be used to determine the rate of the reaction at any instant in time. The rate is given by the negative of the slope of a straight line tangent to the curve at that time. Such a graph is shown in Fig. 14.2; here a tangent is drawn at $t = 40,000$ seconds. The slope of this line is $\Delta[H_2O_2]/\Delta t$. The negative of the slope is the rate of decomposition at 40,000 seconds

Figure 14.2

A graph of concentration versus time for the 1.000 M solution of H_2O_2 shown in Fig. 14.1. The rate at any instant of time is equal to the slope of a line tangent to this curve at that time. A tangent (the purple line) is shown for $t = 40,000$ s.

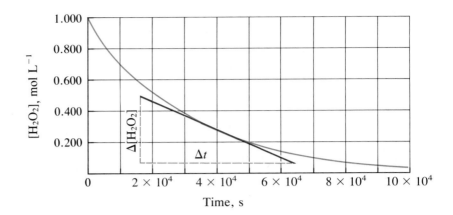

$(8.90 \times 10^{-6}$ mol L^{-1} $s^{-1})$. The **initial rate** of the reaction—the rate when no products are present—can be determined from the slope of the tangent at zero time.

The rates at which the concentrations of reactants or products change during reactions are rarely constant. As the reactants are consumed, rates usually decrease until they reach zero. In an irreversible reaction, such as the decomposition of hydrogen peroxide, the rate of the reaction reaches zero when all of the reactant has been consumed. In a reversible reaction (Section 2.11), the rate becomes zero when equilibrium is reached. In order to establish the rate of a reversible chemical reaction, we study it at the beginning of the reaction, before equilibrium is reached.

14 .2 Factors Affecting Reaction Rates

The rates at which reactants are consumed and products are formed during chemical reactions vary greatly. The following five factors affect the rates of chemical reactions: the nature of the reacting substances; the state of subdivision of the reactants; the temperature of the reactants; the concentration of the reactants; and the presence of a catalyst.

Figure 14.3

Twenty-four hours before this photograph was taken, a piece of iron and a piece of sodium were placed in air. The sodium has reacted completely during this time; the iron has not.

1. **The Nature of the Reacting Substances.** The rate of a reaction depends on the nature of the participating substances. Any simple combination of two ions of opposite charge usually occurs very rapidly. The reaction of an acid with a base is an example.

$$H_3O^+ + OH^- \longrightarrow 2H_2O$$

The acid–base reaction of solutions of hydrochloric acid and sodium hydroxide proceeds as rapidly as the two solutions can be mixed—it is almost instantaneous. Such acid–base reactions are much faster than the decomposition of hydrogen peroxide, a process involving the rearrangement of molecules:

$$2H_2O_2 \longrightarrow 2H_2O + O_2$$

Even similar reactions may have different rates under the same conditions if different reactants are involved. For example, when small pieces of the metals iron and sodium are left in air, the sodium reacts completely overnight, whereas the iron is barely affected (Fig. 14.3). The active metals calcium and sodium both react with water to form hydrogen gas and the metal hydroxide. Yet calcium reacts at a moderate rate, whereas sodium reacts so rapidly that the reaction is of almost explosive violence.

2. The State of Subdivision of the Reactants. Except for substances in the gaseous state or in solution, reactions occur at the boundary, or interface, between two phases. Hence the rate of a reaction between two phases depends to a great extent on the area of surface contact between them. Finely divided liquids and solids, because of the greater surface area available, react more rapidly than the same amount of the substance in a large body. For example, large pieces of iron react slowly with acids; finely divided iron reacts much more rapidly (Fig. 14.4). Large pieces of wood smolder, smaller pieces burn rapidly, and grain dust (which, like wood, is composed of cellulose) may burn at an explosive rate (see photograph below).

3. Temperature of the Reactants. Chemical reactions are accelerated by increases in temperature. The oxidation of either wood or coal is very slow at ordinary temperatures, but both burn at high temperatures. Foods cook faster at higher temperatures than at lower ones. We use a burner or a hot plate in the laboratory to increase the speed of reactions that proceed slowly at ordinary temperatures. In many cases, the rate of a reaction in a homogeneous system is approximately doubled by an increase in temperature of only 10°C. This rule is a rough approximation, however, and applies only to reactions that last longer than a second or two.

The photograph at the beginning of this chapter illustrates the important effect of temperature on the rates at which reactions occur. A warm lizard runs faster than a cold one, because the chemical reactions that move its muscles occur more rapidly at higher temperatures than at lower ones.

4. Concentration of the Reactants. At a fixed temperature, the rate of a given reaction depends on the concentration of the reactants. Reaction rates often increase when the concentration of one or more of the reactants increases. For example, the rate at which limestone ($CaCO_3$) deteriorates as a result of reaction with the pollutant sulfur dioxide depends on the amount of sulfur dioxide in the air (Fig. 14.5). In a highly

Figure 14.4

Iron powder reacts rapidly with dilute hydrochloric acid because the powder has a large total surface area. An iron horseshoe nail reacts more slowly.

Grain dust (very finely divided grain) can burn at an explosive rate. If the dust is suspended in a confined space, such as a grain elevator, an explosion can result. A grain dust explosion in this storage elevator destroyed several silos.

Hydrogen peroxide foams when dropped on a piece of liver because an enzyme in the liver catalyzes its decomposition to oxygen and water. Note that the H_2O_2 in the beaker does not appear to be decomposing.

polluted atmosphere where the concentration of sulfur dioxide is high, it deteriorates more rapidly than in less polluted air. Similarly, Fig. 14.6 shows that phosphorus burns much more rapidly in an atmosphere of pure oxygen than in air, which is only about 20 percent oxygen.

5. The Presence of a Catalyst. Many reactions can be accelerated by catalysts (Section 2.12), substances that affect the rates of chemical reactions but are not themselves used up by the reactions. The catalytic converter (Fig. 14.7) in an automobile exhaust system contains a catalyst that increases the rates of oxidation of CO and unburned hydrocarbons (to CO_2 and H_2O) as well as the rates of decomposition of nitrogen oxides (to N_2 and O_2), so that the polluting carbon monoxide, hydrocarbons, and nitrogen oxides are destroyed before they leave the exhaust system.

Many biological reactions are catalyzed by enzymes, which are complex substances produced by living organisms. For example, a pure solution of sugar in water does not react with oxygen, even over a period of years. However, an enzyme produced by yeast cells catalyzes the reaction between sugar and oxygen, boosting its rate so much that alcohol forms in a matter of hours. A solution of hydrogen peroxide decomposes to oxygen and water, but complete decomposition can take months if no catalyst is present. However, you may have noticed that hydrogen peroxide foams when it is applied to an open cut. An enzyme in the body catalyzes the decomposition of hydrogen peroxide, and the rapid evolution of oxygen gas causes the foaming.

🔵.3 Rate Equations

We can describe the relationship between the rate of a chemical reaction and the concentration of the reactants quantitatively by using an equation based on experimental mea-

Figure 14.6
Phosphorus burns much more rapidly in an atmosphere of 100% oxygen (left) than in air (right), which is only about 20% oxygen. The amount of light produced per second is greater for the faster reaction, so the flame is brighter.

surements. Such equations are referred to as **rate equations** or **rate laws.** In general, a rate equation has the form

$$\text{Rate} = k[A]^m[B]^n[C]^p \ldots$$

in which [A], [B], and [C] represent molar concentrations of reactants (or sometimes products or other substances), k is the **rate constant** for the particular reaction at a particular temperature, and the exponents m, n, and p are usually positive integers (although fractions and negative numbers sometimes appear). *Both k and the exponents m, n, and p must be determined experimentally by observing the variation in the rate of a reaction as the concentrations of the reactants are varied.*

We have seen that the rate of decomposition of hydrogen peroxide (Table 14.1) decreases with decreasing concentration. The rate at any instant of time can be read from the curve shown in Fig. 14.2 and is directly proportional to the concentration of hydrogen peroxide at that time.

$$\text{Rate} = k[H_2O_2] \tag{1}$$

The brackets have their customary meaning; they indicate the molar concentration of H_2O_2. The rate constant k is independent of the concentration of H_2O_2, but it does vary

Figure 14.7
A catalytic converter used to decrease pollutants in the exhaust of automobiles.

with temperature. At 40°C, k is 3.2×10^{-5} s^{-1}; at 50°C, $k = 7.2 \times 10^{-5}$ s^{-1}. The rate for the reaction of hydrochloric acid with sodium hydroxide is described by a similar expression:

$$\text{Rate} = k[H_3O^+][OH^-] \tag{2}$$

In this equation, k stands for a different quantity than in Equation (1), because the rate constant depends on the nature of the reacting substances. The value of k in Equation (2) is 1.4×10^{11} L mol^{-1} s^{-1}.

The following examples illustrate how experimental rate data can be used to determine rate equations.

Example 14.2

One of the reactions occurring in the ozone layer in the upper atmosphere is the combination of nitric oxide, NO, with ozone, O_3.

$$NO + O_3 \longrightarrow NO_2 + O_2$$

This reaction has been studied in the laboratory, and the following rate data reflect what was observed at 25°C.

[NO], mol L^{-1}	[O$_3$], mol L^{-1}	$\dfrac{\Delta[NO_2]}{\Delta t}$, mol L^{-1} s^{-1}
1.00×10^{-6}	3.00×10^{-6}	0.660×10^{-4}
1.00×10^{-6}	6.00×10^{-6}	1.32×10^{-4}
1.00×10^{-6}	9.00×10^{-6}	1.98×10^{-4}
2.00×10^{-6}	9.00×10^{-6}	3.96×10^{-4}
3.00×10^{-6}	9.00×10^{-6}	5.94×10^{-4}

Determine the rate equation and the rate constant for the reaction at 25°C.

The rate equation will have the form

$$\text{Rate} = k[NO]^m[O_3]^n$$

The values of m and n must be determined from the experimental data. In the first three lines in the data table, [NO] is constant and [O$_3$] varies. The reaction rate changes in direct proportion to the change in [O$_3$]. When [O$_3$] doubles, the rate doubles; when [O$_3$] increases by a factor of 3, the rate increases by a factor of 3. Thus the rate is directly proportional to [O$_3$], or

$$\text{Rate} = k'[O_3]$$

Hence n in the rate equation must be equal to 1. Writing [O$_3$] is equivalent to writing [O$_3$]^1.

In the last three lines in the data table, [NO] varies as [O$_3$] is constant. When [NO] doubles, the rate doubles, and when [NO] triples, the rate also triples. Thus the rate is also directly proportional to [NO], and m in the rate equation is also equal to 1.

The rate equation is thus

$$\text{Rate} = k[NO][O_3]$$

The value of k can be determined from one set of concentrations and the corresponding rate.

$$k = \frac{\text{Rate}}{[NO][O_3]}$$

$$= \frac{0.660 \times 10^{-4} \text{ mol L}^{-1} \text{ s}^{-1}}{(1.00 \times 10^{-6} \text{ mol L}^{-1})(3.00 \times 10^{-6} \text{ mol L}^{-1})}$$

$$= 2.20 \times 10^7 \text{ L mol}^{-1} \text{ s}^{-1}$$

In Example 14.2 the exponents m and n in the rate equation happen to be the same as the coefficients in the chemical equation for the reaction. This is not always the case, as the following example illustrates.

Example 14.3

Acetaldehyde decomposes when heated to yield methane and carbon monoxide according to the equation

$$CH_3CHO(g) \xrightarrow{\Delta} CH_4(g) + CO(g)$$

Determine the rate equation and the rate constant for the reaction from the following experimental data:

$[CH_3CHO]$, mol L^{-1}	$\dfrac{\Delta[CH_3CHO]}{\Delta t}$, mol L^{-1} s^{-1}
1.75×10^{-3}	2.06×10^{-11}
3.50×10^{-3}	8.24×10^{-11}
7.00×10^{-3}	3.30×10^{-10}

The rate equation will have the form

$$\text{Rate} = k[CH_3CHO]^n$$

From the experimental data we can see that when $[CH_3CHO]$ doubles, the rate increases by a factor of 4; when $[CH_3CHO]$ increases by a factor of 4, the rate increases by a factor of 16. Thus the rate is proportional to the square of the concentration, or

$$\text{Rate} = k[CH_3CHO]^2$$

The value of k can be determined from one concentration and the corresponding rate.

$$k = \frac{\text{Rate}}{[CH_3CHO]^2}$$

$$= \frac{3.30 \times 10^{-10} \text{ mol L}^{-1} \text{ s}^{-1}}{(7.0 \times 10^{-3} \text{ mol L}^{-1})^2}$$

$$= 6.73 \times 10^{-6} \text{ L mol}^{-1} \text{ s}^{-1}$$

It is not unusual for a rate equation not to reflect the overall stoichiometry of a chemical reaction. In some cases one or more of the reactants may not even appear in the rate equation (see Example 14.4).

14.4 Order of a Reaction

One way to describe the effect of the concentrations of reactants on the rate of a reaction is to use the order of the reaction. **The order with respect to one of the reactants is equal to the power to which the concentration of that reactant is raised in the rate equation.**

Consider a reaction for which the rate equation is

$$\text{Rate} = k[A]^m[B]^n$$

If the exponent m is 1, the reaction is **first order** with respect to reactant A (or first order in A, as is sometimes said). If n is 1, the reaction is first order with respect to reactant B. The rate of a reaction that is first order with respect to a reactant is directly proportional to the concentration of that reactant. If m is 2, the reaction is **second order** with respect to A. If n is 2, the reaction is second order in B. The rate of a reaction that is second order with respect to a reactant is proportional to the square of the concentration of that reactant. If n or m is zero, the reaction is **zero order** with respect to the reactant A or B, respectively, and the rate of the reaction does not change as the concentration of that reactant changes. Note that $[B]^0$ is equal to 1 whatever the value of $[B]$.

The overall order of a reaction is the sum of the orders with respect to each reactant. If $m = 1$ and $n = 1$, the reaction is first order in A and first order in B. The overall order of the reaction is given by $m + n$; therefore the overall order of the reaction in this particular case is second order.

Example 14.4

Experiment shows that the reaction of nitrogen dioxide with carbon monoxide,

$$NO_2(g) + CO(g) \longrightarrow NO(g) + CO_2(g)$$

is second order in NO_2 and zero order in CO at 100°C. What is the rate equation for the reaction?

The rate equation will have the form

$$\text{Rate} = k[NO_2]^m[CO]^n$$

The reaction is second order in NO_2; thus $m = 2$. The reaction is zero order in CO; thus $n = 0$. The rate equation is

$$\text{Rate} = k[NO_2]^2[CO]^0 = k[NO_2]^2$$

Remember that a number raised to the zero power is equal to 1, so $[CO]^0 = 1$.

Example 14.5

What are the orders with respect to each reactant and the overall order of the reaction

$$NO(g) + O_3(g) \longrightarrow NO_2(g) + O_2(g)$$

in Example 14.2, Section 14.3?

The rate equation for the reaction was found to be

$$\text{Rate} = k[\text{NO}][\text{O}_3]$$

Thus the reaction is first order with respect to both NO and O_3. The overall reaction is second order because the sum of the exponents is 2.

The rate equation for the reaction

$$\text{H}_2(g) + 2\text{NO}(g) \longrightarrow \text{N}_2\text{O}(g) + \text{H}_2\text{O}(g)$$

is

$$\text{Rate} = k[\text{NO}]^2[\text{H}_2]$$

What are the orders with respect to each reactant, and what is the overall order of the reaction?

Example 14.6

The reaction is second order with respect to NO and first order with respect to H_2. The overall reaction is third order, because the sum of the exponents $(2 + 1)$ is 3.

⑭.5 Half-Life of a Reaction

The half-life of a reaction, $t_{1/2}$, is the time required for half of the original concentration of the limiting reactant to be consumed. In each succeeding half-life, half of the remaining concentration of the reactant is used up. Figure 14.1, which illustrates the decomposition of hydrogen peroxide, displays the concentration after each of several successive half-lives. During the first half-life (from 0 seconds to 21,600 seconds), the concentration decreases from 1.000 M to 0.500 M. During the second half-life (from 21,600 seconds to 43,200 seconds), it decreases from 0.500 M to 0.250 M; during the third half-life, it decreases from 0.250 M to 0.125 M. The concentration decreases by half during each successive period of 21,600 seconds. The decomposition of hydrogen peroxide is a first-order reaction, and, as shown below, the half-life of a first-order reaction is independent of the concentration of the reactant. However, half-lives of higher-order reactions depend on the concentrations of the reactants.

First-Order Reactions

An equation relating the rate constant k to the initial concentration $[A_0]$ and the concentration $[A]$ present after any given time t can be derived for a first-order reaction. The derivation requires more advanced mathematics than we have been using, so we will not present it here, but the resulting equation is

$$\ln \frac{[A_0]}{[A]} = kt \qquad (1)$$

In this equation, ln is the notation for a natural logarithm, a logarithm to the base e. If $\ln x = y$, then $y = e^x$, where e is a constant equal to 2.7183 (to five significant figures). In terms of common logarithms to the base 10, $\ln x = 2.303 \log x$. (See Appendix A.3 for more discussion on logarithms and exponents.)

Example 14.7

The rate constant for the first-order decomposition of cyclobutane, C_4H_8 (see Section 14.9), at 500°C is 9.2×10^{-3} s^{-1}. How long will it take for 80.0% of a sample of 0.100 M C_4H_8 to decompose—that is, for the concentration of C_4H_8 to decrease to 0.0200 M?

The initial concentration of C_4H_8, $[A_0]$, is 0.100 mol L^{-1}; the concentration at time t, $[A]$, is 0.0200 mol L^{-1}; and k is 9.2×10^{-3} s^{-1}.

$$\ln \frac{[A_0]}{[A]} = kt$$

$$t = \ln \frac{[A_0]}{[A]} \times \frac{1}{k}$$

$$= \ln \left(\frac{0.100 \text{ mol L}^{-1}}{0.0200 \text{ mol L}^{-1}} \right) \times \frac{1}{9.2 \times 10^{-3} \text{ s}^{-1}}$$

$$= 1.609 \times \frac{1}{9.2 \times 10^{-3} \text{ s}^{-1}}$$

$$= 1.7 \times 10^2 \text{ s}$$

The equation for determining the half-life for a first-order reaction can be derived from Equation (1) as follows.

$$\ln \frac{[A_0]}{[A]} = kt$$

$$t = \ln \frac{[A_0]}{[A]} \times \frac{1}{k}$$

If the time t is the half-life, $t_{1/2}$, the concentration of A at the end of this time is equal to $\frac{1}{2}$ of the initial concentration. Hence, at time $t_{1/2}$, $[A] = \frac{1}{2}[A_0]$.

Therefore

$$t_{1/2} = \ln \frac{[A_0]}{\frac{1}{2}[A_0]} \times \frac{1}{k}$$

$$= \ln 2 \times \frac{1}{k} = \frac{0.693}{k}$$

Thus

$$t_{1/2} = \frac{0.693}{k} \qquad (2)$$

You can see in Equation (2) that the half-life of a first-order reaction is inversely proportional to the rate constant k. A fast reaction has a large k and a short half-life; a slow reaction has a smaller k and a longer half-life.

Example 14.8

Calculate the rate constant for the first-order decomposition of hydrogen peroxide in water at 40°C, using the data given in Fig. 14.1.

The half-life for the decomposition of H_2O_2 is 2.16×10^4 s.

$$t_{1/2} = \frac{0.693}{k}$$

$$k = \frac{0.693}{t_{1/2}} = \frac{0.693}{2.16 \times 10^4 \text{ s}} = 3.21 \times 10^{-5} \text{ s}^{-1}$$

Second-Order Reactions

The equations that relate the concentrations of reactants and the rate constant of second-order reactions are fairly complicated. We will limit ourselves to two of the simpler cases: (1) reactions that are second order with respect to one reactant and (2) second-order reactions that are first order with respect to each of two reactants, but only for the special case in which the initial concentrations of both reactants are the same. In such cases, the equation relating the rate constant k to the initial concentration $[A_0]$ of any of the reactants, and to the concentration $[A]$ present after any given time t, is

$$\frac{1}{[A]} - \frac{1}{[A_0]} = kt \qquad (3)$$

Example 14.9

The reaction of an organic ester (a compound with the general formula RCOOR′, where R and R′ are alkyl groups; Chapter 30) with a strong base is second order with a rate constant equal to 4.50 L mol^{-1} min^{-1}. If the initial concentrations of ester and base are both 0.0200 M, what is the concentration remaining after 10.0 min?

$$\frac{1}{[A]} - \frac{1}{[A_0]} = kt$$

We know that $[A_0] = 0.0200$ mol L^{-1}, $k = 4.50$ L mol^{-1} min^{-1}, and $t = 10.0$ min. Therefore,

$$\frac{1}{[A]} - \frac{1}{0.0200 \text{ mol L}^{-1}} = 4.50 \text{ L mol}^{-1} \text{ min}^{-1} \times 10.0 \text{ min}$$

or

$$\frac{1}{[A]} = 4.50 \text{ L mol}^{-1} \text{ min}^{-1} \times 10.0 \text{ min} + \frac{1}{0.0200 \text{ mol L}^{-1}}$$

$$= 45.0 \text{ L mol}^{-1} + \frac{1}{0.0200} \text{ mol}^{-1} \text{ L}$$

$$= 45.0 \text{ L mol}^{-1} + 50.0 \text{ L mol}^{-1}$$

$$= 95.0 \text{ L mol}^{-1}$$

Then

$$[A] = \frac{1}{95.0 \text{ L mol}^{-1}} = 0.0105 \text{ mol L}^{-1}$$

Hence 0.0105 mol of both the ester and the strong base remains per liter at the end of 10.0 min, compared to the 0.0200 mol per liter of each that was originally present.

The equation used for calculating the half-life of a second-order reaction in which the initial concentrations of both reactants are the same can be derived from Equation (3) as follows:

$$\frac{1}{[A]} - \frac{1}{[A_0]} = kt$$

If $t = t_{1/2}$, then

$$[A] = \tfrac{1}{2}[A_0]$$

Therefore,

$$\frac{1}{\tfrac{1}{2}[A_0]} - \frac{1}{[A_0]} = \frac{1 - \tfrac{1}{2}}{\tfrac{1}{2}[A_0]} = kt$$

$$\frac{\tfrac{1}{2}}{\tfrac{1}{2}[A_0]} = \frac{1}{[A_0]} = kt$$

Thus

$$t_{1/2} = \frac{1}{k[A_0]} \qquad (4)$$

For a second-order reaction, $t_{1/2}$ depends on the concentration, and the half-life increases as the reaction proceeds because the concentrations of reactants decrease. The half-life of a first-order reaction is independent of the concentration. Consequently, the use of the half-life concept is more complex for second-order reactions. For example, the rate constant of a second-order reaction cannot be calculated directly from the half-life unless the initial concentration is known; this is not true for first-order reactions.

Example 14.10

Calculate the half-life for the second-order reaction described in Example 14.9 ($k = 4.50$ L mol^{-1} min^{-1}) if the initial concentrations of both reactants are 0.0200 M.

The half-life of the second-order reaction in Example 14.9 can be calculated from the equation

$$t_{1/2} = \frac{1}{k[A_0]}$$

Thus

$$t_{1/2} = \frac{1}{k[A_0]} = \frac{1}{(4.50 \text{ L mol}^{-1} \text{ min}^{-1})(0.0200 \text{ mol L}^{-1})} = 11.1 \text{ min}$$

Example 14.11

What is the half-life for the reaction in Examples 14.9 and 14.10 if the initial concentrations of both reactants are 0.0300 M?

$$t_{1/2} = \frac{1}{k[A_0]} = \frac{1}{(4.50 \text{ L mol}^{-1} \text{ min}^{-1})(0.0300 \text{ mol L}^{-1})} = 7.41 \text{ min}$$

The increase in the initial concentrations from 0.0200 M to 0.0300 M shortens the half-life for this particular reaction from 11.1 min (Example 14.10) to 7.41 min.

The Molecular Explanation of Reaction Rates

🟊.6 Collision Theory of the Reaction Rate

Chemists believe that before atoms, molecules, or ions can react, they must collide with one another. In a few reactions every collision between reactants leads to products, and the rates of such reactions are determined solely by how rapidly the reactants can diffuse together. These reactions are called **diffusion-controlled reactions.** Diffusion-controlled reactions are very fast; hence they have large rate constants. For a typical diffusion-controlled second-order gas-phase reaction at 25°C, such as the reaction of an oxygen atom with a nitrogen molecule,

$$O + N_2 \longrightarrow NO + N$$

the rate constant falls in the range 10^{10} to 10^{12} L mol^{-1} s^{-1}. The diffusion-controlled reaction between hydronium ions and hydroxide ions in water at 25°C,

$$H_3O^+ + OH^- \longrightarrow 2H_2O$$

has a rate constant of 1.4×10^{11} L mol^{-1} s^{-1}. At these rates, more than 95% of the reactants would be consumed in 10^{-11} second.

Most reactions, however, occur at a much slower rate, because only a very small fraction of the collisions in these slower reactions give products. In the majority of collisions, the reactants simply bounce away unchanged. For a collision to lead to a reaction, the following two things must occur:

1. The colliding species must be oriented in such a way that the atoms that are bonded together in the product come into contact.
2. The collision must occur with enough energy for the valence shells of the reacting species to penetrate into each other so that the electrons can rearrange and form new bonds (and new chemical species).

The gas-phase reaction of nitrogen dioxide with carbon monoxide,

$$NO_2 + CO \longrightarrow NO + CO_2$$

above 225°C illustrates the factors necessary for effective collision. During the reaction, an oxygen atom is transferred from an NO_2 molecule to a CO molecule. There are many orientations of the NO_2 and CO molecules during collision that do not place an oxygen atom of the NO_2 molecule close to the carbon atom of the CO molecule. Three of these are indicated in Fig. 14.8(a, b, and c). These collisions are not effective in producing a chemical reaction. Only a collision in which an oxygen atom strikes the carbon atom [Fig. 14.8(d)] can produce a reaction.

Even when the orientation is correct, a collision may not lead to reaction. As the oxygen atom of an NO_2 molecule approaches the carbon atom of a CO molecule, the electrons in the two molecules begin to repel each other. Unless the molecules possess a kinetic energy greater than a certain minimum value, the two molecules bounce away from each other before they can get close enough to react. If the molecules are moving fast enough, then the repulsion between their electrons is not strong enough to keep them

Figure 14.8

Some possible collisions between
NO_2 and CO molecules. Only in (d)
are the molecules correctly oriented
for transfer of an oxygen atom from
NO_2 to CO to give NO and CO_2.

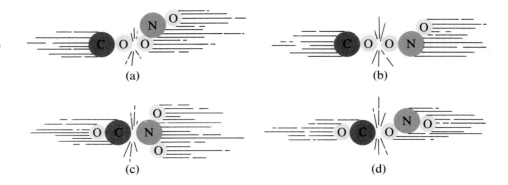

(a)　　　　　　　　　　(b)

(c)　　　　　　　　　　(d)

apart, and the molecules can get close enough for a C—O bond to begin to form as the
N—O bond begins to break. Using dots to represent partially formed or broken bonds,
we can write the resulting species as follows:

$$NO_2 + CO \longrightarrow \left[O \!\!\diagup^{N\cdots O \cdots C \equiv O} \right]$$

The species $O{=}N\cdots O\cdots C{\equiv}O$, which contains the partially formed $C\cdots O$ and the
partially broken $N\cdots O$ bonds, is called the **activated complex, or transition state.** An
activated complex is a combination of reacting molecules that is intermediate between
reactants and products and in which some bonds have weakened and new bonds have
begun to form. Ordinarily, an activated complex cannot be isolated. It breaks down to
give either reactants or products, depending on the conditions under which the reaction
takes place.

$$NO_2 + CO \longrightarrow \left[O \!\!\diagup^{N\cdots O \cdots C \equiv O} \right] \begin{array}{l} \nearrow NO_2 + CO \quad \text{(reactants)} \\ \qquad\qquad \text{or} \\ \searrow NO + CO_2 \quad \text{(products)} \end{array}$$

The collision theory shows why reaction rates increase as concentrations increase.
With increased concentration of any of the reacting substances, the chances for collisions between molecules are increased because more molecules are present per unit of
volume. More collisions mean a faster reaction rate.

⓮.7 Activation Energy and the Arrhenius Equation

The minimum energy necessary to form an activated complex during a collision between
reactants is called the **activation energy, E_a** (Fig. 14.9). In a slow reaction the activation energy is much larger than the average energy content of the molecules. Hence only
a few of the molecules, the fast-moving ones, have relatively high energies. The collisions between the fast-moving molecules are the most likely to result in reactions. In
very fast reactions, the fraction of molecules possessing the necessary activation energy
is large, so most collisions between molecules result in reaction.

The energy relationships for the general reaction of a molecule of A with a molecule
of B to form molecules of C and D are shown in Fig. 14.10.

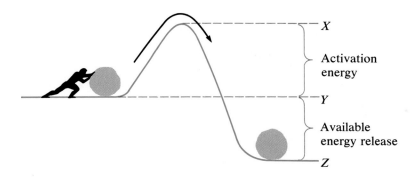

Figure 14.9

Illustration of activation energy. The boulder can release the energy created by falling the distance from height Y to height Z. However, energy must be put into the system (the activation energy) to lift it over the barrier before it can fall to Z. The activation energy is released as the boulder falls through the distance X to Y, and the additional energy is then released as it falls from Y to Z. The net energy released is that provided by the fall from Y to Z.

$$A + B \rightleftharpoons C + D$$

The figure shows that after the activation energy E_a is exceeded, and as C and D begin to form, the system loses energy until its total energy is lower than that of the initial mixture. The forward reaction (that between molecules A and B) therefore tends to take place readily when sufficient energy is available in any one collision to exceed the activation energy E_a. In Fig. 14.10, ΔE represents the difference in energy between the reactants (A and B) and the products (C and D). The sum of E_a and ΔE represents the activation energy for the reverse reaction,

$$C + D \longrightarrow A + B$$

For a given reaction, the rate constant is related to the activation energy by a relationship known as the **Arrhenius equation:**

$$k = A \times e^{-E_a/RT}$$

R is a constant with the value 8.314 J mol^{-1} K^{-1}, T is temperature on the Kelvin scale, E_a is the activation energy in joules per mole, e is the constant 2.7183, and A is a constant called the **frequency factor,** which is related to the frequency of collisions and the orientation of the reacting molecules. A indicates how many collisions have the correct orientation to lead to products. The remainder of the equation, $e^{-E_a/RT}$, gives the fraction of the collisions in which the energy of the reacting species is greater than E_a, the activation energy for the reaction.

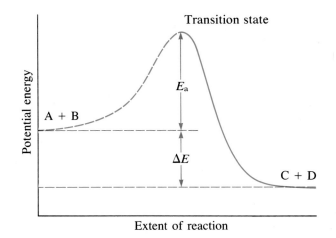

Figure 14.10

Potential energy relationships for the reaction $A + B \rightleftharpoons C + D$. The energy represented by the broken portion of the curve is that for the system with a molecule of A and a molecule of B present. The energy represented by the solid portion of the curve is that for the system with a molecule of C and a molecule of D present. The activation energy for the forward reaction is represented by E_a; the activation energy for the reverse reaction is represented by $(E_a + \Delta E)$. The species present at the peak corresponds to the transition state.

Figure 14.11

As the activation energy of a reaction decreases, the number of molecules with at least this much energy increases, as shown by the yellow shaded areas.

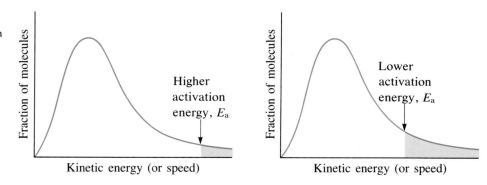

The Arrhenius equation describes quantitatively much of what we have already discussed about reaction rates. Reactions with similar frequency factors but different activation energies E_a have different rate constants, because the rate constants are proportional to $e^{-E_a/RT}$. For two reactions at the same temperature, the reaction with the higher activation energy has the lower rate constant and the slower rate. The larger value of E_a results in a smaller value for $e^{-E_a/RT}$, reflecting the smaller fraction of molecules with sufficient energy to react. Alternatively, the reaction with the smaller E_a has a larger fraction of molecules with enough energy to react (Fig. 14.11). This will be reflected as a larger value of $e^{-E_a/RT}$, a larger rate constant, and a faster rate for the reaction. An increase in temperature has the same effect as a decrease in activation energy. A larger fraction of molecules has the necessary energy to react (Fig. 14.12), as indicated by an increase in the value of $e^{-E_a/RT}$. The rate constant is also directly proportional to the frequency factor, A. Hence a change in conditions or reactants that increases the number of collisions in which the orientation of the molecules is right for reaction results in an increase in A and, consequently, an increase in k.

In order to determine E_a for a reaction, we must measure k at different temperatures and evaluate E_a from the Arrhenius equation. The Arrhenius equation may be rewritten as follows:

$$\ln k = \ln A - \frac{E_a}{RT}$$

A plot of $\ln k$ against $1/T$ gives a straight line with the slope $-E_a/R$, from which E_a may be determined.

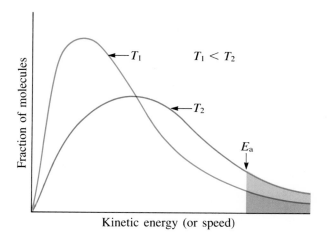

Figure 14.12

At a higher temperature, T_2, more molecules have an energy greater than E_a, as shown by the yellow shaded area.

The variation of the rate constant with temperature for the decomposition of HI(g) to $H_2(g)$ and $I_2(g)$ is given in the following table. What is the activation energy for the reaction?

Example
14.12

T, K	$1/T$, K^{-1}	k, L mol^{-1} s^{-1}	ln k
555	1.80×10^{-3}	3.52×10^{-7}	-14.860
575	1.74×10^{-3}	1.22×10^{-6}	-13.617
645	1.55×10^{-3}	8.59×10^{-5}	-9.362
700	1.43×10^{-3}	1.16×10^{-3}	-6.759
781	1.28×10^{-3}	3.95×10^{-2}	-3.231

A graph of ln k against $1/T$ is given in Fig. 14.13. In order to determine the slope of the line, we need two values of ln k, which are determined from the line at two values of $1/T$ (one near each end of the line is preferable). For example, the value of ln k determined from the line when $1/T = 1.25 \times 10^{-3}$ is -2.593; the value when $1/T = 1.78 \times 10^{-3}$ is -14.447. The slope of this line is given by the following expression:

$$\text{Slope} = \frac{\Delta(\ln k)}{\Delta(1/T)}$$

$$= \frac{(-14.447) - (-2.593)}{(1.78 \times 10^{-3} \text{ K}^{-1}) - (1.25 \times 10^{-3} \text{ K}^{-1})}$$

$$= \frac{-11.854}{0.53 \times 10^{-3} \text{ K}^{-1}} = -2.2 \times 10^4 \text{ K}$$

$$= -\frac{E_a}{R}$$

Thus $\qquad -E_a = \text{slope} \times R = -2.2 \times 10^4 \text{ K} \times 8.314 \text{ J mol}^{-1} \text{ K}^{-1}$

$\qquad E_a = 1.8 \times 10^5 \text{ J mol}^{-1} = 1.8 \times 10^2 \text{ kJ mol}^{-1}$

Figure 14.13

A graph of the linear relationship between ln k and $1/T$ for the reaction $2HI \longrightarrow H_2 + I_2$, according to the Arrhenius equation.

⑭.8 Elementary Reactions

A balanced equation for a chemical reaction indicates what is reacting and what is produced, but it says nothing about how the reaction actually takes place. The process, or pathway, by which a reaction occurs is called the **reaction mechanism,** or the **reaction path.**

Reactions often occur in steps. The decomposition of ozone, for example, is believed to follow a mechanism with two steps:

$$O_3 \longrightarrow O_2 + O \tag{1}$$

$$O + O_3 \longrightarrow 2O_2 \tag{2}$$

The two steps add up to the overall reaction for the decomposition,

$$2O_3 \longrightarrow 3O_2$$

The oxygen atom produced in the first step is used in the second and does not appear as a final product. Species that are produced in one step and consumed in another are called **intermediates.**

Each of the steps in a reaction mechanism is called an **elementary reaction.** Elementary reactions occur exactly as they are written and cannot be broken down into simpler steps. An overall reaction can often be broken down into a number of steps. Although the overall reaction indicates that two molecules of ozone react to give three molecules of oxygen, the reaction path does not involve the collision of two ozone molecules. Instead, a molecule of ozone decomposes to an oxygen molecule and an intermediate oxygen atom, and then the oxygen atom reacts with a second ozone molecule to give two oxygen molecules. These two elementary reactions occur exactly as they are written in Equations (1) and (2).

⑭.9 Unimolecular Elementary Reactions

An elementary reaction is **unimolecular** if the rearrangement of a *single* molecule or ion produces one or more molecules of product. A unimolecular reaction may be one of several elementary reactions in a complex mechanism, or it may be the only reaction in a mechanism. Reaction (1) in Section 14.8,

$$O_3 \longrightarrow O_2 + O$$

illustrates a unimolecular elementary reaction occurring in a two-step reaction mechanism. The gas-phase decomposition of cyclobutane, C_4H_8, to ethylene, C_2H_4, occurs via a one-step unimolecular mechanism.

All that is required for these unimolecular reactions to occur is the separation of parts of single reactant molecules into products. The reaction of cyclobutane also shows that an overall reaction can be an elementary reaction as well.

Chemical bonds do not simply fall apart during chemical reactions. The decomposition of C_4H_8, for example, requires the input of 261 kilojoules of energy per mole to distort the molecules into activated complexes that can decompose into products. (The activation energy for this reaction is 261 kilojoules per mole of C_4H_8 reacting.)

In a sample of C_4H_8, the very few molecules that contain enough energy to form activated complexes react by the process indicated above. Others collide with rapidly moving molecules and pick up additional energy. If this energy is sufficient to form the activated complex, then the activated molecules too can undergo reaction. In effect, a particularly energetic collision knocks the reacting molecules into the geometry of the activated complex. However, only a small fraction of gas molecules travel at sufficiently high speeds with large enough kinetic energies to accomplish this (Fig. 14.11). Hence, at any one time, only a few molecules pick up enough energy from collisions to react.

Doubling the concentration of C_4H_8 molecules in a sample gives twice as many molecules per liter. Although the fraction of molecules with enough energy to react remains the same, the total number of such molecules is twice as great. Consequently, the change in the amount of C_4H_8 per liter and thus the reaction rate ($-\Delta[C_4H_8]/\Delta t$) are twice as great. The reaction rate is directly proportional to the concentration of C_4H_8.

$$\text{Rate} = k[C_4H_8]$$

This relationship applies to any unimolecular elementary reaction; the reaction rate is directly proportional to the concentration of the reactant, and the reaction exhibits first-order behavior. Hence the proportionality constant is the rate constant for the particular unimolecular reaction.

14.10 Bimolecular Elementary Reactions

The collision *and combination* of two reactants to give an activated complex in an elementary reaction is called a **bimolecular reaction.** Equation (2) in Section 14.8,

$$O + O_3 \longrightarrow 2O_2$$

is an example of a bimolecular elementary reaction that occurs in a two-step reaction mechanism. The reaction of nitrogen dioxide with carbon monoxide (Section 14.6) and the decomposition of two hydrogen iodide molecules to give hydrogen, H_2, and iodine, I_2 (Fig. 14.14), are examples of reactions with mechanisms that consist of a single bimolecular elementary reaction.

For the bimolecular elementary reaction

$$A + B \longrightarrow \text{products}$$

the rate equation is first order in A and first order in B.

$$\text{Rate} = k[A][B]$$

Figure 14.14

Probable mechanism for the dissociation of two HI molecules to produce one molecule of H_2 and one molecule of I_2.

Two HI molecules   Transition state   Hydrogen molecule   Iodine molecule

Doubling the concentration of either A or B doubles the total number of molecular collisions (and the number of effective collisions) between molecules A and B. The rate of reaction is doubled. Doubling the concentrations of *both* A and B quadruples the number of collisions and the rate of reaction (Fig. 14.15). If the initial concentrations of both A and B are tripled, then the reaction proceeds nine times as fast. For the bimolecular elementary reaction

$$A + A \longrightarrow products$$

the rate equation is second order in A.

$$Rate = k[A][A] = k[A]^2$$

14.11 Termolecular Elementary Reactions

An elementary **termolecular reaction** involves the simultaneous collision of any combination of three atoms, molecules, or ions. Termolecular elementary reactions are uncommon, because the probability of three particles colliding simultaneously is less than a thousandth of the probability of two particles colliding. There are, however, a few established termolecular elementary reactions. The reaction of nitric oxide with oxygen,

$$2NO + O_2 \longrightarrow 2NO_2$$

Figure 14.15

A schematic representation of the effect of concentration on the number of possible collisions and hence on the rate of reaction.

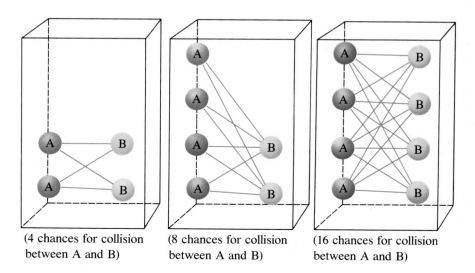

(4 chances for collision between A and B)   (8 chances for collision between A and B)   (16 chances for collision between A and B)

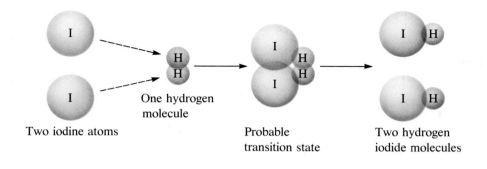

Two iodine atoms   One hydrogen molecule   Probable transition state   Two hydrogen iodide molecules

Figure 14.16

The termolecular step in the mechanism for the reaction of H_2 and I_2 to produce two HI molecules involves two I atoms and one H_2 molecule. The first step (not shown) involves the dissociation of an iodine molecule into two iodine atoms ($I_2 \longrightarrow 2I$). In the termolecular step (shown here) two iodine atoms and one hydrogen molecule combine to produce two HI molecules.

the reaction of nitric oxide with chlorine,

$$2NO + Cl_2 \longrightarrow 2NOCl$$

and the reaction of hydrogen with iodine (Fig. 14.16),

$$H_2 + I_2 \longrightarrow 2HI$$

all involve termolecular steps.

For a termolecular elementary reaction involving three different reactants,

$$A + B + C \longrightarrow products$$

the rate equation is first order in A, B, and C.

$$Rate = k[A][B][C]$$

For the termolecular elementary reaction

$$2A + B \longrightarrow products$$

the rate equation is second order in A and first order in B.

$$Rate = k[A]^2[B]$$

⑭.12 Reaction Mechanisms

The stepwise sequence of elementary reactions that converts reactants into products is called the reaction mechanism, or reaction path. The decomposition of C_4H_8 ($C_4H_8 \longrightarrow 2C_2H_4$), for example, has a one-step mechanism (Section 14.9); the decomposition of ozone ($2O_3 \longrightarrow 3O_2$), a two-step mechanism (Section 14.8). Because elementary reactions involving three or more reactants are rare, it is reasonable to expect that complex reactions take place in several steps.

Even an apparently simple reaction such as the formation of ethylene, C_2H_4, from ethane, C_2H_6, may proceed by a complex mechanism. Ethylene (Section 2.12) may be prepared by the pyrolysis (decomposition by heating) of ethane, a component of natural gas, at temperatures of 500°–800°C.

$$C_2H_6(g) \xrightarrow{\triangle} C_2H_4(g) + H_2(g)$$

The actual mechanism is much more complex than is suggested by this equation and involves three stages:

1. **Initiation.** The reaction begins with a unimolecular reaction in which a C_2H_6 molecule splits at its weakest point, the C—C bond.

$$H-\underset{\underset{H}{|}}{\overset{\overset{H}{|}}{C}}-\underset{\underset{H}{|}}{\overset{\overset{H}{|}}{C}}-H \xrightarrow{\Delta} 2CH_3 \qquad (1)$$

The CH_3 group abstracts a hydrogen atom from another C_2H_6 molecule in a bimolecular reaction.

$$CH_3 + C_2H_6 \longrightarrow CH_4 + C_2H_5 \qquad (2)$$

2. Propagation. The C_2H_5 group undergoes a unimolecular dissociation.

$$C_2H_5 \longrightarrow C_2H_4 + H \qquad (3)$$

The hydrogen atom produced in Equation (3) reacts with another C_2H_6 molecule in a bimolecular reaction.

$$H + C_2H_6 \longrightarrow C_2H_5 + H_2 \qquad (4)$$

The C_2H_5 group produced in Equation (4) reacts according to Equation (3), producing another hydrogen atom to undergo reaction as in Equation (4) and produce another C_2H_5. The reactions given by Equations (3) and (4) produce C_2H_4 and H_2, which are the principal products of the pyrolysis. Normally, each initiation [Equations (1) and (2)] is followed by about a hundred cycles of propagation [Equations (3) and (4)] before termination.

3. Termination. The chain of propagation reactions may be stopped by one of the following bimolecular reactions:

$$2C_2H_5 \longrightarrow C_4H_{10}$$

$$2C_2H_5 \longrightarrow C_2H_4 + C_2H_6$$

The C_2H_5 produced in Equation (4) can react according to Equation (3) to produce another hydrogen atom for Equation (4). This reinitiates the series of elementary reactions represented by Equations (3) and (4), and they repeat themselves over and over. Such a mechanism, involving repeating reactions, is known as a **chain mechanism.**

Some of the elementary reactions in a reaction path are relatively slow. The slowest reaction step determines the maximum rate, because a reaction can proceed no faster than its slowest step. The slowest step, therefore, is the **rate-determining step** of the reaction.

We can write the rate equation for each elementary reaction in a reaction mechanism (Sections 14.9–14.11), but *we cannot write a correct rate equation or establish the order for an overall reaction simply by inspection of the overall balanced equation.* We must determine the overall rate equation from experimental data and deduce the mechanism from the rate equation (and sometimes from other data). The reaction of NO_2 and CO (Sections 14.4 and 14.6) is an excellent example.

$$NO_2 + CO \longrightarrow CO_2 + NO$$

For temperatures above 225°C, the rate equation has been found to be

$$\text{Rate} = k[NO_2][CO]$$

For temperatures above 225°C, therefore, the reaction is first order with respect to NO_2 and first order with respect to CO. This is consistent with a single-step bimolecular mechanism.

At temperatures below 225°C, the reaction is described by a rate equation that is second order in NO_2:

$$\text{Rate} = k[NO_2]^2$$

This is consistent with a mechanism that involves the following two elementary reactions, the first of which is slow and is therefore the rate-determining step:

$$NO_2 + NO_2 \longrightarrow NO_3 + NO \qquad \text{(slow)}$$

$$NO_3 + CO \longrightarrow NO_2 + CO_2 \qquad \text{(fast)}$$

(The sum of the two equations gives the net overall reaction.)

In general, when the rate-determining step is the first step, it provides the rate equation for the overall mechanism. However, when the rate-determining step occurs later in the mechanism, the rate equation may be complex. The oxidation of iodide ion by hydrogen peroxide illustrates this point.

$$H_2O_2 + 3I^- + 2H_3O^+ \longrightarrow 4H_2O + I_3^-$$

In a solution with a high concentration of acid, one reaction pathway has the following rate equation:

$$\text{Rate} = k[H_2O_2][I^-][H_3O^+]$$

This rate equation is consistent with several mechanisms, three of which follow:

Mechanism A

$$H_2O_2 + H_3O^+ + I^- \longrightarrow 2H_2O + HOI \qquad \text{(slow)}$$

$$HOI + H_3O^+ + I^- \longrightarrow 2H_2O + I_2 \qquad \text{(fast)}$$

$$I_2 + I^- \longrightarrow I_3^- \qquad \text{(fast)}$$

Mechanism B

$$H_3O + I^- \longrightarrow HI + H_2O \qquad \text{(fast)}$$

$$H_2O_2 + HI \longrightarrow H_2O + HOI \qquad \text{(slow)}$$

$$HOI + H_3O^+ + I^- \longrightarrow 2H_2O + I_2 \qquad \text{(fast)}$$

$$I_2 + I^- \longrightarrow I_3^- \qquad \text{(fast)}$$

Mechanism C

$$H_3O^+ + H_2O_2 \longrightarrow H_3O_2^+ + H_2O \qquad \text{(fast)}$$

$$H_3O_2^+ + I^- \longrightarrow H_2O + HOI \qquad \text{(slow)}$$

$$HOI + H_3O^+ + I^- \longrightarrow 2H_2O + I_2 \qquad \text{(fast)}$$

$$I_2 + I^- \longrightarrow I_3^- \qquad \text{(fast)}$$

In mechanism A the slow step is the first elementary reaction, so the rate equation for the overall reaction is equal to that for this step. In mechanisms B and C the rate-determining step is the second elementary reaction, and the overall rate equation is not simply the rate equation for this step. To derive the rate equations for mechanisms B and C requires some familiarity with equilibrium constants, which will be introduced in the next chapter. However, because mechanisms A, B, and C all have the same overall rate equation, it is not possible to distinguish among them on this basis alone. Additional experimental information is required to distinguish which reaction pathway actually leads to product. Moreover, the rate equation provides no information about what happens after the rate-determining step. The subsequent steps must be worked out from other chemical knowledge or from other measurements.

The determination of the mechanism of a reaction is important in selecting conditions that provide a good yield of the desired product. Knowing a reaction's mechanism sometimes helps a chemist to prepare a previously unknown compound. Compared to the number of known chemical reactions, rather few reaction mechanisms have been completely characterized. The study of reaction mechanisms, or the **kinetics of reaction,** is a very active research area.

🔟₄.13 Catalysts

The rate of many reactions can be accelerated by catalysts (Section 14.2). Such substances may be divided into two general classes: **homogeneous catalysts** and **heterogeneous catalysts.**

Homogeneous Catalysts

A homogeneous catalyst is present in the same phase as the reactants. It interacts with a reactant to form an intermediate substance, which then decomposes or reacts with another reactant to regenerate the original catalyst and give product.

The ozone in the stratosphere (the upper atmosphere) that protects the earth from ultraviolet radiation is formed when ultraviolet light interacts with oxygen molecules. As shown in Section 14.8, ozone decomposes by the following mechanism:

$$O_3(g) \longrightarrow O_2(g) + O(g) \tag{1}$$

$$O(g) + O_3(g) \longrightarrow 2O_2(g) \tag{2}$$

The rate of decomposition of ozone is influenced by the presence of nitric oxide, NO. Nitric oxide catalyzes the decomposition of ozone by the following mechanism:

$$NO(g) + O_3(g) \longrightarrow NO_2(g) + O_2(g) \tag{3}$$

$$O_3(g) \longrightarrow O_2(g) + O(g) \tag{4}$$

$$NO_2(g) + O(g) \longrightarrow NO(g) + O_2(g) \tag{5}$$

The overall chemical change for Equations (3) through (5) is the same as for Equations (1) and (2):

$$2O_3 \longrightarrow 3O_2$$

Because the nitric oxide is not permanently used up in these reactions, it is a catalyst. The rate of decomposition of ozone is greater in the presence of nitric oxide because of the catalytic activity of NO. Certain compounds that contain chlorine also catalyze the decomposition of ozone (Section 22.7).

As we noted in Section 14.2, the rates of many biological reactions are increased by enzymes, organic molecules that act as catalysts (see Section 31.5).

Heterogeneous Catalysts

Heterogeneous catalysts act by furnishing a surface at which a reaction can occur. Typically, gas-phase and liquid-phase reactions catalyzed by heterogeneous catalysts occur on the surface of the catalyst rather than within the gas or liquid phase.

Heterogeneous catalysis has at least four steps: (1) adsorption of the reactant onto the surface of the catalyst, (2) activation of the adsorbed reactant, (3) reaction of the adsorbed reactant, and (4) diffusion of the product from the surface into the gas or liquid phase (desorption). Any one of these steps may be slow and thus may be the rate-determining step. In general, however, the overall rate of the reaction is faster than it would be if the reactants were in the gas or liquid phase. The steps that are believed to occur in the reaction of compounds containing a carbon–carbon double bond with hydrogen on a nickel catalyst are illustrated in Fig. 14.17. This is the catalyst used in the hydrogenation of polyunsaturated fats and oils (which contain several carbon–carbon double bonds) to produce saturated fats and oils (which contain only carbon–carbon single bonds).

Other significant industrial processes that involve the use of heterogeneous catalysts include the preparation of sulfuric acid (Section 2.12), the preparation of ammonia (Section 2.12), the oxidation of ammonia to nitric acid (Section 23.14), and the synthesis of methanol, CH_3OH (Section 30.9). Heterogeneous catalysts are also used in the catalytic converters found on most gasoline-powered automobiles (Fig. 14.7).

Both homogeneous and heterogeneous catalysts function by providing a reaction path that has a lower activation energy than would be found in the absence of the catalyst (Fig. 14.18). This lower activation energy results in an increase in rate (Section 14.7). Note that a catalyst decreases the activation energy for both the forward and the reverse reactions and hence *accelerates both the forward and the reverse reactions*.

Figure 14.17

Steps in the catalysis by nickel of the reaction $C_2H_4 + H_2 \longrightarrow C_2H_6$. Both molecules are adsorbed by weak attractive forces. Activation occurs when the bonding electrons in the molecules rearrange to form bonds to metal atoms. Following the reaction of the activated atoms, the weakly adsorbed C_2H_6 molecule escapes from the surface.

Figure 14.18

Potential energy diagram showing the
effect of a catalyst on the activation
energy of a reaction.

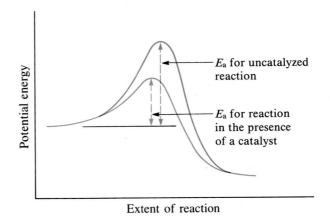

E_a for uncatalyzed
reaction

E_a for reaction
in the presence
of a catalyst

Extent of reaction

Some substances, called **inhibitors,** decrease the rate of a chemical reaction. In
many cases, these are substances that react with and ''poison'' some catalyst in the
system and thereby prevent its action. Many biological poisons are inhibitors that reduce
the catalytic activity of an organism's enzymes. Catalytic converters are poisoned by
lead, so lead-free fuels must be used in automobiles equipped with such converters.

For Review

Summary

The **rate** at which a chemical reaction proceeds can be defined as either the decrease in
concentration of a reactant or the increase in concentration of a product per unit of time.
In general, the rate of a given reaction increases as the temperature or the concentration
of a reactant increases. The rate of a reaction can also be increased by a **catalyst,** a
substance that increases the rate of a reaction but is not permanently changed by the
reaction. Reactions involving two phases proceed more rapidly the more finely divided
the condensed phase. The rate of a given reaction can be described by an experimentally
determined **rate equation** of the form

$$\text{Rate} = k[A]^m[B]^n[C]^p \ldots$$

in which [A], [B], and [C] represent molar concentrations of reactants (or sometimes
products or other substances); m, n, and p are usually, but not always, positive integers;
and k is the rate constant. The exponents, m, n, p, etc., describe the **order of the
reaction** with respect to each specific reactant. The **overall order of the reaction** is the
sum of the exponents. The **half-life** of a reaction is the time required for half of the
original reactant to be consumed.

Before atoms, molecules, or ions can react, they must collide. When every collision
leads to reaction, the rate is controlled by how rapidly the reactants diffuse together.
These **diffusion-controlled reactions** are very fast. Most reactions occur more slowly
because the reacting species must be oriented correctly when they collide and because
they must possess a certain minimum energy, the **activation energy,** in order to form an

activated complex, or transition state. The rate constant for a reaction is related to these effects by the **Arrhenius equation:**

$$k = A \times e^{-E_a/RT}$$

The collection of individual steps, or **elementary reactions,** by which reactants are converted into products during the course of an overall reaction is called the **reaction mechanism,** or **reaction path.** The overall rate of a reaction is determined by the rate of the slowest step, the **rate-determining step.** Although it is not possible to write a rate equation for an overall reaction without data from experimental observations, once the elementary reactions have been determined, rate equations can be written by inspection for each elementary reaction. **Unimolecular elementary reactions** have first-order rate equations, **bimolecular elementary reactions** have second-order rate equations, and **termolecular elementary reactions** (which are uncommon) have third-order rate equations.

Key Terms and Concepts

activated complex (14.6)	diffusion-controlled reaction (14.6)	rate-determining step (14.12)
activation energy (14.7)	elementary reaction (14.8)	rate equation (14.3)
Arrhenius equation (14.7)	frequency factor (14.7)	rate of reaction (14.1)
bimolecular reaction (14.10)	half-life of a reaction (14.5)	reaction mechanism (14.8, 14.12)
catalysts (14.13)	heterogeneous catalysts (14.13)	termolecular reaction (14.11)
chain mechanism (14.12)	homogeneous catalysts (14.13)	transition state (14.6)
collision theory of the reaction rate (14.6)	order of reaction (14.4)	unimolecular reaction (14.9)
	rate constant (14.3)	

early stuff + prpl ex)
are more imp., but read + try
to understand later stuff

Exercises

Answers for selected even-numbered exercises marked by red numbers appear at the end of the book. The worked-out solutions to all even-numbered exercises appear in the *Solutions Guide*.

Reaction Rates and Rate Equations

1. Explain how each of the factors that determine the rate of a reaction is responsible for changing the rate.
2. How do the rate of a reaction and its rate constant differ?
3. Doubling the concentration of a reactant increases the rate of a reaction four times. What is the order of the reaction with respect to that reactant?
4. Nitrogen(II) oxide reacts with chlorine according to the equation

$$2NO(g) + Cl_2(g) \longrightarrow 2NOCl(g)$$

The following initial rates of reaction have been observed for certain reactant concentrations.

[NO], mol L^{-1}	[Cl_2], mol L^{-1}	Rate, mol L^{-1} h^{-1}
0.50	0.50	1.14
1.00	0.50	4.56
1.00	1.00	9.12

What is the rate equation that describes the rate's dependence on the concentrations of NO and Cl_2?

5. The rate constant for the decomposition at 45°C of dinitrogen pentaoxide, N_2O_5, dissolved in chloroform, $CHCl_3$, is 6.2×10^{-4} min^{-1}.

$$2N_2O_5 \longrightarrow 4NO_2 + O_2$$

The decomposition is first order in N_2O_5.
(a) What is the rate of the reaction when [N_2O_5] = 0.40 M?
(b) What is the concentration of N_2O_5 remaining at the end of 1 h if the initial concentration of N_2O_5 was 0.40 M?

6. One of the reactions involved in the formation of photochemical smogs is

$$O_3(g) + NO(g) \longrightarrow O_2(g) + NO_2(g)$$

The rate constant for this reaction is 1.2×10^7 L mol^{-1} s^{-1}. The reaction is first order in O_3 and first order in NO. Calculate the rate of formation of NO_2 in air in which the O_3 concentration is 2×10^{-8} M and the NO concentration 7×10^{-8} M.

7. Most of the nearly 16 billion pounds of HNO_3 produced in the United States during 1989 was prepared by the following sequence of reactions, each run in a separate reaction vessel.

$$4NH_3(g) + 5O_2(g) \longrightarrow 4NO(g) + 6H_2O(g) \quad (1)$$

$$2NO(g) + O_2(g) \longrightarrow 2NO_2(g) \quad (2)$$

$$3NO_2(g) + H_2O(l) \longrightarrow 2HNO_3(aq) + NO(g) \quad (3)$$

The first reaction is run by burning ammonia in air over a platinum catalyst. This reaction is fast. The reaction in Equation (3) is also fast. The second reaction limits the rate at which nitric acid can be prepared from ammonia. If Equation (2) is second order in NO and first order in O_2, what is the rate of formation of NO_2 when the oxygen concentration is 0.50 M and the nitric oxide concentration is 0.75 M? The rate constant for the reaction is 5.8×10^{-6} L^2 mol^{-2} s^{-1}.

8. Nitrosyl chloride, NOCl, decomposes to NO and Cl_2.

$$2NOCl(g) \longrightarrow 2NO(g) + Cl_2(g)$$

Determine the rate equation and the rate constant for this reaction from the following data:

[NOCl], M	0.20	0.40	0.60
Rate, mol L^{-1} s^{-1}	1.60×10^{-9}	6.40×10^{-9}	1.44×10^{-8}

9. Hydrogen reacts with nitrogen(II) oxide to form nitrogen(I) oxide, (laughing gas) according to the equation

$$H_2(g) + NO(g) \longrightarrow N_2O(g) + H_2O(g)$$

Determine the rate equation and the rate constant for the reaction from the following data:

[NO], M	0.30	0.60	0.60
[H₂], M	0.35	0.35	0.70
Rate, mol L^{-1} s^{-1}	2.835×10^{-3}	1.134×10^{-2}	2.268×10^{-2}

10. The following data have been determined for the reaction

$$I^- + OCl^- \longrightarrow IO^- + Cl^-$$

[I⁻], M	0.10	0.20	0.30
[OCl⁻], M	0.050	0.050	0.010
Rate, mol L^{-1} s^{-1}	3.05×10^{-4}	6.10×10^{-4}	1.83×10^{-4}

Determine the rate equation and the rate constant for this reaction.

11. A liter of a 1 M solution of H_2O_2 slowly decomposes into H_2O and O_2. If 0.50 mol of H_2O_2 decomposes during the first 6 h of the reaction, explain why only 0.25 mol decomposes during the next 6-h period.

12. Radioactive materials decay by a first-order process. The very dangerous isotope strontium-90 decays with a half-life of 28 years.

$$^{90}_{38}Sr \longrightarrow ^{90}_{39}Y + e^-$$

What is the rate constant for this decay?

13. Determine the rate constant for the decomposition of H_2O_2 shown in Fig. 14.1 from the data given in the figure.

14. The decomposition of SO_2Cl_2 to SO_2 and Cl_2 is a first-order reaction with $k = 2.2 \times 10^{-5}$ s^{-1} at 320°C.
(a) Determine the half-life of this reaction.
(b) At 320°C, how much $SO_2Cl_2(g)$ remains in a 1.00-L flask 90.0 min after the introduction of 0.0238 mol of SO_2Cl_2? Assume the rate of the reverse reaction is so slow that it can be ignored.

15. Radioactive phosphorus is used in the study of biochemical reaction mechanisms. The isotope phosphorus-33 decays with a rate constant of 4.85×10^{-2} day^{-1}.

$$^{33}_{15}P \longrightarrow ^{33}_{16}S + e^-$$

What is the half-life for this decay?

16. The half-life for the first-order radioactive decay of ^{14}C is 5730 years. What is the rate constant in units of yr^{-1}?

17. For the reaction $A \longrightarrow B + C$, the following data were obtained at 30°C:

[A], M	0.233	0.356	0.557
Rate, mol L^{-1} s^{-1}	4.17×10^{-4}	6.37×10^{-4}	9.97×10^{-4}

(a) What is the order of the reaction with respect to [A], and what is the rate equation?
(b) What is the rate constant?

18. For the reaction $Q \longrightarrow W + X$, the following data were obtained at 30°C:

[Q], M	0.170	0.212	0.357
Rate, mol L^{-1} s^{-1}	6.68×10^{-3}	1.04×10^{-2}	2.94×10^{-2}

(a) What is the order of the reaction with respect to [Q], and what is the rate equation?
(b) What is the rate constant?

19. The reaction of compound A to give compounds C and D was found to be second order in A. The rate constant for the reaction was determined to be 2.42 L mol^{-1} s^{-1}. If the initial concentration is 0.0500 mol/L, what is the value of $t_{1/2}$?

20. The half-life of a reaction of compound A to give compounds D and E is 8.50 min when the initial concentration of A is 0.150 mol/L. How long will it take for the concentration to drop to 0.0300 mol/L if the reaction is first order with respect to A? Second order with respect to A?

Collision Theory of Reaction Rates

21. Chemical reactions occur when reactants collide. For what reasons may a collision fail to produce a chemical reaction?
22. When every collision between reactants leads to a reaction, what determines the rate at which the reaction occurs?
23. What is the activation energy of a reaction, and how is this energy related to the activated complex of the reaction?
24. Account for the relationship between the rate of a reaction and its activation energy.
25. How does an increase in temperature of 10°C affect the rate of many reactions? Explain this effect in terms of the collision theory of the reaction rate.
26. If the rate of a reaction doubles for every 10°C rise in temperature, how much faster does the reaction proceed at 45°C than at 25°C? at 95°C than at 25°C?
27. In an experiment, a sample of $NaClO_3$ was 90% decomposed in 48 min. Approximately how long would this decomposition have taken if the sample had been heated 20°C higher?
28. The rate constant at 325°C for the decomposition reaction $C_4H_8 \longrightarrow 2C_2H_4$ (Section 14.9) is 6.1×10^{-8} s^{-1}, and the activation energy is 261 kJ per mole of C_4H_8. Determine the frequency factor for the reaction.
29. The rate constant for the decomposition of acetaldehyde, CH_3CHO, to methane, CH_4, and carbon monoxide, CO, in the gas phase is 1.1×10^{-2} L mol^{-1} s^{-1} at 703 K and 4.95 L mol^{-1} s^{-1} at 865 K. Determine the activation energy for this decomposition.
30. An elevated level of the enzyme alkaline phosphatase (ALP) in the serum is an indication of possible liver or bone disorder. The level of serum ALP is so low that it is very difficult to measure directly. However, ALP catalyzes a number of reactions, and its relative concentration can be determined by measuring the rate of one of these reactions under controlled conditions. One such reaction is the conversion of *p*-nitrophenyl phosphate (PNPP) to *p*-nitrophenoxide ion (PNP) and phosphate ion. Control of temperature during the test is very important; the rate of the reaction increases 1.47 times if the temperature changes from 30°C to 37°C. What is the activation energy for the ALP-catalyzed conversion of PNPP to PNP and phosphate?

Elementary Reactions, Reaction Mechanisms, Catalysts

31. Define (a) unimolecular reaction, (b) bimolecular reaction, (c) elementary reaction, and (d) overall reaction.

32. What is the rate equation for the elementary termolecular reaction A + 2B $\longrightarrow$ products? For 3A $\longrightarrow$ products?
33. Why are elementary reactions involving three or more reactants very uncommon?
34. In general, can we predict the effect of doubling the concentration of A on the rate of the overall reaction A + B $\longrightarrow$ C? Can we predict the effect if the reaction is known to be an elementary reaction?
35. Which of the following equations, as written, could describe elementary reactions?
    (a) $Cl_2 + CO \longrightarrow Cl_2CO$
    Rate = $k[Cl_2]^{3/2}[CO]$
    (b) $PCl_3 + Cl_2 \longrightarrow PCl_5$
    Rate = $k[PCl_3][Cl_2]$
    (c) $2NO + 2H_2 \longrightarrow N_2 + 2H_2O$
    Rate = $k[NO][H_2]$
    (d) $2NO + O_2 \longrightarrow 2NO_2$
    Rate = $k[NO]^2[O_2]$
    (e) $NO + O_3 \longrightarrow NO_2 + O_2$
    Rate = $k[NO][O_3]$
36. Account for the increase in reaction rate brought about by a catalyst.
37. Describe how a homogeneous catalyst and a heterogeneous catalyst function.
38. (a) Chlorine atoms resulting from decomposition of chlorofluoromethanes, such as CCl_2F_2, catalyze the decomposition of ozone in the ozone layer of the earth's atmosphere. One simplified mechanism for the decomposition is

$$O_3 \xrightarrow{\text{Sunlight}} O_2 + O$$

$$O_3 + Cl \longrightarrow O_2 + ClO$$

$$ClO + O \longrightarrow Cl + O_2$$

Explain why chlorine atoms are catalysts in the gas-phase transformation

$$2O_3 \rightleftharpoons 3O_2$$

(b) Nitric oxide is also involved in the decomposition of ozone by the mechanism

$$O_3 \xrightarrow{\text{Sunlight}} O_2 + O$$

$$O_3 + NO \longrightarrow NO_2 + O_2$$

$$NO_2 + O \longrightarrow NO + O_2$$

Is NO a catalyst for the decomposition? Explain your answer.
39. Write the rate equation for each of the elementary reactions given in both parts of Exercise 38.

Additional Exercises

40. Some bacteria are resistant to the antibiotic penicillin because they produce penicillinase, an enzyme with a molecular mass of 30,000, which converts penicillin into inactive molecules. Although the kinetics of enzyme-catalyzed reac-

tions can be complex, at low concentrations this reaction can be described by a rate equation that is first order in the catalyst (penicillinase) and that also involves the concentration of penicillin. From the following data 1.0 L of a solution containing 0.15 μg (0.15×10^{-6} g) of penicillinase, determine the order of the reaction with respect to penicillin and the value of the rate constant.

[Penicillin], M	Rate, mol L^{-1} min^{-1}
2.0×10^{-6}	1.0×10^{-10}
3.0×10^{-6}	1.5×10^{-10}
4.0×10^{-6}	2.0×10^{-10}

41. The hydrolysis of the sugar sucrose to the sugars glucose and fructose,

$$C_{12}H_{22}O_{11} + H_2O \longrightarrow C_6H_{12}O_6 + C_6H_{12}O_6$$

follows a first-order rate equation for the disappearance of sucrose:

$$\text{Rate} = k[C_{12}H_{22}O_{11}]$$

(The products of the reaction, glucose and fructose, have the same molecular formulas but differ in the arrangement of the atoms in their molecules.)
(a) In neutral solution, $k = 2.1 \times 10^{-11}$ s^{-1} at 27°C and 8.5×10^{-11} s^{-1} at 37°C. Determine the activation energy, the frequency factor, and the rate constant for this equation at 47°C.
(b) When a solution of sucrose with an initial concentration of 0.150 M reaches equilibrium, the concentration of sucrose is 1.65×10^{-7} M. How long will it take the solution to reach equilibrium at 27°C in the absence of a catalyst? Because the concentration of sucrose at equilibrium is so low, assume that the reaction is irreversible.

42. Why does assuming that the reaction is irreversible simplify the calculation in part (b) of Exercise 41?

43. Match each graph with the appropriate caption.
(a) A plot of rate against [A] for a reaction that is first order in A.
(b) A plot of rate against [A] for a reaction that is second order in A.

(c) A plot of the change in concentration of A with time.
(d) A plot of ln k against $1/T$.

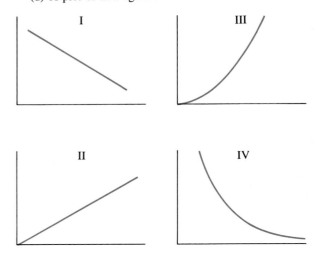

44. Explain why an egg cooks more slowly in boiling water in Denver than in New York City. *Hint:* Consider the effect of temperature on reaction rate and the effect of pressure on boiling point (Section 11.6).

45. The rate of the reaction

$$S_2O_3{}^{2-} + 2H_3O^+ \longrightarrow S + SO_2 + 3H_2O$$

depends on the hydronium ion concentration; it increases as $[H_3O^+]$ increases. Explain why sulfur forms more slowly in a 1 M solution of acetic acid than in a 1 M solution of hydrochloric acid. *Hint:* Section 12.9 contains useful information.

46. Two reactions could initiate the pyrolysis of ethane to ethylene (Section 14.12):

$$C_2H_6 \longrightarrow 2CH_3$$

or

$$C_2H_6 \longrightarrow C_2H_5 + H$$

In these reactions, the activation energy is essentially equal to the bond energy (Section 7.9) of the bond broken in the reaction. Explain why the first of these reactions should be more effective than the second reaction in initiating the pyrolysis of ethane to ethylene.

An Introduction to Chemical Equilibrium

15

Disruption of the oxygen–ozone equilibrium has created a hole in the ozone layer above the Antarctic.

In the previous chapter we learned how to describe the rate of a chemical reaction by using a rate law. We also learned how to predict the effect that changing the concentration or temperature has on the rate. However, this information says nothing about the percent conversion of reactants to products. In order to discuss the percent conversion, we will introduce the concept of chemical equilibrium in this chapter.

The opening photograph for this chapter was taken by a satellite above the southern hemisphere. The colors represent different concentrations of ozone and show the ozone concentration is significantly depleted above the Antarctic. In the ozone layer, ozone is continually forming and decomposing simultaneously in such a way that its concentra-

Figure 15.1

Brown NO_2 reacts with itself to form colorless N_2O_4. As the color indicates, at the end of the reaction (after the concentrations of NO_2 and N_2O_4 stop changing), not all of the NO_2 has been converted to N_2O_4. A state of equilibrium results.

tion normally is constant. Some effect above the Antarctic has upset this equilibrium, and consequently the ozone concentration has been reduced (see Section 29.5).

⓯.1 The State of Equilibrium

When the products of a reaction cannot escape from the reaction mixture, many reactions do not give a 100% yield of products. Some reactants may remain after the concentrations of reactants and products stop changing. For example, when a sample of nitrogen dioxide (NO_2, a brown gas) is placed in a flask, it forms dinitrogen tetraoxide (N_2O_4, a colorless gas) by the reaction

$$2NO_2 \longrightarrow N_2O_4$$

As the reaction proceeds, the color becomes lighter as brown NO_2 is converted to colorless N_2O_4. However, even after the concentrations of reactant and product stop changing, the brown color of the mixture of gases (Fig. 15.1) shows that some NO_2 remains. When there is no further change in concentration of reactant and product, a reaction is said to be at **equilibrium.**

The formation of N_2O_4 from NO_2 is a reversible reaction (Section 2.11); NO_2 forms from the decomposition of N_2O_4 as soon as some N_2O_4 is produced by the forward reaction. At the end of the reaction (at equilibrium), the concentrations no longer change because the rate of formation of NO_2 by the reverse reaction is exactly equal to the rate of formation of N_2O_4 by the forward reaction. **Equilibrium is reached in a system when the reactants combine to form products at the same rate at which the products combine to form reactants** (Fig. 15.2). At equilibrium there is no apparent change in the amounts of reactants and products present, and the equilibrium is a **dynamic equilibrium** because both the forward and the reverse reactions are proceeding (at the same rate).

Figure 15.2

Jugglers provide an illustration of equilibrium. Each person throws clubs to the other person at the same rate at which he receives clubs from that person. Because clubs are thrown continuously in both directions, the number of clubs moving in each direction is constant, and the number of clubs each juggler has at a given time remains constant.

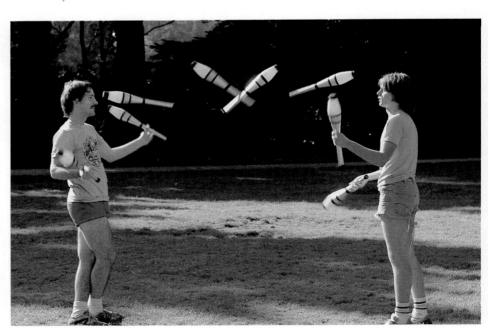

A state of equilibrium can be detected because the concentration of reactants and products does not appear to change. However, it is important to be certain that the absence of change is due to equilibrium and not to a reaction rate that is so slow that changes in concentration are difficult to detect.

In Section 2.11 we indicated that equations for reversible reactions are often written with a double arrow. We also will use the double arrow with reactions that are at equilibrium. For example, the reaction

$$2NO_2 \rightleftharpoons N_2O_4$$

is shown in Fig. 15.1. When we wish to speak about one particular component of a reversible reaction, we will use a single arrow. For example, at the equilibrium shown in Fig. 15.1, the rate of the reaction

$$2NO_2 \longrightarrow N_2O_4$$

is equal to the rate of the reaction

$$N_2O_4 \longrightarrow 2NO_2$$

As a second example of an equilibrium, let us consider the evaporation of bromine.

$$Br_2(l) \rightleftharpoons Br_2(g)$$

Figure 15.3

An equilibrium between liquid bromine and bromine vapor.

Figure 15.3 shows a sample of liquid bromine in equilibrium with bromine vapor. When liquid bromine was poured into the bottle there was no bromine vapor present, but as evaporation proceeded the amount of liquid decreased and the amount of vapor increased. No vapor could escape because the bottle is capped, so an equilibrium between the liquid and the vapor was established. Note that if the bottle were not capped, the bromine vapor could escape and no equilibrium would be reached.

The point at which equilibrium occurs varies with the conditions under which a reaction takes place. Knowing the effect of a change in conditions on an equilibrium enables you to select conditions that control the relative amounts of the substances present at equilibrium. For example, it was known for many years that nitrogen and hydrogen react to form ammonia.

$$N_2 + 3H_2 \rightleftharpoons 2NH_3$$

However, it became possible to manufacture ammonia in useful quantities by this reaction only after the factors that influence its equilibrium were understood (see Section 23.11). The calculation of yields of ammonia at equilibrium under various conditions of temperature and pressure has been extremely important in the fertilizer industry, in the manufacture of nitric acid, and in other applications of ammonia. Fritz Haber, a German chemist, received the 1918 Nobel prize in chemistry for work in which he used equilibrium concepts to develop a means of synthesizing ammonia on a commercial scale.

⓯.2 Reaction Quotients and Equilibrium Constants

A general equation for a reversible chemical reaction may be written

$$mA + nB + \cdots \rightleftharpoons xC + yD + \cdots$$

We can write a ratio called the **reaction quotient, Q,** for this general equation by using the concentrations of the reactants and products and the coefficients m, n, x, and y in the equation. This ratio is

$$Q = \frac{[C]^x[D]^y \cdots}{[A]^m[B]^n \cdots}$$

where brackets mean "molar concentration of," as introduced in Section 14.1. The reaction quotient of a chemical reaction is equal to the product of the molar concentrations of the products (the substances to the right of the arrow in the chemical equation that describes the reaction) divided by the product of the molar concentrations of the reactants (the substances to the left of the arrow), after the concentration of each substance is raised to a power equal to the coefficient preceding that substance in the balanced chemical equation.

The reaction quotient for the reaction

$$2NO_2 \rightleftharpoons N_2O_4$$

is given by the expression

$$Q = \frac{[N_2O_4]}{[NO_2]^2}$$

and the value of Q depends on the concentrations of N_2O_4 and NO_2 *present at the time when Q is determined* whether the reaction is at equilibrium or not. If the concentration of N_2O_4 is large and the concentration of NO_2 is small, the reaction quotient is large. If the concentration of N_2O_4 is small and the concentration of NO_2 is large, Q is small.

Example 15.1

Write the formula for the reaction quotient for each of the following reactions.
(1) $3O_2(g) \rightleftharpoons 2O_3(g)$
(2) $N_2(g) + 3H_2(g) \rightleftharpoons 2NH_3(g)$
(3) $4NH_3(g) + 7O_2(g) \rightleftharpoons 4NO_2(g) + 6H_2O(g)$

(1) $3O_2(g) \rightleftharpoons 2O_3(g)$

$$Q = \frac{[O_3]^2}{[O_2]^3}$$

(2) $N_2(g) + 3H_2(g) \rightleftharpoons 2NH_3(g)$

$$Q = \frac{[NH_3]^2}{[N_2][H_2]^3}$$

(3) $4NH_3(g) + 7O_2(g) \rightleftharpoons 4NO_2(g) + 6H_2O(g)$

$$Q = \frac{[NO_2]^4[H_2O]^6}{[NH_3]^4[O_2]^7}$$

The value of the reaction quotient changes as a reaction approaches equilibrium. When pure reactants are mixed, Q equals zero because there are no products present at that point. As the reaction proceeds, the value of Q increases as the concentrations of the products increase and the concentrations of the reactants simultaneously decrease (Fig. 15.4). At some point the reaction reaches equilibrium, and the value of the reaction quotient no longer changes because the concentrations no longer change. The value of the reaction quotient for a reaction that is at equilibrium is called the **equilibrium constant, K,** of the reaction.

Figure 15.4

(a) The change in the concentrations of reactants and products as the reaction $2SO_2(g) + O_2(g) \rightleftharpoons 2SO_3(g)$ approaches equilibrium. (b) The change in the value of the reaction quotient as the reaction approaches equilibrium.

Gaseous nitrogen dioxide forms dinitrogen tetraoxide according to the equation $2NO_2 \rightleftharpoons N_2O_4$. When 0.10 mol of NO_2 is added to a 1.0-L flask at 25°C, the concentration changes so that at equilibrium $[NO_2] = 0.016$ M and $[N_2O_4] = 0.042$ M. What is the value of the reaction quotient before any reaction occurs? What is the value of the equilibrium constant for the reaction?

Example 15.2

For the reaction $2NO_2 \rightleftharpoons N_2O_4$, the formula for the reaction quotient is $Q = [N_2O_4]/[NO_2]^2$. Before any product is formed, $[NO_2] = 0.10$ mol/1.0 L = 0.10 M, and $[N_2O_4] = 0$ M. Before any reaction occurs, then,

$$Q = \frac{[N_2O_4]}{[NO_2]^2} = \frac{(0)}{(0.10)^2} = 0$$

At equilibrium, the value of the equilibrium constant is equal to the value of the reaction quotient. At equilibrium,

$$K = Q = \frac{[N_2O_4]}{[NO_2]^2}$$

$$= \frac{(0.042)}{(0.016)^2}$$

$$= 1.6 \times 10^2$$

The equilibrium constant is 1.6×10^2.

The magnitude of an equilibrium constant is a measure of the yield of a reversible reaction. A large value for K indicates that equilibrium is attained only after the reactants have been largely converted into products. When K is very small—much less than 1—equilibrium is attained when only a small proportion of the reactants have been converted into products.

When a reaction is at equilibrium at a given temperature, the concentration of reactants and products is such that the reaction quotient is always equal to the equilibrium constant. Regardless of how we might change individual concentrations and temporarily upset an equilibrium, the composition of the system always adjusts itself to a new condition of equilibrium for which $[C]^x[D]^y \cdots /[A]^m[B]^n \cdots$, the reaction quotient, again has the value K, provided that the temperature does not change.

Example 15.3

$CO(g)$ and $H_2O(g)$ react reversibly according to the equation $CO(g) + H_2O(g) \rightleftharpoons CO_2(g) + H_2(g)$. When various mixtures of CO, H_2O, CO_2, and H_2 reacted at 800°C in a closed container, the following concentrations were found after the concentrations stopped changing. Show that the equilibrium constant is the same (within the limits imposed by the uncertainty of the data) in all cases. The subscript i on the first block of data indicates that these data describe the *initial* concentrations—that is, the concentrations of the reactants and products that were mixed before any reaction occurred.

	Experiment 1	Experiment 2	Experiment 3
Before Reaction			
$[CO]_i$	0.0243 M	0 M	0.0094 M
$[H_2O]_i$	0.0243 M	0 M	0.0055 M
$[CO_2]_i$	0 M	0.0468 M	0.0005 M
$[H_2]_i$	0 M	0.0468 M	0.0046 M
At Equilibrium			
$[CO]$	0.0135 M	0.0260 M	0.0074 M
$[H_2O]$	0.0135 M	0.0260 M	0.0035 M
$[CO_2]$	0.0108 M	0.0208 M	0.0025 M
$[H_2]$	0.0108 M	0.0208 M	0.0066 M

At equilibrium, the value of the equilibrium constant is equal to the value of the reaction quotient for the reaction.

For Experiment 1:

$$K = Q = \frac{[CO_2][H_2]}{[CO][H_2O]}$$

$$= \frac{(0.0108)(0.0108)}{(0.0135)(0.0135)} = 0.640$$

For Experiment 2:

$$K = Q = \frac{[CO_2][H_2]}{[CO][H_2O]}$$

$$= \frac{(0.0208)(0.0208)}{(0.0260)(0.0260)} = 0.640$$

For Experiment 3:

$$K = Q = \frac{[CO_2][H_2]}{[CO][H_2O]}$$

$$= \frac{(0.0025)(0.0066)}{(0.0074)(0.0035)} = 0.64$$

Each of these experiments begins with different concentrations of reactants and products, yet all the reaction quotients calculated from the concentrations of reactants and products at equilibrium are the same, within the limits of the significant figures of the data.

Note that the equilibrium concentrations of reactants and products in Experiment 2 in Example 15.3 were produced when the *products* of the reaction were heated in a closed container. This results from the reversibility of the reaction under conditions where equilibrium can be established.

The mathematical expression for the reaction quotient is a mathematical statement of the law of chemical equilibrium, or the **law of mass action: When a reversible reaction has attained equilibrium at a given temperature, the reaction quotient, Q, is a constant.**

Technically, we should calculate the value of an equilibrium constant by using the activities of the reactants and products (see Section 12.22) rather than their concentrations. However, the activity of a dilute solute is closely approximated by its molar concentration, so concentrations are commonly used in calculating equilibrium constants involving dissolved species. The activity of a gas is approximated by its pressure (in atmospheres), so pressures are commonly used in equilibrium constant expressions. However, because the molar concentration of a gas is directly proportional to its pressure, molar concentrations of gases are also used in equilibrium constants. The activity of a pure solid, a pure liquid, or the solvent in a dilute solution is 1.

15.3 The Relationship of Rates of Reaction and Equilibrium Constants

Let us consider the oxidation of carbon monoxide by nitrogen dioxide in a closed flask at 300°C.

$$NO_2 + CO \rightleftharpoons NO + CO_2$$

At the beginning of the reaction, the flask contains only NO_2 and CO. Above 225°C the rate of the forward reaction, rate$_f$ (Section 14.12), is given by the expression

$$rate_f = k_f[NO_2][CO]$$

At first no molecules of NO and CO_2 are present, so there can be no reverse reaction to re-form NO_2 and CO. The rate of the reverse reaction, rate$_r$, is zero (Fig. 15.5). However, as soon as the products (NO and CO_2) begin to form, they also begin to react to re-form the reactants. Initially the rate is relatively slow because their concentrations are low. However, as the concentrations of NO and CO_2 increase, the rate of the reverse reaction, rate$_r$, also increases. The rate of this reaction above 225°C is given by

$$rate_r = k_r[NO][CO_2]$$

Meanwhile, the concentrations of NO_2 and CO decrease, so the rate of the forward reaction, rate$_f$, also decreases. Consequently, the two reaction rates approach each other

Figure 15.5

Rates of reaction of forward and reverse reactions for $NO_2(g) +$ $CO(g) \rightleftharpoons NO(g) + CO_2(g)$, assuming that only NO_2 and CO are present initially.

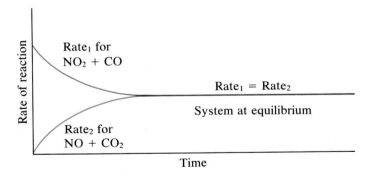

and finally become equal. When $rate_r = rate_f$, equilibrium is established because the concentrations no longer change. At equilibrium we can write

$$rate_r = rate_f$$

$$k_r[NO][CO_2] = k_f[NO_2][CO]$$

or, by rearranging,

$$\frac{k_f}{k_r} = \frac{[NO][CO_2]}{[NO_2][CO]}$$

Because k_f and k_r are constants, the ratio k_f/k_r is also constant, and the expression can be written

$$K = \frac{k_f}{k_r} = \frac{[NO][CO_2]}{[NO_2][CO]}$$

K is the equilibrium constant for the reaction. Just as the rate constants k_f and k_r are specific for each reaction at a definite temperature, K is likewise a constant specific to this system in equilibrium at a given temperature.

It is important to remember that although the rates of reaction, $rate_f$ and $rate_r$, are equal at equilibrium, the molar concentrations of the reactants and products in the equilibrium mixture are usually not equal. However, the individual concentration of each reactant and product remains constant *at equilibrium*, because the rate at which any one reactant is being used up in one reaction is equal to the rate at which it is being formed by the opposite reaction.

15.4 Predicting the Direction of Reaction of a Reversible Reaction

If A, B, C, and D, the components of a mixture, are related by the reversible reaction

$$mA + nB + \cdots \rightleftharpoons xC + yD + \cdots \qquad Q = \frac{[C]^x[D]^y \cdots}{[A]^m[B]^n \cdots}$$

and the mixture is prepared in such proportions that the reaction quotient Q is not equal to the equilibrium constant K, then the system is not in equilibrium. Its composition will change until equilibrium is established. We can predict the direction of the change in composition by comparing Q with K. If Q is less than K ($Q < K$), the reactants will be used up faster than they are formed, and the relative amounts of products will increase until Q is equal to K. The reaction is said to *shift to the right* or to *proceed toward products*. If Q is greater than K ($Q > K$), products will be converted to reactants faster than they are formed, and the relative amounts of reactants will increase until Q is equal to K. The reaction is said to *shift to the left* or to *proceed toward reactants*. If Q is equal to K, the reaction is at equilibrium and no change in concentrations will occur.

Example 15.4

Example 15.3 describes three experiments involving the reaction $CO(g) + H_2O(g) \rightleftharpoons CO_2(g) + H_2(g)$, for which $K = 0.64$. The data given below are the starting concentrations of reactants and products in three additional experiments. Determine in which direction the reaction shifts as it goes to equilibrium in each of these three experiments.

	Experiment 1	Experiment 2	Experiment 3
$[CO]_i$	0.0203 M	0.011 M	0.0094 M
$[H_2O]_i$	0.0203 M	0.0011 M	0.0025 M
$[CO_2]_i$	0.0040 M	0.037 M	0.0015 M
$[H_2]_i$	0.0040 M	0.046 M	0.0076 M

Experiment 1:

$$Q = \frac{[CO_2][H_2]}{[CO][H_2O]}$$

$$= \frac{(0.0040)(0.0040)}{(0.0203)(0.0203)} = 0.039$$

Because $Q < K$ (0.039 < 0.64), the reaction in Experiment 1 is expected to shift to the right and the relative amounts of products to increase until equilibrium is established.

Experiment 2:

$$Q = \frac{[CO_2][H_2]}{[CO][H_2O]}$$

$$= \frac{(0.037)(0.046)}{(0.011)(0.0011)} = 140$$

Because $Q > K$ (140 > 0.64), the reaction in Experiment 2 is expected to shift to the left and the relative amounts of products to decrease until equilibrium is established.

Experiment 3:

$$Q = \frac{[CO_2][H_2]}{[CO][H_2O]}$$

$$= \frac{(0.0015)(0.0076)}{(0.0094)(0.0025)} = 0.48$$

Because $Q < K$ (0.48 < 0.64), the reaction in Experiment 3 is expected to shift to the right and the relative amounts of products to increase until equilibrium is established.

Reactions reach equilibrium only if the reactants and products cannot escape from the reaction mixture. This is easier to understand when we consider the tendency of the concentrations to change until the reaction quotient is equal to the equilibrium constant. For example, calcium carbonate (limestone, $CaCO_3$) may be completely converted to calcium oxide, CaO, and carbon dioxide, CO_2, when heated at 900°C in an open container (Section 13.7).

$$CaCO_3(s) \rightleftharpoons CaO(s) + CO_2(g) \qquad Q = \frac{[CaO][CO_2]}{[CaCO_3]}$$

When calcium carbonate is first exposed to heat, there is essentially no calcium oxide or carbon dioxide present, and the equilibrium quotient is less than the equilibrium constant. Thus the reaction shifts to the right, producing calcium oxide and carbon dioxide. In an open container, the gaseous carbon dioxide escapes from the reaction mixture, so the value of the reaction quotient is *always* less than the value of the equilibrium constant. The reaction keeps producing products as long as the carbon dioxide escapes from the mixture (and as long as any $CaCO_3$ remains), because Q never reaches the value of K. In a closed container, on the other hand, the value of Q increases until the reaction reaches equilibrium because the carbon dioxide cannot escape.

In the commercial production of quicklime, CaO, from limestone, $CaCO_3$, the carbon dioxide is removed as fast as it is formed by means of a stream of air; this causes the reaction to proceed to the right, producing a better yield of CaO. Because the concentration of carbon dioxide never reaches the equilibrium concentration, equilibrium is never established.

⓯.5 Calculations Involving Equilibrium Concentrations

We know that after equilibrium has been established, the value of the reaction quotient of a reaction is equal to its equilibrium constant. Thus we can use the mathematical expression for Q to determine a number of quantities associated with a reaction at equilibrium. In this chapter and in Chapters 17 and 18, we will discuss many different calculations involving equilibrium in several different kinds of reactions. It may help if you keep in mind that there are only three basic types of such calculations:

1. **Calculation of an Equilibrium Constant.** When we know the concentrations of reactants and products at equilibrium, we can calculate the equilibrium constant for the reaction.

2. **Calculation of a Missing Equilibrium Concentration.** When we know the equilibrium constant and all equilibrium concentrations except one, we can calculate the missing concentration.

3. **Calculation of Equilibrium Concentrations from Initial Concentrations.** When we know the equilibrium constant and a set of concentrations of reactants and products that are not at equilibrium, we can calculate the changes in concentrations as the system comes to equilibrium and, from those, the new concentrations at equilibrium.

We will see in Chapters 19 and 20 that if we can determine the equilibrium constant for a chemical reaction, we can evaluate thermodynamic parameters and electrochemical properties of the change. Conversely, if we know thermodynamic parameters or electro-chemical parameters for a reaction, we can evaluate the equilibrium constant for the change.

We will consider calculations of types 1 (equilibrium constant) and 2 (missing equilibrium concentration) in this section and save type 3 (equilibrium concentrations from initial concentrations) for subsequent sections. Calculations of type 3 can be some-what more involved.

1. Calculation of an Equilibrium Constant. Examples 15.2 and 15.3 showed how to determine the equilibrium constant of a reaction if we know the concentrations of reactants and products at equilibrium. The following example shows how to use the stoichiometry of the reaction and a combination of initial concentrations and equilibrium concentrations to determine an equilibrium constant.

Iodine molecules react reversibly with iodide ions to produce triiodide ions.

$$I_2(aq) + I^-(aq) \rightleftharpoons I_3^-(aq)$$

If a solution is prepared with the concentrations of both I_2 and I^- equal to 1.000×10^{-3} M before reaction and if the concentration of I_2 changes to 6.61×10^{-4} M at equilibrium, what is the equilibrium constant for the reaction?

Example 15.5

At equilibrium, the equilibrium constant for the reaction is equal to its reaction quotient.

$$I_2(aq) + I^-(aq) \rightleftharpoons I_3^-(aq) \qquad K = Q = \frac{[I_3^-]}{[I_2][I^-]}$$

In order to determine the equilibrium constant, we must determine the concentrations of I_2, I^-, and I_3^- at equilibrium and then use these concentrations to find the equilibrium constant.

The change in concentration of I_2, $\Delta[I_2]$, is the difference between its final concentration (the equilibrium concentration, 6.61×10^{-4} M) and its initial concentration (1.000×10^{-3} M). That is,

$$\Delta[I_2] = [I_2] - [I_2]_i$$

$$= 6.61 \times 10^{-4} \text{ M} - 1.000 \times 10^{-3} \text{ M}$$

$$= -3.39 \times 10^{-4} \text{ M}$$

The change in the concentration of I^-, $\Delta[I^-]$, is equal to the change in the concentration of I_2 because the chemical equation indicates that for each 1 mol of I_2 that reacts, 1 mol of I^- reacts. That is,

$$\Delta[I^-] = \Delta[I_2] = -3.39 \times 10^{-4} \text{ M}$$

The equilibrium concentration of I^- is equal to the initial concentration of I^- plus the change in its concentration.

$$[I^-] = 1.000 \times 10^{-3} \text{ M} + \Delta[I^-] = 1.000 \times 10^{-3} \text{ M} + (-3.39 \times 10^{-4} \text{ M})$$

$$= 6.61 \times 10^{-4} \text{ M}$$

The change in the concentration of I_3^-, $\Delta[I_3^-]$, is equal to the negative of the change in concentration of I_2 and of I^-. The chemical equation indicates that 1 mol of

Example 15.5 continued

I_3^- is formed and its concentration increases as 1 mol of I_2 or I^- reacts and their concentrations decrease.

$$\Delta[I_3^-] = -\Delta[I_2] = -\Delta[I^-]$$

$$= -(-3.39 \times 10^{-4} \text{ M})$$

$$= 3.39 \times 10^{-4} \text{ M}$$

The equilibrium concentration of I_3^- is equal to the initial concentration of I_3^- plus the change in its concentration.

$$[I_3^-] = 0 + \Delta[I_3^-] = 0 + 3.39 \times 10^{-4} \text{ M}$$

$$= 3.39 \times 10^{-4} \text{ M}$$

To find the equilibrium constant, we simply substitute the equilibrium concentrations into the expression for the equilibrium constant and evaluate it.

$$K = Q = \frac{[I_3^-]}{[I_2][I^-]}$$

$$= \frac{(3.39 \times 10^{-4} \text{ M})}{(6.61 \times 10^{-4} \text{ M})(6.61 \times 10^{-4} \text{ M})}$$

$$= 776 \text{ M}^{-1} = 776 \text{ (mol L}^{-1})^{-1} = 776 \text{ mol}^{-1} \text{ L}$$

Units for reaction quotients or equilibrium constants differ, depending on the reaction and the corresponding equilibrium constant expression. In some cases the units cancel out. Here are several examples of units for equilibrium constants.

Reaction	Equilibrium Equation	Units
$3O_2 \rightleftharpoons 2O_3$	$K = \dfrac{[O_3]^2}{[O_2]^3}$	$\dfrac{(\text{mol L}^{-1})^2}{(\text{mol L}^{-1})^3} = \dfrac{1}{\text{mol L}^{-1}} = \text{mol}^{-1} \text{ L}$
$N_2O_4 \rightleftharpoons 2NO_2$	$K = \dfrac{[NO_2]^2}{[N_2O_4]}$	$\dfrac{(\text{mol L}^{-1})^2}{\text{mol L}^{-1}} = \text{mol L}^{-1}$
$N_2 + 3H_2 \rightleftharpoons 2NH_3$	$K = \dfrac{[NH_3]^2}{[N_2][H_2]^3}$	$\dfrac{(\text{mol L}^{-1})^2}{(\text{mol L}^{-1})(\text{mol L}^{-1})^3} = \dfrac{1}{(\text{mol L}^{-1})^2} = \text{mol}^{-2} \text{ L}^2$
$N_2 + O_2 \rightleftharpoons 2NO$	$K = \dfrac{[NO]^2}{[N_2][O_2]}$	$\dfrac{(\text{mol L}^{-1})^2}{(\text{mol L}^{-1})(\text{mol L}^{-1})} = (\text{no units})$

It is common practice to omit the units of Q or K; we will do so in most examples.

2. Calculation of a Missing Equilibrium Concentration. If we know the equilibrium constant for a reaction and know the concentrations *at equilibrium* of all reactants and products except one, we can calculate the missing concentration.

At 2000°C, the equilibrium constant for the reaction

$$N_2(g) + O_2(g) \rightleftharpoons 2NO(g)$$

is 4.1×10^{-4} (no units; they cancel). Find the concentration of $NO(g)$ in a mixture of $NO(g)$, $N_2(g)$, and $O_2(g)$ in which, at equilibrium, $[N_2] = 0.036$ mol L^{-1} and $[O_2] = 0.0089$ mol L^{-1}.

Example 15.6

Note that in this example we know the equilibrium constant and all of the concentrations except that of NO. At equilibrium, the reaction quotient is equal to the equilibrium constant. Thus we have

$$K = Q = \frac{[NO]^2}{[N_2][O_2]}$$

Because we know K, $[N_2]$, and $[O_2]$, we can solve for $[NO]$ by rearranging this equation.

$$[NO]^2 = K[N_2][O_2]$$
$$[NO] = \sqrt{K[N_2][O_2]}$$
$$= \sqrt{(4.1 \times 10^{-4}) \times (0.036 \text{ mol } L^{-1}) \times (0.0089 \text{ mol } L^{-1})}$$
$$= \sqrt{1.31 \times 10^{-7} \text{ (mol } L^{-1})^2}$$
$$= 3.6 \times 10^{-4} \text{ mol } L^{-1}$$

Thus $[NO]$ is 3.6×10^{-4} mol L^{-1} at equilibrium under these conditions.

We can check our answer by substituting all equilibrium concentrations into the expression for the reaction quotient to see whether it is equal to the equilibrium constant.

$$K = Q = \frac{[NO]^2}{[N_2][O_2]}$$
$$= \frac{(3.6 \times 10^{-4} \text{ mol } L^{-1})^2}{(0.036 \text{ mol } L^{-1})(0.0089 \text{ mol } L^{-1})}$$
$$= 4.0 \times 10^{-4}$$

The answer checks; our calculated value gives the equilibrium constant within the error associated with the significant figures in the problem.

The equilibrium constant for the reaction of nitrogen and hydrogen to produce ammonia at a certain temperature is 6.00×10^{-2} mol^{-2} L^2. Calculate the equilibrium concentration of ammonia if the equilibrium concentrations of nitrogen and hydrogen are 4.26 M and 2.09 M, respectively.

Example 15.7

The balanced equation and the equilibrium constant expression are:

$$N_2(g) + 3H_2(g) \rightleftharpoons 2NH_3(g)$$

$$K = \frac{[NH_3]^2}{[N_2][H_2]^3} = 6.00 \times 10^{-2} \text{ mol}^{-2} \text{ L}^2$$

We substitute the known equilibrium concentrations of N_2 and H_2 into the equilibrium constant expression and solve for $[NH_3]$.

**Example
15.7**
continued

$$K = \frac{[NH_3]^2}{(4.26 \ mol \ L^{-1})(2.09 \ mol \ L^{-1})^3} = 6.00 \times 10^{-2} \ mol^{-2} \ L^2$$

$$[NH_3]^2 = (6.00 \times 10^{-2} \ mol^{-2} \ L^2)(4.26 \ mol \ L^{-1})(2.09 \ mol \ L^{-1})^3$$

$$= 2.33 \ (mol \ L^{-1})^2$$

$$[NH_3] = \sqrt{2.33 \ (mol \ L^{-1})^2} = 1.53 \ mol \ L^{-1}$$

To check our answer, we calculate the equilibrium constant from the equilibrium concentrations.

$$K = Q = \frac{[NH_3]^2}{[N_2][H_2]^3}$$

$$= \frac{(1.53 \ M)^2}{(4.26 \ M)(2.09 \ M)^3}$$

$$= 6.02 \times 10^{-2} \ M^{-2} = 6.02 \times 10^{-2} \ mol^{-2} \ L^2$$

The answer checks; the calculated equilibrium constant agrees with that given within the error associated with the significant figures in the problem.

15.6 Calculation of Equilibrium Concentrations

As indicated in the previous section, if we know the equilibrium constant and a set of concentrations of reactants and products that are not at equilibrium, we can calculate the changes in concentrations as the system comes to equilibrium, as well as the new concentrations at equilibrium. The typical procedure can be summarized as follows:

1. Write a balanced equation for the equilibrium reaction.
2. Write the expression for the reaction quotient, and calculate Q from the initial concentrations in order to determine the direction in which the reaction must shift to reach equilibrium.
3. Define the changes in the initial concentrations that are needed for the reaction to reach equilibrium. Generally, we represent the *smallest* change with the symbol Δ and express the other changes in terms of the smallest change.
4. Define missing equilibrium concentrations in terms of the initial concentrations and the changes in concentration determined in Step 3.
5. Substitute the equilibrium concentrations into the expression for the equilibrium constant, and solve for the unknown change.
6. Calculate the equilibrium concentrations.
7. Check your calculated equilibrium concentrations by substituting them into the equilibrium expression and determining whether they give the equilibrium constant.

Before we consider an example of calculating equilibrium concentrations, let us examine the relationship between changes in concentration and the chemical equation that describes the reaction.

Upon heating, ammonia reversibly decomposes into nitrogen and hydrogen according to the equation

$$2NH_3(g) \rightleftharpoons N_2(g) + 3H_2(g)$$

If a sample of ammonia decomposes such that the concentration of N_2 increases by 0.11 M, the change in concentration of N_2, $\Delta[N_2]$, is 0.11 M. The change is positive because the concentration of N_2 increases.

The change in the concentration of H_2, $\Delta[H_2]$, is also positive; the concentration of H_2 increases as ammonia decomposes. The change in the concentration of H_2 equals 3 times the change in the concentration of N_2, because the chemical equation indicates that for each 1 mole of N_2 that is produced, 3 moles of H_2 is produced.

$$\Delta[H_2] = 3 \times \Delta[N_2]$$
$$= 3 \times (0.11 \text{ M})$$
$$= 0.33 \text{ M}$$

The magnitude of the change in concentration of NH_3, $\Delta[NH_3]$, is twice that of $\Delta[N_2]$; the equation indicates that 2 moles of NH_3 must decompose for each 1 mole of N_2 formed. However, the change is negative because the concentration of ammonia *decreases* as it decomposes, and the final concentration of NH_3 is less than the initial concentration of NH_3 ($\Delta[NH_3] = [NH_3]_{final} - [NH_3]_{initial}$).

$$\Delta[NH_3] = -2 \times \Delta[N_2]$$
$$= -2 \times (0.11 \text{ M})$$
$$= -0.22 \text{ M}$$

These changes are directly related to the coefficients in the equation

$$2NH_3(g) \rightleftharpoons N_2(g) + 3H_2(g)$$
$$\Delta[NH_3] = -2 \times \Delta[N_2] \qquad \Delta[N_2] = 0.11 \text{ M} \qquad \Delta[H_2] = 3 \times \Delta[N_2]$$

Note that all the changes on one side of the arrows are of the same sign and that all the changes on the other side of the arrows are of the opposite sign.

If we did not know the magnitude of the change in the concentration of N_2, we could represent it by the symbol Δ.

$$\Delta[N_2] = \Delta$$

The changes in the other concentrations would then be represented

$$\Delta[H_2] = 3 \times \Delta[N_2] = 3\Delta$$
$$\Delta[NH_3] = -2 \times \Delta[N_2] = -2\Delta$$

The coefficients in the Δ terms are identical to those in the balanced equation for the reaction.

$$2NH_3(g) \rightleftharpoons N_2(g) + 3H_2(g)$$
$$\text{Change:} \quad -2\Delta \qquad \Delta \qquad 3\Delta$$

This is always the case, so the simplest way to find the coefficients for the Δ's is to use the coefficients in the balanced chemical equation. The sign of the coefficient is positive when the concentration increases; it is negative when the concentration decreases.

In solving equilibrium problems that involve changes in concentration, sometimes it is convenient to set up a table of initial concentrations, the changes in these concentrations as the reaction reaches equilibrium, and the final concentrations at equilibrium. Some textbooks use the symbol x to represent the change. However, we use the symbol Δ to emphasize the fact that we solve for the changes in concentrations, and then use the changes to find the concentrations at the final equilibrium.

Example 15.8

Under certain conditions, the equilibrium constant for the decomposition of $PCl_5(g)$ into $PCl_3(g)$ and $Cl_2(g)$ is 0.0211 mol L^{-1}. What are the equilibrium concentrations of PCl_5, PCl_3, and Cl_2 when the initial concentration of PCl_5 was 1.00 M?

Step 1. The balanced equation for the decomposition of PCl_5 is

$$PCl_5(g) \rightleftharpoons PCl_3(g) + Cl_2(g)$$

Step 2. For this reaction the initial value of Q is

$$Q = \frac{[PCl_3][Cl_2]}{[PCl_5]}$$

$$= \frac{(0 \text{ mol } L^{-1})(0 \text{ mol } L^{-1})}{1.00 \text{ mol } L^{-1}} = 0 \text{ mol } L^{-1}$$

Because $Q < K$ ($0 < 0.0211$), the reaction will shift to the right.

Steps 3 and 4. Let us represent the change in concentration of PCl_3 by the symbol Δ; PCl_3 increases in concentration as the reaction shifts to the right, so the change is positive. The change in concentration of Cl_2 is equal to the change in concentration of PCl_3, because the coefficients in the chemical equation are identical (1 mol Cl_2/1 mol PCl_3). The change in concentration of PCl_5 is $-\Delta$, because PCl_5 decreases in concentration as the reaction shifts to the right. The magnitude of the change is equal to the change in the concentration of PCl_3 because the chemical equation indicates that 1 mol of PCl_5 reacts for each 1 mol of PCl_3 that forms (1 mol PCl_5/1 mol PCl_3). The changes in concentration and the expressions for the equilibrium concentrations are summarized, with the concentrations given in the problem in color, in the following table:

	PCl_5	PCl_3	Cl_2
Initial Concentration, M	1.00	0	0
Change, M	$-\Delta$	Δ	Δ
Equilibrium Concentration, M	$1.00 + (-\Delta) = 1.00 - \Delta$	$0 + \Delta = \Delta$	$0 + \Delta = \Delta$

Step 5. Substituting the expressions for the equilibrium concentrations into the equation for the equilibrium constant gives

$$K = \frac{[PCl_3][Cl_2]}{[PCl_5]} = 0.0211$$

$$= \frac{(\Delta)(\Delta)}{(1.00 - \Delta)}$$

We now have an equation that contains only one variable. We can solve this equation for the change in concentration by using the quadratic formula (Appendix Section A.4).

$$0.0211 = \frac{(\Delta)(\Delta)}{(1.00 - \Delta)}$$

$$0.0211(1.00 - \Delta) = \Delta^2$$

$$\Delta^2 + 0.0211\Delta - 0.0211 = 0$$

For an equation of the form $ax^2 + bx + c = 0$,

$$x = \frac{-b \pm \sqrt{b^2 - 4ac}}{2a}$$

In this problem, $x = \Delta$, $a = 1$, $b = 0.0211$, and $c = -0.0211$. Substituting in the quadratic formula yields

$$\Delta = \frac{-0.0211 \pm \sqrt{(0.0211)^2 - 4(1)(-0.0211)}}{2(1)}$$

$$= \frac{-0.0211 \pm \sqrt{(4.45 \times 10^{-4}) + (8.44 \times 10^{-2})}}{2}$$

$$= \frac{-0.0211 \pm 0.2913}{2}$$

Hence

$$\Delta = \frac{-0.0211 + 0.2913}{2} \quad \text{or} \quad \Delta = \frac{-0.0211 - 0.2913}{2}$$

$$= 0.135 \qquad\qquad\qquad = -0.156$$

Quadratic equations often have two different solutions, one that is physically possible and one that is not physically possible. In this case, the second solution is not physically possible because we have defined the change Δ as a positive change; the second solution (-0.156) is a negative change. (The solution of a quadratic equation that has no physical meaning is called an extraneous root.) Thus

$$\Delta = 0.135$$

Step 6. The equilibrium concentrations are

$$[PCl_5] = 1.00 - 0.135 = 0.86 \text{ M}$$

$$[PCl_3] = \Delta = 0.135 \text{ M}$$

$$[Cl_2] = \Delta = 0.135 \text{ M}$$

Step 7. Substitution into the expression for K (to check the calculation) gives

$$K = \frac{[PCl_3][Cl_2]}{[PCl_5]}$$

$$= \frac{(0.135)(0.135)}{(0.86)}$$

$$= 0.021 \text{ M}$$

The equilibrium constant calculated from the equilibrium concentrations given in Step 6 is equal to the value of K given in the problem within the limits of error due to the significant figures. Thus the calculated equilibrium concentrations check.

Example 15.9

Acetic acid, CH_3CO_2H, reacts with ethanol, C_2H_5OH, to form water and ethyl acetate, $CH_3CO_2C_2H_5$, the solvent responsible for the odor in some nail polish removers.

$$CH_3CO_2H + C_2H_5OH \rightleftharpoons CH_3CO_2C_2H_5 + H_2O$$

The equilibrium constant for this reaction (when it is done with dioxane as a solvent) is 4.0. What are the equilibrium concentrations when 0.15 mol of CH_3CO_2H, 0.15 mol of C_2H_5OH, 0.40 mol of $CH_3CO_2C_2H_5$, and 0.40 mol of H_2O are mixed in enough dioxane to make 1.0 liter of solution?

Steps 1 and 2. The equation is given. Before the reaction starts,

$$Q = \frac{[CH_3CO_2C_2H_5][H_2O]}{[CH_3CO_2H][C_2H_5OH]}$$

$$= \frac{(0.40 \text{ mol L}^{-1})(0.40 \text{ mol L}^{-1})}{(0.15 \text{ mol L}^{-1})(0.15 \text{ mol L}^{-1})}$$

$$= 7.1$$

Because $Q > K$ (7.1 > 4.0), the reaction will shift to the left to decrease the amount of products.

Steps 3 and 4. The reaction shifts to the left, so the concentrations of CH_3CO_2H and C_2H_5OH increase. Although we could label the change in concentration of either CH_3CO_2H or C_2H_5OH as Δ, let us choose the increase in concentration of CH_3CO_2H to be Δ. From the chemical equation, we can see that 1 mol of C_2H_5OH is formed for each 1 mol of CH_3CO_2H formed. The change in concentration of C_2H_5OH equals Δ, which is also the change in concentration of CH_3CO_2H. The equation indicates that 1 mol of H_2O and 1 mol of $CH_3CO_2C_2H_5$ are consumed for each 1 mol of CH_3CO_2H produced, so the changes in the concentrations of both $CH_3CO_2C_2H_5$ and H_2O are $-\Delta$. This gives the following table of values.

	CH_3CO_2H	C_2H_5OH	$CH_3CO_2C_2H_5$	H_2O
Initial Concentration, M	0.15	0.15	0.40	0.40
Change, M	Δ	Δ	$-\Delta$	$-\Delta$
Equilibrium Concentration, M	$0.15 + \Delta$	$0.15 + \Delta$	$0.40 + (-\Delta)$	$0.40 + (-\Delta)$

Step 5. Now solve for the changes in concentrations and the new concentrations.

$$4.0 = K = \frac{[CH_3CO_2C_2H_5][H_2O]}{[CH_3CO_2H][C_2H_5OH]}$$

$$= \frac{(0.40 - \Delta)(0.40 - \Delta)}{(0.15 + \Delta)(0.15 + \Delta)}$$

or

$$= \frac{(0.40 - \Delta)^2}{(0.15 + \Delta)^2}$$

We can simplify this equation by taking the square root of both sides. The resulting equation can be readily solved for Δ.

$$\sqrt{4.0} = \sqrt{\frac{(0.40 - \Delta)^2}{(0.15 + \Delta)^2}}$$

$$2.0 = \frac{(0.40 - \Delta)}{(0.15 + \Delta)}$$

$$0.30 + 2.0\Delta = 0.40 - \Delta$$

$$2.0\Delta + \Delta = 0.40 - 0.30$$

$$3.0\Delta = 0.10$$

$$\Delta = 0.033$$

Step 6. The equilibrium concentrations are

$$[CH_3CO_2H] = 0.15 + \Delta = 0.15 + 0.033 = 0.18 \text{ M}$$

$$[C_2H_5OH] = 0.15 + \Delta = 0.15 + 0.033 = 0.18 \text{ M}$$

$$[CH_3CO_2C_2H_5] = 0.40 - \Delta = 0.40 - 0.033 = 0.37 \text{ M}$$

$$[H_2O] = 0.40 - \Delta = 0.40 - 0.033 = 0.37 \text{ M}$$

Step 7. Finally, check the solution.

$$K = \frac{[CH_3CO_2C_2H_5][H_2O]}{[CH_3CO_2H][C_2H_5OH]}$$

$$= \frac{(0.37)(0.37)}{(0.18)(0.18)}$$

$$= 4.2$$

The answer checks within the limits of the significant figures. If we had used 0.183 and 0.367 instead of 0.18 and 0.37, the check would have given a value of 4.0 for K. However, the significant figures in the data and the equilibrium constant limit the equilibrium concentrations to two significant figures.

In subsequent examples, we will sometimes not label each problem-solving step explicitly, but each step will be used.

⓵⓹.7 Techniques for Solving Equilibrium Problems

The features that sometimes make equilibrium problems difficult for students are usually related to identifying the relative changes in reactants and products (the Δ's) and then solving the equilibrium constant equation for the unknown change. As noted in Section 15.6, the coefficients in the Δ terms are identical to those in the balanced equation for the reaction, so we use the coefficients in the balanced chemical equation as the coefficients for the Δ's. Several different techniques can be used to solve the equilibrium constant equation; which one we use depends on the size of the change and the equilibrium constant. In this section, we will see that each of the following four techniques can be used when appropriate.

1. Assume that the change is small compared with the initial concentrations, and neglect Δ when it is added to or subtracted from an initial concentration.
2. Use successive approximations to converge on the solution.
3. Assume the reaction goes to completion in one direction and then comes back to equilibrium.
4. Solve the equilibrium equation with the quadratic formula, or take advantage of a special simplifying mathematical feature of the equation as illustrated in Example 15.9.

There are a number of uncertainties associated with equilibrium calculations that make the results of the calculations relatively inaccurate. The concentrations and pressures used in the calculations are only approximations of the activities of the reactants and products (Section 15.2). Many equilibrium constants are known to only two significant figures, and this imposes uncertainty on the results of equilibrium calculations. Moreover, equilibrium constants are determined experimentally and are subject to experimental error. Most chemists accept the results of a simplified equilibrium calculation if it is within 5% of the value that a more thorough calculation using the same data would yield. We will use this "5% test" in the following examples, which illustrate how to use the techniques listed above for solving equilibrium constant equations.

1. **The Assumption That Δ Is Small.** If the value of the reaction quotient for the initial concentrations is close to the value of the equilibrium constant—that is, if *both* Q and K are much larger than 1 or *both* are much smaller than 1—then Q and K are of the same magnitude, and the concentration changes necessary for Q to become equal to K may be small. Under these conditions, it may be possible to assume that Δ is small relative to the initial concentrations and to neglect some Δ's in solving the equilibrium equation, as shown in the next example.

Example 15.10

Find the concentration of $NO(g)$ at equilibrium when a mixture of $O_2(g)$ with a concentration of 0.50 M and $N_2(g)$ with a concentration of 0.75 M is heated at 700°C.

$$N_2(g) + O_2(g) \rightleftharpoons 2NO(g) \qquad K = 4.1 \times 10^{-9}$$

Steps 1 and 2. The equation is given. Before the reaction starts, Q is zero because no product is present. The reaction will shift to the right.

Steps 3 and 4. The table of initial concentrations, changes, and equilibrium concentrations for this problem follows.

	N_2	O_2	NO
Initial Concentration, M	0.75	0.50	0
Change, M	$-\Delta$	$-\Delta$	2Δ
Equilibrium Concentration, M	$0.75 + (-\Delta)$	$0.50 + (-\Delta)$	$0 + 2\Delta = 2\Delta$

Step 5. At equilibrium,

$$K = 4.1 \times 10^{-9} = \frac{[NO]^2}{[N_2][O_2]}$$

$$= \frac{(2\Delta)^2}{(0.75 - \Delta)(0.50 - \Delta)}$$

Both Q (0) and K (4.1×10^{-9}) are much less than 1 in this problem. Thus we assume that only small changes in concentrations (Δ is small) are necessary to make Q equal to K and that Δ is sufficiently small, relative to the initial concentrations (0.50 and 0.75), for 0.75 to be a close approximation to the value of $0.75 - \Delta$ and for 0.50 to be a close approximation to $0.50 - \Delta$. With these approximations, we can write the equation

$$4.1 \times 10^{-9} = \frac{(2\Delta)^2}{(0.75)(0.50)}$$

This equation is readily solved.

$$4.1 \times 10^{-9} = \frac{(2\Delta)^2}{(0.75)(0.50)}$$

$$\Delta^2 = \frac{(4.1 \times 10^{-9})(0.75)(0.50)}{4}$$

$$= 3.84 \times 10^{-10}$$

$$\Delta = \sqrt{3.84 \times 10^{-10}}$$

$$= 2.0 \times 10^{-5}$$

Now check the assumption that Δ is small relative to 0.50 and 0.75.

$$\frac{\Delta}{0.50} = \frac{2.0 \times 10^{-5}}{0.50} = 4.0 \times 10^{-5} \qquad (4.0 \times 10^{-3}\%)$$

$$\frac{\Delta}{0.75} = \frac{2.0 \times 10^{-5}}{0.75} = 2.7 \times 10^{-5} \qquad (2.7 \times 10^{-3}\%)$$

Δ is less than 5% of both 0.50 and 0.75, so the assumption is valid. The change in concentration of NO is 2Δ, or 4.0×10^{-5} M.

Step 6. The concentration of NO at equilibrium is equal to the change in concentration of NO, which is 4.0×10^{-5} M.

Step 7.

$$K = 4.1 \times 10^{-9} = \frac{[NO]^2}{[N_2][O_2]}$$

$$= \frac{(4.0 \times 10^{-5})^2}{(0.75)(0.50)}$$

$$= 4.3 \times 10^{-9}$$

Substituting the equilibrium concentrations into the expression for the equilibrium constant shows that the calculated values check.

In the example, we did not assume that Δ was zero. We assumed that Δ was small enough for the term $0.50 - \Delta$ to be approximately equal to 0.50 and for the term $0.75 - \Delta$ to be approximately equal to 0.75. These two approximations simplified the equilibrium constant equation so that it could be solved much more easily.

2. The Use of Successive Approximations. As an introduction to the use of successive approximations, consider the equilibrium for the decomposition of $PCl_5(g)$ into $PCl_3(g)$ and $Cl_2(g)$.

Example 15.11

In Example 15.8 we considered a set of conditions for the reaction

$$PCl_5(g) \rightleftharpoons PCl_3(g) + Cl_2(g) \qquad K = 0.0211$$

that led to the equilibrium equation

$$0.0211 = \frac{(\Delta)(\Delta)}{1.00 - \Delta}$$

Let us now solve this equation using successive approximations.

First approximation. In Example 15.8, Q for the initial reaction mixture was seen to be zero. Both Q and K are less than 1, so let us initially assume that Δ is small relative to 1.00; that is, we assume we can approximate $(1.00 - \Delta)$ as 1.00. This gives

$$0.0211 = \frac{(\Delta)(\Delta)}{1.00}$$

which is readily solved.

$$\Delta^2 = 0.0211$$

$$\Delta = \sqrt{0.0211} = 0.145$$

Now we check to see whether Δ is less than 5% of 1.00—and thus whether it is small enough to be neglected.

$$\frac{\Delta}{1.00} = \frac{0.145}{1.00} = 0.145$$

Δ is not small enough to neglect (it is 14.5% of 1.00), so this particular approximation does *not* give a satisfactory solution to the equilibrium equation. However, it does give us useful information for a second approximation.

Second approximation. In the first approximation, we approximated the term $(1.00 - \Delta)$ as 1.00 and then solved the equation. Although this first approximation is not valid, using it gives a better value for Δ than simply assuming Δ is small. The value of $(1.00 - \Delta)$ is closer to $(1.00 - 0.145) = 0.855$ than to the value of 1.00 assumed in the first approximation. Let us use this second approximate value of $(1.00 - \Delta)$ to solve the equilibrium equation.

$$0.0211 = \frac{(\Delta)(\Delta)}{1.00 - \Delta}$$

$$= \frac{(\Delta)(\Delta)}{1.00 - 0.145}$$

$$= \frac{(\Delta)(\Delta)}{0.855}$$

$$\Delta^2 = 0.0211 \times 0.855 = 0.0180$$

$$\Delta = \sqrt{0.0180} = 0.134$$

The values of Δ obtained in the first and second approximations are close to each other, but they differ by more than 5%. Thus a third approximation is necessary.

Third approximation. A still better approximation of the value of $(1.00 - \Delta)$, found by using the value of Δ obtained from the second approximation, is

$$1.00 - \Delta = 1.00 - 0.134 = 0.866$$

$$0.0211 = \frac{(\Delta)(\Delta)}{1.00 - \Delta}$$

$$= \frac{(\Delta)(\Delta)}{1.00 - 0.134}$$

$$= \frac{(\Delta)(\Delta)}{0.866}$$

$$\Delta^2 = 0.0211 \times 0.866 = 0.0183$$

$$\Delta = 0.135$$

This value for Δ differs by less than 5% from that obtained in the second approximation (and is the same value we obtained using the quadratic equation in Example 15.8). Hence we may conclude that $\Delta = 0.135$.

---

3. Assume the Reaction Goes to Completion and Then Comes to Equilibrium. It is not uncommon to encounter a reaction for which the reaction quotient for the initial mixture is much less than 1 and the equilibrium constant is much larger than 1, or vice versa. For example, we might wish to know the equilibrium concentration of HF produced by the reaction of a mixture of H_2 with a concentration of 0.10 M and F_2 with a concentration of 0.050 M according to the equation

$$H_2(g) + F_2(g) \rightleftharpoons 2HF(g) \qquad K = 115$$

In this case, Q is much less than 1 ($Q = 0$), and K is greater than 1 ($K = 115$).

In such cases it may simplify determination of the equilibrium concentrations to attack the problem in two steps: (a) Assume that the reaction goes to completion, giving an intermediate mixture *that is not at equilibrium* and that contains a 100% yield of products (and perhaps some excess of one reactant). (b) Calculate the equilibrium concentrations as the intermediate mixture of products (and reactants) comes to equilibrium. If we use the intermediate mixture in our calculation, Q will be closer to K and the approximations discussed in this section will be applicable for solving the equilibrium equation. This is a valid approach for calculating equilibrium concentrations, because the concentrations are the same whether the equilibrium results from a shift of the reaction either to the right or to the left (Section 15.2).

Example 15.12

Determine the equilibrium concentrations that result from the reaction of a mixture of 0.10 M H_2 and 0.050 M F_2 according to the equation

$$H_2(g) + F_2(g) \rightleftharpoons 2HF(g) \qquad K = 115$$

Because Q is less than 1 and K is greater than 1, let us determine an intermediate set of concentrations that result from the formation of a 100% yield of product and then calculate the concentration of HF in the equilibrium mixture that results when the intermediate mixture comes to equilibrium.

The simplest way to determine the concentrations of reactants and products in the hypothetical intermediate mixture is to consider what happens when 1.0 L of the initial mixture reacts. A 1.0-L sample would contain 0.050 mol of F_2 and 0.10 mol of H_2. The 0.050 mol of F_2 in 1.0 L of the initial mixture would yield 0.10 mol of HF in the intermediate mixture. Thus [HF] in the intermediate mixture would be 0.10 M. The 0.050 mol of F_2 would react with 0.050 mol of H_2, leaving 0.050 mol of H_2 that did not react. The $[H_2]$ in the intermediate mixture would be 0.050 M. All of the F_2 in the initial mixture would react, so $[F_2]$ in the intermediate mixture would be zero. The following table summarizes the concentrations in the initial mixture (shown in red) and in the intermediate mixture (shown in blue).

	H_2	F_2	HF
Initial Concentration, M	0.10	0.050	0
Change, M	−0.050	−0.050	0.10
Intermediate Concentration, M	0.050	0	0.10

Now we use the concentrations of the products and excess reactants in the intermediate mixture and determine the concentrations in an equilibrium mixture, using the changes summarized in the following table. As described in Section 15.6, the symbol Δ is used to represent an increase in concentration.

	H_2	F_2	HF
Intermediate Concentration, M	0.050	0	0.10
Change, M	Δ	Δ	-2Δ
Equilibrium Concentration, M	$0.050 + \Delta$	$0 + \Delta$	$0.10 + (-2\Delta)$

At equilibrium,
$$K = 115 = \frac{[HF]^2}{[H_2][F_2]}$$

$$= \frac{(0.10 - 2\Delta)^2}{(0.050 + \Delta)(\Delta)}$$

Both K and Q are greater than zero for the intermediate mixture, so let us try to solve this equation by assuming that Δ is small. We will try the approximations that $(0.10 - 2\Delta) = 0.10$ and $(0.050 + \Delta) = 0.050$. This gives

$$115 = \frac{(0.10 - 2\Delta)^2}{(0.050 + \Delta)(\Delta)}$$

$$= \frac{(0.10)^2}{(0.050)(\Delta)}$$

$$\Delta = \frac{(0.10)^2}{(0.050)(115)}$$

$$= 0.0017$$

A check of the approximation shows that

$$\frac{2\Delta}{0.10} = \frac{0.0034}{0.10} = 0.034 \qquad (3.4\%)$$

$$\frac{\Delta}{0.050} = \frac{0.0017}{0.050} = 0.034 \qquad (3.4\%)$$

Because Δ is less than 5% of the intermediate concentrations, a second approximation is not necessary.

With the value of Δ, we can calculate the equilibrium concentrations.

$$[H_2] = 0.050 + \Delta = 0.050 + 0.0017 = 0.052 \text{ M}$$

$$[F_2] = 0 + \Delta = 0 + 0.0017 = 0.0017 \text{ M}$$

$$[HF] = 0.10 - 2\Delta = 0.10 - 2(0.0017) = 0.10 \text{ M}$$

To check our calculations, we use

$$K = \frac{[HF]^2}{[H_2][F_2]}$$

$$= \frac{(0.10)^2}{(0.052)(0.0017)}$$

$$= 1.1 \times 10^2$$

The values check within the limits of the significant figures.

15.8 Effect of Change of Concentration on Equilibrium

A chemical system at equilibrium can be shifted out of equilibrium by changing the concentration of reactants or products. The concentrations of both reactants and products then undergo additional changes to return the system to equilibrium. Figure 15.6 shows a system in which a shift in equilibrium is caused by a decrease in the concentration of a reactant.

15 An Introduction to Chemical Equilibrium

Figure 15.6

(a) Test tube contains 0.1 M Fe^{3+}.
(b) Thiocyanate ion has been added to solution in (a), forming the red $Fe(NCS)^{2+}$ ion.

$$Fe^{3+}(aq) + SCN^-(aq) \rightleftharpoons Fe(NCS)^{2+}(aq)$$

(c) Silver nitrate has been added to the solution in (b), precipitating some of the SCN^- as the white $AgNCS(s)$ seen in the bottom of the tube.

$$Ag^+(aq) + SCN^-(aq) \rightleftharpoons AgNCS(s)$$

The decrease in SCN^- concentration shifts the equilibrium among Fe^{3+}, SCN^-, and $Fe(NCS)^{2+}$ to the left, decreasing the concentration (and color) of the red $Fe(NCS)^{2+}$.

(a)   (b)   (c)

Thiocyanate anions, SCN^-, react with iron(III) cations, Fe^{3+}, to form soluble red cations, $Fe(NCS)^{2+}$.

$$Fe^{3+}(aq) + SCN^-(aq) \rightleftharpoons Fe(NCS)^{2+}(aq) \tag{1}$$

Figure 15.6(a) shows an aqueous solution of Fe^{3+}. Figure 15.6(b) shows the same solution after some SCN^- is added; the red color of the $Fe(NCS)^{2+}$ ion is readily apparent. Part (c) of Fig. 15.6 shows the same solution as in part (b) after the addition of silver nitrate, $AgNO_3$, which introduces silver ion, Ag^+, into the solution. Silver ion reacts with thiocyanate ion to form insoluble silver thiocyanate, $AgSCN$.

$$Ag^+(aq) + SCN^-(aq) \rightleftharpoons AgSCN(s) \tag{2}$$

With the formation of the precipitate of $AgSCN$, the concentration of SCN^- in the solution is reduced, changing the value of $[Fe(NCS)^{2+}]/[Fe^{3+}][SCN^-]$, the reaction quotient, such that it is larger than the equilibrium constant. Reaction (1) shifts to the left and increases the concentration of SCN^- partway back to its original concentration, thereby reducing the concentration of the $Fe(NCS)^{2+}$ ion and reducing the value of the reaction quotient until it is again equal to the value of the equilibrium constant for the reaction. A new equilibrium is attained, and the fainter red color in the solution after addition of $AgNO_3$ is in complete accord with equilibrium theory, which calls for a decrease in $[Fe(NCS)^{2+}]$.

The effect of a change in concentration on a system at equilibrium is illustrated further by the equilibrium $H_2(g) + I_2(g) \rightleftharpoons 2HI(g)$, for which K is 50.0 at 400°C. A mixture of gases at 400°C with $[H_2] = [I_2] = 0.221$ M and $[HI] = 1.563$ M is at equilibrium; for this mixture, $Q = 50.0$. If H_2 is introduced into the system so quickly that its concentration doubles before it begins to react (new $[H_2] = 0.442$ M), the reaction will shift so that a new equilibrium is reached, at which $[H_2] = 0.374$ M, $[I_2] = 0.153$ M, and $[HI] = 1.692$ M. If these values are substituted in the expression for the equilibrium constant for this system, we have

$$Q = \frac{[HI]^2}{[H_2][I_2]} = \frac{(1.692)^2}{(0.374)(0.153)} = 50.0 = K$$

Hence by doubling the concentration of H_2 causing the reaction to shift to the right, we have caused the formation of more HI, used up about one-third of the I_2 that was present at the first equilibrium, and used up some, *but not all,* of the excess H_2 that was added.

The effect of a change in concentration on a system at equilibrium is an example of **Le Châtelier's principle: When a stress (such as a change in concentration, pressure, or temperature) is applied to a system in equilibrium, the equilibrium shifts in a way that tends to relieve the stress.** In the case of the formation of the $Fe(NCS)^{2+}$ ion, the stress on the system is the removal of free SCN^- ion. The stress is relieved when the reaction shifts to the left and a portion of the $Fe(NCS)^{2+}$ ions decompose, producing additional free SCN^- (and Fe^{3+}) to relieve the stress. In the HI system, the stress on the system is the introduction of additional H_2. The stress is relieved when the reaction shifts to the right, uses up some of the excess H_2, and forms additional HI.

Addition of a reactant or product to a reaction at equilibrium causes a shift in the reaction, because it upsets the equality of the rates of the forward and reverse reactions. For example, if the system

$$A + B \rightleftharpoons C + D$$

is in equilibrium and an additional quantity of either A or B (or both) is added, the rate of the forward reaction increases because the concentration of the reacting molecules increases [Fig. 15.7(a)]. The rate of the forward reaction becomes greater than that of the reverse reaction, so the system is out of equilibrium. However, as the concentrations of C and D increase, the rate of the reverse reaction increases, while the decrease in the concentrations of A and B causes the rate of the forward reaction to decrease. The rates of the two reactions become equal again, and a second state of equilibrium is reached. Although the concentrations of A, B, C, and D have changed, the reaction quotient [C][D]/[A][B] is again equal to its original value of K.

The equilibrium is said to have shifted to the right because in the new state of equilibrium, the products C and D are present in greater concentration than before the addition of the reactants. Increasing the concentration of either C or D, or both, would shift the equilibrium to the left by increasing the rate of the *reverse* reaction and thereby increasing the concentrations of A and B.

Figure 15.7

(a) The effect of adding some reactant A on the rates of the forward and reverse reactions for A + B $\rightleftharpoons$ C + D when the system is initially at equilibrium. (b) The effect of removing some reactant A on the rates of the forward and reverse reactions for A + B $\rightleftharpoons$ C + D when the system is initially at equilibrium.

(a)

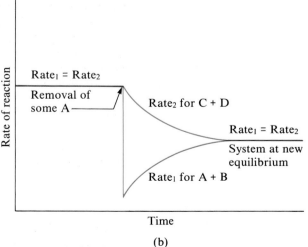

(b)

A system can also be shifted out of equilibrium by *decreasing* the rate of the forward or the reverse reaction [Fig. 15.7(b)]. The rate of the reverse reaction can be decreased and the equilibrium shifted to the right by removing one or more of the products. The equilibrium can be shifted to the left by removing one or more of the reactants.

⓯.9 Effect of Change in Pressure on Equilibrium

Changes in pressure measurably affect systems in equilibrium only when gases are involved, and then only when the chemical reaction produces a change in the total number of gaseous molecules in the system. As the pressure on a gaseous system increases, the gases are compressed, the total number of molecules per unit of volume increases, and their molar concentrations increase. The stress in this case is an increase in the number of molecules per unit of volume. A chemical reaction that reduces the total number of molecules per unit of volume relieves the stress and will, in accordance with Le Châtelier's principle, be favored.

Consider the effect of an increase in pressure on the system in which one molecule of nitrogen and three molecules of hydrogen interact to form two molecules of ammonia.

$$N_2(g) + 3H_2(g) \rightleftharpoons 2NH_3(g)$$

The formation of ammonia decreases the total number of molecules in the system by 50%, thus reducing the total pressure exerted by the system. Experiment shows that an increase in pressure does drive the reaction to the right. On the other hand, a decrease in the pressure on the system favors decomposition of ammonia into hydrogen and nitrogen. These observations are fully in accordance with Le Châtelier's principle.

Let us now consider the reaction in which a molecule of nitrogen interacts with a molecule of oxygen to form two molecules of nitric oxide.

$$N_2(g) + O_2(g) \rightleftharpoons 2NO(g)$$

Because there is no change in the total number of molecules in the system during reaction, a change in pressure does not favor either formation or decomposition of gaseous nitric oxide.

Whenever gases are involved in a reaction, the partial pressure of each gas can be substituted for its concentration in the expression for the reaction quotient or the equilibrium constant, because the concentration of a gas at constant temperature varies directly with the pressure. This relationship can be derived from the ideal gas equation (Section 10.8),

$$PV = nRT$$

The molar concentration of the gas, designated C, is the number of moles, n, in 1 liter of the gas. Substituting 1 L for V, and rearranging the equation, we get

$$P(1 \text{ L}) = nRT$$

$$P = \frac{n}{1 \text{ L}} RT$$

$$= CRT$$

Because R is a constant and T is constant when the temperature does not change, the quantity RT is a constant at constant temperature. Thus at constant temperature, the pressure of a gas is directly proportional to its concentration, or

$$P = \text{constant} \times C$$

For the system

$$N_2(g) + 3H_2(g) \rightleftharpoons 2NH_3(g)$$

we can write the reaction quotient, using the pressures of the gases, as

$$Q_p = \frac{P_{NH_3}^2}{P_{N_2}P_{H_2}^3}$$

At equilibrium,

$$K_p = Q_p = \frac{P_{NH_3}^2}{P_{N_2}P_{H_2}^3}$$

The subscript p is used to designate reaction quotients and equilibrium constants that are obtained by using the pressures of gases instead of their concentrations. The equilibrium constant, K_p, is still a constant, but its numerical value and units may differ from the equilibrium constant found for the same reaction by using concentrations.

The unit we use to express K_p for the reaction to produce ammonia, when the three partial pressures are expressed in atmospheres, is

$$K_p = \frac{\text{atm}^2}{\text{atm} \times \text{atm}^3} = \frac{1}{\text{atm}^2} = \text{atm}^{-2}$$

We solve equilibrium problems involving pressures with the same procedures that we have applied to problems involving concentrations.

Example 15.13

Nitrogen at a pressure of 2.00 atm, hydrogen at a pressure of 6.00 atm, and ammonia at a pressure of 5.00 atm are placed in a reaction vessel. What are the pressures of these gases when equilibrium is established?

$$N_2(g) + 3H_2(g) \rightleftharpoons 2NH_3(g) \qquad K_p = 1.645 \times 10^2 \text{ atm}^{-2}$$

The reaction quotient for the initial pressures of gases is

$$Q_p = \frac{P_{NH_3}^2}{P_{N_2}P_{H_2}^3}$$

$$= \frac{(5.00 \text{ atm})^2}{(2.00 \text{ atm})(6.00 \text{ atm})^3}$$

$$= 0.0579 \text{ atm}^{-2}$$

The reaction will shift to the right because Q_p is less than K_p.

Q_p and K_p are of different magnitudes ($Q_p < 1$; $K_p > 1$). Thus we determine an intermediate set of pressures that would result from the formation of a 100% yield of product and for which Q_p would be greater than 1. Then we calculate the pressures in the equilibrium mixture that results when the intermediate mixture comes to equilibrium. This is similar to the approach used in Example 15.12.

The pressure of a gas is directly proportional to its concentration, so the change in pressure of a gas, Δ_p, can be treated in the same way as the change in concentration, Δ.

Example 15.13 continued

When the initial mixture undergoes a reaction that gives a 100% yield of NH_3, the concentration of NH_3 increases 2 times as much as the concentration of N_2 decreases. The pressure of NH_3 also increases 2 times as much as the pressure of N_2 decreases. A reaction that produces a 100% yield of NH_3 consumes all of the N_2. Thus Δ_p for N_2 is -2.00 atm, and Δ_p for NH_3 is 4.00 atm. The concentration of H_2 decreases 3 times as much as the concentration of N_2. The pressure of H_2 decreases 3 times as much as the pressure of N_2, and Δ_p for H_2 is $3 \times \Delta_p$ for N_2, or 3×-2.00 atm $= -6.00$ atm. The following table summarizes the pressures in the initial mixture and the intermediate mixture.

	N_2	H_2	NH_3
Initial Pressure, atm	2.00	6.00	5.00
Change, atm	−2.00	−6.00	4.00
Intermediate Pressure, atm	0	0	9.00

Now we can set up a table of pressures and changes in pressures as the intermediate mixture comes to equilibrium. Q_p for the intermediate mixture is larger than the equilibrium constant, so the reaction of the intermediate mixture will shift to the left and the change in pressure of N_2 and the change in pressure of H_2 will both be positive.

	N_2	H_2	NH_3
Intermediate Pressure, atm	0	0	9.00
Change, atm	Δ_p	$3\Delta_r$	$-2\Delta_p$
Equilibrium Pressure, atm	Δ_p	$3\Delta_p$	$9.00 - 2\Delta_p$

At equilibrium,

$$K_p = \frac{P_{NH_3}^2}{P_{N_2}P_{H_2}^3} = 1.645 \times 10^2$$

$$= \frac{(9.00 - 2\Delta_p)^2}{(\Delta_p)(3\Delta_p)^3}$$

Q_p for the intermediate mixture and K_p are both larger than 1, so let us assume, as an approximation, that Δ_p is small and that $(9.00 - 2\Delta_p) = 9.00$. This gives the simplified equation

$$1.645 \times 10^2 = \frac{(9.00)^2}{(\Delta_p)(3\Delta_p)^3}$$

This equation can be solved as follows:

$$27\Delta_p{}^4 = \frac{(9.00)^2}{1.645 \times 10^2}$$

$$\Delta_p{}^4 = 0.01824$$

$$\Delta_p{}^2 = \sqrt{\Delta_p{}^4} = \sqrt{0.01824} = 0.1350$$

$$\Delta_p = \sqrt{\Delta_p{}^2} = \sqrt{0.1350}$$

$$= 0.3675$$

Now check the assumptions that Δ_p is small and that $(9.00 - 2\Delta_p)$ can be equated to 9.00 (determine whether $2\Delta_p$ is less than 5% of 9.00).

$$\frac{2\Delta_p}{9.00} = \frac{2 \times 0.3675}{9.00} = 0.0817 \qquad (8.17\%)$$

$2\Delta_p$ is larger than 5% of the initial pressure, so a second approximation is necessary.

As a second approximation, let us assume that $(9.00 - 2\Delta_p) = [9.00 - (2 \times 0.3675)] = 8.26$. With this approximation,

$$1.645 \times 10^2 = \frac{(9.00 - 2\Delta_p)^2}{(\Delta_p)(3\Delta_p)^3}$$

$$1.645 \times 10^2 = \frac{(8.26)^2}{(\Delta_p)(3\Delta_p)^3}$$

$$27\Delta_p{}^4 = \frac{(8.26)^2}{1.645 \times 10^2}$$

$$\Delta_p{}^4 = 0.01536$$

$$\Delta_p{}^2 = \sqrt{\Delta_p{}^4} = \sqrt{0.01536} = 0.1239$$

$$\Delta_p = \sqrt{\Delta_p{}^2} = \sqrt{0.1239}$$

$$= 0.3520$$

The change in Δ_p between the first and second approximations is

$$\frac{(0.3675 - 0.3520)}{0.3520} = 0.0440 \qquad (4.40\%)$$

which is less than a 5% change. Thus we can take 0.352 atm as the change in pressure of N_2 as the intermediate mixture reaches equilibrium. The pressures at equilibrium are

$$P_{N_2} = \Delta_p = 0.352 \text{ atm}$$

$$P_{H_2} = 3\Delta_p = 1.06 \text{ atm}$$

$$P_{NH_3} = 9.00 - 2\Delta_p = 9.00 - (2 \times 0.352) = 8.30 \text{ atm}$$

A check of these pressures shows that

$$Q_p = \frac{P_{NH_3}^2}{P_{N_2}P_{H_2}^3}$$

**Example
15.13
continued**

$$= \frac{(8.30 \text{ atm})^2}{(0.352 \text{ atm})(1.06 \text{ atm})^3}$$

$$= 164 \text{ atm}^{-2}$$

The answer checks.

The following example illustrates that equilibrium problems do not always lead to complicated equations that require successive approximations or other techniques to solve.

**Example
15.14**

A vessel contains gaseous CO, CO_2, H_2, and H_2O at equilibrium at 980°C. The pressures of these gases are as follows: CO, 0.150 atm; CO_2, 0.200 atm; H_2, 0.090 atm; and H_2O, 0.200 atm. Hydrogen is pumped into the vessel, and the equilibrium pressure of CO changes to 0.230 atm. Calculate the partial pressures of the other substances at the new equilibrium, assuming no change in temperature and the following reaction:

$$CO_2(g) + H_2(g) \rightleftharpoons CO(g) + H_2O(g)$$

This example involves calculating an equilibrium constant for a reaction at equilibrium under one set of conditions and then calculating the concentrations of the reactants at a new equilibrium.

Before we can calculate pressures after the addition of hydrogen, we need to determine the equilibrium constant (a calculation of type 1, Section 15.5, page 456). K_p can be determined from the equilibrium pressures of the reactants and products before the additional hydrogen is added.

$$K_p = \frac{P_{CO}P_{H_2O}}{P_{CO_2}P_{H_2}} = \frac{(0.150 \text{ atm})(0.200 \text{ atm})}{(0.200 \text{ atm})(0.0900 \text{ atm})}$$

$$= 1.67$$

(Units cancel out, so the equilibrium constant in this particular case has no units.)

Now consider the situation at the new equilibrium. We do not have enough information to calculate a reaction quotient for the intermediate mixture of gases (the mixture after hydrogen has been added but before it begins to react), because we do not know the new pressure of hydrogen at that point. This fact (that we cannot determine Q) should serve to alert us that this problem is not a routine equilibrium problem.

Let us set up a table showing what we know about the initial pressures in the intermediate mixture (after H_2 is added, but before it reacts), the changes, and what we know about the pressures at the new equilibrium.

	P_{CO_2}	P_{H_2}	P_{CO}	P_{H_2O}
Intermediate Pressure, atm	0.200	?	0.150	0.200
Change, atm	$-\Delta_p$	$-\Delta_p$	Δ_p	Δ_p
Equilibrium Pressure, atm	$0.200 - \Delta_p$	$? - \Delta_p$	0.230	$0.200 + \Delta_p$

At the new equilibrium, P_{CO} is 0.230 atm. P_{CO} increases by 0.080 atm (from 0.150 atm to 0.230 atm); thus Δ_p is 0.080 atm. The balanced equation tells us that for each increase of 1 mol of CO, the H_2O concentration also increases by 1 mol; hence the change in pressure of H_2O equals the change in pressure of CO (0.080 atm). The balanced equation also tells us that for every 1 mol of CO produced, 1 mol of CO_2 must be consumed, so the change in the pressure of CO_2 must equal the negative of the change in pressure of CO. Thus

$$P_{CO_2} = 0.200 - \Delta = 0.200 \text{ atm} - 0.0800 \text{ atm} = 0.120 \text{ atm}$$

$$P_{H_2O} = 0.200 + \Delta = 0.200 \text{ atm} + 0.0800 \text{ atm} = 0.280 \text{ atm}$$

Now we can calculate the pressure of H_2 at the new equilibrium, because we know the equilibrium constant and all of the equilibrium pressures except that of H_2.

$$K_p = \frac{P_{CO}P_{H_2O}}{P_{CO_2}P_{H_2}}$$

$$1.67 = \frac{(0.230 \text{ atm})(0.280 \text{ atm})}{(0.120 \text{ atm})(P_{H_2})}$$

$$P_{H_2} = \frac{(0.230 \text{ atm})(0.280 \text{ atm})}{(0.120 \text{ atm})(1.67)}$$

$$= 0.321 \text{ atm}$$

The partial pressures for CO, H_2O, CO_2, and H_2 at the new equilibrium are 0.230 atm, 0.280 atm, 0.120 atm, and 0.321 atm, respectively.

15.10 Effect of Change in Temperature on Equilibrium

The effect of temperature changes on systems at equilibrium may be summarized by **van't Hoff's law: When the temperature of a system in equilibrium is raised, the equilibrium is displaced in such a way that heat is absorbed.** This generalization is a special case of Le Châtelier's principle (Section 15.8).

Heating a mixture of the gases H_2, I_2, and HI at equilibrium reduces the amount of HI in the equilibrium mixture. This is an example of the application of van't Hoff's law. When hydrogen reacts with gaseous iodine, heat is evolved.

$$H_2(g) + I_2(g) \longrightarrow 2HI(g) \qquad \Delta H = -9.4 \text{ kJ (exothermic)}$$

Recall that ΔH refers to the forward reaction going to completion (100% yield of HI). If we write this equation as shown in Section 4.4,

$$H_2(g) + I_2(g) \longrightarrow 2HI(g) + 9,400 \text{ J}$$

heat can be seen to be a product of the reaction. Thus increasing the temperature of the reaction may be regarded as increasing the amount of one of the products of the reaction. The reaction shifts to the left to relieve the stress, and there is an increase in the concentration of H_2 and I_2 and a reduction in the concentration of HI. Lowering the temperature of this system favors the formation of hydrogen iodide.

The concentrations of a reaction at equilibrium change as the temperature changes; consequently, the equilibrium constant for the reaction changes as the temperature changes. Lowering the temperature in the HI system increases the equilibrium constant, because the concentration of HI at the new equilibrium increases and the concentrations of H_2 and I_2 decrease. Raising the temperature decreases the value of the equilibrium constant, because the concentration of HI at the new equilibrium decreases and the concentrations of H_2 and I_2 increase. The value of the equilibrium constant

$$K = \frac{[HI]^2}{[H_2][I_2]}$$

decreases from 67.5 at 357°C to 50.0 at 400°C.

The equation for the formation of ammonia from hydrogen and nitrogen is

$$N_2(g) + 3H_2(g) \rightleftharpoons 2NH_3(g) \qquad \Delta H = -92.2 \text{ kJ}$$

The reaction is exothermic, and we can shift the equilibrium to the right to favor the formation of more ammonia by lowering the temperature. However, equilibrium is reached more slowly because of the large decrease of reaction rate with decreasing temperature. In the commercial production of ammonia, it is not feasible to use temperatures much lower than 500°C. At lower temperatures, even in the presence of a catalyst, the reaction proceeds too slowly to be practical.

The effect of temperature on the equilibrium between NO_2 and N_2O_4 is indicated in Figure 15.8.

$$2NO_2(g) \rightleftharpoons N_2O_4(g) \qquad \Delta H = -57.20 \text{ kJ}$$

The negative ΔH value tells us that the reaction is exothermic and could be written

$$2NO_2(g) \rightleftharpoons N_2O_4(g) + 57.20 \text{ kJ}$$

At higher temperatures, the gas mixture has a deep brown color, indicative of a preponderance of brown NO_2 molecules. If, however, we put a stress on the system by cooling the mixture (withdrawing heat), the equilibrium shifts to the right to supply some of the heat lost by cooling. The concentration of colorless N_2O_4 increases, and the concentration of brown NO_2 decreases. The decreased concentration of NO_2 causes the brown color to fade.

Figure 15.8

The effect of temperature on the equilibrium between NO_2 and N_2O_4.

$$2NO_2(g) \rightleftharpoons N_2O_4(g)$$

$\Delta H = -57.20$ kJ (exothermic)
At the lower temperature (right), the brown color of the NO_2 is much fainter than at the higher temperature (left). This is due to a shift of the equilibrium from NO_2 to colorless N_2O_4 as heat is removed.

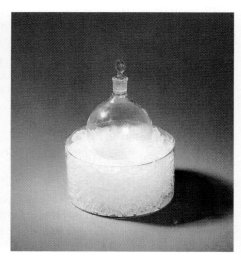

⑮.11 Effect of a Catalyst on Equilibrium

Iron powder is used as a catalyst in the production of ammonia from nitrogen and hydrogen to increase the rate of reaction of these two elements.

$$N_2 + 3H_2 \xrightarrow[\text{Fe}]{\triangle} 2NH_3$$

However, this same catalyst serves equally well to increase the rate of the reverse reaction—that is, the decomposition of ammonia into its constituent elements.

$$2NH_3 \xrightarrow[\text{Fe}]{\triangle} N_2 + 3H_2$$

Thus the net effect of iron in the reversible reaction

$$N_2 + 3H_2 \rightleftharpoons 2NH_3$$

is to cause equilibrium to be reached more rapidly. *A catalyst has no effect on the value of an equilibrium constant or on equilibrium concentrations.* It merely increases the rate of both the forward and the reverse reactions to the same extent so that equilibrium is reached more rapidly.

⑮.12 Homogeneous and Heterogeneous Equilibria

A **homogeneous equilibrium** is an equilibrium within a single phase, such as a mixture of gases or a solution. Most of the equilibria that have been considered in this chapter are homogeneous equilibria involving reversible changes in only one phase, the gas or the liquid phase.

A **heterogeneous equilibrium** is an equilibrium between two or more different phases. Liquid water in equilibrium with ice, liquid water in equilibrium with water vapor, and a solid in contact with its saturated solution are examples of heterogeneous equilibria. Each of these equilibria involves some kind of boundary surface between two phases.

The equilibrium between calcium carbonate, calcium oxide, and carbon dioxide is a heterogeneous equilibrium.

$$CaCO_3(s) \rightleftharpoons CaO(s) + CO_2(g)$$

The expression for the equilibrium constant for this reversible reaction is

$$K = \frac{[CaO][CO_2]}{[CaCO_3]}$$

The concentrations and pressures used in an equilibrium constant are approximations of the activities of the reactants and products (Section 15.2). The activity of a pure solid, such as $CaCO_3$ or CaO, is 1. The activity of a pure liquid or a solvent in a dilute solution is also 1. Thus the concentration of a pure solid, a pure liquid, or a solvent is not a satisfactory approximation of its activity; the activities, rather than the concentrations, should be used in expressions for equilibrium constants involving these species. Because the activities of pure solids, pure liquids, and solvents in dilute solutions are 1,

Figure 15.9

The thermal decomposition of calcium carbonate in a closed system is an example of a heterogeneous equilibrium.

CO₂ (gas)

CaO and CaCO₃ (solids)

these activities need not appear in expressions for reaction quotients or equilibrium constants. The equilibrium expression for the reaction

$$CaCO_3(s) \rightleftharpoons CaO(s) + CO_2(g)$$

is

$$K = [CO_2]$$

The expression for the equilibrium constant in terms of pressure is

$$K_p = P_{CO_2}$$

This equation means that at a given temperature there is only one pressure at which gaseous carbon dioxide can be in equilibrium with solid calcium carbonate and calcium oxide. A sample of $CaCO_3$ placed in a cylinder with a movable piston (Fig. 15.9) and heated at 900°C decomposes into CaO and CO_2. At equilibrium the pressure of carbon dioxide in the cylinder will equal K_p (actually 1.04 atm), if the piston is held stationary.

$$K_p = P_{CO_2} = 1.04 \text{ atm} \qquad \text{(at 900°C)}$$

At this pressure, because equilibrium has been reached, $CaCO_3$ decomposes into CaO and CO_2 at the same rate at which CaO and CO_2 react to produce $CaCO_3$. If we increase the pressure by pushing the piston down and compressing the gas, more CO_2 will combine with CaO to form $CaCO_3$, and the pressure will again drop to 1.04 atm. If, on the other hand, we decrease the pressure by raising the piston, just enough $CaCO_3$ will decompose to bring the pressure exerted by the CO_2 back to its equilibrium value of 1.04 atm.

Other examples of heterogeneous equilibria include the equilibrium of bromine vapor with liquid bromine (Fig. 15.3) and the equilibrium of water vapor either with ice or with liquid water. The equilibrium constant for the reaction

$$Br_2(l) \rightleftharpoons Br_2(g)$$

is

$$K_p = P_{Br_2}$$

There is no term for the liquid Br_2 because the activity of a pure liquid is 1.

⑮.13 The Distribution Law and Extraction

A good example of heterogeneous equilibria is the distribution of a solute in two immiscible solvents that are in contact but separated by a phase boundary. One such solute is iodine, which is soluble in both water and carbon tetrachloride. When an aqueous solution of iodine is shaken vigorously with a sufficient quantity of carbon tetrachloride, the greater part of the iodine leaves the water and goes into the carbon tetrachloride. After shaking is stopped, the carbon tetrachloride, colored violet by the iodine, settles to the bottom of the container. The equilibrium between the iodine in the water and in the carbon tetrachloride may be represented by

$$I_2 \text{ (in } H_2O) \rightleftharpoons I_2 \text{ (in } CCl_4)$$

Applying the law of mass action to the equilibrium system, we have

$$K = \frac{[I_2 \text{ (in } CCl_4)]}{[I_2 \text{ (in } H_2O)]}$$

The equilibrium constant for systems of this type is called the **distribution ratio,** and it has the value of 90 for this particular system at room temperature. In other words, the molar concentration of iodine in the carbon tetrachloride is 90 times that in the aqueous layer when equilibrium is established. Thus most of the iodine in a water solution can be removed by a single treatment with carbon tetrachloride. This process is known as **extraction.** If the aqueous layer is extracted a second time with a fresh portion of carbon tetrachloride, the concentration of iodine in the water solution is reduced to a negligibly small value.

For Review

Summary

A reaction has reached **equilibrium** when it appears that there is no change in the concentrations of reactants or products. The equilibrium is a **dynamic equilibrium,** because the rate of formation of products via the forward reaction is equal to the rate at which the products re-form reactants via the reverse reaction. For any reaction

$$mA + nB + \cdots \rightleftharpoons xC + yD + \cdots$$

at equilibrium, the **reaction quotient Q** is equal to the **equilibrium constant K** for the reaction.

$$K = Q = \frac{[C]^x[D]^y \cdots}{[A]^m[B]^n \cdots}$$

If a reactant or product is a pure solid, a pure liquid, or the solvent in a dilute solution, the concentration of this component does not appear in the expression for the equilibrium constant. At equilibrium, the values of [A], [B], [C], [D] $\cdots$ may vary, but the reaction quotient will always equal K. The addition or removal of a reactant or product may shift a reaction out of equilibrium, but the reaction will proceed such that the concentrations change and the reaction quotient again becomes equal to the equilibrium constant.

We can decide whether a reaction is at equilibrium by comparing the reaction quotient with the equilibrium constant for the reaction. If $Q = K$, the reaction is at equilibrium. If $Q > K$, the concentrations of products are greater than at equilibrium and the reaction will shift to the left, increasing the amounts of reactants and decreasing the amounts of products. If $Q < K$, the concentrations of products are less than at equilibrium and the reaction will shift to the right, increasing the amounts of products and decreasing the amounts of reactants.

There are three basic types of equilibrium calculations: (1) calculation of an equilibrium constant from the concentrations of reactants and products at equilibrium, (2) calculation of a missing equilibrium concentration, given the equilibrium constant and all equilibrium concentrations except one, and (3) calculation of all equilibrium concentrations from initial concentrations and the equilibrium constant.

A change in temperature changes the value of the equilibrium constant. A change in pressure generally affects a system in equilibrium only when gases are involved. The effect of a change in conditions is described by **Le Châtelier's principle:** If a stress such as a change in temperature, pressure, or concentration is applied to a system at equilibrium, the equilibrium shifts in a way that relieves the effects of the stress. **Van't Hoff's law** is a special case of Le Châtelier's principle.

A catalyst increases the rate of the forward and reverse reactions equally. Hence a catalyst in a reversible reaction causes the reaction to come to equilibrium more rapidly, but the catalyst has no effect on the value of the equilibrium constant or on the equilibrium concentrations.

A **homogeneous equilibrium** is an equilibrium within a single phase. A **heterogeneous equilibrium** is an equilibrium between two or more phases and involves a boundary surface between those phases.

Key Terms and Concepts

approximations (15.7)
distribution ratio (15.13)
effects of changes in concentration on equilibrium (15.8)
effects of changes in pressure on equilibrium (15.9)

effects of changes in temperature on equilibrium (15.10)
equilibrium (15.1)
equilibrium constant (15.2)
extraction (15.13)
heterogeneous equilibrium (15.12)

homogeneous equilibrium (15.12)
law of mass action (15.2)
Le Châtelier's principle (15.8)
reaction quotient (15.2)
successive approximations (15.7)
van't Hoff's law (15.10)

Exercises

Answers for selected even-numbered exercises marked by red numbers appear at the end of the book. The worked-out solutions to all even-numbered exercises appear in the *Solutions Guide*.

Equilibrium, Reaction Quotients, and Equilibrium Constants

1. Is it possible to tell whether the sample in the photograph in Fig. 15.1 was prepared from NO_2 or from N_2O_4? Explain your answer.

2. Explain why an equilibrium between $Br_2(l)$ and $Br_2(g)$ would not be established if the top were removed from the bottle shown in Fig. 15.3.

3. Sketch graphs, similar to Fig. 15.4, for Q and the concentrations of NO_2 and N_2O_4 as the 0.10 mol of NO_2 described in Example 15.2 comes to equilibrium. Plot points where $[NO_2] = 0.10$ M, 0.080 M, 0.060 M, 0.040 M, 0.020 M, and the equilibrium concentration.

4. Sketch graphs, similar to Fig. 15.4, for Q and the concentrations of CO, H_2O, CO_2, and H_2 as the mixture of gases described in Experiment 3 of Example 15.3 comes to equilibrium. Plot points where $[CO_2] = 0.0005$ M, 0.0010 M, 0.0015 M, 0.0020 M, and 0.0025 M.

5. Explain why there may be an infinite number of values for the reaction quotient of a reaction at a given temperature but there can be only one value for the equilibrium constant.

6. Write the mathematical expression for the reaction quotient for each of the following reactions:
   (a) $N_2(g) + 3H_2(g) \rightleftharpoons 2NH_3(g)$
   (b) $CH_4(g) + Cl_2(g) \rightleftharpoons CH_3Cl(g) + HCl(g)$
   (c) $N_2(g) + O_2(g) \rightleftharpoons 2NO(g)$

   (d) $2SO_2(g) + O_2(g) \rightleftharpoons 2SO_3(g)$
   (e) $4NH_3(g) + 5O_2(g) \rightleftharpoons 4NO(g) + 6H_2O(g)$
   (f) $N_2O_4(g) \rightleftharpoons 2NO_2(g)$
   (g) $CO_2(g) + H_2(g) \rightleftharpoons CO(g) + H_2O(g)$
   (h) $NH_4Cl(s) \rightleftharpoons NH_3(g) + HCl(g)$
   (i) $BaSO_3(s) \rightleftharpoons BaO(s) + SO_2(g)$
   (j) $2Pb(NO_3)_2(s) \rightleftharpoons 2PbO(s) + 4NO_2(g) + O_2(g)$
   (k) $2H_2(g) + O_2(g) \rightleftharpoons 2H_2O(l)$
   (l) $S_8(g) \rightleftharpoons 8S(g)$

7. The initial concentrations of reactants and products are given for each of the following systems. Calculate the reaction quotient and determine the direction in which each system will shift to reach equilibrium.
   (a) $2NH_3(g) \rightleftharpoons N_2(g) + 3H_2(g)$ $K = 17$
       $[NH_3] = 0.200$ M $[N_2] = 1.000$ M $[H_2] = 1.000$ M
   (b) $2NH_3(g) \rightleftharpoons N_2(g) + 3H_2(g)$ $K = 17$
       $[NH_3] = 0.300$ M $[N_2] = 0.200$ M $[H_2] = 0.100$ M
   (c) $2SO_3(g) \rightleftharpoons 2SO_2(g) + O_2(g)$ $K = 0.230$
       $[SO_3] = 1.00$ M $[SO_2] = 1.00$ M $[O_2] = 1.00$ M
   (d) $2SO_3(g) \rightleftharpoons 2SO_2(g) + O_2(g)$ $K = 0.230$
       $[SO_3] = 0.00$ M $[SO_2] = 1.00$ M $[O_2] = 1.00$ M
   (e) $2NO(g) + Cl_2(g) \rightleftharpoons 2NOCl(g)$ $K = 4.6 \times 10^4$
       $[NO] = 1.00$ M $[Cl_2] = 1.00$ M $[NOCl] = 0$ M
   (f) $N_2(g) + O_2(g) \rightleftharpoons 2NO(g)$ $K = 0.050$
       $[N_2] = 0.100$ M $[O_2] = 0.200$ M $[NO] = 1.00$ M

8. Calculate the reaction quotient and determine the direction in which each of the following systems will shift to reach equilibrium.
   (a) A 5.0-L flask containing 17 g of NH_3, 14 g of N_2, and 12 g of H_2:

   $$N_2(g) + 3H_2(g) \rightleftharpoons 2NH_3(g) \qquad K = 0.060$$

(b) A 2.00-L flask containing 230 g of $SO_3(g)$:

$$2SO_3(g) \rightleftharpoons 2SO_2(g) + O_2(g) \qquad K = 0.230$$

(c) A 1.0-L flask containing 0.050 mol of $NO(g)$, 1.10 g of $Cl_2(g)$, and 3.0×10^{23} molecules of NOCl:

$$2NO(g) + Cl_2(g) \rightleftharpoons 2NOCl(g) \qquad K = 4.6 \times 10^4$$

9. A sample of $NH_3(g)$ was formed from $H_2(g)$ and $N_2(g)$ at 500°C. The equilibrium mixture was found to contain 1.35 mol H_2 per liter, 1.15 mol N_2 per liter, and 4.12×10^{-1} mol NH_3 per liter. What is the value of the equilibrium constant for the formation of NH_3?

10. Ethanol and acetic acid interact to form ethyl acetate, an important industrial solvent, and water according to the equation

$$C_2H_5OH + CH_3CO_2H \rightleftharpoons CH_3CO_2C_2H_5 + H_2O$$

When 1 mol each of C_2H_5OH and CH_3CO_2H are allowed to react in a sealed tube, equilibrium is established when $\frac{1}{3}$ mol of each of the reactants remains. Calculate the equilibrium constant for the reaction. (*Note:* Water is not a solvent in this reaction.)

11. Most of the nearly 87 billion pounds of sulfuric acid produced in the United States during 1989 resulted from the reaction sequence

$$S_8(g) + 8O_2(g) \longrightarrow 8SO_2(g) \qquad (1)$$

$$2SO_2(g) + O_2(g) \xrightarrow{V_2O_5} 2SO_3(g) \qquad (2)$$

$$SO_3(g) + H_2O(l) \longrightarrow H_2SO_4(l) \qquad (3)$$

V_2O_5 is required in Equation (2) because the oxidation of SO_2 to SO_3 is slow in the absence of a catalyst. Under a specific set of conditions at 500°C, equilibrium pressures of SO_2, O_2, and SO_3 in the reaction of Equation (2) have been determined to be 0.342 atm, 0.173 atm, and 0.988 atm, respectively. What is K_p for this reaction?

12. At 1 atm and 25°C, NO_2 with an initial concentration of 1.00 M is 3.3×10^{-3}% decomposed into NO and O_2. Calculate the equilibrium constant for the reaction.

$$2NO_2 \rightleftharpoons 2NO + O_2$$

13. A 0.72-mol sample of PCl_5 is put into a 1.00-L vessel and heated. At equilibrium, the vessel contains 0.40 mol of $PCl_3(g)$ and 0.40 mol of $Cl_2(g)$. Calculate the value of the equilibrium constant for the decomposition of PCl_5 to PCl_3 and Cl_2 at this temperature.

14. Nitrogen and hydrogen form when ammonia decomposes according to the equation $2NH_3 \rightleftharpoons N_2 + 3H_2$. An equilibrium mixture of these substances at 400°C was found to contain 0.45 mol of nitrogen, 0.63 mol of hydrogen, and 0.24 mol of ammonia per liter. Calculate the equilibrium constant for the system.

15. Analysis of the gases in a 4.0-L sealed reaction vessel containing NH_3, N_2, and H_2 at equilibrium at 400°C established the presence of 4.8 mol N_2 and 0.64 mol H_2. At 400°C, $K = 0.50$ mol^{-2} L^2.

$$N_2(g) + 3H_2(g) \rightleftharpoons 2NH_3(g)$$

Calculate the equilibrium molar concentration of NH_3.

16. The equilibrium constant for the gaseous reaction

$$H_2 + I_2 \rightleftharpoons 2HI$$

is 50.2 at 448°C. Calculate the number of grams of HI that are in equilibrium with 1.25 mol of H_2 and 63.5 g of iodine in a 5.00-L flask at this temperature.

17. Calculate the equilibrium constant for the reaction

$$2SO_2(g) + O_2(g) \rightleftharpoons 2SO_3(g)$$

from the equilibrium concentrations $[SO_2] = 0.590$ M, $[O_2] = 0.045$ M, and $[SO_3] = 0.260$ M.

18. Calculate the equilibrium constant K_p for the reaction

$$2NO(g) + Cl_2(g) \rightleftharpoons 2NOCl(g)$$

from the equilibrium pressures: NO, 0.050 atm; Cl_2, 0.30 atm; NOCl, 1.2 atm.

19. The rate of the reaction $H_2(g) + I_2(g) \rightarrow 2HI(g)$ at 25°C is given by

$$\text{rate} = 1.7 \times 10^{-18} \, [H_2][I_2]$$

The rate of decomposition of gaseous HI to $H_2(g)$ and $I_2(g)$ at 25°C is given by

$$\text{rate} = 2.4 \times 10^{-21} \, [HI]^2$$

What is the equilibrium constant for the formation of gaseous HI from the gaseous elements at 25°C?

Calculation of Equilibrium Concentrations

20. Calculate the concentration of all species present when 0.50 M HF decomposes according to the equation

$$2HF(g) \rightleftharpoons H_2(g) + F_2(g) \qquad K = 1.0 \times 10^{-13}$$

21. Calculate the equilibrium concentrations that result when 1.0 M Cl_2 and 1.0 M H_2O react and come to equilibrium according to the equation

$$2Cl_2(g) + 2H_2O(g) \rightleftharpoons 4HCl(g) + O_2(g) \qquad K = 3.2 \times 10^{-14}$$

22. For the reaction

$$2NO(g) + Cl_2(g) \rightleftharpoons 2NOCl(g)$$

$K = 4.6 \times 10^4$ mol^{-1} L. Calculate the concentrations of all species at equilibrium for each of the following starting mixtures.

(a) 2.0 mol of pure NOCl in a 1-L flask
(b) 4.0 mol NO and 2.0 mol Cl_2 in a 1.0-L flask
(c) 2.0 M NO and 2.0 M NOCl
(d) 2.0 M NO, 1.0 M Cl_2, and 2.0 M NOCl
(e) 1.0 mol NO, 1.0 mol Cl_2, and 1.0 mol NOCl in a 1.0-L flask

23. Calculate the equilibrium concentrations for each of the systems in Exercise 7.

24. Calculate the equilibrium concentrations for each of the systems in Exercise 8.
25. A sample of 1.0 mol of Cl_2 and 1.0 mol of Br_2 is placed in a 2.5-L flask and allowed to come to equilibrium.

$$Cl_2(g) + Br_2(g) \rightleftharpoons 2BrCl(g) \quad K = 4.7 \times 10^{-2}$$

(a) What are the equilibrium concentrations?
(b) What mass of product is produced at equilibrium?

26. Calculate the equilibrium concentration of NO_2 in 1 L of a solution prepared from 0.129 mol of N_2O_4 with chloroform as the solvent. For the reaction $N_2O_4 \rightleftharpoons 2NO_2$, in chloroform, $K = 1.07 \times 10^{-5}$.

27. Antimony pentachloride decomposes according to the equation

$$SbCl_5(g) \rightleftharpoons SbCl_3(g) + Cl_2(g)$$

An equilibrium mixture in a 5.00-L flask at 448°C contains 3.85 g of $SbCl_5$, 9.14 g of $SbCl_3$, and 2.84 g of Cl_2. How many grams of each will be found if the mixture is transferred into a 2.00-L flask at the same temperature?

28. The equilibrium constant K for the reaction

$$PCl_5(g) \rightleftharpoons PCl_3(g) + Cl_2(g)$$

is 0.0211 at a certain temperature. What are the equilibrium concentrations of PCl_5, PCl_3, and Cl_2 starting with a concentration of PCl_5 of 0.100 M?

29. The equilibrium constant for the reaction

$$H_2(g) + CO_2(g) \rightleftharpoons H_2O(g) + CO(g)$$

is 1.6 at 990°C. Calculate the number of moles of each component in the final equilibrium mixture obtained from adding 1.00 mol of H_2, 2.0 mol of CO_2, 0.75 mol of H_2O, and 1.0 mol of CO to a 5.00-L container at 990°C.

30. The equilibrium constant for the reaction

$$CO + H_2O \rightleftharpoons CO_2 + H_2$$

is 5.0 at a given temperature.
(a) Upon analysis, an equilibrium mixture of the substances present at the given temperature was found to contain 0.20 mol of CO, 0.30 mol of water vapor, and 0.90 mol of H_2 in a liter. How many moles of CO_2 were there in the equilibrium mixture?
(b) Maintaining the same temperature, additional H_2 was added to the system, and some water vapor was removed by drying. A new equilibrium mixture was thereby established containing 0.40 mol of CO, 0.30 mol of water vapor, and 1.2 mol of H_2 in a liter. How many moles of CO_2 were in the new equilibrium mixture? Compare this with the quantity in part (a), and discuss whether the second value is reasonable. Explain how it is possible for the water vapor concentration to be the same in the two equilibrium solutions even though some vapor was removed before the second equilibrium was established.

31. A 1.00-L vessel at 400°C contains the following equilibrium concentrations: N_2, 1.00 M; H_2, 0.50 M; and NH_3, 0.25 M. How many moles of hydrogen must be removed from the vessel in order to increase the concentration of nitrogen to 1.1 M?

Calculation of Equilibrium Pressures

32. For which of the reactions in Exercise 6 does K (calculated using concentrations) equal K_p (calculated using pressures)?

33. The initial pressures of reactants and products are given for each of the following systems.
(i) Calculate the reaction quotient and determine the direction in which each system will shift to reach equilibrium.
(ii) Derive the equations that describe the relationships between the changes in pressure of the reactants and products as the reactions go to equilibrium.

(a) $2NH_3(g) \rightleftharpoons N_2(g) + 3H_2(g)$
$$K_p = 6.8 \times 10^4 \text{ atm}^2$$
Initial pressures: $NH_3 = 2.00$ atm, $N_2 = 10.00$ atm, $H_2 = 10.00$ atm

(b) $2NH_3(g) \rightleftharpoons N_2(g) + 3H_2(g)$
$$K_p = 6.8 \times 10^4 \text{ atm}^2$$
Initial pressures: $NH_3 = 3.00$ atm, $N_2 = 2.00$ atm, $H_2 = 1.00$ atm

(c) $2SO_3(g) \rightleftharpoons 2SO_2(g) + O_2(g) \quad K_p = 16.5$ atm
Initial pressures: $SO_3 = 1.00$ atm, $SO_2 = 1.00$ atm, $O_2 = 1.00$ atm

(d) $2SO_3(g) \rightleftharpoons 2SO_2(g) + O_2(g) \quad K_p = 16.5$ atm
Initial pressures: $SO_2 = 1.00$ atm, $O_2 = 1.00$ atm

(e) $2NO(g) + Cl_2(g) \rightleftharpoons 2NOCl(g)$
$$K_p = 2.5 \times 10^3 \text{ atm}^{-1}$$
Initial pressures: $NO = 1.00$ atm, $Cl_2 = 1.00$ atm

(f) $N_2(g) + O_2(g) \rightleftharpoons 2NO(g) \quad K_p = 0.050$
Initial pressures: $NO = 10.0$ atm

34. For the reaction

$$2NO(g) + Cl_2(g) \rightleftharpoons 2NOCl(g)$$

$K_p = 2.5 \times 10^3$ atm^{-1}. Calculate the pressures of all species at equilibrium for each of the following starting mixtures:
(a) 2.0 atm of pure NOCl
(b) 4.0 atm NO and 2.0 atm Cl_2
(c) 2.0 atm NO and 2.0 atm NOCl
(d) 2.0 atm NO, 1.0 atm Cl_2, and 2.0 atm NOCl
(e) 1.0 atm NO, 1.0 atm Cl_2, and 1.0 atm NOCl

35. Determine the equilibrium pressures for the systems described in Exercise 33.

36. The equilibrium constant K_p for the decomposition of nitrosyl bromide is 1.0×10^{-2} atm at 25°C.

$$2NOBr(g) \rightleftharpoons 2NO(g) + Br_2(g)$$

What percentage of NOBr is decomposed at 25°C and a total pressure of 0.25 atm?

Le Châtelier's Principle

37. Under what conditions do changes in pressure affect systems in equilibrium?

38. How will an increase in temperature affect each of the following equilibria? An increase in pressure?
    (a) $N_2(g) + 3H_2(g) \rightleftharpoons 2NH_3(g)$ $\Delta H = -92.2$ kJ
    (b) $H_2O(l) \rightleftharpoons H_2O(g)$ $\Delta H = 41$ kJ
    (c) $N_2(g) + O_2(g) \rightleftharpoons 2NO(g)$ $\Delta H = 181$ kJ
    (d) $3O_2(g) \rightleftharpoons 2O_3(g)$ $\Delta H = 285$ kJ
    (e) $CaCO_3(s) \rightleftharpoons CaO(s) + CO_2(g)$ $\Delta H = 176$ kJ

39. For each of the following reactions between gases at equilibrium, determine the effect on the equilibrium concentrations of the products when the temperature is decreased and when the external pressure on the system is decreased.
    (a) $2H_2O(g) \rightleftharpoons 2H_2(g) + O_2(g)$ $\Delta H = 484$ kJ
    (b) $N_2(g) + O_2(g) \rightleftharpoons 2NO(g)$ $\Delta H = 181$ kJ
    (c) $N_2(g) + 3H_2(g) \rightleftharpoons 2NH_3(g)$ $\Delta H = -92.2$ kJ
    (d) $2O_3(g) \rightleftharpoons 3O_2(g)$ $\Delta H = -285$ kJ
    (e) $H_2(g) + F_2(g) \rightleftharpoons 2HF(g)$ $\Delta H = 541$ kJ

40. Suggest four ways in which the equilibrium concentration of ammonia can be increased for the reaction given in Exercise 38(a).

41. (a) Write the expression for the equilibrium constant for the reversible reaction

    $$N_2 + O_2 \rightleftharpoons 2NO \qquad \Delta H = 181 \text{ kJ}$$

    (b) What will happen to the concentration of NO at equilibrium if (1) more O_2 is added? (2) N_2 is removed? (3) the pressure on the system is increased? (4) the temperature of the system is increased?

42. At 25°C and at 1 atmosphere, the partial pressures in an equilibrium mixture of N_2O_4 and NO_2 are $P_{N_2O_4} = 0.70$ atm and $P_{NO_2} = 0.30$ atm. Calculate the partial pressures of these two gases when they are in equilibrium at 9.0 atm and 25°C.

43. In a 3.0-L vessel, the following equilibrium partial pressures are measured: N_2, 190 torr; H_2, 317 torr; NH_3, 1000 torr. Hydrogen is removed from the vessel until the partial pressure of nitrogen, at equilibrium, is 250 torr. Calculate the partial pressures of the other substances under the new conditions.

Heterogeneous Equilibria

44. A 0.72-mol sample of PCl_5 is put into a 1.00-L vessel and heated. At equilibrium the vessel contains 0.40 mol of $PCl_3(g)$ as well as some $Cl_2(g)$ and undissociated $PCl_5(g)$. What is the equilibrium constant for the decomposition of PCl_5 to PCl_3 and Cl_2 at this temperature?

45. At a temperature of 60°C the vapor pressure of water is 0.196 atm. What is the equilibrium constant for the transformation $H_2O(l) \rightleftharpoons H_2O(g)$ at 60°C?

46. A sample of ammonium chloride was heated in a closed container.

    $$NH_4Cl(s) \rightleftharpoons NH_3(g) + HCl(g)$$

At equilibrium the pressure of $NH_3(g)$ was found to be 1.75 atm. What is the equilibrium constant for the decomposition at this temperature?

47. Sodium sulfate 10-hydrate, $Na_2SO_4 \cdot 10H_2O$, dehydrates according to the equation

    $$Na_2SO_4 \cdot 10H_2O(s) \rightleftharpoons Na_2SO_4(s) + 10H_2O(g)$$

    with $K_p = 4.08 \times 10^{-25}$ at 25°C. What is the pressure of water vapor in equilibrium with a sample of $Na_2SO_4 \cdot 10H_2O$?

48. Under what conditions will the reversible decomposition

    $$CaCO_3(s) \rightleftharpoons CaO(s) + CO_2(g)$$

    proceed to completion in a closed container so that no $CaCO_3$ remains?

49. At a temperature of 40°C the vapor pressure of water is 0.0728 atm. What is the equilibrium constant for the transformation $H_2O(l) \rightleftharpoons H_2O(g)$ at 40°C?

50. What is the minimum mass of $CaCO_3$ required to establish equilibrium at a certain temperature in a 6.50-L container if the equilibrium constant is 0.050 mol L^{-1} for the decomposition reaction of $CaCO_3$ at that temperature? Justify the units given in the problem for the equilibrium constant.

    $$CaCO_3(s) \rightleftharpoons CaO(s) + CO_2(g)$$

Additional Exercises

51. Explain why the reaction shown in Fig. 14.1 does not come to equilibrium.

52. What would happen to the color of the solution in Fig. 15.6(b) if a small amount of NaOH were added and $Fe(OH)_3$ precipitated?

53. Write the formula of the reaction quotient for the ionization of HOCN in water (see Section 12.9).

54. Write the formula of the reaction quotient for the ionization of NH_3 in water (see Section 12.9).

55. What is the value of the equilibrium constant for the change $H_2O(l) \rightleftharpoons H_2O(g)$ at 30°C? (See Section 10.11 for useful information.)

56. What is the value of the equilibrium constant for the change $H_2O(l) \rightleftharpoons H_2O(g)$ at 100°C?

57. The binding of oxygen by hemoglobin (Hb), giving oxyhemoglobin (HbO_2), is partially regulated by the concentration of H_3O^+ and dissolved CO_2 in the blood. Although the equilibrium is complicated, it can be summarized as

    $$HbO_2 + H_3O^+ + CO_2 \rightleftharpoons CO_2-Hb-H^+ + O_2 + H_2O$$

    (a) Write the equilibrium constant expression for this reaction.
    (b) Explain why the production of lactic acid and CO_2 in a muscle during exertion stimulates release of O_2 from the oxyhemoglobin in the blood passing through the muscle.

58. For the reaction A $\longrightarrow$ B + C the following data were obtained at 30°C.

Experiment	[A], mol L^{-1}	Rate, mol $L^{-1} h^{-1}$
1	0.170	0.0500
2	0.340	0.100
3	0.680	0.200

(a) What is the rate equation, and what is the order of the reaction?

(b) Calculate k for the reaction.

(c) The equilibrium constant for the reaction is 0.500. What is the rate constant for the reverse reaction?

59. The reaction between hydrogen, $H_2(g)$, and sulfur, $S_8(g)$, to produce H_2S is exothermic at 25°C. How should the pressure and temperature be adjusted in order to improve the equilibrium yield of H_2S, assuming that all reactants and products are in the gaseous state? How will these conditions affect the rate of attainment of equilibrium?

60. One possible mechanism for the reaction of H_2O_2 with I^- in acid solution (see Section 14.12) is

$$H_3O^+ + I^- \longrightarrow HI + H_2O \quad \text{(fast)}$$
$$H_2O_2 + HI \longrightarrow H_2O + HOI \quad \text{(slow)}$$
$$HOI + H_3O^+ + I^- \longrightarrow 2H_2O + I_2 \quad \text{(fast)}$$
$$I_2 + I^- \longrightarrow I_3^- \quad \text{(fast)}$$

(a) Write the rate equation for the slow elementary reaction.

(b) Write the equilibrium constant expression for the first elementary reaction.

(c) Solve the equilibrium constant expression from part (b) for [HI], and substitute this concentration into the rate equation from part (a) to obtain the overall rate equation for this mechanism.

61. Using the expression for the equilibrium constant for the fast reaction of H_3O^+ with H_2O_2 and the rate equation for the slow elementary reaction of $H_3O_2^+$ with I^-, derive the overall rate equation based on Mechanism C in Section 14.12 for the reaction of H_2O_2 with I^- in acid solution.

62. The hydrolysis of the sugar sucrose to the sugars glucose and fructose,

$$C_{12}H_{22}O_{11} + H_2O \longrightarrow C_6H_{12}O_6 + C_6H_{12}O_6$$

follows a first-order rate equation for the disappearance of sucrose.

$$\text{Rate} = k[C_{12}H_{22}O_{11}]$$

In neutral solution, $k = 2.1 \times 10^{-11} \text{ s}^{-1}$ at 27°C. (The products of the reaction, glucose and fructose, have the same molecular formulas but differ in the arrangement of the atoms in their molecules.)

(a) The equilibrium constant for the reaction is 1.36×10^5 at 27°C. What are the concentrations of glucose, fructose, and sucrose after a 0.150 M aqueous solution of sucrose has reached equilibrium? Remember that the activity of a solvent (the effective concentration) is 1.

(b) How long will the reaction of a 0.150 M solution of sucrose require to reach equilibrium at 27°C in the absence of a catalyst? Because the concentration of sucrose at equilibrium is so low, assume that the reaction is irreversible.

16

Acids and Bases

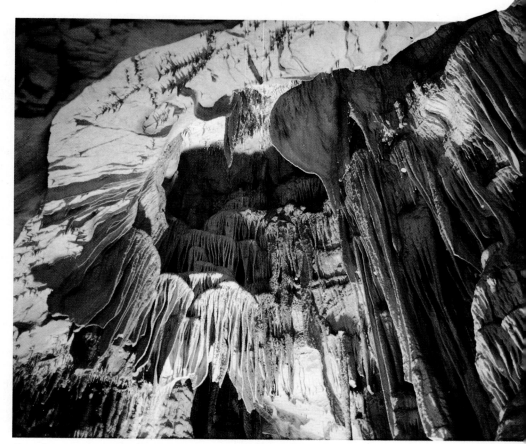

Cave formations result from acid–base reactions involving $CaCO_3$.

Acids and bases have been defined in a number of ways. When Boyle first characterized them in 1680, he noted that acids dissolve many substances, change the color of certain natural dyes (for example, they change litmus from blue to red), and lose these characteristic properties after coming in contact with alkalies (bases). In the eighteenth century it was recognized that acids have a sour taste, react with limestone to liberate a gaseous substance (CO_2), and interact with alkalies to form neutral substances. In 1787 Lavoisier proposed that acids are binary compounds of oxygen and considered oxygen to be responsible for their acidic properties. The hypothesis that oxygen is an essential component of acids was disproved by Davy in 1811 when he showed that hydrochloric acid contains no oxygen. Davy contributed greatly to the development of the modern acid–base concept by concluding that hydrogen, rather than oxygen, is the essential constituent of acids. In 1814 Gay-Lussac concluded that acids are substances that can neutralize alkalies and that these two classes of substances can be defined only in terms of each other. Davy and Gay-Lussac provided the foundation for our current concepts of acids and bases in aqueous solutions.

The significance of hydrogen was reemphasized in 1884 when Arrhenius defined an acid as a compound that dissolves in water to yield hydrogen ions (now recognized to be hydronium ions), and a base as a compound that dissolves in water to yield hydroxide ions. In 1923 the close relationship between acids and bases was pointed out by both Johannes Brønsted, a Danish chemist, and Thomas Lowry, an English chemist. Their models for acid–base behavior define acids as proton donors and bases as proton acceptors. An even broader view of the relationship between acids and bases was developed by the American chemist G. N. Lewis. The Lewis theory defines acids as electron-pair acceptors and defines bases as electron-pair donors.

In this chapter we will consider first the description of acid–base behavior presented by Brønsted and Lowry and then the more specific way in which the Brønsted–Lowry concept applies to aqueous solutions. Later in the chapter, we will proceed to the more generalized Lewis concept.

The Brønsted–Lowry Concept of Acids and Bases

16.1 The Protonic Concept of Acids and Bases

A compound that donates a proton (a hydrogen ion, H^+) to another compound is called a Brønsted acid, and a compound that accepts a proton is called a Brønsted base (Section 2.10). Stated simply, an acid is a proton donor, and a base is a proton acceptor.

An **acid–base reaction** is the transfer of a proton from a proton donor (acid) to a proton acceptor (base). Acids may be molecules, such as HCl, H_2SO_4, CH_3CO_2H, and H_2O; anions, such as HSO_4^-, $H_2PO_4^-$, HS^-, and HCO_3^-; or cations, such as H_3O^+, NH_4^+, and $[Al(H_2O)_6]^{3+}$. Bases also may be molecules, such as H_2O, NH_3, and CH_3NH_2; anions, such as OH^-, HS^-, HCO_3^-, CO_3^{2-}, F^-, and PO_4^{3-}; or cations, such as $[Al(H_2O)_5OH]^{2+}$. The most familiar bases are ionic compounds such as $NaOH$ and $Ca(OH)_2$ that contain the hydroxide ion, OH^-. The hydroxide ion accepts protons from acids to form water.

$$H_3O^+ + OH^- \longrightarrow 2H_2O$$

In our discussions of acid–base properties, we will sometimes identify specific ions as acids or bases. Remember, however, that no solid or solution can contain only cations or only anions. For every ion in a solid or solution there must be an ion of opposite charge, **a counter ion,** in order for the solid or solution to be electrically neutral. We may leave these counter ions out of net ionic equations, if they do not affect the acid–base properties of the system, but they are still present in the solution.

When an acid donates a proton, it forms the **conjugate base** of the acid. The conjugate base is a base because it can accept a proton (to re-form the acid).

Acid		Proton	Conjugate Base
HCl	$\longrightarrow$	H^+ +	Cl^-
H_2SO_4	$\longrightarrow$	H^+ +	HSO_4^-
H_2O	$\longrightarrow$	H^+ +	OH^-
HSO_4^-	$\longrightarrow$	H^+ +	SO_4^{2-}
NH_4^+	$\longrightarrow$	H^+ +	NH_3
$[Fe(H_2O)_6]^{3+}$	$\longrightarrow$	H^+ +	$[Fe(H_2O)_5(OH)]^{2+}$

In a similar behavior when a base accepts a proton, it forms the **conjugate acid** of the base. The conjugate acid is an acid because it can give up a proton (and thus re-form the base).

Base		Proton		Conjugate Acid
H_2O	+	H^+	$\longrightarrow$	H_3O^+
NH_3	+	H^+	$\longrightarrow$	NH_4^+
OH^-	+	H^+	$\longrightarrow$	H_2O
S^{2-}	+	H^+	$\longrightarrow$	HS^-
CO_3^{2-}	+	H^+	$\longrightarrow$	HCO_3^-
F^-	+	H^+	$\longrightarrow$	HF
$[Fe(H_2O)_5OH]^{2+}$	+	H^+	$\longrightarrow$	$[Fe(H_2O)_6]^{3+}$

In order for an acid to act as a proton donor, a base (proton acceptor) must be present to receive the proton. An acid does not form its conjugate base unless some other base is present to accept the proton. When the second base accepts the proton, it forms its conjugate acid, a second acid. Hydrogen chloride, HCl, reacts with anhydrous ammonia, NH_3, to form ammonium ions, NH_4^+, and chloride ions, Cl^-.

$$HCl + NH_3 \rightleftharpoons NH_4^+ + Cl^-$$
$$\text{Acid}_1 \quad \text{Base}_2 \quad \text{Acid}_2 \quad \text{Base}_1$$

During this reaction, hydrogen chloride (acid$_1$) gives up a proton to form chloride ion, its conjugate base (base$_1$); ammonia acts as a proton acceptor and therefore is a base (base$_2$). The proton combines with ammonia to give its conjugate acid, the ammonium ion (acid$_2$). The equations for several other acid–base reactions are as follows:

Acid$_1$	Base$_2$		Acid$_2$	Base$_1$
HNO_3 +	NH_3	$\rightleftharpoons$	NH_4^+ +	NO_3^-
HNO_3 +	F^-	$\rightleftharpoons$	HF +	NO_3^-
HSO_4^- +	CO_3^{2-}	$\rightleftharpoons$	HCO_3^- +	SO_4^{2-}
NH_4^+ +	S^{2-}	$\rightleftharpoons$	HS^- +	NH_3

A white cloud of finely divided solid NH_4Cl is produced by the acid–base reaction that results when the colorless gases HCl and NH_3 mix. (The gases in this photograph escaped from the concentrated solutions of HCl and NH_3.)

In all of these acid–base reactions, the forward reaction is the transfer of a proton from acid$_1$ to base$_2$. The reverse reaction is the transfer of a proton from acid$_2$ to base$_1$. Base$_1$ and base$_2$ are in competition for the proton, and the species that are present in the greatest concentrations depend on which base competes most effectively for the proton. In all of the examples given in the foregoing table, base$_2$ is the stronger base. As a result, at equilibrium the system consists primarily of a mixture of acid$_2$ and base$_1$.

When a Brønsted acid stronger than water dissolves in water, protons are transferred from the acid molecules to water molecules, giving hydronium ions, H_3O^+, and the acid is said to **ionize**. For example, when hydrogen chloride dissolves in water and ionizes, a proton is transferred from the hydrogen chloride to a water molecule. Water is the proton acceptor and acts as a base in this reaction.

$$HCl + H_2O \rightleftharpoons H_3O^+ + Cl^-$$

$$\text{Acid}_1 \quad \text{Base}_2 \quad \quad \text{Acid}_2 \quad \text{Base}_1$$

The **hydronium ion** is the conjugate acid of water. The properties common to Brønsted acids in aqueous solution are those of the hydronium ions that are produced when the acids donate hydrogen ions to water molecules.

When a base such as ammonia dissolves in water and ionizes, water functions as a proton donor and hence as an acid.

$$H_2O + NH_3 \rightleftharpoons NH_4^+ + OH^-$$

$$\text{Acid}_1 \quad \text{Base}_2 \quad \quad \text{Acid}_2 \quad \text{Base}_1$$

The **hydroxide ion** is the conjugate base of water. The hydroxide ion is a stronger base than ammonia, so this reaction gives only a small amount of NH_4^+ and OH^-; the majority of ammonia molecules do not react.

The two preceding equations show that under the appropriate conditions, water can function either as an acid or as a base. The behavior of water depends on the nature of the solute dissolved in it. The ability of water to act as either an acid or a base is also illustrated by the fact that a small fraction of water molecules in pure water provide protons to other water molecules to form hydronium ions and hydroxide ions.

$$H_2O + H_2O \rightleftharpoons H_3O^+ + OH^-$$

$$\text{Acid}_1 \quad \text{Base}_2 \quad \quad \text{Acid}_2 \quad \text{Base}_1$$

This type of reaction, in which a substance ionizes when one molecule of the substance reacts with another molecule of the substance, is referred to as **autoionization,** or **self-ionization.** Pure water exhibits self-ionization to a very slight extent. Only about 2 out of every 10^9 molecules in a sample of pure water are ionized at 25°C.

The very slight ionization of pure water is reflected in the small value of the equilibrium constant for the reaction

$$H_2O(l) + H_2O(l) \rightleftharpoons H_3O^+(aq) + OH^-(aq)$$

Because this reaction is reversible, we can write the equilibrium equation

$$K_w = [H_3O^+][OH^-]$$

where the equilibrium constant, K_w, is called the **ion product for water.** As in Chapter 15, the brackets represent "molar concentration of." The notation $[H_3O^+]$, for example, means the molar concentration of hydronium ion. Note that this is one of those equilibria that involve the solvent of a dilute solution as a reactant; water is both the reactant and the solvent for the hydronium and hydroxide ions. In such a case, the concentration of the solvent does not appear in the equilibrium equation (see Section 15.2).

At 25°C, K_w has the value 1.0×10^{-14}. This is an important equilibrium constant; you should memorize it. The degree of ionization of water and the resulting concentrations of hydronium ion and hydroxide ion increase as the temperature increases. At 100°C, K_w is about 1×10^{-12}, 100 times larger than the K_w value at 25°C.

What are the hydronium ion concentration and the hydroxide ion concentration in pure water at 25°C?

Example 16.1

The self-ionization of water yields the same number of hydronium and hydroxide ions. Therefore, in pure water, $[H_3O^+] = [OH^-]$. At 25°C,

$$K_w = [H_3O^+][OH^-] = [H_3O^+]^2 = [OH^-]^2 = 1.0 \times 10^{-14}$$

so $$[H_3O^+] = [OH^-] = \sqrt{1.0 \times 10^{-14}} = 1.0 \times 10^{-7}$$

The hydronium ion concentration and the hydroxide ion concentration are equal, and both equal 1.0×10^{-7} M.

Because water undergoes self-ionization, all aqueous solutions contain both hydronium ions and hydroxide ions. When an acid is added to pure water, the hydronium ion concentration, $[H_3O^+]$, becomes larger than 1.0×10^{-7}, and the hydroxide ion concentration, $[OH^-]$, becomes less than 1.0×10^{-7}, but never zero. When a base is added to water, $[OH^-]$ becomes greater than 1.0×10^{-7}, and $[H_3O^+]$ decreases, but not to zero. In any aqueous solution (solution in water), the concentrations of hydronium ion and hydroxide ion are inversely proportional (Section 10.3).

16.2 Amphiprotic Species

Certain molecules and ions may exhibit either acidic or basic behavior under the appropriate conditions. A species that, like water, may either gain or lose a proton is said to be **amphiprotic.** Water may lose a proton to a base, such as NH_3, or gain a proton from an acid, such as HCl.

The proton-containing anions previously given in Section 16.1 are also amphiprotic, which can be seen from the following equations involving HS^- and HCO_3^-.

Acid$_1$	Base$_2$		Acid$_2$	Base$_1$
HS$^-$	+ OH$^-$	$\rightleftharpoons$	H$_2$O	+ S^{2-}
HBr	+ HS$^-$	$\rightleftharpoons$	H$_2$S	+ Br$^-$
HCO$_3^-$	+ CN$^-$	$\rightleftharpoons$	HCN	+ CO$_3^{2-}$
H$_3$O$^+$	+ HCO$_3^-$	$\rightleftharpoons$	H$_2$CO$_3$	+ H$_2$O

The hydroxides of some metals, especially those near the boundary between metals and nonmetals in the periodic table, are amphiprotic and so react either as acids or bases.

Acid$_1$	Base$_2$		Acid$_2$	Base$_1$
[Al(H$_2$O)$_3$(OH)$_3$] +	OH$^-$	$\rightleftharpoons$	H$_2$O	+ [Al(H$_2$O)$_2$(OH)$_4$]$^-$
H$_3$O$^+$	+ [Al(H$_2$O)$_3$(OH)$_3$]	$\rightleftharpoons$	[Al(H$_2$O)$_4$(OH)$_2$]$^+$ +	H$_2$O

In the first reaction, one of the water molecules of the hydrated aluminum hydroxide loses a proton to the hydroxide ion. In the second reaction, the aluminum hydroxide accepts a proton from the hydronium ion. In both cases the insoluble hydrated aluminum hydroxide dissolves.

16.3 The Strengths of Brønsted Acids and Bases

The reaction of a Brønsted acid with water is given by the general equation

$$HA + H_2O \rightleftharpoons H_3O^+ + A^-$$

where A$^-$ is the conjugate base of the acid HA and the hydronium ion is the conjugate acid of water. Water is the base that reacts with the acid HA. A **strong acid** gives a 100% yield (or very nearly so) of hydronium ions and the conjugate base of the acid when it ionizes in water. A **weak acid** gives small yields of hydronium ions (ordinarily 10% or less). Thus the strength of an acid can be measured by its tendency to form hydronium ions in aqueous solution by donating protons to water molecules.

One way of measuring the relative strengths of acids is by measuring their percent ionization in aqueous solutions. In solutions of the same concentration, stronger acids ionize to a greater extent, and so give higher yields of hydronium ions than do weaker acids. The following data on percent ionization demonstrate that the order of acid strength for the acids CH$_3$CO$_2$H, HNO$_2$, and HSO$_4^-$ is CH$_3$CO$_2$H < HNO$_2$ < HSO$_4^-$.

$$CH_3CO_2H + H_2O \rightleftharpoons H_3O^+ + CH_3CO_2^- \qquad \text{(1.3\% ionization in 0.10 M soln)}$$

$$HNO_2 + H_2O \rightleftharpoons H_3O^+ + NO_2^- \qquad \text{(6.5\% ionization in 0.10 M soln)}$$

$$HSO_4^- + H_2O \rightleftharpoons H_3O^+ + SO_4^{2-} \qquad \text{(29\% ionization in 0.10 M soln)}$$

An equilibrium constant, called the **ionization constant, K_a,** can be determined for the ionization of an acid. For the reaction of an acid HA,

$$HA + H_2O \rightleftharpoons H_3O^+ + A^-$$

the magnitude of the ionization constant is given by the equation

$$K_a = \frac{[H_3O^+][A^-]}{[HA]}$$

where the concentrations are those at equilibrium. Although water is a reactant in the reaction, it is the solvent as well, so $[H_2O]$ does not appear in this equation. The larger the percent ionization of an acid, the larger the concentration of H_3O^+ and A^- relative to the concentration of the nonionized acid, HA. Thus another measure of the strength of an acid is the magnitude of its ionization constant. A stronger acid has a larger ionization constant than does a weaker acid. For the acids CH_3CO_2H, HNO_2, and HSO_4^- the ionization constants are

$$CH_3CO_2H + H_2O \rightleftharpoons H_3O^+ + CH_3CO_2^- \qquad K_a = \frac{[H_3O^+][CH_3CO_2^-]}{[CH_3CO_2H]} = 1.8 \times 10^{-5}$$

$$HNO_2 + H_2O \rightleftharpoons H_3O^+ + NO_2^- \qquad K_a = \frac{[H_3O^+][NO_2^-]}{[HNO_2]} = 4.5 \times 10^{-4}$$

$$HSO_4^- + H_2O \rightleftharpoons H_3O^+ + SO_4^{2-} \qquad K_a = \frac{[H_3O^+][SO_4^{2-}]}{[HSO_4^-]} = 1.2 \times 10^{-2}$$

The ionization constants increase as the strengths of the acids increase. (A table of ionization constants of weak acids appears in Appendix F.)

The reaction of a Brønsted base with water is given by

$$B + H_2O \rightleftharpoons HB^+ + OH^-$$

where HB^+ is the conjugate acid of the base B and the hydroxide ion is the conjugate base of water. Water is the acid that reacts with the Brønsted base. A **strong base** gives a 100% yield (or very nearly so) of hydroxide ions and the conjugate acid of the base when it reacts with water. Soluble ionic hydroxides are strong bases because they dissolve in water to give a 100% yield of hydroxide ions. A **weak base** gives a small yield of hydroxide ions (ordinarily 10% or less). The strength of a base can be measured by its tendency to form hydroxide ions in aqueous solution.

Because hydroxide ions are formed by ionization of the base, one way to measure the relative strengths of bases is to measure their percent ionization in aqueous solutions. In solutions of the same concentration, stronger bases give higher yields of hydroxide ion than do weaker bases. The following data demonstrate that the order of base strength for the bases NO_2^-, $CH_3CO_2^-$, and NH_3 is $NO_2^- < CH_3CO_2^- < NH_3$.

$$NO_2^- + H_2O \rightleftharpoons HNO_2 + OH^- \qquad \text{(0.0015\% ionization in 0.10 M soln)}$$

$$CH_3CO_2^- + H_2O \rightleftharpoons CH_3CO_2H + OH^- \qquad \text{(0.0075\% ionization in 0.10 M soln)}$$

$$NH_3 + H_2O \rightleftharpoons NH_4^+ + OH^- \qquad \text{(1.3\% ionization in 0.10 M soln)}$$

An equilibrium constant, called an ionization constant K_b, can be determined for the reaction of a base with water. For the reaction of a base B at equilibrium,

$$B + H_2O \rightleftharpoons HB^+ + OH^-$$

the magnitude of the ionization constant is given by the equation

$$K_b = \frac{[HB^+][OH^-]}{[B]}$$

The concentration of water does not appear in this equation because water is the solvent as well as a reactant. The larger the percent ionization of the base, the larger the concentration of HB^+ and OH^- relative to the concentration of the free base, B. Thus the size of its ionization constant is also a measure of the strength of a base. Stronger bases have larger ionization constants than do weaker bases. This may be seen in the ionization constants of the three bases, the base strengths of which increase in the order $NO_2^- < CH_3CO_2^- < NH_3$.

$$NO_2^- + H_2O \rightleftharpoons HNO_2 + OH^- \qquad K_b = \frac{[HNO_2][OH^-]}{[NO_2^-]} = 2.22 \times 10^{-11}$$

$$CH_3CO_2^- + H_2O \rightleftharpoons CH_3CO_2H + OH^- \qquad K_b = \frac{[CH_3CO_2H][OH^-]}{[CH_3CO_2^-]} = 5.6 \times 10^{-10}$$

$$NH_3 + H_2O \rightleftharpoons NH_4^+ + OH^- \qquad K_b = \frac{[NH_4^+][OH^-]}{[NH_3]} = 1.8 \times 10^{-5}$$

A table of ionization constants of weak bases appears in Appendix G.

The extent to which an acid, HA, donates protons to water molecules depends on the strength of the conjugate base, A^-, of the acid. If A^- is a strong base and accepts protons readily, any protons that are donated to water molecules are recaptured by A^-. Thus there is relatively little A^- and H_3O^+ in solution, and the acid, HA, is weak. If A^- is a weak base and does not readily accept protons, the solution contains primarily A^- and H_3O^+, and the acid is strong. *Strong acids form very weak conjugate bases, and weak acids form stronger conjugate bases.*

Table 16.1 lists a series of acids and bases in order of the decreasing strengths of the acids and the corresponding increasing strengths of the bases. The acid and base in a given row are conjugate to each other. That is, each base is the conjugate base of the acid that appears in the same row, and each acid is the conjugate acid of the base that appears in the same row. For example, we could refer to F^- as the conjugate base of the acid HF. Alternately, we could refer to HF as the conjugate acid of the base F^-.

The first six acids in Table 16.1 are the common strong acids. These acids are completely dissociated in aqueous solution. The conjugate bases of these acids are weaker bases than water. When one of these acids dissolves in water, the protons are transferred to water, the stronger base.

Those acids that lie between the hydronium ion and water in Table 16.1 form conjugate bases that can compete with water for possession of a proton. Both hydronium ions and nonionized acid molecules are present in equilibrium in a solution of one of these acids. Compounds that are weaker acids than water (they are found below water in the column of acids in the table) exhibit no observable acid behavior when dissolved in water. Their conjugate bases are stronger than the hydroxide ion, and if any conjugate base were formed, it would react with water to re-form the acid.

The extent to which a base forms hydroxide ion in aqueous solution depends on the strength of the base relative to that of the hydroxide ion, as shown in the last column in Table 16.1. A strong base, such as one of those lying below hydroxide ion, accepts protons from water to form the conjugate acid and hydroxide ion in 100% yield. Those bases lying between water and hydroxide ion accept protons from water, but a mixture of the hydroxide ion and the base results. Bases that are weaker than water (those that lie above water in the column of bases) show no observable basic behavior in aqueous solution.

According to the Brønsted–Lowry concept, stronger acids have weaker conjugate bases, and stronger bases have weaker conjugate acids (Fig. 16.1). We can express this

—based on ionisation of H_2O

Table 16.1   The Relative Strengths of Conjugate Acid–Base Pairs

Acid			Base	
Perchloric acid	$HClO_4$	*these are the only strong acids, all others are weak*	ClO_4^-	Perchlorate ion
Sulfuric acid	H_2SO_4		HSO_4^-	Hydrogen sulfate ion
Hydrogen iodide	HI	Stronger acids than H_3O^+; form H_3O^+ in 100% yield in H_2O.	I^-	Iodide ion
Hydrogen bromide	HBr		Br^-	Bromide ion
Hydrogen chloride	HCl		Cl^-	Chloride ion
Nitric acid	HNO_3		NO_3^-	Nitrate ion
Hydronium ion	H_3O^+		H_2O	Water
Hydrogen sulfate ion	HSO_4^-		SO_4^{2-}	Sulfate ion
Phosphoric acid	H_3PO_4		$H_2PO_4^-$	Dihydrogen phosphate ion
Hydrogen fluoride	HF		F^-	Fluoride ion
Nitrous acid	HNO_2		NO_2^-	Nitrite ion
Acetic acid	CH_3CO_2H		$CH_3CO_2^-$	Acetate ion
Carbonic acid	H_2CO_3		HCO_3^-	Hydrogen carbonate ion
Hydrogen sulfide	H_2S		HS^-	Hydrogen sulfide ion
Ammonium ion	NH_4^+		NH_3	Ammonia
Hydrogen cyanide	HCN		CN^-	Cyanide ion
Hydrogen carbonate ion	HCO_3^-		CO_3^{2-}	Carbonate ion
Water	H_2O		OH^-	Hydroxide ion
Hydrogen sulfide ion	HS^-		S^{2-}	Sulfide ion
Ethanol	C_2H_5OH	Stronger bases than OH^-; form OH^- in 100% yield in H_2O. *grab H^+ from H_2O*	$C_2H_5O^-$	Ethoxide ion
Ammonia	NH_3		NH_2^-	Amide ion
Hydrogen	H_2		H^-	Hydride ion
Methane	CH_4		CH_3^-	Methide ion

Increasing acid strength →

Increasing base strength →

relationship mathematically by using the ionization constant for an acid and its conjugate base. As will be shown in Section 17.11, the ionization constant of an acid is inversely proportional to the ionization constant of its conjugate base. The mathematical relationship is

$$K_a \times K_b = K_w = 1.0 \times 10^{-14} \quad \text{(at 25°C)} \qquad (1)$$

The ionization constant of acetic acid, K_a for CH_3CO_2H, is 1.8×10^{-5}. The conjugate base of acetic acid is the acetate ion, $CH_3CO_2^-$. The ionization constant of the acetate ion, K_b for $CH_3CO_2^-$, is 5.6×10^{-10}. The product of these two ionization constants is equal to K_w.

Relative acid strength

Stronger acids							Weaker acids

K_a 10^{-1} 10^{-3} 10^{-5} 10^{-7} 10^{-9} 10^{-11} 10^{-13}

Relative conjugate base strength

Weaker bases							Stronger bases

K_b 10^{-13} 10^{-11} 10^{-9} 10^{-7} 10^{-5} 10^{-3} 10^{-1}

Figure 16.1

The relative strengths of conjugate acid–base pairs, as indicated by their ionization constants in aqueous solution.

$$K_a \times K_b = (1.8 \times 10^{-5}) \times (5.6 \times 10^{-10})$$
$$= 1.0 \times 10^{-14} = K_w$$

Example 16.2 Show that Equation (1) holds for the nitrite ion, NO_2^-, and its conjugate acid.

The conjugate acid of NO_2^- is HNO_2. K_b for NO_2^- is given in this section as 2.22×10^{-11}, and K_a for HNO_2 is given as 4.5×10^{-4}.

$$K_a \times K_b = (4.5 \times 10^{-4}) \times (2.22 \times 10^{-11})$$
$$= 1.0 \times 10^{-14} = K_w$$

Example 16.3 Is NH_4^+ a stronger acid or a weaker acid than HCN at 25°C?

We can determine the relative acid strengths of NH_4^+ and HCN by comparing their ionization constants. The ionization constant of HCN is given in Appendix F as 4×10^{-10}. The ionization constant of NH_4^+ is not listed, but the ionization constant of its conjugate base, NH_3, is listed in Appendix G as 1.8×10^{-5}. We can determine the ionization constant of NH_4^+ from this value by using Equation (1).

$$K_a \times K_b = K_w = 1.0 \times 10^{-14}$$

$$K_a = \frac{K_w}{K_b}$$

$$= \frac{1.0 \times 10^{-14}}{1.8 \times 10^{-5}}$$

$$= 5.6 \times 10^{-10}$$

Because K_a for NH_4^+ (5.6×10^{-10}) is slightly larger than K_a for HCN (4×10^{-10}), NH_4^+ is the slightly stronger acid.

An acid will donate a proton to the conjugate base of a weaker acid (any acid that has a smaller ionization constant and hence lies below it in Table 16.1). Nitrous acid (HNO_2; K_a, 4.5×10^{-4}) is a stronger acid than acetic acid (CH_3CO_2H; K_a, 1.8×10^{-5}), so nitrous acid reacts with acetate ion to form nitrite ion and acetic acid.

$$HNO_2 + CH_3CO_2^- \rightleftharpoons NO_2^- + CH_3CO_2H$$

The nitrite ion, NO_2^-, the conjugate base of nitrous acid, is a weaker base than the acetate ion, $CH_3CO_2^-$, the conjugate base of acetic acid. Thus the acetate ion competes more effectively for the proton than does the nitrite ion.

16.4 Acid–Base Neutralization

An **acid–base neutralization** reaction occurs when an acid and a base are mixed. However, even when stoichiometrically equivalent quantities are combined in an aqueous solution, the resulting solution may not be neutral; it could contain either excess hydronium ions or excess hydroxide ions. The nature of the particular acid and base involved determines whether the solution is acidic, neutral, or basic. The following four equations illustrate some reactions that take place when equivalent quantities of acids and bases react in aqueous solution.

1. *A strong acid and a strong base yield a neutral solution.* The equation for the reaction of hydrochloric acid, a solution of a strong acid, with sodium hydroxide, a strong base, is

$$H_3O^+(aq) + Cl^-(aq) + Na^+(aq) + OH^-(aq) \longrightarrow Na^+(aq) + Cl^-(aq) + 2H_2O(l)$$

Both the strong acid and the strong base are completely ionized in solution. The reaction goes to completion, and water molecules, sodium ions, and chloride ions are the only products. The solution is therefore neutral.

2. *A strong acid and a weak base yield a weakly acidic solution.* The equation for the reaction of hydrochloric acid with the weak base ammonia is

$$H_3O^+(aq) + Cl^-(aq) + NH_3(aq) \rightleftharpoons NH_4^+(aq) + Cl^-(aq) + H_2O(l)$$

(Because ammonia is a weak base, few of the ammonia molecules are ionized in solution before the reaction.) The conjugate acid of ammonia, the ammonium ion, is a weak acid. After the initial reaction of NH_3 with HCl, a small fraction of the ammonium ions that are formed give up protons to water molecules, thus producing a weakly acidic solution.

3. *A weak acid and a strong base yield a weakly basic solution.* The equation for the reaction of the weak acid acetic acid with sodium hydroxide is

$$CH_3CO_2H(aq) + Na^+(aq) + OH^-(aq) \rightleftharpoons Na^+(aq) + CH_3CO_2^-(aq) + H_2O(l)$$

Acetic acid is a weak acid, and its conjugate base, the acetate ion, is a weak base. A small fraction of the acetate ions produced by the neutralization reaction pick up protons from water, produce OH^- ions, and give a weakly basic solution.

4. *A weak acid plus a weak base can yield either an acidic, basic, or neutral solution.* This is the most complex of the four types of reactions. When the weak acid and the weak base are of *unequal* strengths, the solution can be either acidic or basic, depending on the relative strengths of the two substances. We need to be familiar with the equilibrium concepts discussed in Chapter 17 in order to predict whether the resulting solution will be acidic or basic. However, if the weak acid and the weak base have the *same* strength, the solution is neutral. For example, acetic acid ($K_a = 1.8 \times 10^{-5}$) is as strong an acid as ammonia ($K_b = 1.8 \times 10^{-5}$) is a base. The equation for the reaction of acetic acid with ammonia is

$$CH_3CO_2H(aq) + NH_3(aq) \rightleftharpoons NH_4^+(aq) + CH_3CO_2^-(aq)$$

The weak base NH_3 takes up about the same amount of protons to form ammonium ion as acetic acid gives up to form acetate ion. Although the reaction does not go to completion, the solution is neutral.

16.5 The Relative Strengths of Strong Acids and Bases

The strongest acids, such as HCl, HBr, and HI, *appear* to have about the same strength in water. The water molecule is such a strong base compared to the conjugate bases Cl^-, Br^-, and I^- that ionization of the strong acids HCl, HBr, and HI is nearly complete in aqueous solutions. Hence in water these acids are all strong and appear to have equal types of reaction. This tendency of water to equalize any differences in strength among strong acids is known as the **leveling effect** of water. In solvents less strongly basic than water, HCl, HBr, and HI differ markedly in their tendency to give up a proton to the solvent. In ethanol, a weaker base than water, the extent of ionization increases in the order HCl < HBr < HI, and it is evident that HI is the strongest of these acids.

Water also exerts a leveling effect on the strengths of very strong bases. For example, the oxide ion, O^{2-}, and the amide ion, NH_2^-, are such strong bases that they react completely with water.

$$O^{2-} + H_2O \longrightarrow OH^- + OH^-$$

$$NH_2^- + H_2O \longrightarrow NH_3 + OH^-$$

Thus O^{2-} and NH_2^- appear to have the same base strength in water; they both give a 100% yield of hydroxide ion.

In binary compounds of hydrogen with nonmetals, the acid strength (the tendency to lose a proton) increases as the H—A bond strength decreases down a group in the periodic table. For Group VIIA the order of increasing acidity is HF < HCl < HBr < HI, in the absence of any leveling effect due to the solvent. Likewise, for Group VIA the order of increasing acid strength is $H_2O < H_2S < H_2Se < H_2Te$.

Across a row in the periodic table, the acid strength of binary hydrogen compounds increases with increasing electronegativity of the nonmetal atom, because the polarity of the H—A bond increases. Thus the order of increasing acidity (for removal of one proton) across the second row is $CH_4 < NH_3 < H_2O < HF$; across the third row it is $SiH_4 < PH_3 < H_2S < HCl$.

Compounds containing oxygen and one or more hydroxide groups can be acidic, basic, or amphoteric (Section 2.10), depending on the position in the periodic table (and thus the electronegativity, Section 7.5) of E, the element bonded to the oxygen and hydroxide group. Such compounds have the general formula $O_nE(OH)_m$ and include sulfuric acid, $O_2S(OH)_2$, sulfurous acid, $OS(OH)_2$, nitric acid, O_2NOH, perchloric acid, O_3ClOH, and aluminum hydroxide, $Al(OH)_3$.

$$-\overset{\displaystyle |}{\underset{\displaystyle |}{E}}-O-H$$

Bond *b*

Bond *a*

If the central atom, E, has a low electronegativity, its attraction for electrons is low. Little tendency exists for the central atom to form a strong covalent bond with the oxygen atom, and the bond between the element and oxygen is more readily broken than that between oxygen and hydrogen. Hence bond *a* is ionic, hydroxide ions are released to the solution, and the material behaves as a base. Large atomic size, small nuclear charge, and low oxidation number lower the electronegativity of E and are characteristic of the more metallic elements.

If, on the other hand, the element E has a relatively high electronegativity, it strongly attracts the electrons it shares with the oxygen atom, giving rise to a relatively strong covalent bond between E and oxygen. The oxygen–hydrogen bond is thereby weakened, because electrons are displaced toward E. Bond *b* is polar and readily releases hydrogen ions to the solution, so the material behaves as an acid. Small atomic size, large nuclear charge, and high oxidation number increase the electronegativity of E and are characteristic of the more nonmetallic elements. As the electronegativity of E increases, the O—H bond becomes weaker, and the acid strength increases.

Increasing the oxidation number of a given element E also increases the acidity of an oxyacid, because this increases the attraction of E for the electrons it shares with oxygen and thereby weakens the O—H bond. Sulfuric acid, $O_2\overset{+6}{S}(OH)_2$, is more acidic than sulfurous acid, OS(OH)$_2$; likewise nitric acid, $\overset{+5}{O_2NOH}$, is more acidic than nitrous acid, $\overset{+3}{ONOH}$. In each of these pairs, the oxidation number of the central atom (indicated by the small superior number) is larger for the stronger acid.

The hydroxides of elements with intermediate electronegativities and relatively high oxidation numbers (for example, elements near the diagonal line separating the metals from the nonmetals in the periodic table) are usually **amphoteric.** This means that the hydroxides act as acids when they react with strong bases and as bases when they react with strong acids. The amphoterism of aluminum hydroxide is reflected in its solubility in both strong acids and strong bases. In strong bases, the relatively insoluble hydrated aluminum hydroxide, [Al(H$_2$O)$_3$(OH)$_3$], is converted to the soluble ion, [Al(H$_2$O)$_2$(OH)$_4$]$^-$, by reaction with hydroxide ion (Section 16.2). In strong acids, it is converted in the first step to the soluble ion [Al(H$_2$O)$_4$(OH)$_2$]$^+$ by reaction with hydronium ion and in two additional steps to the soluble ion [Al(H$_2$O)$_6$]$^{3+}$. The net equation is

$$[Al(H_2O)_3(OH)_3] + 3H_3O^+ \rightleftharpoons [Al(H_2O)_6]^{3+} + 3H_2O$$

The different direction in the trend of acid strengths for the binary hydrogen halides arises from the fact that the halogen is attached directly to a hydrogen in the binary acid (instead of to an oxygen, which, in oxyacids, is attached to a hydrogen). In either kind of compound, as we go from a larger halogen to a smaller (that is, from I to Br to Cl), a progressive shrinking of the electron shells takes place, including a pulling closer of the adjacent atom, whether the adjacent atom be hydrogen (as in the hydrogen halides) or oxygen (as in the oxyacids). As the adjacent atom is pulled closer, it is brought into a region of higher electron density. If you picture the valence electrons as being inside a smaller volume for the smaller halogen, you can visualize the higher electron density. If the adjacent atom being pulled closer is a hydrogen atom (as is the case with the hydrogen halides), it is held more tightly by the higher electron density and is pulled loose with greater difficulty. Conversely, the hydrogen atom is in a region of lower electron density when attached to a larger halogen, so it is attracted less tightly and is pulled away more easily.

🔟.6 Properties of Brønsted Acids in Aqueous Solution

Because aqueous solutions of acids contain higher concentrations of hydronium ions than does pure water, these solutions all exhibit the following properties, which are due to the presence of the hydronium ion.

1. They have a sour taste.
2. They change the color of certain indicators (organic dyes). That is, they change litmus from blue to red and bromcresol green from green to yellow (Fig. 16.2).
3. They react with most representative metals and with the first-row transition metals (except copper) to liberate hydrogen gas. For example,

$$2H_3O^+(aq) + Zn(s) \longrightarrow Zn^{2+}(aq) + H_2(g) + 2H_2O(l)$$

4. They react with many basic metal oxides and hydroxides to form salts and water.

$$2H_3O^+ + FeO \longrightarrow Fe^{2+} + 3H_2O$$

$$2H_3O^+ + Fe(OH)_2 \longrightarrow Fe^{2+} + 4H_2O$$

Magnesium reacts with a solution of acetic acid, producing hydrogen gas and magnesium acetate.

Figure 16.2

The blue-green solution contains the indicator bromcresol green in a neutral solution; the yellow solution contains the same indicator in an acidic solution.

When solid CuO is added to a colorless solution of HNO_3, a blue solution of $Cu(NO_3)_2$ is produced.

5. They react with the salts of either weaker or volatile acids, such as carbonates or sulfides, to give a new salt and a new acid.

$$2H_3O^+ + CaCO_3 \longrightarrow H_2CO_3 + Ca^{2+} + 2H_2O$$
$$\hookrightarrow H_2O + CO_2(g)$$

$$2H_3O^+ + FeS \longrightarrow H_2S(g) + Fe^{2+} + 2H_2O$$

16.7 Preparation of Brønsted Acids

Brønsted acids may be prepared by any of the following methods.

1. *By direct union of the constituent elements.* Because binary compounds of hydrogen with more electronegative nonmetals are acids (Section 16.5), the direct reaction of hydrogen with such nonmetals as F_2, Cl_2, Br_2, and S_8 yields an acid.

$$H_2 + Br_2 \longrightarrow 2HBr$$
$$8H_2 + S_8 \overset{\Delta}{\rightleftharpoons} 8H_2S$$

2. *By the reaction of water with an oxide of a nonmetal.* Most oxides of nonmetals are acidic (Section 6.5). The action of water on such a nonmetal oxide forms an acid.

$$SO_3 + H_2O \longrightarrow H_2SO_4$$
$$P_4O_{10} + 6H_2O \longrightarrow 4H_3PO_4$$
$$CO_2 + H_2O \rightleftharpoons H_2CO_3$$

3. *By the metathesis reaction* (Section 2.11):
   (a) of a salt of a volatile acid with a nonvolatile or slightly volatile acid.

$$NaF(s) + H_2SO_4(l) \longrightarrow NaHSO_4(s) + HF(g)$$

   (b) of a salt with an acid to produce a second acid and an insoluble precipitate.

$$Ca_3(PO_4)_2(s) + 3H_2SO_4(l) \longrightarrow 2H_3PO_4(l) + 3CaSO_4(s)$$

   (c) of a salt of a weak acid with a strong acid.

$$Na^+(aq) + CH_3CO_2{}^-(aq) + H_3O^+(aq) + Cl^-(aq) \longrightarrow$$
$$CH_3CO_2H(aq) + Na^+(aq) + Cl^-(aq) + H_2O(l)$$

4. *By the reaction of water with certain nonmetal halides containing polar bonds.*

$$PBr_3 + 3H_2O \longrightarrow H_3PO_3 + 3HBr$$

$$PCl_5 + 4H_2O \longrightarrow H_3PO_4 + 5HCl$$

$$SiI_4 + 4H_2O \longrightarrow Si(OH)_4 + 4HI$$

16.8 Monoprotic, Diprotic, and Triprotic Acids

Acids can be classified in terms of the number of protons per molecule that they can give up in a reaction. Acids such as HCl, HNO_3, and HCN that contain one ionizable hydrogen atom in each molecule are called **monoprotic acids.** Their reactions with water are

$$HCl + H_2O \longrightarrow H_3O^+ + Cl^-$$

$$HNO_3 + H_2O \longrightarrow H_3O^+ + NO_3^-$$

$$HCN + H_2O \rightleftharpoons H_3O^+ + CN^-$$

Acetic acid, CH_3CO_2H, is also monoprotic because only one of the four hydrogen atoms in each molecule is given up as a proton in reactions with bases.

$$\begin{array}{c} H \\ | \\ H-C-CO_2H + H_2O \rightleftharpoons H_3O^+ + H-C-CO_2^- \\ | \\ H \end{array}$$

Diprotic acids contain two ionizable hydrogen atoms per molecule; ionization of such acids occurs in two stages. The first ionization always takes place to a greater extent than the second ionization. For example, carbonic acid ionizes as follows:

$$H_2CO_3 + H_2O \rightleftharpoons H_3O^+ + HCO_3^- \quad \text{(first ionization)}$$

$$HCO_3^- + H_2O \rightleftharpoons H_3O^+ + CO_3^{2-} \quad \text{(second ionization)}$$

Triprotic acids, such as phosphoric acid, ionize in three steps:

$$H_3PO_4 + H_2O \rightleftharpoons H_3O^+ + H_2PO_4^- \quad \text{(first ionization)}$$

$$H_2PO_4^- + H_2O \rightleftharpoons H_3O^+ + HPO_4^{2-} \quad \text{(second ionization)}$$

$$HPO_4^{2-} + H_2O \rightleftharpoons H_3O^+ + PO_4^{3-} \quad \text{(third ionization)}$$

16.9 Properties of Brønsted Bases in Aqueous Solution

When a Brønsted base stronger than water dissolves in water, a solution containing a higher concentration of hydroxide ions than that found in pure water is formed. The following properties are common to Brønsted bases in aqueous solution and are due to the presence of the hydroxide ion.

(a)   (b)

Figure 16.3

(a) The colorless liquid is a solution of the indicator phenolphthalein in a neutral solution; the pink liquid is a solution of the same indicator in a basic solution. (b) The red liquid is a basic solution of the indicator alizarin; the yellow liquid is a neutral solution of the same indicator.

1. They have a bitter taste.
2. They change the colors of certain indicators. For example, they change litmus from red to blue and phenolphthalein from colorless to red (Fig. 16.3).
3. They neutralize acids, forming water and a solution of a salt.

$$M^+ + OH^- + H_3O^+ + A^- \longrightarrow M^+ + A^- + 2H_2O$$

16.10 Preparation of Hydroxide Bases

Bases containing hydroxide ion (hydroxide bases) may be prepared by the following four methods.

1. *By the reaction of active metals with water.* The metals of Group IA, and Ca, Sr, and Ba of Group IIA, react directly with a stoichiometric amount of water to give strong bases.

$$2K + 2H_2O \longrightarrow 2KOH + H_2$$

$$Ca + 2H_2O \longrightarrow Ca(OH)_2 + H_2$$

When an excess of water is present, aqueous solutions of the bases form.

2. *By the reaction of oxides of active metals with water.* The soluble oxides of active metals react with water to give bases (Section 13.5).

$$Li_2O + H_2O \longrightarrow 2LiOH$$

$$SrO + H_2O \longrightarrow Sr(OH)_2$$

When an excess of water is present, aqueous solutions of the bases may form.

3. *By the metathesis reaction of a salt with a base to give a solution of a second base and an insoluble precipitate.*

$$2Na^+ + SO_4^{2-} + Ba^{2+} + 2OH^- \longrightarrow BaSO_4(s) + 2Na^+ + 2OH^-$$

4. *By the electrolysis of certain salt solutions* (Section 13.6).

$$2Na^+ + 2Cl^- + 2H_2O \xrightarrow{\text{Electrolysis}} 2Na^+ + 2OH^- + H_2(g) + Cl_2(g)$$

Calcium reacts with water and produces hydrogen gas and a solution of the base $Ca(OH)_2$.

⑯.11 Salts

The products of a neutralization reaction in aqueous solution are water and a salt (Section 2.10). Among the cations most frequently found in salts are simple metal ions such as Na^+, K^+, Ca^{2+}, and Ba^{2+}. Solvated metal ions such as $[Al(H_2O)_6]^{3+}$ and polyatomic cations such as NH_4^+ and $(CH_3)_3NH^+$ are also found. The simple anions of salts include F^-, Cl^-, Br^-, and I^-. Many salts contain polyatomic anions such as NO_3^-, SO_4^{2-}, PO_4^{3-}, $CH_3CO_2^-$, and CN^-.

Salts may be formed by other reactions too. For example, Brønsted acid–base reactions, Lewis acid–base reactions (Section 16.14), metathesis reactions, and the direct reactions between metals and nonmetals can all produce salts.

A solution of salt can be neutral, acidic, or basic, depending on the cation and anion present. Salts, such as NaCl and CaI_2, that contain a nonacidic ion and a nonbasic ion give neutral solutions. Salts, such as NaF and $Ca(CH_3CO_2)_2$, that consist of a nonacidic ion and a weakly basic ion give weakly basic solutions, because the weakly basic ions react with water and form hydroxide ions.

$$F^- + H_2O \rightleftharpoons HF + OH^-$$

$$CH_3CO_2^- + H_2O \rightleftharpoons CH_3CO_2H + OH^-$$

Similarly, salts, such as NH_4Cl and $NaHSO_4$, that contain a weakly acidic ion and a nonbasic ion give weakly acidic solutions, because the weakly acidic ions donate protons to water molecules and form hydronium ions.

$$NH_4^+ + H_2O \rightleftharpoons H_3O^+ + NH_3$$

$$HSO_4^- + H_2O \rightleftharpoons H_3O^+ + SO_4^{2-}$$

The solution of a salt that contains an ion that is a weak acid and an ion that is a weak base can give a solution that is neutral, acidic, or basic, depending on the relative strengths of the weak acid and the weak base. Examples of such salts include NH_4CN and $[Al(H_2O)_6](CH_3CO_2)_3$.

A salt that contains neither a replaceable hydrogen nor a hydroxide group is sometimes called a **normal salt;** examples include NaCl, K_2SO_4, and $Ca_3(PO_4)_2$. When only

The pink color of the phenolphthalein in this solution of NaF indicates that the solution is basic.

The yellow color of bromcresol green in this solution of $NaHSO_4$ indicates that the solution is acidic.

part of the acidic hydrogens of a polyprotic acid are replaced by a cation, the compound is known as a **hydrogen salt;** examples include sodium hydrogen carbonate, $NaHCO_3$ (often called sodium bicarbonate or baking soda), and sodium dihydrogen phosphate, NaH_2PO_4.

When only part of the hydroxide groups of an ionic metal hydroxide are replaced by another anion, the compound is known as a **hydroxysalt** or basic salt; examples include barium hydroxychloride, $Ba(OH)Cl$, and bismuth dihydroxychloride, $Bi(OH)_2Cl$. Some hydroxysalts readily lose the elements of one or more molecules of water and form **oxysalts.** For example, bismuth dihydroxychloride breaks down to give bismuth oxychloride, $BiOCl$, an oxysalt.

$$Bi(OH)_2Cl \longrightarrow BiOCl + H_2O$$

16.12 Quantitative Reactions of Acids and Bases

Using chemical reactions to determine the concentration of a solution (to **standardize** a solution) or to determine the amount of a substance present in a sample using a **standard solution** (a solution of known concentration) makes up the branch of quantitative analysis called **volumetric analysis.** Because the end point of a titration (Section 3.13) involving a neutralization reaction can be detected readily by use of an indicator, solutions of acids and bases are often used in volumetric analyses.

Example 16.4

Titration of a 40.00-mL sample of a solution of H_3PO_4 requires 35.00 mL (0.03500 L) of 0.1500 M KOH to reach the end point. Determine the molar concentration of H_3PO_4 if the reaction is

$$2KOH + H_3PO_4 \longrightarrow K_2HPO_4 + 2H_2O$$

The following steps are required for this problem.

Volume of KOH	→	Moles of KOH	→	Moles of H_3PO_4	→	Molarity of of H_3PO_4

$$0.03500 \text{ L KOH} \times \frac{0.1500 \text{ mol KOH}}{1 \text{ L KOH}} = 5.250 \times 10^{-3} \text{ mol KOH}$$

$$5.250 \times 10^{-3} \text{ mol KOH} \times \frac{1 \text{ mol } H_3PO_4}{2 \text{ mol KOH}} = 2.625 \times 10^{-3} \text{ mol } H_3PO_4$$

$$\frac{2.625 \times 10^{-3} \text{ mol } H_3PO_4}{0.04000 \text{ L}} = 0.06562 \text{ M}$$

Example 16.5

You may have used crystalline potassium hydrogen phthalate, $KHC_8H_4O_4$, as a standard acid in the laboratory, because it is easy to purify and weigh. If you titrate 1.5024 g of this acid with 37.28 mL of NaOH solution, what is the concentration of the NaOH solution?

$$KHC_8H_4O_4 + NaOH \longrightarrow KNaC_8H_4O_4 + H_2O$$

You can determine the concentration of NaOH from the number of moles of NaOH in 37.28 mL (0.03728 L) of the solution. To determine the concentration requires the following steps.

$$\boxed{\text{Mass of}\ KHC_8H_4O_4} \longrightarrow \boxed{\text{Moles of}\ KHC_8H_4O_4} \longrightarrow \boxed{\text{Moles of}\ NaOH} \longrightarrow \boxed{\text{Molarity of of NaOH}}$$

$$1.5024\ \text{g}\ KHC_8H_4O_4 \times \frac{1\ \text{mol}\ KHC_8H_4O_4}{204.223\ \text{g}\ KHC_8H_4O_4}$$

$$= 7.3567 \times 10^{-3}\ \text{mol}\ KHC_8H_4O_4$$

$$7.3567 \times 10^{-3}\ \text{mol}\ KHC_8H_4O_4 \times \frac{1\ \text{mol}\ NaOH}{1\ \text{mol}\ KHC_8H_4O_4}$$

$$= 7.3567 \times 10^{-3}\ \text{mol}\ NaOH$$

$$\frac{7.3567 \times 10^{-3}\ \text{mol}\ NaOH}{0.03728\ \text{L}} = 0.1973\ \text{M}$$

We can solve titration problems using mole relationships, as described here and in Section 3.13. An alternative method using equivalents is described in the next section.

16.13 Equivalents of Acids and Bases

An **equivalent of a Brønsted acid** is the amount of the acid that will provide 1 mole of protons (H^+) in a reaction. An **equivalent of a base** is the amount of the base that will provide 1 mole of hydroxide ions in a reaction or will react with 1 mole of protons. In an acid–base reaction, 1 equivalent of an acid will react with 1 equivalent of a base.

In an acid–base reaction, protons (H^+) are transferred from the acid to the base, and the number of protons transferred is used in the calculation of the mass of an equivalent of the acid and the base. When hydrochloric acid reacts with sodium hydroxide, a proton is transferred to the hydroxide ion.

$$HCl + NaOH \longrightarrow NaCl + H_2O$$

When 1 mole of hydrochloric acid reacts with 1 mole of sodium hydroxide, 1 mole of protons (6.022×10^{23} protons) is transferred to 1 mole of hydroxide ions (6.022×10^{23} hydroxide ions). It follows, then, that 1 equivalent (equiv) of hydrochloric acid is the same as 1 mole (36.5 g) of HCl (1 equiv HCl/1 mol HCl) and that 1 equivalent of sodium hydroxide is the same as 1 mole (40.0 g) of NaOH (1 equiv NaOH/1 mol NaOH). However, 1 mole of sulfuric acid can react with 2 moles of sodium hydroxide, transferring 2 moles of protons from the acid to the base.

$$H_2SO_4 + 2NaOH \longrightarrow Na_2SO_4 + 2H_2O$$

Hence 1 equivalent of sulfuric acid is equal to $\frac{1}{2}$ mole of the acid (2 equiv H_2SO_4/1 mol H_2SO_4).

The number of protons *actually transferred* in an acid–base reaction determines the mass of an equivalent of the acid or the base. For example, phosphoric acid may react with potassium hydroxide in any one of three ways:

$$H_3PO_4 + KOH \longrightarrow KH_2PO_4 + H_2O \tag{1}$$

$$H_3PO_4 + 2KOH \longrightarrow K_2HPO_4 + 2H_2O \tag{2}$$

$$H_3PO_4 + 3KOH \longrightarrow K_3PO_4 + 3H_2O \tag{3}$$

The numbers of moles of protons transferred, per mole of H_3PO_4, in the three reactions are 1, 2, and 3 moles, respectively. Thus an equivalent of H_3PO_4 in the three cases is equal to 1 mole, $\frac{1}{2}$ mole, and $\frac{1}{3}$ mole of H_3PO_4, respectively. *It must be emphasized that the mass of an equivalent of an acid or a base must be deduced from the reaction, not merely from the formula of the substance.*

Example 16.6

Calculate the mass of an equivalent of H_3PO_4 in Equations (1), (2), and (3).

The molar mass of H_3PO_4 is 98.00 g/mol. In Equation (1), 1 mol of H_3PO_4 provides 1 mol of H^+ (1 equiv H_3PO_4/1 mol H_3PO_4).

$$\frac{98.00 \text{ g } H_3PO_4}{1 \text{ mol } H_3PO_4} \times \frac{1 \text{ mol } H_3PO_4}{1 \text{ equiv } H_3PO_4} = \frac{98.00 \text{ g } H_3PO_4}{1 \text{ equiv } H_3PO_4}$$

Thus the mass of an equivalent of H_3PO_4 in Equation (1) is 98.00 g.

In Equation (2), 1 mol of H_3PO_4 provides 2 mol of H^+ (2 equiv H_3PO_4/1 mol H_3PO_4).

$$\frac{98.00 \text{ g } H_3PO_4}{1 \text{ mol } H_3PO_4} \times \frac{1 \text{ mol } H_3PO_4}{2 \text{ equiv } H_3PO_4} = \frac{49.00 \text{ g } H_3PO_4}{1 \text{ equiv } H_3PO_4}$$

The mass of an equivalent of H_3PO_4 in Equation (2) is therefore 49.00 g.

In Equation (3), 1 mol of H_3PO_4 provides 3 mol of H^+ (3 equiv H_3PO_4/1 mol H_3PO_4).

$$\frac{98.00 \text{ g } H_3PO_4}{1 \text{ mol } H_3PO_4} \times \frac{1 \text{ mol } H_3PO_4}{3 \text{ equiv } H_3PO_4} = \frac{32.67 \text{ g } H_3PO_4}{1 \text{ equiv } H_3PO_4}$$

Hence the mass of an equivalent of H_3PO_4 in Equation (3) is 32.67 g.

The **normality, N,** of a solution is the number of equivalents of solute per liter of solution. (Compare this with the definition of molarity given in Section 3.8.)

$$\text{Normality} = \frac{\text{equivalents of solute}}{\text{liters of solution}} = \frac{\text{equiv}}{L}$$

Normality may also be determined from the molarity of the solution, provided that the reaction is known.

$$\text{Normality} = \frac{\text{moles of solute}}{\text{liters of solution}} \times \frac{\text{equivalents of solute}}{\text{moles of solute}} = \frac{\text{equiv}}{L}$$

A solution that contains 1 equivalent of solute in 1 liter of solution is a 1 N (one normal) solution. Provided that both hydrogens react, a 1 N solution of sulfuric acid contains 1 equivalent, or 98 g/2 = 49 g, of H_2SO_4 per liter; a 2 N solution of H_2SO_4 contains 2 equivalents, or 98 g, per liter; and a 0.01 N solution contains 0.49 g per liter. A 1 N solution of sulfuric acid, if both hydrogens react, is identical to a 0.5 M solution of sulfuric acid; each contains 49 g of solute per liter of solution.

It should be evident that a 1 M solution of hydrochloric acid is also 1 N, because 1 mole of HCl is equal to 1 equivalent of HCl. However, a 1 M solution of sulfuric acid (98 g/L) is 2 N, because 1 mole of H_2SO_4 is equal to 2 equivalents of H_2SO_4, if both hydrogens react.

Calculate the normality of a solution containing 3.65 g of HCl per 0.500 L of solution. The mass of an equivalent of HCl is 36.5 g.

Example 16.7

$$3.65 \text{ g HCl} \times \frac{1 \text{ equiv HCl}}{36.5 \text{ g HCl}} = 0.100 \text{ equiv HCl}$$

$$\frac{0.100 \text{ equiv}}{0.500 \text{ L}} = 0.200 \text{ N HCl}$$

What is the normality of a solution of $Ba(OH)_2$ that contains 0.01713 g of $Ba(OH)_2$ per 0.1000 L of solution?

Example 16.8

$$Ba(OH)_2 + 2HCl \longrightarrow BaCl_2 + 2H_2O$$

Both of the hydroxide ions react, so 1 mol of $Ba(OH)_2$ provides 2 mol of OH^-. Hence there is 1 mol of $Ba(OH)_2$ per 2 equiv of $Ba(OH)_2$. This problem requires the following steps.

$$\boxed{\begin{array}{c} \text{Mass of} \\ Ba(OH)_2 \end{array}} \longrightarrow \boxed{\begin{array}{c} \text{Moles of} \\ Ba(OH)_2 \end{array}} \longrightarrow \boxed{\begin{array}{c} \text{Equivalents of} \\ \text{of } Ba(OH)_2 \end{array}} \longrightarrow \boxed{\begin{array}{c} \text{Normality} \\ \text{of solution} \end{array}}$$

$$0.01713 \text{ g Ba(OH)}_2 \times \frac{1 \text{ mol Ba(OH)}_2}{171.34 \text{ g Ba(OH)}_2} = 1.000 \times 10^{-4} \text{ mol Ba(OH)}_2$$

$$1.000 \times 10^{-4} \text{ mol Ba(OH)}_2 \times \frac{2 \text{ equiv Ba(OH)}_2}{1 \text{ mol Ba(OH)}_2} = 2.000 \times 10^{-4} \text{ equiv Ba(OH)}_2$$

$$\frac{2.000 \times 10^{-4} \text{ equiv Ba(OH)}_2}{0.1000 \text{ L}} = 2.000 \times 10^{-3} \text{ N}$$

How many grams of H_2SO_4 are contained in 1.2 L of 0.50 N H_2SO_4 solution that reacts according to this equation?

Example 16.9

$$H_2SO_4 + Ba(OH)_2 \longrightarrow BaSO_4 + 2H_2O$$

This problem may be solved by the following steps.

$$\boxed{\begin{array}{c} \text{Volume of} \\ \text{solution} \end{array}} \longrightarrow \boxed{\begin{array}{c} \text{Equivalents} \\ \text{of } H_2SO_4 \end{array}} \longrightarrow \boxed{\begin{array}{c} \text{Moles of} \\ H_2SO_4 \end{array}} \longrightarrow \boxed{\begin{array}{c} \text{Mass of} \\ H_2SO_4 \end{array}}$$

A 0.50 N H_2SO_4 solution contains 0.50 equiv/L.

$$1.2 \text{ L} \times \frac{0.50 \text{ equiv H}_2SO_4}{1.0 \text{ L}} = 0.60 \text{ equiv H}_2SO_4$$

Because each mole of H_2SO_4 provides two protons in the acid–base reaction, 1 mol of H_2SO_4 is equal to 2 equiv of H_2SO_4.

Example 16.9 continued

$$0.60 \text{ equiv } H_2SO_4 \times \frac{1 \text{ mol } H_2SO_4}{2 \text{ equiv } H_2SO_4} = 0.30 \text{ mol } H_2SO_4$$

$$0.30 \text{ mol } H_2SO_4 \times \frac{98.1 \text{ g } H_2SO_4}{1 \text{ mol } H_2SO_4} = 29 \text{ g } H_2SO_4$$

Example 16.10

Calculate the normality of a solution containing 2.35 g of H_3PO_4 per 0.600 L of solution, for a reaction in which two of the hydrogens react.

The problem may be solved by the following steps.

Mass of H_3PO_4 → Moles of H_3PO_4 → Equivalents of H_3PO_4 → Normality of H_3PO_4

(In the following solution, Steps 1 and 2 are combined in one overall calculation.) The molar mass of H_3PO_4 is 98.00 g/mol.

$$2.35 \text{ g } H_3PO_4 \times \frac{1 \text{ mol } H_3PO_4}{98.00 \text{ g } H_3PO_4} \times \frac{2 \text{ equiv } H_3PO_4}{1 \text{ mol } H_3PO_4} = 4.80 \times 10^{-2} \text{ equiv } H_3PO_4$$

$$\frac{4.80 \times 10^{-2} \text{ equiv}}{0.600 \text{ L}} = 8.00 \times 10^{-2} \text{ N } H_3PO_4$$

The Lewis Concept of Acids and Bases

16.14 Definitions and Examples

In 1923, G. N. Lewis proposed a generalized model of acid–base behavior in which acids and bases are not restricted to proton donors and proton acceptors. **According to the Lewis concept, an acid is any species (molecule or ion) that can accept a pair of electrons, and a base is any species (molecule or ion) that can donate a pair of electrons.** An acid–base reaction occurs when a base donates a pair of electrons to an acid. A Lewis acid–base adduct, a compound that contains a coordinate covalent bond between the Lewis acid and the Lewis base, is formed. The following equations illustrate the general application of the Lewis model.

The boron atom in boron trifluoride, BF_3, has only six electrons in its valence shell. Consequently, BF_3 is a very good **Lewis acid** and reacts with many Lewis bases; fluoride ion is the **Lewis base** in this reaction:

$$\left[:\overset{..}{\underset{..}{F}}: \right]^- + \overset{..}{\underset{..}{F}} : \overset{:\overset{..}{F}:}{\underset{:\overset{..}{F}:}{B}} : \overset{..}{\underset{..}{F}} : \longrightarrow \left[:\overset{..}{\underset{..}{F}} : \overset{:\overset{..}{F}:}{\underset{:\overset{..}{F}:}{B}} : \overset{..}{\underset{..}{F}} : \right]$$

Base   Acid   Acid–base adduct

In the following reaction, each of two ammonia molecules, Lewis bases, donates a pair of electrons to a silver ion, the Lewis acid.

$$2H : \overset{\overset{\displaystyle H}{|}}{\underset{\underset{\displaystyle H}{|}}{N}} : \quad + Ag^+ \longrightarrow \left[H : \overset{\overset{\displaystyle H}{|}}{N} : Ag : \overset{\overset{\displaystyle H}{|}}{N} : H \right]^+$$

Base   Acid   Acid–base
                                      adduct

$$2NH_3 + Ag^+ \longrightarrow [Ag(NH_3)_2]^+$$

An analogous reaction, in which four ammonia molecules serve as Lewis bases, each donating a pair of electrons to a copper ion that serves as the Lewis acid, is shown in Fig. 16.4.

$$4NH_3 + Cu^{2+} \longrightarrow [Cu(NH_3)_4]^{2+}$$

Nonmetal oxides act as Lewis acids and react with oxide ions, the Lewis base, to form oxyanions.

$$Ca^{2+} \left[: \overset{..}{\underset{..}{O}} : \right]^{2-} + \quad \overset{\overset{\displaystyle :O:}{}}{\underset{\underset{\displaystyle :O:}{}}{S}} : : \overset{..}{O} : \longrightarrow Ca^{2+} \left[: \overset{\overset{\displaystyle :O:}{}}{\underset{\underset{\displaystyle :O:}{}}{O}} : \overset{..}{S} : \overset{..}{O} : \right]^{2-}$$

Base   Acid   Acid–base
                                             adduct

Figure 16.4

The tube on the left contains a 0.1 M solution of $CuSO_4$. The tube on the right contains $[Cu(NH_3)_4]^{2+}$ prepared by adding NH_3 to a 0.1 M solution of $CuSO_4$.

Many Lewis acid–base reactions are displacement reactions in which one Lewis base displaces another Lewis base from an acid–base adduct or in which one Lewis acid displaces another Lewis acid.

$$\left[H : \overset{\overset{\displaystyle H}{|}}{N} : Ag : \overset{\overset{\displaystyle H}{|}}{N} : H \right]^+ + 2 : C \equiv N : ^- \longrightarrow [: N \equiv C : Ag : C \equiv N :]^- + 2 : \overset{\overset{\displaystyle H}{|}}{\underset{\underset{\displaystyle H}{|}}{N}} : H$$

Acid–base adduct   Base   New adduct   New base

$$Ca^{2+} \left[: \overset{\overset{\displaystyle :O:}{}}{\underset{\underset{\displaystyle :O:}{}}{C}} : : \overset{..}{O} : \right]^{2-} + SO_3 \longrightarrow Ca^{2+} \left[: \overset{\overset{\displaystyle :O:}{}}{\underset{\underset{\displaystyle :O:}{}}{O}} : \overset{..}{S} : \overset{..}{O} : \right]^{2-} + CO_2$$

Acid–base adduct   Acid   New adduct   New acid

$$H : \overset{..}{\underset{..}{Cl}} : \quad + : \overset{..}{O} : H \longrightarrow H : \overset{..}{O} : H^+ + : \overset{..}{\underset{..}{Cl}} : ^-$$

Acid–base   Base   New adduct   New base
adduct

The last displacement reactions shows how the reaction of a Brønsted acid with a base fits into the Lewis model. A Brønsted acid such as HCl is an acid–base adduct according to the Lewis concept, and proton transfer occurs because a more stable acid–base adduct is formed. Thus, although the definitions of acids and bases in the two theories are quite different, the theories overlap considerably.

For Review

Summary

A compound that can donate a proton (a hydrogen ion) to another compound is called a **Brønsted acid.** The compound that accepts the proton is called a **Brønsted base.** The species remaining after a Brønsted acid has lost a proton is the **conjugate base** of the acid. When a Brønsted base gains a proton, its **conjugate acid** forms. Thus an **acid–base reaction** occurs when a proton is transferred from a reactant acid to a reactant base, with formation of the conjugate base of the reactant acid and formation of the conjugate acid of the reactant base. **Amphiprotic species** can act as both proton donors and proton acceptors. Water is the most important amphiprotic species. It can form both the hydronium ion, H_3O^+, and the hydroxide ion, OH^-.

The strengths of Brønsted acids and bases in aqueous solutions can be determined by measurements of percent ionization or of ionization constants. Stronger acids form weaker conjugate bases, and weaker acids form stronger conjugate bases. Thus **strong acids** are completely ionized in aqueous solution because their conjugate bases are weaker bases than water. **Weak acids** are only partially ionized because their conjugate bases are strong enough to compete successfully with water for possession of protons. **Strong bases** react with water to give a 100% yield of hydroxide ion. **Weak bases** give only small yields of hydroxide ion. The strengths of the binary acids increase from left to right across a period of the periodic table ($CH_4 < NH_3 < H_2O < HF$), and they increase down a group ($HF < HCl < HBr < HI$). The strengths of oxyacids that contain the same central element increase as the oxidation number of the element increases ($H_2SO_3 < H_2SO_4$). The strengths of oxyacids also increase as the electronegativity of the central element increases [$H_2SeO_4 < H_2SO_4$; $Al(OH)_3 < Si(OH)_4 < H_3PO_4 < H_2SO_4 < HClO_4$].

The characteristic properties of aqueous solutions of Brønsted acids are due to the presence of hydronium ions; those of aqueous solutions of Brønsted bases are due to the presence of hydroxide ions. The **neutralization** that occurs when aqueous solutions of acids and bases are mixed results from the reaction of the hydronium and hydroxide ions to form water. **Salts** are also formed in neutralization reactions.

The concentration of an acid or a base in solution may be described in terms of the number of moles per liter (**molarity**) or in terms of the number of equivalents per liter (**normality**). An **equivalent** of an acid is the amount of the acid that will provide 1 mole of protons in a reaction. An equivalent of a base is the amount of the base that will provide 1 mole of hydroxide ions or will accept 1 mole of protons.

A **Lewis acid** is a molecule or ion that can accept a pair of electrons. A **Lewis base** is a molecule or ion that can donate a pair of electrons. Thus a Lewis acid–base reaction results in the formation of a coordinate covalent bond.

Key Terms and Concepts

amphiprotic (16.2)
amphoteric (16.5)
Brønsted acid (16.1)
Brønsted base (16.1)
conjugate acid (16.1)
conjugate base (16.1)
diprotic acid (16.8)
equivalent (16.13)

hydrogen salt (16.11)
hydroxysalt (16.11)
Lewis acid (16.14)
Lewis base (16.14)
monoprotic acid (16.8)
neutralization (16.4)
normal salt (16.11)
normality (16.13)

oxysalt (16.11)
salt (16.11)
strong acid (16.3)
strong base (16.3)
triprotic acid (16.8)
weak acid (16.3)
weak base (16.3)

Exercises

Answers for selected even-numbered exercises marked by red numbers appear at the end of the book. The worked-out solutions to all even-numbered exercises appear in the *Solutions Guide*.

Brønsted Acids and Bases

1. According to the Brønsted–Lowry concept, what is an acid? A base?
2. Write the equation for each of the following acting as a Brønsted acid.
   (a) H_3O^+ (c) H_2O (e) NH_4^+
   (b) HCl (d) CH_3CO_2H (f) HSO_4^-
3. Write the equation for each of the following acting as a Brønsted base.
   (a) H_2O (c) NH_3 (e) S^{2-}
   (b) OH^- (d) CN^- (f) $H_2PO_4^-$
4. What is the conjugate acid formed when each of the following reacts as a base?
   (a) OH^- (d) HSO_4^- (g) NH_2^-
   (b) F^- (e) HCO_3^- (h) H^-
   (c) H_2O (f) NH_3 (i) N^{3-}
   Is each conjugate acid strong or weak?
5. What is the conjugate base formed when each of the following reacts as an acid?
   (a) OH^- (d) HBr (g) HS^-
   (b) H_2O (e) HSO_4^- (h) PH_3
   (c) HCO_3^- (f) NH_3 (i) H_2O_2
6. What is the conjugate base of each of the following?
   (a) NH_4^+ (c) HNO_3 (e) CH_3CO_2H
   (b) HCl (d) $HClO_4$ (f) HCN
   Is each conjugate base strong or weak?
7. Write an equation for the reaction of each of the following with water.
   (a) HCl (d) NH_2^- (f) F^-
   (b) HNO_3 (e) $HClO_4$ (g) NH_4^+
   (c) NH_3
   What is the role played by water in each of these acid–base reactions?
8. (a) Identify the strong Brønsted acids and the strong Brønsted bases in the list of important industrial chemicals in Table 2.5.
   (b) List those compounds in Table 2.5 that can behave as Brønsted acids with strengths lying between those of H_3O^+ and H_2O.
   (c) List those compounds in Table 2.5 that can behave as Brønsted bases with strengths lying between those of H_2O and OH^-.
9. Hydrogen chloride can be prepared by the acid–base reaction of pure sulfuric acid with solid sodium chloride (see Section 2.11). Write the balanced chemical equation for the reaction, and identify the conjugate acid–base pairs in this reaction.
10. Identify and label the Brønsted acid, its conjugate base, the Brønsted base, and its conjugate acid in each of the following equations.
    (a) $HNO_3 + H_2O \longrightarrow H_3O^+ + NO_3^-$
    (b) $CN^- + H_2O \rightleftharpoons HCN + OH^-$
    (c) $H_2SO_4 + Cl^- \longrightarrow HCl + HSO_4^-$
    (d) $HSO_4^- + OH^- \longrightarrow SO_4^{2-} + H_2O$
    (e) $O^{2-} + H_2O \longrightarrow 2OH^-$
    (f) $[Cu(H_2O)_3(OH)]^+ + [Al(H_2O)_6]^{3+} \rightleftharpoons$
    $[Cu(H_2O)_4]^{2+} + [Al(H_2O)_5(OH)]^{2+}$
    (g) $H_2S + NH_2^- \longrightarrow HS^- + NH_3$
11. Gastric juice, the digestive fluid produced in the stomach, contains hydrochloric acid, HCl. Milk of magnesia, a suspension of solid $Mg(OH)_2$ in an aqueous medium, is sometimes used to neutralize excess stomach acid. Write a complete balanced equation for the neutralization reaction, and identify the conjugate acid–base pairs.
12. Nitric acid reacts with insoluble manganese(II) oxide to form soluble manganese(II) nitrate, $Mn(NO_3)_2$. Write the balanced chemical equation for the reaction of an aqueous solution of HNO_3 with MnO, and indicate the conjugate acid–base pairs.
13. What are amphiprotic species? Illustrate with suitable equations.
14. State which of the following species are amphiprotic, and write chemical equations illustrating the amphiprotic character of the species.
    (a) H_2O (c) S^{2-} (e) HSO_4^-
    (b) $H_2PO_4^-$ (d) CH_4 (f) H_2CO_3

Strengths of Acids and Bases

15. What is the ionization constant for the weak acid $CH_3NH_3^+$ (which is the conjugate acid of the weak base CH_3NH_2)?
16. What is the ionization constant of AsO_4^{3-} (which is the conjugate base of $HAsO_4^{2-}$)?
17. Which is the stronger base, $(CH_3)_3N$ or $H_2BO_3^-$?
18. Which is the stronger acid, NH_4^+ or $HBrO$?
19. Arrange the following in increasing order of base strength: N_3^-, HSe^-, HPO_4^{2-}.
20. Arrange the following in increasing order of acid strength: HSe^-, HPO_4^{2-}, $(CH_3)_2NH_2^+$.
21. Predict which acid in each of the following pairs is the stronger.
    (a) H_2O or H_2Te (c) HSO_4^- or $HSeO_4^-$
    (b) NH_3 or PH_3 (d) HSO_3^- or HSO_4^-
    Explain your reasoning for each.
22. Predict which acid in each of the following pairs is the stronger.
    (a) NH_3 or H_2O (c) NH_3 or H_2S
    (b) H_2O or HF (d) PH_3 or HI
    Explain your reasoning for each.
23. Rank the compounds in each of the following groups in order of increasing acidity, and explain the order you assign.
    (a) $HOCl$, $HOBr$, HOI
    (b) HCl, HBr, HI

(c) HOCl, HOClO, HOClO$_2$, HOClO$_3$

(d) HF, H$_2$O, NH$_3$, CH$_4$

(e) Mg(OH)$_2$, Si(OH)$_4$, ClO$_3$(OH)

(f) NaHSO$_3$, NaHSeO$_3$, NaHSO$_4$

24. Rank the bases in each of the following groups in order of increasing base strength, and explain the order you assign.

(a) H$_2$O, OH$^-$, H$^-$, Cl$^-$

(b) ClO$_4^-$, ClO$^-$, ClO$_2^-$, ClO$_3^-$

(c) NH$_2^-$, HS$^-$, HTe$^-$, PH$_2^-$

(d) BrO$_2^-$, ClO$_2^-$, IO$_2^-$

25. What is the relationship between the extent of ionization of an acid in aqueous solution and the strength of the acid?

26. Both HF and HCN ionize in water to a limited extent. Which of the conjugate bases, F$^-$ or CN$^-$, is the stronger base? See Table 16.1.

27. Soaps are sodium and potassium salts of a family of acids called fatty acids, which are isolated from animal fats. These acids, which are related to acetic acid, CH$_3$CO$_2$H, all contain the carboxyl group, —CO$_2$H, and have about the same strength as acetic acid. Examples include palmitic acid, C$_{15}$H$_{31}$CO$_2$H, and stearic acid, C$_{17}$H$_{35}$CO$_2$H.

(a) Write a balanced chemical equation indicating the formation of sodium palmitate, C$_{15}$H$_{31}$CO$_2$Na, from palmitic acid and sodium carbonate, and a corresponding equation for the formation of sodium stearate.

(b) Is a soap solution acidic, basic, or neutral?

28. Some porcelain cleansers contain sodium hydrogen sulfate, NaHSO$_4$. Is a solution of NaHSO$_4$ acidic, neutral, or basic? These cleansers remove the deposits due to hard water (primarily calcium carbonate, CaCO$_3$) very effectively. Write a balanced chemical equation for one reaction between NaHSO$_4$ and CaCO$_3$.

29. What is meant by the leveling effect of water on strong acids and strong bases?

Lewis Acids and Bases

30. According to the Lewis concept, what is an acid? A base?

31. Write the Lewis structures of the reactants and product of each of the following equations, and identify the Lewis acid and the Lewis base in each.

(a) O^{2-} + SO$_3$ $\longrightarrow$ SO$_4^{2-}$

(b) AlCl$_3$ + Cl$^-$ $\longrightarrow$ AlCl$_4^-$

(c) B(OH)$_3$ + OH$^-$ $\longrightarrow$ B(OH)$_4^-$

(d) CO$_2$ + OH$^-$ $\longrightarrow$ HCO$_3^-$

(e) I$^-$ + I$_2$ $\longrightarrow$ I$_3^-$

32. Calcium oxide is prepared by the decomposition of calcium carbonate at elevated temperatures (Section 13.5). This is the reverse of the Lewis acid–base reaction between CaO and CO$_2$. Write the chemical equation for the reaction of CaO with CO$_2$ showing the Lewis structures of the reactants and product, and identify the Lewis acid and the Lewis base.

33. The reaction of SO$_3$ with H$_2$SO$_4$ to give pyrosulfuric acid, H$_2$S$_2$O$_7$, is a Lewis acid–base reaction that results in the formation of S—O—S bonds. Write the chemical equation for this reaction showing the Lewis structures of the reactants and product, and identify the Lewis acid and the Lewis base.

34. The dissolution of solid Al(NO$_3$)$_3$ in water is accompanied by both a Lewis and a Brønsted acid–base reaction. Write balanced chemical equations for both reactions.

35. Each of the species given below may be considered a Lewis acid–base adduct of a proton with a Lewis base. For each of the following pairs, indicate which adduct is the stronger acid.

(a) HCl or HCN   (d) H$_2$O or NH$_3$

(b) HBr or H$_3$O$^+$ (e) HSO$_4^-$ or HCO$_3^-$

(c) H$_3$O$^+$ or NH$_4^+$

36. Write a balanced chemical equation for the Lewis acid–base reaction between Al(OH)$_4^-$ and CO$_2$, which causes the precipitation of Al(OH)$_3$ when CO$_2$ is added to an aqueous solution of Al(OH)$_4^-$.

Solutions of Brønsted Acids and Bases

37. Write the equation for the essential reaction between aqueous solutions of strong acids and of strong bases.

38. Write equations to show the stepwise ionization of the following polyprotic acids: H$_2$S, H$_2$CO$_3$, and H$_3$PO$_4$.

39. Containers of NaHCO$_3$, sodium hydrogen carbonate (sometimes called sodium bicarbonate), are often kept in chemical laboratories for use in neutralizing any acids or bases that may be accidentally spilled. Write balanced chemical equations for the neutralization by NaHCO$_3$ of (a) a solution of HCl and (b) a solution of KOH.

40. In aqueous solution arsenic acid, H$_3$AsO$_4$, ionizes in three steps. Write an equation for each step, and label the conjugate acid–base pairs. Which arsenic-containing species are amphiprotic?

41. Define the term *salt,* and give examples of normal salts, hydrogen salts, hydroxysalts, and oxysalts.

42. Write equations to illustrate three typical and characteristic reactions of aqueous acids.

43. Contrast the action of water on oxides of metals with that of water on oxides of nonmetals.

44. Give four methods of preparing hydroxide bases and of preparing Brønsted acids.

45. Using equations where appropriate, describe the chemical reaction you would expect from the combination of a solution of HClO$_4$ with each of the following:

(a) aluminum

(b) calcium carbonate

(c) a potassium hydroxide solution

(d) a blue-colored litmus solution

(e) solid sodium oxide

(f) solid aluminum sulfide, Al$_2$S$_3$

(g) ammonia gas

46. Define acid–base *neutralization.* Does your definition imply that the resulting solution is always neutral? Explain.

Titration: Normality

47. Calculate, to one decimal place, the mass of an equivalent of each of the reactants in the following equations.

(a) $Sr(OH)_2 + 2HNO_3 \longrightarrow Sr(NO_3)_2 + 2H_2O$

(b) $LiOH + LiH_2PO_4 \longrightarrow Li_2HPO_4 + H_2O$

(c) $2Al(OH)_3 + 3H_2SO_4 \longrightarrow Al_2(SO_4)_3 + 6H_2O$

(d) $NiCO_3 + 2HF \longrightarrow NiF_2 + H_2O + CO_2$

(e) $KOH + H_2SO_4 \longrightarrow KHSO_4 + H_2O$

(f) $H_2S + Li_3P \longrightarrow Li_2S + PH_3$ (not balanced)

48. Calculate the normality of each of the following solutions.

(a) 5.0 equiv of HCl in 2.0 L of solution

(b) 0.050 equiv of $Ba(OH)_2$ in 0.67 L of solution

(c) 0.0015 equiv of HCl in 100.0 mL of solution

(d) 0.04733 equiv of $HClO_4$ in 98.02 mL of solution

49. A 0.244 M solution of KOH is titrated with H_2SO_4, producing K_2SO_4. If a 48.0-mL sample of the KOH solution is used, what volume of 0.244 M H_2SO_4 is required to reach the end point?

50. What volume of 0.421 M HCl is required to titrate 47.00 mL of 0.204 M KOH?

51. Titration of 0.1500 g of an acid requires 47.00 mL of 0.0120 N NaOH to reach the end point. What is the mass of an equivalent of the acid?

52. Titration of 10.0 mL of a 0.444 N HI solution with NH_3 requires 23.2 mL of the NH_3 solution to reach the end point. What is the normality of the NH_3 solution?

53. What is the molarity of a H_2SO_4 solution if 24.8 mL of the solution is required to titrate 2.50 g of $NaHCO_3$?

$$H_2SO_4 + 2NaHCO_3 \longrightarrow Na_2SO_4 + 2H_2O + 2CO_2$$

54. A sample of solid calcium hydroxide, $Ca(OH)_2$, is allowed to stand in water until a saturated solution is formed. A titration of 50.00 mL of this solution with 5.00×10^{-2} M HCl requires 24.4 mL of the acid to reach the end point.

$$Ca(OH)_2 + 2HCl \longrightarrow CaCl_2 + 2H_2O$$

What is the molarity of a saturated $Ca(OH)_2$ solution? What is the solubility of $Ca(OH)_2$ in grams per liter of solution?

55. A 0.1824-g sample of an acid is titrated with 0.1236 M NaOH, and 23.14 mL is required to reach the end point. What is the mass of an equivalent of the acid?

Additional Exercises

56. In papermaking the use of wood pulp as a source of cellulose and of alum-rosin sizing (which keeps ink from soaking into the pages and blurring) produces a paper that deteriorates in 25–50 years. This is quite satisfactory for most purposes, but it is not suitable for the needs of libraries and archives. The deterioration is due to formation of acids. Alum-rosin slowly produces sulfuric acid under humid conditions. Also, wood pulp contains lignin, which forms carboxylic acids as it ages. These acids are similar to acetic acid in that they contain the acidic $—CO_2H$ group. In order to stop this acidification, books are sometimes soaked in magnesium hydrogen carbonate solution; treated with cyclohexylamine, $C_6H_{11}NH_2$, a base like ammonia but with one hydrogen atom replaced by a $—C_6H_{11}$ group; and treated with gaseous diethyl zinc, $(C_2H_5)_2Zn$, a covalent molecule containing Zn—C bonds. Diethyl zinc is a source of $C_2H_5^-$, which is very much like CH_3^- in its properties. Write balanced equations for these reactions. Use the formula RCO_2H for the carboxylic acids formed from lignin; the exact nature of R is not important in these reactions.

57. In dilute aqueous solution, HF acts as a weak acid. However, pure liquid HF (bp = 19.5°C) is a strong acid. In liquid HF, HNO_3 acts like a base and one molecule of HNO_3 can accept one proton. The acidity of liquid HF can be increased by adding one of several inorganic fluorides that are Lewis acids and accept F^- ions (for example, BF_3 or SbF_5). Write balanced chemical equations for the reaction of pure HNO_3 with pure HF and for that of pure HF with BF_3. Write the Lewis structures of the reactants and products, and identify the conjugate acid–base pairs.

58. Amino acids are biologically important molecules that are the building blocks of proteins. The simplest amino acid is glycine, $H_2NCH_2CO_2H$. The common feature of amino acids is that they contain the groups indicated in color: amino, $—NH_2$, and carboxyl, $—CO_2H$. An amino acid can function as either an acid or a base. For glycine the acid strength of the carboxyl group is about the same as that of acetic acid, CH_3CO_2H, and the base strength of the amino group is slightly greater than that of ammonia, NH_3.

(a) Write the Lewis structures of the ions that form when glycine is dissolved in 1 M HCl and in 1 M KOH.

(b) Write the Lewis structure of glycine when this amino acid is dissolved in water. (*Hint:* Consider the relative base strengths of the $—NH_2$ and $—CO_2^-$ groups.)

59. Using Lewis structures, write balanced equations for the following reactions.

(a) $HF + NH_3 \longrightarrow$

(b) $H_3O^+ + CN^- \longrightarrow$

(c) $Na_2O + SO_3 \longrightarrow$

(d) $Li_3N + H_2O \longrightarrow$

(e) $NH_3 + CH_3^- \longrightarrow$

60. Predict the products of the following reactions, and write a balanced equation for each. There may be more than one reasonable equation, depending on the stoichiometry assumed for the reactants.

(a) $Fe_2O_3(s) + H_2SO_4(l) \longrightarrow$

(b) $Li_2O(s) + SiO_2(s) \xrightarrow{\Delta}$

(c) $HCN(g) + Na(s) \longrightarrow$

(d) $NaHCO_3(s) + NaNH_2(s) \longrightarrow$

(e) $Li_3N(s) + NH_3(l) \longrightarrow$

(f) $BaO(s) + Cl_2O_7(l) \longrightarrow$

(g) $NaF(s) + H_3PO_4(l) \longrightarrow$

(h) $MgH_2(s) + H_2S(g) \longrightarrow$

(i) $NaCH_3(s) + NH_3(g) \longrightarrow$

(j) $KHCO_3(s) + KHS(s) \longrightarrow$

(k) $H_2SO_4(l) + NaCH_3CO_2(s) \longrightarrow$

61. Trichloroacetic acid, CCl_3CO_2H, is amphiprotic.

$$CCl_3CO_2H + B \longrightarrow CCl_3CO_2^- + BH$$

$$HA + CCl_3CO_2H \longrightarrow CCl_3CO_2H_2^+ + A^-$$

Write equations for the reaction of pure $CCl_3CO_2H(l)$ with $H_2O(l)$, $HClO_4(l)$, $HBr(g)$, $NH_3(g)$, and $CH_3CO_2H(l)$. Trichloroacetic acid has an acid strength between that of H_3O^+ and that of HSO_4^-.

62. Write equations for three methods of preparing the insoluble salt $BaSO_4$.

63. What mass of magnesium, when treated with an excess of dilute sulfuric acid, produces the same volume of hydrogen gas as is produced by 2.00 g of aluminum under the same conditions?

64. The reaction of 0.871 g of sodium with an excess of liquid ammonia containing a trace of $FeCl_3$ as a catalyst produced 0.473 L of pure H_2, measured at 25°C and 745 torr. What is the equation for the reaction of sodium with pure liquid ammonia? Show your calculations.

65. The reaction of WCl_6 with Al at about 400°C gives black crystals of a compound containing only tungsten and chlorine. A sample of this compound, when reduced with hydrogen, gives 0.2232 g of tungsten metal and hydrogen chloride, which is absorbed in water. Titration of the hydrochloric acid thus produced requires 46.2 mL of 0.1051 M NaOH to reach the end point. What is the empirical formula of the black tungsten chloride?

Ionic Equilibria of Weak Electrolytes

Red blood cells are immersed in a complex, weakly basic buffer system.

Water is the most important solvent on our planet. Our lives depend on reactions that occur in aqueous solution within our cells. Many aqueous solutions contain ions that result from ionization of electrolytes. The concentrations of these ions are very important in determining the rates, mechanisms, and yields of reactions in such solutions. In this chapter we will consider the solvent water. However, many of the concepts applied to water can also be applied to other polar solvents.

The concentrations of ions in a solution of a strong electrolyte can be calculated from the concentration of the solute, because a strong electrolyte is 100% ionized in solution. However, the concentrations of ions in a solution of a weak electrolyte cannot be determined so easily. Both ions and nonionized molecules of the weak electrolyte are present, and the concentrations of each of these species must be calculated from the concentration of the weak electrolyte and the extent to which it ionizes. These calculations involve the concepts of equilibria introduced in Chapter 15.

Weak acids and weak bases are probably the most significant weak electrolytes. They are important in many purely chemical processes and in those of biological interest. For example, amino acids are both weak acids and weak bases. In this chapter we will consider some ways of expressing concentrations of hydronium ion and hydroxide ion in solutions of weak acids and weak bases. Then we will examine equilibria involving these weak electrolytes.

⓱.1 pH and pOH

Pure water is an extremely weak electrolyte that undergoes self-ionization (Section 16.1) with the formation of very small *but equal* amounts of hydronium and hydroxide ions.

$$H_2O + H_2O \rightleftharpoons H_3O^+ + OH^- \qquad K_w = [H_3O^+][OH^-] = 1.0 \times 10^{-14} \quad \text{(at 25°C)}$$

The degree of ionization of water and the resulting concentrations of hydronium and hydroxide ion increase as the temperature increases. At 100°C, K_w is about 1×10^{-12}, 100 times larger than the value at 25°C.

Because the self-ionization of water yields the same number of hydronium and hydroxide ions, pure water is neutral—neither acidic nor basic. In pure water at 25°C, $[H_3O^+] = [OH^-] = 1.0 \times 10^{-7}$ M.

When an acid is added to pure water, the hydronium ion concentration, $[H_3O^+]$, becomes larger than 1.0×10^{-7} M, and the hydroxide ion concentration, $[OH^-]$, becomes less than 1.0×10^{-7} M, but not zero. Similarly, when a base is added to water $[OH^-]$ becomes greater than 1.0×10^{-7} M, and $[H_3O^+]$ decreases, but not to zero. The product of $[H_3O^+]$ and $[OH^-]$ is always a constant, so the value of neither concentration can ever become zero.

Using the pH scale is a convenient way to represent very small concentrations of hydronium ion in solution and to show changes in very small concentrations. The **pH of a solution** is the negative of the logarithm of the hydronium ion concentration.

$$pH = -\log [H_3O^+]$$

In this equation, *log* is the notation for a common logarithm, a logarithm to the base 10. If $\log x = y$, then $x = 10^y$. Thus we can find the hydronium ion concentration of a solution from its pH by using the relationship

$$[H_3O^+] = 10^{-pH} \text{ M}$$

The **pOH of a solution** is the negative of the logarithm of the hydroxide ion concentration. Thus pOH is another way to indicate the concentration of hydroxide ion of a solution.

$$pOH = -\log [OH^-]$$

We can find the hydroxide ion concentration by using the relationship

$$[OH^-] = 10^{-pOH} \text{ M}$$

We may define **pK_w** as the negative logarithm of the ion product for water (K_w).

$$pK_w = -\log K_w$$

Now we can write the ion product equation for water in terms of pH, pOH, and pK_w.

$$[H_3O^+][OH^-] = K_w$$

$$(-\log [H_3O^+]) + (-\log [OH^-]) = -\log K_w$$

$$pH + pOH = pK_w$$

Because K_w has the value 1.0×10^{-14} at 25°C,

$$pK_w = -\log (1.0 \times 10^{-14}) = -(-14.00) = 14.00$$

it follows that at 25°C

$$pH + pOH = 14.00$$

$$pH = 14.00 - pOH$$

$$pOH = 14.00 - pH$$

A neutral solution, one in which $[H_3O^+] = [OH^-]$, has a pH of 7.00 at 25°C. The pH of an acidic solution ($[H_3O^+] > [OH^-]$) is less than 7; the pH of a basic solution ($[OH^-] > [H_3O^+]$) is greater than 7. The pH of a solution can be measured with a **pH meter** (Fig. 17.1), with a solution of an indicator (Fig. 17.2), or with pH paper (Fig. 17.3).

Table 17.1 shows the relationships between $[H_3O^+]$, $[OH^-]$, pH, and pOH, and gives the values for some common substances at 25°C. Note that pH + pOH = 14.00. The lower the pH (and the higher the pOH), the higher the acidity.

Table 17.1   Relationships of $[H_3O^+]$, $[OH^-]$, pH, and pOH

$[H_3O^+]$	$[OH^-]$	pH	pOH	Sample Solution
10^1	10^{-15}	−1	15	Strongly acidic
10^0 or 1	10^{-14}	0	14	1 M HCl
10^{-1}	10^{-13}	1	13	
10^{-2}	10^{-12}	2	12	Gastric juice / Lime juice — 1 M CH₃CO₂H
10^{-3}	10^{-11}	3	11	Stomach acid
10^{-4}	10^{-10}	4	10	Wine
10^{-5}	10^{-9}	5	9	Coffee
10^{-6}	10^{-8}	6	8	More acidic
10^{-7}	10^{-7}	7	7	Pure water / Blood — Neutral
10^{-8}	10^{-6}	8	6	
10^{-9}	10^{-5}	9	5	More basic
10^{-10}	10^{-4}	10	4	
10^{-11}	10^{-3}	11	3	Milk of magnesia
10^{-12}	10^{-2}	12	2	Household ammonia, NH₃
10^{-13}	10^{-1}	13	1	
10^{-14}	10^0 or 1	14	0	1 M NaOH Strongly basic

The sour taste of a lime and other citrus fruit is due to the acid (citric acid) present in the fruit juice.

Figure 17.1

(a) A pH meter. The pH of a solution is determined electronically from the difference in electrical potentials between the two electrodes when they are dipped into the solution. It is displayed on the scale for convenient reading. (b) Some pairs of pH electrodes are combined into a single unit for convenience.

(a)

(b)

Figure 17.2

Universal indicator assumes a different color in solutions of different pH. Thus it can be added to a solution to determine the pH of the solution. The solutions in the 14 test tubes (left) contain universal indicator and are labeled with their pH. They show the gradations in color of the indicator for pH 1 to 14. The seven test tubes (above) also contain universal indicator and are labeled with the pH of their solutions. They contain 0.1 M solutions of the progressively weaker acids HCl (pH = 1), CH_3CO_2H (pH = 3), and NH_4Cl (pH = 5); pure water, a neutral substance (pH = 7); and 0.1 M solutions of the progressively stronger bases $C_6H_5NH_2$ (pH = 9), NH_3 (pH = 11), and NaOH (pH = 13).

Figure 17.3

pH paper contains a mixture of indicators that give it different colors in solutions of differing pH.

What is the pH of a solution of hydrochloric acid with a concentration of 1.2×10^{-3} M?

Example 17.1

Because hydrochloric acid is a strong acid (Section 16.3), the hydronium ion concentration is the same as the molar concentration of HCl. Thus we have

$$\text{pH} = -\log [\text{H}_3\text{O}^+] = -\log (1.2 \times 10^{-3})$$

$$= -(-2.92) = 2.92$$

(The use of logarithms is explained in Appendix A. On a calculator, take the logarithm of 1.2×10^{-3}; the pH is equal to its negative.)

The answer 2.92 represents *two* significant figures rather than three. The only significant figures in a logarithm are those to the right of its decimal point. The number to the left of the decimal point in a logarithm merely establishes the decimal place in the number that the logarithm represents. The number of significant figures in a logarithm should be equal to the number of significant figures in the number from which the logarithm is obtained. There are two significant figures in the hydronium ion concentration (1.2×10^{-3}) and two in the pH.

Calculate the pH of a 0.10 M solution of nitric acid (a strong acid) and of 0.10 M solutions of nitrous acid (6.5% ionized) and acetic acid (1.3% ionized).

Example 17.2

0.10 M Nitric Acid. Nitric acid is completely ionized in dilute solutions, so the concentration of the hydronium ion is 0.10 M in a 0.10 M solution of HNO_3. Substituting, we have

$$\text{pH} = -\log [\text{H}_3\text{O}^+] = -\log 0.10 = -(-1.00) = 1.00$$

(On a calculator, simply take the logarithm of 0.10; the pH is equal to the negative of this logarithm.)

0.10 M Nitrous Acid. The percent ionization for 0.10 M nitrous acid is 6.5%. Hence the number of moles of hydronium ion in exactly 1 L of solution is $(0.065)(0.10) = 0.0065$ mol. The concentration of H_3O^+ is 6.5×10^{-3} mol/1 L, or 6.5×10^{-3} M.

Example 17.2 continued

$$[H_3O^+] = 6.5 \times 10^{-3} \text{ M}$$

$$pH = -\log [H_3O^+] = -\log (6.5 \times 10^{-3}) = -(-2.19) = 2.19$$

0.10 M Acetic Acid. The percent ionization for 0.10 M acetic acid solution is 1.3%. Hence the number of moles of hydronium ion in exactly 1 L of a solution containing 0.10 mol of acetic acid is $(0.013)(0.10) = 0.0013$ mol. The concentration of H_3O^+ is 0.0013 mol/1 L, or 1.3×10^{-3} M. Thus

$$pH = -\log [H_3O^+] = -\log (1.3 \times 10^{-3}) = -(-2.89) = 2.89$$

Remember, the logarithm 2.89 contains only *two* significant figures. The 2 is not a significant figure.

Note that the strengths of the acids *decrease* as the pH values *increase* (*given the same initial concentration*). Nitric acid (pH = 1.00) is the strongest of the three acids, nitrous acid (pH = 2.19) is weaker, and acetic acid (pH = 2.89) is still weaker. This is what Table 16.1 (Section 16.3) would lead us to expect.

Example 17.3

Water in equilibrium with air contains 4.4×10^{-5}% carbon dioxide. The resulting carbonic acid, H_2CO_3, gives the solution a hydronium ion concentration of 2.0×10^{-6} M, about 20 times larger than that of pure water. Calculate the pH of the solution.

$$pH = -\log [H_3O^+] = -\log (2.0 \times 10^{-6})$$

$$= -(-5.70) = 5.70$$

(On a calculator take the logarithm of 2.0×10^{-6}; the pH is equal to its negative.)

Thus we see that water in contact with air is acidic, rather than neutral, because of dissolved carbon dioxide.

The next two examples illustrate the conversion of pH values to hydronium ion concentrations.

Example 17.4

Calculate the hydronium ion concentration of a solution, the pH of which is 9.0.

$$pH = -\log [H_3O^+] = 9.0$$

$$\log [H_3O^+] = -9.0$$

$$[H_3O^+] = 10^{-9.0} \qquad \text{or} \qquad [H_3O^+] = \text{antilog of } -9.0$$

$$[H_3O^+] = 1 \times 10^{-9} \text{ M}$$

(On a calculator take the antilog, or the "inverse" log, of -9.0, or calculate $10^{-9.0}$.)

Example 17.5

Calculate the hydronium ion concentration of blood, the pH of which is 7.3 (slightly alkaline).

$$pH = -\log [H_3O^+] = 7.3$$

$$\log [H_3O^+] = -7.3$$

$$[H_3O^+] = 10^{-7.3} \quad \text{or} \quad [H_3O^+] = \text{antilog of } -7.3$$

$$[H_3O^+] = 5 \times 10^{-8} \text{ M}$$

(On a calculator simply take the antilog, or the "inverse" log, of -7.3, or calculate $10^{-7.3}$.)

The relationship between pH and pOH is illustrated in the next two examples.

What are the pOH and the pH of a 0.0125 M solution of potassium hydroxide, KOH? **Example 17.6**

Potassium hydroxide is a strong base and is completely ionized in dilute solution (Section 16.3), so $[OH^-] = 0.0125$ M.

$$pOH = -\log [OH^-] = -\log 0.0125$$

$$= -(-1.903) = 1.903$$

The pH can be found from the pOH.

$$pH + pOH = 14.00$$

$$pH = 14.00 - pOH = 14.00 - 1.903 = 12.10$$

Calculate the pOH and the pH of a 0.10 M solution of acetate ion, $CH_3CO_2^-$, at 25°C. **Example 17.7**

$$CH_3CO_2^- + H_2O \rightleftharpoons CH_3CO_2H + OH^-$$

The percent yield of OH^- in this reaction is 0.0075%.

The percent reaction of acetate ion is 0.0075%. Hence the number of moles of acetic acid and of hydroxide ion in exactly 1 L of solution is $(0.000075)(0.10) = 7.5 \times 10^{-6}$ and the concentrations are 7.5×10^{-6} M. Thus

$$pOH = -\log (7.5 \times 10^{-6}) = -(-5.12) = 5.12$$

$$pH = 14.00 - pOH = 14.00 - 5.12 = 8.88$$

The calculated values of pOH and pH ($pOH < 7$; $pH > 7$) show that acetate ion is a weak base in water solution, as expected.

17.2 Ion Concentrations in Solutions of Strong Electrolytes

Chemists usually speak of concentrations of solutions of electrolytes as though the electrolyte were not ionized. They give the number of moles of the electrolyte needed to make a liter of the solution, rather than giving the actual concentrations of the molecules and ions present in the solution (Fig. 17.4).

The concentration of ions in a solution of a *strong* electrolyte can be found directly from the molar concentration of the electrolyte, because strong electrolytes are completely ionized in aqueous solution. In a solution prepared from 2.0 moles of hydrogen chloride and enough water to give 1.0 liter of solution (a 2.0 M solution of hydrochloric

Figure 17.4

This solution contains no HCl molecules even though it is labeled 2.0 M HCl. In the solution, $[H_3O^+]$ = 2.0 M and $[Cl^-]$ = 2.0 M.

acid), the HCl is 100% ionized and the concentration of HCl molecules is zero. Each HCl molecule provides one hydronium ion and one chloride ion; thus the concentrations of H_3O^+ and Cl^- are both equal to 2.0 M. A solution prepared by using 1.0 mole of the ionic compound K_2SO_4 in 2.0 liters of solution (0.50 mol K_2SO_4/1.00 L) is referred to as a 0.50 M solution of potassium sulfate. However, the solution actually contains K^+ and SO_4^{2-} ions with $[K^+]$ equal to 1.0 M and $[SO_4^{2-}]$ equal to 0.50 M, because each formula unit of potassium sulfate contains two potassium ions and one sulfate ion.

The concentration of ions in a solution of a weak electrolyte must be determined from the initial concentration of the weak electrolyte and either the equilibrium constant for its ionization in solution or its percent ionization in solution.

If a solution of a strong acid or a strong base is very dilute, the concentration of the hydronium ion or the hydroxide ion may be greater than the concentration of acid or base used to make the solution. This can occur because the acid (or base) is not the only source of H_3O^+ (or OH^-) in the solution; the self-ionization of water also produces these ions.

$$H_2O + H_2O \rightleftharpoons H_3O^+ + OH^-$$

If the concentration (or ionization) of an acid or of a base is sufficiently low, the ionization of water is larger, and therefore can increase the concentration of H_3O^+ or OH^- so much that it is significantly larger than the concentration of the acid or the base.

As an example, consider the concentrations of hydronium ion in various aqueous solutions of hydrogen chloride. If 1.00×10^{-6} mole of HCl, or more, is used to make 1.00 liter of a solution at 25°C, the hydronium ion concentration essentially equals the concentration of the HCl used to make the solution (Table 17.2 and Fig. 17.5). At lower concentrations of HCl, the concentration of hydronium ion in the solution is larger than the concentration of HCl used to make the solution. For concentrations of HCl less than 1.00×10^{-8} M, the concentration of hydronium ion stabilizes at 1.00×10^{-7} M. The additional hydronium ion (the hydronium ion that is not produced by the ionization of HCl) is produced by the self-ionization of water.

Figure 17.6 is a graph of the concentration of hydroxide ion in various solutions of sodium hydroxide. When the concentration of NaOH is greater than 1.00×10^{-6} M, the concentration of hydroxide ion in these solutions essentially equals the concentration

Figure 17.5

A graph of the concentrations of hydronium ion in 1.00-L solutions of HCl prepared from various amounts of HCl.

Table 17.2	Concentrations in Aqueous Solutions of HCl		
[HCl], M^a		**[H$_3$O$^+$], M^b**	**pH**
0.100	(1.00×10^{-1})	0.100	1.000
0.0100	(1.00×10^{-2})	0.0100	2.000
0.00100	(1.00×10^{-3})	0.00100	3.000
0.000100	(1.00×10^{-4})	0.000100	4.000
0.0000100	(1.00×10^{-5})	0.0000100	5.000
0.00000100	(1.00×10^{-6})	0.00000101	5.996
0.000000427	(4.27×10^{-7})	0.000000450	6.347
0.000000100	(1.00×10^{-7})	0.000000166	6.780
0.0000000100	(1.00×10^{-8})	0.000000101	6.996
0.00000000100	(1.00×10^{-9})	0.000000100	7.000
0.000000000100	(1.00×10^{-10})	0.000000100	7.000

^{a}Concentration of HCl added to aqueous solution.
^{b}Concentration of H$_3$O$^+$ in the resulting solution.

of NaOH used to make the solution. However, the self-ionization of water becomes important when the concentration of the hydroxide ion produced by the base is less than 1.00×10^{-6} M. When [NaOH] is less than 1.00×10^{-8} M, the concentration of OH$^-$ levels off at 1.00×10^{-7} M.

When the concentration of hydronium ion in a solution of an acid is greater than 4.5×10^{-7} M, the self-ionization of water produces less than 5% of the hydronium ion in solution (Table 17.2). Therefore, when calculating [H$_3$O$^+$] in these solutions, we can neglect the self-ionization of water. Similarly, when the concentration of hydroxide ion in a solution of a base is greater than 4.5×10^{-7} M, the self-ionization of water produces less than 5% of the hydroxide ion in solution, and the self-ionization of water can be neglected. Most solutions of acids or bases have hydronium ion or hydroxide ion concentrations greater than 4.5×10^{-7} M, so the self-ionization of water can usually be neglected.

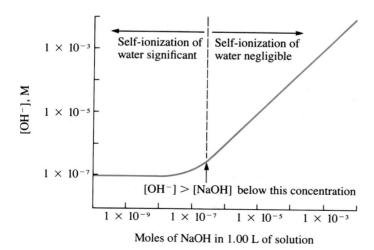

Figure 17.6

A graph of the concentrations of hydroxide ion in 1.00-L solutions of NaOH prepared from various amounts of NaOH.

Figure 17.7
pH paper indicates that a 0.1 M solution of HCl (beaker on left) has a pH of 1 (also see Fig. 17.3). A 0.1 M solution of CH_3CO_2H (beaker on right) is less acidic and has a pH of 3 ($[H_3O^+] = 0.001$ M) because the weak acid CH_3CO_2H is only partially ionized.

pH = 1   pH = 3

⑰.3 The Ionization of Weak Acids

We can tell by measuring the pH of an aqueous solution of known concentration that only a fraction of a weak acid ionizes (Fig. 17.7). The majority of the acid is present as the nonionized (molecular) form. For example, the ionization in a solution of acetic acid is

$$CH_3CO_2H(aq) + H_2O(l) \rightleftharpoons H_3O^+(aq) + CH_3CO_2^-(aq)$$

At equilibrium, K_a, **the ionization constant of the acid,** is equal to the reaction quotient.

$$K_a = Q = \frac{[H_3O^+][CH_3CO_2^-]}{[CH_3CO_2H]} = 1.8 \times 10^{-5}$$

Although water is a reactant in the reaction, it is the solvent as well, so $[H_2O]$ does not appear in the expression for K_a (Section 15.2). Table 17.3 gives the ionization constants for several weak acids; additional ionization constants can be found in Appendix F.

As noted in Section 15.5 for other reversible reactions, we can determine the equilibrium constant and the concentrations of reactants and products in an aqueous solution of a weak acid at equilibrium. These calculations involve the approximations and techniques discussed in Chapter 15 plus additional considerations arising from the fact that there are actually two equilibria present in an aqueous solution of an acid: the ionization of the acid and the self-ionization of water. For now, we will consider systems in which the concentration of hydronium ion is greater than 4.5×10^{-7} M so that we can neglect the contribution of the self-ionization of water to the hydronium ion concentration.

The following examples show how the equilibrium constants in Table 17.3 can be determined.

Table 17.3	Ionization Constants of Some Weak Acids	

Ionization Reaction	K_a at 25°C
$HSO_4^- + H_2O \rightleftharpoons H_3O^+ + SO_4^{2-}$	1.2×10^{-2}
$HF + H_2O \rightleftharpoons H_3O^+ + F^-$	7.2×10^{-4}
$HNO_2 + H_2O \rightleftharpoons H_3O^+ + NO_2^-$	4.5×10^{-4}
$HNCO + H_2O \rightleftharpoons H_3O^+ + NCO^-$	3.46×10^{-4}
$HCO_2H + H_2O \rightleftharpoons H_3O^+ + HCO_2^-$	1.8×10^{-4}
$CH_3CO_2H + H_2O \rightleftharpoons H_3O^+ + CH_3CO_2^-$	1.8×10^{-5}
$HClO + H_2O \rightleftharpoons H_3O^+ + ClO^-$	3.5×10^{-8}
$HBrO + H_2O \rightleftharpoons H_3O^+ + BrO^-$	2×10^{-9}
$HCN + H_2O \rightleftharpoons H_3O^+ + CN^-$	4×10^{-10}

At equilibrium, a solution of acetic acid contains $[CH_3CO_2H] = 0.0788$ M and $[H_3O^+] = [CH_3CO_2^-] = 0.0012$ M. What is the value of K_a for acetic acid? **Example 17.8**

We are asked to calculate an equilibrium constant from equilibrium concentrations—a type of calculation described in Section 15.5. At equilibrium the value of the equilibrium constant is equal to the reaction quotient. Thus

$$K_a = Q = \frac{[H_3O^+][CH_3CO_2^-]}{[CH_3CO_2H]}$$

$$= \frac{(0.0012)(0.0012)}{0.0788}$$

$$= 1.8 \times 10^{-5}$$

The pH of a 0.0516 M solution of nitrous acid, HNO_2, is 2.34. What is its K_a? **Example 17.9**

This is an equilibrium calculation similar to that discussed in Example 15.5 in Section 15.5. We are asked to determine an equilibrium constant from the initial concentrations of reactants and the concentration of one product at equilibrium. (It may not be immediately apparent that we are given a concentration at equilibrium, but remember that pH is simply another way to express the concentration of hydronium ion.)

The equation for the ionization of nitrous acid is

$$HNO_2 + H_2O \rightleftharpoons H_3O^+ + NO_2^-$$

for which K_a equals Q at equilibrium. Thus at equilibrium,

$$K_a = Q = \frac{[H_3O^+][NO_2^-]}{[HNO_2]}$$

We need to know the concentrations of H_3O^+, NO_2^-, and HNO_2 at equilibrium in order to calculate K_a.

We can calculate $[H_3O^+]$ at equilibrium from the pH.

$$pH = -\log [H_3O^+] = 2.34$$

$$\log [H_3O^+] = -2.34$$

$$[H_3O^+] = 10^{-2.34} = 0.0046 \text{ M}$$

Example 17.9 continued

Because the concentration of hydronium ion at equilibrium is greater than 4.5×10^{-7} M, the concentration of H_3O^+ produced by the self-ionization of water can be neglected (Section 17.2).

The concentration of H_3O^+ at equilibrium is due to the amount of H_3O^+ formed as the acid ionizes. From the chemical equation we see that 1 mol of NO_2^- forms for each 1 mol of H_3O^+ formed; thus $[H_3O^+]$ and $[NO_2^-]$ are equal. The equilibrium concentration of HNO_2 is equal to the initial concentration (0.0516 M) minus the amount that ionized to form H_3O^+ (0.0046 M). At equilibrium,

$$[HNO_2] = 0.0516 - 0.0046 = 0.0470 \text{ M}$$

Thus
$$K_a = Q = \frac{[H_3O^+][NO_2^-]}{[HNO_2]}$$

$$= \frac{(0.0046)(0.0046)}{(0.0470)}$$

$$= 4.5 \times 10^{-4}$$

The following examples illustrate cases in which equilibrium concentrations are calculated from initial concentrations and the equilibrium constant—calculations that generally involve the techniques discussed in Sections 15.6 and 15.7. For now we will assume that any hydronium ion produced by the ionization of water can be neglected in these calculations. The contribution of hydronium ion from water will be considered in Section 17.6.

Example 17.10

Calculate the concentrations of H_3O^+, $CH_3CO_2^-$, and CH_3CO_2H in a 0.100 M solution of the acid. K_a for acetic acid is 1.8×10^{-5}.

The equation for the ionization of acetic acid is

$$CH_3CO_2H + H_2O \rightleftharpoons H_3O^+ + CH_3CO_2^- \qquad K_a = 1.8 \times 10^{-5}$$

The initial concentrations are $[CH_3CO_2H] = 0.100$ M, $[H_3O^+] = \sim 0$, and $[CH_3CO_2^-] = 0$ M. Thus the reaction quotient calculated *from the initial concentrations* is zero, and the reaction will shift to the right to reach equilibrium.

The changes in concentration are as follows:

$$\begin{array}{ccccc} CH_3CO_2H & + & H_2O & \rightleftharpoons & H_3O^+ & + & CH_3CO_2^- \\ -\Delta & & & & \Delta & & \Delta \end{array}$$

The concentration of water does not appear in the equilibrium constant, so we do not need to consider its change in concentration, which is very small in any event. A table of initial concentrations (concentrations before the acid ionizes), changes in concentration, and equilibrium concentrations follows (the data given in the problem appear in color). It is always necessary to check the assumption that the final concentration of hydronium ion will be large enough for us to neglect the contribution of the self-ionization of water. We do this by verifying that $[H_3O^+] > 4.5 \times 10^{-7}$ M at equilibrium after calculating the concentration of hydronium ion.

	[CH₃CO₂H]	[H₃O⁺]	[CH₃CO₂⁻]
Initial Concentration, M	0.100	~0	0
Change, M	$-\Delta$	Δ	Δ
Equilibrium Concentration, M	$0.100 + (-\Delta) = 0.100 - \Delta$	$0 + \Delta = \Delta$	$0 + \Delta = \Delta$

At equilibrium, $\dfrac{[H_3O^+][CH_3CO_2^-]}{[CH_3CO_2H]} = K_a = 1.8 \times 10^{-5}$

Substitution of equilibrium concentrations yields

$$\frac{(\Delta)(\Delta)}{0.100 - \Delta} = 1.8 \times 10^{-5}$$

In solving for Δ, the changes in concentrations, we note that both Q for the initial concentrations and K_a are much less than 1, so we will assume that the changes in concentrations needed to make $Q = K$ are so small that $(0.100 - \Delta) = 0.100$. Thus

$$\frac{(\Delta)(\Delta)}{0.100} = 1.8 \times 10^{-5}$$

$$\Delta^2 = 0.100 \times (1.8 \times 10^{-5}) = 1.8 \times 10^{-6}$$

$$\Delta = \sqrt{1.8 \times 10^{-6}}$$

$$= 1.3 \times 10^{-3}$$

To check the assumption that Δ is small compared to 0.100, we find

$$\frac{\Delta}{0.100} = \frac{1.3 \times 10^{-3}}{0.100} = 0.013 \qquad (1.3\% \text{ of } 0.100)$$

Δ is less than 5% of the initial concentration; as discussed in Section 15.7, the assumption is valid.

The equilibrium concentrations are found from the initial concentrations and the changes in these concentrations as indicated in the last line of the table above.

$$[CH_3CO_2H] = 0.100 - \Delta = 0.100 - (1.3 \times 10^{-3}) = 0.099 \text{ M}$$

$$[H_3O^+] = 0 + \Delta = 1.3 \times 10^{-3} \text{ M}$$

$$[CH_3CO_2^-] = 0 + \Delta = 1.3 \times 10^{-3} \text{ M}$$

There are two more checks to be made:

1. Is the arithmetic correct? If so, the value of Q at equilibrium will equal K_a. At equilibrium our values give

$$Q = \frac{[H_3O^+][CH_3CO_2^-]}{[CH_3CO_2H]} = \frac{(1.3 \times 10^{-3}) \times (1.3 \times 10^{-3})}{0.099}$$

$$= 1.7 \times 10^{-5}$$

The answer checks; our calculated values are equal to the equilibrium constant within the margin for error associated with the number of significant figures in the problem.

<table>
<tr><td>

Example
17.10
continued

</td><td>

2. Is the assumption that we can neglect the hydronium ion from water valid? The equilibrium concentration of hydronium ion from the ionization of acetic acid is greater than 4.5×10^{-7} M; so we can neglect the self-ionization of water.

</td></tr>
</table>

Some weak acids ionize to such an extent that we cannot neglect the change in the initial concentration of the acid when solving the equilibrium equation. In such cases, we must solve the equilibrium equations by making successive approximations or by using the quadratic equation as described in Section 15.7.

Example 17.11

Calculate the pH of a 0.15 M solution of $NaHSO_4$. The HSO_4^- ion is a weak acid with a K_a of 1.2×10^{-2}.

In this problem, we need to determine the equilibrium concentration of the hydronium ion that results from the ionization of HSO_4^- so that we can use $[H_3O^+]$ to determine the pH.

The equation for the ionization of HSO_4^- is

$$HSO_4^- + H_2O \rightleftharpoons H_3O^+ + SO_4^{2-} \qquad K_a = 1.2 \times 10^{-2}$$

For this system the initial value of Q is zero, and the reaction will shift to the right with a decrease in $[HSO_4^-]$ and an increase in $[H_3O^+]$ and $[SO_4^{2-}]$.

The changes in concentration are summarized as follows:

$$HSO_4^- + H_2O \rightleftharpoons H_3O^+ + SO_4^{2-}$$
$$-\Delta \qquad\qquad \Delta \qquad \Delta$$

A table of initial concentrations, changes in concentration, and equilibrium concentrations follows (the data given in the problem are shown in color). Again, in setting up this table we made the assumption that the self-ionization of water can be neglected.

	$[HSO_4^-]$	$[H_3O^+]$	$[SO_4^{2-}]$
Initial Concentration, M	0.15	~0	0
Change, M	$-\Delta$	Δ	Δ
Equilibrium Concentration, M	$0.15 + (-\Delta) = 0.15 - \Delta$	$0 + \Delta = \Delta$	$0 + \Delta = \Delta$

At equilibrium,

$$\frac{[H_3O^+][SO_4^{2-}]}{[HSO_4^-]} = K_a = 1.2 \times 10^{-2}$$

Substitution of equilibrium concentrations yields

$$\frac{(\Delta)(\Delta)}{0.15 - \Delta} = 1.2 \times 10^{-2}$$

Let us attempt to solve for the change in the simplest way. Both Q for the initial concentrations and K_a are less than 1, so we will assume that Δ is small and that $0.15 - \Delta = 0.15$. Thus

This disinfectant is acidic because it contains $NaHSO_4$.

$$\frac{(\Delta)(\Delta)}{0.15} = 1.2 \times 10^{-2}$$

$$\Delta^2 = 0.15 \times (1.2 \times 10^{-2}) = 1.8 \times 10^{-3}$$

$$\Delta = \sqrt{1.8 \times 10^{-3}} = 0.042$$

To check the assumption that Δ is small compared to 0.15, we calculate

$$\frac{\Delta}{0.15} = \frac{0.042}{0.15} = 0.28 \qquad (28\%)$$

The change in concentration is not less than 5% of the initial concentration (it is 28% of the initial concentration); the assumption is *not* valid. We must solve the equilibrium equation for the change by one of the other techniques described in Section 15.7. We could use either successive approximations or the quadratic formula, but because we already have a first approximation to the solution, let's use the method of successive approximations to complete the solution.

Second Approximation. As a second approximation to the value of $(0.15 - \Delta)$, we use the value of Δ that was just determined from the approximation $(0.15 - \Delta) = 0.15$. Thus $(0.15 - \Delta) = (0.15 - 0.042) = 0.108$, and the equilibrium equation becomes

$$\frac{(\Delta)(\Delta)}{0.15 - 0.042} = \frac{(\Delta)(\Delta)}{0.108} = 1.2 \times 10^{-2}$$

$$\Delta^2 = 1.296 \times 10^{-3}$$

$$\Delta = 0.036$$

As described in Section 15.7, we can stop making approximations when the value of Δ differs by less than 5% from the value of Δ calculated in the previous approximation. The value of Δ has changed from 0.042 to 0.036. The change in Δ is 0.006.

$$\frac{0.042 - 0.036}{0.042} = \frac{0.006}{0.042} = 0.14 \qquad (14\%)$$

The change is 14%; another approximation is needed.

Third Approximation. We assume that $(0.15 - \Delta)$ is approximately equal to $(0.15 - 0.036) = 0.114$. Under this assumption, the equilibrium equation becomes

$$\frac{(\Delta)(\Delta)}{0.15 - 0.036} = \frac{(\Delta)(\Delta)}{0.114} = 1.2 \times 10^{-2}$$

$$\Delta^2 = 1.368 \times 10^{-3}$$

$$\Delta = \sqrt{1.368 \times 10^{-3}} = 0.037$$

Let us check to see how much this value of Δ differs from that calculated in the second approximation.

$$\frac{0.037 - 0.036}{0.036} = \frac{0.001}{0.036} = 0.028 \qquad (2.8\%)$$

The change is 2.8%; another approximation is not needed.

Example 17.11 continued

Using Δ and the initial concentration of H_3O^+ we can calculate $[H_3O^+]$ and the pH of the solution. However, before we do additional calculations, it wise to check the arithmetic by using the equilibrium concentrations. From the table,

$$[HSO_4^-] = 0.15 - \Delta = 0.15 - 0.037 = 0.11$$

$$[H_3O^+] = 0 + \Delta = 0.037 \text{ M}$$

$$[SO_4^{2-}] = 0 + \Delta = 0.037 \text{ M}$$

The value of Q with these concentrations is

$$Q = \frac{[H_3O^+][SO_4^{2-}]}{[HSO_4^-]} = \frac{(0.037)(0.037)}{(0.11)} = 1.2 \times 10^{-2}$$

The calculated concentrations give a value of Q equal to K_a; the arithmetic checks.

We also need to make sure the contribution of water to the hydronium ion concentration can be neglected. $[H_3O^+]$ is greater than 4.5×10^{-7} M at equilibrium, so the self-ionization of water can be neglected.

Now we can determine the pH of a 0.15 M solution of HSO_4^-.

$$pH = -\log [H_3O^+]$$

$$= -\log (0.037)$$

$$= 1.43$$

The next example shows that only a fraction of the weak acid in a solution is ionized. The example uses HF, one of the stronger weak acids.

Example 17.12

Calculate the percent ionization in a 0.20 M solution of hydrofluoric acid, HF.

The equation for the ionization of hydrofluoric acid and the ionization constant (Table 17.3) are

$$HF + H_2O \rightleftharpoons H_3O^+ + F^- \qquad K_a = 7.2 \times 10^{-4}$$

The reaction quotient for the initial concentration of HF is zero, so the reaction will shift to the right.

An abbreviated version of the table of changes and concentrations follows.

	HF	+ H_2O $\rightleftharpoons$	H_3O^+	+ F^-	$K_a = 7.2 \times 10^{-4}$
Change	$-\Delta$		Δ	Δ	
Initial Concentration, M	0.20		~0	0	
Equilibrium Concentration, M	$0.20 - \Delta$		Δ	Δ	

At equilibrium,

$$K_a = \frac{[H_3O^+][F^-]}{[HF]} = 7.2 \times 10^{-4}$$

Thus

$$\frac{(\Delta)(\Delta)}{0.20 - \Delta} = 7.2 \times 10^{-4}$$

Because both Q and K_a are less than 1, we assume that we can approximate $0.20 - \Delta$ as 0.20 to simplify solving for Δ. Thus

$$\frac{(\Delta)(\Delta)}{0.20} = 7.2 \times 10^{-4}$$

$$\Delta^2 = 0.20 \times (7.2 \times 10^{-4})$$

$$= 1.44 \times 10^{-4}$$

$$\Delta = \sqrt{1.44 \times 10^{-4}} = 1.2 \times 10^{-2}$$

Checking our calculated value of Δ gives

$$\frac{\Delta}{0.20} = \frac{0.012}{0.20} = 0.06 \ (6\%)$$

Because Δ is not less than 5% of the initial concentration of HF (it is 6%), another approximation is necessary.

For the second approximation, we assume $\Delta = 0.012$. Thus

$$\frac{(\Delta)(\Delta)}{0.20 - \Delta} = \frac{(\Delta)(\Delta)}{0.20 - 0.012} = 7.2 \times 10^{-4}$$

$$\frac{(\Delta)(\Delta)}{0.188} = 7.2 \times 10^{-4}$$

$$\Delta^2 = 0.188 \times (7.2 \times 10^{-4})$$

$$= 1.35 \times 10^{-4}$$

$$\Delta = 1.2 \times 10^{-2}$$

Because Δ did not change between the first and second approximations, the approximation that $(0.20 - \Delta) = 0.188$ is valid and we can take Δ to be 0.012.

Now we determine the equilibrium concentrations from the initial concentrations and the changes in these concentrations.

$$[\text{HF}] = 0.20 - \Delta = 0.20 - 0.012 = 0.19 \ \text{M}$$

$$[\text{H}_3\text{O}^+] = [\text{F}^-] = 0 + \Delta = 0.012 \ \text{M}$$

We need to (1) check the arithmetic and (2) determine whether we can neglect the ionization of water.

$$Q = \frac{[\text{H}_3\text{O}^+][\text{F}^-]}{[\text{HF}]} = \frac{(0.012)(0.012)}{0.19} = 7.6 \times 10^{-4}$$

Q agrees with K_a within the significance of the calculation, so the arithmetic is probably correct. The contribution of the ionization of water to the hydronium ion concentration can be neglected because $[\text{H}_3\text{O}^+] > 4.5 \times 10^{-7} \ \text{M}$.

Example 17.12
continued

To calculate percent ionization, we divide the concentration of the acid in the ionized form, which is equal to $[F^-]$, by the initial concentration of the acid, $[HF]_i$, and then multiply by 100. Thus we have

$$\frac{[F^-]}{[HF]_i} \times 100 = \frac{0.012 \text{ M}}{0.20 \text{ M}} \times 100$$

$$= 6.0\% \text{ ionization}$$

The extent to which a weak acid ionizes (the percent ionization) increases with decreasing initial concentration of the acid. As indicated in Table 17.4, for example, 0.100 M acetic acid is 1.3% ionized (98.7% is in the molecular form), whereas 0.0100 M acetic acid is 4.2% ionized (95.8% is in the molecular form). This is because in a more dilute solution at equilibrium, the ions are farther apart and have less tendency to combine to form molecular acetic acid.

Table 17.4 **Percent Ionization of Acetic Acid at Various Concentrations**

Molarity	% Ionized	$[H_3O^+]$ and $[CH_3CO_2^-]$	$[CH_3CO_2H]$
0.100	1.3	0.0013	0.099
0.0800	1.5	0.0012	0.079
0.0300	2.4	0.00074	0.029
0.0100	4.2	0.00042	0.0096

🅱.4 The Ionization of Weak Diprotic Acids

In any solution at equilibrium, all reactions are at equilibrium and the concentrations of ions common to all equilibria are the same. This is the case in a solution that contains a mixture of weak acids of different strengths, each at equilibrium. If K_a for the stronger acid is 20 or more times larger than K_a for the weaker acid, the stronger acid is the dominant producer of hydronium ion, and the weaker acid contributes a negligible amount of hydronium ion to the solution. In such a solution the stronger acid determines the concentration of hydronium ion, and the ionization of the weaker acid is fixed by the concentration of hydronium ion produced by the stronger acid.

When a weak diprotic acid (Section 16.8) dissolves in water, a mixture of acids results. The ion resulting from the first ionization step is also an acid, and it ionizes in the second step. Hydrogen sulfide is an example of a diprotic acid. The first step in the ionization of hydrogen sulfide produces hydronium ions and hydrogen sulfide ions in low yield.

First ionization:

A solution of H_2S is acidic.

$$H_2S + H_2O \rightleftharpoons H_3O^+ + HS^- \qquad K_{H_2S} = \frac{[H_3O^+][HS^-]}{[H_2S]} = 1.0 \times 10^{-7}$$

The hydrogen sulfide ion is also an acid. It ionizes and forms hydronium ions and sulfide ions in even lower yields.

Second ionization:

$$HS^- + H_2O \rightleftharpoons H_3O^+ + S^{2-} \qquad K_{HS^-} = \frac{[H_3O^+][S^{2-}]}{[HS^-]} = 1.0 \times 10^{-19}$$

K_{H_2S} is larger than K_{HS^-} by a factor of 10^{12}, so H_2S is the dominant producer of hydronium ion in the solution. This means that very little of the HS^- formed by the ionization of H_2S ionizes to give hydronium ions (and sulfide ions), and the concentrations of H_3O^+ and HS^- are practically equal in a pure aqueous solution of H_2S.

If the first ionization constant of a diprotic acid is larger than the second by a factor of at least 20, it is convenient and appropriate to treat the first ionization step separately and calculate concentrations resulting from it before calculating concentrations of species resulting from subsequent ionization steps.

The concentration of H_2S in a saturated aqueous solution at room temperature is approximately 0.1 M. Calculate $[H_3O^+]$, $[HS^-]$, and $[S^{2-}]$ in the solution.

Example 17.13

The two equilibria in the solution involving H_2S are

$$H_2S(aq) + H_2O(l) \rightleftharpoons H_3O^+(aq) + HS^-(aq) \qquad K_{H_2S} = 1.0 \times 10^{-7}$$

$$HS^-(aq) + H_2O(l) \rightleftharpoons H_3O^+(aq) + S^{2-}(aq) \qquad K_{HS^-} = 1.0 \times 10^{-19}$$

As indicated by the ionization constants, H_2S is a much stronger acid than HS^-, so H_2S is the dominant producer of hydronium ion in solution. First we calculate the concentrations of species resulting from the ionization of H_2S and then, using the $[H_3O^+]$ and $[HS^-]$ produced by hydrogen sulfide, we calculate the concentrations produced by ionization of the HS^- ion. For H_2S, an abbreviated table of changes and concentrations shows:

	H_2S	$+ H_2O \rightleftharpoons$	H_3O^+	$+ HS^-$
Change	$-\Delta$		Δ	Δ
Initial Concentration, M	0.1		~0	0
Equilibrium Concentration, M	$0.1 - \Delta$		Δ	Δ

Substituting the equilibrium concentrations into the equilibrium equation, and making the assumption that $(0.1 - \Delta) = 0.1$, we get

$$K_{H_2S} = \frac{[H_3O^+][HS^-]}{[H_2S]} = 1.0 \times 10^{-7}$$

$$\frac{(\Delta)(\Delta)}{0.1 - \Delta} = \frac{\Delta^2}{0.1} = 1.0 \times 10^{-7}$$

The value of the change is

$$\Delta = 1 \times 10^{-4}$$

Example 17.13 continued

Thus

$$[H_2S] = 0.1 - \Delta = 0.1 - 0.0001 = 0.1 \text{ M}$$

$$[H_3O^+] = [HS^-] = 0 + \Delta = 0.0001 \text{ M}$$

Calculation of Q using these concentrations shows that the arithmetic is correct. Because Δ is less than 5% of $[H_2S]$, and $[H_3O^+]$ is greater than 4.5×10^{-7} M, our customary assumptions are justified.

Now we calculate the concentration of S^{2-} in a solution with $[H_3O^+]$ and $[HS^-]$ both equal to 1×10^{-4} M. The equilibrium among HS^-, H_3O^+, and S^{2-} is

$$HS^-(aq) + H_2O(l) \Longrightarrow H_3O^+(aq) + S^{2-}(aq) \qquad K_{HS^-} = 1.0 \times 10^{-19}$$

We know K_{HS^-}, $[H_3O^+]$, and $[HS^-]$, so we need to calculate the missing concentration.

$$K_{HS^-} = \frac{[H_3O^+][S^{2-}]}{[HS^-]} = 1.0 \times 10^{-19}$$

$$= \frac{(1 \times 10^{-4})[S^{2-}]}{1 \times 10^{-4}}$$

or

$$[S^{2-}] = \frac{(1.0 \times 10^{-19}) \times (1 \times 10^{-4})}{1 \times 10^{-4}}$$

$$= 1 \times 10^{-19} \text{ M}$$

The concentrations of H_3O^+ and S^{2-} produced by the ionization of HS^- are equal. Thus the concentration of H_3O^+ *produced by the ionization of HS$^-$* is 1×10^{-19} M. This is much smaller than the 1×10^{-4} M produced by the ionization of H_2S, so it is justifiable to neglect the H_3O^+ formed from HS^-.

Note that in a pure aqueous solution of H_2S, $[S^{2-}]$ is equal to K_{HS^-}. *In fact, for any weak diprotic acid, the concentration of the divalent anion is equal to the second ionization constant if K_a for the first step is at least 20 times larger than K_a for the second step.*

If we know two of the three concentrations $[H_3O^+]$, $[A^{2-}]$, and $[H_2A]$ in a solution of a diprotic acid, we can readily determine the third concentration (Section 15.5). By multiplying the expressions for the ionization constants K_{H_2A} and K_{HA^-}, we obtain

$$\frac{[H_3O^+][HA^-]}{[H_2A]} \times \frac{[H_3O^+][A^{2-}]}{[HA^-]} = K_{H_2A} \times K_{HA^-}$$

$$\frac{[H_3O^+]^2[A^{2-}]}{[H_2A]} = K_{H_2A}K_{HA^-}$$

This gives the relationship among $[H_3O^+]$, $[A^{2-}]$, and $[H_2A]$ for the reaction

$$H_2A + 2H_2O \Longrightarrow 2H_3O^+ + A^{2-}$$

Example 17.14

Calculate the equilibrium concentration of sulfide ion in a saturated solution of hydrogen sulfide to which enough hydrochloric acid has been added to make the hydronium ion concentration of the solution 0.1 M at equilibrium. (A saturated H_2S solution is 0.1 M in hydrogen sulfide.)

Because we know the H_2S and H_3O^+ concentrations, we can calculate the sulfide concentration by using the equilibrium

$$H_2S + 2H_2O \rightleftharpoons 2H_3O^+ + S^{2-}$$

$[H_3O^+]$ is 0.1 M at equilibrium because enough hydrochloric acid has been added to make $[H_3O^+]$ equal to 0.1 M. $[H_2S]$ is known to be 0.1 M because the solution is saturated with hydrogen sulfide.

$$K_{H_2S}K_{HS^-} = \frac{[H_3O^+]^2[S^{2-}]}{[H_2S]} = (1.0 \times 10^{-7}) \times (1.0 \times 10^{-19})$$

$$= \frac{(0.1)^2[S^{2-}]}{(0.1)} = 1.0 \times 10^{-26}$$

$$[S^{2-}] = \frac{(1.0 \times 10^{-26})(0.1)}{(0.1)^2}$$

$$= 1.0 \times 10^{-25} \text{ M}$$

(We could use the same equation to calculate the hydronium ion concentration necessary to produce a given sulfide ion concentration in a saturated solution of H_2S.)

A word of caution is necessary here. Combining the ionization steps for a diprotic acid and multiplying the ionization constants together is a convenient way to calculate the concentration of one species at equilibrium, if all the other *equilibrium concentrations* for the reactants involved in the reaction are known. However, using a combined equation to calculate equilibrium concentrations from *initial concentrations* is very tricky, is likely to lead to unacceptably large errors, and will not be considered here. Such calculations should be made by treating each ionization step separately.

It is of interest to note that for many years the value of K_{HS^-} for hydrogen sulfide was thought to be on the order of 1×10^{-13} to 1×10^{-14}. The exact value is exceedingly difficult to determine experimentally but is now known to be much smaller. Recent experimental evidence indicates that it is in the range of 1×10^{-17} to 1×10^{-19}, with 1.0×10^{-19} being a reasonable value. We will use 1.0×10^{-19} in this text.

17.5 The Ionization of Weak Triprotic Acids

A triprotic acid is an acid that has three ionizable hydrogen ions that undergo stepwise ionization (Section 16.8). A typical example of a triprotic acid is phosphoric acid.

First ionization: $\qquad H_3PO_4 + H_2O \rightleftharpoons H_3O^+ + H_2PO_4^-$

Second ionization: $\qquad H_2PO_4^- + H_2O \rightleftharpoons H_3O^+ + HPO_4^{2-}$

Third ionization: $\qquad HPO_4^{2-} + H_2O \rightleftharpoons H_3O^+ + PO_4^{3-}$

Each step in the ionization has a corresponding ionization constant. The expressions for the ionization constants of the three steps are

$$\frac{[H_3O^+][H_2PO_4^-]}{[H_3PO_4]} = K_{H_3PO_4} = 7.5 \times 10^{-3}$$

Some soft drinks are mildly acidic because they contain a small amount of phosphoric acid.

$$\frac{[H_3O^+][HPO_4^{2-}]}{[H_2PO_4^-]} = K_{H_2PO_4^-} = 6.3 \times 10^{-8}$$

$$\frac{[H_3O^+][PO_4^{3-}]}{[HPO_4^{2-}]} = K_{HPO_4^{2-}} = 3.6 \times 10^{-13}$$

In each successive step the degree of ionization is significantly less. This is a general characteristic of polyprotic acids; successive ionization constants often differ by a factor of about 10^5 to 10^6.

This set of three dissociation reactions appears to make calculations of equilibrium concentrations very complicated. However, because the successive ionization constants differ by a factor of 10^5 to 10^6, the calculations can be broken down into a series of steps similar to those for diprotic acids.

Example 17.15 Calculate the concentrations of all species—H_3PO_4, $H_2PO_4^-$, HPO_4^{2-}, PO_4^{3-}, H_3O^+, and OH^- present at equilibrium in a solution containing a total phosphoric acid concentration of 0.100 M.

The three equilibria involving H_3PO_4 and its ions are

$$H_3PO_4 + H_2O \rightleftharpoons H_3O^+ + H_2PO_4^- \qquad K_{H_3PO_4} = 7.5 \times 10^{-3}$$

$$H_2PO_4^- + H_2O \rightleftharpoons H_3O^+ + HPO_4^{2-} \qquad K_{H_2PO_4^-} = 6.3 \times 10^{-8}$$

$$HPO_4^{2-} + H_2O \rightleftharpoons H_3O^+ + PO_4^{3-} \qquad K_{HPO_4^{2-}} = 3.6 \times 10^{-13}$$

As indicated by the ionization constants, H_3PO_4 is a much stronger acid than $H_2PO_4^-$ or HPO_4^{2-}. H_3PO_4 is the dominant producer of hydronium ion in solution. Let us assume that we can neglect the concentration of hydronium ion produced by water and calculate the concentrations resulting from the first step in the ionization of H_3PO_4. Then we calculate the concentration of HPO_4^{2-} produced by the second step of the ionization, using the $[H_3O^+]$ and $[H_2PO_4^-]$ produced in the first step. At this point we can check our assumptions. If they prove correct, we can determine the concentration of PO_4^{3-} by using the $[H_3O^+]$ produced in the first step of the ionization and the $[HPO_4^{2-}]$ produced in the second step.

Ionization of H_3PO_4. Here are the data for the first step in the ionization:

	H_3PO_4	$+ H_2O \rightleftharpoons$	H_3O^+	$+ H_2PO_4^-$	$K_{H_3PO_4} = 7.5 \times 10^{-3}$
Change	$-\Delta$		Δ	Δ	
Initial Concentration, M	0.100		~0	0	
Equilibrium Concentration, M	$0.100 - \Delta$		Δ	Δ	

Substituting the equilibrium concentrations into the equilibrium equation and making the assumption that $(0.100 - \Delta) = 0.100$, we get

$$K_{H_3PO_4} = \frac{[H_3O^+][H_2PO_4^-]}{[H_3PO_4]} = 7.5 \times 10^{-3}$$

$$= \frac{(\Delta)(\Delta)}{0.100 - \Delta} = \frac{\Delta^2}{0.100}$$

$$\Delta = 2.7 \times 10^{-2}$$

Thus $[H_3PO_4] = 0.100 - \Delta = 0.100 - (2.7 \times 10^{-2}) = 0.073$ M

$[H_3O^+] = [H_2PO_4^-] = 0 + \Delta = 0.027$ M

Calculation of Q using these concentrations shows that the arithmetic is correct. However, the concentration of H_3O^+ is greater than 5% of the initial $[H_3PO_4]$.

$$\frac{0.027}{0.100} = 0.27 \qquad (27\%)$$

Our assumption that Δ is small enough to be neglected in comparison to the initial concentration of H_3PO_4 is not justified. The hydronium ion concentration, however, is greater than 4.5×10^{-7} M, so the ionization of water can be neglected. (As we will see when we solve the equilibrium equation by a more appropriate technique, the assumption that Δ is small leads to a $[H_3O^+]$ that is too large. A better approximation will give a lower $[H_3O^+]$; but this also indicates that the hydronium ion from water can be neglected.)

We can solve the equilibrium equation

$$K_{H_3PO_4} = \frac{[H_3O^+][H_2PO_4^-]}{[H_3PO_4]} = 7.5 \times 10^{-3}$$

$$= \frac{(\Delta)(\Delta)}{0.100 - \Delta}$$

Example 17.15 continued

more precisely by using the quadratic equation or by successive approximation. Successive approximation was illustrated in Examples 17.11 and 17.12, so we will use the quadratic equation (Section 15.7 and Example 15.8) in this example.

$$7.5 \times 10^{-3} = \frac{(\Delta)(\Delta)}{0.100 - \Delta}$$

$$\Delta^2 = (7.5 \times 10^{-4}) - (7.5 \times 10^{-3})\Delta$$

$$\Delta^2 + (7.5 \times 10^{-3})\Delta - (7.5 \times 10^{-4}) = 0$$

$$\Delta = \frac{-(7.5 \times 10^{-3}) \pm \sqrt{(7.5 \times 10^{-3})^2 - 4(1)(-7.5 \times 10^{-4})}}{2(1)}$$

$$= \frac{(-7.5 \times 10^{-3}) \pm (5.5 \times 10^{-2})}{2}$$

Hence

$$\Delta = \frac{(-7.5 \times 10^{-3}) + (5.5 \times 10^{-2})}{2} = 2.4 \times 10^{-2} \text{ M}$$

or

$$= \frac{(-7.5 \times 10^{-3}) - (5.5 \times 10^{-2})}{2} = -3.1 \times 10^{-2} \text{ M}$$

(Δ is defined as a positive change, so this is an extraneous root.) Thus

$$\Delta = 2.4 \times 10^{-2}$$

$$[H_3O^+] = 0 + \Delta = 2.4 \times 10^{-2} \text{ M}$$

$$[H_2PO_4^-] = 0 + \Delta = 2.4 \times 10^{-2} \text{ M}$$

$$[H_3PO_4] = 0.100 - \Delta = 0.100 - 0.024 = 0.076 \text{ M}$$

Ionization of $H_2PO_4^-$. To calculate the concentration of HPO_4^{2-}, we use the second step in the ionization of the acid.

$$H_2PO_4^- + H_2O \rightleftharpoons H_3O^+ + HPO_4^{2-}$$

We have noted that if the first ionization constant for a stepwise reaction is larger than the second ionization constant by a factor of 20 or more, the concentrations resulting from the first step of the ionization are not changed by the second step. The concentrations from the first step can then be used to calculate the concentrations of species resulting from subsequent steps (see Example 17.13). This is the case here. We calculate the concentration of HPO_4^{2-} using the concentrations of H_3O^+ and $H_2PO_4^-$ produced in the first step: $[H_3O^+] = 0.024$ M and $[H_2PO_4^-] = 0.024$ M.

$$K_{H_2PO_4^-} = \frac{[H_3O^+][HPO_4^{2-}]}{[H_2PO_4^-]} = 6.3 \times 10^{-8}$$

$$6.3 \times 10^{-8} = \frac{(0.024)[HPO_4^{2-}]}{(0.024)}$$

Thus

$$[HPO_4^{2-}] = \frac{(6.3 \times 10^{-8})(0.024)}{(0.024)}$$

$$= 6.3 \times 10^{-8}$$

This small concentration of HPO_4^{2-} provides a check on our assumption that the increase in H_3O^+ and the decrease in $H_2PO_4^-$ (now known to be 6.3×10^{-8} M) are negligible compared to the quantity of each ion produced in the first step (0.024 M). As noted in Example 17.13, the concentration of the anion produced by the second ionization of a weak polyprotic acid is equal to the value of the second ionization constant of the acid.

Ionization of HPO_4^{2-}. Now we consider the third step of the ionization and determine the concentration of PO_4^{3-}.

$$HPO_4^{2-} + H_2O \rightleftharpoons H_3O^+ + PO_4^{3-}$$

The ionization constant for the second step of the ionization is greater than that of the third step by a factor of about 10^5. The ionization constant for the first step of the ionization is greater than that of the third step by a factor of about 10^{10}. Thus, we can assume that the concentrations of ions produced by the first and second steps are not changed by the third step, and we calculate the concentration of PO_4^{3-} using the concentrations of H_3O^+ produced in the first step and of HPO_4^{2-} produced in the second step: $[H_3O^+] = 0.024$ M and $[HPO_4^{2-}] = 6.3 \times 10^{-8}$ M.

$$K_{HPO_4^{2-}} = \frac{[H_3O^+][PO_4^{3-}]}{[HPO_4^{2-}]} = 3.6 \times 10^{-13}$$

$$= \frac{(0.024)[PO_4^{3-}]}{(6.3 \times 10^{-8})}$$

$$[PO_4^{3-}] = \frac{(3.6 \times 10^{-13})(6.3 \times 10^{-8})}{0.024}$$

$$= 9.4 \times 10^{-19} \text{ M}$$

The quantity of H_3O^+ added to the solution and the decrease in HPO_4^{2-} in the third step are indeed negligible compared to the amounts previously present in the solution.

In summary, the concentrations we have found up to this point are

$$[H_3O^+] = 2.4 \times 10^{-2} \text{ M}$$

$$[H_2PO_4^-] = 2.4 \times 10^{-2} \text{ M}$$

$$[H_3PO_4] = 0.100 - 0.024 = 0.076 \text{ M}$$

$$[HPO_4^{2-}] = 6.3 \times 10^{-8} \text{ M}$$

$$[PO_4^{3-}] = 9.4 \times 10^{-19} \text{ M}$$

Calculation of $[OH^-]$ completes this example.

$$K_w = [H_3O^+][OH^-] = 1.0 \times 10^{-14}$$

$$[OH^-] = \frac{K_w}{[H_3O^+]} = \frac{1.0 \times 10^{-14}}{2.4 \times 10^{-2}}$$

$$= 4.2 \times 10^{-13} \text{ M}$$

17.6   The Ionization of Very Weak Acids

In any aqueous solution of an acid, we have two simultaneous equilibria that produce hydronium ion. These are the ionization of the acid:

$$HA + H_2O \rightleftharpoons H_3O^+ + A^-$$

and the self-ionization of water:

$$H_2O + H_2O \rightleftharpoons H_3O^+ + OH^-$$

The total concentration of hydronium ion, $[H_3O^+]_{total}$, in a solution of an acid is the sum of the hydronium ion concentrations from the acid, $[H_3O^+]_{acid}$, and from the water, $[H_3O^+]_{water}$.

$$[H_3O^+]_{total} = [H_3O^+]_{acid} + [H_3O^+]_{water}$$

As we noted in Section 17.2, if the concentration of hydronium ion produced by an acid is greater than 4.5×10^{-7} M, then $[H_3O^+]_{water}$ can be neglected and $[H_3O^+]_{total}$ is equal to $[H_3O^+]_{acid}$. If an acid is very weak or present in low enough concentration, $[H_3O^+]_{acid}$ may not be greater than 4.5×10^{-7} M (see Table 17.2, for example). Under these conditions, we must consider the ionization of water when calculating the concentrations of molecules and ions in solution.

Before we consider the effect of water on ion concentrations, let us consider why the ionization of water is significant when $[H_3O^+]_{total}$ is less than 4.5×10^{-7} M. In a solution of acid, the total hydronium ion concentration is given by the equation

$$[H_3O^+]_{total} = [H_3O^+]_{acid} + [H_3O^+]_{water}$$

Looking at the equation for the self-ionization of water,

$$H_2O + H_2O \rightleftharpoons H_3O^+ + OH^-$$

we can see that for each 1 mole of H_3O^+ formed by the self-ionization of water, 1 mole of OH^- is produced. Thus the concentration of hydronium ion *produced by water* is equal to the concentration of hydroxide ion, because the only source of hydroxide ion in a solution of an acid is the ionization of water. Thus

$$[H_3O^+]_{water} = [OH^-]_{water}$$

In order for $[H_3O^+]_{water}$ (which equals $[OH^-]_{water}$) to be negligible, it must be less than 5% of $[H_3O^+]_{total}$. That is,

$$[H_3O^+]_{water} = [OH^-]_{water} = 0.05[H_3O^+]_{total} \quad \text{(or less)}$$

The product of the *total* hydronium ion concentration in the solution and the hydroxide ion concentration equals K_w.

$$K_w = [H_3O^+]_{total}[OH^-]_{water}$$

Because $[H_3O^+]_{water} = [OH^-]_{water}$ we can write

$$K_w = [H_3O^+]_{total}[H_3O^+]_{water}$$

and when $[H_3O^+]_{water} = 0.05[H_3O^+]_{total}$, we have

$$K_w = [H_3O^+]_{total} \times 0.05[H_3O^+]_{total}$$

We can now solve this equation for the minimum total hydronium ion concentration at which the contribution of hydronium ion by water can be neglected.

$$K_w = [H_3O^+]_{total} \times 0.05[H_3O^+]_{total}$$

$$[H_3O^+]^2_{total} = \frac{K_w}{0.05} = \frac{1.0 \times 10^{-14}}{0.05}$$

$$[H_3O^+]_{total} = 4.5 \times 10^{-7} \text{ M}$$

Can the contribution of water to the hydronium ion concentration be neglected in a 1.0×10^{-5} M solution of HCN?

Example 17.16

In order to answer this question, we find the concentration of hydronium ion produced by the ionization of HCN and determine whether it is large enough ($[H_3O^+]_{acid} > 4.5 \times 10^{-7}$ M) for us to neglect the self-ionization of water.

	HCN	$+ H_2O \rightleftharpoons H_3O^+ + CN^-$	$K_a = 4 \times 10^{-10}$
Change	$-\Delta$	Δ $\quad$ Δ	
Initial Concentration, M	0.000010	~0 $\quad$ 0	
Equilibrium Concentration, M	$0.000010 - \Delta$	Δ $\quad$ Δ	

At equilibrium,

$$K_a = \frac{[H_3O^+][CN^-]}{[HCN]} = 4 \times 10^{-10}$$

If we assume that the self-ionization of water can be neglected

$$\frac{(\Delta)(\Delta)}{0.000010 - \Delta} = 4 \times 10^{-10}$$

Both Q and K_a are much less than 1, so we will assume that $(0.000010 - \Delta) = 0.000010$ to simplify solving for Δ. Thus

$$\frac{(\Delta)(\Delta)}{0.000010} = 4 \times 10^{-10}$$

and

$$[H_3O^+] = [CN^-] = 6 \times 10^{-8}$$

Checking our assumption that Δ is small gives

$$\frac{\Delta}{0.000010} = \frac{6 \times 10^{-8}}{0.000010} = 6 \times 10^{-3} \quad (0.6\%)$$

Another approximation is not necessary. A check of the calculated equilibrium concentrations ($[H_3O^+] = [CN^-] = 6 \times 10^{-8}$ M and $[HCN] = 1 \times 10^{-5}$ M) gives

$$Q = \frac{[H_3O^+][CN^-]}{[HCN]} = \frac{(6 \times 10^{-8})(6 \times 10^{-8})}{1 \times 10^{-5}} = 4 \times 10^{-10}$$

The arithmetic checks.

However, the contribution of the self-ionization of water cannot be neglected in this solution of HCN, because the calculated concentration of hydronium ion derived from the ionization of HCN (6×10^{-8} M) is less than 4.5×10^{-7} M.

Although the arithmetic used in Example 17.16 checks, the calculation shown does not give the actual concentration of hydronium ion at equilibrium, because the self-ionization of water was neglected. The check we performed by evaluating Q simply showed that the arithmetic was carried out correctly, not that we chose the correct procedure. The correct procedure for determining the concentration of ions is discussed below.

In any aqueous solution of an acid, we have two simultaneous equilibria:

$$HA + H_2O \rightleftharpoons H_3O^+ + A^-$$

$$H_2O + H_2O \rightleftharpoons H_3O^+ + OH^-$$

The total concentration of hydronium ion, $[H_3O^+]_{total}$, regardless of its source, is the correct concentration to use in the equilibrium equation either for the ionization of the acid or for the self-ionization of water. When an acid anion, A^-, or a hydroxide ion combines with a hydronium ion, the source of the H_3O^+ (either from HA or from H_2O) is irrelevant. Thus

$$K_a = \frac{[H_3O^+]_{total}[A^-]}{[HA]}$$

where the concentrations are at equilibrium. We have seen that

$$[H_3O^+]_{total} = [H_3O^+]_{acid} + [H_3O^+]_{water}$$

The concentration of A^- in the solution is equal to $[H_3O^+]_{acid}$ because for each molecule of HA that ionizes, one H_3O^+ ion and one A^- ion result. Likewise, the concentration of OH^- is equal to $[H_3O^+]_{water}$. Thus

$$[H_3O^+]_{total} = [A^-] + [OH^-]$$

If we rearrange this equation to solve for $[A^-]$, we have a term that can be substituted into the equilibrium equation.

$$[A^-] = [H_3O^+]_{total} - [OH^-]$$

$$K_a = \frac{[H_3O^+]_{total}[A^-]}{[HA]}$$

Thus
$$K_a = \frac{[H_3O^+]_{total}\{[H_3O^+]_{total} - [OH^-]\}}{[HA]}$$

Now let us solve this equation for the total hydronium ion concentration in the solution. Multiplication gives

$$K_a = \frac{\{[H_3O^+]_{total} \times [H_3O^+]_{total}\} - \{[H_3O^+]_{total} \times [OH^-]\}}{[HA]}$$

$$= \frac{\{[H_3O^+]^2_{total}\} - \{[H_3O^+]_{total} \times [OH^-]\}}{[HA]}$$

Because $K_w = [H_3O^+]_{total}[OH^-]$, we can write

$$K_a = \frac{[H_3O^+]^2_{total} - K_w}{[HA]}$$

Rearranging gives

$$K_a[HA] = [H_3O^+]^2_{total} - K_w$$

and

$$[H_3O^+]^2_{total} = K_a[HA] + K_w$$

Taking the square root of both sides of the equation yields

$$[H_3O^+]_{total} = \sqrt{K_a[HA] + K_w}$$

We now introduce the only assumption in this derivation. We assume that HA is such a weak acid that the change in concentration of HA upon ionization is negligible. Under this assumption, the concentration of the acid at equilibrium, [HA], is equal to the initial concentration of the acid, $[HA]_i$. Thus

$$[H_3O^+]_{total} = \sqrt{K_a[HA]_i + K_w} \tag{1}$$

This equation enables us to evaluate the total concentration of hydronium ion in a solution of a weak acid when the ionization of water cannot be neglected.

Example 17.17

What is the concentration of H_3O^+ in a 1.0×10^{-5} M solution of HCN?

As shown in Example 17.16, the contribution of the concentration of H_3O^+ derived from water cannot be neglected in calculating the hydronium ion concentration in this solution. Thus we must use Equation (1) to determine the concentration of H_3O^+ in this solution with $[HCN]_i = 1.0 \times 10^{-5}$ M and $K_a = 4 \times 10^{-10}$ for HCN.

$$\begin{aligned}
[H_3O^+]_{total} &= \sqrt{K_a[HA]_i + K_w} \\
&= \sqrt{(4 \times 10^{-10}) \times (1.0 \times 10^{-5}) + (1.0 \times 10^{-14})} \\
&= \sqrt{1.4 \times 10^{-14}} = 1.2 \times 10^{-7} \text{ M} \\
&= 1 \times 10^{-7} \text{ M (to the number of significant figures} \\
&\quad \text{justified by } K_a)
\end{aligned}$$

This $[H_3O^+]$ is twice as large as that calculated ignoring the self-ionization of water (Example 17.16).

17.7 The Ionization of Weak Bases

We can tell by measuring the pH of an aqueous solution of a *weak* base of known concentration that only a fraction of the base reacts with water to produce cations and hydroxide ions (Fig. 17.8). The remaining weak base is present as the unreacted form. For example, in a solution of trimethylamine, $(CH_3)_3N$, the reversible reaction is

$$(CH_3)_3N + H_2O \rightleftharpoons (CH_3)_3NH^+ + OH^-$$

Figure 17.8

pH paper indicates that a 0.1 M solution of NH_3 is weakly basic. The solution has a pOH of 3 ([OH^-] = 0.001 M) because the weak base NH_3 only partially reacts with water. A 0.1 M solution of NaOH has a pOH of 1 because NaOH is a strong base.

pOH = 3

Table 17.5	Ionization Constants of Some Weak Bases	
Base	Ionization	K_b at 25°C
$(CH_3)_2NH$ Dimethylamine	$+ H_2O \rightleftharpoons (CH_3)_2NH_2^+ + OH^-$	7.4×10^{-4}
CH_3NH_2 Methylamine	$+ H_2O \rightleftharpoons CH_3NH_3^+ + OH^-$	4.4×10^{-4}
$(CH_3)_3N$ Trimethylamine	$+ H_2O \rightleftharpoons (CH_3)_3NH^+ + OH^-$	7.4×10^{-5}
NH_3 Ammonia	$+ H_2O \rightleftharpoons NH_4^+ + OH^-$	1.8×10^{-5}
$C_6H_5NH_2$ Aniline	$+ H_2O \rightleftharpoons C_6H_5NH_3^+ + OH^-$	4.6×10^{-10}

At equilibrium, K_b, the **ionization constant of a weak base,** is equal to the reaction quotient for the ionization of the base. At equilibrium for trimethylamine,

$$K_b = Q = \frac{[(CH_3)_3NH^+][OH^-]}{[(CH_3)_3N]} = 7.4 \times 10^{-5}$$

As we noted in Section 16.3, the concentration of water (the solvent for this reaction) does not appear in the equilibrium equation. The ionization constants of several weak bases are given in Table 17.5 and in Appendix G.

We can determine the equilibrium constant and the concentrations of reactants and products of an aqueous solution of a weak base at equilibrium as described in Section 15.5 for other reversible reactions. The mathematics of the calculations are very similar to those described for weak acids, and they involve the same approximations and techniques. We will only consider systems in which the concentration of hydroxide ion produced by the ionization of the base is greater than 4.5×10^{-7} M. Thus we neglect the contribution of water to the hydroxide ion concentration (Section 17.2). The following example illustrates how equilibrium concentrations are calculated from initial concentrations and the equilibrium constant—a type of calculation introduced in Section 15.6.

Example 17.18 Find the concentration of hydroxide ion in a 0.25 M solution of trimethylamine (Fig. 17.9), a weak base with an ionization constant, K_b, of 7.4×10^{-5}.

The abbreviated table of changes and concentrations follows.

	$(CH_3)_3N + H_2O \rightleftharpoons$	$(CH_3)_3NH^+ +$	OH^-	$K_b = 7.4 \times 10^{-5}$
Change	$-\Delta$	Δ	Δ	
Initial Concentration, M	0.25	0	~0	
Equilibrium Concentration, M	$0.25 - \Delta$	Δ	Δ	

(a) (b)

Figure 17.9
The structures of (a) the base tri-methylamine and (b) the cation formed when a proton is added to it. The red lobe represents the unshared pair of electrons in the trimethylamine molecule.

At equilibrium,

$$K_b = \frac{[(CH_3)_3NH^+][OH^-]}{[(CH_3)_3N]} = 7.4 \times 10^{-5}$$

$$\frac{(\Delta)(\Delta)}{0.25 - \Delta} = 7.4 \times 10^{-5}$$

If we assume that Δ is small relative to 0.25, then $(0.25 - \Delta) = 0.25$ and

$$\Delta^2 = 0.25 \times (7.4 \times 10^{-5})$$

$$\Delta = \sqrt{1.8 \times 10^{-5}} = 4.3 \times 10^{-3}$$

The concentration of OH^- is 4.3×10^{-3} M.

A check of our arithmetic shows that

$$Q = \frac{(4.3 \times 10^{-3})(4.3 \times 10^{-3})}{0.25} = 7.4 \times 10^{-5}$$

which equals K_b. Because $[OH^-]$ is greater than 4.5×10^{-7} M, our assumption that we can neglect the ionization of water is valid. To check our assumption about the magnitude of Δ, we determine that

$$\frac{4.3 \times 10^{-3}}{0.25} = 0.017 \quad (1.7\%)$$

The change is less than 5%, so the assumption is justified.

17.8 The Common Ion Effect

The acidity of an aqueous solution of acetic acid decreases when the strong electrolyte sodium acetate, $NaCH_3CO_2$, is added. This can be explained by Le Châtelier's principle (Section 15.8); the addition of acetate ions causes the equilibrium to shift to the left, increasing the concentration of CH_3CO_2H and reducing the concentration of H_3O^+.

$$CH_3CO_2H + H_2O \rightleftharpoons H_3O^+ + CH_3CO_2^-$$

Because sodium acetate and acetic acid have the acetate ion in common, this influence on the equilibrium is known as the **common ion effect.**

The extent to which the concentration of the hydronium ion is decreased may be calculated from the expression for the ionization constant.

Example 17.19

Calculate $[H_3O^+]$ in a 0.10 M solution of CH_3CO_2H that is 0.50 M with respect to $NaCH_3CO_2$.

The equilibrium in this system is

$$CH_3CO_2H + H_2O \rightleftharpoons H_3O^+ + CH_3CO_2^- \qquad K_a = 1.8 \times 10^{-5}$$

Before any reaction in the mixture, $[CH_3CO_2H]$ is 0.10 M, $[H_3O^+]$ is approximately zero, and $[CH_3CO_2^-]$ is 0.50 M. ($NaCH_3CO_2$ is an ionic compound and is completely ionized in solution.) Let the change in concentration of H_3O^+ as the mixture comes to equilibrium be Δ. Because 1 mol of $CH_3CO_2^-$ is formed for each 1 mol of H_3O^+ formed, the change in concentration of $CH_3CO_2^-$ also equals Δ, and the change in concentration of nonionized acetic acid equals $-\Delta$.

	$[CH_3CO_2H]$	$[H_3O^+]$	$[CH_3CO_2^-]$
Initial Concentration, M	0.10	~0	0.50
Change	$-\Delta$	Δ	Δ
Equilibrium Concentration, M	$0.10 + (-\Delta) = 0.10 - \Delta$	$0 + \Delta = \Delta$	$0.50 + \Delta$

$$K_a = \frac{[H_3O^+][CH_3CO_2^-]}{[CH_3CO_2H]}$$

$$1.8 \times 10^{-5} = \frac{(\Delta)(0.50 + \Delta)}{(0.10 - \Delta)}$$

Because both Q and K_a are less than 1, we assume that the change necessary to reach equilibrium is small and that Δ can be neglected; thus we assume that $(0.10 - \Delta) = 0.10$ and $(0.50 + \Delta) = 0.50$.

$$1.8 \times 10^{-5} = \frac{(\Delta)(0.50 + \Delta)}{(0.10 - \Delta)}$$

$$= \frac{(\Delta)(0.50)}{(0.10)}$$

$$\Delta = \frac{(1.8 \times 10^{-5})(0.10)}{0.50}$$

$$= 3.6 \times 10^{-6}$$

Thus
$$[H_3O^+] = 0 + \Delta = 3.6 \times 10^{-6} \text{ M}$$

$$[CH_3CO_2H] = 0.10 - \Delta = 0.10 \text{ M}$$

$$[CH_3CO_2^-] = 0.50 + \Delta = 0.50 \text{ M}$$

The simplifying assumption that Δ is negligibly small compared to either 0.50 or 0.10 was well justified.

We saw in Example 17.10 that the concentration of the hydronium ion in 0.10 M CH_3CO_2H is 0.0013 M. This is reduced to 0.0000036 M by the presence of 0.50 M sodium acetate in the 0.10 M acetic acid solution.

Addition of a base to a weak acid produces a salt of the acid. Hence addition of a base to a solution of a weak acid can create a common ion effect if the amount of base is not sufficient to neutralize all of the weak acid. The solution produced contains both the weak acid and its salt. Similarly, addition of an acid to a solution of weak base can create a common ion effect. Example 17.20 illustrates the creation of a common ion effect by the addition of an acid to a solution of a weak base.

Example 17.20

Exactly 10 mL of a 0.100 M HCl solution is added to 25 mL of 0.100 M NH_3 solution. Calculate the hydroxide ion concentration of the resulting 35 mL of solution.

Hydrogen chloride (HCl), a strong acid, reacts with ammonia (NH_3) to form ammonium chloride (NH_4Cl). We first assume that this reaction gives a 100% yield of NH_4Cl and calculate the amount of NH_4Cl produced (a limiting reagent problem with HCl the limiting reagent, Section 3.12). We then calculate the hydroxide ion concentration in this intermediate solution that contains a mixture of NH_3 and NH_4^+ (a common ion problem involving a weak base and its salt).

Ten milliliters (0.010 L) of 0.100 M HCl contains 0.010 L × (0.100 mol/1 L) = 1.0×10^{-3} mol of HCl. Twenty-five milliliters (0.025 L) of 0.100 M NH_3 contains 0.025 L × (0.100 mol/1 L) = 2.5×10^{-3} mol of ammonia. The 1.0×10^{-3} mol of HCl neutralizes 1.0×10^{-3} mol of NH_3, according to the equation

$$HCl + NH_3 \longrightarrow NH_4^+ + Cl^-$$

producing 1.0×10^{-3} mol of NH_4Cl and leaving 1.5×10^{-3} mol of unreacted NH_3. The concentration of 1.5×10^{-3} mol of NH_3 in 35 mL of solution is

$$[NH_3] = \frac{1.5 \times 10^{-3} \text{ mol}}{0.035 \text{ L}} = 4.3 \times 10^{-2} \text{ M}$$

The concentration of NH_4^+ equals the concentration of NH_4Cl.

$$[NH_4^+] = [NH_4Cl] = \frac{1.0 \times 10^{-3} \text{ mol}}{0.035 \text{ L}} = 2.9 \times 10^{-2} \text{ M}$$

Now we consider the changes as this intermediate mixture comes to equilibrium.

$$NH_3 + H_2O \rightleftharpoons NH_4^+ + OH^-$$

	$[NH_3]$	$[OH^-]$	$[NH_4^+]$
Intermediate Concentration, M	4.3×10^{-2}	~0	2.9×10^{-2}
Change	$-\Delta$	Δ	Δ
Equilibrium Concentration, M	$4.3 \times 10^{-2} - \Delta$	$0 + \Delta = \Delta$	$2.9 \times 10^{-2} + \Delta$

$$K_b = \frac{[NH_4^+][OH^-]}{[NH_3]} = 1.8 \times 10^{-5}$$

Example 17.20

continued

$$= \frac{(2.9 \times 10^{-2} + \Delta)(\Delta)}{4.3 \times 10^{-2} - \Delta}$$

Assuming Δ is small, $(2.9 \times 10^{-2} + \Delta) = 2.9 \times 10^{-2}$ and $(4.3 \times 10^{-2} - \Delta) = 4.3 \times 10^{-2}$. Hence we solve the equation

$$1.8 \times 10^{-5} = \frac{(2.9 \times 10^{-2})(\Delta)}{4.3 \times 10^{-2}}$$

and find that

$$\Delta = 2.7 \times 10^{-5}$$

Here $[OH^-] = 0 + \Delta = 2.7 \times 10^{-5}$ M, a value low enough to justify our approximation that Δ can be neglected relative to 4.3×10^{-2} or 2.9×10^{-2}.

17.9 Buffer Solutions

Mixtures of weak acids and their salts or mixtures of weak bases and their salts are called **buffer solutions,** or **buffers.** They resist a change in pH when small amounts of acid or base are added (Fig. 17.10). An example of a buffer that consists of a weak acid and its salt is a solution of acetic acid and sodium acetate. An example of a buffer that consists of a weak base and its salt is a solution of ammonia and ammonium chloride.

How Buffers Work

Figure 17.10

(a) The color of the indicator in the solutions shows that the buffered solution on the left and the unbuffered solution on the right have the same pH (pH 8). They are basic. (b) After the addition of 1 mL of a 0.01 M HCl solution, the buffered solution has not detectably changed its pH but the unbuffered solution has become acidic.

An acetic acid–sodium acetate mixture acts as a buffer to keep the hydronium ion concentration (and hence the pH) almost constant. If a small amount of sodium hydroxide is added, the hydroxide ions react with the few hydronium ions present. Then more of the acetic acid ionizes, restoring the hydronium ion concentration almost to its original value. If a small amount of hydrochloric acid is added to the buffer solution, most of the hydronium ions from the hydrochloric acid combine with acetate ions, forming acetic acid molecules.

$$H_3O^+ + CH_3CO_2^- \longrightarrow CH_3CO_2H + H_2O$$

Buffered
pH = 8

Unbuffered
pH = 8

(a)

Buffered
pH = 8

Unbuffered
pH = 4

(b)

Thus there is very little increase in the concentration of the hydronium ion, and the pH remains practically unchanged.

An ammonia–ammonium chloride buffer mixture keeps the hydronium ion concentration almost constant, because as hydroxide ions are added, ammonium ions in the buffer mixture react with the hydroxide ions to form ammonia molecules and water, thus reducing the hydroxide ion concentration almost to its original value and leaving the hydronium ion concentration almost constant.

$$NH_4^+ + OH^- \longrightarrow NH_3 + H_2O$$

If hydronium ions are added, ammonia molecules in the buffer mixture react with the hydronium ions to form ammonium ions, thereby reducing the hydronium ion concentration almost to its original value.

$$NH_3 + H_3O^+ \longrightarrow NH_4^+ + H_2O$$

The following example illustrates the change in pH that accompanies the addition of base to a buffered solution of a weak acid and to an unbuffered solution of a strong acid.

Example 17.21

(a) Calculate the pH of a buffer that is a mixture of 0.10 M acetic acid and 0.10 M sodium acetate.

Determination of the pH of the buffer solution requires calculation of $[H_3O^+]$ in a typical common ion equilibrium calculation, as illustrated in Example 17.19. An abbreviated table of changes and concentrations follows.

	$CH_3CO_2H + H_2O \rightleftharpoons H_3O^+ + CH_3CO_2^-$		$K_a = 1.8 \times 10^{-5}$
Change	$-\Delta$	Δ	Δ
Initial			
Concentration, M	0.10	~0	0.10
Equilibrium			
Concentration, M	$0.10 - \Delta$	Δ	$0.10 + \Delta$

Assuming that Δ is negligible compared to 0.10, we get

$$K_a = \frac{[H_3O^+][CH_3CO_2^-]}{[CH_3CO_2H]}$$

$$= \frac{(\Delta)(0.10)}{0.10}$$

$$[H_3O^+] = 0 + \Delta = 1.8 \times 10^{-5} \text{ M}$$

$$pH = -\log [H_3O^+] = -\log (1.8 \times 10^{-5})$$

$$= 4.74$$

(b) Calculate the pH after 1.0 mL of 0.10 M NaOH is added to 100 mL of this buffer, giving a solution with a volume of 101 mL.

This calculation is similar to the one in Example 17.20. First we calculate the concentrations of an intermediate mixture resulting from the complete reaction between the

A buffer consisting of equal concentrations of acetic acid and sodium acetate is acidic, as the indicator in this solution shows.

The buffer is still acidic, with the same pH, after addition of 1 mL of 0.1 M NaOH.

Example 17.21 continued

acid in the buffer and the added base. Then we determine the concentrations as the intermediate mixture comes to equilibrium.

Upon addition of sodium hydroxide to the buffer, some of the acetic acid is neutralized and acetate ion is formed.

$$CH_3CO_2H + OH^- \longrightarrow H_2O + CH_3CO_2^-$$

Before reaction, 0.100 L of the buffer solution contains 0.100 L $\times$ (0.10 mol CH_3CO_2H/1 L) = 1.0×10^{-2} mol of CH_3CO_2H and, similarly, 1.0×10^{-2} mol of $NaCH_3CO_2$. One milliliter (0.0010 L) of 0.10 M sodium hydroxide contains 0.0010 L $\times$ (0.10 mol NaOH/1 L) = 1.0×10^{-4} mol of NaOH. The 1.0×10^{-4} mol of NaOH neutralizes 1.0×10^{-4} mol of CH_3CO_2H, leaving

$$(1.0 \times 10^{-2}) - (0.01 \times 10^{-2}) = 0.99 \times 10^{-2} \text{ mol } CH_3CO_2H$$

and producing 1.0×10^{-4} mol of $NaCH_3CO_2$. This makes a total of

$$(1.0 \times 10^{-2}) + (0.01 \times 10^{-2}) = 1.01 \times 10^{-2} \text{ mol } NaCH_3CO_2$$

After reaction, CH_3CO_2H and $NaCH_3CO_2$ are contained in 101 mL of the intermediate solution, so the concentrations are 9.9×10^{-3} mol/0.101 L = 0.098 M CH_3CO_2H and 1.01×10^{-2} mol/0.101 L = 0.100 M $NaCH_3CO_2$.

Now we calculate the pH of the intermediate solution, which is 0.098 M in CH_3CO_2H and 0.100 M in $NaCH_3CO_2$.

	$CH_3CO_2H + H_2O \rightleftharpoons H_3O^+ + CH_3CO_2^-$			$K_a = 1.8 \times 10^{-5}$
Change	$-\Delta$	Δ	Δ	
Intermediate Concentration, M	0.098	~ 0	0.100	
Equilibrium Concentration, M	$0.098 - \Delta$	Δ	$0.100 + \Delta$	

Assuming that Δ is small compared to 0.100 or 0.098, we get

$$K_a = \frac{[H_3O^+][CH_3CO_2^-]}{[CH_3CO_2H]} = \frac{(\Delta)(0.100)}{0.098}$$

$$[H_3O^+] = 0 + \Delta = 1.76 \times 10^{-5}$$

$$pH = -\log [H_3O^+] = -\log (1.76 \times 10^{-5})$$

$$= 4.75$$

Thus the addition of the base barely changes the pH of the solution.

(c) Calculate the pH after 1.0 mL of 0.10 M NaOH is added to 100 mL of a solution of HCl with a pH of 4.74. The volume of the final solution is 101 mL.

The hydronium ion concentration in a solution of HCl with a pH of 4.74 can be found as follows:

$$pH = -\log [H_3O^+]$$

$$[H_3O^+] = 10^{-pH} = 10^{-4.74} = 1.8 \times 10^{-5}$$

This solution is a 1.8×10^{-5} M solution of HCl. It has the same hydronium ion concentration as the 0.10 M solution of acetic acid–sodium acetate buffer described in part (a) of this example. The solution contains

$$0.100 \text{ L} \times (1.8 \times 10^{-5} \text{ mol HCl/1 L}) = 1.8 \times 10^{-6} \text{ mol HCl}$$

As shown in part (b), 1 mL of 0.10 M NaOH contains 1.0×10^{-4} mol of NaOH. When the NaOH and HCl solutions are mixed, the HCl is the limiting reagent in the reaction. All of the HCl reacts, and the amount of NaOH that remains is

$$(1.0 \times 10^{-4}) - (1.8 \times 10^{-6}) = 9.8 \times 10^{-5} \text{ M}$$

The concentration of NaOH is

$$\frac{9.8 \times 10^{-5} \text{ M NaOH}}{0.101 \text{ L}} = 9.7 \times 10^{-4} \text{ M}$$

The pOH of this solution is

$$\text{pOH} = -\log [\text{OH}^-] = -\log (9.7 \times 10^{-4}) = 3.01$$

$$\text{pH} = 14.00 - \text{pOH} = 10.99$$

The pH changes from 4.74 to 10.99 in this unbuffered solution. This compares to the change of 4.74 to 4.75 that occurred when the same amount of NaOH was added to the buffered solution described in part (b).

A calculation similar to that in part (c) shows that addition of 1.0 mL of a 0.10 M solution of HCl to 100 mL of the buffer solution described in part (b) leaves the pH unchanged. If 1.0 mL of 0.10 M HCl was added to 100 mL of an HCl solution with a pH of 4.74 (1.8×10^{-5} M HCl), the pH would also change dramatically—from 4.74 to 3.00.

The calculations of the changes in pH that occur when either an acid or a base is added to a buffer that is a mixture of a weak base and its salt are analogous to the calculations for a buffer mixture of a weak acid and its salt.

Buffer Capacity

It is important to note that buffer solutions do not have an unlimited capacity to keep the pH relatively constant (Fig. 17.11). When the weak acid of a buffer is used up, no more buffering action toward additional base is possible (Table 17.6 and Fig. 17.12); when the weak base of a buffer is used up, no more buffering action toward additional acid is possible. Furthermore, the buffering action begins to diminish rapidly as a given component nears depletion.

The **buffer capacity** is the amount of acid or base that can be added to a certain volume of a buffer solution before the pH begins to change significantly. Buffer capacity depends on the amounts of the weak acid and its salt, or the amounts of the weak base and its salt, that are in the buffer mixture. For example, 100 mL of a solution that is 0.10 M in acetic acid and 0.10 M in sodium acetate has less buffer capacity than 100 mL of a solution that is 1.00 M in acetic acid and 1.00 M in sodium acetate. Both solutions have the same pH, but the former has less buffer capacity because it contains less acetic acid and acetate ion.

Figure 17.11

The color of the indicator shows that a small amount of acid added to a buffered solution of pH 10 (beaker on left) does not affect the pH of this buffered system (middle beaker). However, a large amount of acid exhausts the buffering capacity of the solution and the pH changes dramatically (beaker on right).

Selection of Suitable Buffer Mixtures

There are four useful rules of thumb for selecting buffer mixtures.

1. A good buffer mixture should have about equal concentrations of the weak acid and its salt or of the weak base and its salt.

2. A buffer solution has generally lost its usefulness when one component of the buffer pair is less than about 10% of the other (Table 17.6 and Fig. 17.12).

Table 17.6 shows a 0.10 M acetic acid–0.10 M acetate ion buffer, for which the initial pH is 4.74. A pH of 5.70 occurs with a mixture in which the acetic acid concentration is only 11% of the acetate ion concentration. This is an indication that the buffer is losing its effectiveness. Figure 17.12 illustrates this graphically. At pH 5.7, the curve is entering its range of rapid rise in pH when additional small increments of NaOH are added.

Figure 17.12

An illustration of buffering action. The graph shows change of pH as an increasing volume of 0.10 M NaOH solution is added to 100 mL of a buffer solution in which, initially, $[CH_3CO_2H] = 0.10$ M and $[CH_3CO_2^-] = 0.10$ M.

Table 17.6   **pH Values, pOH Values, and Ratios of the Weak Acid to Its Salt, as Increasing Increments of a Strong Base Are Added to 100 mL of a Buffer Solution of 0.10 M CH_3CO_2H and 0.10 M $NaCH_3CO_2$**

Volume of 0.10 M NaOH Added, mL	pH	pOH	Ratio $\dfrac{[CH_3CO_2H]}{[CH_3CO_2^-]}$
0	4.74	9.26	1.00
1.0	4.75	9.25	0.98
2.0	4.76	9.24	0.96
5.0	4.79	9.21	0.90
10.0	4.83	9.17	0.82
20.0	4.92	9.08	0.67
30.0	5.01	8.99	0.54
40.0	5.11	8.89	0.43
50.0	5.22	8.78	0.33
60.0	5.35	8.65	0.25
70.0	5.50	8.50	0.18
80.0	5.70	8.30	0.11 $[CH_3CO_2H]$ is 11% of $[CH_3CO_2^-]$
90.0	6.02	7.98	0.050
95.0	6.34	7.66	0.030
96.0	6.43	7.57	0.020
97.0	6.56	7.44	0.015
98.0	6.74	7.26	0.010
99.0	7.04	6.96	0.005
100.0	8.72	5.28	0
101.0	10.70	3.30	0
102.0	11.00	3.00	0

The addition of 100 mL of 0.10 M NaOH provides the exact amount of NaOH to react with all of the acetic acid present in the original 100 mL of 0.10 M CH_3CO_2H, bringing $[CH_3CO_2H]$ to zero. At that point, the solution has lost all of its buffering capacity for added NaOH; further additions of NaOH simply provide free hydroxide ion to the solution.

3. Weak acids and their salts are better as buffers for pH < 7; weak bases and their salts are better as buffers for pH > 7.

4. For a weak acid, HA, and its salt, the ratio $[H_3O^+]/K_a$ should be as close to 1 as possible for effective buffer action. Similarly, for a weak base, B, and its salt, the ratio $[OH^-]/K_b$ should be as close to 1 as possible for effective buffer action. This concept can be developed as follows:

For $HA + H_2O \rightleftharpoons H_3O^+ + A^-$ (where HA is a weak acid and A^- is the anion of the weak acid and thus also the anion of the salt of the weak acid),

$$K_a = \frac{[H_3O^+][A^-]}{[HA]}$$

$$\frac{[H_3O^+]}{K_a} = \frac{[HA]}{[A^-]}$$

Because an ideal buffer has [HA] = [A$^-$] (the ratio [HA]/[A$^-$] = 1), [H$_3$O$^+$]/K_a should also equal 1 for the most effective weak acid–salt buffer action.

For B + H$_2$O $\rightleftharpoons$ BH$^+$ + OH$^-$ (where B is a weak base and BH$^+$ is the cation of the salt of the weak base),

$$K_b = \frac{[BH^+][OH^-]}{[B]}$$

$$\frac{[OH^-]}{K_b} = \frac{[B]}{[BH^+]}$$

An ideal buffer should have the ratio [B]/[BH$^+$] = 1. Therefore, [OH$^-$]/K_b should also equal 1 for the most effective weak base–salt buffer action.

The Henderson-Hasselbalch Equation

Biological scientists often use an expression called the **Henderson-Hasselbalch equation** to relate the pH (or pOH) of a buffered solution, the pK of the acid (or base) in the buffer, and the ratio of the concentrations of the acid (or base) and its salt. It is derived as follows for an acidic solution.

In a solution containing a monoprotic weak acid and its salt

$$K_a = \frac{[H_3O^+][A^-]}{[HA]},$$

we can solve for the hydronium ion concentration by rearranging the equation for the equilibrium constant

$$[H_3O^+] = K_a \times \frac{[HA]}{[A^-]}$$

Now if we take the logarithm of the preceding equation we get

$$\log [H_3O^+] = \log K_a + \log \frac{[HA]}{[A^-]}$$

Multiplying by -1 gives

$$-\log [H_3O^+] = -\log K_a - \log \frac{[HA]}{[A^-]}$$

Because pH = $-\log$ [H$_3$O$^+$], pK_a = $-\log K_a$, and log [A$^-$]/[HA] = $-\log$ [HA]/[A$^-$],

$$pH = pK_a + \log \frac{[A^-]}{[HA]}$$

This equation, the Henderson-Hasselbalch equation, relates the pH, the ionization constant of a weak acid, and the concentrations of the weak acid and its salt in a buffered solution.

In a solution of a weak base (B) and its salt (BH$^+$), the corresponding equation is

$$pOH = pK_b + \log [BH^+]/[B]$$

where pK_b is the negative of the common logarithm of the ionization constant of the weak base.

Buffers play a very important role in chemical processes; they keep hydrogen ion and hydroxide ion concentrations approximately constant over a range of changes in condition, such as the addition of acid, base, or water. Common buffer pairs besides CH_3CO_2H and $CH_3CO_2^-$, and NH_3 and NH_4^+, include H_2CO_3 and HCO_3^-, and $H_2PO_4^-$ and HPO_4^{2-}.

Blood is an important example of a buffered solution, with the principal acid and ion responsible for the buffering action being carbonic acid, H_2CO_3, and the hydrogen carbonate ion, HCO_3^-. When an excess of hydrogen ion enters the blood stream, it is removed primarily by the reaction

$$H_3O^+ + HCO_3^- \longrightarrow H_2CO_3 + H_2O$$

When an excess of the hydroxide ion is present, it is removed by the reaction

$$OH^- + H_2CO_3 \longrightarrow H_2O + HCO_3^-$$

The pH of human blood thus remains very near 7.35, slightly alkaline. Variations are usually less than 0.1 of a pH unit. A change of 0.4 of a pH unit is likely to be fatal.

17.10 Reaction of Salts with Water

The conjugate base of a weak acid reacts with water to increase the concentration of hydroxide ion (Section 16.3). A salt such as $NaCH_3CO_2$, which is formed from a weak acid and a strong base, contains the conjugate base ($CH_3CO_2^-$) of the weak acid and forms aqueous solutions that are basic.

$$CH_3CO_2^- + H_2O \rightleftharpoons CH_3CO_2H + OH^-$$

The conjugate acid of a weak base reacts with water to increase the hydronium ion concentration. A salt such as NH_4Cl, which is formed from a weak base and a strong acid, contains the conjugate acid (NH_4^+) of the weak base and forms aqueous solutions that are acidic.

$$NH_4^+ + H_2O \rightleftharpoons H_3O^+ + NH_3$$

Because both the conjugate base of a strong acid and the conjugate acid of a strong base are very weak, a salt such as NaCl or KNO_3, which is formed from a strong acid and a strong base, yields aqueous solutions that are neutral. A salt of a weak acid and a weak base may form neutral, basic, or acidic solutions, depending on the relative strengths of the conjugate acid and the conjugate base present in the salt.

Reactions of this type, in which water is one of the reactants, are sometimes called **hydrolysis** reactions. The concentrations of ions and molecules that result from the hydrolysis of salts of weak acids and/or weak bases will be discussed in the sections that follow.

17.11 Reaction of a Salt of a Strong Base and a Weak Acid with Water

Sodium acetate, $NaCH_3CO_2$, the salt of the strong base sodium hydroxide and the weak acid acetic acid, dissolves in water to give basic solutions (Fig. 17.13). The sodium ion (the ion of an alkali metal) has no appreciable reaction with water (see Section 17.14),

Figure 17.13

Addition of an indicator to a color-less solution of $NaCH_3CO_2$ shows that the solution is slightly basic.

whereas the acetate ion (the conjugate base of a weak acid) reacts with water to produce hydroxide ions.

$$Na^+ + H_2O \longrightarrow \text{(no appreciable reaction)}$$

$$CH_3CO_2^- + H_2O \rightleftharpoons CH_3CO_2H + OH^-$$

The equilibrium equation for this reaction is

$$\frac{[CH_3CO_2H][OH^-]}{[CH_3CO_2^-]} = K_b$$

This equilibrium constant is simply the ionization constant for the base $CH_3CO_2^-$ (Section 17.7).

The value of the equilibrium constant for the base $CH_3CO_2^-$ can be calculated from the values for the ionization constants of water and acetic acid, the conjugate acid of the anion (Section 16.3). This may be shown as follows. For any aqueous solution,

$$K_w = [H_3O^+][OH^-] \qquad \text{or} \qquad [OH^-] = \frac{K_w}{[H_3O^+]}$$

Substituting $K_w/[H_3O^+]$ for $[OH^-]$ in the expression for the ionization constant for the base, we obtain

$$\frac{[CH_3CO_2H][OH^-]}{[CH_3CO_2^-]} = \frac{[CH_3CO_2H]K_w}{[CH_3CO_2^-][H_3O^+]} = K_b$$

But the expression

$$\frac{[CH_3CO_2H]}{[CH_3CO_2^-][H_3O^+]}$$

is the reciprocal of K_a, or $1/K_a$, for acetic acid. Therefore

$$K_b = \frac{K_w}{K_a} = \frac{1.0 \times 10^{-14}}{1.8 \times 10^{-5}} = 5.6 \times 10^{-10}$$

For any salt of a strong base and a weak acid, the ionization constant of the conjugate base of the weak acid is given by the expression

$$K_b = \frac{K_w}{K_a}$$

where K_a is the ionization constant of the weak acid.

It is sometimes useful to rewrite the expression as

$$K_a \times K_b = K_w$$

for any conjugate acid–base pair. This shows clearly that for a relatively strong acid (large K_a), the conjugate base must be relatively weak (small K_b); conversely, for a relatively weak acid (small K_a), the conjugate base must be relatively strong (large K_b).

Calculate the hydroxide ion concentration, the percent reaction, and the pH of a 0.050 M solution of sodium acetate.

Example 17.22

The equation for the hydrolysis of sodium acetate is

$$CH_3CO_2^- + H_2O \rightleftharpoons CH_3CO_2H + OH^-$$

The acetate ion behaves as a base in this reaction; hydroxide ions are a product. The expression for the equilibrium constant is

$$\frac{[CH_3CO_2H][OH^-]}{[CH_3CO_2^-]} = K_b = \frac{K_w}{K_a}$$

For acetic acid, $K_a = 1.8 \times 10^{-5}$, so

$$K_b = \frac{K_w}{K_a} = \frac{1.0 \times 10^{-14}}{1.8 \times 10^{-5}} = 5.6 \times 10^{-10}$$

The changes and concentrations for the reaction of the base $CH_3CO_2^-$ with water are as follows:

	$CH_3CO_2^-$	$+ H_2O \rightleftharpoons$	CH_3CO_2H	$+ OH^-$
Change	$-\Delta$		Δ	Δ
Initial Concentration, M	0.050		0	~0
Equilibrium Concentration, M	$0.050 - \Delta$		Δ	Δ

Both Q and K_b for this system are much less than 1, so we assume that Δ is small and $(0.050 - \Delta) = 0.050$. Thus we have

$$K_b = \frac{[CH_3CO_2H][OH^-]}{[CH_3CO_2^-]}$$

$$5.6 \times 10^{-10} = \frac{(\Delta)(\Delta)}{0.050 - \Delta}$$

$$= \frac{(\Delta)(\Delta)}{0.050}$$

$$\Delta = 5.3 \times 10^{-6}$$

Example 17.22 continued

The assumption that Δ is small relative to 0.050 is valid, and

$$[OH^-] = [CH_3CO_2H] = 5.3 \times 10^{-6} \text{ M}$$

Thus the concentration of hydroxide ion is 5.3×10^{-6} M, and the percent reaction is equal to

$$\frac{[CH_3CO_2H]}{[CH_3CO_2^-]} \times 100 = \frac{5.3 \times 10^{-6}}{0.050} \times 100 = 0.011\%$$

We can calculate the pH of the solution by first finding the hydronium ion concentration:

$$[H_3O^+] = \frac{K_w}{[OH^-]} = \frac{1.0 \times 10^{-14}}{5.3 \times 10^{-6}} = 1.9 \times 10^{-9}$$

and then using that value as follows:

$$pH = -\log [H_3O^+] = -\log (1.9 \times 10^{-9}) = 8.72$$

This pH corresponds to a basic solution, as expected.

Example 17.23

Calculate the stepwise equilibrium constants for the reaction of sulfide ion with water and the S^{2-}, HS^-, and H_2S concentrations in a 0.0010 M solution of sodium sulfide (see the photograph).

The sulfide ion reacts with water by a two-step process.

First ionization: $\quad S^{2-} + H_2O \rightleftharpoons HS^- + OH^-$

Second ionization: $\quad HS^- + H_2O \rightleftharpoons H_2S + OH^-$

The HS^- ion formed when S^{2-} acts as a base in the first ionization step is also a base, and it reacts with water in the second ionization step.

The equilibrium constant for the first ionization is

$$K_b(S^{2-}) = \frac{K_w}{K_a(HS^-)} = \frac{1.0 \times 10^{-14}}{1.0 \times 10^{-19}} = 1.0 \times 10^5$$

where $K_a(HS^-)$ is the acid ionization constant for HS^- (Appendix F). The equilibrium constant for the second ionization is

$$K_b(HS^-) = \frac{K_w}{K_a(H_2S)} = \frac{1.0 \times 10^{-14}}{1.0 \times 10^{-7}} = 1.0 \times 10^{-7}$$

where $K_a(H_2S)$ is the ionization constant for H_2S (Appendix F). Because $K_b(S^{2-})$ is more than 20 times larger than $K_b(HS^-)$ $\{K_b(S^{2-}) = (1 \times 10^{12}) \times K_b(HS^-)\}$, we can treat the ionization in a stepwise fashion as illustrated in Example 17.14 for H_2S. For the first ionization, we have

$$S^{2-} + H_2O \rightleftharpoons HS^- + OH^- \qquad K_b(S^{2-}) = 1.0 \times 10^5$$

In a 0.0010 M solution of Na_2S, before any reaction of S^{2-} with water, the reaction quotient is zero. Because Q is less than 1 and $K_b(S^{2-})$ is very much larger than 1, the reaction will shift to the right, producing a large yield of HS^- and OH^-. The problem is much easier to solve if we assume that all of the S^{2-} reacts, giving a 100% yield of an intermediate mixture of HS^- and OH^- (see Section 15.7 and Example 15.12). The equilibrium concentrations are calculated as this intermediate mixture comes to equilibrium.

The indicator shows that a 0.001 M solution of Na_2S is very basic.

	$[S^{2-}]$	$[HS^-]$	$[OH^-]$
Initial Concentration, M	0.0010	0	~0
Intermediate Concentration, M	0	0.0010	0.0010

Now let us calculate the equilibrium concentrations from the intermediate concentrations. In the following calculation Δ is the change in the intermediate concentrations. Note that for the intermediate concentrations, Q is infinitely large $\{Q = (0.0010)(0.0010)/0\}$ and is larger than $K_b(S^{2-})$. Thus the concentrations in the intermediate mixture will shift to the left to reach equilibrium, and Δ will be positive for S^{2-}.

	S^{2-} + H_2O $\rightleftharpoons$	HS^-	+	OH^-
Change	Δ	$-\Delta$		$-\Delta$
Intermediate Concentration, M	0	0.0010		0.0010
Equilibrium Concentration, M	Δ	$0.0010 - \Delta$		$0.0010 - \Delta$

In the equilibrium equation,

$$K_b(S^{2-}) = \frac{[HS^-][OH^-]}{[S^{2-}]} = \frac{(0.0010 - \Delta)(0.0010 - \Delta)}{\Delta} = 1.0 \times 10^5$$

If we assume Δ is so small that $0.0010 - \Delta = 0.0010$,

$$K_b(S^{2-}) = \frac{(0.0010)(0.0010)}{\Delta} = 1.0 \times 10^5$$

$$\Delta = \frac{(0.0010)^2}{1.0 \times 10^5} = 1.0 \times 10^{-11}$$

Thus

$$[S^{2-}] = 0 + \Delta = 1.0 \times 10^{-11} \text{ M}$$

$$[HS^-] = 0.0010 - 1.0 \times 10^{-11} = 0.0010 \text{ M}$$

$$[OH^-] = 0.0010 - 1.0 \times 10^{-11} = 0.0010 \text{ M}$$

Now we can employ these concentrations to determine the concentration of H_2S in the solution, using the equilibrium of the second ionization step.

$$HS^- + H_2O \rightleftharpoons H_2S + OH^- \qquad K_b(HS^-) = 1.0 \times 10^{-7}$$

Inasmuch as we already know $K_b(HS^-)$ and the concentrations of HS^- and OH^-, it is a straightforward task to determine the H_2S concentration.

$$K_b(HS^-) = \frac{[H_2S][OH^-]}{[HS^-]}$$

$$1.0 \times 10^{-7} = \frac{[H_2S](0.0010)}{0.0010}$$

$$[H_2S] = 1.0 \times 10^{-7} \text{ M}$$

As indicated in Section 17.4, the concentration of the conjugate acid in the second step of the ionization is equal to the equilibrium constant for the second step.

🅱.12 Reaction of a Salt of a Weak Base and a Strong Acid with Water

Ammonium chloride, NH_4Cl, is a salt of a weak base and a strong acid. The ammonium ion, the conjugate acid of the weak base ammonia, is acidic and reacts with water to produce ammonia and hydronium ions. Note that the chloride ion, being the conjugate base of a strong acid (HCl), has no significant tendency to attract a proton from water and hence has no appreciable effect on the H_3O^+ and OH^- concentrations in the solution.

$$NH_4^+ + H_2O \rightleftharpoons NH_3 + H_3O^+$$

$$Cl^- + H_2O \longrightarrow \text{(no appreciable reaction)}$$

The equilibrium equation is

$$\frac{[NH_3][H_3O^+]}{[NH_4^+]} = K_a$$

The equilibrium constant is simply the ionization constant for the acid NH_4^+.

The value of K_a for NH_4^+ can be determined from K_w and the ionization constant, K_b, for NH_3. The expression for the acid ionization constant, based on the equation

$$NH_4^+ + H_2O \rightleftharpoons NH_3 + H_3O^+$$

is written

$$\frac{[NH_3][H_3O^+]}{[NH_4^+]} = K_a$$

Substituting $K_w/[OH^-]$ for $[H_3O^+]$ in the foregoing equation, we obtain

$$\frac{[NH_3]K_w}{[NH_4^+][OH^-]} = K_a$$

The expression $[NH_3]/[NH_4^+][OH^-]$ is equal to the reciprocal of K_b for NH_3 and equals $1/K_b$ (for NH_3). Hence

$$K_a = \frac{K_w}{K_b} = \frac{1.0 \times 10^{-14}}{1.8 \times 10^{-5}} = 5.6 \times 10^{-10}$$

The equilibrium constant for the ionization of the conjugate acid of any weak base can be calculated from the expression

$$K_a = \frac{K_w}{K_b}$$

where K_b is the ionization constant of the weak base.

🅱.13 Reaction of a Salt of a Weak Base and a Weak Acid with Water

When we dissolve ammonium acetate, $NH_4CH_3CO_2$, in water, we have a solution of ammonium ion (a weak acid) and acetate ion (a weak base), both of which undergo reaction with water.

$$NH_4^+ + H_2O \rightleftharpoons NH_3 + H_3O^+$$

$$CH_3CO_2^- + H_2O \rightleftharpoons CH_3CO_2H + OH^-$$

The extent to which these reactions take place is about the same, because the reactions of ammonium ion and acetate ion with water have nearly equal equilibrium constants. Therefore the products are present in nearly equal concentrations at equilibrium. As H_3O^+ and OH^- are produced by these reactions, they react to form water because the product of their concentrations cannot exceed 1.0×10^{-14}. Thus the solution remains neutral as the reactions proceed.

The net reaction may be seen as the sum of three equations:

$$NH_4^+ + H_2O \rightleftharpoons NH_3 + H_3O^+$$

$$CH_3CO_2^- + H_2O \rightleftharpoons CH_3CO_2H + OH^-$$

$$\underline{H_3O^+ + OH^- \rightleftharpoons 2H_2O}$$

$$NH_4^+ + CH_3CO_2^- \rightleftharpoons CH_3CO_2H + NH_3$$

The equilibrium equation for the net reaction is

$$\frac{[CH_3CO_2H][NH_3]}{[NH_4^+][CH_3CO_2^-]} = K$$

To express the equilibrium constant in terms of the ion product for water and the ionization constants for aqueous ammonia and acetic acid, we multiply the numerator and denominator of the foregoing equation by $[H_3O^+][OH^-]$.

$$\frac{[NH_3]}{[NH_4^+][OH^-]} \times \frac{[CH_3CO_2H]}{[H_3O^+][CH_3CO_2^-]} \times \frac{[H_3O^+][OH^-]}{1} = K$$

We see that

$$K = \frac{K_w}{K_b \text{ (for } NH_3) \times K_a \text{ (for } CH_3CO_2H)}$$

$$= \frac{1.0 \times 10^{-14}}{(1.8 \times 10^{-5})(1.8 \times 10^{-5})} = 3.1 \times 10^{-5}$$

When the ions of a salt of a weak base and a weak acid do not have the same equilibrium constants, the aqueous solution of the salt is either basic or acidic, depending on which ion has the larger equilibrium constant. For example, ammonium cyanide, NH_4CN, reacts with water to give a basic solution because K_b for CN^- is larger than K_a for NH_4^+. The reaction of the cyanide ion with water,

$$CN^- + H_2O \rightleftharpoons HCN + OH^-$$

is more extensive than that of the ammonium ion,

$$NH_4^+ + H_2O \rightleftharpoons NH_3 + H_3O^+$$

and an excess of hydroxide ions accumulates in the solution.

17.14 The Ionization of Hydrated Metal Ions

A large number of metal ions behave as acids when in solution. For example, the aluminum(III) ion of aluminum nitrate reacts with water to give a hydrated aluminum ion, $[Al(H_2O)_6]^{3+}$.

$$Al(NO_3)_3(s) + 6H_2O(l) \longrightarrow [Al(H_2O)_6]^{3+}(aq) + 3NO_3^-(aq)$$

The ion $[Al(H_2O)_6]^{3+}$ is an acid and donates hydrogen ions to water (Fig. 17.14).

$$[Al(H_2O)_6]^{3+} + H_2O \rightleftharpoons [Al(OH)(H_2O)_5]^{2+} + H_3O^+$$

As other polyprotic acids, the hydrated aluminum ion ionizes in stages, as shown by

$$[Al(H_2O)_6]^{3+} + H_2O \rightleftharpoons [Al(OH)(H_2O)_5]^{2+} + H_3O^+$$

$$[Al(OH)(H_2O)_5]^{2+} + H_2O \rightleftharpoons [Al(OH)_2(H_2O)_4]^+ + H_3O^+$$

$$[Al(OH)_2(H_2O)_4]^+ + H_2O \rightleftharpoons [Al(OH)_3(H_2O)_3] + H_3O^+$$

The ionization of a cation carrying more than one charge is not extensive beyond the first stage. Additional examples of the first stage in the ionization of hydrated metal ions are

$$[Fe(H_2O)_6]^{3+} + H_2O \rightleftharpoons [Fe(OH)(H_2O)_5]^{2+} + H_3O^+$$

$$[Cu(H_2O)_4]^{2+} + H_2O \rightleftharpoons [Cu(OH)(H_2O)_3]^+ + H_3O^+$$

$$[Zn(H_2O)_6]^{2+} + H_2O \rightleftharpoons [Zn(OH)(H_2O)_5]^+ + H_3O^+$$

Ions known to be hydrated in solution are often indicated in abbreviated form—that is, indicated without showing the hydration. For example, Al^{3+} is often written instead of $[Al(H_2O)_6]^{3+}$. However, when water participates in a reaction, the hydration becomes important and we use formulas that show the extent of hydration.

Figure 17.14

The pH paper shows that a 0.1 M solution of aluminum nitrate has a pH of 3.

Example 17.24 Calculate the pH of a 0.10 M solution of aluminum chloride that dissolves to give the hydrated aluminum ion $[Al(H_2O)_6]^{3+}$ in solution.

In spite of the unusual appearance of the acid, this is a typical acid ionization problem.

	$[Al(H_2O)_6]^{3+}$ + H_2O $\rightleftharpoons$	H_3O^+ +	$[Al(OH)(H_2O)_5]^{2+}$	$K_a = 1.4 \times 10^{-5}$
Change	$-\Delta$	Δ	Δ	
Initial				
Concentration, M	0.10	~ 0	0	
Equilibrium				
Concentration, M	$0.10 - \Delta$	Δ	Δ	

Substituting in the expression for the ionization constant yields

$$K_a = \frac{[H_3O^+][Al(OH)(H_2O)_5^{2+}]}{[Al(H_2O)_6^{3+}]}$$

$$= \frac{(\Delta)(\Delta)}{0.10 - \Delta} = 1.4 \times 10^{-5}$$

Assuming Δ is small gives $0.10 - \Delta = 0.10$. Thus

$$\Delta^2 = 1.4 \times 10^{-6}$$

$$[H_3O^+] = 0 + \Delta = 1.2 \times 10^{-3} \text{ M}$$

$$pH = -\log [H_3O^+] = -\log (1.2 \times 10^{-3}) = 2.92 \quad \text{(an acid solution)}$$

The constants for the different stages of ionization are not known for many metal ions, so we cannot calculate the extent of their ionization. However, if the hydroxide of a metal ion is insoluble in water, the hydrated metal ion ionizes extensively to give a very acidic solution. In fact, practically all metal ions other than those of the alkali metals ionize to give acidic solutions. Ionization increases as the charge of the metal ion increases or as the size of the metal ion decreases.

⓱.15 Acid–Base Indicators

Certain organic substances change color in dilute solution when the hydronium ion concentration reaches a particular value. For example, phenolphthalein is a colorless substance in any aqueous solution with a hydronium ion concentration greater than 5.0×10^{-9} M (pH less than 8.3). In solutions with a hydronium ion concentration less than 5.0×10^{-9} M (pH greater than 8.3), phenolphthalein is red or pink. Substances such as phenolphthalein, which can be used to determine the pH of a solution, are called **acid–base indicators.** Acid–base indicators are either weak organic acids, HIn, or weak organic bases, InOH, where the letters *In* stand for a complex organic group.

The equilibrium in a solution of the acid–base indicator **methyl orange,** a weak acid, can be represented by the equation

$$\underset{\text{Red}}{\text{HIn}} + \text{H}_2\text{O} \rightleftharpoons \text{H}_3\text{O}^+ + \underset{\text{Yellow}}{\text{In}^-} \qquad K_a = \frac{[\text{H}_3\text{O}^+][\text{In}^-]}{[\text{HIn}]}$$

The anion of methyl orange is yellow, and the nonionized form is red. When acid is added to the solution, the increase in the hydronium ion concentration shifts the equilibrium toward the nonionized red form, in accordance with Le Châtelier's principle.

The indicator's color is the visible result of the ratio of the concentrations of the two species In$^-$ and HIn. For methyl orange,

$$\frac{[\text{In}^-]}{[\text{HIn}]} = \frac{[\text{substance with yellow color}]}{[\text{substance with red color}]} = \frac{K_a}{[\text{H}_3\text{O}^+]}$$

When $[\text{H}_3\text{O}^+]$ has the same numerical value as K_a, the ratio of $[\text{In}^-]$ to $[\text{HIn}]$ is equal to 1, meaning that 50% of the indicator is present in the red acid form and 50% in the yellow ionic form, and the solution appears orange in color. When the hydronium ion concentration increases to a pH of 3.1, about 90% of the indicator is present in the red form and 10% in the yellow form, and the solution turns red. No change in color is visible for any further increase in the hydronium ion concentration.

Addition of a base to the system reduces the hydronium ion concentration and shifts the equilibrium toward the yellow form. At a pH of 4.4 about 90% of the indicator is in the yellow ionic form, and a further decrease in the hydronium ion concentration does not produce a visible color change. The pH range between 3.1 (red) and 4.4 (yellow) is the **color-change interval** of methyl orange; the pronounced color change takes place between these pH values.

The large number of known acid–base indicators cover a wide range of pH values and can be used to determine the approximate pH of an unknown solution by a process of elimination. Table 17.7 lists some of these indicators, their colors, and their color-change intervals (also see Fig. 17.15, page 567). The use of these indicators for specific purposes will be discussed in Section 17.16.

Table 17.7	Some Acid–Base Indicators		
Indicator	Color in the More Acid Range	pH Range	Color in the More Basic Range
Methyl violet	Yellow	0–2	Violet
Thymol blue	Pink	1.2–2.8	Yellow
Bromophenol blue	Yellow	3.0–4.7	Violet
Methyl orange	Pink	3.1–4.4	Yellow
Bromocresol green	Yellow	4.0–5.6	Blue
Bromocresol purple	Yellow	5.2–6.8	Purple
Litmus	Red	4.7–8.2	Blue
Phenolphthalein	Colorless	8.3–10.0	Pink
Thymolphthalein	Colorless	9.3–10.5	Blue
Alizarin yellow G	Colorless	10.1–12.1	Yellow
Trinitrobenzene	Colorless	12.0–14.3	Orange

⓱.16 Titration Curves

Titration curves, plots of the pH against the volume of acid or base added in a titration, show the point where equivalent quantities of acid and base are present (the equivalence point).

The simplest acid–base reactions are those of a strong acid with a strong base. Let us consider the titration of a 25.0-milliliter sample of 0.100 M hydrochloric acid with 0.100 M sodium hydroxide. The values of the pH measured after successive additions of small amounts of NaOH are listed in the first column in Table 17.8, page 568, and shown in Fig. 17.16. The pH increases very slowly at first, increases very rapidly in the middle portion of the curve, and then increases very slowly again. The point of inflection (the midpoint of the vertical part of the curve) is the **equivalence point** for the titration. It indicates when equivalent quantities of acid and base are present. For the titration of a strong acid and a strong base, the equivalence point occurs at a pH of 7 (Table 17.8 and Fig. 17.16). A solution with a pH of 7 is neutral; the hydronium ion concentration is equal to the hydroxide ion concentration.

The titration of a weak acid with a strong base (or of a weak base with a strong acid) is somewhat more complicated than that just discussed, but it follows the same basic principles. Let us consider the titration of 25.0 milliliters of 0.100 M acetic acid (a weak acid) with 0.100 M sodium hydroxide and compare the titration curve with that of the strong acid (Fig. 17.16). Table 17.8 gives the pH values during the titration; Fig. 17.17, page 569, shows the titration curve.

There are important differences between the two titration curves. The titration curve for the weak acid begins at a higher pH value (less acidic) and maintains higher pH values up to the equivalence point. This is because acetic acid is a weak acid and produces only a small quantity of hydronium ions. The pH at the equivalence point is also higher (8.72 rather than 7.00) because the solution contains sodium acetate. The acetate ion is a weak base and raises the pH as described in Section 17.11.

$$CH_3CO_2^- + H_2O \rightleftharpoons CH_3CO_2H + OH^-$$

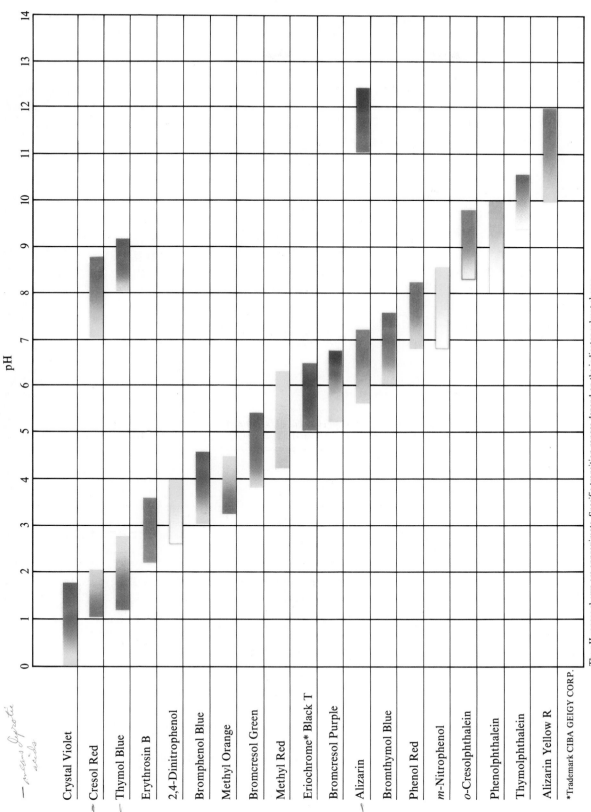

pH

Crystal Violet

Cresol Red

Thymol Blue

Erythrosin B

2,4-Dinitrophenol

Bromphenol Blue

Methyl Orange

Bromcresol Green

Methyl Red

Eriochrome* Black T

Bromcresol Purple

Alizarin

Bromthymol Blue

Phenol Red

m-Nitrophenol

o-Cresolphthalein

Phenolphthalein

Thymolphthalein

Alizarin Yellow R

*Trademark CIBA GEIGY CORP.

The pH ranges shown are approximate. Specific transition ranges depend on the indicator solvent chosen.

Figure 17.15

Ranges of color change for several acid–base indicators.

Table 17.8	pH Values in the Titrations of a Strong Acid with a Strong Base and of a Weak Acid with a Strong Base		

| | | pH Values | |
Volume of 0.100 M NaOH Added, mL	Moles of NaOH Added	0.100 M HCl[a]	0.100 M CH$_3$CO$_2$H[b]
0.0	0.0	1.00	2.87
5.0	0.00050	1.18	4.14
10.0	0.00100	1.37	4.57
15.0	0.00150	1.60	4.92
20.0	0.00200	1.95	5.35
22.0	0.00220	2.20	5.61
24.0	0.00240	2.69	6.13
24.5	0.00245	3.00	6.44
24.9	0.00249	3.70	7.14
25.0	0.00250	7.00	8.72
25.1	0.00251	10.30	10.30
25.5	0.00255	11.00	11.00
26.0	0.00260	11.29	11.29
28.0	0.00280	11.75	11.75
30.0	0.00300	11.96	11.96
35.0	0.00350	12.22	12.22
40.0	0.00400	12.36	12.36
45.0	0.00450	12.46	12.46
50.0	0.00500	12.52	12.52

[a] Titration of 25.00 mL of 0.100 M HCl (0.00250 mol of HCl) with 0.100 M NaOH.
[b] Titration of 25.00 mL of 0.100 M CH$_3$CO$_2$H (0.00250 mol of CH$_3$CO$_2$H) with 0.100 M NaOH.

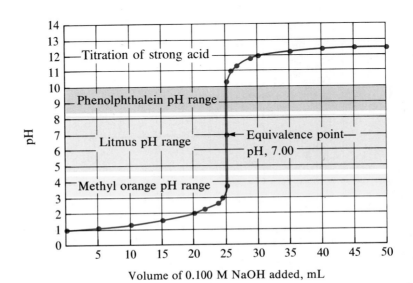

Figure 17.16

Titration curve for the titration of 25.00 mL of 0.100 M HCl (strong acid) with 0.100 M NaOH (strong base). The pH ranges for the color change of phenolphthalein, litmus, and methyl orange are indicated by the shaded areas.

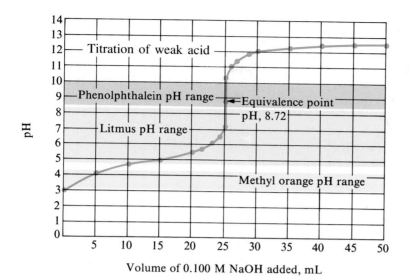

Figure 17.17

Titration curve for the titration of 25.00 mL of 0.100 M CH_3CO_2H (weak acid) with 0.100 M NaOH (strong base). The pH ranges for the color change of phenolphthalein, litmus, and methyl orange are indicated by the shaded areas.

After the equivalence point, the two curves are identical (Table 17.8 and Figs. 17.16 and 17.17) because the pH is dependent on the excess of hydroxide ion in both cases. After an acid is neutralized, whether it is a strong acid (like HCl) or a weak acid (like CH_3CO_2H), it has no further significant effect on the concentration of the hydroxide ion when additional strong base is added.

Titration curves help us pick an indicator that will provide a sharp color change at the equivalence point. The pH ranges for the color changes of three indicators from Table 17.7 are indicated in Figs. 17.16 and 17.17.

Phenolphthalein has a sharp color change over a small added volume of NaOH and hence is suitable for titrations that are either strong acid–strong base or weak acid–strong base. The equivalence point is located in the steeply rising portion of the titration curve, where the curve passes through the color-change interval of the indicator.

Litmus is a suitable indicator for the HCl titration because the titration curve shows that it changes color within 0.10 milliliter of the equivalence point. However, litmus would be a poor choice for the CH_3CO_2H titration because the pH is within the color-change interval of litmus when only about 12 milliliters of NaOH has been added, and it does not leave the range until 25 milliliters has been added. The color change would be very gradual, taking place during the addition of 13 milliliters of NaOH, making it almost useless as an indicator of the equivalence point.

Methyl orange could be used for the HCl titration (Fig. 17.16), although its use would have two disadvantages: (1) it completes its color change slightly before the equivalence point is reached (but very close to it, so this is not too serious), and (2) it changes color, as the plot shows, during the addition of nearly 0.5 milliliter of NaOH, which is not so sharp a color change as that of litmus or phenolphthalein. The titration curve shows that methyl orange would be completely useless as an indicator for the CH_3CO_2H titration. Its color change begins after about 1 milliliter of NaOH has been added and ends when about 8 milliliters has been added. The color change is completed long before the equivalence point (which occurs when 25.0 milliliters of NaOH has been added) is reached and hence provides no indication of the equivalence point.

The pH range in which an equivalence point will be observed can also be determined by calculating a pH curve. For example, the hydronium ion concentration of a 0.100 M solution of acetic acid can be calculated as described in Example 17.10 and then converted to pH. The determination of the hydronium ion concentration in a solution of a mixture of sodium acetate and acetic acid was described in Example 17.19. At the equivalence point, equimolar amounts of sodium hydroxide and acetic acid have been mixed. The problem therefore becomes calculation of the pH of a solution of sodium acetate, a calculation described in Section 17.11. Beyond the equivalence point, the pH is controlled by the excess sodium hydroxide present and can be determined from the concentration of hydroxide ion.

For Review

Summary

Water is an extremely weak electrolyte that undergoes **self-ionization.**

$$2H_2O \rightleftharpoons H_3O^+ + OH^- \qquad K_w = [H_3O^+][OH^-] = 1.0 \times 10^{-14} \text{ at } 25°C$$

Pure water contains equal concentrations of 1.0×10^{-7} M hydronium ion and hydroxide ion at 25°C. The **ion product of water, K_w,** is the equilibrium constant for the self-ionization reaction. All aqueous solutions contain both H_3O^+ and OH^-, and the product $[H_3O^+][OH^-]$ is equal to 1.0×10^{-14} at 25°C.

The concentration of hydronium ion in a solution of an acid in water is greater than 1.0×10^{-7} M and results from two reactions: the ionization of the acid and the self-ionization of water. However, the contribution of water to the total $[H_3O^+]$ in an acid solution can be neglected when the total $[H_3O^+]$ is greater than 4.5×10^{-7} M at 25°C.

The concentration of hydroxide ion in a solution of a base in water is greater than 1.0×10^{-7} M and also results from two reactions: the ionization of the base and the self-ionization of water. The contribution of water to the total $[OH^-]$ in a solution of a base is negligible when the total $[OH^-]$ is greater than 4.5×10^{-7} M at 25°C.

The concentration of H_3O^+ in a solution can be expressed as the pH of the solution; **pH $= -$log $[H_3O^+]$.** The concentration of OH^- can be expressed as the pOH of the solution; **pOH $= -$log $[OH^-]$.** In pure water, pH $= 7$ and pOH $= 7$. In any aqueous solution at 25°C, pH $+$ pOH $= 14.00$.

Although strong electrolytes ionize completely in solution, a solution of a weak electrolyte contains a mixture of molecular and ionic species. The concentration of the nonionized molecules of a weak acid (HA), of hydronium ion, and of the conjugate base (A$^-$) of the weak acid can be determined from K_a, the **ionization constant of the weak acid.** K_a is the equilibrium constant for the reaction.

$$HA + H_2O \rightleftharpoons H_3O^+ + A^- \qquad K_a = \frac{[H_3O^+][A^-]}{[HA]}$$

The concentration of the nonionized molecules of a weak base (B), of hydroxide ion, and of the conjugate acid (HB$^+$) of the weak base can be determined from K_b, the **ionization constant for a weak base.** K_b is the equilibrium constant for the reaction.

$$B + H_2O \rightleftharpoons BH^+ + OH^- \qquad K_b = \frac{[BH^+][OH^-]}{[B]}$$

Determination of equilibrium concentrations of weak acids or weak bases involves the procedures described for other equilibria in Chapter 15. Polyprotic acids (or bases) or mixtures of weak acids (or bases) are treated as though the ionization proceeded in a stepwise fashion; we first calculate the concentrations produced by the stronger acid (or base) and then use them to determine the concentrations resulting from ionization of the weaker acid (or base).

The extent of ionization of a weak acid in solution can be reduced by adding a compound containing the conjugate base of the weak acid (the **common ion effect**) or by adding an acid. Likewise, the ionization of a weak base can be reduced by adding the conjugate acid of the weak base or by adding hydroxide. A solution containing a mixture of an acid and its conjugate base, or of a base and its conjugate acid, is called a **buffer solution.** Unlike the solution of an acid, a base, or most salts, the hydronium ion concentration of a buffer solution does not change greatly when a small amount of acid or base is added to the buffer solution. The base (or acid) in the buffer reacts with the added acid (or base).

The value of the product of the ionization constants of a weak acid and its conjugate base or of a weak base and its conjugate acid is equal to the value of K_w; that is, $K_a K_b = K_w$. The conjugate base of a weak acid exhibits basic behavior and reacts with water to give a basic solution.

$$A^- + H_2O \rightleftharpoons HA + OH^- \qquad K_b = \frac{K_w}{K_a} = \frac{[HA][OH^-]}{[A^-]}$$

where K_b is the ionization constant of the conjugate base (A^-), K_w is the ion product of water, and K_a is the ionization constant of the weak acid (HA). The conjugate acid (HB^+) of a weak base (B) gives an acid solution.

$$HB^+ + H_2O \rightleftharpoons H_3O^+ + B \qquad K_a = \frac{K_w}{K_b} = \frac{[H_3O^+][B]}{[HB^+]}$$

where K_a is the ionization constant of the conjugate acid (HB^+), K_w has its customary value (1.0×10^{-14} at 25°C), and K_b is the ionization constant for the weak base (B). Reactions of this type, in which water is one of the reactants, are sometimes called **hydrolysis reactions.**

The pH of a solution can be determined with a **pH meter** or with **acid–base indicators.** Acid–base indicators are also used to determine the equivalence point in an acid–base titration. The best indicator for titration of an acid and a base is selected by considering the **titration curve** for the acid–base pair.

Key Terms and Concepts

acid–base indicator (17.15)
buffer capacity (17.9)
buffer solution (17.9)
common ion effect (17.8)
diprotic acid (17.4)
equivalence point (17.16)
Henderson-Hasselbalch equation (17.9)

hydrolysis (17.10)
ionization of hydrated metal ions (17.14)
ionization of water (17.1)
ionization of weak acids (17.3, 17.4, 17.5, 17.6)
ionization of weak bases (17.7)

ion product for water (17.1)
pH (17.1)
pK_w (17.1)
pOH (17.1)
stepwise ionization (17.4, 17.5)
titration curve (17.16)
triprotic acid (17.5)

Exercises

Answers for selected even-numbered exercises marked by red numbers appear at the end of the book. The worked-out solutions to all even-numbered exercises appear in the *Solutions Guide*.

Self-ionization of Water; pH and pOH

1. Explain why the concentration of hydronium ion and the concentration of hydroxide ion are the same in a sample of pure water.
2. Draw a graph of the relationship between the pH and the pOH of a solution as $[H_3O^+]$ varies from 1×10^{-13} M to 1×10^{-1} M. Put pOH on the vertical axis and pH on the horizontal axis.
3. Are the concentrations of hydronium ion and hydroxide ion in solutions of an acid or a base in water directly proportional or inversely proportional? Explain your answer. (Inverse and direct proportionality are discussed in Sections 10.3 and 10.4.)
4. Define pH and pOH both in words and mathematically.
5. Is the solution shown in Fig. 17.1(a) prepared from an acid or a base? Explain your answer.
6. The ionization constant for water (K_w) is 9.614×10^{-14} at 60°C. Calculate $[H_3O^+]$, $[OH^-]$, pH, and pOH for pure water at 60°C.
7. Calculate the pH and the pOH of each of the following solutions at 25°C.
   (a) 0.200 M HCl   (c) 0.0071 M Ca(OH)$_2$
   (b) 0.0143 M NaOH   (d) 3 M HNO$_3$
8. What are the hydronium and hydroxide ion concentrations in the solution shown in Fig. 17.1(a)?
9. What are the pH and the pOH in the solution shown in Fig. 17.4?
10. What is the concentration of NaOH in the unbuffered solution shown in part (a) of Fig. 17.10? What is the pOH of this solution?
11. Calculate the hydrogen ion concentration and the hydroxide ion concentration in a blood sample. See Table 17.1 for useful information.
12. Calculate the hydronium ion concentration and the hydroxide ion concentration in lime juice from its pH. See Table 17.1 for useful information.

Solutions of Electrolytes

13. Compare the extent of ionization of strong electrolytes and that of weak electrolytes in water.
14. Equilibrium calculations are not necessary when we are dealing with ionic concentrations in solutions of strong electrolytes such as NaOH and HCl. Why not?
15. What ionic and molecular species are present in an aqueous solution of hydrogen fluoride, HF? In a solution of sulfuric acid?

16. Calculate the concentration of each of the ions in the following solutions of strong electrolytes.
    (a) 0.085 M HNO$_3$
    (b) 1.248 M CoCl$_2$
    (c) 0.107 M [Fe(H$_2$O)$_6$]$_2$(SO$_4$)$_3$
17. For which of the following solutions must we consider the ionization of water when calculating the pH or pOH?
    (a) 3×10^{-8} M HNO$_3$
    (b) 0.1 g HCl in 1.0 L of solution.
    (c) 0.00080 g NaOH in 0.50 L of solution
    (d) 1×10^{-7} M Ca(OH)$_2$
18. For which of the following solutions must we consider the ionization of water when calculating the pH or pOH?
    (a) 6×10^{-7} M KOH
    (b) 3×10^{-5} M H$_2$SO$_4$
    (c) 1×10^{-6} g HBr in 2.0 L of solution
    (d) 0.034 g Sr(OH)$_2$ in 0.234 L of solution

Ionization of Weak Acids

19. Write the formula of the reaction quotient for the ionization of HOCN in water.
20. Write the formula of the reaction quotient for the ionization of HNO$_2$ in water.
21. What two common assumptions simplify calculation of equilibrium concentrations in a solution of a weak acid? How is the correctness of these assumptions checked?
22. From the equilibrium concentrations given, calculate K for each of the following weak acids or weak bases.
    (a) CH$_3$CO$_2$H: $[H_3O^+] = 1.34 \times 10^{-3}$ M;
       $[CH_3CO_2^-] = 1.34 \times 10^{-3}$ M;
       $[CH_3CO_2H] = 9.866 \times 10^{-2}$ M
    (b) HNO$_2$: $[H_3O^+] = 0.011$ M;
       $[NO_2^-] = 0.0438$ M; $[HNO_2] = 1.07$ M
23. Does the ionization of water make a significant contribution to the concentration of hydronium ion in the acid solutions described in Exercise 22? To the hydroxide ion concentrations?
24. Assume that the ionization of water can be neglected, and calculate the hydronium ion concentration in each of the following solutions. Show that the change in the initial concentration of the acid can be neglected. Ionization constants can be found in Appendix F.
    (a) 0.0092 M HClO
    (b) 0.0810 M HCN
25. Assume that the ionization of water can be neglected, and calculate the hydronium ion concentration in each of the following solutions. Show that the change in the initial concentration of the acid can be neglected. Ionization constants can be found in Appendix F.
    (a) 0.138 M CH$_3$CO$_2$H
    (b) 0.0992 M HC$_2$O$_4^-$ $(K_a = 6.4 \times 10^{-5})$
26. Calculate the hydronium ion concentration in each of the

following solutions. Show that the change in the initial concentration of the acid cannot be neglected.
(a) 0.0184 M HCNO   ($K_a = 3.46 \times 10^{-4}$)
(b) 0.100 M HF   ($K_a = 7.2 \times 10^{-4}$)
(c) 0.0655 M $[Fe(H_2O)_6]^{3+}$ ($K_a = 4.0 \times 10^{-3}$ for
$[Fe(H_2O)_6]^{3+} + H_2O \rightleftharpoons [Fe(OH)(H_2O)_5]^{2+} + H_3O^+$)

27. Calculate the hydronium ion concentration in each of the following solutions. Show that the change in concentration of the acid cannot be neglected.
(a) 0.02173 M CH_2ClCO_2H ($K_a = 1.4 \times 10^{-3}$)
(b) 0.10 M HSO_3NH_2 ($K_a = 1.0 \times 10^{-1}$)

28. Formic acid, HCO_2H, is the irritant that causes the body's reaction to an ant's sting. What is the concentration of hydronium ion and the percent ionization in a 0.417 M solution of formic acid?

29. Propionic acid, $C_2H_5CO_2H$ ($K_a = 1.34 \times 10^{-5}$), is used in the manufacture of calcium propionate, a food preservative. What is the hydronium ion concentration in a 0.717 M solution of $C_2H_5CO_2H$?

30. Sodium hydrogen sulfate, $NaHSO_4$, is used as a solid acid in some porcelain cleansers because it reacts with calcium carbonate precipitates. What are the hydronium ion concentration and the percent ionization of the HSO_4^- ion ($K_a = 1.2 \times 10^{-2}$) in a 0.50 M solution of $NaHSO_4$?

31. The ionization constant of lactic acid, $CH_3CHOHCO_2H$, is 1.36×10^{-4}. If 20.0 g of lactic acid is used to make a solution with a volume of 1.00 L, what is the concentration of hydronium ion in the solution?

32. What is the fluoride ion concentration in 0.750 L of a solution that contains 0.1500 g of HF?

33. Calculate the hydronium ion concentration in a 3.4×10^{-5} M solution of HBrO.

34. Calculate the hydronium ion concentration in a 9.2×10^{-6} M solution of HCN.

35. Calculate the pH and pOH of the solutions in Exercise 24.
36. Calculate the pH and pOH of the solutions in Exercise 25.
37. Calculate the pH and pOH of the solutions in Exercise 26.
38. Calculate the pH and pOH of the solutions in Exercise 27.
39. Calculate the pH of a 0.19 M solution of HNO_2.
40. Calculate the pH of a 1.4×10^{-2} M solution of HCNO.
41. How many moles of CH_3CO_2H were used to make the solution of acetic acid shown in Fig. 17.7 if its volume is 125 mL?

42. White vinegar is a 5.0% by mass solution of acetic acid in water. If the density of white vinegar is 1.007 g/cm^3, what is the pH?

Stepwise Equilibria

43. Why is the hydronium ion concentration in a solution that is 0.10 M in HCl and 0.10 M in HCO_2H determined by the concentration of HCl?

44. Evaluate the ionization constants $K_{H_2CO_3}$ and $K_{HCO_3^-}$ as well as the constant for the equilibrium

$$H_2CO_3 + 2H_2O \rightleftharpoons 2H_3O^+ + CO_3^{2-}$$

from the following concentrations found at equilibrium in a solution of H_2CO_3 and $NaHCO_3$.

$$[H_3O^+] = 8.0 \times 10^{-6} \text{ M}$$
$$[HCO_3^-] = 1.6 \times 10^{-3} \text{ M}$$
$$[CO_3^{2-}] = 1.4 \times 10^{-8} \text{ M}$$
$$[H_2CO_3] = 3.0 \times 10^{-2} \text{ M}$$

45. Which of the following concentrations would we find to be equal if we were to calculate the equilibrium concentrations in a 0.134 M solution of H_2CO_3, a diprotic acid: $[H_3O^+]$, $[OH^-]$, $[H_2CO_3]$, $[HCO_3^-]$, $[CO_3^{2-}]$? (No calculations are needed to answer this question.)

46. Which of the following concentrations would we find to be equal if we were to calculate equilibrium concentrations in a 0.20 M solution of H_2S, a diprotic acid: $[H_3O^+]$, $[OH^-]$, $[H_2S]$, $[HS^-]$, $[S^{2-}]$? (No calculations are needed to answer this question.)

47. Calculate the equilibrium concentration of the nonionized acids and all ions in a solution that is 0.25 M in HCO_2H and 0.10 M in HClO.

48. Calculate the equilibrium concentration of the nonionized acids and all ions in a solution that is 0.134 M in HNO_2 and 0.10 M in HBrO.

49. Calculate the equilibrium concentration of the nonionized acid and all ions in a solution that is 0.134 M in H_2CO_3, a diprotic acid.

50. One of the important components of proteins is glycine, $H_3NCH_2CO_2H^+$, which we can abbreviate as H_2gly^+. Calculate the equilibrium concentration of H_3O^+, H_2gly^+, Hgly, and gly$^-$ in a solution that is 0.090 M in H_2gly^+. For glycine, $K_{a_1} = 4.5 \times 10^{-3}$ and $K_{a_2} = 2.5 \times 10^{-10}$.

51. Calculate the concentration of each species present in a 0.050 M solution of H_2S.

52. Calculate the concentration of each species present in a 0.010 M solution of phthalic acid, $C_6H_4(CO_2H)_2$.

$$C_6H_4(CO_2H)_2 + H_2O \rightleftharpoons H_3O^+ + C_6H_4(CO_2H)(CO_2)^-$$
$$(K_a = 1.1 \times 10^{-3})$$
$$C_6H_4(CO_2H)(CO_2)^- + H_2O \rightleftharpoons H_3O^+ + C_6H_4(CO_2)_2^{2-}$$
$$(K_a = 3.9 \times 10^{-6})$$

Ionization of Weak Bases

53. Write the formula of the reaction quotient for the ionization of NH_3 in water.

54. Write the formula of the reaction quotient for the ionization of $N(CH_3)_3$ in water.

55. Calculate the ionization constants of the following weak bases from the concentrations given.
(a) NH_3: $[OH^-] = 3.1 \times 10^{-3}$ M;
$[NH_4^+] = 3.1 \times 10^{-3}$ M; $[NH_3] = 0.533$ M
(b) ClO^-: $[OH^-] = 4.0 \times 10^{-4}$ M;
$[HClO] = 2.38 \times 10^{-5}$ M;
$[ClO^-] = 0.273$ M

56. What two assumptions simplify calculation of equilibrium concentrations in a solution of a weak base? How is the correctness of these assumptions checked?

57. Assume that the ionization of water can be neglected, and calculate the hydroxide ion concentration in each of the following solutions. Show that the change in the initial concentration of the base can be neglected.
(a) 0.0784 M $C_6H_5NH_2$ $(K_b = 4.6 \times 10^{-10})$
(b) 0.1098 M $(CH_3)_3N$ $(K_b = 7.4 \times 10^{-5})$
(c) 0.222 M CN^- $(K_b = 2.5 \times 10^{-5})$

58. Assume that the ionization of water can be neglected, and calculate the hydroxide ion concentration in each of the following solutions. Show that the change in the initial concentration of the base can be neglected.
(a) 0.300 M N_2H_4 $(K_b = 3 \times 10^{-6}$ for
$$N_2H_4 + H_2O \rightleftharpoons N_2H_5^+ + OH^-)$$
(b) 1.13 M BrO^- $(K_b = 5 \times 10^{-6})$

59. Calculate the hydroxide ion concentration in each of the following solutions. Show that the change in the initial concentration of the base cannot be neglected.
(a) 4.113×10^{-3} M CH_3NH_2 $(K_b = 4.4 \times 10^{-4})$
(b) 0.11 M $(CH_3)_2NH$ $(K_b = 7.4 \times 10^{-4})$

60. Calculate the hydroxide ion concentration in each of the following solutions. Show that the change in concentration of the base cannot be neglected.
(a) 0.050 M CH_3NH_2 $(K_b = 4.4 \times 10^{-4})$
(b) 0.00253 M $C_6H_5O^-$ $(K_b = 7.81 \times 10^{-5})$

61. Calculate the pH and pOH of the solutions in Exercise 57.

62. Calculate the pH and pOH of the solutions in Exercise 58.

63. Calculate the pH and pOH of the solutions in Exercise 59.

64. Calculate the pH and pOH of the solutions in Exercise 60.

65. What is the hydroxide ion concentration in a dilute solution of household ammonia that contains 0.3124 mol of NH_3 per liter?

66. The artificial sweetener sodium saccharide, once commonly used in soft drinks, contains the basic ion $C_7H_4NSO_3^-$ $(K_b = 4.8 \times 10^{-3})$. What is the hydroxide ion concentration in a liter of water sweetened with 0.100 g of $Na(C_7H_4NSO_3)$?

67. What is the pH of a 0.252 M solution of NH_3?

68. What is the pH of a 0.083 M solution of CN^-? For the CN^- ion, $K_b = 2.5 \times 10^{-5}$.

69. Nicotine, $C_{10}H_{14}N_2$, is a base that will accept two protons $(K_1 = 7 \times 10^{-7}, K_2 = 1.4 \times 10^{-11})$. What is the concentration of each species present in a 0.050 M solution of nicotine?

70. Calculate the concentration of each species present in a 0.050 M solution of Na_3PO_4.
$$PO_4^{3-} + H_2O \rightleftharpoons HPO_4^{2-} + OH^-$$
$$(K_b = 2.8 \times 10^{-2})$$
$$HPO_4^{2-} + H_2O \rightleftharpoons H_2PO_4^- + OH^-$$
$$(K_b = 1.6 \times 10^{-7})$$
$$H_2PO_4^- + H_2O \rightleftharpoons H_3PO_4 + OH^-$$
$$(K_b = 1.3 \times 10^{-12})$$

71. Say the solution shown in Fig. 17.1 were made with NH_3. How many moles of NH_3 would be required to make the solution if its volume were 110 mL?

72. Calculate the pH and pOH of each of the following solutions of a base.
(a) 0.127 M NH_3
(b) 0.244 M $(CH_3)_3N$
(c) 0.0244 M $(CH_3)_3N$
(d) 0.104 M $H_2BO_3^-$ $(K_b = 1.7 \times 10^{-6})$
(e) 0.479 M SO_3^{2-} $(K_b = 1.6 \times 10^{-7})$

73. Calculate the pH, pOH, and total methylamine concentration in a solution of methylamine that is 6.90% ionized.

74. Is it possible to tell whether the solution shown in Fig. 17.1 was prepared from NaOH or from NH_3? Explain your answer.

75. Sketch graphs similar to Fig. 15.4 for Q and the concentrations of NH_3, NH_4^+, and OH^- when 0.10 mol of NH_3 is added to 1.00 L of water and comes to equilibrium.

Buffers

76. Explain why a buffer can be prepared from a mixture of HF and NaF but not from HCl and NaCl.

77. Draw a graph similar to Fig. 17.12 that describes the change in pH as 0.10 M HCl is added to 100 mL of a buffer that is 0.10 M in ammonia and 0.10 M in ammonium chloride.

78. Explain why the pH does not change significantly when a small amount of an acid or a base is added to a solution that contains equal amounts of H_3PO_4 and NaH_2PO_4.

79. Calculate the pH of each of the following buffer solutions that contain equal volumes of the two solutions with the concentrations indicated.
(a) 0.50 M CH_3CO_2H; 0.50 M $NaCH_3CO_2$
(b) 0.50 M CH_3CO_2H; 0.20 M $NaCH_3CO_2$
(c) 0.40 M NH_3; 0.40 M NH_4Cl
(d) 0.25 M H_3PO_4; 0.15 M NaH_2PO_4
(e) 0.10 M H_2S; 0.20 M NaHS

80. In venous blood, the following equilibrium is set up by dissolved carbon dioxide:
$$H_2CO_3 + H_2O \rightleftharpoons H_3O^+ + HCO_3^-$$
If the pH of the blood is 7.4, what is the ratio of $[HCO_3^-]$ to $[H_2CO_3]$?

81. Calculate the pH of 0.500 L of a 0.0880 M solution of $NaHCO_3$ to which has been added 1.10×10^{-2} mol of HCl.

82. Calculate the pH of a solution resulting from mixing 0.10 L of 0.10 M NaOH with 0.40 L of 0.025 M HF.

83. Calculate the pH of a solution made by mixing equal volumes of 0.30 M NH_3 and 0.030 M HNO_3.

84. Calculate the pH of a solution prepared by mixing 10.0 mL of 0.10 M LiOH and 5.0×10^{-4} mol of benzoic acid. Assume the final volume is 10.0 mL. K_a for benzoic acid is 6.7×10^{-5}.

85. A buffer solution is prepared from 5.0 g of NH_4NO_3 and

0.100 L of 0.10 M NH_3. What is the pH of the buffer if the final volume is 0.100 L?

86. Calculate the pH of 0.750 L of a solution that contains 87.5 g of $Ba(N_3)_2$ and 0.250 mol of HN_3.

87. How many moles of sodium acetate must be added to 1.0 L of a 1.0 M acetic acid solution to prepare a buffer solution with a pH of 5.08? With a pH of 4.20?

88. How many moles of NH_4Cl must be added to 1.0 L of a 1.0 M NH_3 solution to prepare a buffer solution with a pH of 9.00? With a pH of 9.50?

89. Addition of 1.0 mL of 0.10 M NaOH to 0.100 L of the buffer solution discussed in Section 17.9 changed the pH from 4.74 to 4.75. What is the new pH when 1.0 mL of 0.10 M NaOH is added to 0.100 L of an unbuffered solution of hydrochloric acid with a pH of 4.74?

90. A buffer solution is made up of equal volumes of 0.100 M acetic acid and 0.500 M sodium acetate. (a) What is the pH of this solution? (b) What is the pH that results from adding 1.00 mL of 0.100 M HCl to 0.200 L of the buffer solution? (Use 1.80×10^{-5} for the ionization constant of acetic acid.)

91. Which acid in Table 17.3 is most appropriate for preparation of a buffer solution with a pH of 3.1?

92. Which acid in Table 17.3 is most appropriate for preparation of a buffer solution with a pH of 3.7?

Reaction of Salts with Water

93. Why does the salt of a strong acid and a weak base give an acidic solution?

94. Why does the salt of a weak acid and a strong base give a basic solution?

95. Why does the salt of a strong acid and a strong base give an approximately neutral solution?

96. Calculate the ionization constant for each of the following acids or bases.
    (a) F^-
    (b) AsO_4^{3-}
    (c) NO_2^-
    (d) NH_4^+
    (e) $(CH_3)_2NH_2^+$
    (f) $HC_2O_4^-$ (as a base)

97. Calculate the pH of each of the following solutions.
    (a) 0.4735 M NaCN
    (b) 0.1050 M NH_4NO_3
    (c) 0.0270 M $Ca(N_3)_2$
    (d) 0.333 M $[(CH_3)_2NH_2]_2SO_4$
    [Note that $(CH_3)_2NH_2^+$ is the conjugate acid of the weak base $(CH_3)_2NH$, just as NH_4^+ is the conjugate acid of the weak base NH_3.]

98. Calculate the pH of a solution made by mixing equal volumes of 0.040 M aqueous aniline, $C_6H_5NH_2$, and 0.040 M HCl. (K_b for $C_6H_5NH_2 = 4.6 \times 10^{-10}$.)

99. (a) Write the equation for the reaction when potassium cyanide, KCN, behaves as a base.
    (b) What is K_b for this reaction?
    (c) What is the pH of a 0.255 M solution of KCN?

100. The ion HTe^- is an amphiphrotic species; it can act as either an acid or a base. What is K_a for the acid reaction of HTe^- with H_2O? What is K_b for the reaction in which HTe^- functions as a base in water?

101. Sodium nitrite, $NaNO_2$, is used in meat processing. What are $[H_3O^+]$ and the pH of a 0.225 M $NaNO_2$ solution? Is the solution acidic or basic?

102. Novocaine, $C_{13}H_{21}O_2N_2Cl$, is the salt of the base procaine and hydrochloric acid. The ionization constant for procaine is 7×10^{-6}. Find the pH of a 2.0% solution by mass of novocaine, assuming that the density of the solution is 1.0 g/cm^3.

103. Calculate the pH of a 0.470 M solution of lithium carbonate, Li_2CO_3.

Titration Curves and Indicators

104. Determine a theoretical titration curve for the titration of 20.0 mL of 0.100 M $HClO_4$, a strong acid, with 0.200 M KOH.

105. Determine a theoretical titration curve for the titration of 25.0 mL of 0.150 M NH_3 with 0.150 M HCl.

106. Which of the indicators listed in Table 17.7 would be appropriate for the titration described in Exercise 104? For that described in Exercise 105?

107. Why does an acid–base indicator change color over a range of pH values rather than at a specific pH?

108. The indicator dinitrophenol is an acid with a K_a of 1.1×10^{-4}. In a 1.0×10^{-4} M solution, it is colorless in acid and yellow in base. Calculate the pH range over which it goes from 10% ionized (colorless) to 90% ionized (yellow).

109. The hydronium ion concentration at the half-equivalence point (the point at which half of the amount of base necessary to reach the equivalence point has been added) in the titration of a weak acid with a strong base is equal to K_a for the weak acid. Explain.

Additional Exercises

110. What is the pH of a solution prepared by mixing equal volumes of the solutions shown in Fig. 17.7?

111. Draw a curve similar to that shown in Fig. 17.5 for a series of solutions of HF. Plot $[H_3O^+]_{total}$ on the vertical axis and the total concentration of HF (the sum of the concentrations of both the ionized and nonionized HF molecules) on the horizontal axis. Let the total concentration of HF vary from 1×10^{-10} M to 1×10^{-2} M.

112. Draw a curve similar to that shown in Fig. 17.6 for a series of solutions of NH_3. Plot $[OH^-]$ on the vertical axis and the total concentration of NH_3 (both ionized and nonionized NH_3 molecules) on the horizontal axis. Let the total concentration of NH_3 vary from 1×10^{-10} M to 1×10^{-2} M.

113. The pH of a sample of acid rain is 4.07. Assuming that the acidity is due to the presence of HNO_2 in the rain, find the total concentration of HNO_2.

114. Using the K_a values in Appendix F, place $[Al(H_2O)_6]^{3+}$ in the correct location in Table 16.1, the table of relative strengths of conjugate acid–base pairs in Section 16.3.

115. A typical urine sample contains 2.3% by mass of the base urea, $CO(NH_2)_2$.

$$CO(NH_2)_2 + H_2O \rightleftharpoons CO(NH_2)(NH_3)^+ + OH^-$$
$$(K_b = 1.5 \times 10^{-14})$$

The density of the urine sample is 1.06 g/cm^3, and the pH of the sample is 6.35. Calculate the concentration of $CO(NH_2)_2$ and of $CO(NH_2)(NH_3)^+$ in the sample.

116. The solutions of ammonia used for cleaning windows usually contain about 10% NH_3 by mass. If a solution that is exactly 10% by mass has a density of 0.99 g/cm^3, what are the pH and the hydroxide ion concentration?

117. In many detergents, phosphates have been replaced with silicates as water conditioners. If 125 g of a detergent that contains 8.0% Na_2SiO_3 by weight is used in 4.0 L of water, what are the pH and the hydroxide ion concentration in the wash water?

$$SiO_3^{2-} + H_2O \rightleftharpoons SiO_3H^- + OH^-$$
$$(K_b = 1.6 \times 10^{-3})$$

$$SiO_3H^- + H_2O \rightleftharpoons SiO_3H_2 + OH^-$$
$$(K_b = 3.1 \times 10^{-5})$$

118. Saccharin, $C_7H_4NSO_3H$, is a weak acid ($K_a = 2.1 \times 10^{-12}$). If 0.250 L of diet cola with a buffered pH of 5.48 was prepared from 2.00×10^{-3} g of sodium saccharide, $Na(C_7H_4NSO_3)$, what are the final concentrations of saccharin and sodium saccharide in the solution?

119. The ionization constant for water, K_w, is 5.474×10^{-14} at 50°C. At 50°C, K_b for NH_3 is 1.892×10^{-5}. What is the ionization constant for NH_4^+ at 50°C?

120. What is the pH of 1.000 L of a solution of 100.0 g of glutamic acid ($C_5H_9NO_4$, a diprotic acid; $K_1 = 8.5 \times 10^{-5}$, $K_2 = 3.39 \times 10^{-10}$) to which has been added 20.0 g of NaOH during the preparation of monosodium glutamate, the flavoring agent? What is the pH when exactly 1 mol of NaOH per mole of acid has been added?

The Solubility Product Principle

Barium chromate is only slightly soluble.

In chemical reactions that yield solids (precipitation reactions, Section 2.11), slightly soluble products are often formed. For example, when an aqueous solution of yellow potassium chromate is added drop by drop to a solution of colorless barium nitrate, a cloud of solid yellow-orange barium chromate forms, as shown in the opening photograph in this chapter. A slightly soluble ionic solid, such as barium chromate, dissolves to a very limited extent, and an equilibrium between the solid and a saturated solution of the ions of the solid results.

The rules given in Section 12.5 (''The Solubilities of Common Metal Compounds'') enable us to predict the solubilities of a variety of simple common salts. However, they provide no quantitative information about solubilities. In this chapter we shall be concerned with the concentrations of ions present during the formation or dissolution of slightly soluble ionic compounds. This will entail the application of equilibrium concepts to reactions involving the precipitation and dissolution of slightly soluble ionic compounds.

The Formation of Precipitates

🔟.1 The Solubility Product

A slightly soluble electrolyte dissolves until a saturated solution—a solution of its ions in equilibrium with undissolved solute—is formed. When the solution is saturated, some of the solid continues to dissolve, but at the same time an equal amount of the ions in the solution combines to yield crystals of the solid. The opposing processes have equal rates; a state of equilibrium exists. For example, when solid silver chloride is added to pure water, the equilibrium is described by the equation

$$AgCl(s) \underset{\text{Precipitation}}{\overset{\text{Dissolution}}{\rightleftharpoons}} Ag^+(aq) + Cl^-(aq) \qquad \text{(saturated solution)}$$

For an equilibrium involving the precipitation or dissolution of the slightly soluble electrolyte $M_pX_q(s)$

$$M_pX_q(s) \rightleftharpoons pM^{m+}(aq) + qX^{x-}(aq)$$

where M_pX_q is composed of the ions M^{m+} and X^{x-}, we write the equilibrium constant equation as

$$K_{sp} = [M^{m+}]^p[X^{x-}]^q$$

The reaction quotient for a dissolution reaction *at equilibrium* has a value called K_{sp}, **the solubility product.** Because the reactants are solids, the concentrations of the reactants do not appear in the expressions for the solubility products (Section 15.2). Note that an equilibrium involving a dissolution reaction is a heterogeneous equilibrium (Section 15.12).

For the equilibrium involving the dissolution of AgCl, which is

$$AgCl(s) \rightleftharpoons Ag^+(aq) + Cl^-(aq)$$

the solubility product is

$$K_{sp} = [Ag^+][Cl^-]$$

The product of the concentrations of Ag^+ and Cl^- must be equal to the solubility product when a saturated solution is in equilibrium with undissolved solute.

Apatite is a slightly soluble mineral that dissolves according to the equation

$$Ca_5(PO_4)_3OH(s) \rightleftharpoons 5Ca^{2+}(aq) + 3PO_4^{3-}(aq) + OH^-(aq)$$

Crystal of the mineral apatite, $Ca_5(PO_4)_3OH$. Pure apatite is white, but like most other minerals, this sample is colored because of the presence of impurities.

For this dissolution at equilibrium,

$$K_{sp} = Q = [Ca^{2+}]^5[PO_4^{3-}]^3[OH^-]$$

For a salt like magnesium ammonium phosphate, which dissolves according to the equation

$$MgNH_4PO_4(s) \rightleftharpoons Mg^{2+}(aq) + NH_4^+(aq) + PO_4^{3-}(aq)$$

at equilibrium we have

$$K_{sp} = Q = [Mg^{2+}][NH_4^+][PO_4^{3-}]$$

A table of solubility products appears in Appendix D. The magnitude of each of these equilibrium constants is much smaller than 1, because the compounds listed are only slightly soluble.

In this chapter we will be concerned with four aspects of the equilibria between slightly soluble electrolytes and their solutions:

1. Determination of the solubility product of a slightly soluble electrolyte from its solubility—the calculation of an equilibrium constant from equilibrium concentrations (Section 15.5).
2. Determination of the solubility of a slightly soluble electrolyte from its solubility product—a calculation of equilibrium concentrations from initial concentrations (which are zero in this case) and the equilibrium constant (Section 15.6).
3. Determination of the concentration of one ion in an equilibrium mixture resulting from the dissolution of a slightly soluble electrolyte from the concentration of the remaining ions and its solubility product—a calculation of a missing concentration (Section 15.5).
4. Determination of the change in solubility of a slightly soluble electrolyte resulting from a change in the equilibrium concentration of one of its ions—a calculation of equilibrium concentrations from initial concentrations and the equilibrium constant (Section 15.6) and an application of Le Châtelier's principle (Section 15.8).

18.2 Calculation of Solubility Products from Solubilities

The solubility product of a slightly soluble electrolyte can be calculated from its solubility in moles per liter. When the concentrations are given in other units, such as grams per liter, we must convert them to moles per liter. The following two examples illustrate the calculation of equilibrium constants from equilibrium concentrations—a type of calculation described in Section 15.5.

Example 18.1

The solubility of the artist's pigment chrome yellow, $PbCrO_4$, is 4.3×10^{-5} g L^{-1}. Calculate the solubility product for $PbCrO_4$.

In this case, the reaction is

$$PbCrO_4(s) \rightleftharpoons Pb^{2+}(aq) + CrO_4^{2-}(aq)$$

and the equilibrium constant is the solubility product of $PbCrO_4$.

$$K_{sp} = [Pb^{2+}][CrO_4^{2-}]$$

Example 18.1

continued

Yellow lead chromate, $PbCrO_4$, the colored compound in this paint, is not appreciably soluble in water.

We need to know the equilibrium concentrations of Pb^{2+} and CrO_4^{2-} in order to perform the calculation.

We are given the solubility of $PbCrO_4$ in grams per liter. By determining the solubility of $PbCrO_4$ in moles per liter, we can find the equilibrium concentrations and, from them, K_{sp}. We use the molar mass of $PbCrO_4$ (323.2 g/1 mol) to convert the solubility of $PbCrO_4$ in grams per liter to moles per liter.

$$\frac{4.3 \times 10^{-5} \text{ g } PbCrO_4}{1 \text{ L}} \times \frac{1 \text{ mol } PbCrO_4}{323.2 \text{ g } PbCrO_4}$$

$$= \frac{1.33 \times 10^{-7} \text{ mol } PbCrO_4}{1 \text{ L}} = 1.33 \times 10^{-7} \text{ M}$$

Because 1 mol of $PbCrO_4$ gives 1 mol of $Pb^{2+}(aq)$ and 1 mol of $CrO_4^{2-}(aq)$, both $[Pb^{2+}]$ and $[CrO_4^{2-}]$ are equal to the molar solubility of $PbCrO_4$. Now we substitute the equilibrium concentrations of Pb^{2+} and CrO_4^{2-} into the expression for K_{sp}.

$$[Pb^{2+}][CrO_4^{2-}] = K_{sp}$$

$$(1.33 \times 10^{-7})(1.33 \times 10^{-7}) = 1.8 \times 10^{-14} = K_{sp}$$

Example 18.2

Silver chromate, Ag_2CrO_4 is not appreciably soluble in water.

Calculate the solubility product, K_{sp}, of silver chromate, Ag_2CrO_4, the molar solubility of which is 1.3×10^{-4} mol L^{-1}.

The equation for the dissolution of silver chromate and the solubility product are

$$Ag_2CrO_4(s) \rightleftharpoons 2Ag^+(aq) + CrO_4^{2-}(aq) \qquad K_{sp} = [Ag^+]^2[CrO_4^{2-}]$$

From the equation for the dissolution of Ag_2CrO_4, we can see that 1 mol of $CrO_4^{2-}(aq)$ is formed for each mol of Ag_2CrO_4 that dissolves (1 mol CrO_4^{2-}/1 mol Ag_2CrO_4), and that 2 mol of $Ag^+(aq)$ are formed (2 mol Ag^+/1 mol Ag_2CrO_4).

$$\frac{1.3 \times 10^{-4} \text{ mol } Ag_2CrO_4}{1 \text{ L}} \times \frac{2 \text{ mol } Ag^+}{1 \text{ mol } Ag_2CrO_4} = \frac{2.6 \times 10^{-4} \text{ mol } Ag^+}{1 \text{ L}}$$

$$\frac{1.3 \times 10^{-4} \text{ mol } Ag_2CrO_4}{1 \text{ L}} \times \frac{1 \text{ mol } CrO_4^{2-}}{1 \text{ mol } Ag_2CrO_4} = \frac{1.3 \times 10^{-4} \text{ mol } CrO_4^{2-}}{1 \text{ L}}$$

Thus $[Ag^+] = 2.6 \times 10^{-4}$ M and $[CrO_4^{2-}] = 1.3 \times 10^{-4}$ M.

Substituting the equilibrium concentrations of Ag^+ and CrO_4^{2-} in the expression for the solubility product gives

$$[Ag^+]^2[CrO_4^{2-}] = K_{sp}$$

$$(2.6 \times 10^{-4})^2(1.3 \times 10^{-4}) = 8.8 \times 10^{-12} = K_{sp}$$

Note that $[Ag^+]$ is squared in this expression.

⑱.3 Calculation of Solubilities from Solubility Products

The molar solubility of a slightly soluble electrolyte can be calculated from its solubility product. The following two examples illustrate such calculations. In these examples, equilibrium concentrations are calculated from initial concentrations and equilibrium constants, techniques introduced in Sections 15.5 and 15.6.

Example 18.3

The solubility product for silver chloride is 1.8×10^{-10} (Appendix D). Calculate the molar solubility of silver chloride.

The molar solubility of AgCl is equal to the molar concentration of Ag^+ or Cl^- in a saturated solution of silver chloride in water. This means that we need to determine the equilibrium concentration of Ag^+ or Cl^- from the initial concentrations (which are 0 M before any AgCl dissolves) and the equilibrium constant (K_{sp}) for the dissolution of AgCl.

The equilibrium is described by the equation

$$AgCl(s) \rightleftharpoons Ag^+(aq) + Cl^-(aq) \qquad K_{sp} = [Ag^+][Cl^-] = 1.8 \times 10^{-10}$$

The following table gives the initial concentrations of Ag^+ and Cl^-, the changes in concentration as equilibrium is established, and the concentrations at equilibrium.

	$[Ag^+]$	$[Cl^-]$
Initial Concentration, M	0	0
Change	Δ	Δ
Equilibrium Concentration, M	$0 + \Delta = \Delta$	$0 + \Delta = \Delta$

The change in the concentration of Ag^+, Δ, is positive because [Ag+] increases as solid AgCl dissolves. The change in the concentration of Cl^- is equal to the change in $[Ag^+]$ because, as indicated by the chemical equation, 1 mol of Cl^- forms for each 1 mol of Ag^+ that forms. The concentration of AgCl does not appear in either the solubility product or the table because AgCl is a solid (Sections 15.2 and 15.12). Substitution into the equilibrium equation gives, at equilibrium,

$$K_{sp} = [Ag^+][Cl^-]$$
$$1.8 \times 10^{-10} = (\Delta)(\Delta) = \Delta^2$$
$$\Delta = \sqrt{1.8 \times 10^{-10}} = 1.3 \times 10^{-5}$$
$$[Ag^+] = [Cl^-] = 1.3 \times 10^{-5} \text{ M}$$

The molar solubility of AgCl is 1.3×10^{-5} moles per liter because 1 mol of AgCl must dissolve for each 1 mol of Ag^+ or Cl^- that is produced.

A precipitate of insoluble silver chloride, AgCl, forms when solutions of $AgNO_3$ and NaCl are mixed.

Example 18.4

Although most mercury compounds are very poisonous, sixteenth-century physicians used calomel, Hg_2Cl_2, as a medication. Their patients did not die of mercury poisoning (usually) because calomel is quite insoluble. Calculate the molar solubility of Hg_2Cl_2 ($K_{sp} = 1.1 \times 10^{-18}$, Appendix D).

Example 18.4 continued

Mercury(I) chloride is essentially insoluble in water.

The equation for the dissolution of Hg_2Cl_2 is

$$Hg_2Cl_2(s) \rightleftharpoons Hg_2^{2+}(aq) + 2Cl^-(aq) \qquad K_{sp} = 1.1 \times 10^{-18}$$

where Hg_2^{2+} is the diatomic mercury(I) ion. The number of moles of Hg_2Cl_2 that dissolve in 1 L of solution (the molar solubility of Hg_2Cl_2) is equal to the concentration of Hg_2^{2+} ions in the solution that results, because for each 1 mol of Hg_2Cl_2 that dissolves, 1 mol of Hg_2^{2+} forms. The molar solubility of Hg_2Cl_2 also equals half the concentration of Cl^- in the solution, because for each 1 mol of Hg_2Cl_2 that dissolves, 2 mol of Cl^- form.

The table of changes and concentrations follows.

	$[Hg_2^{2+}]$	$[Cl^-]$
Initial Concentration, M	0	0
Change	Δ	2Δ
Equilibrium Concentration, M	$0 + \Delta = \Delta$	$0 + 2\Delta = 2\Delta$

Note that the change in the concentration of Cl^- is twice as large as the change in the concentration of Hg_2^{2+}, because for each 1 mol of Hg_2^{2+} that forms, 2 mol of Cl^- form. We substitute the equilibrium concentrations into the expression for K_{sp} and calculate the value of Δ.

$$K_{sp} = [Hg_2^{2+}][Cl^-]^2$$

$$1.1 \times 10^{-18} = (\Delta)(2\Delta)^2$$

$$4\Delta^3 = 1.1 \times 10^{-18}$$

$$\Delta = \left(\frac{1.1 \times 10^{-18}}{4}\right)^{1/3} = 6.5 \times 10^{-7}$$

$$[Hg_2^{2+}] = 0 + \Delta = 6.5 \times 10^{-7} \text{ M}$$

$$[Cl^-] = 0 + 2\Delta = 2(6.5 \times 10^{-7}) = 1.3 \times 10^{-6} \text{ M}$$

The molar solubility of Hg_2Cl_2 is 6.5×10^{-7} M.

18.4 The Precipitation of Slightly Soluble Electrolytes

As noted in Section 18.1 the dissolution of a slightly soluble electrolyte involves the equilibrium

$$M_pX_q(s) \rightleftharpoons pM^{m+}(aq) + qX^{x-}(aq) \qquad K_{sp} = [M^{m+}]^p[X^{x-}]^q$$

When a solution of a soluble salt of the M^{m+} ion is mixed with a solution of a soluble salt of the X^{x-} ion, the solid M_pX_q precipitates if the value of the reaction quotient for the resulting mixture of M^{m+} and X^{x-} is greater than the solubility product of M_pX_q. If the reaction quotient is greater than the solubility product, the reaction shifts to the left, as we noted in Section 15.4, and the concentrations of the ions are reduced by formation of the solid until the value of Q equals K_{sp}.

When a solution of $AgNO_3$ and a solution of $NaCl$ are mixed, we can expect silver chloride to precipitate if the reaction quotient calculated from the concentrations in the mixture is greater than the solubility product of silver chloride.

Does silver chloride precipitate when equal volumes of a 2×10^{-4} M solution of $AgNO_3$ and a 2×10^{-4} M solution of $NaCl$ are mixed?

Example 18.5

The equation for the equilibrium between solid silver chloride, silver ion, and chloride ion is

$$AgCl(s) \rightleftharpoons Ag^+(aq) + Cl^-(aq) \qquad K_{sp} = [Ag^+][Cl^-] = 1.8 \times 10^{-10}$$

We can expect this reaction to shift to the left and AgCl to precipitate if the reaction quotient calculated from the concentrations in the mixture of $AgNO_3$ and $NaCl$ is greater than the solubility product of silver chloride.

The volume doubles when we mix equal volumes, so each concentration is reduced to half its initial value. Consequently, immediately upon mixing, $[Ag^+]$ and $[Cl^-]$ are both equal to

$$\tfrac{1}{2}(2 \times 10^{-4})\ M = 1 \times 10^{-4}\ M$$

The reaction quotient, Q, is *momentarily* greater than K_{sp} for AgCl.

$$K_{sp} = 1.8 \times 10^{-10}$$

$$Q = [Ag^+][Cl^-] = (1 \times 10^{-4})(1 \times 10^{-4}) = 1 \times 10^{-8} > K_{sp}$$

The system is not at equilibrium, and silver chloride does precipitate as the reaction shifts to the left until the reaction quotient is equal to the solubility product and equilibrium is established—that is, until

$$Q = [Ag^+][Cl^-] = K_{sp}$$

The ions Ag^+ and Cl^- are present in equal concentrations in a saturated solution of AgCl in pure water in contact with solid AgCl, and the reaction quotient $[Ag^+][Cl^-]$ equals K_{sp}. If we add NaCl to the solution, the reaction shifts to the left to relieve the stress produced by the additional Cl^- ion, in accordance with Le Châtelier's principle (Section 15.8). In quantitative terms, the added Cl^- causes the reaction quotient to be larger than the solubility product, and AgCl forms until the reaction quotient again equals K_{sp}. At the new equilibrium, $[Ag^+]$ is less and $[Cl^-]$ is greater than in the solution of AgCl in pure water. The greater we make $[Cl^-]$, the smaller $[Ag^+]$ becomes. However, we can never reduce $[Ag^+]$ to zero, because the product of $[Ag^+]$ and $[Cl^-]$ always equals the solubility product at equilibrium.

Does magnesium hydroxide, $Mg(OH)_2$, precipitate when a solution is prepared with initial concentrations of $[Mg^{2+}] = 0.0010$ M and $[OH^-] = 0.00050$ M?

Example 18.6

This problem asks whether the reaction

$$Mg(OH)_2(s) \rightleftharpoons Mg^{2+}(aq) + 2OH^-(aq) \qquad K_{sp} = 1.5 \times 10^{-11}$$

shifts to the left and forms solid $Mg(OH)_2$ when $[Mg^{2+}] = 0.0010$ M and $[OH^-] = 0.00050$ M. The reaction shifts to the left if $Q > K_{sp}$, where K_{sp}, the equilibrium

Example 18.6

continued

constant for the dissolution of $Mg(OH)_2$, is 1.5×10^{-11} (Appendix D). The reaction quotient for the solution *before any reaction occurs* is

$$Q = [Mg^{2+}][OH^-]^2 = (0.0010)(0.00050)^2$$
$$= 2.5 \times 10^{-10}$$

Because $Q > K_{sp}$, we can expect the reaction to shift to the left and form solid magnesium hydroxide. $Mg(OH)_2(s)$ forms until the concentrations of magnesium ion and hydroxide ion are reduced sufficiently that the value of Q is equal to K_{sp}.

18.5 Calculation of Concentrations Necessary to Form a Precipitate

We have seen that when a solution of a soluble salt of the M^{m+} ion is mixed with a solution of a soluble salt of the X^{x-} ion, the solid, M_pX_q, precipitates if the value of Q for the mixture of M^{m+} and X^{x-} is greater than K_{sp} for M_pX_q. Thus, if we know the concentration of one of the ions of a slightly soluble electrolyte and the value for the solubility product of the electrolyte, we can calculate the concentration that the other ion must exceed for precipitation to begin. Most chemists consider that precipitation begins when the concentration of the added ion is large enough that the reaction quotient becomes equal to the solubility product constant. At this point, addition of the smallest amount more of the added ion results in precipitation.

Example 18.7

If a solution contains 0.001 mol of CrO_4^{2-} per liter, what concentration of Ag^+ ion must be added as $AgNO_3$ before Ag_2CrO_4 begins to precipitate? Neglect any increase in volume upon adding the solid silver nitrate ($K_{sp} = 9 \times 10^{-12}$, Appendix D).

We can write the equilibrium involved in the problem as

$$Ag_2CrO_4(s) \rightleftharpoons 2Ag^+(aq) + CrO_4^{2-}(aq) \qquad K_{sp} = 9 \times 10^{-12}$$

A mixture of Ag^+ and CrO_4^{2-} does not begin to form solid Ag_2CrO_4 until the reaction quotient for this mixture is equal to the equilibrium constant. When $Q = K_{sp}$, the first trace of solid Ag_2CrO_4 appears. At this point,

$$Q = K_{sp} = [Ag^+]^2[CrO_4^{2-}] = 9 \times 10^{-12}$$

Because we know K_{sp} and $[CrO_4^{2-}]$, we can solve for the concentration of Ag^+ that is necessary to produce the first trace of solid.

$$Q = K_{sp} = [Ag^+]^2[CrO_4^{2-}]$$
$$9 \times 10^{-12} = [Ag^+]^2(0.001)$$
$$[Ag^+]^2 = \frac{9 \times 10^{-12}}{0.001} = 9 \times 10^{-9}$$
$$[Ag^+] = 9.5 \times 10^{-5} \text{ M} = 1 \times 10^{-4} \text{ M} \quad \text{(rounded)}$$

A concentration of Ag^+ of 1×10^{-4} M is necessary to initiate the precipitation of Ag_2CrO_4 under these conditions.

The calculation in this example is one of those introduced in Section 15.5—calculation of the concentration of a species in an equilibrium mixture from the concentrations of the other species and the equilibrium constant.

18.6 Calculation of Concentrations Following Precipitation

It is sometimes useful to know the concentration of an ion that remains in solution after precipitation. This, too, can be determined using the solubility product: If we know the value of K_{sp} and the concentration of one ion in solution, we can calculate the concentration of the second ion remaining in solution. Although the conditions are different (we are calculating concentrations after precipitation is complete, rather than at the start of precipitation), the calculation is the same type as that in Example 18.7—calculation of the concentration of a species in an equilibrium mixture from the concentrations of the other species and the equilibrium constant (Section 15.5).

Example 18.8

Clothing washed in water that has a manganese concentration exceeding 0.1 mg L^{-1} (1.8 × 10^{-6} M) may be stained by the manganese. A laundry wishes to add a base to precipitate manganese as the hydroxide, Mn(OH)$_2$ (K_{sp} = 4.5 × 10^{-14}). At what pH is [Mn^{2+}] equal to 1.8 × 10^{-6} M?

The dissolution of Mn(OH)$_2$ is described by the equation

$$Mn(OH)_2(s) \rightleftharpoons Mn^{2+}(aq) + 2OH^-(aq) \qquad K_{sp} = 4.5 \times 10^{-14}$$

We need to calculate the equilibrium concentration of hydroxide ion when the concentration of Mn^{2+} is 1.8 × 10^{-6} M. At equilibrium,

$$K_{sp} = [Mn^{2+}][OH^-]^2$$

$$4.5 \times 10^{-14} = (1.8 \times 10^{-6})[OH^-]^2$$

$$[OH^-]^2 = \frac{4.5 \times 10^{-14}}{1.8 \times 10^{-6}} = 2.5 \times 10^{-8}$$

$$[OH^-] = 1.6 \times 10^{-4} \text{ M}$$

The pH of the solution can be calculated from the pOH (Section 17.1).

$$pOH = -\log [OH^-] = -\log (1.6 \times 10^{-4}) = 3.80$$

$$pH = 14.00 - pOH = 14.00 - 3.80 = 10.20$$

Manganese hydroxide, Mn(OH)$_2$, precipitates when a solution of a base is added to a solution of a manganese(II) salt.

If the laundry adds a base, such as the sodium silicate in some detergents, to the wash water until the pH rises to 10.20, the manganese ion will be reduced to a concentration of 1.8 × 10^{-6} M; at that concentration or less, the ion will not stain clothing.

18.7 Solubility and Crystal Size

When the product of the concentrations of the ions, raised to the proper powers, exceeds the solubility product, precipitation *usually* occurs. However, sometimes a supersaturated solution (Section 12.1) is formed, and visible precipitation does not occur immediately. For example, when magnesium is being precipitated as magnesium ammonium phosphate from a solution of low magnesium ion content, the solution may stand for several hours before a visible precipitate appears. Furthermore, even though precipitation may begin immediately, it may not be complete right away. The first crystals to precipitate are often very small and more soluble than the larger ones that form later as the solution stands in contact with the precipitate.

The solubility of fine crystals of barium sulfate has been found to be about twice as great as that of coarse crystals. In fact, small crystals of any substance are more soluble than large ones, because smaller crystals offer a relatively larger surface area. Ions in the interior of a crystal are bound more tightly than those on the faces and edges. The fraction of ions occupying surface positions is greater in a small crystal than in a large crystal, so the tendency for ions to enter solution is greater for the small crystal.

Because small crystals are more soluble than large ones, the smallest crystals tend to dissolve over time, whereas the larger ones tend to grow still larger. True equilibrium is not reached until large, perfect crystals are formed. Solubility products should be determined for solutions in contact with relatively large crystals.

Very small crystals pass through filters and resist centrifugation, so precipitates are often digested (warmed in the solution) to increase the size of the crystals. Heat increases the rate at which large crystals grow from the smaller ones. Simply allowing a precipitate to stand in solution may also yield larger crystals.

⓲.8 Fractional Precipitation

When two anions form slightly soluble compounds with the same cation, or when two cations form slightly soluble compounds with the same anion, the less soluble compound (the compound with the smaller K_{sp}) generally precipitates first upon addition of a precipitating agent to a solution containing both anions (or both cations). When the solubilities of the two compounds differ by a factor of about 20 or more, almost all of the less soluble compound precipitates before any of the more soluble one does. However, any remaining less soluble compound precipitates along with the more soluble one (coprecipitation) when enough precipitating agent is added to cause the more soluble compound to precipitate.

Consider the case in which a solution containing both sodium iodide and sodium chloride is treated with silver nitrate. Silver iodide, being less soluble than silver chloride, is precipitated first. Only after most of the iodide is precipitated does the chloride begin to precipitate.

Example 18.9

A solution contains 0.010 mol of KI and 0.10 mol of KCl per liter. $AgNO_3$ is gradually added to this solution. Which forms first, solid AgI or solid AgCl?

The two equilibria involved are

$$AgCl(s) \rightleftharpoons Ag^+(aq) + Cl^-(aq) \qquad K_{sp} = 1.8 \times 10^{-10} \qquad (1)$$

$$AgI(s) \rightleftharpoons Ag^+(aq) + I^-(aq) \qquad K_{sp} = 1.5 \times 10^{-16} \qquad (2)$$

If the solution contained about *equal* concentrations of Cl^- and I^-, then the silver salt with the smallest K_{sp} (AgI) would precipitate first. The concentrations are not equal, however, so we should find the $[Ag^+]$ at which AgCl begins to precipitate and the $[Ag^+]$ at which AgI begins to precipitate. The salt that forms at the lower $[Ag^+]$

precipitates first. Note that these calculations are of the type described in Examples 18.7 and 18.8—calculation of a missing equilibrium concentration.

For AgI. AgI precipitates when Q equals K_{sp} for AgI. We find the $[Ag^+]$ for which $Q = K_{sp}$.

$$K_{sp} = [Ag^+][I^-] = 1.5 \times 10^{-16}$$

$$1.5 \times 10^{-16} = [Ag^+](0.010)$$

$$[Ag^+] = \frac{1.5 \times 10^{-16}}{0.010} = 1.5 \times 10^{-14} \text{ M}$$

Thus AgI begins to precipitate when $[Ag^+]$ is 1.5×10^{-14} M.

For AgCl. AgCl precipitates when Q equals K_{sp} for AgCl. We find the $[Ag^+]$ for which $Q = K_{sp}$.

$$K_{sp} = [Ag^+][Cl^-] = 1.8 \times 10^{-10}$$

$$1.8 \times 10^{-10} = [Ag^+](0.10)$$

$$[Ag^+] = \frac{1.8 \times 10^{-10}}{0.10} = 1.8 \times 10^{-9} \text{ M}$$

A precipitate of silver iodide, AgI (left), and of silver chloride, AgCl (right).

Thus AgCl begins to precipitate when $[Ag^+]$ is 1.8×10^{-9} M.

AgI begins to precipitate at a lower $[Ag^+]$ than AgCl, so AgI begins to precipitate first.

What is the concentration of I^- in the solution described in Example 18.9 when AgCl begins to precipitate, and what fraction of the original I^- remains in solution at this point?

Example 18.10

We need to calculate the I^- concentration involved in the equilibrium

$$\text{AgI}(s) \rightleftharpoons Ag^+(aq) + I^-(aq) \qquad K_{sp} = 1.5 \times 10^{-16}$$

for a specific concentration of Ag^+, the concentration of Ag^+ when AgCl begins to precipitate. When $[Ag^+] = 1.8 \times 10^{-9}$ M, AgCl begins to precipitate (Example 18.9). Thus

$$K_{sp} = [Ag^+][I^-] = 1.5 \times 10^{-16}$$

$$1.5 \times 10^{-16} = (1.8 \times 10^{-9})[I^-]$$

$$[I^-] = \frac{1.5 \times 10^{-16}}{1.8 \times 10^{-9}} = 8.3 \times 10^{-8} \text{ M}$$

$[I^-]$ is 8.3×10^{-8} M when AgCl begins to precipitate.

The fraction of I^- remaining at this point is determined as follows:

$$\frac{[I^-] \text{ when precipitation of AgCl begins}}{[I^-] \text{ originally present}}$$

$$= \frac{8.3 \times 10^{-8}}{0.010}$$

$$= 8.3 \times 10^{-6}$$

Only about 8 parts in a million of the original I^- remains in solution when AgCl begins to precipitate.

Multiple Equilibria Involving Solubility

The dissolution of a slightly soluble electrolyte involves the equilibrium

$$M_pX_q(s) \rightleftharpoons pM^{m+}(aq) + qX^{x-}(aq) \tag{1}$$

The concentration of one of the ions M^{m+} or X^{x-} in an equilibrium mixture can be shifted by applying Le Châtelier's principle. One way to do this is by adjusting the concentration of the other ion. This can be accomplished by adding a strong electrolyte that contains the second ion and thereby shifting the equilibrium to the left, as illustrated in Examples 18.6–18.8, or by adding a compound that reacts with the second ion and thereby shifting the equilibrium to the right.

When one of the ions in Reaction (1) reacts with another compound, an additional equilibrium is set up in the system. In addition to the equilibrium involving the dissolution of M_pX_q, we have either an equilibrium between M^{m+} and some other chemical species—for example, NH_3:

$$M^{m+} + nNH_3 \rightleftharpoons M(NH_3)_n^{m+} \tag{2}$$

or an equilibrium between X^{x-} and some other species such as H_3O^+:

$$X^{x-} + xH_3O^+ \rightleftharpoons H_xX + xH_2O \tag{3}$$

In any solution at equilibrium, all reactions are at equilibrium simultaneously, and the concentrations of ions common to all equilibria are the same. Thus if Reactions (1) and (2) were at equilibrium in the same solution, the concentration of M^{m+} would be the same in the equations for the reaction quotients of both reactions. At equilibrium,

For Reaction (1): $\quad Q = K_{sp} = [M^{m+}]^p[X^{x-}]^q$

For Reaction (2): $\quad Q = K = \dfrac{[M(NH_3)_n^{m+}]}{[M^{m+}][NH_3]^n}$

and $[M^{m+}]$ has the same value in both equations. The concentration of M^{m+} in Reaction (1) could be controlled by varying the concentration of NH_3 and controlling the amount of M^{m+} in Reaction (2). Similarly, if Reactions (1) and (3) were at equilibrium in the same solution, the concentration of X^{x-} would be the same in both reaction quotients.

For Reaction (1): $\quad Q = K_{sp} = [M^{m+}]^p[X^{x-}]^q$

For Reaction (3): $\quad Q = K = \dfrac{[H_xX]}{[X^{x-}][H_3O^+]^x}$

It is possible, therefore, to adjust the concentration of X^{x-} by using Reaction (3) and thereby affect the concentration of X^{x-} in Reaction (1).

You may have recognized Reaction (3) as the reverse of the acid ionization

$$H_xX + xH_2O \rightleftharpoons xH_3O^+ + X^{x-}$$

For this discussion we wrote Reaction (3) with X^{x-} reacting with H_3O^+, because it made the discussion simpler. In subsequent examples we shall write the reaction as we customarily treat such equilibria (in the direction of the formation of H_3O^+ and X^{x-}).

⓲.9 Dissolution by Formation of a Weak Electrolyte

Slightly soluble solids derived from weak acids often dissolve in strong acids. For example, $CaCO_3$, FeS, and $Ca_3(PO_4)_2$ dissolve in HCl because their anions react and form weak acids (H_2CO_3, H_2S, and $H_2PO_4^-$). The resulting decrease in the concentration of the anion results in a shift of the equilibrium concentrations to the right in accordance with Le Châtelier's principle.

When hydrochloric acid is added to solid calcium carbonate, the hydronium ion from the acid combines with the carbonate ion and forms the hydrogen carbonate ion, a weak acid.

$$H_3O^+(aq) + CO_3^{2-}(aq) \rightleftharpoons HCO_3^-(aq) + H_2O(l)$$

Additional hydronium ion reacts with the hydrogen carbonate ion according to the equation

$$H_3O^+(aq) + HCO_3^-(aq) \rightleftharpoons H_2CO_3(aq) + H_2O(l)$$

Finally, the solution becomes saturated with the weak electrolyte carbonic acid. Carbonic acid is unstable and carbon dioxide gas is evolved.

$$H_2CO_3(aq) \rightleftharpoons H_2O(l) + CO_2(g)$$

Calcium carbonate dissolves in an acid solution with evolution of gaseous CO_2.

These reactions reduce the carbonate ion concentration, and additional calcium carbonate dissolves. If enough acid is present, the concentration of carbonate ion is reduced to such a low level that the reaction quotient for the dissolution of calcium carbonate remains less than the solubility product of calcium carbonate even after all of the calcium carbonate has dissolved. Even an acid as weak as acetic acid gives enough hydronium ion to dissolve calcium carbonate, because acetic acid is a stronger acid than either the hydrogen carbonate ion or carbonic acid. (Check the K_a values for acetic acid, hydrogen carbonate ion, and carbonic acid in Appendix F to verify this statement.)

Lead sulfate is only slightly soluble. It dissolves in solutions of ammonium acetate, because the formation of soluble lead acetate, a weak electrolyte, reduces the concentration of lead ion and the reaction shifts completely to the right. The reaction quotient for the dissolution of lead sulfate (the product of the lead ion and sulfate ion concentrations) becomes smaller than the value of the solubility product for lead sulfate.

$$PbSO_4(s) \rightleftharpoons Pb^{2+}(aq) + SO_4^{2-}(aq) \tag{1}$$

$$Pb^{2+}(aq) + 2CH_3CO_2^-(aq) \rightleftharpoons Pb(CH_3CO_2)_2(aq) \tag{2}$$

For Equation (1): $Q = [Pb^{2+}][SO_4^{2-}] < K_{sp}$

The formation of water causes most metal hydroxides—such as $Al(OH)_3$, $Mg(OH)_2$, and $Fe(OH)_3$—to dissolve in solutions of acids.

$$Al(OH)_3(s) \rightleftharpoons Al^{3+}(aq) + 3OH^-(aq) \tag{3}$$

$$3H_3O^+(aq) + 3OH^-(aq) \rightleftharpoons 6H_2O(l)$$

Net: $Al(OH)_3(s) + 3H_3O^+(aq) \longrightarrow Al^{3+}(aq) + 6H_2O(l)$

For Equation (3): $Q = [Al^{3+}][OH^-]^3 < K_{sp}$

$$Mg(OH)_2(s) \rightleftharpoons Mg^{2+}(aq) + 2OH^-(aq) \qquad (4)$$

$$2NH_4^+(aq) + 2OH^-(aq) \rightleftharpoons 2NH_3(aq) + 2H_2O(l)$$

Net: $Mg(OH)_2(s) + 2NH_4^+(aq) \longrightarrow Mg^{2+}(aq) + 2H_2O(l) + 2NH_3(aq)$

For Equation (4): $\qquad Q = [Mg^{2+}][OH^-]^2 < K_{sp}$

The following examples illustrate how to treat multiple equilibria involving reaction of the anion to form a weak electrolyte. Reactions of the cation will be discussed in Section 18.11.

Example 18.11

Calculate the concentration of hydronium ion required to prevent the precipitation of ZnS in a solution that is 0.050 M in ZnCl$_2$ and saturated with H$_2$S (0.10 M H$_2$S).

We need to consider two equilibria in this system.

$$ZnS(s) \rightleftharpoons Zn^{2+}(aq) + S^{2-}(aq) \qquad K_{sp} = 1 \times 10^{-27} \qquad (1)$$

$$2H_2O(l) + H_2S(aq) \rightleftharpoons 2H_3O^+(aq) + S^{2-}(aq) \qquad K = 1.0 \times 10^{-26} \qquad (2)$$

(The value of K_{sp} comes from Appendix D, and the ionization constant for H$_2$S is discussed in Section 17.4.) ZnS does not precipitate according to Reaction (1) if the reaction quotient is less than K_{sp} for ZnS. So we first find the $[S^{2-}]$ at which the first trace of ZnS appears. We then find the conditions necessary to keep $[S^{2-}]$ lower than this. The concentration of sulfide ion can be controlled by adding hydronium ion and thereby shifting Reaction (2) to the left, so we find the hydronium ion concentration that will keep the $[S^{2-}]$ below the value necessary to cause the precipitation of ZnS. We first determine the maximum possible value of $[S^{2-}]$.

$$K_{sp} = [Zn^{2+}][S^{2-}]$$

$$1 \times 10^{-27} = (0.050)[S^{2-}]$$

$$[S^{2-}] = \frac{1 \times 10^{-27}}{0.050} = 2 \times 10^{-26} \text{ M}$$

Thus when $[Zn^{2+}] = 0.050$ M, ZnS does not precipitate unless $[S^{2-}]$ is greater than 2×10^{-26} M.

Zinc sulfide is insoluble in neutral solution (left) but dissolves in acidic solution (right). The pH paper shows that the pH of the solution is less than 1.

The concentration of S^{2-} can be adjusted by changing the concentration of H_3O^+ (Section 17.4).

$$\frac{[H_3O^+]^2[S^{2-}]}{[H_2S]} = K = 1.0 \times 10^{-26}$$

Now we find $[H_3O^+]$ for a solution in which $[S^{2-}]$ is equal to 2×10^{-26} M.

$$K = \frac{[H_3O^+]^2[S^{2-}]}{[H_2S]}$$

$$1.0 \times 10^{-26} = \frac{[H_3O^+]^2(2 \times 10^{-26})}{0.10}$$

$$[H_3O^+]^2 = \frac{(0.10)(1.0 \times 10^{-26})}{2 \times 10^{-26}} = 5.0 \times 10^{-2}$$

$$[H_3O^+] = 2.2 \times 10^{-1} \text{ M} = 0.2 \text{ M}$$

$[S^{2-}]$ is equal to 2×10^{-26} M when $[H_3O^+] = 0.2$ M. When $[H_3O^+]$ is greater than 0.2 M, $[S^{2-}]$ is less than 2×10^{-26} M and precipitation of ZnS does not occur.

Calculate the concentration of ammonium ion, supplied by NH_4Cl, that is required to prevent the precipitation of $Mg(OH)_2$ in a liter of solution containing 0.10 mol of ammonia and 0.10 mol of Mg^{2+}.

Example 18.12

Two equilibria are involved in this system.

$$Mg(OH)_2(s) \rightleftharpoons Mg^{2+}(aq) + 2OH^-(aq) \qquad K_{sp} = 1.5 \times 10^{-11} \quad (1)$$

$$NH_3(aq) + H_2O(l) \rightleftharpoons NH_4^+(aq) + OH^-(aq) \qquad K_b = 1.8 \times 10^{-5} \quad (2)$$

If $Mg(OH)_2$ is not to form, then the reaction quotient for Equation (1), $[Mg^{2+}][OH^-]^2$, must be less than K_{sp} for $Mg(OH)_2$. $[OH^-]$ can be reduced by the addition of NH_4^+, which shifts Reaction (2) to the left and reduces $[OH^-]$.

First we use the equilibrium constant of Reaction (1) to determine the $[OH^-]$ at which the first trace of $Mg(OH)_2$ forms when $[Mg^{2+}] = 0.10$ M.

$$K_{sp} = [Mg^{2+}][OH^-]^2$$

$$1.5 \times 10^{-11} = (0.10)[OH^-]^2$$

$$[OH^-]^2 = \frac{1.5 \times 10^{-11}}{0.10} = 1.5 \times 10^{-10}$$

$$[OH^-] = 1.2 \times 10^{-5} \text{ M}$$

Magnesium hydroxide precipitates in a 0.1 M solution of NH_3 but redissolves when NH_4Cl is added.

Solid $Mg(OH)_2$ does not form in a 0.10 M solution of magnesium ion when $[OH^-]$ is less than 1.2×10^{-5} M.

Now we calculate the $[NH_4^+]$ needed to reduce $[OH^-]$ to 1.2×10^{-5} M. Note that NH_4Cl is added to the solution to supply the NH_4^+. We can assume that the reaction of NH_3 with water gives a negligible concentration of NH_4^+, compared to the

Example 18.12 continued

NH_4^+ supplied by the added NH_4Cl. According to Le Châtelier's principle (Section 15.8), the addition of NH_4^+ suppresses the reaction of NH_3 with water.

$$K_b = \frac{[NH_4^+][OH^-]}{[NH_3]}$$

$$1.8 \times 10^{-5} = \frac{[NH_4^+](1.2 \times 10^{-5})}{(0.10)}$$

$$[NH_4^+] = \frac{(1.8 \times 10^{-5})(0.10)}{1.2 \times 10^{-5}} = 0.15 \text{ M}$$

When $[NH_4^+]$ equals 0.15 M, $[OH^-]$ will be 1.2×10^{-5} M. Any $[NH_4^+]$ greater than 0.15 M will reduce $[OH^-]$ below 1.2×10^{-5} M and prevent the formation of $Mg(OH)_2$.

The concentration of hydronium ion or hydroxide ion in pure water is sufficient to change the solubility of some salts of very weak acids or bases. These salts hydrolyze when they dissolve in water. When a relatively insoluble sulfide such as lead sulfide, PbS, dissolves in water, an appreciable amount of the sulfide ion hydrolyzes to form the hydrogen sulfide ion and, in some cases, hydrogen sulfide.

$$PbS(s) \rightleftharpoons Pb^{2+}(aq) + S^{2-}(aq)$$

$$S^{2-}(aq) + H_2O(l) \rightleftharpoons HS^-(aq) + OH^+(aq)$$

$$HS^-(aq) + H_2O(l) \rightleftharpoons H_2S(aq) + OH^-(aq)$$

Under these conditions, the concentration of the lead ion is not the same as that of the sulfide ion; rather, it equals the sum of the concentrations of the sulfide ion, S^{2-}, the hydrogen sulfide ion, HS^-, and the hydrogen sulfide, H_2S.

$$[Pb^{2+}] = [S^{2-}] + [HS^-] + [H_2S]$$

$[Pb^{2+}]$ is equal to the sum of the concentrations of all the sulfur-containing species, because even though some of the sulfide ions produced by the dissolution of PbS react and form HS^- or H_2S, one lead ion is produced for each sulfide ion formed by the original dissolution of PbS. This means that in calculating the solubility of a slightly soluble sulfide from the solubility product, we must consider the reactions of the S^{2-} ion and the HS^- ion with water.

The insoluble carbonates behave similarly to the sulfides. When a relatively insoluble carbonate such as barium carbonate, $BaCO_3$, is dissolved in water, its solubility is increased as a result of the reaction of the carbonate ion with water.

$$CO_3^{2-} + H_2O \rightleftharpoons HCO_3^- + OH^-$$

$$HCO_3^- + H_2O \rightleftharpoons H_2CO_3 + OH^-$$

The concentration of the barium ion is equal to the sum of the concentrations of the carbonate ion, CO_3^{2-}, the hydrogen carbonate ion, HCO_3^-, and carbonic acid, H_2CO_3.

⑱.10 Dissolution by Changing an Ion to Another Species

The solubility products of some metal sulfides are sufficiently large that the hydronium ion from a strong acid lowers the sulfide ion concentration (by forming the weak electrolyte hydrogen sulfide) enough to dissolve the metal sulfide. For example, iron(II) sulfide is readily dissolved by hydrochloric acid according to the equation

$$FeS(s) \rightleftharpoons Fe^{2+}(aq) + S^{2-}(aq)$$

$$2H_3O^+(aq) + S^{2-}(aq) \rightleftharpoons H_2S(g) + 2H_2O(l)$$

Net: $\quad FeS(s) + 2H_3O^+(aq) \rightleftharpoons Fe^{2+}(aq) + H_2S(g) + 2H_2O(l)$

$$[Fe^{2+}][S^{2-}] < K_{sp}$$

However, other metal sulfides, such as lead sulfide, have solubility products so small that even very high concentrations of hydronium ion from strong acids are not sufficient to lower the sulfide ion concentration enough to dissolve them. To dissolve these sulfides, the sulfide ion concentration must be decreased by oxidizing the sulfide to elemental sulfur.

$$3S^{2-}(aq) + 2NO_3^-(aq) + 8H_3O^+(aq) \longrightarrow 3S(s) + 2NO(g) + 12H_2O(l)$$

Lead sulfide dissolves in nitric acid, then, because the sulfide ion is oxidized to sulfur, making the reaction quotient less than the solubility product:

$$Q = [Pb^{2+}][S^{2-}] < K_{sp}$$

⑱.11 Dissolution by Formation of a Complex Ion

Many slightly soluble electrolytes dissolve when the concentration of the metal ion in solution is reduced through the formation of complex (polyatomic) ions in a Lewis acid–base reaction (Section 16.14). For example, silver chloride dissolves in a solution of ammonia because the silver ion reacts with ammonia to form the complex ion $Ag(NH_3)_2^+$.

$$AgCl(s) \rightleftharpoons Ag^+(aq) + Cl^-(aq)$$

$$Ag^+(aq) + 2NH_3(aq) \rightleftharpoons Ag(NH_3)_2^+(aq)$$

Net: $\quad AgCl(s) + 2NH_3(aq) \rightleftharpoons Ag(NH_3)_2^+(aq) + Cl^-(aq)$

Aluminum hydroxide dissolves in a solution of sodium hydroxide or other strong base because of the formation of the complex ion $Al(OH)_4^-$.

$$Al(OH)_3(s) \rightleftharpoons Al^{3+}(aq) + 3OH^-(aq)$$

$$Al^{3+}(aq) + 4OH^-(aq) \rightleftharpoons Al(OH)_4^-(aq)$$

Net: $\quad Al(OH)_3(s) + OH^-(aq) \rightleftharpoons Al(OH)_4^-(aq)$

Mercury(II) sulfide dissolves in a solution of sodium sulfide because HgS reacts with the S^{2-} ion, forming $HgS_2{}^{2-}$.

$$HgS(s) \rightleftharpoons Hg^{2+}(aq) + S^{2-}(aq)$$

$$Hg^{2+}(aq) + 2S^{2-}(aq) \rightleftharpoons HgS_2{}^{2-}(aq)$$

Net: $\quad HgS(s) + S^{2-}(aq) \rightleftharpoons HgS_2{}^{2-}(aq)$

The stability of a complex ion is described by an equilibrium constant for the formation of the complex ion from its components. The larger the equilibrium constant, the more stable the complex. For example, the complex ion $Cu(CN)_2{}^-$ forms by the reaction

$$Cu^+(aq) + 2CN^-(aq) \rightleftharpoons Cu(CN)_2{}^-(aq)$$

The equilibrium constant for this reaction is the **formation constant, K_f,** the equilibrium constant for the reaction of the components of a complex ion to form the complex ion in solution.

$$K_f = \frac{[Cu(CN)_2{}^-]}{[Cu^+][CN^-]^2} = 1 \times 10^{16}$$

The formation constant is sometimes referred to as the **stability constant** or **association constant.** Appendix E contains a table of formation constants.

Alternatively, the stability of a complex ion can be described by its **dissociation constant, K_d,** the equilibrium constant for the decomposition of a complex ion into its components in solution. For $Cu(CN)_2{}^-$ the dissociation is

$$Cu(CN)_2{}^-(aq) \rightleftharpoons Cu^+(aq) + 2CN^-(aq)$$

and $\qquad K_d = \dfrac{[Cu^+][CN^-]^2}{[Cu(CN)_2{}^-]} = 1 \times 10^{-16}$

It should be apparent that K_d is the inverse of K_f.

$$K_d = \frac{1}{K_f}$$

The smaller K_d, the more stable the complex.

As an example of dissolution by complex ion formation, let us consider the dissolution of silver chloride in aqueous ammonia. Silver chloride dissolves in water, giving a small concentration of Ag^+ ($[Ag^+] = 1.3 \times 10^{-5}$ M, as we found in Example 18.4).

$$AgCl(s) \rightleftharpoons Ag^+(aq) + Cl^-(aq)$$

However, if NH_3 is present in the water, the complex ion, $Ag(NH_3)_2{}^+$, can form according to the equation

$$Ag^+(aq) + 2NH_3(aq) \rightleftharpoons Ag(NH_3)_2{}^+(aq)$$

The formation constant, K_f, for $Ag(NH_3)_2{}^+$ is 1.6×10^7.

$$K_f = \frac{[Ag(NH_3)_2{}^+]}{[Ag^+][NH_3]^2} = 1.6 \times 10^7$$

The large size of this formation constant indicates that most of the free silver ions produced by the dissolution of AgCl combine with NH_3 to form $Ag(NH_3)_2{}^+$. As a consequence, the concentration of silver ions, $[Ag^+]$, is reduced, and the reaction quotient for the dissolution of silver chloride, $[Ag^+][Cl^-]$, falls below the solubility product of AgCl.

$$Q = [Ag^+][Cl^-] < K_{sp}$$

More silver chloride then dissolves. If the concentration of ammonia is great enough, all of the silver chloride dissolves.

Example 18.13

Calculate the concentration of the silver ion in a solution that initially is 0.10 M with respect to $Ag(NH_3)_2^+$.

The complex ion $Ag(NH_3)_2^+$ is in equilibrium with its components, as represented by the equation

$$Ag^+(aq) + 2NH_3(aq) \rightleftharpoons Ag(NH_3)_2^+(aq)$$

We write the equation as a formation reaction because the equilibrium constants listed in Appendix E for complex ions are formation constants. For this reaction, the reaction quotient is larger than the equilibrium constant $[K_f = 1.6 \times 10^7, Q = 0.10/(0 \times 0)$ or is infinitely large], so the reaction shifts to the left to reach equilibrium. Let the change in the concentration of Ag^+ be Δ. One mol of $Ag(NH_3)_2^+$ would dissociate to give 1 mol of Ag^+ and 2 mol of NH_3, so the change in $[NH_3]$ is 2Δ. In summary,

	Ag^+	$+$	$2NH_3$	$\rightleftharpoons$	$Ag(NH_3)_2^+$	$K_f = 1.6 \times 10^7$
Change	Δ		2Δ		$-\Delta$	
Initial Concentration, M	0		0		0.10	
Equilibrium Concentration, M	$0 + \Delta$		$0 + 2\Delta$		$0.10 - \Delta$	

At equilibrium,

$$K_f = \frac{[Ag(NH_3)_2^+]}{[Ag^+][NH_3]^2}$$

$$1.6 \times 10^7 = \frac{(0.10 - \Delta)}{(\Delta)(2\Delta)^2}$$

Both Q and K_f are much larger than 1, so let us assume that the changes in concentrations needed to reach equilibrium are small. Thus $0.10 - \Delta$ is assumed to be 0.10.

$$1.6 \times 10^7 = \frac{(0.10)}{(\Delta)(2\Delta)^2}$$

$$\Delta^3 = \frac{0.10}{4(1.6 \times 10^7)} = 1.6 \times 10^{-9}$$

$$\Delta = (1.6 \times 10^{-9})^{1/3} = 1.2 \times 10^{-3}$$

Hence

$$[Ag^+] = 0 + \Delta = 1.2 \times 10^{-3} \text{ M}$$

$$[NH_3] = 0 + 2\Delta = 2.4 \times 10^{-3} \text{ M}$$

Because only 1.2% of the $Ag(NH_3)_2^+$ dissociates to Ag^+ and NH_3, the assumption that Δ is small is justified.

Example 18.14

Unexposed silver halides are removed from photographic film when they react with sodium thiosulfate ($Na_2S_2O_3$, called hypo) to form the complex ion $Ag(S_2O_3)_2^{3-}$ ($K_f = 4.7 \times 10^{13}$). What mass of $Na_2S_2O_3$ is required to prepare 1.00 L of a solution that will dissolve 1.00 g of AgBr by the formation of $Ag(S_2O_3)_2^{3-}$?

Two equilibria are involved when AgBr dissolves in a solution containing the $S_2O_3^{2-}$ ion.

$$AgBr(s) \rightleftharpoons Ag^+(aq) + Br^-(aq) \qquad K_{sp} = 3.3 \times 10^{-13} \quad (1)$$

$$Ag^+(aq) + 2S_2O_3^{2-}(aq) \rightleftharpoons Ag(S_2O_3)_2^{3-}(aq) \qquad K_f = 4.7 \times 10^{13} \quad (2)$$

In order for 1.00 g of AgBr to dissolve and form 1.00 L of solution, the $[Ag^+]$ in the solution that results must be low enough for the reaction quotient for Reaction (1) to be smaller than the equilibrium constant (K_{sp}) for this reaction. We can reduce $[Ag^+]$ by adding $S_2O_3^{2-}$ and thus cause Reaction (2) to shift to the right.

Let us first calculate the $[Br^-]$ produced by the dissolution of 1.00 g of AgBr and then determine the maximum possible concentration of Ag^+ that can be present without causing reprecipitation of AgBr.

$$1.00 \text{ g AgBr} \times \frac{1 \text{ mol AgBr}}{187.77 \text{ g AgBr}} = 5.33 \times 10^{-3} \text{ mol AgBr}$$

$$5.33 \times 10^{-3} \text{ mol AgBr} \times \frac{1 \text{ mol Br}^-}{1 \text{ mol AgBr}} = 5.33 \times 10^{-3} \text{ mol Br}^-$$

$$\frac{5.33 \times 10^{-3} \text{ mol Br}^-}{1.00 \text{ L}} = 5.33 \times 10^{-3} \text{ M} = [Br^-]$$

The dissolution of 1.00 g of AgBr produces a Br^- concentration of 5.33×10^{-3} M. If AgBr is not to precipitate,

$$[Ag^+][Br^-] = K_{sp} = 3.3 \times 10^{-13}$$

$$[Ag^+](5.33 \times 10^{-3}) = 3.3 \times 10^{-13}$$

$$[Ag^+] = \frac{3.3 \times 10^{-13}}{5.33 \times 10^{-3}}$$

$$= 6.19 \times 10^{-11} \text{ M}$$

An exposed and developed photographic film. The transparent or light gray parts are the portions of the film that were not exposed to light or were lightly exposed. At these portions of the film, the silver halide is dissolved during the developing process by the sodium thiosulfate (hypo) through formation of the soluble $Ag(S_2O_3)_2^{3-}$ complex ion. The darker gray or black parts are the portions of the film that were exposed to light, reducing the metal halide to metallic silver (gray or black, depending on degree of exposure).

In order for the AgBr to dissolve completely and to remain dissolved, $[Ag^+]$ must be reduced to 6.19×10^{-11} M by the addition of $S_2O_3^{2-}$. Now we determine the $[S_2O_3^{2-}]$ at which $[Ag^+] = 6.19 \times 10^{-11}$ M. Because 5.33×10^{-3} mol of AgBr dissolves,

$$(5.33 \times 10^{-3}) - (6.19 \times 10^{-11}) = 5.33 \times 10^{-3} \text{ mol Ag}(S_2O_3)_2^{3-}$$

must form. Thus $[Ag(S_2O_3)_2^{3-}] = 5.33 \times 10^{-3}$ M. To form 5.33×10^{-3} mol of $Ag(S_2O_3)_2^{3-}$ requires $2 \times (5.33 \times 10^{-3})$ mol of $S_2O_3^{2-}$. However, the total number of moles of $S_2O_3^{2-}$ that must be added to the solution is equal to the amount that reacts in forming the complex plus the amount of free $S_2O_3^{2-}$ in solution at equilibrium.

$$Ag^+ + 2S_2O_3^{2-} \rightleftharpoons Ag(S_2O_3)_2^{3-} \qquad K_f = 4.7 \times 10^{13}$$

At equilibrium, $[Ag^+] = 6.19 \times 10^{-11}$ M, $[Ag(S_2O_3)_2^{3-}] = 5.33 \times 10^{-3}$ M, and the equilibrium constant, K_f, $= 4.7 \times 10^{13}$. We find the unknown $S_2O_3^{2-}$ concentration as follows:

$$K_f = \frac{[Ag(S_2O_3)_2^{3-}]}{[Ag^+][S_2O_3^{2-}]^2}$$

$$4.7 \times 10^{13} = \frac{5.33 \times 10^{-3}}{(6.19 \times 10^{-11})[S_2O_3^{2-}]^2}$$

$$[S_2O_3^{2-}]^2 = \frac{5.33 \times 10^{-3}}{(6.19 \times 10^{-11})(4.7 \times 10^{13})} = 1.83 \times 10^{-6}$$

$$[S_2O_3^{2-}] = 1.35 \times 10^{-3} \text{ M}$$

When $[S_2O_3^{2-}]$ is 1.35×10^{-3} M, $[Ag^+]$ is 6.19×10^{-11} M and all AgBr dissolves. The total amount of $S_2O_3^{2-}$ that must be added to the solution via the addition of $Na_2S_2O_3$ is

$$2 \times (5.33 \times 10^{-3} \text{ mol } S_2O_3^{2-}) + 1.35 \times 10^{-3} \text{ mol } S_2O_3^{2-} = 1.20 \times 10^{-2} \text{ mol } S_2O_3^{2-}$$

$$= 1.20 \times 10^{-2} \text{ mol } Na_2S_2O_3$$

$$1.20 \times 10^{-2} \text{ mol Na}_2S_2O_3 \times \frac{158.1 \text{ g Na}_2S_2O_3}{1 \text{ mol Na}_2S_2O_3} = 1.9 \text{ g Na}_2S_2O_3$$

Thus 1.00 L of a solution prepared from 1.9 g $Na_2S_2O_3$ dissolves 1.0 g of AgBr.

For Review

Summary

The value of the equilibrium constant for an equilibrium involving the precipitation or dissolution of a slightly soluble electrolyte is called the **solubility product, K_{sp},** of the electrolyte.

$$M_pX_q(s) \rightleftharpoons pM^{m+}(aq) + qX^{x-}(aq) \qquad K_{sp} = [M^{m+}]^p[X^{x-}]^q$$

The solubility product of a slightly soluble electrolyte can be calculated from its solubility (in moles per liter); conversely, its solubility can be calculated from its K_{sp}.

A slightly soluble electrolyte begins to precipitate when the magnitude of the reaction quotient for the dissolution reaction exceeds the magnitude of the solubility product. Precipitation continues until the reaction quotient equals the solubility product. Consequently, if we have a solution containing one of the ions of a slightly soluble electrolyte, we can calculate what amount of the other ions of the electrolyte must be added to cause precipitation to begin or to reduce the concentration of the first ion to any desired value.

Many slightly soluble electrolytes contain anions of weak acids. These electrolytes often dissolve in acidic solution, because reaction of the anions with water to give the weak acid reduces the concentration of the anion to the point where the reaction quotient is less than the solubility product. The ion product can also be reduced by changing the ion to another species or by the formation of a complex ion. The stability of a complex ion is described by its **formation constant, K_f,** or its **dissociation constant, K_d.**

Key Terms and Concepts

association constant (18.11)
coprecipitation (18.8)
complex ion (18.11)
dissociation constant (18.11)
dissolution of precipitates (18.9, 18.10, 18.11)

formation constant (18.11)
fractional precipitation (18.8)
hydrolysis (18.9)
molar solubility (18.2)

precipitation (18.4, 18.5)
solubility product (18.1)
stability constant (18.11)
supersaturated solution (18.7)

Exercises

Answers for selected even-numbered exercises marked by red numbers appear at the end of the book. The worked-out solutions to all even-numbered exercises appear in the *Solutions Guide*.

Solubility Products

1. A saturated solution of a slightly soluble electrolyte in contact with some of the solid electrolyte is said to be a system in equilibrium. Explain. Why is such a system called a heterogeneous equilibrium?

2. How do the concentrations of Ag^+ and CrO_4^{2-} in a liter of water above 1.0 g of solid Ag_2CrO_4 change when 100 g of solid Ag_2CrO_4 is added to the system? Explain.

3. How do the concentrations of Pb^{2+} and S^{2-} change when K_2S is added to a saturated solution of PbS?

4. Under what circumstances, if any, does a sample of solid AgCl completely dissolve in pure water?

5. Refer to Appendix D for solubility products for calcium salts. Determine which of the calcium salts listed is most soluble in moles per liter and which is most soluble in grams per liter.

6. Solid silver bromide is in equilibrium with a saturated solution of its ions, Ag^+ and Br^-. How, if at all, is this equilibrium affected when (a) more solid silver bromide is added? (b) silver nitrate is added? (c) sodium bromide is added? (d) the temperature is raised? (The solubility increases with temperature.)

7. Write the expression for the solubility product of each of the following slightly soluble electrolytes.

(a) $PbCl_2$
(b) Ag_2S
(c) $Sr_3(PO_4)_2$
(d) $SrSO_4$

8. Write the expression for the solubility product of each of the following slightly soluble electrolytes.

(a) LaF_3
(b) $Pb(OH)_2$
(c) Ag_2SO_4
(d) $CaCO_3$

9. Which of the following compounds precipitates from a solution that has the concentrations indicated? (See Appendix D for K_{sp} values.)

(a) $KClO_4$: $[K^+] = 0.01$ M; $[ClO_4^-] = 0.01$ M

(b) K_2PtCl_6: $[K^+] = 0.01$ M; $[PtCl_6^{2-}] = 0.01$ M

(c) PbI_2: $[Pb^{2+}] = 0.003$ M; $[I^-] = 1.3 \times 10^{-3}$ M

(d) Ag_2S: $[Ag^+] = 1 \times 10^{-10}$ M; $[S^{2-}] = 1 \times 10^{-13}$ M

10. Which of the following compounds precipitates from a solution that has the concentrations indicated? (See Appendix D for K_{sp} values.)

(a) $CaCO_3$: $[Ca^{2+}] = 0.003$ M, $[CO_3^{2-}] = 0.003$ M

(b) $Co(OH)_2$: $[Co^{2+}] = 0.01$ M, $[OH^-] = 1 \times 10^{-7}$ M

(c) $CaHPO_4$: $[Ca^{2+}] = 0.01$ M, $[HPO_4^{2-}] = 2 \times 10^{-6}$ M

(d) $Pb_3(PO_4)_2$: $[Pb^{2+}] = 0.01$ M,
$[PO_4^{3-}] = 1 \times 10^{-13}$ M

11. Calculate the solubility product of each of the following from the solubility given.
    (a) AgBr, 5.7×10^{-7} mol L^{-1}
    (b) $CaCO_3$, 6.9×10^{-3} g L^{-1}
    (c) PbF_2, 2.1×10^{-3} mol L^{-1}
    (d) Ag_2CrO_4, 4.3×10^{-2} g L^{-1}
    (e) Ag_2SO_4, 4.47 g L^{-1}

12. The *Handbook of Chemistry and Physics* gives solubilities for the following compounds in grams per 100 mL of water. Because these compounds are only slightly soluble, assume that the volume does not change on dissolution, and calculate the solubility product for each.
    (a) TlCl, 0.29 g/100 mL
    (b) $Ce(IO_3)_4$, 1.5×10^{-2} g/100 mL
    (c) $Gd_2(SO_4)_3$, 3.98 g/100 mL
    (d) InF_3, 4.0×10^{-2} g/100 mL

13. Calculate the concentrations of ions in a saturated solution of each of the following (see Appendix D for solubility products).
    (a) AgI
    (b) Ag_2SO_4
    (c) $Mn(OH)_2$
    (d) $Sr(OH)_2 \cdot 8H_2O$

14. Calculate the molar solubility of each of the following minerals from its K_{sp}.
    (a) alabandite, MnS: $K_{sp} = 4.3 \times 10^{-22}$
    (b) anglesite, $PbSO_4$: $K_{sp} = 1.8 \times 10^{-8}$
    (c) brucite, $Mg(OH)_2$: $K_{sp} = 1.5 \times 10^{-11}$
    (d) fluorite, CaF_2: $K_{sp} = 3.9 \times 10^{-11}$

15. Most barium compounds are very poisonous; however, barium sulfate is often administered internally as an aid in the X-ray examination of the lower intestinal track. This use of $BaSO_4$ is possible because of its insolubility. Calculate the molar solubility of $BaSO_4$ ($K_{sp} = 1.08 \times 10^{-10}$) and the mass of barium present in 1 L of water saturated with $BaSO_4$.

16. Public Health Service standards for drinking water set a maximum of 250 mg/L of SO_4^{2-}, or $[SO_4^{2-}] = 2.60 \times 10^{-3}$ M, because of its cathartic action (it is a laxative). Does natural water that is saturated with $CaSO_4$ ("gyp" water) as a result of passing through soil containing gypsum, $CaSO_4 \cdot 2H_2O$, meet these standards? What is $[SO_4^{2-}]$ in such water?

17. The first step in the preparation of magnesium metal is the precipitation of $Mg(OH)_2$ from sea water by the addition of $Ca(OH)_2$. The concentration of $Mg^{2+}(aq)$ in sea water is 5.37×10^{-2} M. Using the solubility product for $Mg(OH)_2$, calculate the pH at which $[Mg^{2+}]$ is reduced to 5.37×10^{-5} M by the addition of $Ca(OH)_2$.

18. Calculate the concentration of Tl^+ when TlCl ($K_{sp} = 1.9 \times 10^{-4}$) just begins to precipitate from a solution that is 0.0250 M in Cl^-.

19. Calculate the concentration of Sr^{2+} when SrF_2 ($K_{sp} = 3.7 \times 10^{-12}$) starts to precipitate from a solution that is 0.0025 M in F^-.

20. Calculate the concentration of F^- required to begin precipitation of CaF_2 in a solution that is 0.010 M in Ca^{2+}.

21. Iron concentrations greater than 5.4×10^{-6} M in water used for laundry purposes can cause staining. What $[OH^-]$ is required to reduce $[Fe^{2+}]$ to this level by precipitation of $Fe(OH)_2$?

22. (a) Calculate $[Ag^+]$ in a saturated aqueous solution of AgBr ($K_{sp} = 3.3 \times 10^{-13}$).
    (b) What will $[Ag^+]$ be when enough KBr has been added to make $[Br^-] = 0.050$ M?
    (c) What will $[Br^-]$ be when enough $AgNO_3$ has been added to make $[Ag^+] = 0.020$ M?

23. The solubility product of $CaSO_4 \cdot 2H_2O$ is 2.4×10^{-5}. What mass of this salt will dissolve in 1.0 L of 0.010 M K_2SO_4?

24. Calculate the maximum concentration of lead(II) ion in a solution of lead(II) sulfate in which the concentration of sulfate ions is 0.0045 M.

25. In one experiment a precipitate of $BaSO_4$ ($K_{sp} = 1.08 \times 10^{-10}$) was washed with 0.100 L of distilled water; in another experiment a precipitate of $BaSO_4$ was washed with 0.100 L of 0.010 M H_2SO_4. Calculate the quantity of $BaSO_4$ that dissolved in each experiment, assuming that the wash liquid became saturated with $BaSO_4$.

26. A volume of 0.800 L of a 2×10^{-4} M $Ba(NO_3)_2$ solution is added to 0.200 L of 5×10^{-4} M Li_2SO_4. Does $BaSO_4$ precipitate? Explain your answer.

Solubility Products and Ionization Constants

27. Which of the following compounds, when dissolved in a 0.01 M solution of $HClO_4$, has a solubility greater than in pure water: CuCl, $CaCO_3$, MnS, $PbBr_2$, CaF_2? Explain your answer.

28. A solution of 0.075 M $CoBr_2$ is saturated with H_2S ($[H_2S] = 0.10$ M). What is the minimum pH at which CoS ($K_{sp} = 4.5 \times 10^{-27}$) precipitates?

29. (a) What are the concentrations of Ca^{2+} and CO_3^{2-} in a saturated solution of $CaCO_3$ ($K_{sp} = 4.8 \times 10^{-9}$)?
    (b) What are the concentrations of Ca^{2+} and CO_3^{2-} in a buffer solution with a pH of 4.55 in contact with an excess of $CaCO_3$?

30. To a 0.10 M solution of $Pb(NO_3)_2$ is added enough $HF(g)$ to make $[HF] = 0.10$ M. (a) Does PbF_2 precipitate from this solution? (b) What is the minimum pH at which PbF_2 precipitates?

31. Using the solubility product, calculate the molar solubility of AgCN (a) in pure water and (b) in a buffer solution with a pH of 3.00.

32. Calculate the molar solubility of $Sn(OH)_2$ (a) in pure water (pH = 7) and (b) in a buffer solution containing equal concentrations of NH_3 and NH_4^+.

33. A 0.125 M solution of $Mn(NO_3)_2$ is saturated with H_2S

([H$_2$S] = 0.10 M). At what pH does MnS (K_{sp} = 4.3 × 10^{-22}) begin to precipitate?

34. Calculate the concentration of Cd^{2+} resulting from the dissolution of CdCO$_3$ in a solution that is 0.250 M in CH$_3$CO$_2$H, 0.375 M in NaCH$_3$CO$_2$, and 0.010 M in H$_2$CO$_3$.

35. A volume of 50 mL of 1.8 M NH$_3$ is mixed with an equal volume of a solution containing 0.95 g of MgCl$_2$. What mass of NH$_4$Cl must be added to the resulting solution to prevent the precipitation of Mg(OH)$_2$?

36. Calculate the molar solubility of BaF$_2$ in a buffer solution containing 0.20 M HF and 0.20 M NaF.

Separation of Ions

37. (a) With what volume of water must a precipitate containing NiCO$_3$ be washed to dissolve 0.100 g of this compound? Assume that the wash water becomes saturated with NiCO$_3$ (K_{sp} = 1.36 × 10^{-7}).
   (b) If the NiCO$_3$ were a contaminant in a sample of CoCO$_3$ (K_{sp} = 1.0 × 10^{-12}), what mass of CoCO$_3$ would have been lost? Keep in mind that both NiCO$_3$ and CoCO$_3$ dissolve in the same solution.

38. A solution is 0.010 M in both Cu^{2+} and Cd^{2+}. What percentage of Cd^{2+} remains in the solution when 99.9% of the Cu^{2+} has been precipitated as CuS by adding sulfide?

39. A solution is 0.15 M in both Pb^{2+} and Ag$^+$. If Cl$^-$ is added to this solution, what is [Ag$^+$] when PbCl$_2$ begins to precipitate?

40. The maximum allowable chloride ion concentration in drinking water is 0.25 g/L (7.1 × 10^{-3} M). A commercial kit for the analysis of chloride ion in water contains K$_2$CrO$_4$, which is dissolved in a water sample as an indicator, and a standard solution of AgNO$_3$, which is used as a titrant. As the AgNO$_3$ solution is added to the water sample drop by drop, insoluble white AgCl is formed. After "all" of the chloride ion has been precipitated, the next drop of AgNO$_3$ solution reacts with the K$_2$CrO$_4$ to form an orange-colored precipitate of Ag$_2$CrO$_4$, which indicates the end of the titration. What percentage of the initial chloride ion content remains unprecipitated when the first trace of Ag$_2$CrO$_4$ forms in a solution for which initial [Cl$^-$] = 7.1 × 10^{-3} M and [CrO$_4^{2-}$] = 1.0 × 10^{-4} M? Assume that the titration does not change the volume of the solution.

41. A solution that is 0.10 M in both Pb^{2+} and Fe^{2+} and 0.30 M in HCl is saturated with H$_2$S ([H$_2$S] = 0.10 M). What concentrations of Pb^{2+} and Fe^{2+} remain in the solution?

42. What reagent might be used to separate the ions in each of the following mixtures, which are 0.1 M with respect to each ion? In some cases it may be necessary to control the pH. (*Hint:* Consider the K_{sp} values given in Appendix D.)
   (a) Hg$_2^{2+}$ and Cu^{2+} (d) Zn^{2+} and Sr^{2+}
   (b) SO$_4^{2-}$ and Cl$^-$ (e) Ba^{2+} and Mg^{2+}
   (c) Hg^{2+} and Co^{2+} (f) CO$_3^{2-}$ and OH$^-$

Formation Constants of Complex Ions

43. Calculate the cadmium ion concentration, [Cd^{2+}], in a solution prepared by mixing 0.100 L of 0.0100 M Cd(NO$_3$)$_2$ with 0.150 L of 0.100 M NH$_3$(aq).

44. Calculate the silver ion concentration, [Ag$^+$], of a solution prepared by dissolving 1.00 g of AgNO$_3$ and 10.0 g of KCN in sufficient water to make 1.00 L of solution.

45. Sometimes equilibria for complex ions are described in terms of dissociation constants, K_d. For the complex ion AlF$_6^{3-}$ the dissociation reaction is

$$AlF_6^{3-} \rightleftharpoons Al^{3+} + 6F^-$$

and $$K_d = \frac{[Al^{3+}][F^-]^6}{[AlF_6^{3-}]} = 2 \times 10^{-24}$$

   (a) Calculate the value of the formation constant, K_f, for AlF$_6^{3-}$.
   (b) Using the value of the formation constant for the complex ion Co(NH$_3$)$_6^{2+}$, calculate the dissociation constant.

46. Calculate the concentration of Ni^{2+} in a 1.0 M solution of [Ni(NH$_3$)$_6$](NO$_3$)$_2$.

47. Calculate the concentration of Zn^{2+} in a 0.30 M solution of [Zn(CN)$_4$]$^{2-}$.

48. What are the concentrations of Ag$^+$, CN$^-$, and Ag(CN)$_2^-$ in a saturated solution of AgCN?

49. The equilibrium constant for the reaction

$$Hg^{2+}(aq) + 2Cl^-(aq) \rightleftharpoons HgCl_2(aq)$$

   is 1.6 × 10^{13}. Is HgCl$_2$ a strong electrolyte or a weak electrolyte? What are the concentrations of Hg^{2+} and Cl$^-$ in a 0.015 M solution of HgCl$_2$?

Dissolution of Precipitates

50. (a) Which of the following slightly soluble compounds has a solubility greater than that calculated from its solubility product because of hydrolysis of the anion present: CoSO$_3$, CuI, PbCO$_3$, PbCl$_2$, Tl$_2$S, KClO$_4$?
   (b) For which compound in part (a) is hydrolysis the most extensive?

51. Both AgCl and AgI dissolve in NH$_3$.
   (a) What mass of AgCl dissolves in 1.0 L of 1.0 M NH$_3$?
   (b) What mass of AgI dissolves in 1.0 L of 1.0 M NH$_3$?

52. Calculate the minimum number of moles of cyanide ion that must be added to 100 mL of solution to dissolve 2 × 10^{-2} mol of silver cyanide, AgCN.

53. Calculate the minimum concentration of ammonia needed in 1.0 L of solution to dissolve 3.0 × 10^{-3} mol of silver bromide.

54. A roll of 35-mm black-and-white film contains about 0.27 g of unexposed AgBr before developing. What mass of

$Na_2S_2O_3 \cdot 5H_2O$ (hypo) in 1.0 L of developer is required to dissolve the AgBr as $Ag(S_2O_3)_2{}^{3-}$ ($K_f = 4.7 \times 10^{13}$)?

55. Calculate the volume of 1.50 M CH_3CO_2H required to dissolve a precipitate composed of 350 mg each of $CaCO_3$, $SrCO_3$, and $BaCO_3$.

Additional Exercises

56. Even though $Ca(OH)_2$ is an inexpensive base, its limited solubility restricts its use. What is the pH of a saturated solution of $Ca(OH)_2$?

57. What mass of NaCN must be added to 1 L of 0.010 M $Mg(NO_3)_2$ in order to produce the first trace of $Mg(OH)_2$?

58. The calcium ions in human blood serum are necessary for coagulation. In order to prevent coagulation when a blood sample is drawn for laboratory tests, an anticoagulant is added to the sample. Potassium oxalate, $K_2C_2O_4$, can be used as an anticoagulant because it removes the calcium as a precipitate of $CaC_2O_4 \cdot H_2O$. In order to prevent coagulation, it is necessary to remove all but 1.0% of the Ca^{2+} in serum. If normal blood serum with a buffered pH of 7.40 contains 9.5 mg of Ca^{2+} per 100 mL of serum, what mass of $K_2C_2O_4$ is required to prevent the coagulation of a 10-mL blood sample that is 55% serum by volume? [All volumes are accurate to two significant figures. Note that the volume of fluid (serum) in a 10-mL blood sample is 5.5 mL. Assume that the K_{sp} value for CaC_2O_4 in serum is the same as in water.]

59. About 50% of urinary calculi (kidney stones) consist of calcium phosphate, $Ca_3(PO_4)_2$. The normal midrange calcium content excreted in the urine is 0.10 g of Ca^{2+} per day. The normal midrange amount of urine passed may be taken as 1.4 L per day. What is the maximum concentration of phosphate ion that urine can contain before a calculus begins to form?

60. The pH of normal urine is 6.30, and the total phosphate concentration ($[PO_4{}^{3-}] + [HPO_4{}^{2-}] + [H_2PO_4{}^-] + [H_3PO_4]$) is 0.020 M. What is the minimum concentration of Ca^{2+} necessary to induce calculus formation? (See Exercise 59 for additional information.)

61. Magnesium metal (a component of alloys used in aircraft and a reducing agent used in the production of uranium, titanium, and other active metals) is isolated from sea water by the following sequence of reactions:

$$Mg^{2+}(aq) + Ca(OH)_2(aq) \longrightarrow Mg(OH)_2(s) + Ca^{2+}(aq)$$

$$Mg(OH)_2(s) + 2HCl(aq) \longrightarrow MgCl_2(s) + 2H_2O(l)$$

$$MgCl_2(l) \xrightarrow{\text{Electrolysis}} Mg(s) + Cl_2(g)$$

Sea water has a density of 1.026 g/cm^3 and contains 1272 parts per million of magnesium as $Mg^{2+}(aq)$ by mass. What mass, in kilograms, of $Ca(OH)_2$ is required to precipitate 99.9% of the magnesium in 1.00×10^3 L of sea water?

62. Calculate $[HgCl_4{}^{2-}]$ in a solution prepared by adding 8.0×10^{-3} mol of NaCl to 0.100 L of a 0.040 M $HgCl_2$ solution.

63. In a titration of cyanide ion, 28.72 mL of 0.0100 M $AgNO_3$ is added before precipitation begins. (The reaction of Ag^+ with CN^- goes to completion, producing the $[Ag(CN)_2]^-$ complex. Precipitation of solid AgCN takes place when excess Ag^+ is added to the solution, above the amount needed to complete the formation of $[Ag(CN)_2]^-$.) How many grams of NaCN were in the original sample?

64. A 0.010-mol sample of solid AgCN is rendered soluble in 1 L of solution by adding just enough excess cyanide ion to form $[Ag(CN)_2]^-$. When all of the solid silver cyanide has just dissolved, the concentration of free cyanide ion is 1.125×10^{-7} M. Neglecting hydrolysis of the cyanide ion, determine the concentration of free, uncomplexed silver ion in the solution. If more cyanide ion is added (without changing the volume) until the equilibrium concentration of free cyanide ion is 1.0×10^{-6} M, what will be the equilibrium concentration of free silver ion?

19 Chemical Thermodynamics

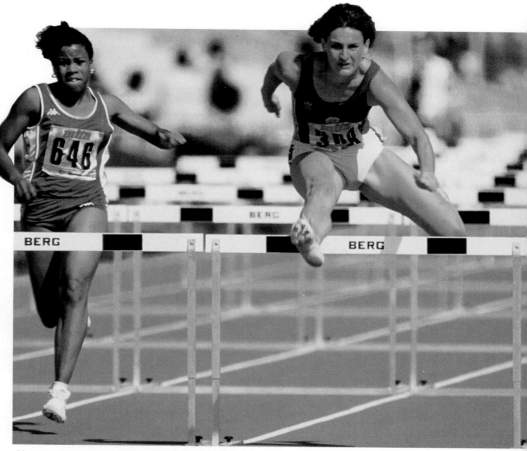

Chemical reactions produce work and heat in the body.

When we consider a potential chemical reaction, such as the biological oxidation of glucose to carbon dioxide and water, we often have several questions. Will the substances react when put together? If they do react, what will be the final concentrations of reactants and products when equilibrium is established? If a reaction occurs, how much heat, if any, will be produced? How fast will the reaction go? What is its mechanism? The last two questions can be answered by exploring the kinetics of the reaction (Chapter 14). The first three are the topic of this chapter, in which we consider energy changes and changes in randomness, or disorder, that accompany chemical processes. We shall see that these changes can be determined quantitatively and that their values can be used to predict whether a chemical reaction will occur. Finally, we shall see that the equilibrium constant for a reaction can be calculated from these values.

In several of the preceding chapters we have pointed out chemical processes that are accompanied by changes in the internal energy of the system. For example, removing the electron from a hydrogen atom, breaking a carbon–hydrogen bond, evaporating water, melting ice, and forming calcium oxide and carbon dioxide from calcium carbonate all proceed with an increase in internal energy. These changes are endothermic (Fig. 19.1), and because energy must be added to the system to get them to go, the internal energy of the system increases. On the other hand, burning of carbon (charcoal or coal), digestion of food, combustion of hydrogen and oxygen, condensation of water vapor to a solid or a liquid, reaction of hydrochloric acid and sodium hydroxide, and reaction of sodium with water all proceed spontaneously, with the evolution of heat (Fig. 19.2) and a decrease in internal energy. When we discussed the formation of solutions, we noted that processes that increase the disorder of the system also tend to be spontaneous. These familiar concepts of changes in internal energy or in the amount of disorder can be used in analyzing the behavior of chemical systems. They will prove helpful as we learn to predict whether a reaction will proceed, the amounts of reactants and products present at equilibrium, and the energy changes associated with a reaction.

Figure 19.1

The decomposition of $CaCO_3$ to CaO and CO_2 is an endothermic change; heating is required.

Figure 19.2

Carbon burns in an exothermic reaction; heat is evolved.

Internal Energy and Enthalpy

⓳.1 Spontaneous Processes, Energy, and Disorder

Chemical thermodynamics is the study of the energy transformations that accompany chemical and physical changes. The part of the universe that undergoes a change (the part we study) is called the **system;** the rest of the universe is called the **surroundings.** In our study of chemical thermodynamics we shall examine the energy transformations that occur within a system and any transfer of energy that may occur between the system and the surroundings.

Two fundamental laws of nature are particularly important in thermodynamics.

1. *Systems tend to attain a state of minimum energy.* For example, suppose we have a system that consists of a box containing an assembled jigsaw puzzle. If we drop the box, it falls to the floor. During this change in the box's position, part of its potential energy (energy due to its height above the floor) is converted to kinetic energy. When the box hits the floor, that kinetic energy is converted to heat. The loss of heat indicates that the system (the box and the puzzle) has gone to a lower energy state. It certainly has a lower potential energy, because it cannot fall as far as it could before the change in its position.

2. *Systems tend toward a state of maximum disorder.* The assembled jigsaw puzzle in the box would almost certainly be partly disassembled (more disordered) after the fall. The latter fact may not seem very important or fundamental, but no one would try to assemble a jigsaw puzzle by dropping the separated pieces on the floor, whereas the reverse process (making the system more disordered) is readily accomplished by dropping the assembled puzzle. A system tends to become less orderly because there are so many more ways to be disorderly than to be orderly. The probability of a system becoming more disordered or more random is greater than that of its becoming more ordered.

A physical or a chemical change that occurs spontaneously is accompanied by one or both of these two shifts—a shift toward a minimum energy and/or a shift to a more disordered state. The effects of a shift toward minimum energy and a shift toward a more disordered state are discussed in connection with the formation of solutions in Section 12.7. It would be beneficial for you to reread that section now.

⓳.2 Internal Energy, Heat, and Work

The **internal energy of a system, E,** is simply the total of all of the possible kinds of energy present in that portion of the universe that we choose to study—the total of kinetic energies, ionization energies of the electrons, bond energies, vibrational energies, lattice energies, and so on that are present in the system. In Section 4.3 we described how the internal energy of a system varies with the loss or gain of heat by the system and with the work done by or on the system as it undergoes a chemical or physical change. In this section we shall consider how to calculate the energy change

Figure 19.3

When an initial state composed of 6.0×10^{23} H$_2$ molecules undergoes a change to a final state composed of 1.2×10^{24} H atoms, the internal energy of the system increases by 436 kJ, and $\Delta E = 436$ kJ. The system consists of 1.2×10^{24} H atoms in both states, but the arrangements of the atoms are different.

SYSTEM: 1.2×10^{24} H atoms
    (2.0 mol H atoms)

SURROUNDINGS

Initial State of System

6.0×10^{23} H$_2$ molecules
(1.0 mol H$_2$ molecules)
Internal energy $= E_1$,
an unknown value

436 kJ added
from surroundings

$\Delta E = 436$ kJ
    $= E_2 - E_1$

Final State of System

1.2×10^{24} H atoms
(2.0 mol H atoms)
Internal energy $= E_2$
    $= E_1 + 436$ kJ

associated with one type of work, called expansion work, and review how the combination of work and loss or gain of heat changes the internal energy of a system.

We cannot measure the value of E for a system; we can only determine the change in internal energy, ΔE, that accompanies a change in the system. In Section 7.9 we saw that for a hydrogen–hydrogen bond, the bond energy is 436 kilojoules per mole of bonds. Thus a system consisting of 1 mole of hydrogen molecules can be converted into 2 moles of hydrogen atoms with the input of 436 kilojoules of heat or other energy (Fig. 19.3). During this process the internal energy changes (increases) by 436 kilojoules. Although we cannot measure its initial internal energy, E_1, when the system exists as 1 mole of hydrogen molecules, or its final energy, E_2, when it exists as 2 moles of hydrogen atoms, we can measure the difference in internal energy between the two states. The internal energy of the 2 moles of hydrogen atoms is 436 kilojoules greater than the internal energy of 1 mole of hydrogen molecules, because 436 kilojoules of energy has been added to the system. The difference between E_2 and E_1 is equal to the change in internal energy.

$$\Delta E = E_2 - E_1$$

The value of ΔE is positive when energy is transferred from the surroundings to the system. When energy is transferred from the system to the surroundings, ΔE is negative.

Energy is transferred into or out of a system in one, or both, of two ways: by heat transfer and/or by work. In Section 4.2 we discussed how to measure the amount of heat, q, transferred. We saw that when heat flows into the system from the surroundings, the value of q is positive ($q > 0$). When heat flows from the system to the surroundings, the value of q is negative ($q < 0$). For example, if a system consisting of 18 grams (1 mole) of steam at 100°C condensed to liquid water at 100°C and did no work, the internal energy of the system would decrease, because 40.7 kilojoules of heat would flow from the system: $q = -40.7$ kJ.

In Section 4.3 we saw that when a system does work on the surroundings, the internal energy of the system decreases by the amount of work it does; when work is done on the system by the surroundings, the internal energy of the system increases by the amount of work done on it. The symbol for the amount of work done by a system is w. When energy is transferred from the system to the surroundings as work, work is done on the surroundings and the value of w is negative ($w < 0$). When energy is transferred to the system from the surroundings as work, the surroundings do work on the system and the value of w is positive ($w > 0$). In this chapter we shall limit our consideration of work to that of expansion against a constant pressure. This kind of work is called **expansion work**.

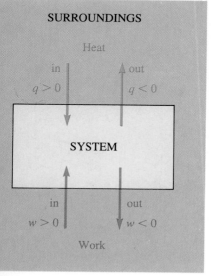

SURROUNDINGS

Heat

in   out
$q > 0$ $q < 0$

SYSTEM

in   out
$w > 0$ $w < 0$

Work

Figure 19.4

The expansion of steam in the cylinders of this steam engine results in expansion work that is converted into kinetic energy.

Gases expanding against a restraining pressure are capable of doing work, as in a steam engine (Fig. 19.4) or an automobile engine. A system with an initial volume V_1 that goes to a larger volume V_2 loses energy because it does expansion work on the surroundings ($w < 0$). When a system with an initial volume V_1 undergoes compression to a smaller volume V_2, the system gains energy because the surroundings do work on the system ($w > 0$, Fig. 19.5). If the restraining pressure, P, remains constant, the amount of work can be calculated from the expression $-P(V_2 - V_1)$. The term $P(V_2 - V_1)$ is an energy term with energy units. Pressure is defined as force per unit of

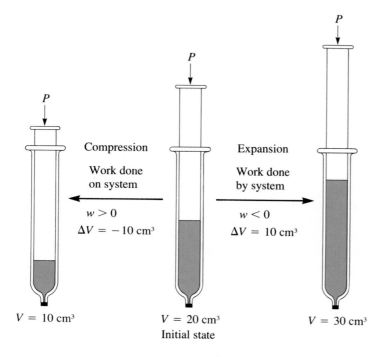

Figure 19.5

When a system consisting of 20 cm³ of a gas expands, the system does work on the surroundings ($w < 0$). When a system consisting of 20 cm³ of a gas is compressed, the surroundings do work on the system ($w > 0$).

area and therefore has units of force/(length)^2; volume has units of (length)^3. Thus the units for work are

$$w = -P\Delta V = -P(V_2 - V_1) = \frac{\text{force}}{\text{length}^2} \times \text{length}^3 = \text{force} \times \text{length}$$

Units of force × length are units of work, or energy. If the pressure is expressed in pascals (newtons/meter^2) and the volume change in cubic meters (m^3), the resulting product has units of newton meters, which is the same as joules, or pascal meters^3 (Section 4.1).

Example 19.1

Determine the amount of work, in joules, done when a system consisting of 1.0 cm^3 of liquid water at 0°C freezes under a constant pressure of 1.0 atm (101,325 Pa) and forms 1.1 cm^3 of ice (see the figure).

H$_2$O (*l*)   H$_2$O (*s*)

When 1.0 cm^3 of liquid water freezes, it expands to a volume of 1.1 cm^3.

As the water freezes it expands against a restraining pressure of 1 atm and pushes back the atmosphere (Section 4.3). Thus the system does work on its surroundings. The amount of work done on the surroundings, w, can be calculated from the expression $w = -P\Delta V = -P(V_2 - V_1)$. The original volume of the system, V_1, was given as 1.0 cm^3; the final volume, V_2, as 1.1 cm^3. We must convert these volumes to cubic meters (m^3) and express the pressure in pascals in order to get units of joules from the equation.

$$V_1 = 1.0 \text{ cm}^3 \times \frac{1 \text{ m}^3}{1 \times 10^6 \text{ cm}^3} = 1.0 \times 10^{-6} \text{ m}^3$$

$$V_2 = 1.1 \text{ cm}^3 \times \frac{1 \text{ m}^3}{1 \times 10^6 \text{ cm}^3} = 1.1 \times 10^{-6} \text{ m}^3$$

$$w = -P\Delta V = -P(V_2 - V_1)$$

$$= -101,325 \text{ Pa} \times (1.1 \times 10^{-6} \text{ m}^3 - 1.0 \times 10^{-6} \text{ m}^3)$$

$$= -101,325 \text{ Pa} \times (1 \times 10^{-7} \text{ m}^3) = -1 \times 10^{-2} \text{ Pa m}^3$$

$$= -1 \times 10^{-2} \text{ J}$$

The negative value of w indicates that work is done by the system. The magnitude of w indicates that very little work is done by this expansion. In Examples 19.2 and 19.3, we will see that other changes may involve a great deal more work.

19.3   The First Law of Thermodynamics

The **first law of thermodynamics** is actually the law of conservation of energy (Section 1.3): **The total amount of energy in the universe is constant.** The first law is often considered in a rather special form. When an amount of heat, q, is added to a system with an internal energy, E_1, and the surroundings then do some work, w, on the system, the system ends up with a new internal energy, E_2. The law of conservation of energy requires that the final internal energy of the system be equal to its initial internal energy plus the energy added as heat from the surroundings plus the energy added as work from the surroundings.

$$E_2 = E_1 + q + w$$

or

$$E_2 - E_1 = q + w$$

$E_2 - E_1$ is the change in the internal energy of the system, or ΔE.

$$\Delta E = E_2 - E_1 = q + w$$

In other words, the change in the internal energy of a given system equals the heat transferred to the system from the surroundings plus the work transferred from the surroundings to the system. The value of ΔE may be either positive or negative, depending on the relative values and signs of q and w.

If ΔE is the energy change for the system and ΔE_{sur} is the energy change for the surroundings,

$$\Delta E + \Delta E_{sur} = 0$$

This emphasizes the fact, expressed by the first law, that the total amount of energy in the universe is constant.

(a) If 600 J of heat is added to a system with an internal energy E_1 and the system does 450 J of work on the surroundings, what is the energy change in the system?

Example 19.2

To calculate ΔE we use the expression relating ΔE, q, and w.

$$\Delta E = q + w$$

Because heat is added to the system, q is positive ($q > 0$), so q is $+600$ J. The value of w is negative ($w < 0$), because work is done on the surroundings; w is -450 J.

$$\Delta E = q + w = (+600 \text{ J}) + (-450 \text{ J}) = +150 \text{ J}$$

The internal energy of the system increases by 150 J.

(b) What energy change do the surroundings undergo?

$$\Delta E + \Delta E_{sur} = 0$$
$$150 \text{ J} + \Delta E_{sur} = 0$$
$$\Delta E_{sur} = -150 \text{ J}$$

The energy of the surroundings decreases by 150 J.

(c) Can we determine the internal energy E_2 of the system in the new state?

We cannot determine the internal energy of the system. All we can say is that its final internal energy, E_2, is 150 J greater than its initial internal energy, E_1.

$$\Delta E = E_2 - E_1 = 150 \text{ J}$$
$$E_2 = E_1 + 150 \text{ J}$$

A system consisting of 18.02 g (1 mol) of $H_2O(g)$ at 100°C and 1 atm with a volume of 30.12 L (0.03012 m³) condenses at a constant pressure of 1 atm to $H_2O(l)$ at 100°C and 1 atm with a density of 0.9584 g/cm³. There is 40,668 J of heat released to the surroundings. Calculate ΔE for this process.

Example 19.3

Because

$$\Delta E = q + w$$

we need two values to determine ΔE: the amount of heat transferred to or from the system and the amount of work done on or by the system. The problem tells us that 40,668 J of heat is transferred from the water to the surroundings, so q is $-40,668$ J. The sign is negative because heat leaves the system.

Example 19.3 continued

The amount of work (in joules) involved in this change can be calculated from the expression

$$w = -P\Delta V = -P(V_2 - V_1)$$

if P is expressed in pascals (1 atm = 101,325 Pa; Section 10.2) and V_2 and V_1 are expressed in cubic meters.

The value of V_1 is given as 0.03012 m³. The value of V_2 can be calculated from the mass of water and its density.

$$V_2 = 18.02 \text{ g} \times \frac{1 \text{ cm}^3}{0.9584 \text{ g}} = 18.80 \text{ cm}^3$$

$$= 18.80 \text{ cm}^3 \times \left(\frac{1 \text{ m}}{100 \text{ cm}}\right)^3 = 1.880 \times 10^{-5} \text{ m}^3$$

Now the value of w can be determined.

$$w = -P(V_2 - V_1)$$

$$= -101,325 \text{ Pa} \times (1.880 \times 10^{-5} \text{ m}^3 - 3012 \times 10^{-5} \text{ m}^3)$$

$$= 3050 \text{ Pa m}^3 = 3050 \text{ J}$$

As indicated in Section 19.2, units of Pa m³ are equivalent to joules. Note that the value of w is positive, indicating that work is done on the system as its volume decreases from 0.03012 m³ to 0.00001880 m³ at a constant pressure of 101,325 Pa (1 atm). Now that we know both q (−40,668 J) and w (3050 J), we can calculate ΔE.

$$\Delta E = q + w$$

$$= (-40,668 \text{ J}) + (3050 \text{ J})$$

$$= -37,618 \text{ J} = -37.618 \text{ kJ}$$

The internal energy of the system decreases by 37,618 J ($\Delta E < 0$), because the system gives up 40,668 J to the surroundings ($q < 0$), and the surroundings do 3050 J of work on the system ($w > 0$). These changes are summarized in Fig. 19.6.

Figure 19.6

Work and heat changes accompanying the change in a system consisting of 1.000 mol of O atoms and 2.000 mol of H atoms combined as water molecules as the water undergoes a change from the gas phase (initial state) to the liquid phase (final state) at 100°C and 1 atm.

SYSTEM: 1.000 mol O atoms
2.000 mol H atoms

SURROUNDINGS

Initial State of System		**Final State of System**
1.000 mol gaseous H_2O molecules $T = 100$°C, $P = 1$ atm $V = 30.12$ L, Internal energy $= E_1$	40.668 kJ lost to surroundings $q = -40.668$ kJ	1.000 mol liquid H_2O $T = 100$°C, $P = 1$ atm $V = 18.80$ mL Internal energy $= E_2$
	3.050 kJ added to system as work from surroundings $w = 3.050$ kJ	$= E_1 - 40.668$ kJ $+ 3.050$ kJ

⑲.4 State Functions

A mole of water that condenses from a gas to a liquid at 100°C and 1 atmosphere (as in Example 19.3) undergoes a change in internal energy, ΔE, that is simply the difference between the internal energies of 1 mole of liquid H_2O at 100°C and of 1 mole of gaseous H_2O at 100°C. This difference does not depend on how we convert the steam to liquid water. We could convert the gas directly to liquid at 100°C and 1 atmosphere:

$$H_2O(g) \longrightarrow H_2O(l)$$

or we could use a two-step process. We could first convert the $H_2O(g)$ to 1 mole of $H_2(g)$ and $\frac{1}{2}$ mole of $O_2(g)$ and then reconvert the $H_2(g)$ and $O_2(g)$ to 1 mole of $H_2O(l)$ at 100°C and 1 atmosphere:

$$H_2O(g) \longrightarrow H_2(g) + \tfrac{1}{2}O_2(g) \longrightarrow H_2O(l)$$

Either way, ΔE for the process is -37.618 kilojoules.

When a property of a system (its density or its internal energy, for example) does not depend on how the system gets to the state that exhibits that property, the property is said to be a **state function.** How a system goes from an initial state to a final state is irrelevant to the value of a state function of the system in its final state. The change in the value of a state function equals its value in the final state minus its value in the initial state. For example, the change in internal energy that accompanies the condensation of a mole of water (-37.618 kJ) is a change in a state function—the internal energy of the water.

A second example of a change in a state function is the change in the potential energy of a tennis ball as it is moved from a second-floor window ledge to a third-floor window ledge. (The potential energy is a measure of how hard the ball would hit the ground if it fell.) The change in potential energy is the same whether the ball is taken directly from the second to the third floor or carried to the roof and then back to the third floor. The potential energy of the tennis ball is a state function; any difference in the path by which it is moved from the second to the third floor makes no difference in how hard the ball will hit the ground if it falls from the third-floor window.

In contrast to state functions, there are other functions whose values depend on the paths followed. The distinction between the two types of functions can be illustrated by the expression

$$\Delta E = E_2 - E_1 = q + w$$

The internal energy, E, is a state function; ΔE of a reaction is the same regardless of how that reaction is carried out. On the other hand, the values of q and w are not constant; they vary with the process used. As an example of how an energy change can be independent of the path used to cause it, consider the tennis ball again. More work is required to carry the tennis ball from the second floor to the roof and back to the third floor of a ten-story building than to carry it directly from the second floor to the third floor, but the change in its potential energy is the same for both paths. Similarly, the change in energy, ΔE, associated with the transformation of $H_2O(g)$ to $H_2O(l)$ at a given temperature and pressure is always the same and is a state function. However, q and w depend on the way the transformation is carried out, so they are not state functions. Quantities that are state functions are designated by capital letters; those that are not, by lowercase letters.

Figure 19.7

The heat released when 2 mol of Al and 1 mol of Fe_2O_3 at 25°C react and form 1 mol of Al_2O_3 and 2 mol of Fe at 25°C is the enthalpy change of the reaction $2Al + Fe_2O_3 \longrightarrow Al_2O_3 + 2Fe$. The heat is released in two stages. This photograph shows that heat is released as the reaction occurs; additional heat is released as the molten iron and hot Al_2O_3 cool back down to 25°C.

⓵⓽.5   Enthalpy Changes

The amount of heat, q, absorbed or released by a system undergoing a chemical or physical change is usually not a state function; it varies with the way the process occurs. However, if the change occurs in such a way that the only work done is due to a change in volume of the system at constant pressure, q is a state function. The amount of heat, q, exchanged when the only work done by the system is expansion work at constant pressure is called the **enthalpy change, ΔH,** of the system ($\Delta H = q$). Most chemical reactions occur under the essentially constant pressure of the atmosphere. Consequently, the enthalpy change of these or any other changes that occur at constant pressure can be determined by measuring the amount of heat transferred during the process (Fig. 19.7).

The change in internal energy for a reaction that occurs at constant pressure can be calculated from the equation

$$\Delta E = q + w = \Delta H + w$$

Because the reaction occurs at constant pressure and the only work done results from the change in volume of the system, the work term in this case is equal to $-P(V_2 - V_1)$, or $-P\Delta V$.

At constant pressure *and constant volume,*

$$-P\Delta V = 0 \quad \text{and} \quad \Delta H = \Delta E$$

Remember that when ΔH for a chemical reaction is negative, the system evolves heat to the surroundings, and the reaction is exothermic. When ΔH for a chemical reaction is positive, heat is absorbed by the system from the surroundings, and the reaction is endothermic (Section 4.4).

At this point we need to digress briefly and discuss the notation used to indicate enthalpy changes for processes that occur at different temperatures with different pressures and concentrations of reactants and products. The use of 298.15 K (25°C) and 1 atmosphere as standard state conditions was noted in Section 4.4. A process that occurs under standard state conditions and that converts a system's reactants, at unit activities, to products, at unit activities, has an enthalpy change that is labeled as ΔH°_{298}. The subscript 298 is used to specify that the temperature is 298.15 K. A solid, a pure liquid, or a solvent has an activity of 1 (unit activity). The activity of a gas is approximated by its pressure (in atmospheres); thus we will consider a gas with a pressure of 1 atmosphere to have unit activity. The activity of a dissolved solute is approximated by its concentration, and we will consider a 1 molar solution to have unit activity.

The enthalpy change of a process that occurs at some temperature other than 298.15 K but that involves reactants and products that all have unit activities is given the symbol ΔH°. The symbol ΔH is used to indicate an enthalpy change with no restrictions on the temperature or the activities of the components. The various symbols used to indicate enthalpy changes are summarized in Table 19.1.

The difference between the enthalpy change for a process at 298.15 K and for the same process at some other temperature is generally small and is often neglected. Thus we often make the approximation that ΔH°_{298} equals ΔH° for the same process.

The enthalpy changes that we have seen in Section 4.4 include enthalpy of combustion and standard molar enthalpy of formation, enthalpy of vaporization, and enthalpy of fusion. In addition, enthalpy changes are used to define ionization energy and electron affinity (Section 6.3), covalent bond energy (Section 7.9), and lattice energy (Section 11.19).

Table 19.1 **Symbols for Various Thermodynamic Parameters**

Enthalpy Change	Free Energy Change	Entropy Change	Conditions
ΔH°_{298}	ΔG°_{298}	ΔS°_{298}	Standard state conditions, unit activities (T = 298.15 K, pure solids, pure liquids, P = 1 atm, 1 M concentrations)
ΔH°	ΔG°	ΔS°	Unit activities (Pure solids, pure liquids, P = 1 atm, 1 M concentrations)
ΔH	ΔG	ΔS	No restrictions

We have seen how to calculate the enthalpy change for a reaction that can be carried out in a series of steps using Hess's law (Section 4.5). The enthalpy change of a process that can be written as the sum of several steps is equal to the sum of the enthalpy changes of all the steps. The Born–Haber cycle (Section 11.20) is an application of Hess's law.

Example 19.4

Calculate the enthalpy change for the following reaction at 25°C and 1 atm

$$S(s) + 1\tfrac{1}{2}O_2(g) \longrightarrow SO_3(g)$$

from the enthalpy of formation of $SO_2(g)$ (-296.8 kJ mol^{-1}) and the enthalpy change for the following reaction

$$SO_2(g) + \tfrac{1}{2}O_2(g) \longrightarrow SO_3(g) \qquad \Delta H^\circ_{298} = -98.9 \text{ kJ}$$

The enthalpy change for the process that converts a system at 25°C consisting of 1 mole of $S(s)$ and $1\tfrac{1}{2}$ moles of $O_2(g)$ (at 1 atmosphere pressure) to 1 mole of $SO_3(g)$ (at 1 atmosphere pressure), ΔH°_{298}, is the sum of the enthalpy changes of two reactions: the reaction that converts $S(s)$ to $SO_2(g)$ and the reaction that converts $SO_2(g)$ to $SO_3(g)$. The enthalpy change of the first reaction is simply the standard molar enthalpy of formation of $SO_2(g)$. Thus

$S(s) + O_2(g) \longrightarrow SO_2(g)$	$\Delta H^\circ_{298} = \Delta H^\circ_{f_{SO_2(g)}} = -296.8$ kJ
$SO_2(g) + \tfrac{1}{2}O_2(g) \longrightarrow SO_3(g)$	$\Delta H^\circ_{298} = -98.9$ kJ
$S(s) + 1\tfrac{1}{2}O_2(g) \longrightarrow SO_3(g)$	$\Delta H^\circ_{298} = -296.8$ kJ $+ (-98.9$ kJ$) = -395.7$ kJ

The value of ΔH°_{298} for the bottom reaction is the sum of the ΔH°_{298} values for the two reactions that add up to it.

We have also seen how Hess's law can be used to determine the standard state enthalpy change of any reaction if the standard molar enthalpies of formation of the reactants and products are available (Section 4.5). The steps that we used were the decompositions of the reactants into their component elements (for which the enthalpy changes are proportional to the negative of the enthalpies of formation of the reactants) followed by recombinations of the elements to give the products (for which the enthalpy changes are proportional to the enthalpies of formation of the products).

Example 19.5

Using the standard molar enthalpies of formation of the compounds involved, calculate the standard state enthalpy change, ΔH_{298}°, for the reaction

$$Na_2O(s) + CO_2(g) \longrightarrow Na_2CO_3(s)$$

The standard state enthalpy change can be calculated from the following sum:

$$Na_2O(s) \longrightarrow 2Na(s) + \tfrac{1}{2}O_2(g) \qquad \Delta H_1 = -\Delta H_{f_{Na_2O(s)}}^{\circ}$$

$$CO_2(g) \longrightarrow C(s) + O_2(g) \qquad \Delta H_2 = -\Delta H_{f_{CO_2(g)}}^{\circ}$$

$$\underline{2Na(s) + C(s) + \tfrac{3}{2}O_2(g) \longrightarrow Na_2CO_3(s) \qquad \Delta H_3 = \Delta H_{f_{Na_2CO_3(s)}}^{\circ}}$$

$$Na_2O(s) + CO_2(g) \longrightarrow Na_2CO_3(s) \qquad H_{298}^{\circ} = \Delta H_1 + \Delta H_2 + \Delta H_3$$

$$\Delta H_{298}^{\circ} = \Delta H_1 + \Delta H_2 + \Delta H_3 = -\Delta H_{f_{Na_2O(s)}}^{\circ} - \Delta H_{f_{CO_2(g)}}^{\circ} + \Delta H_{f_{Na_2CO_3(s)}}^{\circ}$$

Using the values of the standard molar enthalpies of formation, we find the value of ΔH_{298}° to be

$$\Delta H_{298}^{\circ} = -(-415.9 \text{ kJ}) - (-393.51 \text{ kJ}) + (-1130.8 \text{ kJ})$$

$$= -321.4 \text{ kJ}$$

The equation that was used to calculate ΔH in Example 19.5, $\Delta H_{298}^{\circ} = -\Delta H_{f_{Na_2O(s)}}^{\circ} - \Delta H_{f_{CO_2(g)}}^{\circ} + \Delta H_{f_{Na_2CO_3(s)}}^{\circ}$, is a specific example of a useful equation for that type of calculation: *The enthalpy change for a chemical reaction run under standard state conditions is equal to the sum of the standard molar enthalpies of formation of all the products, each multiplied by the number of moles of the product in the balanced chemical equation, minus the corresponding sum for the reactants.*

$$\Delta H_{298}^{\circ} = \sum \Delta H_{f_{products}}^{\circ} - \sum \Delta H_{f_{reactants}}^{\circ}$$

For the reaction

$$mA + nB \longrightarrow xC + yD$$

$$\Delta H_{298}^{\circ} = [x \times \Delta H_{f_C}^{\circ} + y \times \Delta H_{f_D}^{\circ}] - [m \times \Delta H_{f_A}^{\circ} + n \times \Delta H_{f_B}^{\circ}]$$

When using this equation, it is important to remember that the standard molar enthalpy of formation of an element in its most stable state (gas, liquid, or solid) is zero (Section 4.4).

Example 19.6

Calculate ΔH° at 298.15 K for the reaction

$$2Ag_2S(s) + 2H_2O(l) \longrightarrow 4Ag(s) + 2H_2S(g) + O_2(g)$$

The standard molar enthalpies of formation, ΔH_f°, of the compounds involved can be found in Table 19.2 on page 618.

$$\Delta H_{298}^{\circ} = 4 \Delta H_{f_{Ag(s)}}^{\circ} + 2 \Delta H_{f_{H_2S(g)}}^{\circ} + \Delta H_{f_{O_2(g)}}^{\circ} - 2 \Delta H_{f_{Ag_2S(s)}}^{\circ} - 2 \Delta H_{f_{H_2O(l)}}^{\circ}$$

Remember that the standard molar enthalpy of formation of an element in its most stable state is zero (Section 4.4); hence $\Delta H_{f_{O_2(g)}}^{\circ} = \Delta H_{f_{Ag(s)}}^{\circ} = 0 \text{ kJ}$.

$$\Delta H^\circ_{298} = 4 \text{ mol Ag}(s) \times (0 \text{ kJ mol}^{-1}) + 2 \text{ mol H}_2\text{S}(g) \times (-20.6 \text{ kJ mol}^{-1})$$
$$+ 1 \text{ mol O}_2(g) \times (0 \text{ kJ mol}^{-1}) - 2 \text{ mol Ag}_2\text{S}(s) \times (-32.6 \text{ kJ mol}^{-1})$$
$$- 2 \text{ mol H}_2\text{O}(l) \times (-285.8 \text{ kJ mol}^{-1})$$
$$= [-41.2 - (-65.2) - (-571.6)] \text{ kJ} = 595.6 \text{ kJ}$$

The reaction is endothermic.

$$2\text{Ag}_2\text{S}(s) + 2\text{H}_2\text{O}(l) \longrightarrow 4\text{Ag}(s) + 2\text{H}_2\text{S}(g) + \text{O}_2(g) \qquad \Delta H^\circ_{298} = 595.6 \text{ kJ}$$

Calculate ΔH° at 298.15 K for the reaction

Example 19.7

$$2\text{Na}(s) + 2\text{H}_2\text{O}(l) \longrightarrow 2\text{NaOH}(s) + \text{H}_2(g)$$

The standard molar enthalpies of formation for the reactants and products involved are as follows: $\text{H}_2\text{O}(l)$, -285.8 kJ mol^{-1}; NaOH(s), -426.8 kJ mol^{-1}; Na and H_2, 0 kJ mol^{-1}.

$$\Delta H^\circ_{298} = 2 \Delta H^\circ_{f_{\text{NaOH}(s)}} + \Delta H^\circ_{f_{\text{H}_2(g)}} - 2 \Delta H^\circ_{f_{\text{Na}(s)}} - 2 \Delta H^\circ_{f_{\text{H}_2\text{O}(l)}}$$

$$\Delta H^\circ_{298} = 2 \text{ mol NaOH}(s) \times (-426.8 \text{ kJ mol}^{-1}) + 1 \text{ mol H}_2(g) \times (0 \text{ kJ mol}^{-1})$$
$$- 2 \text{ mol Na}(s) \times (0 \text{ kJ mol}^{-1}) - 2 \text{ mol H}_2\text{O}(l) \times (-285.8 \text{ kJ mol}^{-1})$$

$$= [-853.5 + 571.6] \text{ kJ} = -281.9 \text{ kJ}$$

The reaction evolves heat; it is exothermic.

Entropy and Free Energy

⓲.6 The Spontaneity of Chemical and Physical Changes

A **spontaneous change,** in a thermodynamic sense, is a change in a system that proceeds without any outside influence on the system (Fig. 19.8). For example, when we add solid salt to water, the solid dissolves without any outside influence—the dissolution is spontaneous. Liquid water freezes to ice spontaneously at $-1°C$; ice melts spontaneously at 25°C; when a solution of an acid is added to a solution of a base, the hydronium ions and hydroxide ions combine spontaneously; and carbon combines spontaneously with oxygen to give carbon monoxide and/or carbon dioxide. Changes may be spontaneous even though they are very slow; the definition of a spontaneous change does not include time. For those who own diamonds (which are essentially pure carbon), it is fortunate that the spontaneous reaction of carbon with oxygen is very slow at room temperature.

Those exothermic changes for which ΔH is very negative (a large amount of heat given off) are frequently spontaneous. Enough heat to melt and ignite the metal may be produced by the spontaneous reaction of sodium with water; the reaction is exothermic (Example 19.7).

$$2Na(s) + 2H_2O(l) \longrightarrow 2NaOH(s) + H_2(g) \qquad \Delta H^\circ_{298} = -281.9 \text{ kJ}$$

Because of the large negative value of ΔH, we would expect this reaction to occur spontaneously at 25°C and 1 atmosphere, and it does. The reaction in Example 19.6,

$$2Ag_2S(s) + 2H_2O(l) \longrightarrow 4Ag(s) + 2H_2S(g) + O_2(g) \qquad \Delta H^\circ_{298} = 595.6 \text{ kJ}$$

is endothermic, and we should not expect it to occur spontaneously. However, we would expect the reverse reaction ($\Delta H^\circ_{298} = -595.6$ kJ) to occur spontaneously, and it does. Silver tarnishes when exposed to hydrogen sulfide and air.

Predictions based solely on the value of ΔH° are not always valid, particularly when ΔH° has a value near zero. For example, a reaction that proceeds spontaneously at one temperature and pressure may not proceed spontaneously at another temperature and pressure. At 25°C and 1 atmosphere of pressure, the reaction

$$2Ag(s) + \tfrac{1}{2}O_2(g) \longrightarrow Ag_2O(s)$$

proceeds spontaneously; ΔH°_{298} is -31 kilojoules. However, above about 200°C this reaction is not spontaneous, even though ΔH changes very little with the change in temperature. A crystalline solid melts spontaneously above its melting temperature, even though melting is an endothermic change ($\Delta H > 0$). Below its melting temperature it does not melt spontaneously, yet the ΔH value changes very little. Whether chemical reactions and physical changes proceed spontaneously *can* depend on temperature and pressure, yet temperature and pressure changes often have virtually no effect on the value of ΔH for a reaction.

It is evident, then, that we must consider another factor in addition to ΔH when determining whether a given reaction will proceed spontaneously. This factor is the entropy change that occurs as the change in the system takes place.

Figure 19.8

Pink solid MnS and a solution of $NaNO_3$ form spontaneously when a solution of Na_2S is added to a solution of $Mn(NO_3)_2$.

❶⓿.7 Entropy and Entropy Changes

Consider two changes that are spontaneous but not exothermic: the melting of ice at room temperature,

$$H_2O(s) \longrightarrow H_2O(l) \qquad \Delta H^\circ = 6.0 \text{ kJ}$$

and the decomposition of calcium carbonate at high temperature,

$$CaCO_3(s) \longrightarrow CaO(s) + CO_2(g) \qquad \Delta H^\circ = 178 \text{ kJ}$$

The disorder of both of these systems increases when these reactions occur. Water molecules are held in fixed positions in a regular, repeating array in an ice crystal (Fig. 11.22). When the ice melts, the water molecules are free to move through the liquid as well as to change their orientations. The molecules in the liquid are much more randomly distributed than those in the solid. Thus the amount of order is higher in the solid than in the liquid. As calcium carbonate decomposes, the system changes from an ordered array of calcium ions and carbonate ions in solid calcium carbonate to an ordered array of calcium and oxide ions in solid calcium oxide plus a disordered collection of carbon dioxide molecules in the gas phase. The arrangement of the carbon dioxide molecules in the gas phase is even more random (the disorder is greater) than that of an equal number of water molecules in the liquid phase.

The randomness, or the amount of disorder, of a system can be determined quantitatively and is referred to as the entropy, S, of the system. The greater the randomness, or disorder, in a system, the higher is its entropy. Entropy is one of the most important of scientific concepts; as we shall see, an entropy increase corresponding to an increase in disorder is the major driving force in many chemical and physical processes. Every substance has an entropy as one of its characteristic properties, just as it has color, hardness, volume, melting point, density, and enthalpy. Like E, the internal energy of a system, the entropy, S, of a system is a state function. The entropy of a system is equal to the sum of the entropies of its components.

The **entropy change, ΔS,** for a chemical change is equal to the sum of the entropies of the products of that change minus the sum of the entropies of the reactants. For the reaction $mA + nB \longrightarrow xC + yD$, the entropy change is

$$\Delta S = \Sigma S_{products} - \Sigma S_{reactants}$$

$$= [(x \times S_C) + (y \times S_D)] - [(m \times S_A) + (n \times S_B)]$$

where S_A is the entropy of A, S_B is the entropy of B, and so on. A positive value for ΔS ($\Delta S > 0$) indicates an increase in randomness, or disorder, during the change; a negative value for ΔS ($\Delta S < 0$) indicates a decrease in randomness, or an increase in order.

The change to a more random and less ordered system when a solid melts corresponds to an increase in entropy ($\Delta S > 0$). Similarly, entropy increases as liquid molecules go to the still more disordered and random state characteristic of gases (Fig. 19.9). The amount of change in the entropy value is a measure of the increase in the randomness, or disorder, of a system.

The notation used to indicate entropy changes for processes that occur at different temperatures with different pressures and concentrations of reactants and products is analogous to that used for enthalpy changes (Table 19.1). The entropy change for a process that occurs under standard state conditions and that converts a system's components, at unit activities, to products, at unit activities, is labeled ΔS°_{298}. To review several points we made in Section 19.5, remember that solids, pure liquids, and solvents have an activity of 1 (unit activity), the activity of a gas is approximated by its pressure in atmospheres (we consider a gas with a pressure of 1 atmosphere to have unit activity), and the activity of a dissolved solute is approximated by its concentration (we consider a 1 molar solution to have unit activity).

Increasing entropy

$\Delta S > 0$

$\Delta S < 0$

$\Delta S > 0$

$\Delta S < 0$

Crystalline solid   Liquid   Gas

Figure 19.9

The entropy of a substance increases ($\Delta S > 0$) as it transforms from an ordered solid to a less ordered liquid and then to a still less ordered gas. The entropy decreases ($\Delta S < 0$) as the substance transforms from a gas to a liquid and then to a solid.

The entropy change of a process that occurs at some temperature other than 298.15 K but that involves reactants and products that all have unit activities is given the symbol $\Delta S°$. The symbol ΔS is used to indicate an entropy change with no restrictions on the temperature or the activities of the components. The difference between the entropy *change* for a process at 298.15 K and that same process at some other temperature is generally small and is often neglected. It is common practice to make the approximation that $\Delta S°_{298}$ equals $\Delta S°$ for the same process.

It is possible to measure the absolute entropy of a substance by using the technique described in Section 19.13. Absolute standard molar entropy values for several substances are listed in Table 19.2 and in Appendix I. Each of these $S°_{298}$ values represents the actual entropy content of 1 mole of a substance. The superscript symbol in $S°_{298}$ indicates that the value is for a substance in a standard state (298.15 K, 1 atm, unit

Table 19.2   **Standard Molar Enthalpies of Formation, Standard Molar Free Energies of Formation, and Absolute Standard Molar Entropies (298.15 K, 1 atm)[a]**

Substance	$\Delta H°_f$, kJ mol^{-1}	$\Delta G°_f$, kJ mol^{-1}	$S°_{298}$, J mol^{-1} K^{-1}
Carbon			
C(s) (graphite)	0	0	5.74
C(g)	716.68	671.29	157.99
CO(g)	−110.5	−137.2	197.56
CO$_2$(g)	−393.5	−394.4	213.6
CH$_4$(g)	−74.81	−50.75	186.15
Chlorine			
Cl$_2$(g)	0	0	222.96
Cl(g)	121.7	105.7	165.09
Copper			
Cu(s)	0	0	33.15
CuS(s)	−53.1	−53.6	66.5
Hydrogen			
H$_2$(g)	0	0	130.57
H(g)	218.0	203.3	114.6
H$_2$O(g)	−241.8	−228.6	188.71
H$_2$O(l)	−285.8	−237.2	69.91
HCl(g)	−92.31	−95.3	186.8
H$_2$S(g)	−20.6	−33.6	205.7
Oxygen			
O$_2$(g)	0	0	205.03
Silver			
Ag$_2$O(s)	−31.0	−11.2	121.0
Ag$_2$S(s)	−32.6	−40.7	144.0

[a] See Appendix I for additional values.

activities). Note that solids (most ordered) tend to have lower entropies than liquids (less ordered) and that liquids tend to have lower entropies than gases (least ordered) (Fig. 19.9). In the same physical state, substances with simple molecules tend to have lower entropies than substances with more complicated molecules. Because larger molecules have more atoms per molecule to move about, they can exhibit greater randomness or disorder; thus they have higher entropies. Hard crystalline substances, such as diamond, tend to be more ordered and to have lower entropies than softer materials, such as graphite or sodium.

It is important to remember that the entropy of a single substance varies with temperature. In subsequent sections we will assume that the entropy *change* for a process, ΔS, is independent of temperature, but we cannot make the same assumption about the entropy, S, of a single substance.

The following examples show how absolute standard molar entropies can be used to calculate entropy changes.

Determine the entropy change for the process $H_2O(l) \longrightarrow H_2O(g)$ when both $H_2O(l)$ and $H_2O(g)$ are in their standard states at 25°C.

Example 19.8

The entropy change for this reaction is the sum of the entropies of the products, $H_2O(g)$ in this case, minus the sum of the entropies of the reactants, $H_2O(l)$ in this case. Entropy values are listed in Table 19.2.

$$\Delta S^{\circ}_{298} = S^{\circ}_{H_2O(g)} - S^{\circ}_{H_2O(l)}$$

$$= 1 \text{ mol } H_2O(g) \times (188.71 \text{ J mol}^{-1} \text{ K}^{-1})$$

$$- 1 \text{ mol } H_2O(l) \times (69.91 \text{ J mol}^{-1} \text{ K}^{-1})$$

$$= 118.80 \text{ J K}^{-1}$$

The value for ΔS°_{298} is positive, indicating greater disorder in gaseous H_2O than in liquid H_2O. This makes sense because the molecules are in much more rapid and random motion in the gaseous state than they are in the liquid state.

Calculate the entropy change for the following reaction when the reactants and products are in their standard states at 25°C.

Example 19.9

$$2H_2(g) + O_2(g) \longrightarrow 2H_2O(l)$$

Note that absolute standard molar entropies of the elements are not zero at 25°C.

$$\Delta S^{\circ}_{298} = 2 S^{\circ}_{H_2O(l)} - 2 S^{\circ}_{H_2(g)} - S^{\circ}_{O_2(g)}$$

$$= 2 \text{ mol } H_2O(l) \times (69.91 \text{ J mol}^{-1} \text{ K}^{-1})$$

$$- 2 \text{ mol } H_2(g) \times (130.57 \text{ J mol}^{-1} \text{ K}^{-1})$$

$$- 1 \text{ mol } O_2(g) \times (205.03 \text{ J mol}^{-1} \text{ K}^{-1})$$

$$= -326.35 \text{ J K}^{-1}$$

As this reaction proceeds, the entropy *of the system* decreases. We will see in a subsequent section that the entropy of the surroundings increases accordingly.

⑲.8 Free Energy Changes

The effects of randomness and enthalpy on a chemical reaction are such that, when possible, reactions proceed spontaneously toward a state of minimum energy (ΔH negative) and maximum disorder (ΔS positive) (Sections 12.7 and 19.1). The enthalpy change and the entropy change of a reaction can be combined to give the change in another state function, the **free energy, G,** of the system. The relationship between the **free energy change, ΔG,** the enthalpy change, and the entropy change for a reaction is given by the expression

$$\Delta G = \Delta H - T\Delta S$$

where T is the temperature of the reaction on the Kelvin scale. The free energy change gives an unambiguous prediction of the spontaneity of a chemical reaction run at constant temperature and pressure, because it combines the effects of both ΔH and ΔS. **Reactions for which the value of ΔG is negative ($\Delta G < 0$) are spontaneous.**

The notation used to indicate free energy changes for processes that occur at different temperatures with different pressures and concentrations of reactants and products is similar to that used for enthalpy changes and entropy changes (Table 19.1). The free energy change for a process that occurs under standard state conditions and that converts a system's reactants, at unit activities, to products, at unit activities, is labeled ΔG°_{298}. The free energy change of a process that occurs at some temperature other than 298.15 K but that involves reactants and products that all have unit activities is given the symbol ΔG°. The symbol ΔG is used to indicate a free energy change, with no restrictions on the temperature or the activities of the components.

In the free energy equation, $\Delta G = \Delta H - T\Delta S$, when $T\Delta S$ is small compared to ΔH, then ΔG and ΔH have nearly the same value and each predicts the spontaneity of a given reaction. However, when the value of $T\Delta S$ is significant compared to that of ΔH, only the ΔG value can be used to predict spontaneity in a reliable way. The ΔH term of the free energy equation represents the energy, in the form of heat, involved in a reaction at constant pressure; hence it corresponds to a difference in energy between the initial and final states in a process. The ΔS term of the free energy equation (and hence the $T\Delta S$ term), on the other hand, corresponds to the difference in the amount of order of the products and reactants.

The free energy equation $\Delta G = \Delta H - T\Delta S$ tells us that a process that is exothermic (ΔH negative) and produces a more disordered system (ΔS positive) proceeds spontaneously (both ΔH and ΔS contribute to a more negative value for ΔG) (Fig. 19.10 and Table 19.3). A process that is endothermic (ΔH positive) and produces a more ordered system (ΔS negative) does not proceed spontaneously (both ΔH and ΔS contribute to a more positive value for ΔG). If a process is exothermic (ΔH negative) but produces a more ordered system (ΔS negative) or if a process is endothermic (ΔH positive) but produces a less ordered system (ΔS positive), then ΔH and ΔS are working in opposite directions, and the relative sizes and signs of ΔH and $T\Delta S$ determine the spontaneity or nonspontaneity of the process.

Note that T is always positive because it is measured on the Kelvin scale; therefore ΔS (which can be either positive or negative) determines the sign of the $T\Delta S$ term. Also, as T increases, the value of $T\Delta S$ gets larger and ΔS plays an increasingly important role in the value of ΔG.

Again, it should be emphasized that predicting whether a given process will proceed spontaneously says *nothing whatever about the rate*. A reaction with a negative ΔG

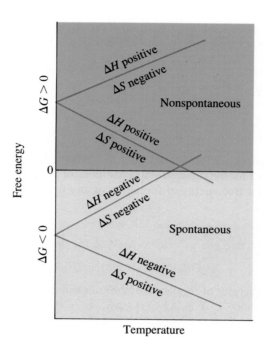

Figure 19.10

A graphical representation of the dependence of both ΔG and the spontaneity of a process on the temperature for the four combinations of ΔH and ΔS.

value will proceed spontaneously, but it may do so at a very rapid rate or at an incredibly slow rate.

19.9 Determination of Free Energy Changes

Free energy is a state function. Hence values of ΔG°_{298}, the free energy change for a reaction run under standard state conditions, can be calculated from standard molar free energies of formation, ΔG°_f, in the same way that ΔH°_{298} values are calculated from standard molar enthalpies of formation. The free energy change of a chemical process

Table 19.3   Examples of Spontaneous and Nonspontaneous Reactions

ΔH	ΔS	Example	ΔH°_{298}(kJ)	ΔS°_{298}(J K^{-1})	Comment
−	+	$H_2(g) + Cl_2(g) \longrightarrow 2HCl(g)$	−185	141	Spontaneous at all
		$C(s) + O_2(g) \longrightarrow CO_2(g)$	−394	3	temperatures
−	−	$H_2O(g) \longrightarrow H_2O(l)$	−44	−119	Spontaneous at lower tem-
		$2SO_2(g) + O_2(g) \longrightarrow 2SO_3(g)$	−198	−187	peratures, nonspontaneous at higher temperatures
+	+	$NH_4Cl(s) \longrightarrow NH_3(g) + HCl(g)$	176	284	Nonspontaneous at lower tem-
		$N_2(g) + O_2(g) \longrightarrow 2NO(g)$	180	25	peratures, spontaneous at higher temperatures
+	−	$3O_2(g) \longrightarrow 2O_3(g)$	286	−137	Nonspontaneous at all
		$2H_2O(l) + O_2(g) \longrightarrow 2H_2O_2(l)$	196	−126	temperatures

equals the sum of the free energies of formation of the products minus the sum of the free energies of formation of the reactants. For the reaction

$$mA + nB \longrightarrow xC + yD$$

the free energy change is

$$\Delta G^\circ_{298} = \Sigma\ \Delta G^\circ_{products} - \Sigma\ \Delta G^\circ_{reactants}$$

$$= [(x \times \Delta G^\circ_{f_C}) + (y \times \Delta G^\circ_{f_D})] - [(m \times \Delta G^\circ_{f_A}) + (n \times \Delta G^\circ_{f_B})]$$

Standard molar free energy of formation values for several substances are given in Table 19.2 and in Appendix I for the standard state conditions of 25°C and 1 atmosphere. Note that the standard molar free energy of formation of any free element in its most stable state is zero.

Example 19.10

Calculate the standard free energy change, ΔG°_{298}, for the reaction

$$2Ag_2S(s) + 2H_2O(l) \longrightarrow 4Ag(s) + 2H_2S(g) + O_2(g)$$

Standard molar free energies of formation of the compounds involved can be found in Table 19.2 or Appendix I. For $Ag_2S(s)$, ΔG°_f is -40.7 kJ mol^{-1}; for $H_2O(l)$, -237.2 kJ mol^{-1}; for $H_2S(g)$, -33.6 kJ mol^{-1}; and for $Ag(s)$ and $O_2(g)$, 0 kJ mol^{-1}. Thus

$$\Delta G^\circ_{298} = 4\ \Delta G^\circ_{f_{Ag(s)}} + 2\ \Delta G^\circ_{f_{H_2S(g)}} + \Delta G^\circ_{f_{O_2(g)}} - 2\ \Delta G^\circ_{f_{Ag_2S(s)}} - 2\ \Delta G^\circ_{f_{H_2O(l)}}$$

$$= 4\ \text{mol Ag}(s) \times (0\ \text{kJ mol}^{-1}) + 2\ \text{mol H}_2\text{S}(g) \times (-33.6\ \text{kJ mol}^{-1})$$

$$+ 1\ \text{mol O}_2(g) \times (0\ \text{kJ mol}^{-1}) - 2\ \text{mol Ag}_2\text{S}(s) \times (-40.7\ \text{kJ mol}^{-1})$$

$$- 2\ \text{mol H}_2\text{O}(l) \times (-237.2\ \text{kJ mol}^{-1})$$

$$= 488.6\ \text{kJ}$$

The positive value of ΔG°_{298} indicates that the reaction should not occur spontaneously as written but that the reverse reaction ($\Delta G^\circ_{298} = -488.6$ kJ) should occur spontaneously at 25°C and 1 atm.

The value of the free energy change for a process can also be calculated from the values of the enthalpy change and the entropy change for the process.

Example 19.11

The reaction of calcium oxide with the pollutant, sulfur trioxide,

$$CaO(s) + SO_3(g) \longrightarrow CaSO_4(s)$$

has been proposed as one way of removing SO_3 from the smoke resulting from burning high-sulfur coal. Using the following ΔH°_f and S°_{298} values, calculate the standard free energy change for the reaction under standard state conditions.

$$CaO(s)\colon \Delta H^\circ_f = -635.5\ \text{kJ mol}^{-1};\ S^\circ_{298} = 40\ \text{J mol}^{-1}\ \text{K}^{-1}$$

$$SO_3(g)\colon \Delta H^\circ_f = -395.7\ \text{kJ mol}^{-1};\ S^\circ_{298} = 256.6\ \text{J mol}^{-1}\ \text{K}^{-1}$$

$$CaSO_4(s)\colon \Delta H^\circ_f = -1432.7\ \text{kJ mol}^{-1};\ S^\circ_{298} = 107\ \text{J mol}^{-1}\ \text{K}^{-1}$$

This calculation can be approached in either of two ways.

1. We can calculate ΔH°_{298} and ΔS°_{298} for the reaction from the data, as shown in Sections 19.5 and 19.7, and then calculate ΔG°_{298} from the free energy equation.

$$\Delta G^\circ_{298} = \Delta H^\circ_{298} - T\Delta S^\circ_{298}$$

2. Using ΔS°_{298} and ΔH°_f for each compound, we can determine ΔG°_f for each compound, and we can calculate ΔG°_{298} for the reaction from these data by using the technique illustrated in Example 19.10.

We will use the first approach.

$$\Delta H^\circ_{298} = \Delta H^\circ_{f_{CaSO_4(s)}} - \Delta H^\circ_{f_{CaO(s)}} - \Delta H^\circ_{f_{SO_3(g)}}$$

$$= 1 \text{ mol } CaSO_4(s) \times (-1432.7 \text{ kJ mol}^{-1}) - 1 \text{ mol } CaO(s)$$

$$\times (-635.5 \text{ kJ mol}^{-1}) - 1 \text{ mol } SO_3(g) \times (-395.7 \text{ kJ mol}^{-1})$$

$$= -401.5 \text{ kJ} = -401,500 \text{ J}$$

Note that the units of ΔH were initially *kilojoules* but were converted to joules because the units of ΔS are *joules* per kelvin. We must use the same energy units for ΔH and ΔS when calculating ΔG.

$$\Delta S^\circ_{298} = S^\circ_{CaSO_4(s)} - S^\circ_{CaO(s)} - S^\circ_{SO_3(g)}$$

$$= 1 \text{ mol } CaSO_4(s) \times (107 \text{ J mol}^{-1} \text{ K}^{-1}) - 1 \text{ mol } CaO(s)$$

$$\times (40 \text{ J mol}^{-1} \text{ K}^{-1}) - 1 \text{ mol } SO_3(g) \times (256.6 \text{ J mol}^{-1} \text{ K}^{-1})$$

$$= -189.6 \text{ J K}^{-1}$$

$$\Delta G^\circ_{298} = \Delta H^\circ_{298} - T\Delta S^\circ_{298}$$

$$= -401,500 \text{ J} - [298.15 \text{ K} \times (-189.6 \text{ J K}^{-1})]$$

$$= -401,500 \text{ J} + 56,529 \text{ J}$$

$$= -344,971 \text{ J} = -345.0 \text{ kJ}$$

19.10 The Second Law of Thermodynamics

When a process occurs in a closed system—a system in which no heat can get in or out—ΔH must be zero. When the process is spontaneous, the free energy change, ΔG, is negative, and because ΔH is zero, the entropy change, ΔS, must be positive. Thus the entropy increases in a closed system when a spontaneous process occurs. The universe is a closed system; the universe includes everything; nothing can get in or out. **The second law of thermodynamics states that any spontaneous change that occurs in the universe must be accompanied by an increase in the entropy of the universe.**

It is difficult to apply the second law in its pure form. However, a useful modification can be developed from the free energy equation presented in Section 19.8.

$$\Delta G = \Delta H - T\Delta S \qquad \text{(all values pertaining to the system)}$$

Dividing by T gives

$$\frac{\Delta G}{T} = \frac{\Delta H}{T} - \Delta S \qquad \text{(for the system)}$$

It can be shown that

$$\Delta S_{sur} = -\frac{\Delta H_{sys}}{T} \qquad \text{(at constant temperature and pressure)}$$

where ΔS_{sur} is the change in entropy for the surroundings, and ΔH_{sys} is the change in enthalpy for the system.

Thus

$$\frac{\Delta G_{sys}}{T} = -\Delta S_{sur} - \Delta S_{sys}$$

or

$$-\frac{\Delta G_{sys}}{T} = \Delta S_{sur} + \Delta S_{sys}$$

$$\Delta S_{univ} = \Delta S_{sur} + \Delta S_{sys}$$

Hence

$$-\frac{\Delta G_{sys}}{T} = \Delta S_{univ}$$

This equation is valid only at constant temperature and pressure, when no work other than expansion work is done, because of the conditions that apply to the relationships from which it is derived.

This equation indicates that when ΔG_{sys} is negative, corresponding to a spontaneous change, the entropy of the universe must increase—that is, ΔS_{univ} must be positive. Thus it can be seen that **for a spontaneous change to take place at constant temperature and pressure, the entropy of the universe must increase.**

19.11 Free Energy Changes and Nonstandard States

Many chemical reactions occur when the reactants and products are not in their standard states (see Fig. 19.11, for example). We can determine the free energy change, ΔG, of such a reaction from the free energy change, $\Delta G°$, of the same reaction when both the reactants and the products are at unit activities (pure solids or liquids, $P = 1$ atm, concentrations $= 1$ M) by using the equation

$$\Delta G = \Delta G° + RT \ln Q \qquad (1)$$

In this equation T is the temperature on the Kelvin scale, R is a constant (8.314 J K^{-1}), and Q is the reaction quotient of the chemical reaction. For the chemical reaction

$$m\text{A} + n\text{B} + \cdots \longrightarrow x\text{C} + y\text{D} + \cdots$$

Figure 19.11

The free energy change for the reaction of methane with oxygen in this flame [CH$_4$(g) + 2O$_2$(g) $\longrightarrow$ CO$_2$(g) + 2H$_2$O(g)] is not equal to $\Delta G°_{298}$ for the reaction. Neither is it equal to $\Delta G°$. The reactants (CH$_4$ and O$_2$) and the products (CO$_2$ and H$_2$O) are far from unit activities (1 atm), and the temperature is not equal to 25°C.

the reaction quotient is

$$Q = \frac{[C]^x[D]^{y \cdots}}{[A]^m[B]^{n \cdots}}$$

Thus the reaction quotient Q has the same form as the equilibrium constant K for the reaction. However, Q has no fixed value; its magnitude is determined by the concentrations of reactants and products at whatever stage in the reaction we choose to evaluate Q. When A and B are first mixed, no products are present, and Q is equal to zero. The value of Q increases as the reaction proceeds. Only when the reaction has reached equilibrium is Q equal to K. As with the equilibrium constant (Section 15.2), strictly speaking, the activities of the reactants and products should be used to evaluate Q. However, we will continue to use pressure (in atmospheres) for gases, concentrations (in moles per liter) for dissolved species, and unity for solvents and for pure solids and liquids as good approximations of the activities of these species.

Example 19.12

The reaction of calcium oxide with sulfur trioxide (Example 19.11) rarely occurs under standard state conditions. Calculate ΔG for this reaction at 25°C when the pressure of SO_3 is 0.15 atm.

To determine ΔG under these nonstandard state conditions at 25°C (298 K), we use Equation (1)

$$\Delta G = \Delta G^{\circ}_{298} + RT \ln Q$$

For the reaction $CaO(s) + SO_3(g) \longrightarrow CaSO_4(s)$,

$$Q = \frac{[CaSO_4]}{[CaO]P_{SO_3}}$$

CaO and $CaSO_4$ are solids, so their concentrations (activities) are 1. The activity of the gas SO_3 is taken as its pressure in atmospheres, 0.15.

$$Q = \frac{1}{(1) \times (0.15)} = 6.67$$

In Example 19.11, ΔG°_{298} was shown to be -345.0 kJ. Thus

$$\Delta G = \Delta G^{\circ}_{298} + RT \ln Q$$

$$= -345.0 \text{ kJ} + RT \ln Q$$

Note that R has units of J K^{-1}, which have to be converted to kJ K^{-1}.

$$\Delta G = -345.0 \text{ kJ} + (8.314 \text{ J K}^{-1})\left(\frac{1 \text{ kJ}}{10^3 \text{ J}}\right)(298.15 \text{ K})(\ln 6.67)$$

$$= -345.0 \text{ kJ} + 4.7 \text{ kJ}$$

$$= -340.3 \text{ kJ}$$

The change of conditions caused a change in ΔG from -345.0 kJ to -340.3 kJ, but the reaction is still spontaneous under these conditions.

Example 19.13

The partial pressure of carbon dioxide in the atmosphere is 0.0033 atm. Calculate ΔG for the conversion of limestone ($CaCO_3$) to quicklime (CaO) in air at 1000°C.

$$CaCO_3(s) \longrightarrow CaO(s) + CO_2(g)$$

To determine ΔG we must consider a process that converts the initial state (1 mol of solid $CaCO_3$) to the final state (1 mol of solid CaO and 1 mol of gaseous CO_2 with a pressure of 0.0033 atm) under nonstandard conditions. First we need to calculate $\Delta G°$ for a CO_2 pressure of 1 atm at 1000°C, assuming that $\Delta H°$ and $\Delta S°$ for the reaction are equal to $\Delta H°_{298}$ and $\Delta S°_{298}$, respectively.

We then calculate ΔG when the pressure of CO_2 is 0.0033 atm. $\Delta H°_{298}$ and $\Delta S°_{298}$ can be calculated from the values in Appendix I.

$$\Delta H°_{298} = (1 \text{ mol } CaO(s) \times -635.5 \text{ kJ}) + (1 \text{ mol } CO_2(g) \times -393.51 \text{ kJ})$$
$$- (1 \text{ mol } CaCO_3(s) \times -1206.9 \text{ kJ}) = 177.9 \text{ kJ}$$

$$\Delta S°_{298} = (1 \text{ mol } CaO(s) \times 40 \text{ J}) + (1 \text{ mol } CO_2(g) \times 213.6 \text{ J})$$
$$- (1 \text{ mol } CaCO_3(s) \times 92.9 \text{ J}) = 161 \text{ J K}^{-1}$$

Next, assuming $\Delta H° = \Delta H°_{298}$ and $\Delta S° = \Delta S°_{298}$, we find that

$$\Delta G° = \Delta H° - T\Delta S° = 177.9 \text{ kJ} - 1273 \text{ K} \times 0.161 \text{ kJ K}^{-1} = -27 \text{ kJ}$$

(This value of $\Delta G°$ indicates that the decomposition of limestone is spontaneous at 1000°C.)

Now we can calculate ΔG.

$$\Delta G = \Delta G° + RT \ln Q$$

$$Q = \frac{P_{CO_2}[CaO]}{[CaCO_3]} = \frac{0.0033 \times 1}{1} = 0.0033$$

$$\Delta G = -27 \text{ kJ} + (8.314 \text{ J K}^{-1})\left(\frac{1 \text{ kJ}}{1000 \text{ J}}\right)(1273 \text{ K})(\ln 0.0033)$$

$$= -27 \text{ kJ} + (-60.5 \text{ kJ}) = -87 \text{ kJ}$$

Changing the pressure of $CO_2(g)$ reduces the free energy change from -27 kJ (at a pressure of 1 atm) to -87 kJ (at a pressure of 0.0033 atm) and makes the reaction even more spontaneous at 1000°C.

⑲.12 The Relationship Between Free Energy Changes and Equilibrium Constants

When ΔG for any reaction (A + B $\longrightarrow$ C + D, for example) is negative, the reaction occurs spontaneously as written, and the quantities of products increase. When ΔG is positive, the reverse reaction occurs spontaneously; that is, the species on the right react to give increased quantities of the species on the left. What is the situation at equilibrium, which, by definition, is the state wherein the quantities of reactants and products do not change? At equilibrium, ΔG can be neither positive nor negative; it can only be zero. At equilibrium, we therefore have

$$\Delta G = 0 = \Delta G^\circ + RT \ln Q$$

In this equation the value determined for ΔG° is for unit activities of the reactants and products at temperature T (see Example 19.14). Because the reaction is at equilibrium, the value of the reaction quotient must be equal to that of the equilibrium constant for the reaction (Q is equal to K), so we have

$$\Delta G = 0 = \Delta G^\circ + RT \ln K$$

$$\Delta G^\circ = -RT \ln K \qquad (1)$$

This derivation shows us that the value of the standard state free energy change, ΔG°, for a reaction can be used to determine the equilibrium constant for that reaction and that values of ΔG° can be determined experimentally from equilibrium constants (Fig. 19.12).

Figure 19.12

The value of the equilibrium constant ($K_p = 0.282$ atm) for the phase change $Br_2(l) \longrightarrow Br_2(g)$ at 25°C can be used to determine ΔG°_{298} (3.14 kJ) for the change.

Calculate the standard state free energy change for the ionization of acetic acid at 0°C.

$$CH_3CO_2H(aq) + H_2O(l) \longrightarrow H_3O^+(aq) + CH_3CO_2^-(aq)$$

The equilibrium constant for the reaction has been found to be 1.657×10^{-5}.

At equilibrium, $\Delta G^\circ = -RT \ln K$, where

$$K = \frac{[H_3O^+][CH_3CO_2^-]}{[CH_3CO_2H]} = 1.657 \times 10^{-5}$$

Example 19.14

Thus

$$\Delta G^\circ = -(8.314 \text{ J K}^{-1})(273.15 \text{ K})[\ln (1.657 \times 10^{-5})]$$

$$= -(8.314 \text{ J K}^{-1})(273.15 \text{ K})(-11.0079) = 2.500 \times 10^4 \text{ J}$$

$$= 25.00 \text{ kJ}$$

Therefore the free energy change for the *complete* transformation at 0°C of 1 L of 1 M acetic acid in water into 1 mol of hydrogen ion and 1 mol of acetate ion, both at 1 M

Example 19.14 continued

concentrations in water, would be 25.00 kJ. $\Delta G°$ is positive, so the reaction is not spontaneous. However, the reverse reaction,

$$H_3O^+(aq) + CH_3CO_2^-(aq) \longrightarrow CH_3CO_2H(aq) + H_2O(l)$$

is spontaneous ($\Delta G° = -25.00$ kJ).

Example 19.15

Using data in Appendix I, calculate the value of K at 298.15 K for the reaction

$$H_2(g) + \tfrac{1}{2}O_2(g) \longrightarrow H_2O(g)$$

We can evaluate the equilibrium constant for this reaction by using the equation

$$\Delta G°_{298} = -RT \ln K$$

Because this reaction involves formation of 1 mol of $H_2O(g)$ from the elements, $\Delta G°_{298}$ for the reaction is equal to the standard molar free energy of formation of water vapor, -228.59 kJ (Appendix I), or $-228,590$ J. Therefore

$$-228,590 \text{ J} = -(8.314 \text{ J K}^{-1})(298.15 \text{ K})(\ln K)$$

$$\ln K = \frac{-228,590 \text{ J}}{-(8.314 \text{ J K}^{-1})(298.15 \text{ K})} = 92.22$$

$$K = 1.1 \times 10^{40}$$

Note that when reactants are gases, the equilibrium constant calculated from Equation (1) involves the pressures of the gases in atmospheres. Thus

$$K = \frac{P_{H_2O(g)}}{P_{H_2(g)} \times P_{O_2(g)}^{1/2}} = 1.1 \times 10^{40}$$

Now we see one reason why calculation of the value of $\Delta G°$ is useful. It enables us to predict the value of the equilibrium constant for a reaction and thus to determine whether a reaction will give significant amounts of products.

If we combine the equations $\Delta G° = -RT \ln K$ and $\Delta G° = \Delta H° - T\Delta S°$, we have

$$\Delta G° = \Delta H° - T\Delta S° = -RT \ln K \tag{2}$$

As the temperature varies, $\Delta H°$ and $\Delta S°$ change only slightly, so if we assume that they are indeed independent of temperature, we can obtain a simple equation relating the equilibrium constant and temperature.

Consider an equilibrium reaction at two different temperatures, T_1 and T_2, with equilibrium constants K_{T_1} and K_{T_2}.

$$\Delta H° - T_1\Delta S° = -RT_1 \ln K_{T_1} \tag{3}$$

$$\Delta H° - T_2\Delta S° = -RT_2 \ln K_{T_2} \tag{4}$$

Equations (3) and (4) can be rearranged by dividing Equation (3) by T_1 and Equation (4) by T_2. This gives

$$\frac{\Delta H°}{T_1} - \Delta S° = -R \ln K_{T_1} \tag{5}$$

$$\frac{\Delta H°}{T_2} - \Delta S° = -R \ln K_{T_2} \tag{6}$$

Subtracting Equation (6) from Equation (5) gives

$$\frac{\Delta H^\circ}{T_1} - \frac{\Delta H^\circ}{T_2} - \Delta S^\circ - (-\Delta S^\circ) = -R \ln K_{T_1} - (-R \ln K_{T_2})$$

or

$$\Delta H^\circ\left(\frac{1}{T_1} - \frac{1}{T_2}\right) = R \ln \frac{K_{T_2}}{K_{T_1}}$$

Alternatively, multiplying the left side by $T_1 T_2 / T_1 T_2$ and dividing both sides by R, we get

$$\frac{\Delta H^\circ (T_2 - T_1)}{RT_1 T_2} = \ln \frac{K_{T_2}}{K_{T_1}} \qquad (7)$$

Equations (1) and (7) prove to be quite useful. If we know ΔG°_{298}, we can determine the equilibrium constant, K, at 298 K by using Equation (1). Then, if we know ΔH°_{298}, we can obtain K for any other temperature by means of Equation (7) (within the limitation that both ΔH° and ΔS° are independent of T). We can calculate the value of ΔG° at a temperature other than 298 K if ΔG°_{298} and ΔH°_{298} are known, because the value of ΔS°_{298} can be determined by using the equation

$$\Delta G^\circ_{298} = \Delta H^\circ_{298} - T\Delta S^\circ_{298} \qquad (T = 298 \text{ K})$$

Then, because both ΔH° and ΔS° are essentially independent of temperature, we can calculate ΔG° at other temperatures.

(a) For the reaction

$$CuS(s) + H_2(g) \longrightarrow Cu(s) + H_2S(g)$$

calculate ΔG°_{298} and ΔH°_{298}.

Example 19.16

$$\Delta G^\circ_{298} = \Delta G^\circ_{f_{Cu(s)}} + \Delta G^\circ_{f_{H_2S(g)}} - \Delta G^\circ_{f_{CuS(s)}} - \Delta G^\circ_{f_{H_2(g)}}$$

$$= 1 \text{ mol Cu}(s) \times (0 \text{ kJ mol}^{-1}) + 1 \text{ mol } H_2S(g) \times (-33.6 \text{ kJ mol}^{-1})$$

$$- 1 \text{ mol CuS}(s) \times (-53.6 \text{ kJ mol}^{-1}) - 1 \text{ mol } H_2(g) \times (0 \text{ kJ mol}^{-1})$$

$$= 20.0 \text{ kJ} \qquad \text{(reaction is not spontaneous)}$$

$$\Delta H^\circ_{298} = \Delta H^\circ_{f_{Cu(s)}} + \Delta H^\circ_{f_{H_2S(g)}} - \Delta H^\circ_{f_{CuS(s)}} - \Delta H^\circ_{f_{H_2(g)}}$$

$$= 1 \text{ mol Cu}(s) \times (0 \text{ kJ mol}^{-1}) + 1 \text{ mol } H_2S(g) \times (-20.6 \text{ kJ mol}^{-1})$$

$$- 1 \text{ mol CuS}(s) \times (-53.1 \text{ kJ mol}^{-1}) - 1 \text{ mol } H_2(g) \times (0 \text{ kJ mol}^{-1})$$

$$= 32.5 \text{ kJ} \qquad \text{(reaction is endothermic)}$$

(b) Calculate the value for the equilibrium constant, K, at 298.15 K and 1 atm.

$$K = \frac{P_{H_2S}}{P_{H_2}} \qquad \text{(where } P \text{ is the partial pressure of a gas in atm)}$$

$$\Delta G^\circ_{298} = -RT \ln K \qquad (R = 8.314 \text{ J K}^{-1})$$

**Example
19.16
continued**

Then

$$\ln K = \frac{\Delta G°}{-RT}$$

$$= \frac{20.0 \times 10^3 \text{ J}}{-(8.314 \text{ J K}^{-1})(298.15 \text{ K})}$$

$$= -8.0684$$

$$K = 3.13 \times 10^{-4} \qquad \text{(at 298.15 K)}$$

Note that at 298.15 K the equilibrium constant has a value less than 1, indicating that the elements in the reaction are present in larger quantities as reactants than as products and that the equilibrium therefore lies far to the left.

(c) Estimate the value for K at 798 K and 1 atm.

$$\frac{\Delta H°(T_2 - T_1)}{RT_1 T_2} = \ln \frac{K_{T_2}}{K_{T_1}}$$

Then

$$\frac{32,500 \text{ J} (798 \text{ K} - 298 \text{ K})}{(8.314 \text{ J K}^{-1})(798 \text{ K})(298 \text{ K})} = \ln \frac{K_{798}}{K_{298}}$$

$$8.2191 = \ln \frac{K_{798}}{K_{298}}$$

$$\ln K_{798} - \ln K_{298} = 8.2191$$

$$\ln K_{298} = -8.0684 \qquad \text{[calculated in part (b)]}$$

Therefore

$$\ln K_{798} = 8.2191 + (-8.0684) = 0.1507$$

$$K = 1.16 \qquad \text{(at 798 K)}$$

Note that the equilibrium constant at 798 K is greater than 1, indicating that the elements are present in greater quantities as products than as reactants and that the equilibrium has been displaced to the right.

(d) Calculate $\Delta S°_{298}$.

Although we could calculate $\Delta S°_{298}$ from absolute standard molar entropy values (Section 19.7), let us use a different method because we already have values for $\Delta G°_{298}$ and $\Delta H°_{298}$.

$$\Delta G°_{298} = \Delta H°_{298} - T\Delta S°_{298}$$

$$\Delta S°_{298} = \frac{\Delta H°_{298} - \Delta G°_{298}}{T} = \frac{32,500 \text{ J} - 20,000 \text{ J}}{298.15 \text{ K}}$$

$$= 41.9 \text{ J K}^{-1}$$

Note that this value for $\Delta S°_{298}$ is positive and favors a spontaneous reaction, whereas the positive value of $\Delta H°_{298}$ is unfavorable for reaction. This is, therefore, a case where $\Delta S°_{298}$ is sufficiently large that $\Delta H°_{298}$ is not a valid indicator of spontaneity, and $\Delta G°_{298}$ must be considered. In particular, whether the reaction is spontaneous is expected to depend on the temperature.

We found in part (a) that $\Delta G°_{298} = +20.0$ kJ, which indicates that at 25°C (298 K) the reaction is not spontaneous. Let us now calculate $\Delta G°$ at the higher temperature, assuming that $\Delta H°_{298}$ [from part (a)] and $\Delta S°_{298}$ [from part (d)] do not change significantly as the temperature increases.

(e) Estimate $\Delta G°$ at 798 K and 1 atm.

$$\Delta G° = \Delta H° - T\Delta S°$$

$$= 32{,}500 \text{ J} - (798 \text{ K})(41.9 \text{ J K}^{-1})$$

$$= -936 \text{ J} = -0.936 \text{ kJ}$$

At the higher temperature $\Delta G°$ is negative, showing that at 798 K the reaction *is* spontaneous. $\Delta H°$, being relatively independent of temperature, still has a value of about 32.5 kJ at 798 K and hence does not indicate the change to spontaneity.

(f) Estimate the temperature at which $\Delta G°$ is equal to zero, assuming that $\Delta H°$ and $\Delta S°$ do not change significantly as the temperature increases.

$$\Delta G° = \Delta H° - T\Delta S°$$

$$0 = 32{,}500 \text{ J} - T(41.9 \text{ J K}^{-1})$$

$$T = \frac{32{,}500 \text{ J}}{41.9 \text{ J K}^{-1}} = 776 \text{ K}$$

Hence $\Delta G° = 0$ at 776 K. At temperatures below 776 K the values of $\Delta G°$ are positive; at temperatures above 776 K they are negative. Therefore, above 776 K the reaction is spontaneous; below 776 K the reaction as written is not spontaneous—indeed, it is spontaneous in the opposite direction.

(a) Determine the temperature at which liquid water and gaseous water are in equilibrium with each other at 1 atm.

Example 19.17

Because the two states are in equilibrium, the free energy change, $\Delta G°$, in going from the liquid to the gas is zero. Assuming again that $\Delta H°$ and $\Delta S°$ are independent of temperature, for the reaction $H_2O(l) \longrightarrow H_2O(g)$,

$$\Delta H°_{298} = \Delta H°_{f_{H_2O(g)}} - \Delta H°_{f_{H_2O(l)}} = 1 \text{ mol } H_2O(g) \times (-241.8 \text{ kJ mol}^{-1})$$

$$- 1 \text{ mol } H_2O(l) \times (-285.8 \text{ kJ mol}^{-1})$$

$$= 44.0 \text{ kJ} = 44{,}000 \text{ J}$$

$$\Delta S°_{298} = S°_{H_2O(g)} - S°_{H_2O(l)}$$

$$= 1 \text{ mol } H_2O(g) \times (188.71 \text{ J mol}^{-1} \text{ K}^{-1})$$

$$- 1 \text{ mol } H_2O(l) \times (69.91 \text{ J mol}^{-1} \text{ K}^{-1})$$

$$= 118.80 \text{ J K}^{-1}$$

$$\Delta G° = \Delta H° - T\Delta S° = 0 \qquad (\Delta G° = 0 \text{ at equilibrium})$$

We assume $\Delta H°$ and $\Delta S°$ to be independent of temperature, so $\Delta H° = \Delta H°_{298}$ and $\Delta S° = \Delta S°_{298}$. Thus

$$T = \frac{\Delta H°}{\Delta S°} = \frac{44{,}000 \text{ J}}{118.80 \text{ J K}^{-1}}$$

$$= 370 \text{ K} = 97°C$$

The correct answer, of course, is 373 K (100°C), the boiling point of water at 1 atm, but the calculation of the value 370 K was based on the assumptions that $\Delta H°$

**Example
19.17
continued**

and $\Delta S°$ are independent of temperature. This is a good place to reemphasize that these assumptions are only approximately correct. They are sufficiently close to be highly useful, but for really exact calculations, values of $\Delta H°$ and $\Delta S°$ at the temperature in question must be used.

(b) Recalculate the temperature at which liquid water and gaseous water are in equilibrium with each other at 1 atm, this time using the known values of $\Delta H°$ and $\Delta S°$ at the temperature 97°C.

$$\Delta H° \text{ at } 97°C = 40,720 \text{ J}; \qquad \Delta S° \text{ at } 97°C = 109.1 \text{ J K}^{-1}$$

Note that the values of $\Delta H°_{298}$ (44,000 J) and $\Delta S°_{298}$ (118.80 J K^{-1}) are close enough to the values at 97°C for an approximate calculation but are not sufficiently close for an exact calculation.

Again using

$$\Delta G° = \Delta H° - T\Delta S° = 0 \qquad (\Delta G° = 0 \text{ at equilibrium})$$

we find that

$$T = \frac{\Delta H°_{370}}{\Delta S°_{370}} = \frac{40,720 \text{ J}}{109.1 \text{ J K}^{-1}} = 373.2 \text{ K}$$

or
$$373.2 - 273.2 = 100.0°C$$

In this part of the example, we obtained the experimental value of 100°C. If the calculation is repeated with the values of $\Delta H°$ and $\Delta S°$ at 100°C (40,656 J and 108.95 J K^{-1}), a value of $T = 100.0°C$ is again obtained, indicating that the values for $\Delta H°$ and $\Delta S°$ at 97°C are close enough to give the correct temperature of 100.0°C (to four significant figures).

At temperatures below 373 K the value of $T\Delta S°$ for the vaporization of liquid water becomes smaller, and hence a smaller term is subtracted from $\Delta H°$ to give $\Delta G°$ ($\Delta G° = \Delta H° - T\Delta S°$). Thus $\Delta G°$ is positive (it equals zero at the equilibrium state at 373 K), indicating that *at temperatures below 373 K (100°C) at 1 atmosphere of pressure, the spontaneous change is from gaseous H_2O to liquid H_2O.* At temperatures higher than 373 K, $T\Delta S°$ becomes larger, and hence a larger term is subtracted from $\Delta H°$. Thus $\Delta G°$ is negative, indicating that *at temperatures above 373 K (100°C) at 1 atmosphere of pressure, the spontaneous change is from liquid H_2O to gaseous H_2O.*

Here the heat effect ($\Delta H°$) and the entropy effect ($\Delta S°$) work at cross purposes; $\Delta S°$ is positive (increasing disorder, indicating favorable conditions for the change) and $\Delta H°$ is positive (endothermic, indicating unfavorable conditions for the change). Neither $\Delta H°$ nor $\Delta S°$ alone is sufficient to predict spontaneity. $\Delta G°$ (which combines $\Delta H°$, $\Delta S°$, and T) is the quantity on which we must base such predictions. As shown above, $\Delta G°$ is positive at temperatures below 373 K (100°C) and negative at temperatures above 373 K.

🔟.13 The Third Law of Thermodynamics

In the preceding sections we have considered the changes in state functions that accompany chemical or physical changes; we have not tried to obtain values for the functions in any particular state. In fact, it is not possible to measure values for E, H, and G.

(a)

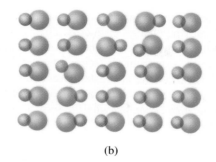
(b)

Figure 19.13

(a) A representation of a perfect crystal of hydrogen chloride at 0 K. The HCl molecules are polar, the smaller hydrogen atom bearing a partial positive charge and the larger chlorine atom bearing a partial negative charge. The entropy of this perfect crystal is zero at 0 K. (b) As the temperature rises above 0 K, the vibration of molecules produces some disorder and the entropy increases.

However, it is possible to measure the **absolute entropy** of a pure substance at any given temperature. The reason for this is found in the **third law of thermodynamics: The entropy of any pure, perfect crystalline element or compound at absolute zero (0 K) is equal to zero.** At absolute zero all molecular motion is at a minimum, and at that temperature a pure crystalline substance has no disorder; its entropy is zero (Fig. 19.13). All molecular motion is also at a minimum in an impure substance at absolute zero, but the impurity can be distributed in different ways, giving rise to disorder (and a nonzero value for entropy).

If we take a pure crystalline substance at absolute zero (with an entropy of zero) and measure the entropy change as its temperature is increased to any temperature T, then we have measured the absolute entropy of the substance at the temperature T. Hence we can find *absolute entropies* of pure substances; in contrast, for free energy and enthalpy, we can find only differences between two values, not the absolute values. Absolute entropies enable us to compare the relative amounts of disorder present in different pure substances, and they can be used to determine entropy changes (Section 19.7). Caution must be exercised when using absolute entropies, however, because the absolute entropy of a pure elemental substance at standard state conditions is *not* equal to zero. Table 19.2 and Appendix I contain absolute standard molar entropies, S°_{298}, of some common substances at standard state conditions.

For Review

Summary

Chemical thermodynamics is the study of the energy transformations and transfers that accompany chemical and physical changes. From such a study we can determine whether a change will occur spontaneously and how far it will proceed—the equilibrium position of the change. The spontaneity of a chemical change is determined by the changes in potential energy and in disorder that accompany the change.

The **first law of thermodynamics** states that in any change that occurs in nature, the total energy of the universe remains constant. Thus by measuring the energy lost or gained by the system we can determine the energy change within it. Energy can be lost from a system as the system does **work, w,** on the surroundings ($w < 0$) or as the surroundings do work on the system ($w > 0$). The amount of work due to expansion is given by the expression $-P(V_2 - V_1)$ when the expansion is carried out at constant pressure. Energy can also be transferred as **heat, q.** In an **endothermic process** heat is transferred into the system from the surroundings ($q > 0$). In an **exothermic process** heat is transferred from the system to the surroundings ($q < 0$).

Although the amounts of heat and work accompanying a change may vary depending on how the change is carried out, the change in internal energy of the system is independent of how the change is accomplished. A property, such as internal energy, that does not depend on how the system gets from one state to another is called a **state function.** When a chemical change is carried out at constant pressure such that the only work done is expansion work, q is a state function and is called the **enthalpy change, ΔH,** of the reaction. The enthalpy change accompanying the formation of 1 mole of a substance from the elements in their most stable states, all at 298.15 K and 1 atm (a **standard state**), is called the **standard molar enthalpy of formation of the substance, ΔH_f°.** Using **Hess's law,** we can describe the enthalpy change of any reaction as the sum of the standard molar enthalpies of all the products minus those of all the reactants.

A **spontaneous change**—a change in a system that will proceed without any outside influence—is favored when the change is exothermic or when the change leads to an increase in the randomness, or disorder, of the system. The randomness of a system can be determined quantitatively and is called the **entropy, S,** of the system. S is a state function, and values of S_{298}° for many substances in a standard state have been measured and tabulated. The entropy change, ΔS°, for many reactions can be calculated as the sum of the **absolute standard molar entropies** of all products minus the sum of those of all reactants. A positive value of ΔS° ($\Delta S^\circ > 0$) indicates that the disorder of the system has increased, whereas a negative value of ΔS° ($\Delta S^\circ < 0$) indicates that the disorder of the system has decreased. The **second law of thermodynamics** states that any spontaneous change that occurs in the universe must be accompanied by an increase in the entropy of the universe.

The **free energy change, ΔG,** of a reaction is the difference between the enthalpy change of the reaction and the product of the temperature and entropy change of the reaction.

$$\Delta G = \Delta H - T\Delta S$$

For a reaction at constant temperature and pressure, a negative value of ΔG ($\Delta G < 0$) indicates that the reaction is spontaneous. Values of ΔG_{298}° can be calculated from **standard molar free energies of formation, ΔG_f°,** or from the values of ΔH_{298}° and ΔS_{298}° for the reaction.

The free energy change of a reaction that involves reactants or products at concentrations other than 1 M or pressures other than 1 atm, ΔG, can be determined using the equation

$$\Delta G = \Delta G^\circ + RT \ln Q$$

where R is equal to 8.314 J K^{-1} and Q is the reaction quotient. When a reaction has reached equilibrium, Q is equal to K, the equilibrium constant for the reaction, and ΔG is equal to zero. Thus, at equilibrium,

$$\Delta G^\circ = -RT \ln K$$

The **third law of thermodynamics** states that the entropy of a pure crystalline substance at 0 K is equal to zero. Thus a measurement of the entropy change of such a substance as it is heated from 0 K to a higher temperature gives the absolute entropy of the substance at the higher temperature. The entropy change for a chemical reaction can be determined by subtracting the sum of the absolute molar entropies of all the reactants from the sum of those of all the products.

$$\Delta S^\circ = \Sigma\, S_{products}^\circ - \Sigma\, S_{reactants}^\circ$$

Key Terms and Concepts

absolute entropy (19.13)
chemical thermodynamics (19.1)
endothermic process (19.5)
enthalpy change (19.5)
entropy (19.7)
entropy change (19.7)
equilibrium constant (19.12)
exothermic process (19.5)
expansion work (19.2)

first law of thermodynamics (19.3)
free energy change (19.8, 19.9)
heat (19.2)
Hess's law (19.5)
internal energy (19.2)
reaction quotient (19.11)
second law of thermodynamics
(19.10)

spontaneous change (19.6)
standard molar entropy (19.7)
state function (19.4)
surroundings (19.1)
system (19.1)
third law of thermodynamics (19.13)
work (19.2)

Exercises

Answers for selected even-numbered exercises marked by red numbers appear at the end of the book. The worked-out solutions to all even-numbered exercises appear in the *Solutions Guide*.

Heat, Work, and Internal Energy

1. State the first law of thermodynamics in words and by using an equation.
2. Calculate the missing value of ΔE, q, or w for a system, given the following data:
   (a) $q = 570$ J; $w = 300$ J
   (b) $\Delta E = -7500$ J; $w = -4500$ J
   (c) $\Delta E = -250$ J; $q = 300$ J
   (d) The system absorbs 2.000 kJ of heat and does 1425 J of work on the surroundings.
3. Calculate the missing value of ΔE, q, or w for a system given the following data:
   (a) $q = 570$ J; $w = -300$ J
   (b) $\Delta E = -7500$ J; $w = 4500$ J
   (c) $\Delta E = 250$ J; $q = 300$ J
   (d) The system absorbs 1.000 kJ of heat and does 650 J of work on the surroundings.
4. In which of the following changes at constant pressure is work done by the surroundings on the system? By the system on the surroundings? Is no work done in any of these changes? What is the value of w in each case: $w > 0$, $w < 0$, or $w = 0$ or almost 0?

Initial State	Final State
(a) $H_2O(g)$	$H_2O(l)$
(b) $H_2O(s)$	$H_2O(g)$
(c) $2Na(s) + Cl_2(g)$	$2NaCl(s)$
(d) $H_2(g) + Cl_2(g)$	$2HCl(g)$
(e) $Na_2SO_4 \cdot 10H_2O(s)$	$Na_2SO_4(s) + 10H_2O(g)$
(f) $NO_2(g) + CO(g)$	$NO(g) + CO_2(g)$

5. In which of the following changes at constant pressure is work done by the surroundings on the system? By the system on the surroundings? Is essentially no work done? What is the value of w in each case: $w > 0$, $w < 0$, or $w = 0$ or almost 0?

Initial State	Final State
(a) $H_2O(s)$	$H_2O(l)$
(b) $H_2O(g)$	$H_2O(s)$
(c) $2Na(s) + 2H_2O(l)$	$2NaOH(s) + H_2(g)$
(d) $3H_2(g) + N_2(g)$	$2NH_3(g)$
(e) $CaCO_3(s)$	$CaO(s) + CO_2(g)$
(f) $N_2(g) + O_2(g)$	$2NO(g)$

6. Calculate the work involved in compressing a system consisting of exactly 1 mol of H_2O as it changes from a gas at 373 K (volume = 30.6 L) to a liquid at 373 K (volume = 18.9 mL) under a constant pressure of 1 atm. Does this work increase or decrease the internal energy of the system?
7. In expanding against a constant pressure of 0.50 atm from 10.0 L to 16.0 L, a gas absorbs 125 J of heat. What is the change in internal energy of the gas?
8. What work is done when 1.00 mol of solid $CaCO_3$ (volume = 34.2 mL) decomposes at 25°C and a pressure of exactly 1.00 atm to give solid CaO (volume = 16.9 mL) and $CO_2(g)$? (Assume the gaseous CO_2 exhibits ideal behavior.)
9. Assume that the only change in volume is due to the production of hydrogen and calculate w, the work done, when 2.00 mol of Zn dissolves in hydrochloric acid, giving H_2 at 35°C and 1.00 atm.

$$Zn(s) + 2HCl(aq) \longrightarrow ZnCl_2(aq) + H_2(g)$$

10. Assume that the gases exhibit ideal behavior and calculate w, the work done, when 17.0 g of $CH_4(g)$ is burned at 775°C and 2.00 atm according to the following reaction:

$$CH_4(g) + 2O_2(g) \longrightarrow CO_2(g) + 2H_2O(g)$$

Enthalpy Changes; Hess's Law

11. What is the difference between ΔH and ΔH_{298}° for a reaction?
12. The enthalpy, H, of a system has been referred to as the *heat content* of the system. Why might this follow from the relationship between ΔH and q?
13. (a) Using the data in Appendix I, calculate the standard

enthalpy change, ΔH_{298}°, for each of the following reactions.

(1) $2Al(s) + 3F_2(g) \longrightarrow 2AlF_3(s)$
(2) $CaO(s) + H_2O(l) \longrightarrow Ca(OH)_2(s)$
(3) $Fe_2O_3(s) + 3CO(g) \longrightarrow 2Fe(s) + 3CO_2(g)$
(4) $CaSO_4 \cdot 2H_2O(s) \longrightarrow CaSO_4(s) + 2H_2O(g)$

(b) Which of these reactions are exothermic?

14. (a) Using the data in Appendix I, calculate the standard enthalpy change, ΔH_{298}°, for each of the following reactions.

(1) $2LiOH(s) + CO_2(g) \longrightarrow Li_2CO_3(s) + H_2O(g)$
(2) $CH_4(g) + N_2(g) \longrightarrow HCN(g) + NH_3(g)$
(3) $CS_2(g) + 3Cl_2(g) \longrightarrow CCl_4(g) + S_2Cl_2(g)$
(4) $N_2(g) + O_2(g) \longrightarrow 2NO(g)$

(b) Which of these reactions are exothermic?

15. The decomposition of hydrogen peroxide, H_2O_2, has been used to provide thrust in the control jets of various space vehicles. How much heat is produced by the decomposition of exactly 1 mol of H_2O_2 under standard conditions?

$$H_2O_2(l) \longrightarrow H_2O(g) + \tfrac{1}{2}O_2(g)$$

16. In 1774 Joseph Priestley prepared oxygen by heating red mercury(II) oxide with the light from the sun focused through a lens. How much heat is required to decompose 1 mol of $HgO(s)$ to $Hg(l)$ and $O_2(g)$ under standard state conditions?

17. How many kilojoules of heat are liberated when 49.70 g of manganese are burned to form $Mn_3O_4(s)$ at standard state conditions? ΔH_f° of Mn_3O_4 is equal to -1388 kJ mol^{-1}.

18. The enthalpy of formation of $OsO_4(s)$, $\Delta H_{f_{OsO_4(s)}}^{\circ}$, is -391 kJ mol^{-1} at 298 K, and the enthalpy of sublimation is 56.4 kJ mol^{-1}. What is ΔH_{298}° for the process $Os(s) + 2O_2(g) \longrightarrow OsO_4(g)$?

19. The oxidation of the sugar glucose, $C_6H_{12}O_6$, is described by the following equation:

$$C_6H_{12}O_6(s) + 6O_2(g) \longrightarrow 6CO_2(g) + 6H_2O(l)$$
$$\Delta H^{\circ} = -2816 \text{ kJ}$$

Metabolism of glucose gives the same products, although the glucose reacts with oxygen in a series of steps in the body. (a) How much heat, in kilojoules, is produced by the metabolism of 1.0 g of glucose? (b) How many nutritional Calories are produced by the metabolism of 1.0 g of glucose? (1 cal = 4.184 J; 1 nutritional Cal = 1000 cal)

20. The white pigment TiO_2 is prepared by the hydrolysis of titanium tetrachloride, $TiCl_4$, in the gas phase.

$$TiCl_4(g) + 2H_2O(g) \longrightarrow TiO_2(s) + 4HCl(g)$$

How much heat is evolved in the production of exactly 1 mol of $TiO_2(s)$ under standard state conditions of 25°C and 1 atm?

21. For the conversion of graphite to diamond

$$C(s, \text{ graphite}) \longrightarrow C(s, \text{ diamond}), \Delta H^{\circ} = 1.90 \text{ kJ mol}^{-1}$$

do the enthalpies of combustion of graphite and carbon dif-

fer? That is, are the enthalpy changes for the following reactions the same or different?

$$C(s, \text{ graphite}) + O_2(g) \longrightarrow CO_2(g)$$
$$C(s, \text{ diamond}) + O_2(g) \longrightarrow CO_2(g)$$

Entropy Changes and Absolute Entropy

22. What is the relationship between entropy and disorder?
23. What is the absolute standard molar entropy of a pure substance?
24. Arrange the following systems, each of which consists of 1 mol of substance, in order of increasing entropy: $H_2O(g)$ at 100°C, $N_2(s)$ at -215°C, $C_2H_5OH(g)$ at 100°C, $H_2O(l)$ at 25°C, $H_2O(s)$ at -215°C, $C_2H_5OH(s)$ at 0 K.
25. State the second law of thermodynamics in terms of entropy changes for the universe. State the second law of thermodynamics in terms of free energy changes.
26. State the third law of thermodynamics.
27. Does the entropy of each of the following systems increase, decrease, or not change in going from the initial to the final state? If the entropy does change, give the sign of ΔS and explain your answers.

Initial State	Final State
(a) $NaCl(s)$ at 298 K	$NaCl(s)$ at 0 K
(b) $H_2O(s)$ at 273 K and 1 atm	$H_2O(l)$ at 273 K and 1 atm
(c) 1 mol Si and 1 mol O_2	1 mol SiO_2
(d) 1 mol $CaCO_3$	1 mol CaO and 1 mol CO_2

28. (a) Using the data in Appendix I, calculate ΔS_{298}°, the standard entropy change, for each of the following reactions.

(1) $2Al(s) + 3F_2(g) \longrightarrow 2AlF_3(s)$
(2) $CaO(s) + H_2O(l) \longrightarrow Ca(OH)_2(s)$
(3) $Fe_2O_3(s) + 3CO(g) \longrightarrow 2Fe(s) + 3CO_2(g)$
(4) $CaSO_4 \cdot 2H_2O(s) \longrightarrow CaSO_4(s) + 2H_2O(g)$

(b) For which of these reactions are the entropy changes favorable for the reaction to proceed spontaneously?

29. (a) Using the data in Appendix I, calculate the standard entropy change for each reaction in part (a) of Exercise 14.

(b) For which of the reactions in Exercise 14 are the entropy changes favorable for the reaction to proceed spontaneously?

30. What is the entropy change for condensation of 59.7 g of chloroform, $CHCl_3(g) \longrightarrow CHCl_3(l)$, under standard state conditions?

31. What is ΔS_{298}° for the following reaction?

$$2NH_3(g) \longrightarrow N_2(g) + 3H_2(g)$$

32. What is ΔS_{298}° for the formation of ozone, $O_3(g)$, from oxygen, O_2?

Free Energy Changes

33. Why is the emphasis in thermodynamics on the free energy change as a system changes rather than on the values of the free energies of the initial and final states?

34. What is the difference between ΔH and ΔG for a system undergoing a change at constant temperature and pressure?

35. What is a spontaneous reaction?

36. Explain why the free energy change of a reaction varies with temperature.

37. Under what conditions is ΔG equal to $\Delta G°$ for the reaction $2H_2O_2(l) \longrightarrow 2H_2O(l) + O_2(g)$?

38. (a) Using the data in Appendix I, calculate the standard free energy changes for the reactions given in part (a) of Exercise 14.
    (b) Which of those reactions are spontaneous? Why?

39. (a) Using the data in Appendix I, calculate the standard free energy changes for the following reactions.
    (1) $2Al(s) + 3F_2(g) \longrightarrow 2AlF_3(s)$
    (2) $CaO(s) + H_2O(l) \longrightarrow Ca(OH)_2(s)$
    (3) $Fe_2O_3(s) + 3CO(g) \longrightarrow 2Fe(s) + 3CO_2(g)$
    (4) $CaSO_4 \cdot 2H_2O(s) \longrightarrow CaSO_4(s) + 2H_2O(g)$
    (b) Which of those reactions are spontaneous?

40. As ammonium nitrate dissolves spontaneously in water at constant pressure, heat is absorbed and the solution gets cold. What is the sign of ΔH for this process? Is it possible to identify the sign of ΔS for this process? Why?

41. As sulfuric acid dissolves spontaneously in water at constant pressure, heat is produced and the solution gets hot. What is the sign of ΔH for this process? Is it possible to identify the sign of ΔS for this process? Why?

42. The reaction $3O_2(g) \longrightarrow 2O_3(g)$ is endothermic and proceeds with a decrease in the entropy of the system. Is this likely to be a spontaneous reaction? Explain your reasoning.

43. Using the data given in Table 19.2, show that H, S, and G are state functions by calculating $\Delta H°_{298}$, $\Delta S°_{298}$, and $\Delta G°_{298}$ for the formation of $HCl(g)$ from $H_2(g)$ and $Cl_2(g)$ by two pathways, both at standard state conditions.

Path 1: $H_2(g) + Cl_2(g) \longrightarrow 2HCl(g)$

Path 2: $H_2(g) \longrightarrow 2H(g)$

$Cl_2(g) \longrightarrow 2Cl(g)$

$2H(g) + 2Cl(g) \longrightarrow 2HCl(g)$

44. The standard molar enthalpies of formation of $NO(g)$, $NO_2(g)$, and $N_2O_3(g)$ are 90.25 kJ mol^{-1}, 33.2 kJ mol^{-1}, and 83.72 kJ mol^{-1}, respectively. Their standard molar entropies are 210.65 J mol^{-1} K^{-1}, 239.9 J mol^{-1} K^{-1}, and 312.2 J mol^{-1} K^{-1}, respectively.
    (a) Use the foregoing data to calculate the free energy change for the following reaction at 25.0°C.

$N_2O_3(g) \longrightarrow NO(g) + NO_2(g)$

    (b) Repeat the above calculation for 0.00°C and 100.0°C, assuming that the enthalpy and entropy changes do not vary with a change in temperature. Is the reaction spontaneous at 0.00°C? At 100.0°C?

45. For a certain process at 300 K, $\Delta G = -77.0$ kJ and $\Delta H = -56.9$ kJ. Find the entropy change for this process at this temperature.

46. Hydrogen chloride, $HCl(g)$, and ammonia, $NH_3(g)$, escape from bottles of their solutions and react to form the white glaze often seen on glass in chemistry laboratories.

$HCl(g) + NH_3(g) \longrightarrow NH_4Cl(s)$

    (a) Calculate the free energy change, $\Delta G°_{298}$, for this reaction.
    (b) At what temperature will $\Delta G°$ for the reaction be equal to zero?

Free Energy Changes and Equilibrium Constants

47. Explain why equilibrium constants change with temperature.

48. No matter what their bond energy, all compounds decompose if heated to a sufficiently high temperature. Why will the reaction $AB(g) \longrightarrow A(g) + B(g)$, where A and B represent atoms, eventually become spontaneous with $K > 1$ as the temperature of the system is increased?

49. Calculate the equilibrium constant for the decomposition of solid NH_4Cl to $HCl(g)$ and $NH_3(g)$. $\Delta G°_{298}$ for this reaction is 89.7 kJ (see Exercise 46).

50. Consider the reaction

$I_2(g) + Cl_2(g) \longrightarrow 2ICl(g)$

    (a) For this reaction $\Delta H°_{298} = -26.9$ kJ and $\Delta S°_{298} = 11.3$ J K^{-1}. Calculate $\Delta G°_{298}$ for the reaction.
    (b) Calculate the equilibrium constant for this reaction at 25.0°C.

51. If the standard entropy of vaporization of H_2O is equal to 109 J mol^{-1} K^{-1} and the standard enthalpy of vaporization is 40.62 kJ mol^{-1}, calculate the normal boiling temperature of water in °C.

52. Will the conversion of graphite to diamond become spontaneous at any temperature?

53. Consider the decomposition of $CaCO_3(s)$ into $CaO(s)$ and $CO_2(g)$ at 1 atm.
    (a) Estimate the minimum temperature at which you would conduct the reaction.
    (b) Calculate the equilibrium vapor pressure of $CO_2(g)$ above $CaCO_3(s)$ in a closed container at 298 K.

54. If the standard enthalpy of vaporization of CH_2Cl_2 is 29.0 kJ mol^{-1} at 25.0°C and the standard entropy of vaporization is 92.5 J mol^{-1} K^{-1}, calculate the normal boiling temperature of CH_2Cl_2.

55. At 298 K the equilibrium constant, K_p, for the reaction $N_2O_4(g) \rightleftharpoons 2NO_2(g)$ is 0.142. What is $\Delta G°_{298}$ for the reaction?

56. Calculate ΔG°_{298} for the reaction of 1 mol of $H_3O^+(aq)$ with 1 mol of $OH^-(aq)$, using the equilibrium constant for the self-ionization of water at 298 K.

$$2H_2O(l) \rightleftharpoons H_3O^+(aq) + OH^-(aq) \quad K_w = 1.00 \times 10^{-14}$$

57. Consider the decomposition of dinitrogen trioxide described in Exercise 44.

$$N_2O_3(g) \longrightarrow NO(g) + NO_2(g)$$

At what temperature does this reaction become spontaneous?

58. The pollutant gas hydrogen sulfide is removed from natural gas by the reaction

$$2H_2S(g) + SO_2(g) \longrightarrow 3S(s) + 2H_2O(g)$$

What is the equilibrium constant for this reaction? Is the reaction endothermic or exothermic?

59. (a) Calculate ΔG° for each of the following reactions from the equilibrium constant at the temperature given.

    (1) $N_2(g) + O_2(g) \longrightarrow 2NO(g)$
        $T = 2000°C$, $K_p = 4.1 \times 10^{-4}$
    (2) $H_2(g) + I_2(g) \longrightarrow 2HI(g)$
        $T = 400°C$, $K_p = 50.0$
    (3) $CO_2(g) + H_2(g) \longrightarrow CO(g) + H_2O(g)$
        $T = 980°C$, $K_p = 1.67$
    (4) $CaCO_3(s) \longrightarrow CaO(s) + CO_2(g)$
        $T = 900°C$, $K_p = 1.04$

  (b) Assume that ΔH° does not vary with temperature and calculate ΔS° for these reactions.

Additional Exercises

60. (a) Water gas, a mixture of H_2 and CO, is an important industrial fuel produced by the reaction of steam with red-hot coke (essentially pure carbon).

$$C(s) + H_2O(g) \longrightarrow CO(g) + H_2(g)$$

Assuming that coke has the same enthalpy of formation as graphite, calculate ΔH°_{298} for this reaction.

  (b) Methanol, a liquid fuel that may possibly replace gasoline, can be prepared from water gas and additional hydrogen at high temperatures and pressures in the presence of a suitable catalyst.

$$2H_2(g) + CO(g) \longrightarrow CH_3OH(g)$$

Under the conditions of the reaction, methanol forms as a gas. Calculate ΔH°_{298} for this reaction and for the condensation of gaseous methanol to liquid methanol.

  (c) Calculate the heat of combustion of 1 mol of liquid methanol to $H_2O(g)$ and $CO_2(g)$.

61. Consider the vaporization of bromine liquid to bromine gas, $Br_2(l) \longrightarrow Br_2(g)$, at 25°C.

  (a) Calculate the change in enthalpy and the change in entropy at standard state conditions.

  (b) Discuss the relative disorder in bromine liquid compared to that in bromine gas. State what you can about the spontaneity of the vaporization.

  (c) Estimate the value of ΔG°_{298} for the vaporization of bromine from the values of ΔH°_{298} and ΔS°_{298} you determined in part (a).

  (d) State what you can about the spontaneity of the process from the value you obtained for ΔG°_{298} in part (c).

  (e) Estimate the temperature at which liquid Br_2 and gaseous Br_2 with a pressure of 1 atm are in equilibrium (assume that ΔH° and ΔS° are independent of temperature).

  (f) State in which direction the process would be spontaneous at 298 K and at 398 K, using the temperature value you obtained in part (e).

  (g) Compare ΔH°, ΔS°, and ΔG° in terms of their usefulness in predicting the spontaneity of the vaporization of bromine.

62. Carbon dioxide decomposes into CO and O_2 at elevated temperatures. What is the equilibrium partial pressure of oxygen in a sample at 1000°C for which the initial pressure of CO_2 was 1.15 atm?

63. Carbon tetrachloride, an important industrial solvent, is prepared by the chlorination of methane at 850 K.

$$CH_4(g) + 4Cl_2(g) \longrightarrow CCl_4(g) + 4HCl(g)$$

  (a) What is the equilibrium constant for the reaction at 850 K?

  (b) Will the reaction vessel need to be heated or cooled to keep the temperature of the reaction constant?

64. Acetic acid, CH_3CO_2H, can form a dimer, $(CH_3CO_2H)_2$, in the gas phase.

$$2CH_3CO_2H(g) \longrightarrow (CH_3CO_2H)_2(g)$$

The dimer is held together by two hydrogen bonds with a total strength of 66.5 kJ per mole of dimer.

At 25°C the equilibrium constant for the dimerization is 1.3×10^3 (pressure in atm). What is ΔS° for the reaction?

65. At 1000 K the equilibrium constant for the decomposition of bromine molecules, $Br_2(g) \rightleftharpoons 2Br(g)$, is 2.8×10^4 (pressure in atm). What is ΔG° for the reaction? Assume that the bond energy of Br_2 does not change between 298 K and 1000 K, and calculate the approximate value of ΔS° for the reaction at 1000 K.

66. Nitric acid, HNO_3, can be prepared by the following sequence of reactions:

$$4NH_3(g) + 5O_2(g) \longrightarrow 4NO(g) + 6H_2O(g)$$
$$2NO(g) + O_2(g) \longrightarrow 2NO_2(g)$$
$$3NO_2(g) + H_2O(l) \longrightarrow 2HNO_3(l) + NO(g)$$

How much heat is evolved when 1 mol of $NH_3(g)$ is converted to $HNO_3(l)$? Assume that all reactants and products are in their standard states at 25°C and 1 atm.

Electrochemistry and Oxidation–Reduction

Corrosion of iron is an electrochemical process.

The most apparent applications of electrochemistry in our daily lives are the batteries we use to power our portable radios, cassette players, toys, and power tools and to start our cars. These batteries are galvanic cells, which produce electrical energy by chemical reactions. In other applications, which may not be so obvious, electrical energy is used to bring about chemical changes. The aluminum in our soft drink cans, the chlorine used to purify swimming pools, and many other commercial products are manufactured in electrolytic cells, in which electrical energy is used to bring about a chemical change. When you recharge a battery, you are using electrical energy to accomplish the chemical change that returns the battery to the state where it can again deliver electricity.

Electrochemistry deals with chemical changes produced by an electric current and with the production of electricity by chemical reactions. Energy changes in chemical reactions (Chemical Thermodynamics, Chapter 19) are studied electrochemically when possible, because the quantity of electrical energy produced or consumed during electrochemical changes can be measured very accurately. The free energy change of a reaction (ΔG) and its equilibrium constant can be determined by electrochemical measurements. Furthermore, an understanding of the reactions that take place at the electrodes of electrochemical cells clarifies the process of oxidation and reduction and chemical reactivity.

Many electrochemical processes are important in science and industry. Electrical energy is used in the manufacture of hydrogen, oxygen, ozone, hydrogen peroxide, chlorine, sodium hydroxide, and oxygen compounds of the halogens (Chapter 22). Electrical energy is also used in production of many other chemicals, electrorefining of metals (Chapter 13), electroplating of metals and alloys, and production of metal articles by electrodeposition.

Galvanic Cells and Cell Potentials

20.1 Galvanic Cells

When a strip of magnesium is added to a solution of hydrochloric acid, the magnesium and hydrochloric acid react spontaneously, and hydrogen gas and a solution of magnesium chloride are produced (Fig. 20.1).

$$Mg(s) + 2H_3O^+(aq) + 2Cl^-(aq) \longrightarrow H_2(g) + Mg^{2+}(aq) + 2Cl^-(aq) + 2H_2O(l)$$

Hydrochloric acid solution   Magnesium chloride solution

This oxidation–reduction reaction (Section 2.11, Part 4) has two "halves." In one half, the magnesium metal loses electrons (is oxidized), giving the Mg^{2+} ion and two electrons. The net ionic equation for the oxidation half of the reaction is

$$Mg(s) \longrightarrow Mg^{2+}(aq) + 2e^-$$

In the other half, two hydronium ions combine with the electrons (are reduced), giving hydrogen gas and water. The net ionic equation for the reduction half of the reaction is

$$2H_3O^+(aq) + 2e^- \longrightarrow H_2(g) + 2H_2O(l)$$

These reactions, each of which constitutes either the oxidation step or the reduction step of the overall reaction, are called **half-reactions.** The net ionic equation for the reaction is the sum of the two half-reactions, with the coefficients of the reactants and products in each half-reaction adjusted such that both half-reactions involve the same number of electrons. This is necessary because the electrons produced by the oxidation half-reaction are consumed in the reduction half-reaction. Because both of the foregoing half-reactions involve two electrons, the coefficients do not need adjusting.

Figure 20.1

Magnesium metal reacts spontaneously with hydrochloric acid, producing hydrogen and magnesium chloride.

Oxidation half-reaction:	$Mg(s) \longrightarrow Mg^{2+}(aq) + 2e^-$
Reduction half-reaction:	$2H_3O^+(aq) + 2e^- \longrightarrow H_2(g) + 2H_2O(l)$
Sum:	$Mg(s) + 2H_3O^+(aq) \longrightarrow H_2(g) + Mg^{2+}(aq) + 2H_2O(l)$

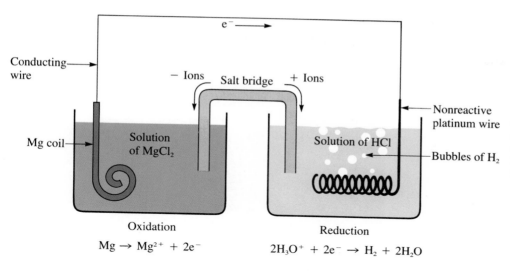

Figure 20.2

The oxidation of magnesium to magnesium ion occurs in the left dish in this apparatus; the reduction of hydronium ion to hydrogen and water occurs in the right dish. The wire conducts electrons from the left dish to the nonreactive electrode in the right dish, and the salt bridge allows ions to migrate from one side to the other.

The oxidation half of the reaction and the reduction half of the reaction can be run in two separate containers without the magnesium actually coming in contact with the hydrochloric acid. Figure 20.2 shows a diagram of an apparatus for doing this. The oxidation of the magnesium metal occurs on a magnesium strip immersed in a solution of magnesium chloride in the dish on the left side of the diagram. The net change in this dish is the oxidation half-reaction,

$$Mg(s) \longrightarrow Mg^{2+}(aq) + 2e^-$$

The electrons produced by this oxidation are conducted by the wire to a nonreactive electrode (a platinum wire) immersed in a solution of hydrochloric acid in the dish on the right side of the diagram. The electrode does not react with the acid but simply conducts the electrons to the hydrochloric acid solution. The electrons combine with hydronium ions present in the acid solution and produce hydrogen gas and water. The net change in this dish is the reduction half-reaction,

$$2H_3O^+(aq) + 2e^- \longrightarrow H_2(g) + 2H_2O(l)$$

The net ionic equation for the reaction occurring in the apparatus is the sum of the two halves of the reaction:

$$Mg(s) + 2H_3O^+(aq) \longrightarrow H_2(g) + Mg^{2+}(aq) + 2H_2O(l)$$

Figure 20.3 is a photograph of one such apparatus in action. Bubbles of hydrogen can be seen in the right-hand dish.

In addition to the wire, the two parts of the apparatus are connected by a **salt bridge,** a tube containing a concentrated solution of an electrolyte (Section 12.8) such as potassium chloride. The salt bridge allows the ions of the electrolyte to migrate, but the solutions in the two dishes cannot mix. As magnesium ions are produced in the left dish, enough chloride ions from the salt bridge migrate into that dish for the solution to remain electrically neutral. That is, the total number of negative charges on the negative ions in the left dish remains equal to the total number of positive charges on the positive ions in the dish. As hydronium ions are destroyed in the right dish, potassium ions from the salt bridge replace them and maintain equal numbers of positive and negative charges in the right dish.

The reaction shown in Fig. 20.3 is the same as that shown in Fig. 20.1; electrons are transferred from magnesium to hydronium ions, and hydrogen gas and magnesium ions

Figure 20.3

An apparatus for the reaction of magnesium with hydrochloric acid. Magnesium ions form in the left beaker; hydrogen gas forms in the right beaker.

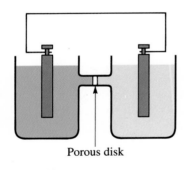

Porous disk

Figure 20.4

Two half-cells connected by a porous disk.

Figure 20.5

No reaction occurs when two half-cells are connected by a wire but no salt bridge or porous disk.

are produced in both cases. However, in the apparatus shown in Fig. 20.3, the reaction takes place without any contact of the reactants. The electrons are transferred from the magnesium to the hydronium ions through a wire. This flow of electrons constitutes an electric current and is important from a practical point of view, because the energy made available can be used to do electrical work. For example, the electric current can be used to do work in an electric motor, to light an electric lamp, or to produce some other form of energy. The apparatus shown in Figs. 20.2 and 20.3 is a simple battery.

A battery is a type of **galvanic cell** (sometimes called a **voltaic cell**)—a device in which chemical energy is converted to electrical energy. A galvanic cell consists of two **half-cells** arranged so that half of the reaction occurs in one half-cell and the other half of the reaction occurs in the other half-cell. The sum of the two half-reactions is called the **cell reaction.** The half of the reaction that produces electrons is the **oxidation half-reaction;** the half-cell where oxidation occurs is called the **anode** of the cell. The half of the reaction that accepts electrons is the **reduction half-reaction;** the half-cell where reduction occurs is called the **cathode** of the cell. (It will help you recall these definitions if you remember that *anode* and *oxidation* both start with a vowel and that *cathode* and *reduction* both start with a consonant.)

For a galvanic cell to deliver electrical energy, the two half-cells must be connected by an external wire through which the electrons pass and by a salt bridge or porous disk (Fig. 20.4) that allow ions to flow with no mixing of the solutions in the two half-cells. If the two solutions were allowed to mix, a direct reaction would take place and the half-cells would be shorted out.

The importance of the salt bridge or porous plug becomes apparent when we consider what happens without one. When our two half-cells are connected by a wire but no salt bridge or porous plug (Fig. 20.5), a few electrons pass from the magnesium strip through the wire into the acid solution, but then the current stops. The right half-cell becomes negatively charged because of the transfer of electrons into it, and the left half-cell becomes positively charged because electrons leave it. The attraction of electrons by the positive charge in the left half-cell and the repulsion of electrons by the negative charge in the right half-cell prevent any further transfer of electrons. Adding a salt bridge allows the two half-cells to lose their excess charge and permits more electrons to flow.

Example 20.1

Identify the anode, the cathode, and the net ionic half-reactions in a Daniell cell, a battery first constructed in 1836 by the English chemist John Fredrick Daniell. A Daniell cell (Fig. 20.6) consists of a piece of copper metal (Cu) with crystals of copper(II) sulfate in a saturated solution of copper(II) sulfate below a piece of zinc metal (Zn) suspended near the top of the cell in a dilute solution of zinc sulfate. (The crystals of copper sulfate simply keep the copper sulfate solution saturated.) The zinc sulfate solution floats on the denser solution of copper(II) sulfate. Because of the difference in density between the two solutions, they mix very slowly and the boundary between them acts like a porous disk. The cell reaction is

$$Zn(s) + Cu^{2+}(aq) + SO_4^{2-}(aq) \longrightarrow Cu(s) + Zn^{2+}(aq) + SO_4^{2-}(aq)$$

The anode of the cell is the half-cell where oxidation (loss of electrons) occurs. Zinc metal is oxidized, so the anode consists of the zinc metal and the solution of zinc sulfate. The net ionic oxidation half-reaction at the anode is

$$Zn(s) \longrightarrow Zn^{2+}(aq) + 2e^-$$

The cathode is the half-cell where reduction (gain of electrons) occurs. Copper(II) ion is reduced to copper metal during the reaction, so the cathode consists of the copper metal and the copper sulfate solution. The net ionic reduction reaction at the cathode is

$$Cu^{2+}(aq) + 2e^- \longrightarrow Cu(s)$$

When the two metals are connected by a wire, the zinc metal is oxidized and electrons from the zinc flow through the wire to the copper metal, where the copper(II) ions in the solution are reduced to metallic copper.

Figure 20.6

The Daniell cell. Sheet copper (Cu) is surrounded by saturated copper(II) sulfate solution and crystals of copper sulfate; zinc plate (Zn) is surrounded by zinc sulfate solution.

20.2 Cell Potentials

A galvanic cell may be thought of as possessing a "driving force" or "electrical pressure" that pushes electrons through the external circuit (the wire in Fig. 20.3). This driving force is called the **cell potential (E_{cell})** or the **electromotive force** of the cell. The cell potential is measured in units of volts. One **volt (V)** is the potential required to impart 1 joule (J) of energy to a charge of 1 coulomb (C); 1 V = 1 J/1 C.

When 1 **coulomb** of charge (the charge on 1/96,485 mole of electrons) moves from a higher potential to a lower potential, 1 joule of energy is available when the potential difference is 1 volt.

$$1 \text{ J} = 1 \text{ V} \times 1 \text{ C}$$

More energy is available when the potential difference or the amount of charge moved is larger. Less energy is available when the potential difference or the amount of charge moved is smaller.

The potential of a cell can be measured with a voltmeter, a device that measures voltage when the cell passes a current through a known resistance. However, when current flows, the heating that results from resistance in the wires and in the cell wastes some of the potentially useful energy of the cell. A voltmeter therefore measures a potential that is less than the maximum potential of the cell. To determine the maximum potential of the cell, we must measure its potential under conditions of zero current so that no energy is wasted. This can be accomplished with a potentiometer, a device that produces a voltage opposite to that of the cell potential. The voltage supplied by the potentiometer is adjusted so that no current flows from the cell. At this point, the voltage supplied by the potentiometer is equal to the maximum potential of the cell.

Let us consider a version of the Daniell cell described in Example 20.1. This galvanic cell is constructed from two half-cells, one a strip of metallic zinc immersed in a 1.0 M solution of zinc sulfate and the other a strip of metallic copper immersed in a 1.0 M solution of copper sulfate (Fig. 20.7) and operated at 25°C. The half-reaction at the anode is

$$Zn(s) \longrightarrow Zn^{2+}(aq) + 2e^-$$

The half-reaction at the cathode is

$$Cu^{2+}(aq) + 2e^- \longrightarrow Cu(s)$$

The sulfate ion is unchanged during the reaction. Hence the net ionic equation for the cell reaction is

$$Zn(s) + Cu^{2+}(aq) \longrightarrow Cu(s) + Zn^{2+}(aq)$$

A potentiometer placed in the circuit of the cell at the beginning of the reaction, before the concentrations change, indicates that the cell potential is 1.10 volts. The cell was constructed such that at the beginning of the reaction, the reactants and products are at standard state conditions (pure solids or 1 M concentrations, 1 atm pressure, 25°C;

Figure 20.7

A cell constructed from a Zn^{2+}/Zn electrode (left) and a Cu^{2+}/Cu electrode (right) produces a potential of 1.10 V when the temperature is 25°C and the concentrations are 1 M.

Figure 20.8
When a zinc strip is immersed in a solution of copper sulfate, copper metal and a colorless solution of zinc sulfate form. On the left is a zinc strip and a solution of copper sulfate. The beaker on the right shows the system after the reaction is almost complete; the blue color that is due to the presence of Cu^{2+} in the solution has almost disappeared, and copper metal can be seen.

see Section 4.4), and the cell potential is called the **standard cell potential, $E°_{cell}$.** The superscript indicates that all reactants and products are at standard state conditions. For the net ionic reaction,

$$Zn(s) + Cu^{2+}(aq) \longrightarrow Cu(s) + Zn^{2+}(aq)$$

the standard cell potential, $E°_{cell}$, is 1.10 V.

The potential of any cell depends on the nature of the chemical reaction taking place in the cell, the concentration of reactants and products, and the temperature of the cell, which we will take as 25°C unless otherwise noted. Information related to cell potentials is usually tabulated at standard state conditions.

A galvanic cell has a positive voltage when the cell reaction is spontaneous. If a reaction occurs in a galvanic cell with a positive potential (Fig. 20.7), the same reaction will be spontaneous when the reactants are mixed (Fig. 20.8).

Just as each cell has a cell potential, each half-reaction has a half-reaction potential. We can determine the cell potential from the sum of the potentials of the two half-cells that compose it, just as we can determine an overall cell reaction from the sum of two half-reactions. The cell potential E_{cell} is the sum of the half-cell potential E_{ox} of the anode and the half-cell potential E_{red} of the cathode.

$$E_{cell} = E_{ox} + E_{red}$$

For the cell illustrated in Fig. 20.7 operating under standard state conditions, the anode potential is 0.763 volts and the cathode potential is 0.337 volts. Their sum is equal to $E°_{cell}$.

Anode:	$Zn(s) \longrightarrow Zn^{2+}(aq) + 2e^-$	$E°_{ox} = 0.763$ V
Cathode:	$Cu^{2+}(aq) + 2e^- \longrightarrow Cu(s)$	$E°_{red} = 0.337$ V
Sum:	$Zn(s) + Cu^{2+}(aq) \longrightarrow Cu(s) + Zn^{2+}(aq)$	$E°_{cell} = E°_{ox} + E°_{red}$
		$= 1.100$ V

Example 20.2

What is the standard cell potential of a nickel–cadmium cell, the galvanic cell in a rechargeable nickel–cadmium battery? The cell reaction is

$$Cd(s) + NiO_2(s) + 2H_2O(l) \longrightarrow Cd(OH)_2(s) + Ni(OH)_2(s)$$

The standard state half-cell potentials are

Anode: $Cd(s) + 2OH^-(aq) \longrightarrow Cd(OH)_2(s) + 2e^-$ $E^\circ_{ox} = 0.40$ V

Cathode: $NiO_2(s) + 2H_2O(l) + 2e^- \longrightarrow Ni(OH)_2(s) + 2OH^-$ $E^\circ_{red} = 0.49$ V

The cell reaction is the sum of the anode half-reaction and the cathode half-reaction. The cell potential is the sum of the half-cell potentials for these two half-reactions. Note that the hydroxide ion in the anode half-reaction cancels the hydroxide ion in the cathode half-reaction.

Anode: $Cd(s) + 2OH^-(aq) \longrightarrow Cd(OH)_2(s) + 2e^-$ $E^\circ_{ox} = 0.40$ V

Cathode: $NiO_2(s) + 2H_2O(l) + 2e^- \longrightarrow Ni(OH)_2(s) + 2OH^-$ $E^\circ_{red} = 0.49$ V

Sum: $Cd(s) + NiO_2(s) + 2H_2O(l) \longrightarrow Cd(OH)_2(s) + Ni(OH)_2(s)$ $E^\circ_{cell} = E^\circ_{ox} + E^\circ_{red}$

$$= 0.40 \text{ V} + 0.49 \text{ V}$$

$$= 0.89 \text{ V}$$

The standard state cell potential is 0.89 volts.

20.3 Standard Electrode Potentials

The term *electrode* can refer to a conductor that delivers electricity into a cell and that may or may not enter into the cell reaction. The term **electrode** is also used to refer to a complete half-cell, in which a conductor is in contact with a mixture of the oxidized and reduced forms of some chemical species. One such electrode comprises a strip of metal placed in a solution containing ions of the metal—for example, the strip of zinc immersed in the solution of zinc sulfate in Fig. 20.7. The metal strip is both the conductor and the reduced species; the metal ions are the oxidized species. Other electrodes are made up of a nonreactive conductor immersed in a solution that contains molecules or ions of the oxidized and reduced species. One such electrode consists of a platinum wire (an inert conductor) dipped into a solution of bromine (the oxidized species) and bromide ion (the reduced species).

Although the potential of a galvanic cell can be calculated by adding the potentials of the electrodes that make up the cell, there is no satisfactory method for measuring the actual potential of an individual electrode. We can only measure the sum of the potentials of two electrodes. However, if one electrode is *assigned* a standard potential, potentials of other electrodes can be measured by comparison to the assigned value of the standard. The electrode that is used as the reference electrode is the **standard hydrogen electrode, which is assigned a potential of zero volts.** The potentials of all other electrodes are reported relative to the standard hydrogen electrode. (This approach is similar to arbitrarily establishing sea level as zero elevation and reporting all elevations in terms of how much higher or lower than this level they are.)

The standard hydrogen electrode is a **gas electrode.** Gas electrodes are half-cells with a gas as either the oxidized or the reduced species. Such an electrode is set up by bubbling the gas around an inert conductor—a conductor that carries electrons but does not enter into the electrode reaction. A hydrogen electrode (Fig. 20.9) is constructed in such a way that hydrogen gas is bubbled around a platinum foil or wire covered with very finely divided platinum and immersed in a solution of hydrogen ions. The net ionic equation for the electrode is

$$2H_3O^+ + 2e^- \longrightarrow H_2 + 2H_2O$$

The potential of a gas electrode changes with changing pressure of the gas and with changing concentration of the other components, so we must be careful to keep the pressures and concentrations constant when measuring standard potentials. A standard hydrogen electrode is prepared by bubbling hydrogen gas at a temperature of 25°C and a pressure of 1 atm around platinum immersed in a solution containing a 1 M concentration of hydronium ions (standard state conditions).

To measure the potential of an electrode relative to the standard hydrogen electrode, we need a galvanic cell consisting of the electrode being measured and a standard hydrogen electrode. A cell for measuring the potential of a copper electrode is shown in Fig. 20.10. The Cu^{2+}/Cu electrode consists of a copper strip in contact with a 1 M solution of copper ion. The oxidation half-reaction is

$$H_2(g) + 2H_2O(l) \longrightarrow 2H_3O^+(aq) + 2e^-$$

The reduction half-reaction is

$$Cu^{2+}(aq) + 2e^- \longrightarrow Cu(s)$$

The net cell reaction is

$$H_2(g) + 2H_2O(l) + Cu^{2+}(aq) \longrightarrow 2H_3O^+(aq) + Cu(s)$$

The copper strip in the Cu^{2+} solution and the platinum wire of the hydrogen electrode are connected to a potentiometer that shows the cell potential—the potential difference, in volts, between the two electrodes. For this cell the potential is 0.337 volts. Because the cell potential is the sum of the potentials of the copper electrode and the hydrogen

Figure 20.9

Diagram of a simple standard hydrogen electrode. F indicates the platinized platinum foil; P, the port for escape of hydrogen bubbles; B, part of the salt bridge.

Figure 20.10

A galvanic cell with a hydrogen electrode and a Cu^{2+}/Cu electrode.

electrode (which has an assigned potential of zero volts), the cell potential is equal to the potential of the copper electrode. That is,

$$E^\circ_{cell} = E^\circ_{ox} \qquad \text{(for the hydrogen electrode)}$$

$$+ E^\circ_{red} \qquad \text{(for the copper electrode)}$$

$$0.337 \text{ V} = 0 \text{ V} + E^\circ_{red}$$

$$E^\circ_{red} = 0.337 \text{ V} - 0 \text{ V} = 0.337 \text{ V}$$

By international agreement, the values of electrode potentials are given for the reduction process. **Standard reduction potentials, E°_{red},** are potentials measured with respect to the standard hydrogen electrode at 25°C with 1 M concentration (unit activity) of each ion in solution and 1 atmosphere pressure (unit activity) of each gas involved. The potential of the Cu^{2+}/Cu electrode that we discussed is a standard reduction potential. When a potential is measured for an oxidation process (an oxidation potential), it can be converted to a reduction potential by reversing the sign of the voltage. **The reduction potential and the oxidation potential of the same electrode have the same absolute value but are of opposite sign.**

Once a standard electrode potential has been established relative to the standard hydrogen electrode, it can be used to determine other electrode potentials.

Example 20.3

A galvanic cell operating at 25°C with an anode consisting of an iron strip immersed in a 1 M solution of iron(II) perchlorate (a Fe^{2+}/Fe electrode) and a cathode consisting of a copper strip immersed in a 1 M solution of copper(II) perchlorate (a Cu^{2+}/Cu electrode, $E^\circ_{red} = 0.337$ V) has a potential of 0.777 V (Fig. 20.11). The cell reaction is

$$Fe(s) + Cu^{2+}(aq) \longrightarrow Fe^{2+}(aq) + Cu(s)$$

What is the standard reduction potential of the Fe^{2+}/Fe electrode?

Figure 20.11

A galvanic cell with a Fe^{2+}/Fe electrode and a Cu^{2+}/Cu electrode.

The cell temperature is 25°C and all reactants and products are at standard state conditions, so all potentials in this example are standard state potentials. The standard cell potential (0.777 V) is the sum of the standard electrode potential of the anode and the standard electrode potential of the cathode. Oxidation occurs at the anode, so iron metal is oxidized in the anode half-reaction. Copper(II) ion is reduced in the cathode half-reaction.

Anode: $\qquad$ $Fe(s) \longrightarrow Fe^{2+}(aq) + 2e^-$ $\qquad$ $E = E^\circ_{ox}$

Cathode: $\qquad$ $2e^- + Cu^{2+}(aq) \longrightarrow Cu(s)$ $\qquad$ $E = E^\circ_{red} = 0.337 \text{ V}$

Sum: $\qquad$ $Fe(s) + Cu^{2+}(aq) \longrightarrow Fe^{2+}(aq) + Cu(s)$ $\qquad$ $E^\circ_{cell} = E^\circ_{ox} + E^\circ_{red}$

$$E^\circ_{cell} = E^\circ_{ox} + 0.337 \text{ V}$$

We can determine the potential of the iron electrode as follows:

$$E^\circ_{cell} = E^\circ_{ox} + 0.337 \text{ V}$$

$$E^\circ_{ox} = E^\circ_{cell} - 0.337 \text{ V}$$

$$= 0.777 \text{ V} - 0.337 \text{ V} = 0.440 \text{ V}$$

The iron electrode is the anode of the cell and is engaged in an oxidation half-reaction. In order to find the standard reduction potential for the electrode, we must reverse the sign of the oxidation potential.

$$E^\circ_{red} = -E^\circ_{ox}$$

$$= -0.440 \text{ V}$$

The standard reduction potential of the iron electrode is −0.440 V.

$$Fe^{2+}(aq) + 2e^- \longrightarrow Fe(s) \qquad E^\circ_{red} = -0.440 \text{ V}$$

Table 20.1 lists the standard reduction potentials of several electrodes. (A more extensive table is given in Appendix H.) These values can be used to determine the cell potentials for a variety of cells. Remember that the table lists reduction potentials; the potential of an electrode involved in an oxidation process (an anode) is opposite in sign to the reduction potential.

The standard reduction potentials in Table 20.1 refer only to ion concentrations of 1 M in aqueous solution, gases at 1 atm pressure, and a temperature of 25°C. (For simplicity, the phases of the reactants and products are generally not listed in these tables.) When the conditions change, the potentials change, and some members may even change places in the table. The effect of the concentration on potential is illustrated by the reduction potentials for the hydrogen electrode at two different concentrations. Under standard state conditions,

$$2H_3O^+ \text{ (1 M)} + 2e^- \longrightarrow H_2 \text{ (1 atm)} + 2H_2O \qquad E^\circ_{red} = 0.00 \text{ V}$$

When the concentration of hydronium ion is changed to that in neutral water, 1×10^{-7} M, the electrode potential decreases.

$$2H_3O^+ \text{ (1} \times 10^{-7} \text{ M)} + 2e^- \longrightarrow H_2 \text{ (1 atm)} + 2H_2O \qquad E^\circ_{red} = -0.41 \text{ V}$$

The values given in Table 20.1 do not apply to nonaqueous solutions or to molten salts, although similar tables can be constructed for them. The electrode potentials are

Table 20.1　　Standard Reduction Potentials

Half-reaction	$E°$, V
$K^+ + e^- \longrightarrow K$	-2.925
$Ba^{2+} + 2e^- \longrightarrow Ba$	-2.90
$Ca^{2+} + 2e^- \longrightarrow Ca$	-2.87
$Na^+ + e^- \longrightarrow Na$	-2.714
$Mg^{2+} + 2e^- \longrightarrow Mg$	-2.37
$Al^{3+} + 3e^- \longrightarrow Al$	-1.66
$Zn(OH)_2 + 2e^- \longrightarrow Zn + 2OH^-$	-1.245
$Mn^{2+} + 2e^- \longrightarrow Mn$	-1.18
$Fe(OH)_2 + 2e^- \longrightarrow Fe + 2OH^-$	-0.877
$Zn^{2+} + 2e^- \longrightarrow Zn$	-0.763
$Cr^{3+} + 3e^- \longrightarrow Cr$	-0.74
$Fe^{2+} + 2e^- \longrightarrow Fe$	-0.440
$Cd^{2+} + 2e^- \longrightarrow Cd$	-0.403
$PbSO_4 + 2e^- \longrightarrow Pb + SO_4{}^{2-}$	-0.356
$Co^{2+} + 2e^- \longrightarrow Co$	-0.277
$Ni^{2+} + 2e^- \longrightarrow Ni$	-0.250
$Sn^{2+} + 2e^- \longrightarrow Sn$	-0.136
$Pb^{2+} + 2e^- \longrightarrow Pb$	-0.126
$2H_3O^+ + 2e^- \longrightarrow H_2 + 2H_2O$	0.00
$Sn^{4+} + 2e^- \longrightarrow Sn^{2+}$	$+0.15$
$AgCl + e^- \longrightarrow Ag + Cl^-$	$+0.222$
$Hg_2Cl_2 + 2e^- \longrightarrow 2Hg + 2Cl^-$	$+0.27$
$Cu^{2+} + 2e^- \longrightarrow Cu$	$+0.337$
$NiO_2 + 2H_2O + 2e^- \longrightarrow Ni(OH)_2 + 2OH^-$	$+0.49$
$I_2 + 2e^- \longrightarrow 2I^-$	$+0.5355$
$MnO_4{}^- + 2H_2O + 3e^- \longrightarrow MnO_2 + 4OH^-$	$+0.588$
$Fe^{3+} + e^- \longrightarrow Fe^{2+}$	$+0.771$
$Hg_2{}^{2+} + 2e^- \longrightarrow 2Hg$	$+0.789$
$Ag^+ + e^- \longrightarrow Ag$	$+0.7991$
$Br_2(l) + 2e \longrightarrow 2Br^-$	$+1.0652$
$Pt^{2+} + 2e^- \longrightarrow Pt$	$\sim +1.20$
$O_2 + 4H_3O^+ + 4e^- \longrightarrow 6H_2O$	$+1.23$
$Cl_2 + 2e^- \longrightarrow 2Cl^-$	$+1.3595$
$Au^{3+} + 3e^- \longrightarrow Au$	$+1.50$
$MnO_4{}^- + 8H_3O^+ + 5e^- \longrightarrow Mn^{2+} + 12H_2O$	$+1.51$
$PbO_2 + SO_4{}^{2-} + 4H_3O^+ + 2e^- \longrightarrow$ $PbSO_4 + 6H_2O$	$+1.685$
$F_2 + 2e^- \longrightarrow 2F^-$	$+2.87$

different from those in water, and the members sometimes fall in a different order in the series.

The position of a metal in the table of reduction potentials, when the electrodes are arranged from the most negative to the most positive, is the same as in the activity series (Section 13.1). The activity series (or the table of standard reduction potentials) correlates many chemical properties of the elements; three of the more important ones are given in the following list.

1. The metals with large negative reduction potentials at the top of the series are good reducing agents in the free state. They are the metals that are most easily oxidized to their ions by the removal of electrons (the active metals, Chapter 13).

2. The elements with large positive reduction potentials at the bottom of the series are good oxidizing agents when in the oxidized form—that is, when the metals are in the form of ions and the nonmetals are in the elemental state.

3. The reduced form of any element reduces the oxidized form of any element below it. For example, metallic zinc reduces copper(II) ions (Fig. 20.8) according to the equation

$$Zn + Cu^{2+} \longrightarrow Cu + Zn^{2+}$$

Most elemental metals reduce the halogens, and iodide ion (the reduced form of iodine) reduces the elemental halogens. For example, it reduces elemental bromine (Fig. 20.12), forming iodine and bromide ion (the reduced form of bromine).

20.4 Calculation of Cell Potentials

The values in Table 20.1 can be used to determine standard state cell potentials. Two points are important to remember when using these values.

1. $E°$ values are for reduction half-reactions, and the sign of a reduction potential must be reversed when it is used as a potential for an oxidation half-reaction.

2. Changing the stoichiometric coefficients of a half-cell equation does not change the value of $E°$, because electrode potentials are intensive properties (Section 1.4). For example, from Table 20.1,

$$Ag^+(aq) + e^- \longrightarrow Ag(s) \qquad E°_{red} = 0.7991 \text{ V}$$

$E°_{red}$ does not change when we double the quantities involved.

$$2Ag^+(aq) + 2e^- \longrightarrow 2Ag(s) \qquad E°_{red} = 0.7991 \text{ V}$$

Figure 20.12

Iodide ion (in test tube) reduced bromine from the solution of bromine in water (yellow liquid), producing iodine and colorless bromide ion. The iodine has been extracted into an organic layer, giving the characteristic purple color.

Write the cell reaction and determine the standard state potential for the cell diagrammed in Fig. 20.13, page 652.

Example 20.4

The anode half-reaction is

$$Co(s) \longrightarrow Co^{2+}(aq) + 2e^-$$

The cathode half-reaction is

$$Fe^{3+}(aq) + e^- \longrightarrow Fe^{2+}(aq)$$

The platinum wire in the cell is an inert electrode that delivers the electrons from the anode to the solution of iron(III) ions and iron(II) ions.

The cell reaction is the sum of the anode half-reaction and the cathode half-reaction. However, the two foregoing equations cannot simply be added to find the cell reaction. The numbers of electrons in the two equations differ. One cobalt atom produces two electrons; one iron(III) ion reacts with one electron. Hence, twice as many Fe^{3+} ions as Co atoms are required in the cell reaction in order to make the numbers of electrons in the two half-reactions equal. In order to describe the correct ratio of Co and Fe^{3+}, we must double the number of reactants and products in the cathode half-reaction (the half-reaction must be multiplied by 2). Thus we have

Anode half-reaction: $\qquad\qquad Co(s) \longrightarrow Co^{2+}(aq) + 2e^-$

Cathode half-reaction: $\qquad \underline{2Fe^{3+}(aq) + 2e^- \longrightarrow 2Fe^{2+}(aq)}$

Cell reaction: $\qquad\qquad Co(s) + 2Fe^{3+}(aq) \longrightarrow Co^{2+}(aq) + 2Fe^{2+}(aq)$

Example 20.4 continued

Figure 20.13
A galvanic cell with a Co^{2+}/Co anode and a Fe^{3+}/Fe^{2+} cathode.

A simple way to adjust the coefficients of the half-reactions is to multiply them by the smallest whole numbers that give equal numbers of electrons in both. In this example, multiplying the cathode half-reaction by 2 gives two electrons, which is equal to the number of electrons in the anode reaction.

The cell potential is equal to the sum of the potentials of the anode and cathode. The electrode potential of the cathode is equal to the potential given in Table 20.1; $E_{red}^\circ = 0.771$ V. The electrode potential of the anode is opposite in sign to that given in the table: $E_{ox}^\circ = -E_{red}^\circ = -(-0.277$ V). Thus we have

Anode:	$Co(s) \longrightarrow Co^{2+}(aq) + 2e^-$	$E_{ox}^\circ = 0.277$ V
Cathode:	$2Fe^{3+}(aq) + 2e^- \longrightarrow 2Fe^{2+}(aq)$	$E_{red}^\circ = 0.771$ V
Sum:	$Co(s) + 2Fe^{3+}(aq) \longrightarrow Co^{2+}(aq) + 2Fe^{2+}(aq)$	$E_{cell}^\circ = E_{ox}^\circ + E_{red}^\circ$

$$= 0.227 \text{ V} + 0.771 \text{ V}$$

$$= 0.998 \text{ V}$$

Note that doubling the number of reactants and products in the cathode half-reaction does not change the value of the standard reduction potential for the half-reaction.

A line notation is sometimes used to represent the electrodes in a galvanic cell. The cell involving a reaction between zinc and a solution of hydrochloric acid under standard state conditions can be diagrammed as follows:

$$Zn \,|\, Zn^{2+} \text{ (1 M)} \xrightarrow{e^-} \| \quad H_3O^+ \text{ (1 M)} \,|\, H_2 \text{ (1 atm)} \,|\, Pt$$

The diagram indicates zinc metal in contact with a 1 M solution of zinc ions. The anion accompanying the zinc ion is not shown because it is not involved in the reaction, and water is usually not shown. The solution of zinc ion is connected by a salt bridge or porous disk, represented by $\|$, to a 1 M solution of hydronium ions (in the hydrochloric acid) in a hydrogen electrode with a gaseous hydrogen pressure of 1 atmosphere. A single vertical line, $|$, is used to separate two different phases; two different species in the same phase are separated by a semicolon. The anode is always written on the left in such a diagram. The arrow and the symbol for the electron are not standard notation. We use them to show the direction of electron flow in the external circuit.

Determine the standard cell potential, and write equations for the half-reactions and the cell reaction, for the cell described by the following line notation. **Example 20.5**

$$Fe \mid Fe^{2+} (1 \text{ M}) \quad \parallel \quad MnO_4^- (1 \text{ M}); Mn^{2+} (1 \text{ M}); H_3O^+ (1 \text{ M}) \mid Pt$$

The species to the left of the double line are involved in the anode half-reaction,

$$Fe(s) \longrightarrow Fe^{2+}(aq) + 2e^-$$

The species to the right of the double line are involved in the cathode half-reaction,

$$MnO_4^-(aq) + 8H_3O^+(aq) + 5e^- \longrightarrow Mn^{2+}(aq) + 12H_2O(l)$$

The cell reaction is the sum of these half-reactions, but the two foregoing equations cannot simply be added because the numbers of electrons in the two differ. When we multiply the anode half-reaction by 5 and multiply the cathode half-reaction by 2, we have 10 electrons in each. The standard potential for the cathode half-reaction can be found in Table 20.1; $E_{red}^\circ = 1.51$ V. The potential for the anode half-reaction is opposite in sign to its standard reduction potential (Table 20.1): $E_{ox}^\circ = -E_{red}^\circ = -(-0.440)$ V $= 0.440$ V. Now we have

Anode:
$$5Fe(s) \longrightarrow 5Fe^{2+}(aq) + 10e^- \qquad E_{ox}^\circ = 0.440 \text{ V}$$

Cathode:
$$2MnO_4^-(aq) + 16H_3O^+(aq) + 10e^- \longrightarrow 2Mn^{2+}(aq) + 24H_2O(l) \qquad E_{red}^\circ = 1.51 \text{ V}$$

Sum:
$$5Fe(s) + 2MnO_4^-(aq) + 16H_3O^+(aq) \longrightarrow 5Fe^{2+}(aq) + 2Mn^{2+}(aq) + 24H_2O(l)$$

$$E_{cell}^\circ = E_{ox}^\circ + E_{red}^\circ$$
$$= 0.440 \text{ V} + 1.51 \text{ V}$$
$$= 1.95 \text{ V}$$

The standard cell potential is 1.95 V.

A positive cell potential indicates that a cell reaction proceeds spontaneously to the right and that the cell delivers an electric current. A negative potential indicates that the reaction does not proceed spontaneously to the right but rather proceeds spontaneously to the left.

Calculate the potential of a cell made with a standard bromine electrode as the anode and a standard chlorine electrode as the cathode. **Example 20.6**

The half-reactions and standard potentials (Table 20.1) are

Anode:
$$2Br^-(aq) \longrightarrow Br_2(l) + 2e^- \qquad E_{ox}^\circ = -1.0652 \text{ V}$$

Cathode:
$$Cl_2(g) + 2e^- \longrightarrow 2Cl^-(aq) \qquad E_{red}^\circ = +1.3595 \text{ V}$$

Sum:
$$2Br^-(aq) + Cl_2(g) \longrightarrow Br_2(l) + 2Cl^-(aq) \qquad E_{cell}^\circ = +0.2943 \text{ V}$$

The cell potential is 0.2943 V, so the cell reaction proceeds spontaneously to the right, as the equation is written.

20.5 Cell Potential, Electrical Work, and Free Energy

Galvanic cells are sources of electrical energy that can be used to do work. In this section we shall explore the relationship between the potential of a cell and the work that it can deliver. This is the link between electrochemistry and thermodynamics.

The work that can be accomplished by electrons passing through a wire depends on the cell potential (or some other potential if the electrons are supplied by another source, such as a generator) that pushes the electrons through the circuit. As noted in Section 20.2, a potential of 1 volt imparts 1 joule of energy to a charge of 1 coulomb. If the energy is expended as work, we have

$$\text{potential (V)} = \frac{\text{work (J)}}{\text{charge (C)}}$$

or
$$\text{work} = \text{charge} \times \text{potential}$$

One joule of work can be produced or consumed (depending on whether the charge moves with or against the potential) when 1 coulomb of charge passes between two electrodes with a potential difference of 1 volt (or when 1 coulomb of charge passes between any two points with a potential difference of 1 volt).

When a cell produces a current, the current can be used to do work on the surroundings—by running an electric motor, for example. Although this work is not the same as expansion work (Section 19.2), the energy of the cell (the system) is reduced because it does work on the surroundings. The sign of the work is negative ($w < 0$). When a cell produces a current, the cell potential is positive; thus the magnitude of the cell potential and the amount of work w available from the cell have opposite signs and are related by the equations

$$-w = nFE_{\text{cell}} \qquad \text{and} \qquad w = -nFE_{\text{cell}}$$

where the product nF is the charge, in coulombs, passed through the circuit and E_{cell} is the potential produced by the cell. The charge nF is determined by multiplying the number of moles of electrons n that pass through the circuit by the charge on 1 mole of electrons F. The charge on 1 mole of electrons is called a **faraday** (**F**): $1\ F = 96{,}485\ \text{C mol}^{-1}$, or, because $1\ \text{C} = 1\ \text{J V}^{-1}$, $1\ F = 96{,}485\ \text{J V}^{-1}\ \text{mol}^{-1}$.

The maximum amount of work w_{max} available from a process carried out at constant temperature and pressure is equal to the free energy change, ΔG, for the process.

$$w_{\text{max}} = \Delta G$$

This equation gives the upper limit of available work. The actual amount of work a cell can do is less than w_{max}. For electrical work to be done, a current must flow. When a current flows, some energy is wasted because resistance in the circuit gives rise to heat. The heat produced by the system reduces the total amount of work the system can actually do. (Remember that a reduction in energy in a system can result both from evolution of heat and from work; Section 19.2.)

We can write an equation that relates the potential of a cell and the free energy of the cell reaction, because the maximum amount of work available can be related to the cell potential and to the free energy change of the cell reaction.

$$w_{\text{max}} = -nFE_{\text{cell}} = \Delta G \tag{1}$$

For our purposes, the important part of Equation (1) is the relationship between the free energy change and the cell potential.

$$\Delta G = -nFE_{cell}$$

For standard state conditions,

$$\Delta G° = -nFE°_{cell}$$

These equations relate the free energy change for a cell reaction, where the initial state is that of the reactants in the cell (the concentration, pressure, phase, and temperature of the reactants) and the final state is that of the products in the cell (the concentration, pressure, phase, and temperature of the products). The equations indicate that we can find ΔG for a reaction if we know the potential of a cell that has a cell reaction that is the same as the reaction for which the ΔG value applies. The equation also shows that a galvanic cell spontaneously produces current when it has a positive potential. A positive potential corresponds to a negative value of ΔG, which is the criterion for spontaneity of a reaction (Section 19.8).

Calculate the standard free energy change at 25°C for the reaction

$$Cd(s) + Pb^{2+}(aq) \longrightarrow Cd^{2+}(aq) + Pb(s)$$

Example 20.7

The half-reactions and calculation of the potential of the cell follow.

Anode:	$Cd(s) \longrightarrow Cd^{2+}(aq) + 2e^-$		$E°_{ox} = +0.403$ V
Cathode:	$Pb^{2+}(aq) + 2e^- \longrightarrow Pb(s)$		$E°_{red} = -0.126$ V
Sum:	$Cd(s) + Pb^{2+}(aq) \longrightarrow Cd^{2+}(aq) + Pb(s)$		$E°_{cell} = +0.277$ V

The cell potential is 0.277 V. We calculate $\Delta G°$ for the change, taking into account that 2 mol of electrons are transferred when the ratio of reactants and products is that indicated by the cell reaction. We will use the value of F with kilojoules (96.485 kJ V^{-1} mol^{-1}).

$$\Delta G° = -nFE°_{cell}$$

$$= -2 \text{ mol}(96.485 \text{ kJ V}^{-1} \text{ mol}^{-1})(0.277 \text{ V})$$

$$= -53.5 \text{ kJ}$$

The negative value for $\Delta G°$ indicates that the reaction is spontaneous both when it is run in a galvanic cell and when cadmium metal and Pb^{2+} ion are mixed.

Determine the cell potential, write the cell reaction, determine whether the cell reaction is spontaneous, and determine $\Delta G°$ for the cell reaction for the cell indicated by the following line diagram.

Example 20.8

$$Pt \mid Fe^{2+} \text{ (1 M)}; Fe^{3+} \text{ (1 M)} \parallel Sn^{2+} \text{ (1 M)}; Sn^{4+} \text{ (1 M)} \mid Pt$$

The anode of this cell involves the oxidation of Fe^{2+} to Fe^{3+}. The cathode involves the reduction of Sn^{4+} to Sn^{2+}. We can write the half-reactions and standard half-cell potentials (Table 20.1) and determine the cell potential as follows. The anode half-reaction must be multiplied by 2 to make the number of electrons the same in both half-reactions.

Example 20.8 continued

Anode:	$2[Fe^{2+}(aq) \longrightarrow Fe^{3+}(aq) + e^-]$		$E_{ox}^{\circ} = -0.771$ V
Cathode:	$Sn^{4+}(aq) + 2e^- \longrightarrow Sn^{2+}(aq)$		$E_{red}^{\circ} = +0.15$ V
Sum:	$Sn^{4+}(aq) + 2Fe^{2+}(aq) \longrightarrow Sn^{2+}(aq) + 2Fe^{3+}(aq)$		$E_{cell}^{\circ} = -0.62$ V

The cell potential is negative, -0.62 V. This means that the cell reaction is not spontaneous as written and that electrons do not flow as indicated. In this cell, electrons flow from the right electrode to the left electrode. The negative cell potential also means that ΔG° for the reaction is positive and that the reaction shifts to the left in a solution containing 1 M concentrations of Sn^{4+}, Fe^{2+}, Sn^{2+}, and Fe^{3+}, so that the concentrations of Sn^{4+} and Fe^{2+} increase while the concentrations of Sn^{2+} and Fe^{3+} decrease.

ΔG° is calculated as follows (keep in mind that 2 mol of electrons are involved in this reaction).

$$\Delta G^{\circ} = -nFE_{cell}^{\circ}$$

$$= -2 \text{ mol}(96.485 \text{ kJ V}^{-1} \text{ mol}^{-1})(-0.62 \text{ V})$$

$$= +120 \text{ kJ}$$

The value for ΔG° is positive, confirming that the reaction is not spontaneous.

20.6 The Effect of Concentration on Cell Potentials

Up to this point, we have concentrated on cell potentials determined for cells with reactants and products in standard states; however, cells need not operate at standard state conditions. As pointed out in Section 20.3, the reduction potential of a half-reaction changes when the concentrations change, so cell potentials differ when the reactants or products are not at standard state conditions.

We can derive a relationship between the cell potential at nonstandard state conditions, the cell potential at standard state conditions, and the reaction quotient (Section 15.2) for the cell reaction. The free energy change for a reaction can be written (Section 19.12) as

$$\Delta G = \Delta G^{\circ} + RT \ln Q$$

where ΔG° is the free energy change for the reaction under standard state conditions, ΔG is the free energy change under some other set of conditions, and Q is the reaction quotient for the reaction at the second set of conditions. Because $\Delta G = -nFE_{cell}$ and $\Delta G^{\circ} = -nFE_{cell}^{\circ}$, we can write

$$-nFE_{cell} = -nFE_{cell}^{\circ} + RT \ln Q$$

Dividing through by $-nF$ gives

$$E_{cell} = E_{cell}^{\circ} - \frac{RT}{nF} \ln Q$$

where

E°_{cell} = the cell potential under standard state conditions

R = the gas constant (8.314 J K^{-1})

T = the Kelvin temperature

F = the Faraday constant, 96.485 kJ V^{-1} mol^{-1}

n = the number of moles of electrons exchanged in the cell reaction

Q = the reaction quotient

This equation is known as the **Nernst equation.** It was named after W. H. Nernst, a German chemist and physicist who was awarded the Nobel prize in 1920 for his contributions to thermodynamics.

For use with cells at 25°C, the Nernst equation is often written in a special form utilizing common logarithms:

$$E_{\text{cell}} = E^\circ_{\text{cell}} - \frac{0.05916 \text{ V}}{n} \log Q$$

where

E_{cell} = the cell potential for a cell at nonstandard state conditions

E°_{cell} = the *standard state* cell potential

n = the number of electrons in the cell reaction

Q = the reaction quotient for the cell reaction

The constant 0.05916 contains the value of RT/F and the conversion from natural to common logarithms. It has units of volts.

Calculate the potential at 25°C for the cell

$$\text{Cd}\,|\,\text{Cd}^{2+}\,(2.00 \text{ M})\,\|\,\text{Pb}^{2+}\,(0.0010 \text{ M})\,|\,\text{Pb}$$

Example 20.9

The cell reaction and standard state potential of the cell were determined in Example 20.7.

$$\text{Cd}(s) + \text{Pb}^{2+}(aq) \longrightarrow \text{Cd}^{2+}(aq) + \text{Pb}(s) \qquad E^\circ_{\text{cell}} = 0.277 \text{ V}$$

The line notation indicates that the Pb^{2+} ion in the reaction has a concentration of 0.0010 M and that the Cd^{2+} ion has a concentration of 2.00 M. These are not standard state concentrations, so we need to use the Nernst equation to determine how the standard state cell potential changes as the concentrations of the reactants and products in the cell reaction change. We can use the special form of the equation because the cell is at 25°C.

$$E_{\text{cell}} = E^\circ_{\text{cell}} - \frac{0.05916 \text{ V}}{n} \log Q$$

In this equation $n = 2$, because 2 mol of electrons are exchanged in the cell reaction.

Example 20.9 continued

For the reaction,

$$Q = \frac{[Cd^{2+}]}{[Pb^{2+}]} = \frac{2.00}{0.0010}$$

and

$$E_{cell} = E^\circ_{cell} - \frac{0.05916 \text{ V}}{n} \log Q$$

$$= 0.277 \text{ V} - \frac{0.05916 \text{ V}}{2} \log (2.00/0.0010)$$

$$= 0.277 \text{ V} - \frac{0.05916 \text{ V}}{2} (3.301)$$

$$= 0.277 \text{ V} - 0.0976 \text{ V} = 0.179 \text{ V}$$

The cell potential decreases from 0.277 V at standard state concentrations to 0.179 V at the nonstandard concentrations.

The magnitude of a cell potential is a measure of the spontaneity of a reaction. The change from 0.277 V to 0.179 V as Q changes from 1 to 2000, which we determined in Example 20.9 for the reaction

$$Cd(s) + Pb^{2+}(aq) \longrightarrow Cd^{2+}(aq) + Pb(s)$$

indicates that the spontaneity of this reaction decreases when the concentration of the reactant Pb^{2+} decreases and the concentration of the product Cd^{2+} increases. This is similar, but not exactly identical, to the idea expressed by Le Châtelier's principle (Section 15.8). Reducing the amount of reactant relative to the amount of product (as described by the reaction quotient) decreases the driving force of a reaction (as indicated by the cell potential). Increasing the amount of reactant relative to the amount of product (as described by the reaction quotient) increases the driving force of a reaction (as indicated by the cell potential).

20.7 Relationship of the Cell Potential and the Equilibrium Constant

Electrochemical measurements make it possible to gather data that can be used to determine thermodynamic parameters and equilibrium constants for a wide variety of chemical changes. Section 20.5 described the relationship between the free energy change of a cell reaction and its standard state potential.

$$\Delta G^\circ = -nFE^\circ_{cell}$$

In Section 19.12 we saw that the relationship between the standard state free energy change of a reaction and its equilibrium constant is

$$\Delta G^\circ = -RT \ln K$$

Hence, if we know the standard state cell potential for a reaction, we can calculate its standard free energy change and, from that, the equilibrium constant for the reaction.

Using these two equations, we can derive a simple relationship between the potential of a reaction under standard state conditions and its equilibrium constant K. Because both $-nFE^°_{cell}$ and $-RT \ln K$ are equal to $\Delta G°$, we can write

$$-nFE^°_{cell} = \Delta G° = -RT \ln K$$

or

$$-nFE^°_{cell} = -RT \ln K$$

Dividing through by $-nF$ gives

$$E^°_{cell} = \frac{RT}{nF} \ln K \qquad (1)$$

Equation (1) enables us to use the standard potential of a cell reaction to calculate the equilibrium constant for the reaction or to use the equilibrium constant to calculate the standard potential of the cell.

Sometimes it is convenient to use a simpler version of Equation (1) for cells at 25°C (298.15 K). After conversion to the common logarithm, and with substitution of R, T, and F, the expression becomes

$$E^°_{cell} = \frac{0.05916 \text{ V}}{n} \log K \qquad \text{(at 25°C)} \qquad (2)$$

Example 20.10

Calculate the equilibrium constant at 25°C for the cell discussed in Example 20.7.

$$Cd\,|\,Cd^{2+}\,(1 \text{ M})\,\|\,Pb^{2+}\,(1 \text{ M})\,|\,Pb$$

The cell reaction and standard state potential of the cell were determined in Example 20.7.

$$Cd(s) + Pb^{2+}(aq) \longrightarrow Cd^{2+}(aq) + Pb(s) \qquad E^°_{cell} = 0.277 \text{ V}$$

Two electrons are involved in this cell reaction, so $n = 2$.

The equilibrium constant can be determined from Equation (2).

$$E^°_{cell} = \frac{0.05916 \text{ V}}{n} \log K$$

$$\log K = E^°_{cell} \times \frac{n}{0.05916 \text{ V}}$$

$$= 0.277 \text{ V} \times \frac{2}{0.05916 \text{ V}} = 9.36$$

$$K = 10^{9.36} = 2.3 \times 10^9$$

At equilibrium the molar concentration of cadmium ion in the solution is more than a billion times that of lead ion!

$$K = \frac{[Cd^{2+}]}{[Pb^{2+}]} = 2.3 \times 10^9$$

The next example illustrates that it is also possible to use Equation (1) or Equation (2) to calculate an equilibrium constant for a reaction for which K is less than 1.

Example 20.11

Determine the equilibrium constant at 25°C for the reaction

$$Br_2(l) + 2Cl^-(aq) \longrightarrow 2Br^-(aq) + Cl_2(g)$$

We need to find the standard cell potential for this reaction and the number of electrons exchanged in the cell reaction in order to use Equation (2) to determine K. We find the cell potential as follows, using potentials from Table 20.1.

Anode:	$2Cl^-(aq) \longrightarrow Cl_2(g) + 2e^-$	$E^\circ_{ox} = -1.3595$ V
Cathode:	$Br_2(l) + 2e^- \longrightarrow 2Br^-(aq)$	$E^\circ_{red} = +1.0652$ V
Sum:	$Br_2(l) + 2Cl^-(aq) \longrightarrow 2Br^-(aq) + Cl_2(g)$	$E^\circ_{cell} = -0.2943$ V

Two electrons are involved in the half-reactions, so $n = 2$.

$$E^\circ_{cell} = \frac{0.05916 \text{ V}}{n} \log K$$

$$\log K = E^\circ_{cell} \times \frac{n}{0.05916 \text{ V}}$$

$$= -0.2943 \text{ V} \times \frac{2}{0.05916 \text{ V}} = -9.949$$

$$K = 10^{-9.949} = 1.12 \times 10^{-10}$$

Equation (1) and the Nernst equation can be used to explain why a battery runs down—that is, why a battery ultimately drops to zero voltage as it is used. As the reaction in a cell proceeds, the cell reaction approaches equilibrium. When the cell reaction reaches equilibrium and the concentrations of reactants and products are equal to the equilibrium concentrations, the reaction quotient is equal to the equilibrium constant; $Q = K$. At this point,

$$\frac{RT}{nF} \ln Q = \frac{RT}{nF} \ln K$$

Substituting this relationship into the Nernst equation (Section 20.6) gives

$$E_{cell} = E^\circ_{cell} - \frac{RT}{nF} \ln K$$

We know

$$E^\circ_{cell} = \frac{RT}{nF} \ln K$$

so we can write

$$E_{cell} = \frac{RT}{nF} \ln K - \frac{RT}{nF} \ln K = 0$$

Thus when the concentrations in a cell reaction are equal to the equilibrium concentrations, the potential of the cell is zero. A cell reaction that is spontaneous (one that proceeds to the right to increase the relative amounts of products) has a positive potential. A nonspontaneous cell reaction (one that proceeds to the left to increase the relative amounts of reactants) has a negative cell potential. A reaction that is at equilibrium, a condition in which the amounts of reactants and products do not change (Section 15.1), has a potential of zero. The relationships among $E°_{cell}$, $\Delta G°$, and K are as follows:

$E°_{cell}$	$\Delta G°$	K	Reaction Under Standard State Conditions
Positive	Negative	>1	Spontaneous
0	0	=1	At equilibrium
Negative	Positive	<1	Nonspontaneous

Batteries

A battery consists of one galvanic cell or of several galvanic cells connected in series so that the potentials of the individual cells combine to give the total potential of the battery. Batteries are special types of galvanic cells that generally deliver a large current and can endure rough handling.

20.8 Primary Cells

Primary cells, such as most flashlight batteries, cannot be recharged because the electrodes and electrolytes cannot be restored to their original states by an external electrical potential. The Daniell cell and dry cells are examples of primary cells. The Daniell cell (Fig. 20.6) was described in Example 20.1.

The familiar flashlight battery, or Leclanche cell (Fig. 20.14), is one form of dry cell. It consists of a zinc container, which serves as the electrode for the anode; a carbon (graphite) cathode; and a moist mixture of ammonium chloride, manganese dioxide, zinc chloride, and an inert filler such as sawdust. This mixture is separated from the zinc anode by a porous paper liner that serves the same purpose as a salt bridge in a galvanic cell. When the cell delivers a current, the zinc anode is oxidized, forming zinc ions and electrons, which are involved in the reduction of manganese(IV) oxide at the cathode. This reduction is not completely understood, but one possible reaction involves the reduction of the manganese from an oxidation state of $+4$ in MnO_2 to $+3$ in $MnO(OH)$

$$e^- + NH_4^+ + MnO_2 \longrightarrow NH_3 + MnO(OH)$$

The ammonia that is produced unites with some of the zinc ions, forming the complex ion $[Zn(NH_3)_4]^{2+}$. This reaction helps to hold down the concentration of zinc ions, thereby keeping the potential of the zinc electrode more nearly constant. It also prevents the accumulation of an insulating layer of ammonia molecules on the cathode, a condition called **polarization,** which would stop the action of the cell.

A second type of dry cell, the alkaline cell (Fig. 20.15), also uses zinc and manga-

Paste of MnO_2, NH_4Cl, $ZnCl_2$, water, and filler

Figure 20.14

Cross section of a flashlight battery, a dry cell.

Anode (MnO_2 and KOH)

Seal and insulation

Separator

Cathode (Zn and KOH

Figure 20.15

Cross section of a small alkaline cell used in watches and calculators.

nese dioxide, but the electrolyte contains potassium hydroxide instead of ammonium chloride. Many of the small button-shaped batteries used in cameras, calculators, and watches are alkaline cells.

The small Rubin–Mallory cell is used in hearing aids. It utilizes a zinc container as the anode and a mercury–mercury oxide electrode with a carbon rod as the cathode. The electrolyte is sodium or potassium hydroxide. The cell produces a potential of 1.35 volts. The half-reactions and net cell reaction are

Anode: $\qquad$ $Zn + 2OH^- \longrightarrow Zn(OH)_2 + 2e^-$

Cathode: $\qquad$ $HgO + H_2O + 2e^- \longrightarrow Hg + 2OH^-$

Net cell reaction: $\qquad$ $Zn + HgO + H_2O \longrightarrow Zn(OH)_2 + Hg$

20.9 Secondary Cells

Secondary cells are galvanic cells that can be regenerated by passing a current of electricity through the cell in the reverse direction of that of discharge. This recharges the cell. The lead storage battery and the nickel–cadmium cell are examples of secondary cells.

The battery in an automobile is a lead storage battery (a lead–acid battery). Its electrodes are lead alloy plates in the form of grids. The openings of one set of grids are filled with lead(IV) oxide and the openings of the other with spongy lead metal. Dilute sulfuric acid serves as the electrolyte. When the battery (Fig. 20.16) discharges (delivers a current), the spongy lead is oxidized to lead ions, which combine with sulfate ions of the electrolyte and coat the lead electrode with insoluble lead sulfate. The anode half-reaction is

$$Pb + SO_4^{2-} \longrightarrow PbSO_4(s) + 2e^-$$

Electrons from the lead electrode flow through an external circuit and enter the lead(IV) oxide electrode. The lead(IV) oxide is reduced to lead(II) ions, and water is formed. Again lead ions combine with sulfate ions of the sulfuric acid electrolyte, and this plate also becomes coated with lead sulfate. The cathode half-reaction is

$$PbO_2 + 4H_3O^+ + SO_4^{2-} + 2e^- \longrightarrow PbSO_4 + 6H_2O$$

The lead storage battery can be recharged by passing electrons in the reverse direction through each cell by applying an external potential. The cell becomes an electrolytic cell during recharging. An **electrolytic cell** is a cell in which electrical energy is converted to chemical energy—the opposite of the process that occurs in a galvanic cell. The half-reactions are just the reverse of those that occur when the cell is producing a current. Electrons forced into the lead electrode reduce lead ions from the lead sulfate, so this electrode becomes the cathode during recharging. Electrons are withdrawn from the lead(IV) oxide electrode, making it the anode, and lead ions from the lead sulfate are oxidized.

The charge and discharge at the two plates may be summarized as follows:

$$Pb + SO_4^{2-} \underset{\text{Charge}}{\overset{\text{Discharge}}{\rightleftharpoons}} PbSO_4(s) + 2e^- \qquad \text{(at the lead plate)}$$

$$PbO_2 + 4H_3O^+ + SO_4^{2-} + 2e^- \underset{\text{Charge}}{\overset{\text{Discharge}}{\rightleftharpoons}} PbSO_4(s) + 6H_2O \qquad \text{(at the lead dioxide plate)}$$

During recharging, hydronium ions and sulfate ions are regenerated.

Figure 20.16

One cell of a lead storage battery. A 12-volt automobile battery contains six of these cells.

Sulfuric acid, electrolyte

Lead grid filled with spongy lead

Lead grid filled with PbO_2

The net cell reaction of the lead storage battery is obtained by adding the two electrode reactions together.

$$Pb + PbO_2 + 4H_3O^+ + 2SO_4{}^{2-} \underset{\text{Charge}}{\overset{\text{Discharge}}{\rightleftharpoons}} 2PbSO_4(s) + 6H_2O$$

This equation indicates that the amount of sulfuric acid decreases as the cell discharges and increases as the cell is charged. Sulfuric acid is much denser than water, so a lead storage battery can be tested by determining the density of the electrolyte. As can be calculated from the potentials in Table 20.1, a single standard lead cell has a potential of 2.05 volts. The potential falls off slowly as the cell is used. A 12-volt automobile battery contains six lead storage cells.

The rechargeable cells used in calculators and battery-operated tools are based on nickel and cadmium electrodes (Example 20.2). Cadmium metal serves as the anode, while nickel(IV) oxide is reduced to nickel(II) hydroxide at the cathode. The electrolyte is a hydroxide solution. When the cell delivers a current, cadmium is oxidized at the anode.

Anode: $\qquad\qquad Cd + 2OH^- \longrightarrow Cd(OH)_2 + 2e^-$

NiO_2 is reduced at the cathode.

Cathode: $\qquad NiO_2 + 2H_2O + 2e^- \longrightarrow Ni(OH)_2 + 2OH^-$

These reactions are reversed during charging. The net reaction is

$$Cd + NiO_2 + 2H_2O \underset{\text{Charge}}{\overset{\text{Discharge}}{\rightleftharpoons}} Cd(OH)_2 + Ni(OH)_2$$

The anode is positive and the cathode negative in an electrolytic cell, whereas the anode is negative and the cathode positive in a galvanic cell. *For all types of cells, however, the electrode where oxidation occurs is the anode, and the electrode where reduction occurs is the cathode.* Figure 20.17 shows diagrammatically the relationship between a galvanic cell and an electrolytic cell. The sign convention is such that when a galvanic cell is supplying the current for an electrolytic cell, the negative electrode of

Figure 20.17

Illustration of the relationship between a galvanic cell (in this case, a Daniell cell) and an electrolytic cell. The galvanic cell (left) provides the electric current to run the electrolytic cell (right). Note that regardless of whether the cell is galvanic or electrolytic, oxidation occurs at the anode and reduction at the cathode.

one cell is connected to the negative electrode of the other cell, and likewise the positive electrodes of the two cells are connected.

20.10 Fuel Cells

Fuel cells are galvanic cells in which electrode materials, usually in the form of gases, are supplied continuously and are consumed to produce electricity.

A typical fuel cell, of the type currently used in the space shuttle, is based on the reaction of hydrogen and oxygen to form water. Hydrogen gas is diffused through the anode, a porous electrode with a catalyst such as finely divided platinum or palladium on its surface. Oxygen is diffused through the cathode, a porous electrode impregnated with cobalt oxide, platinum, or silver as a catalyst. The two electrodes are separated by a concentrated solution of sodium hydroxide or potassium hydroxide (Fig. 20.18) as an electrolyte.

Hydrogen diffuses through the anode and is absorbed on the surface in the form of hydrogen atoms, which react with hydroxide ions of the electrolyte to form water.

$$H_2 \xrightarrow{\text{Catalyst}} 2H$$

$$\underline{2H + 2OH^- \longrightarrow 2H_2O + 2e^-}$$

Net anode reaction: $\quad H_2 + 2OH^- \longrightarrow 2H_2O + 2e^-$

The electrons produced at the anode flow through the external circuit to the cathode. The oxygen adsorbed on the cathode's surface is reduced to hydroxide ions.

Cathode reaction: $\quad O_2 + 2H_2O + 4e^- \longrightarrow 4OH^-$

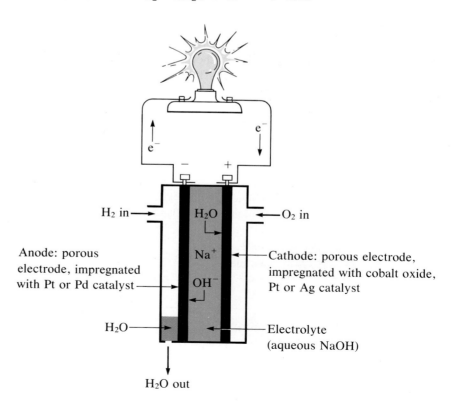

Figure 20.18

Diagram of a hydrogen–oxygen fuel cell. It would take several such cells to light an ordinary 110-V bulb.

The hydroxide ions replace those that react at the anode. As in all galvanic cells, the electrical output of the cell results from the flow of electrons through the external circuit from anode to cathode.

The overall cell reaction is the combination of hydrogen and oxygen to produce water.

Anode: $\qquad 2H_2 + 4OH^- \longrightarrow 4H_2O + 4e^-$

Cathode: $\qquad \dfrac{O_2 + 2H_2O + 4e^- \longrightarrow 4OH^-}{}$

Cell reaction: $\qquad 2H_2 + O_2 \longrightarrow 2H_2O$

A great deal of effort is being spent investigating other fuels, such as methane and other hydrocarbons, and other electrode systems.

20.11 Corrosion

Many metals, particularly iron, undergo corrosion when exposed to air and water (Fig. 20.19). Losses caused by corrosion of metals total billions of dollars annually in the United States.

Iron will not rust in dry air or in water that is free of dissolved oxygen. Both air and water are involved in the corrosion process. The presence of an electrolyte in the water accelerates corrosion, particularly when the solution is acidic. Heated portions of a metal corrode more rapidly than unheated ones. Finally, iron in contact with a less active metal, such as tin, lead, or copper, corrodes more rapidly than iron that is either alone or in contact with a more active metal, such as zinc or magnesium.

Corrosion appears to be an electrochemical process (Fig. 20.20). When iron is in contact with a drop of water, the iron tends to oxidize.

Anode: $\qquad Fe \longrightarrow Fe^{2+} + 2e^-$

The electrons from the oxidation pass through the iron to the edge of the drop, where they reduce oxygen from the air to hydroxide ion.

Cathode: $\qquad O_2 + 2H_2O + 4e^- \longrightarrow 4OH^-$

The iron(II) ions and hydroxide ions diffuse together and combine, forming insoluble iron(II) hydroxide.

$$Fe^{2+} + 2OH^- \longrightarrow Fe(OH)_2(s)$$

This precipitate is rapidly oxidized by oxygen to rust, an iron(III) compound with the approximate composition $Fe_2O_3 \cdot H_2O$.

Figure 20.19

Iron rusts when exposed to air and water.

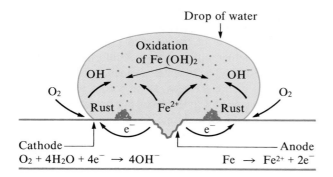

Figure 20.20

The electrochemical corrosion of iron. The iron in the anodic region dissolves, forming Fe^{2+} ions and causing the pit to form. The electrons travel to the cathodic region, where they react with O_2 with the formation of OH^- ions. The combination of Fe^{2+} and OH^- followed by oxidation produces rust.

Many methods and devices have been employed to prevent or retard corrosion. Iron can be protected against corrosion by coating it with an organic material such as paint, lacquer, grease, or asphalt; with another metal such as zinc, copper, nickel, chromium, or tin; with a ceramic enamel, like that used on sinks, bathtubs, stoves, refrigerators, and washers; or with an adherent oxide, which is formed by exposing iron to superheated steam, thereby giving it an adherent coating of Fe_3O_4. Some alloys of iron are corrosion-resistant. Some examples include stainless steel (Fe, Cr, and Ni) and Duriron (Fe and Si).

Another method of preventing the corrosion of iron or steel involves an application of electrochemistry called cathodic protection. Cathodic protection is used on iron and steel, such as underground pipeline, that is in contact with soil. If the iron is connected by a wire to a more active metal, such as zinc, aluminum, or magnesium, the iron becomes a cathode at which oxygen is reduced, rather than an anode where iron is oxidized. The difference in activity of the two metals causes a current to flow between them, producing corrosion of the more active metal and protecting the iron. With magnesium as the more active metal, the following reactions occur.

Anode:	$2Mg \longrightarrow 2Mg^{2+} + 4e^-$
Cathode:	$O_2 + 2H_2O + 4e^- \longrightarrow 4OH^-$
Sum:	$2Mg + O_2 + 2H_2O \longrightarrow 2Mg^{2+} + 4OH^-$

In this series of reactions no iron is oxidized. The active metal is slowly consumed and must be replaced periodically, but this is less expensive than replacing a pipeline.

Some of the more active metals such as aluminum and magnesium, which might be expected to corrode rapidly, are protected by a tightly adhering oxide coat of the metal oxide that forms when the metal is exposed to air (Section 13.2). The metal is made passive by this coating.

Electrolytic Cells

20.12 The Electrolysis of Molten Sodium Chloride

In Section 13.3 we saw that lithium, sodium, magnesium, calcium, and aluminum are extracted from their compounds by **electrolysis,** the input of electrical energy as a direct current of electricity, which forces a nonspontaneous reaction to occur. As an example of this type of reaction, let us examine the electrolysis of molten sodium chloride a little more carefully than we did in that section.

The Downs cell used for the commercial electrolysis of molten sodium chloride (Fig. 13.9) is complicated because of the need to prevent the product sodium from reacting with air and from reacting with the product chlorine. A simpler representation of the cell is given in Fig. 20.21. The essential elements of this cell are a container of molten sodium chloride, two inert electrodes, and a porous separator that permits diffusion of ions from one side of the cell to the other but prevents the sodium produced at one electrode from reacting with the chlorine produced at the other.

Molten sodium chloride contains equal numbers of sodium ions and chloride ions, which move about with considerable freedom. When an electrochemical cell containing molten NaCl is connected to a source of direct current, the sodium ions combine with

Figure 20.21
The electrolysis of molten sodium chloride. The reduction of sodium ions at the cathode produces sodium metal, and the oxidation of chloride ions at the anode produces chlorine gas. The separator prevents the reaction of the sodium and chlorine that are produced.

electrons to form sodium atoms (metallic sodium). The cathode half-reaction is

$$Na^+ + e^- \longrightarrow Na$$

The chloride ions give up one electron each and become chlorine atoms, which then combine to form molecules of chlorine gas. The anode half-reaction is

$$2Cl^- \longrightarrow Cl_2 + 2e^-$$

The net reaction for the electrolytic production of sodium and chlorine from molten sodium chloride is the sum of the two half-reactions.

Cathode: $\qquad\qquad 2Na^+ + 2e^- \longrightarrow 2Na$

Anode: $\qquad\qquad\quad 2Cl^- \longrightarrow Cl_2 + 2e^-$

Sum: $\qquad\qquad 2Na^+ + 2Cl^- \longrightarrow 2Na + Cl_2$

or $\qquad\qquad\quad 2NaCl(l) \longrightarrow 2Na(l) + Cl_2(g)$

The electrolysis of molten LiCl, $MgCl_2$, or $CaCl_2$ (Section 13.3) is very similar to that of NaCl. The metal is produced by reduction of the metal ion at the cathode, and chlorine is produced by oxidation of the chloride ion at the anode.

20.13 The Electrolysis of Aqueous Solutions

When an electrolyte is dissolved in water and an electric current is passed through it, several reactions are possible. The ions of the electrolyte or the water itself can be oxidized or reduced. The half-reactions that occur depend on the ease of oxidation or reduction of the ions relative to that of water.

1. Electrolysis of Hydrochloric Acid. When an aqueous solution of hydrochloric acid is electrolyzed, the hydronium ions are reduced to hydrogen gas at the cathode.

$$2H_3O^+ + 2e^- \longrightarrow H_2 + 2H_2O$$

Two oxidations are possible at the anode, the oxidation of chloride ion and the oxidation of water:

$$2Cl^- \longrightarrow Cl_2 + 2e^- \qquad E^\circ_{ox} = -1.36 \text{ V} \qquad (1)$$

$$6H_2O \longrightarrow O_2 + 4H_3O^+ + 4e^- \qquad E^\circ_{ox} = -1.23 \text{ V} \qquad (2)$$

Chloride ion and water are oxidized with almost equal ease, so the concentration of the chloride ion plays a significant role in determining the product. With a high chloride ion concentration, Reaction (1) occurs, and chlorine is formed at the anode. If the chloride concentration is low, Reaction (2) occurs as well, and oxygen is formed in addition to the chlorine. In a very dilute solution of hydrochloric acid, very little chlorine is formed, and the primary product is oxygen.

In a concentrated solution of hydrochloric acid, chlorine is produced at the anode, and the overall cell reaction can be obtained by adding the electrode reactions.

Cathode: $\qquad$ $2H_3O^+ + 2e^- \longrightarrow H_2 + 2H_2O$

Anode: $\qquad$ $2Cl^- \longrightarrow Cl_2 + 2e^-$

Sum: $\qquad$ $2H_3O^+ + 2Cl^- \longrightarrow H_2 + Cl_2 + 2H_2O$

2. Electrolysis of a Solution of Sodium Chloride. Hydrogen gas, chlorine, and an aqueous solution of sodium hydroxide are produced when a concentrated solution of sodium chloride is electrolyzed during the production of sodium hydroxide (Section 13.6 and Fig. 20.22). Chlorine is formed at the anode, and hydrogen gas and hydroxide ion are formed at the cathode. In order to account for these products, we need to consider all of the possible electrode reactions.

There are two species that might be reduced at the cathode: the sodium ion and water.

$$Na^+ + e^- \longrightarrow Na \qquad\qquad E^\circ_{red} = -2.714 \text{ V} \qquad (3)$$

$$2H_2O + 2e^- \longrightarrow H_2 + 2OH^- \qquad E^\circ_{red} = -0.828 \text{ V} \qquad (4)$$

Water is much more easily reduced than sodium ion, so hydroxide ion and hydrogen gas form according to Equation (4). The hydroxide ions migrate toward the anode.

As we have just seen, both chloride ion and water can be oxidized at the anode.

$$2Cl^- \longrightarrow Cl_2 + 2e^- \qquad\qquad (5)$$

$$6H_2O \longrightarrow O_2 + 4H_3O^+ + 4e^- \qquad\qquad (6)$$

In order to optimize the production of chlorine, a concentrated sodium chloride solution is used. The net reaction for the electrolysis of concentrated aqueous sodium chloride can be obtained by adding the electrode reactions.

Anode: $\qquad$ $2H_2O + 2e^- \longrightarrow H_2 + 2OH^-$

Cathode: $\qquad$ $2Cl^- \longrightarrow Cl_2 + 2e^-$

Sum: $\qquad$ $2H_2O + 2Cl^- \longrightarrow H_2 + Cl_2 + 2OH^-$

Figure 20.22

The electrolysis of an aqueous solution of sodium chloride. The reduction of water at the cathode produces hydrogen gas and hydroxide ions, and the oxidation of chloride ions at the anode produces chlorine gas. A solution of sodium hydroxide remains.

Hydroxide ions are formed during the electrolysis as chloride ions are removed from solution. Because the sodium ions remain unchanged, sodium hydroxide accumulates in the solution as electrolysis proceeds.

3. Electrolysis of a Solution of Sulfuric Acid. Sulfuric acid ionizes in water in two steps:

$$H_2SO_4 + H_2O \longrightarrow H_3O^+ + HSO_4^- \quad \text{(essentially complete)}$$

$$HSO_4^- + H_2O \rightleftharpoons H_3O^+ + SO_4^{2-}$$

As in a solution of hydrochloric acid, the reduction at the cathode is

$$2H_3O^+ + 2e^- \longrightarrow H_2 + 2H_2O$$

Two oxidations are possible at the anode: oxidation of the sulfate ion to the peroxydisulfate ion (Section 22.15) and oxidation of water.

$$2SO_4^{2-} \longrightarrow S_2O_8^{2-} + 2e^-$$

$$6H_2O \longrightarrow O_2 + 4H_3O^+ + 4e^-$$

Oxygen and hydronium ions form because water is more easily oxidized than sulfate ion.

The net reaction is the sum of the anode and cathode reactions. (The cathode reaction is multiplied by 2 to balance the number of electrons in the oxidation and reduction.)

Cathode:	$4H_3O^+ + 4e^- \longrightarrow 2H_2 + 4H_2O$
Anode:	$6H_2O \longrightarrow O_2 + 4H_3O^+ + 4e^-$
Sum:	$2H_2O \longrightarrow 2H_2 + O_2$

The electrolysis of an aqueous solution of sulfuric acid produces hydrogen and oxygen in a 2:1 ratio (Fig. 20.23). Although hydronium ion from the sulfuric acid is consumed by cathodic reduction, it is regenerated at the anode at the same rate at which it disappears at the cathode. Water is consumed, and the sulfuric acid becomes more concentrated as electrolysis proceeds.

Figure 20.23

The electrolysis of a dilute solution of H_2SO_4.

㉒.14 Electrolytic Deposition of Metals

Electrolysis is used to deposit metals from aqueous solutions. Chrome plating, bronzing (Fig. 20.24), and refining copper all employ this process. Bronzing and refining copper are particularly interesting because copper is both the anode and the cathode in these processes.

The electrodes used in the electrolytic cells we have considered thus far are electrically conducting, unreactive materials such as graphite or platinum. However, when a more reactive metal is used in the anode of an electrolytic cell, the anode reaction may involve oxidation of the metal. When a strip of metallic copper is used in an anode, the copper dissolves as the following anodic reaction occurs.

$$Cu \longrightarrow Cu^{2+} + 2e^-$$

The copper(II) ions formed are reduced at the cathode, and copper plates out onto the cathode.

$$Cu^{2+} + 2e^- \longrightarrow Cu$$

Figure 20.24

A pair of bronzed baby shoes.

Figure 20.25

The electrolytic refining of copper.

$$Cu \rightarrow Cu^{2+} + 2e^- \qquad Cu^{2+} + 2e^- \rightarrow Cu$$

If the cathode consists of a pair of baby shoes dusted with graphite powder to make them conducting, they become bronzed. If the cathode consists of a sheet of copper metal, refined copper is recovered.

Crude copper is refined electrochemically to improve its electrical conductivity. If impurities are not removed, they can reduce copper's conductivity by over 10%, so impure copper wires may get dangerously hot when they conduct electricity. When impure copper is used as an anode, impurities such as gold and silver, which do not oxidize so easily as copper, do not dissolve (are not oxidized) and fall to the bottom of the cell, forming a mud from which they are readily recovered (Fig. 20.25). Impurities such as zinc and iron, which oxidize more easily than copper, are oxidized and go into the solution as ions. When the electrical potential between the electrodes is carefully regulated, these ions are not reduced at the cathode; only the more easily reduced copper is deposited. The refined copper is deposited either upon a thin sheet of pure copper,

Figure 20.26

In the electrochemical purification of copper, ultrapure sheets of copper (the cathodes) are placed between sheets of impure copper (the anodes) in a tank containing a solution of $CuSO_4$. During the electrolysis, pure copper is deposited on the cathodes.

which serves as a cathode, or upon some other metal from which the deposit can be stripped (Fig. 20.26).

A similar electrochemical technique is used to refine aluminum by the Hoopes process (Section 13.3).

20.15 Faraday's Law of Electrolysis

In 1832–1833 Michael Faraday performed experiments demonstrating that the amount of a substance undergoing a chemical change at each electrode during electrolysis is directly proportional to the quantity of electricity that passes through the electrolytic cell (Fig. 20.27). This observation has come to be known as **Faraday's law of electrolysis.**

The quantity of electricity can be expressed as the number of moles of electrons passing through a cell. The quantity of a substance undergoing chemical change is related to the number of electrons that are involved in its half-reaction and can be expressed in terms of the moles of substance or in terms of equivalents of the substance. An electrochemical **equivalent** is the amount of a substance that combines with or releases 1 mole of electrons. Thus 1 equivalent of an oxidizing agent combines with 1 mole of electrons; and 1 equivalent of a reducing agent releases 1 mole of electrons. The number of equivalents of solute in a liter of solution (equivalents per liter) is called the **normality** of the solution. A solution that contains 1 equivalent of a substance per liter is called a 1 N solution. One liter of a 1 N solution will combine with or release 1 mole of electrons.

Experimental results show that 1 electron reduces 1 silver ion, whereas 2 electrons are required to reduce 1 copper(II) ion.

$$Ag^+ + e^- \longrightarrow Ag$$
$$Cu^{2+} + 2e^- \longrightarrow Cu$$

Therefore 6.022×10^{23} electrons reduce 6.022×10^{23} silver ions (1 mole) to silver atoms. The mass of silver produced is 107.9 grams; thus the mass of 1 equivalent of silver is the same as the mass of 1 mole. Because 2 electrons are required to reduce 1

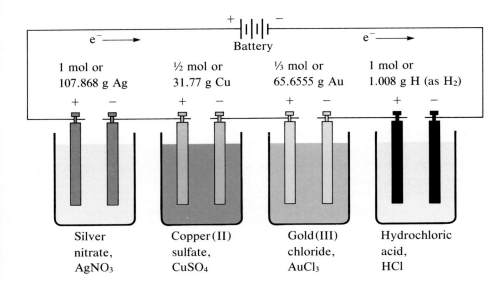

Figure 20.27

Amounts of various elements discharged at the cathode by 1 faraday of electricity (96,485 C, or 1 mol of electrons).

Cu^{2+} ion to atomic copper, 6.022×10^{23} electrons reduce only $\frac{1}{2}$ of a mole of copper. Thus the mass of 1 equivalent of copper is $\frac{1}{2}$ the mass of 1 mole.

A faraday is the charge on 1 mole of electrons (Section 20.5). When 1 faraday is passed through an electrochemical cell, 1 mole of electrons passes through the cell, 1 equivalent of a substance is reduced at the cathode, and 1 equivalent of a substance is oxidized at the anode. Other units of electricity that you will encounter often are the coulomb and the ampere. The relationships between these units are as follows:

1 faraday = 6.022×10^{23} electrons = 1 mole of electrons
= 96,485 coulombs (C)
1 coulomb = quantity of electricity involved when a current of 1 ampere (A) flows for 1 second
= 1 A s
1 ampere = 1 coulomb per second = 1 C/1 s

Handle calculations involving passage of an electric current (measured in amperes) through a cell just like any other stoichiometry problem: Convert the current in amperes to coulombs, then to faradays, and finally to moles of electrons. Use the moles of electrons as you would moles of any other reactant.

Example 20.12

Calculate the mass of copper produced by the reduction of Cu^{2+} ion at the cathode during the passage of 1.600 ampere of current through a solution of copper(II) sulfate for 1.000 hour.

Copper(II) ion is reduced at the cathode according to the equation

$$Cu^{2+} + 2e^- \longrightarrow Cu$$

If we know the number of moles of copper produced by the current, we can determine the mass of copper produced. We can calculate the moles of copper if we know the moles of electrons that pass through the cell. The moles of electrons can be determined from the amperage and time of the current flow. The chain of calculations is

| Amps and time | → | Coulombs | → | Faradays, moles of electrons | → | Moles of copper | → | Mass of copper |

$$1.600 \text{ A} \times 1.000 \text{ h} \times \frac{60 \text{ min}}{1 \text{ h}} \times \frac{60 \text{ s}}{1 \text{ min}} = 5760 \text{ A s} = 5760 \text{ C}$$

$$5760 \text{ C} \times \frac{1 \text{ faraday}}{96,485 \text{ C}} = 5.970 \times 10^{-2} \text{ faraday}$$

$$5.970 \times 10^{-2} \text{ faraday} \times \frac{1 \text{ mol e}^-}{1 \text{ faraday}} = 5.970 \times 10^{-2} \text{ mol e}^-$$

The foregoing half-reaction at the cathode is used to relate moles of electrons to the mass of copper produced.

$$5.970 \times 10^{-2} \text{ mol e}^- \times \frac{1 \text{ mol Cu}}{2 \text{ mol e}^-} = 2.985 \times 10^{-2} \text{ mol Cu}$$

$$2.985 \times 10^{-2} \text{ mol Cu} \times \frac{63.55 \text{ g Cu}}{1 \text{ mol Cu}} = 1.897 \text{ g Cu}$$

**Example
20.13**

Very large currents are used in many industrial electrolytic cells. How much time is required to produce exactly 1 metric ton (1000 kg) of magnesium by passage of a current of 150,000 A through molten $MgCl_2$? Assume a 100% yield of magnesium based on the current.

We need to determine the time required to produce 1000 kg of magnesium. If we know the number of coulombs, C, passed through the melt, we can calculate the time, in seconds, from the relationship $C = A \times s$, because we know the number of amperes, A. The number of coulombs is available from the number of faradays (moles of electrons) passed through the cell. The number of moles of electrons can be determined from the number of moles of Mg produced; 2 mol of electrons are used per mole of Mg produced ($Mg^{2+} + 2\ e^- \longrightarrow Mg$). The moles of Mg can be determined from the mass of Mg to be produced. The chain of calculations is

$$\boxed{\begin{array}{c} \text{Mass} \\ \text{of} \\ \text{Mg} \end{array}} \longrightarrow \boxed{\begin{array}{c} \text{Moles} \\ \text{of} \\ \text{Mg} \end{array}} \longrightarrow \boxed{\begin{array}{c} \text{Moles} \\ \text{of} \\ \text{electrons} \end{array}} \longrightarrow \boxed{\text{Coulombs}} \longrightarrow \boxed{\text{Time}}$$

$$1000\ \text{kg Mg} \times \frac{1000\ \text{g}}{1\ \text{kg}} \times \frac{1\ \text{mol Mg}}{24.305\ \text{g Mg}} = 4.114 \times 10^4\ \text{mol Mg}$$

$$4.114 \times 10^4\ \text{mol Mg} \times \frac{2\ \text{mol e}^-}{1\ \text{mol Mg}} = 8.229 \times 10^4\ \text{mol e}^-$$

$$8.229 \times 10^4\ \text{mol e}^- \times \frac{96,485\ \text{C}}{1\ \text{mol e}^-} = 7.940 \times 10^9\ \text{C}$$

We can rearrange the equation $C = A \times s$ and solve for s (s = C/A), because we know the current in amps and the number of coulombs passed through the melt.

$$s = \frac{C}{A} = \frac{7.940 \times 10^9\ \text{C}}{150,000\ \text{C s}^{-1}} = 5.293 \times 10^4\ \text{s}$$

It requires 5.293×10^4 s, or 14.70 h, to produce 1 metric ton of magnesium with a current of 150,000 A.

Oxidation–Reduction Reactions

Oxidation–reduction reactions (redox reactions) involve oxidation and reduction of the reactants (Section 2.11, Part 4). The chemical changes occurring in electrochemical cells involve oxidation of one species at the anode and reduction of another species at the cathode; thus the net reactions of most electrochemical cells are oxidation–reduction reactions.

$\textcircled{20}$.16 Balancing Redox Equations by the Half-Reaction Method

Equations for oxidation–reduction reactions can become quite complicated and difficult to balance by trial and error. The half-reaction method for balancing redox equations provides a systematic approach. In this method the overall reaction is broken down into two half-reactions, one representing the oxidation step and the other the reduction step. Each half-reaction is balanced separately, the numbers of electrons in both half-reactions are made the same, and then the two half-reactions are added to give the balanced equation. This is the same process that is used to write a cell reaction (Section 20.1). After balancing an equation we should always check to be sure both atoms and charges are balanced.

Example 20.14

Iron(II) is oxidized to iron(III) by chlorine. Use the half-reaction method to balance the equation for the reaction

$$Fe^{2+} + Cl_2 \longrightarrow Fe^{3+} + Cl^-$$

The oxidation half-reaction is oxidation of Fe^{2+} to Fe^{3+}.

$$Fe^{2+} \longrightarrow Fe^{3+} + e^-$$

The half-reaction for the reduction of Cl_2 to Cl^- has 2 electrons on the left side of the equation.

$$Cl_2 + 2e^- \longrightarrow 2Cl^-$$

In the oxidation half-reaction 1 electron is lost, whereas in the reduction half-reaction 2 electrons are gained. We multiply the oxidation half-reaction by 2 to balance the electrons.

$$2Fe^{2+} \longrightarrow 2Fe^{3+} + 2e^-$$

When the balanced half-reactions are added together, the two electrons on either side of the equation cancel one another, and the balanced equation is obtained.

$$2Fe^{2+} \longrightarrow 2Fe^{3+} + 2e^-$$
$$\underline{Cl_2 + 2e^- \longrightarrow 2Cl^-}$$
$$2Fe^{2+} + Cl_2 \longrightarrow 2Fe^{3+} + 2Cl^-$$

Example 20.15

The dichromate ion oxidizes iron(II) to iron(III) in acid solution. Balance the equation

$$Cr_2O_7{}^{2-} + H_3O^+ + Fe^{2+} \longrightarrow Cr^{3+} + Fe^{3+} + H_2O$$

by the half-reaction method.

The oxidation half-reaction is

$$Fe^{2+} \longrightarrow Fe^{3+} + e^-$$

The reduction half-reaction involves the change

$$Cr_2O_7{}^{2-} \longrightarrow 2Cr^{3+}$$

In acid solution, excess oxide combines with hydronium ion to give water; thus this half-reaction also involves H_3O^+ as a reactant and H_2O as a product. By inspection we can see that the 7 atoms of oxygen from the $Cr_2O_7^{2-}$ ion require 14 H_3O^+ ions.

$$Cr_2O_7^{2-} + 14H_3O^+ \longrightarrow 2Cr^{3+} + 21H_2O$$

To balance this reduction half-reaction in terms of ion charges and electrons, we must have 6 electrons on the left side of the equation.

$$Cr_2O_7^{2-} + 14H_3O^+ + 6e^- \longrightarrow 2Cr^{3+} + 21H_2O$$

Now we multiply the oxidation half-reaction by 6 so that both half-reactions will involve the same number of electrons.

$$6Fe^{2+} \longrightarrow 6Fe^{3+} + 6e^-$$

On addition of the balanced half-reactions, the 6 electrons on either side of the equation cancel one another, and we have

$$6Fe^{2+} \longrightarrow 6Fe^{3+} + 6e^-$$
$$\underline{Cr_2O_7^{2-} + 14H_3O^+ + 6e^- \longrightarrow 2Cr^{3+} + 21H_2O}$$
$$Cr_2O_7^{2-} + 14H_3O^+ + 6Fe^{2+} \longrightarrow 2Cr^{3+} + 6Fe^{3+} + 21H_2O$$

Example 20.16

In acidic solution, hydrogen peroxide oxidizes Fe^{2+} to Fe^{3+}. Use the half-reaction method to balance the equation

$$H_2O_2 + H_3O^+ + Fe^{2+} \longrightarrow H_2O + Fe^{3+}$$

The oxidation half-reaction is

$$Fe^{2+} \longrightarrow Fe^{3+} + e^-$$

The reduction half-reaction involves the reduction of H_2O_2 to H_2O in acid solution.

$$H_2O_2 \longrightarrow ?H_2O$$

By inspection we can see that there is sufficient oxygen in 1 molecule of H_2O_2 to form 2 molecules of water. This requires 2 hydronium ions, which release 2 additional water molecules, making a total of 4.

$$H_2O_2 + 2H_3O^+ \longrightarrow 4H_2O$$

Then 2 electrons are needed to balance the positive charges.

$$H_2O_2 + 2H_3O^+ + 2e^- \longrightarrow 4H_2O$$

So that both half-reactions will involve the same number of electrons, we multiply the oxidation half-reaction by 2.

$$2Fe^{2+} \longrightarrow 2Fe^{3+} + 2e^-$$

Now we add the two half-reactions.

$$2Fe^{2+} \longrightarrow 2Fe^{3+} + 2e^-$$
$$\underline{H_2O_2 + 2H_3O^+ + 2e^- \longrightarrow 4H_2O}$$
$$H_2O_2 + 2H_3O^+ + 2Fe^{2+} \longrightarrow 4H_2O + 2Fe^{3+}$$

When using the half-reaction method in basic solution, you must remember that in a *basic solution* excess oxide combines with water to give hydroxide ion:

$$O^{2-} + H_2O \longrightarrow 2OH^-$$

and excess hydrogen combines with hydroxide ion to give water:

$$H_3O^+ + OH^- \longrightarrow 2H_2O$$

Example 20.17 Hydrogen peroxide reduces MnO_4^- to MnO_2 in basic solution. Write a balanced equation for the reaction.

Initially we have

$$H_2O_2 + MnO_4^- \longrightarrow MnO_2$$

and we know that the reaction is in basic solution. The reduction half-reaction involves the change

$$MnO_4^- \longrightarrow MnO_2$$

Because it is in basic solution, the excess oxide combines with water to give hydroxide ion. Thus H_2O is needed as a reactant and OH^- is a product.

$$MnO_4^- + 2H_2O \longrightarrow MnO_2 + 4OH^-$$

Adding electrons to balance the charge gives us the following half-reaction:

$$MnO_4^- + 2H_2O + 3e^- \longrightarrow MnO_2 + 4OH^-$$

The oxidation half-reaction involves oxidation of hydrogen peroxide. Oxygen already has an oxidation number of -1 in H_2O_2, so it can be oxidized only to O_2, with an oxidation number of zero. The oxidation half-reaction must involve the change

$$H_2O_2 \longrightarrow O_2$$

In basic solution, excess hydrogen combines with hydroxide ion to give water.

$$H_2O_2 + 2OH^- \longrightarrow O_2 + 2H_2O$$

Adding electrons to balance the charge gives us

$$H_2O_2 + 2OH^- \longrightarrow O_2 + 2H_2O + 2e^-$$

After multiplying to get the same number of electrons in both half-reactions, we add them to give the overall equation.

$$2MnO_4^- + 4H_2O + 6e^- \longrightarrow 2MnO_2 + 8OH^-$$
$$\underline{3H_2O_2 + 6OH^- \longrightarrow 3O_2 + 6H_2O + 6e^-}$$
$$2MnO_4^- + 4H_2O + 3H_2O_2 + 6OH^- \longrightarrow 2MnO_2 + 8OH^- + 3O_2 + 6H_2O$$

Cancellation of identical species on the left and right sides of this equation gives

$$2MnO_4^- + 3H_2O_2 \longrightarrow 2MnO_2 + 3O_2 + 2OH^- + 2H_2O$$

20.17 Some Half-Reactions

When redox equations are balanced by the half-reaction method, the correct half-reactions must be used. Study carefully the half-reactions in Table 20.2; you will encounter them frequently in balancing redox equations. The products listed are the *major products* under the conditions given, but often they are not the sole products.

20.18 Balancing Redox Equations by the Change in Oxidation Number Method

Oxidation and reduction always occur together and to the same extent; the total increase in oxidation number due to oxidation must equal the total decrease in oxidation number due to reduction. This makes it possible to use changes in oxidation number in balancing redox equations.

Table 20.2   Important Half-Reactions

$X_2 + 2e^- \longrightarrow 2X^-$	The halogens F_2, Cl_2, Br_2, and I_2 as oxidizing agents
$O_2 + 4H_3O^+ + 4e^- \longrightarrow 6H_2O$	Oxygen as an oxidizing agent in acid solution
$2H_3O^+ + 2e^- \longrightarrow H_2 + 2H_2O$	The hydrogen ion as an oxidizing agent
$H_2 + 2H_2O \longrightarrow 2H_3O^+ + 2e^-$	Molecular hydrogen as a reducing agent in aqueous solution
$M \longrightarrow M^{n+} + ne^-$	Metals as reducing agents
$M^{n+} + ne^- \longrightarrow M$	Metal ions as oxidizing agents
$M^{n+} \longrightarrow M^{n+x} + xe^-$	Oxidation of a metal ion to a higher oxidation number; for example, $$Cr^{2+} \longrightarrow Cr^{3+} + e^-$$
$M^{n+} + xe^- \longrightarrow M^{n-x}$	Reduction of a metal ion to a lower oxidation number; for example, $$Fe^{3+} + e^- \longrightarrow Fe^{2+}$$
$H_2O_2 + 2H_3O^+ + 2e^- \longrightarrow 4H_2O$	Hydrogen peroxide as an oxidizing agent in acid solution
$H_2O_2 + 2H_2O \longrightarrow O_2 + 2H_3O^+ + 2e^-$	Hydrogen peroxide as a reducing agent in acid solution
$MnO_4^- + 8H_3O^+ + 5e^- \longrightarrow Mn^{2+} + 12H_2O$	Permanganate ion as an oxidizing agent in acid solution
$MnO_4^- + 2H_2O + 3e^- \longrightarrow MnO_2 + 4OH^-$	Permanganate ion as an oxidizing agent in neutral or basic solution
$Cr_2O_7^{2-} + 14H_3O^+ + 6e^- \longrightarrow 2Cr^{3+} + 21H_2O$	Dichromate ion as an oxidizing agent in acid solution
$NO_3^- + 2H_3O^+ + e^- \longrightarrow NO_2 + 3H_2O$	Concentrated nitric acid as an oxidizing agent toward less active metals, such as Cu, Ag, and Pb, and certain anions, such as Br^-
$NO_3^- + 4H_3O^+ + 3e^- \longrightarrow NO + 6H_2O$	Dilute nitric acid as an oxidizing agent toward less active metals and certain nonmetals, such as Br^-
$2NO_3^- + 10H_3O^+ + 8e^- \longrightarrow N_2O + 15H_2O$	Dilute nitric acid as an oxidizing agent toward moderately active metals, such as Zn and Fe
$H_2SO_4 + 2H_3O^+ + 2e^- \longrightarrow SO_2 + 4H_2O$	Concentrated sulfuric acid as an oxidizing agent toward HBr, C, and Cu
$H_2SO_4 + 6H_3O^+ + 6e^- \longrightarrow S + 10H_2O$	Concentrated sulfuric acid as an oxidizing agent toward H_2S
$H_2SO_4 + 8H_3O^+ + 8e^- \longrightarrow H_2S + 12H_2O$	Concentrated sulfuric acid as an oxidizing agent toward HI
$NO_2^- + 2H_3O^+ + e^- \longrightarrow NO + 3H_2O$	Nitrous acid as an oxidizing agent
$NO_2^- + 3H_2O \longrightarrow NO_3^- + 2H_3O^+ + 2e^-$	Nitrous acid as a reducing agent
$HClO + H_3O^+ + 2e^- \longrightarrow Cl^- + 2H_2O$	Hypochlorous acid as an oxidizing agent

Example 20.18
Use the changes in oxidation number to balance the equation for the reaction of antimony and chlorine to form antimony(III) chloride.

First we write the reactants and products of the reaction and then indicate the oxidation number of each atom in the reactants and products (Section 2.7. Remember that elements in the free state are always assigned an oxidation number of zero.)

$$\overset{0}{Sb} + \overset{0}{Cl_2} \longrightarrow \overset{+3 \; -1}{SbCl_3}$$

We indicate the changes in oxidation number that occur during the reaction. An ascending arrow (↑) denotes an increase in oxidation number, and a descending arrow (↓) denotes a decrease in oxidation number.

$$\overset{0}{Sb} \longrightarrow \overset{+3}{Sb} \quad \uparrow 3 \qquad \text{(total increase of 3 in oxidation number per formula unit, Sb)}$$

$$\overset{0}{Cl_2} \longrightarrow \overset{-1}{2Cl} \quad \downarrow 2 \qquad \text{(total decrease of 2 in oxidation number per formula unit, } Cl_2)$$

To balance the equation we must select the proper numbers of antimony and chlorine atoms so that the total increase in oxidation number will equal the total decrease. If we use 2 atoms of antimony and 3 molecules (6 atoms) of chlorine, there will be both an increase and a decrease of 6 units of oxidation number.

$$\overset{0}{Sb} \longrightarrow \overset{+3}{Sb} \quad \uparrow \qquad 3 \times 2 = 6$$

$$\overset{0}{Cl_2} \longrightarrow \overset{-1}{2Cl} \quad \downarrow \qquad 2 \times 3 = 6$$

The balanced equation, then, is

$$2Sb + 3Cl_2 \longrightarrow 2SbCl_3$$

Example 20.19
The chloride ion is oxidized by the permanganate ion in acid solution to give the manganese(II) ion, molecular chlorine, and water. Balance the equation

$$MnO_4^- + Cl^- + H_3O^+ \longrightarrow Mn^{2+} + Cl_2 + H_2O$$

using the changes in oxidation number.

After we assign oxidation numbers, it becomes evident that manganese is reduced from +7 to +2 and that chlorine is oxidized from −1 to 0.

$$\overset{+7}{MnO_4^-} + Cl^- + H_3O^+ \longrightarrow Mn^{2+} + \overset{0}{Cl_2} + H_2O$$

$$2Cl^- \longrightarrow \overset{0}{Cl_2} \quad \uparrow \qquad 2 \times 5 = 10$$

$$\overset{+7}{Mn} \longrightarrow Mn^{2+} \quad \downarrow \qquad 5 \times 2 = 10$$

We can see that 10 chloride ions increase by 10 units of oxidation number in going to 5 chlorine molecules (10 chlorine atoms) and that 2 manganese atoms decrease by 10 units of oxidation number.

$$2MnO_4^- + 10Cl^- + ?H_3O^+ \longrightarrow 2Mn^{2+} + 5Cl_2 + ?H_2O$$

Now we balance the ion charges on both sides of the equation. On the right side of the equation the only charged particles are the 2 manganese ions, with a total ionic charge of +4. The sum of the charges on the left must also be equal to +4. The sum of the charges on the 2 permanganate ions and the 10 chloride ions is -12, so 16 hydronium ions are necessary to give a sum of +4.

$$-2 - 10 + 16 = +4$$

The 16 hydronium ions produce 24 molecules of water.

$$2MnO_4^- + 10Cl^- + 16H_3O^+ \longrightarrow 2Mn^{2+} + 5Cl_2 + 24H_2O$$

To check the balancing, note that there are 24 oxygen atoms on each side of the arrow.

Very active reducing agents such as zinc can reduce dilute nitric acid to ammonium ion. Using the changes in oxidation number, balance the equation for this reduction with zinc.

Example 20.20

First we write the reactants and products of the reaction and assign oxidation numbers to the atoms that undergo a change in oxidation number.

$$\overset{0}{Zn} + \overset{+5}{NO_3^-} + H_3O^+ \longrightarrow Zn^{2+} + \overset{-3}{NH_4^+} + H_2O$$

Then we balance the equation with regard to the atoms that change in oxidation number.

$$\overset{0}{Zn} \longrightarrow Zn^{2+} \quad \uparrow \quad 2 \times 4 = 8$$

$$\overset{+5}{N} \longrightarrow \overset{-3}{N} \quad \downarrow \quad 8 \times 1 = 8$$

$$4Zn + NO_3^- + ?H_3O^+ \longrightarrow 4Zn^{2+} + NH_4^+ + ?H_2O$$

Next we balance the ion charges to find the number of hydronium ions required.

$$4Zn + NO_3^- + 10H_3O^+ \longrightarrow 4Zn^{2+} + NH_4^+ + ?H_2O$$

Of the 30 hydrogen atoms on the left, 4 are found in the ammonium ion on the right. Thus the other 26 hydrogen atoms form 13 molecules of water on the right.

$$4Zn + NO_3^- + 10H_3O^+ \longrightarrow 4Zn^{2+} + NH_4^+ + 13H_2O$$

To check the balancing of the equation, we note that there are 13 oxygen atoms on each side of the arrow. We also note that the net charge on each side of the arrow is +9. Charges and atoms thus balance, respectively, on each side.

For Review

Summary

In a **galvanic cell,** chemical changes are used to produce electrical energy. In an **electrolytic cell,** electrical energy is used to produce a chemical change. In both types of cells the electrode at which oxidation occurs is the **anode,** and the electrode at which reduction occurs is the **cathode.**

The potential that causes electrons from a galvanic cell to move from one electrode to the other through an external circuit is called the **cell potential, E_{cell},** of the cell. The potential of a cell can be regarded as the sum of the electrode potential of the anode and the electrode potential of the cathode. A positive E_{cell} value indicates that the cell reaction occurs spontaneously as written. **Standard reduction potentials** are tabulated for a variety of reduction (cathode) **half-reactions** with ion concentrations of 1 M, gas pressures of 1 atmosphere, and a temperature of 25°C. The potential of an oxidation half-cell (the anode half-reaction) has the same absolute value as the reduction potential but is opposite in sign. The more positive the potential associated with a half-reaction, the greater the tendency of that reaction to occur as written. The standard free energy change, ΔG°_{298}, for a cell reaction can be calculated from the potential of a cell based on the reaction. At standard conditions,

$$\Delta G^{\circ}_{298} = -nFE^{\circ}_{cell}$$

The equilibrium constant for the reaction is related to the standard free energy change and thus to E°. At 25°C

$$E^{\circ}_{cell} = \frac{0.05916 \text{ V}}{n} \log K$$

Electrode potentials vary with the concentrations of the reactants and products involved in the half-reaction. We can calculate them from standard electrode potentials, using the **Nernst equation:**

$$E_{cell} = E^{\circ}_{cell} - \frac{RT}{nF} \ln Q$$

or, in simplified form,

$$E_{cell} = E^{\circ}_{cell} - \frac{0.05916 \text{ V}}{n} \log Q$$

where n is the number of moles of electrons involved in the cell reaction.

Examples of batteries include the Daniell cell and the familiar flashlight battery, a dry cell. These are **primary cells,** which cannot be recharged. The lead storage battery is an example of a **secondary cell,** which is rechargeable.

Typical changes carried out in electrolytic cells include electrolysis of molten sodium chloride, producing sodium and chlorine; of an aqueous solution of hydrogen chloride, producing hydrogen and chlorine; of an aqueous solution of sodium chloride, producing hydrogen, chlorine, and a solution of sodium hydroxide; and of a solution of sulfuric acid, producing hydrogen and oxygen. The extent of the chemical changes in these processes can be related to the amount of electricity that passes through the cell. A **faraday,** which corresponds to passage of 1 mole of electrons, reduces 1 **equivalent** of a substance at the cathode or is produced by the oxidation of 1 equivalent of a substance at the anode. The amount of electrical charge possessed by a mole of electrons is 96,485 coulombs; 1 **coulomb** is the quantity of electricity involved when a current of 1 ampere flows for 1 second.

Oxidation–reduction (redox) reactions can be considered to consist of two half-reactions. After the half-reactions are balanced, we can add them to obtain the overall balanced equation for the reaction. Redox equations can also be balanced by considering the changes in oxidation number that accompany the reaction.

Key Terms and Concepts

anode (20.1)
cathode (20.1)
cell potential (20.2)
change in oxidation number method
    for balancing redox equations
    (20.18)
coulomb (20.2)
electrode (20.3)
electrolysis (20.12)
electrolytic cell (20.9)
equilibrium constants (20.7)
equivalent (20.15)

faraday (20.5)
Faraday's law (20.15)
free energy change (20.5)
fuel cell (20.10)
galvanic cell (20.1)
gas electrode (20.3)
half-cell (20.1)
half-reaction (20.1)
half-reaction method for balancing
    redox equations (20.16)
line notation (20.4)
maximum work (20.5)

Nernst equation (20.6)
normality (20.15)
primary cell (20.8)
salt bridge (20.1)
secondary cell (20.9)
spontaneity of cell reactions (20.5)
standard cell potential (20.2)
standard electrode potential (20.3)
standard hydrogen electrode (20.3)
standard reduction potential (20.3)
volt (20.2)

Exercises

Answers for selected even-numbered exercises marked by red numbers appear at the end of the book. The worked-out solutions to all even-numbered exercises appear in the *Solutions Guide*.

1. Define *anode* and *cathode*.
2. Complete and balance each of the following half-reactions. (In each case indicate whether oxidation or reduction occurs.)
   (a) $Sn^{4+} \longrightarrow Sn^{2+}$
   (b) $[Ag(NH_3)_2]^+ \longrightarrow Ag$
   (c) $Hg_2Cl_2 \longrightarrow Hg$
   (d) $O_2 \longrightarrow H_2O$ (in acid)
   (e) $O_2 \longrightarrow OH^-$ (in base)
   (f) $SO_3^{2-} \longrightarrow SO_4^{2-}$ (in acid)
   (g) $MnO_4^- \longrightarrow Mn^{2+}$ (in acid)
   (h) $Cl^- \longrightarrow ClO_3^-$ (in base)

Standard Reduction Potentials and Cell Potentials

3. Diagram galvanic cells that have the following net reactions.
   (a) $Mn + 2Ag^+ \longrightarrow Mn^{2+} + Ag$
   (b) $Sn^{4+} + H_2 + 2H_2O \longrightarrow Sn^{2+} + 2H_3O^+$
4. Diagram galvanic cells that have the following net reactions.
   (a) $Zn + I_2 \longrightarrow Zn^{2+} + 2I^-$
   (b) $Cr_2O_7^{2-} + 14H_3O^+ + 6I^- \longrightarrow$
   $\qquad\qquad\qquad\qquad 3I_2 + 2Cr^{3+} + 21H_2O$

5. Define *standard reduction potential*.
6. Why is the potential for the standard hydrogen electrode listed as 0.00 V?
7. Which is the better oxidizing agent in each of the following pairs at standard conditions?
   (a) Cr^{3+} or Co^{2+}
   (b) I_2 or Mn^{2+}
   (c) MnO_4^- or $Cr_2O_7^{2-}$ (in acid solution)
   (d) Pb^{2+} or Sn^{4+}
8. Which is the better reducing agent in each of the following pairs at standard conditions?
   (a) F^- or Cu (c) Sn^{2+} or Fe^{2+}
   (b) H_2 or I^- (d) Fe^{2+} or Cr
9. Calculate the potential of a cell based on the following reactions at standard conditions.
   (a) $Zn + I_2 \longrightarrow Zn^{2+} + 2I^-$
   (b) $Cd + Pb^{2+} \longrightarrow Cd^{2+} + Pb$
   (c) $Pt^{2+} + 2Cl^- \longrightarrow Pt + Cl_2$
10. Calculate the cell potential of a cell based on the following reactions at standard conditions.
   (a) $Mn + 2AgCl \longrightarrow Mn^{2+} + 2Cl^- + 2Ag$
   (b) $MnO_4^- + 8H_3O^+ + 5Au \longrightarrow$
   $\qquad\qquad\qquad Mn^{2+} + 12H_2O + 5Au^+$
   (c) $Fe + NiO_2 + 2H_2O \longrightarrow Fe(OH)_2 + Ni(OH)_2$
11. Determine the potential for each of the following cells:
   (a) $Co\,|\,Co^{2+}(1\ M)\,||\,Cr^{3+}(1\ M)\,|\,Cr$
   (b) $Ni\,|\,Ni^{2+}(1\ M)\,||\,Br^-(1\ M)\,|\,Br_{2(l)}\,|\,Pt$
12. Determine the potential for each of the following cells.

(a) $Pb; PbSO_4(s)|SO_4^{2-}(1\ M)\|H_3O^+,$
$$(1\ M)|H_2,\ (1\ atm)|Pt$$
(b) $Pt|Mn^{2+}\ (1\ M); MnO_4^-\ (1\ M); H_3O^+$
$$(1\ M)\|Fe^{3+}(1\ M); Fe^{2+}(1\ M)|Pt$$

13. Write the cell reaction for a galvanic cell based on each of the following pairs of half-reactions, and calculate the potential of the cell under standard conditions.
    (a) $Sc^{3+} + 3e^- \longrightarrow Sc$
    $Ag^+ + e^- \longrightarrow Ag$
    (b) $S + 2e^- \longrightarrow S^{2-}$
    $Cl_2 + 2e^- \longrightarrow 2Cl^-$

14. Write the cell reaction for a galvanic cell based on each of the following pairs of half-reactions, and calculate the potential of the cell under standard conditions.
    (a) $ZnS + 2e^- \longrightarrow Zn + S^{2-}$
    $CdS + 2e^- \longrightarrow Cd + S^{2-}$
    (b) $Co(OH)_3 + e^- \longrightarrow Co(OH)_2 + OH^-$
    $Cr(OH)_4^- + 3e^- \longrightarrow Cr + 4OH^-$
    (c) $HClO_2 + 2H_3O^+ + 2e^- \longrightarrow HClO + 3H_2O$
    $ClO_3^- + 3H_3O^+ + 2e^- \longrightarrow HClO_2 + 4H_2O$

15. Rechargeable nickel–cadmium cells are used in calculators and other battery-powered devices. Communication satellites also use these cells. The cell reaction is

$$NiO_2 + Cd + 2H_2O \longrightarrow Ni(OH)_2 + Cd(OH)_2$$

Calculate the cell potential, using the following half-cell potentials:

$$NiO_2 + 2H_2O + 2e^- \longrightarrow Ni(OH)_2 + 2OH^-$$
$$E° = +0.49\ V$$

$$Cd(OH)_2 + 2e^- \longrightarrow Cd + 2OH^-$$
$$E° = -0.81\ V$$

16. (a) Calculate the standard state potential of a single lead storage cell.
    (b) A lead storage battery, such as that used in an automobile, contains six lead storage cells. What maximum voltage is expected of such a battery?

17. Under standard conditions the potential of the cell diagrammed below is $+1.05$ V. What is the metal M? Show your calculations.

$$M|M^{n+}\|Cu^+|Cu$$

18. What is the cell with the highest potential that could be constructed from the metals iron, nickel, copper, and silver?

The Nernst Equation

19. Why is the Nernst equation important in electrochemistry?
20. Why does the potential of a galvanic cell change as the concentrations of the species involved in the cell reaction change?
21. Show by suitable equations that the electrode reaction for the zinc electrode is a reversible one.
22. Calculate the potential for each of the following half-reactions. *Note:* e^- does not appear in Q.

(a) $Sn^{2+}(0.0100\ M) + 2e^- \longrightarrow Sn$
(b) $Hg \longrightarrow Hg^{2+}(0.2500\ M) + 2e^-$
(c) $O_2(0.0010\ atm) + 4H_3O^+(0.100\ M) + 4e^-$
$$\longrightarrow 6H_2O(l)$$

23. Calculate the potential for each of the following half-reactions, using the Nernst equation. *Note:* e^- does not appear in Q.
    (a) $Cr_2O_7^{2-}(0.150\ M) + 14H_3O^+(0.100\ M) + 6e^-$
    $$\longrightarrow 2Cr^{3+}(0.000100\ M) + 21H_2O(l)$$
    (b) $Mn^{2+}(0.0125\ M) + 12H_2O(l) \longrightarrow$
    $$MnO_4^-(0.0125\ M) + 8H_3O^+(0.100\ M) + 5e^-$$
    (c) $Sn^{4+}(0.00010\ M) + 2e^- \longrightarrow Sn^{2+}(4.0\ M)$

24. Hypochlorous acid, HOCl, is a stronger oxidizing agent in acidic solution than in neutral solution. Calculate the potential for the reduction of HOCl to Cl^- in a solution with a pH of 7.00 in which [HOCl] and $[Cl^-]$ both equal 1.00 M.

25. The standard reduction potential of oxygen in acidic solution is 1.23 V ($O_2 + 4H_3O^+ + 4e^- \longrightarrow 6H_2O$). Calculate the standard reduction potential of oxygen in basic solution, and compare your result with the value in Appendix H. (*Hint:* What is $[H_3O^+]$ when $[OH^-]$ is 1 M?)

26. Calculate the voltage produced by each of the following cells:
    (a) $Zn|Zn^{2+}(0.0100\ M)\|Cu^{2+}(1.00\ M)|Cu$
    (b) $Al|Al^{3+}(0.250\ M)\|Co^{2+}(0.0500\ M)|Co$

27. Calculate the potential of each of the following cells:
    (a) $Pt|Br_2(l)|Br^-(0.450\ M)\|$
    $$Cl^-(0.0500\ M)|Cl_2(g)(0.900\ atm)|Pt$$
    (b) $Pt|H_2(g)\ (0.790\ atm)|H_3O^+\ (0.500\ M)\|$
    $$Cl^-\ (0.0500\ M)|Cl_2(g)\ (0.100\ atm)|Pt$$

28. What is the theoretical potential required to electrolyze a 0.0300 M solution of copper(II) chloride, producing metallic copper and chlorine at 0.300 atm of pressure?

29. A standard zinc electrode is combined with a hydrogen electrode with H_2 at 1 atm. If the cell potential is 0.46 V, what is the pH of the electrolyte in the hydrogen electrode?

Free Energy Changes and Equilibrium Constants

30. For a cell based on each of the following reactions run at standard conditions, calculate the cell potential, the standard free energy change of the reaction, and the equilibrium constant of the reaction.
    (a) $Mn(s) + Cd^{2+}(aq) \longrightarrow Mn^{2+}(aq) + Cd(s)$
    (b) $2Al(s) + 3Co^{2+}(aq) \longrightarrow 2Al^{3+}(aq) + 3Co(s)$
    (c) $2Br^-(aq) + I_2(s) \longrightarrow Br_2(l) + 2I^-(aq)$

31. For a cell based on each of the following reactions run at standard conditions, calculate the cell potential, the standard free energy change of the reaction, and the equilibrium constant of the reaction.
    (a) $Cr_2O_7^{2-} + 3Fe(s) + 14H_3O^+(aq) \longrightarrow$
    $$2Cr^{3+}(aq) + 3Fe^{2+}(aq) + 21H_2O(l)$$
    (b) $2Mn^{2+}(aq) + 24H_2O(l) + 5Fe^{2+}(aq) \longrightarrow$
    $$2MnO_4^-(aq) + 16H_3O^+(aq) + 5Fe(s)$$

32. Calculate the standard free energy change and equilibrium constant for the reaction

$$2Br^- + F_2 \longrightarrow 2F^- + Br_2$$

33. Using the standard reduction potentials for the half-reactions in the hydrogen–oxygen fuel cell, calculate the standard free energy change and equilibrium constant for the combustion of hydrogen.

$$2H_2 + O_2 \longrightarrow 2H_2O$$

34. Copper(I) salts disproportionate in water to form copper(II) salts and copper metal.

$$2Cu^+ \longrightarrow Cu^{2+} + Cu$$

What concentration of Cu^+ remains at equilibrium in 1.00 L of a solution prepared from 1.00 mol of Cu_2SO_4?

35. Use the potentials of the following half-cells and show that hydrogen peroxide, H_2O_2, is unstable with respect to decomposition into oxygen and water.

$$H_2O_2 + 2H_3O^+ + 2e^- \longrightarrow 4H_2O \quad E° = +1.77 \text{ V}$$

$$O_2 + 2H_3O^+ + 2e^- \longrightarrow H_2O_2 + 2H_2O$$
$$E° = +0.68 \text{ V}$$

36. Should each of the following compounds be stable in a 1 M aqueous solution? (*Hint:* Check the possibility of oxidation or reduction of the anion by the cation.)
   (a) $Ba(MnO_4)_2$
   (b) FeI_3
   (c) $Pd[HgBr_4]$
   (d) $[Co(NH_3)_6](ClO)_2$
   (e) $Na_2[Cd(CN)_4]$

Electrolytic Cells and Faraday's Law of Electrolysis

37. How does a galvanic cell differ from an electrolytic cell?
38. By means of description and chemical equations, explain the electrolytic purification of copper from impurities such as silver, zinc, and gold.
39. In this and other chapters we note commercial electrolytic processes for the preparation of several substances, some of which are hydrogen, oxygen, chlorine, and sodium hydroxide. Write equations for the net cell reaction and the individual electrode half-reactions that describe these commercial processes.
40. Using a line diagram of the type

Anode | anode soln ‖ cathode soln | cathode

diagram the electrolytic cell for each of the following cell reactions:
   (a) $MgCl_2 \longrightarrow Mg + Cl_2$ (using Mg and inert carbon as electrodes)
   (b) $2NaCl(aq) + 2H_2O \longrightarrow 2NaOH(aq) + H_2 + Cl_2$ (using inert electrodes of specially treated titanium, Ti)
   (c) $Fe + Cu^{2+} \longrightarrow Fe^{2+} + Cu$
   (d) $Cl_2 + 2Br^- \longrightarrow Br_2 + 2Cl^-$ (using platinum electrodes)

41. Write the anode half-reaction, the cathode half-reaction, and the cell reaction for each of the following electrolytic cells.
   (a) $C | NaCl(l) | Cl_2 ‖ NaCl(l) | Na(l) | Fe$
   (b) $Pt | Cl_2 | Cl^- ‖ H^+ | H_2 | Pt$

42. Write the anode half-reaction, the cathode half-reaction, and the cell reaction for each of the following electrolytic cells.
   (a) $C | CO_2 | O^{2-} ‖ Al^{3+} | Al$
   (b) $Pb; PbSO_4; PbO_2 | H_2SO_4(aq) ‖ H_2SO_4(aq) | PbSO_4; Pb$

43. State Faraday's law. What is a faraday of electricity?
44. Calculate the value of the Faraday constant, F, from the charge on a single electron, 1.6021×10^{-19} C.
45. How many moles of electrons are involved in each of the following electrochemical changes?
   (a) 0.800 mol of I_2 is converted to I^-
   (b) 118.7 g of Sn^{2+} is converted to Sn^{4+}
   (c) 27.6 g of SO_3 is converted to SO_3^{2-}
   (d) 0.174 g of MnO_4^- is converted to Mn^{2+}
   (e) 1.0 L of O_2 at STP is converted to H_2O in acid solution
   (f) 100 mL of 0.50 M Cu^{2+} is converted to Cu
   (g) 15.80 mL of 0.1145 M MnO_4^- is converted to Mn^{2+}
46. How many faradays of electricity are involved in each of the electrochemical changes described in Exercise 45?
47. How many coulombs of electricity are involved in each of the electrochemical changes described in Exercise 45?
48. Aluminum is manufactured by the electrolysis of a molten mixture of Al_2O_3 and Na_3AlF_6. How many moles of electrons are required to convert 1.0 mol of Al^{3+} to Al? How many faradays? How many coulombs?
49. How many moles of electrons are required to prepare 1.000 metric ton (1000 kg) of chlorine gas by electrolysis of an aqueous solution of sodium chloride as described in Section 20.13? How many faradays? How many coulombs? Assume that the efficiency of the electrochemical cell is 100%; that is, every electron involved results in the production of a chlorine atom. (In an actual commercial cell the efficiency is about 65%.)
50. Ammonium perchlorate, NH_4ClO_4, which is used in the solid fuel in the booster rockets on the space shuttle, is prepared from sodium perchlorate, $NaClO_4$, which is produced commercially by the electrolysis of a hot, stirred solution of sodium chloride.

$$NaCl + 4H_2O \longrightarrow NaClO_4 + 4H_2$$

How many moles of electrons are required to produce 1.00 kg of sodium perchlorate? How many faradays? How many coulombs?
51. Electrolysis of a sulfuric acid solution with a certain amount of current produces 0.3718 g of hydrogen. What mass of silver would be produced by the same amount of current? What mass of copper?
52. How many grams of zinc are deposited from a solution of zinc(II) sulfate by 3.40 faradays of electricity?
53. Say we conducted an experiment, using the apparatus depicted in Fig. 20.27. How many grams of gold would be

plated out of solution by the current required to plate out 4.97 g of copper? How many moles of hydrogen would simultaneously be released from the hydrochloric acid solution? How many moles of oxygen would be freed at each anode in the copper sulfate and silver nitrate solutions?

54. How many moles of electrons flow through a lamp that draws a current of 2.0 A for 1.0 min?

55. How many grams of cobalt are deposited from a solution of cobalt(II) chloride that is electrolyzed with a current of 20.0 A for 54.5 min?

56. How many faradays of electricity would be required to reduce 21.0 g of $Na_2[CdCl_4]$ to metallic cadmium? How long would this take (in minutes) with a current of 7.5 A?

57. Chromium metal can be plated electrochemically from an acidic aqueous solution of CrO_3. (a) What is the half-reaction for the process? (b) What mass of chromium, in grams, is deposited by a current of 2.50 A passing for 20.0 min? (c) How long does it take to deposit 1.0 g of chromium using a current of 10.0 A?

58. A single commercial electrolytic cell for the production of chlorine draws a current of 150,000 A. Assume that the efficiency of the cell is 100%, and calculate the mass of chlorine, in kilograms, produced by such a cell in 1.0 h.

59. Which metals listed in Table 20.1 could be purified by an electrolysis similar to that used to purify copper?

60. Why are different products obtained when molten $ZnCl_2$ is electrolyzed than when a solution of $ZnCl_2$ is electrolyzed? Why do a solution of $CuCl_2$ and molten $CuCl_2$ give the same products upon electrolysis?

Oxidation–Reduction Reactions

61. Balance each of the following redox equations.
  (a) $P + Cl_2 \longrightarrow PCl_5$
  (b) $IF_5 + Fe \longrightarrow FeF_3 + IF_3$
  (c) $Sn^{2+} + Cu^{2+} \longrightarrow Sn^{4+} + Cu^+$
  (d) $H_2S + Hg_2^{2+} + H_2O \longrightarrow Hg + S + H_3O^+$
  (e) $CN^- + ClO_2 \longrightarrow CNO^- + Cl^-$
  (f) $Fe^{2+} + Ce^{4+} \longrightarrow Fe^{3+} + Ce^{3+}$
  (g) $HBrO + H_2O \longrightarrow H_3O^+ + Br^- + O_2$
  (h) $ICl + H_2O \longrightarrow H_3O^+ + Cl^- + HOI$

62. Balance each of the following redox equations.
  (a) $Zn + BrO_4^- + OH^- + H_2O \longrightarrow [Zn(OH)_4]^{2-} + Br^-$
  (b) $H_2SO_4 + HBr \longrightarrow SO_2 + Br_2 + H_2O$
  (c) $MnO_4^- + S^{2-} + H_2O \longrightarrow MnO_2 + S + OH^-$
  (d) $NO_3^- + I_2 + H_3O^+ \longrightarrow IO_3^- + NO_2 + H_2O$
  (e) $Cu + H_3O^+ + NO_3^- \longrightarrow Cu^{2+} + NO_2 + H_2O$
  (f) $Zn + H_3O^+ + NO_3^- \longrightarrow Zn^{2+} + N_2O + H_2O$
  (g) $Cu + H_3O^+ + NO_3^- \longrightarrow Cu^{2+} + NO + H_2O$
  (h) $MnO_4^- + H_2S + H_3O^+ \longrightarrow Mn^{2+} + S + H_2O$
  (i) $MnO_4^- + NO_2^- + H_2O \longrightarrow MnO_2 + NO_3^- + OH^-$
  (j) $MnO_4^{2-} + H_2O \longrightarrow MnO_4^- + OH^- + MnO_2$
  (k) $Br_2 + SO_2 + H_2O \longrightarrow H_3O^+ + Br^- + SO_4^{2-}$

63. Balance each of the following redox equations.
  (a) $Al + [Sn(OH)_4]^{2-} \longrightarrow [Al(OH)_4]^- + Sn + OH^-$

  (b) $Cl^- + H_3O^+ + NO_3^- \longrightarrow Cl_2 + NO_2 + H_2O$
  (c) $H_2S + H_2O_2 \longrightarrow S + H_2O$
  (d) $MnO_4^- + Se^{2-} + H_2O \longrightarrow MnO_2 + Se + OH^-$
  (e) $MnO_4^{2-} + Cl_2 \longrightarrow MnO_4^- + Cl^-$
  (f) $OH^- + NO_2 \longrightarrow NO_3^- + NO_2^- + H_2O$
  (g) $Br_2 + CO_3^{2-} \longrightarrow Br^- + BrO_3^- + CO_2$
  (h) $NH_3 + O_2 \longrightarrow NO + H_2O$
  (i) $C + HNO_3 \longrightarrow NO_2 + H_2O + CO_2$
  (j) $HClO_3 \longrightarrow HClO_4 + ClO_2 + H_2O$
  (k) $ClO_3^- + H_2O + I_2 \longrightarrow IO_3^- + Cl^- + H_3O^+$
  (l) $Cr_2O_7^{2-} + HNO_2 + H_3O^+ \longrightarrow Cr^{3+} + NO_3^- + H_2O$

64. Complete and balance each of the following equations. (Note that when a reaction occurs in acidic solution, H_3O^+ and/or H_2O can be added on either side of the equation, as necessary, to balance the equation properly. When a reaction occurs in basic solution, OH^- and/or H_2O can be added, as necessary, on either side of the equation. No indication of the acidity of the solution is given if neither H_3O^+ nor OH^- is involved as a reactant or product.)
  (a) $Zn + NO_3^- \longrightarrow Zn^{2+} + N_2$ (acidic solution)
  (b) $Zn + NO_3^- \longrightarrow Zn^{2+} + NH_3$ (basic solution)
  (c) $CuS + NO_3^- \longrightarrow Cu^{2+} + S + NO$ (acidic solution)
  (d) $NH_3 + O_2 \longrightarrow NO_2$ (gas phase)
  (e) $H_2SO_4 + HI \longrightarrow I_2 + SO_2$ (acidic solution)
  (f) $Cl_2 + OH^- \longrightarrow Cl^- + ClO_3^-$ (basic solution)
  (g) $H_2O_2 + MnO_4^- \longrightarrow Mn^{2+} + O_2$ (acidic solution)
  (h) $NO_2 \longrightarrow NO_3^- + NO_2^-$ (basic solution)
  (i) $KClO_3 \longrightarrow KCl + O_2$ (no solvent)
  (j) $Fe^{3+} + I^- \longrightarrow Fe^{2+} + I_2$
  (k) $P_4 \longrightarrow PH_3 + HPO_3^{2-}$ (basic solution)
  (l) $P_4 \longrightarrow PH_3 + HPO_3^{2-}$ (acidic solution)

65. Complete and balance the following reactions. (See the instructions for Exercise 64.)
  (a) $Zn + H_3O^+ \longrightarrow$ (acidic solution)
  (b) $MnO_2 + Cl^- \longrightarrow$ (acidic solution)
  (c) $Pb^{4+} + Sn^{2+} \longrightarrow$
  (d) $Fe^{2+} + H_2O_2 \longrightarrow$ (acidic solution)
  (e) $Cl_2 + SO_2 \longrightarrow$ (acidic solution)

  (f) $ZnS + O_2 \xrightarrow{\Delta}$ (no solvent)
  (g) $ClO^- + Sn^{2+} \longrightarrow$ (acidic solution)
  (h) $PbO_2 + SeO_3^{2-} \longrightarrow$ (basic solution)
  (i) $Cr_2O_7^{2-} + Br^- \longrightarrow$ (acidic solution)

Additional Exercises

66. Tarnished silverware is coated with Ag_2S. The tarnish can be removed by placing the silverware in an aluminum pan and covering it with a solution of an inert electrolyte such as NaCl. Explain the electrochemical basis for this procedure.

67. Soon after a copper metal rod is placed in a silver nitrate solution, copper ions are observed in the solution and silver metal has been deposited on the rod. Can the copper rod be considered an electrode? If so, is it an anode or a cathode?

68. The cell potential for the unbalanced chemical reaction

$$Hg_2^{2+} + NO_3^- + H_3O^+ \longrightarrow Hg^{2+} + HNO_2 + H_2O$$

is measured under standard state conditions in the electrochemical cell shown in the accompanying diagram. The cell voltage is positive: $E° = 0.02$ V.

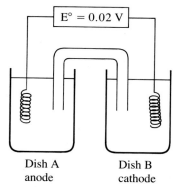

$E° = 0.02$ V

Dish A	Dish B
anode	cathode

(a) Which of the following statements must be true of the solutions in order for the cell to operate with the voltage indicated?
   (i) The solution in dish A must be acidic.
   (ii) The solution in dish B must be acidic.
   (iii) The solutions in both dish A and dish B must be acidic.
   (iv) No acid may be in either dish A or dish B.
(b) Which ions and compounds are in each dish?
(c) Calculate the reduction potential for the half-cell

$$2Hg^{2+} + 2e^- \longrightarrow Hg_2^{2+}$$

given the following:

$$NO_3^- + 3H_3O^+ + 2e^- \longrightarrow HNO_2 + 4H_2O$$
$$E_{red}° = 0.94 \text{ V}$$

(d) What is the value of $\Delta G_{298}°$ for the reaction?
(e) What is the equilibrium constant for the reaction?
(f) At what pH will the cell potential be zero if all the other concentrations remain unchanged?
(g) How many moles of electrons pass through the circuit when 0.60 mol of Hg^{2+} and 0.30 mol of HNO_2 are produced in a cell that contains 0.50 mol of Hg_2^{2+} and 0.40 mol of NO_3^- at the beginning of the reaction?
(h) How long will it take to produce 0.10 mol of HNO_2 by this reaction if a current of 10 A passes through the cell?
(i) Which of the following statements accurately expresses what will happen in a solution that is 1.0 M each in Hg_2^{2+}, NO_3^-, H_3O^+, Hg^{2+}, and HNO_2?
   (i) Hg_2^{2+} will be oxidized and NO_3^- reduced.
   (ii) Hg_2^{2+} will be reduced and NO_3^- oxidized.
   (iii) Hg^{2+} will be oxidized and HNO_2 reduced.
   (iv) Hg^{2+} will be reduced and HNO_2 oxidized.
   (v) There will be no change because the reaction is at standard state conditions.

69. Which of the following statements accurately describes the effect of adding CN^- to the cathode of a cell with the cell reaction

$$Cd + 2Ag^+ \longrightarrow 2Ag + Cd^{2+} \qquad E° = 1.2 \text{ V}$$

   (i) $E°$ increases because $Cd(CN)_4^{2-}$ forms.
   (ii) $E°$ decreases because $Cd(CN)_4^{2-}$ forms.
   (iii) $E°$ increases because $Ag(CN)_2^-$ forms.
   (iv) $E°$ decreases because $Ag(CN)_2^-$ forms.
   (v) Both $Cd(CN)_4^{2-}$ and $Ag(CN)_2^-$ form, so there is no change.

70. Explain briefly how you could determine the solubility product of CuI ($K_{sp} \approx 10^{-7}$) by using an electrochemical measurement.

71. When chlorine dissolves in water, it disproportionates, producing chloride ion and hypochlorous acid (see Section 22.18). Find at what hydrogen ion concentration the potential for the disproportionation changes from a negative value to a positive value, assuming 1.00 atm of pressure and concentrations of 1.00 M for all species except hydrogen ion. (The standard reduction potential for chlorine to chloride ion is 1.36 V, and for hypochlorous acid to chlorine is 1.63 V.) Could chlorine be produced from hypochlorite and chloride ions in solution, through the reverse of the disproportionation reaction, by acidifying the solution with strong acid? Explain.

72. The standard reduction potentials for the reactions

$$Ag^+ + e^- \longrightarrow Ag$$

and

$$AgCl + e^- \longrightarrow Ag + Cl^-$$

are +0.7991 V and +0.222 V, respectively. From these data and the Nernst equation, calculate a value for the solubility product (K_{sp}) for AgCl. Compare your answer with the value given in Appendix D.

73. Calculate the standard reduction potential for the reaction $H_2O + e^- \rightarrow \frac{1}{2}H_2 + OH^-$, using the Nernst equation and the fact that the standard reduction potential for the reaction $H_3O^+ + e^- \rightarrow \frac{1}{2}H_2 + H_2O$ is by definition equal to 0.00 V.

74. The standard reduction potentials for the reactions

$$Ag^+ + e^- \longrightarrow Ag$$

and $\quad [Ag(NH_3)_2]^+ + e^- \longrightarrow Ag + 2NH_3$

are +0.7991 V and +0.373 V, respectively. From these values and the Nernst equation, determine K_f for the $[Ag(NH_3)_2]^+$ ion. Compare your answer with the value given in Appendix E.

75. When gold is plated electrochemically from a basic solution of $[Au(CN)_4]^-$, O_2 forms at one electrode and Au is deposited at the other. Write the half-reactions that occur at the two electrodes and the net reaction for the electrolytic cell. (The cyanide ion, CN^-, is not oxidized or reduced under these conditions.)

76. A lead storage battery is used to electrolyze a solution of hydrogen chloride. Sketch the two cells, label the cathode and anode in each cell, give the sign of each electrode, indicate the direction of flow of electrons through the system, show the movement of ions in the cells, and write the half-reactions that occur at the two electrodes.

77. A current of 9.0 A flowed for 45 min through water containing a small quantity of sodium hydroxide. How many liters of gas were formed at the anode at 27.0°C and 750 torr of pressure?

78. A lead storage battery has initially 200 g of lead and 200 g of PbO_2, plus excess H_2SO_4. Theoretically, how long could this cell deliver a current of 10.0 A, without recharging, if it were possible to operate it so that the reaction goes to completion?

79. A total of 69,500 C of electricity was required to reduce 37.7 g of M^{3+} to the metal. What is M?

80. A current of 10.0 A is applied for 1.0 h to 1.0 L of a solution containing 1.0 mol of HCl. Calculate the pH of the solution at the end of this time.

81. A current of 10.0 A is applied for 1.0 h to 1.0 L of a solution containing 5.0 mol of NaCl. Calculate the pH of the solution at the end of this time.

A Survey of the Nonmetals

21

Enormous quantities of sulfur are produced each year.

In Chapter 6 we learned that the nonmetallic character of elements increases as we go from left to right and from bottom to top in the periodic table. The nonmetals are the elements located in the upper right-hand portion of the periodic table. Under normal conditions, over half of the nonmetals are gases, one is a liquid, and the rest are some of the softest and hardest of solids. The nonmetals exhibit a rich variety of chemical behavior. They include the most reactive and the most nonreactive of the elements, and they form many different ionic and covalent compounds.

In this chapter we present an overview of the properties and chemical behavior of the nonmetals so that you can get a feel for their general chemistry before you deal with one or more of the specific elements. For example, oxygen is discussed briefly in this chapter and is compared with sulfur and selenium, other members of its group. Then, in Chapter 22, we will examine in detail the chemical and physical properties of oxygen, its importance to life, some of its many commercial uses, and its allotrope ozone. The chemical behavior of other nonmetals is also presented in more detail in Chapters 22 and 23.

Properties of the Nonmetals

㉑.1 The Nonmetals

The properties and behavior of the nonmetals in the upper right portion of the periodic table are quite different from the metals on the left side. However, there are no distinct points at which changes from metallic to nonmetallic behavior occur in periods or groups in the periodic table.

As we move from metals to nonmetals, we encounter some elements that are intermediate in their properties. As noted in Chapter 6, these borderline elements, shown in blue in Fig. 21.1, are called **semi-metals** or **metalloids.** The chemical and physical behavior of the five semi-metals will be considered in Chapter 25.

Figure 21.1

The location of the nonmetals, shown in yellow, in the periodic table. Semi-metals are shown in blue, metals in red.

Chemists have slightly different ideas about which elements constitute the semi-metal group and which constitute the nonmetals. For our purposes, we will consider hydrogen and those elements with electronegativities equal to or larger than that of hydrogen as nonmetals. In addition, the noble gases are considered to be nonmetals. The limited number of compounds that they form are covalent, and they exhibit characteristic nonmetal behavior. The nonmetals, then, are hydrogen (Group IA or VIIA); carbon (Group IVA); nitrogen, phosphorus, and arsenic (Group VA); oxygen, sulfur, and selenium (Group VIA); fluorine, chlorine, bromine, iodine, and astatine (Group VIIA); and helium, neon, argon, krypton, xenon, and radon (Group VIIIA). (See Fig. 21.1; the nonmetals are highlighted in yellow.)

Carbon is unique among the elements in the periodic table because of its ability to form stable bonds to itself and subsequently to form long chains, a property called **catenation.** The chemistry of carbon is extremely varied, and there are more compounds of carbon than of any other element in the periodic table except hydrogen. Most of these compounds are best regarded as organic compounds; Chapter 30 introduces organic chemistry, the chemistry of compounds that contain carbon–carbon bonds. Chapter 31 treats biochemistry, the chemistry of carbon compounds found in living systems. In this chapter we shall focus on the inorganic chemistry of carbon.

㉑.2 Periodic Trends and the General Behavior of the Nonmetals

Acquaintance with periodic properties and trends can enhance our understanding and recall of the chemistry of the nonmetals (Table 6.7). Nonmetals exhibit widely differing chemical behaviors, but we can understand and predict similarities and trends if we are familiar with properties such as electronegativity, ionization energy, and size. Many reactions of the nonmetals are Lewis acid–Lewis base, Brønsted acid–Brønsted base, or oxidation–reduction reactions. (To refresh your memory, you may want to review material on these types of reactions in Chapters 2, 7, and 16.)

In many cases, trends in electronegativity enable us to predict the type of bonding in compounds involving the nonmetals, as well as the physical states of the compounds. We know that electronegativity decreases as we move down a given group and increases as we move from left to right across a period. The nonmetals have higher electronegativities than metals, and compounds formed between metals and nonmetals are generally ionic in nature because of the large differences in electronegativity between the metals and the nonmetals. The metals form cations, the nonmetals form anions, and the resulting compounds are solids at 25°C and a pressure of 1 atm. On the other hand, compounds formed between two or more nonmetals have small differences in electronegativity between the atoms, and covalent bonding—sharing of electrons—results. These substances thus tend to be molecular in nature and are gases, liquids, or volatile solids at 25°C and 1 atm of pressure.

In normal chemical processes, nonmetals do not form monatomic positive ions because their ionization energies are too high. All monatomic nonmetal ions are anions; examples include the chloride ion, Cl^-, the nitride ion, N^{3-}, and the selenide ion, Se^{2-}.

The common oxidation numbers that the nonmetals exhibit in their ionic and covalent compounds are shown in Table 21.1. Remember that an element exhibits a positive oxidation number when it is combined with a more electronegative element and exhibits a negative oxidation number when combined with a less electronegative element.

| Table 21.1 | Common Oxidation Numbers of the Nonmetals in Compounds, by Group | | | | |

IA	IVA	VA	VIA	VIIA	VIIIA
H	C	N	O	F	
+1	+4	+5	−1	−1	
−1	to	to	−2		
	−4	−3			
		P–As	S–Se	Cl–I	Xe
		+5	+6	+7	+8
		+3	+4	+5	+6
		−3	−2	+3	+4
				+1	+2
				−1	

Figure 21.2

Hot iron powder is vigorously oxidized by the oxygen in air, forming iron oxides.

The first member of each nonmetal group exhibits different behavior, in many respects, from the other group members. The several reasons for this include smaller size, greater ionization energy, and (most important) the fact that the first member of each group has valence orbitals with principal quantum number 2 (that is, $n = 2$). This means that the first member of each group has only four atomic orbitals (one $2s$ and three $2p$) available for bonding, whereas other group members have empty d orbitals in their valence shells, making possible five, six, or even more bonds around the central atom. For example, nitrogen forms only NF_3 whereas phosphorus forms both PF_3 and PF_5.

Another difference between the first group member and subsequent members is the greater ability of the first member to form π bonds. This is primarily a function of the smaller size of the first member of each group, which allows better overlap of atomic orbitals. Nonmetals other than the first member of each group form π bonds, but not to the same extent, and they form their most stable π bonds to elements that are the first members of a group. For example, sulfur–oxygen π bonds are well known, whereas sulfur does not form stable π bonds to itself.

The variety of oxidation numbers displayed by most of the nonmetals means that many of their chemical reactions involve changes in these oxidation numbers in oxidation–reduction reactions. Four general aspects of the oxidation–reduction chemistry of the nonmetals are listed below.

1. Nonmetals oxidize most metals (Fig. 21.2). The oxidation number of the metal becomes positive as it is oxidized, and that of the nonmetal becomes negative as it is reduced. For example,

$$\overset{0}{4Fe} + \overset{0}{3O_2} \longrightarrow \overset{+3\ -2}{2Fe_2O_3}$$

2. With the exception of nitrogen and carbon, which are poor oxidizing agents, a more electronegative nonmetal oxidizes a less electronegative nonmetal or the anion of the nonmetal (Figs. 21.3 and 21.4).

$$\overset{0}{S} + \overset{0}{O_2} \longrightarrow \overset{+4-2}{SO_2}$$

$$\overset{0}{Cl_2} + 2I^- \longrightarrow \overset{0}{I_2} + 2Cl^-$$

Fluorine and oxygen are the strongest oxidizing agents within their respective groups; each oxidizes all the elements that lie below it in the group. Within any period, the strongest oxidizing agent is found in Group VIIA. A nonmetal often oxidizes an element that lies to its left in the same period. For example,

$$\overset{0}{2As} + \overset{0}{3Br_2} \longrightarrow \overset{+3\ -1}{2AsBr_3}$$

3. The stronger a nonmetal is as an oxidizing agent, the more difficult it is to remove electrons from the anion formed by the nonmetal. This means that the most stable negative ions are formed by elements at the top of the group or in Group VIIA of the period.

4. Fluorine and oxygen are the strongest oxidizing elements known. Fluorine does not form compounds in which it exhibits positive oxidation numbers, and oxygen exhibits a positive oxidation number only when combined with fluorine. For example,

$$\overset{0}{2F_2} + 2OH^- \longrightarrow \overset{+2\ -1}{OF_2}(g) + 2F^- + H_2O$$

With the exception of the noble gases, all nonmetals form compounds with oxygen giving covalent oxides. Most of these oxides are acidic; that is, they react with water to form oxyacids that yield hydronium ions in aqueous solution. Notable exceptions are carbon monoxide, CO, nitrous oxide, N_2O, and nitric oxide, NO. We can describe the general behavior of acidic oxides with the following three statements.

1. Oxides such as SO_2 and N_2O_5, in which the nonmetal exhibits one of its common oxidation numbers, are called **acid anhydrides** and react with water to form acids with no change in oxidation number. The product is an oxyacid. For example,

$$SO_2 + H_2O \longrightarrow H_2SO_3$$

$$N_2O_5 + H_2O \longrightarrow 2HNO_3$$

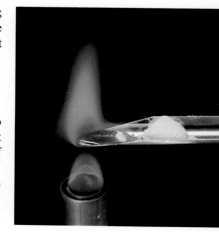

Figure 21.3

When it burns in air, sulfur is oxidized by the more electronegative element oxygen.

Figure 21.4

Chlorine oxidizes I^- to I_2, as indicated by the purple color of I_2 extracted into the lower layer.

2. Those oxides such as NO_2 and ClO_2, in which the nonmetal does not exhibit one of its common oxidation numbers, also react with water. In these reactions the nonmetal is both oxidized and reduced. For example,

$$\overset{+4\,-2}{3NO_2} + H_2O \longrightarrow \overset{+5}{2HNO_3} + \overset{+2}{NO}$$

$$\overset{+4}{6ClO_2} + 3H_2O \longrightarrow \overset{+5}{5HClO_3} + \overset{-1}{HCl}$$

Reactions in which the same element is both oxidized and reduced are called **disproportionation reactions.**

3. The relative acid strength of oxyacids can be predicted on the basis of the electronegativity and oxidation number of the central atom. The acid strength increases as the electronegativity of the central atom increases (see Section 16.5). For example, perchloric acid, $HClO_4$, is stronger than sulfuric acid, H_2SO_4, which in turn is stronger than phosphoric acid, H_3PO_4. For the same central atom, the acid strength increases as the oxidation number of the central atom increases. For example, nitric acid, HNO_3, is a stronger acid than nitrous acid, HNO_2; and sulfuric acid, H_2SO_4, is a stronger acid than sulfurous acid, H_2SO_3.

The binary hydrides of the nonmetals also exhibit acidic behavior in water, though only HCl, HBr, and HI are strong acids. The acid strength of the nonmetal hydrides increases from left to right across a period and down a group. For example, ammonia, NH_3, is a weaker acid than water, H_2O, which is weaker than hydrogen fluoride, HF. Water, H_2O, is also a weaker acid than hydrogen sulfide, H_2S, which is weaker than hydrogen selenide, H_2Se. Similarly, the basicity increases in the opposite direction.

21.3 Structures of the Nonmetals

Metals crystallize in closely packed arrays that do not contain molecules or covalent bonds (see Section 11.14). The structures of the nonmetals differ dramatically from those of metals. Nonmetal structures contain covalent bonds, and many nonmetals consist of individual molecules.

The noble gases are all monatomic, whereas the other nonmetal gases—hydrogen, nitrogen, oxygen, fluorine, and chlorine—exist as the diatomic molecules H_2, N_2, O_2, F_2, and Cl_2. The other halogens are also diatomic; Br_2 is a liquid, and I_2 and At_2 exist as solids. The changes in state as one moves down the halogen family offer an excellent example of the increasing strength of intermolecular dispersion forces with increasing molecular mass and increasing polarizability (see Section 11.3).

Allotropes are two or more forms of the same element that exhibit different structures in the same physical state. Several nonmetals exist as allotropes. In addition to diatomic O_2, elemental oxygen also occurs as the unstable allotrope O_3, which is called ozone (Fig. 21.5). Carbon, phosphorus, and sulfur are other examples of nonmetals that occur as allotropes.

A description of the physical properties of five nonmetals that are covalent solids follow.

Carbon. Graphite is one allotrope of naturally occurring carbon; diamond is the other (Fig. 21.6). Charcoal, coke, and carbon black are microcrystalline, amorphous forms of carbon with the graphite structure.

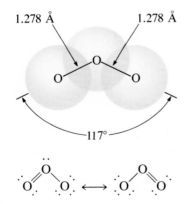

1.278 Å   1.278 Å

117°

Figure 21.5

The molecular structure of ozone. Its electronic structure is described by the resonance forms indicated.

Figure 21.6

The appearance of carbon as diamond and its appearance as graphite are strikingly different. Diamond is translucent; graphite is black. A natural diamond, which has been cut and polished, is shown in the center, surrounded by graphite.

The atoms in a crystal of diamond [Fig. 21.7(a)] are bonded into one giant molecule by single bonds. Each atom is covalently bonded to four others at the corners of a tetrahedron (sp^3 hybridization). The bonds are very strong and they extend throughout the crystal in three dimensions, making the crystal very hard and giving it a high melting point (~4400°C). Diamond does not conduct electricity because it has no mobile electrons. They are all used in sigma bonds.

Graphite is distinctly different from diamond. It is a soft, grayish-black, slippery solid that is not as dense as diamond. It crystallizes in hexagonal plates that have a metallic luster and conduct electricity. The conversion of graphite to diamond has a positive $\Delta H°$, so graphite is the more thermodynamically stable allotrope of carbon.

$$C(graphite) \longrightarrow C(diamond) \qquad \Delta H° = 1.9 \text{ kJ/mol}$$

Because this conversion is endothermic and the density of diamond is greater, diamond formation is favored by high temperature and high pressure. These conditions are applied in the commercial synthesis of industrial-grade diamonds.

The comparative softness, electrical conductivity, and lubricating properties of graphite are related to its structure [Fig. 21.7(b)]. A crystal of graphite consists of layers of carbon atoms, each atom having three atoms as near neighbors in a trigonal planar arrangement. Each carbon atom forms three σ bonds, one to each of its nearest neighbors in the layer, by means of sp^2 hybrid orbitals. The unhybridized p orbital on each

(a)

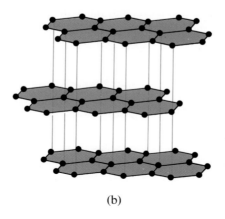

(b)

Figure 21.7

(a) The crystal structure of diamond. Each sphere represents a carbon atom. The black spheres indicate the atoms at the corners and the centers of the faces of a cubic face-centered unit cell. The red spheres indicate the atoms in tetrahedral sites. The covalent bonds are wedge-shaped to help show the perspective. (b) The crystal structure of graphite.

Figure 21.8

The orientation of unhybridized *p* orbitals of the carbon atoms in graphite. Each *p* orbital is perpendicular to the plane of carbon atoms.

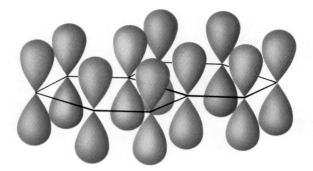

carbon atom projects above and below the layer (Fig. 21.8) and can overlap with the unhybridized *p* orbitals on the adjacent carbon atoms in the same layer. There is one electron for each unhybridized orbital, and these π electrons form π bonds to adjacent carbon atoms.

Many resonance formulas are necessary to describe the electronic structure of a graphite layer; two are shown in Fig. 21.9. The σ and π bonds bind the atoms tightly together *within* the layers. However, layers themselves can be separated easily because only weak van der Waals forces hold them together. These weak bonds give graphite the flaky, soft character that makes it useful as the "lead" in pencils. The word *graphite* is derived from a Greek word meaning "to write." The loosely held electrons of the mobile double bonds are responsible for the electrical conductivity of graphite.

The π bonding in graphite can also be described by molecular orbital theory. The unhybridized *p* orbitals on each carbon atom overlap to give molecular orbitals that extend over the entire layer like bands in a metal (Section 9.15), so an electron in one of these orbitals can move over the entire layer. Because the electron can move, graphite conducts electricity. A portion of one molecular orbital is shown in Fig. 21.10.

Phosphorus. The name *phosphorus* is derived from Greek words meaning "light-bringing." (When phosphorus was first isolated, scientists noted that it glowed in the dark and burned when exposed to air.) Although phosphorus is the only member of its group that is not found in the uncombined state in nature, it exists in many allotropic forms. We will consider three of those forms: **white phosphorus, red phosphorus,** and **black phosphorus.**

White phosphorus [Fig. 21.11(a)] is a white, waxy solid that melts at 44.2°C and boils at 280°C. It is insoluble in water (in which it is stored), is very soluble in carbon disulfide, and bursts into flame in air. As a solid, as a liquid, as a gas, and in solution, white phosphorus exists as P_4 molecules with the four phosphorus atoms arranged at the

Figure 21.9

Two of the many resonance forms of graphite necessary to describe its electronic structure, which is a resonance hybrid.

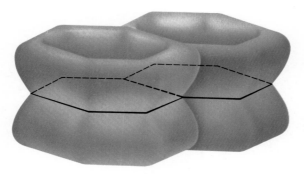

Figure 21.10

A portion of one molecular orbital in graphite, which contains delocalized π electrons.

(a)

(b)

Figure 21.11

(a) White phosphorus stored under water. (b) Red phosphorus.

corners of a regular tetrahedron. Each phosphorus atom is covalently bonded to the other three atoms in the molecule by covalent, single bonds [Figure 21.12(a)]. White phosphorus is the most reactive allotrope and is also very toxic.

Heating white phosphorus to 270–300°C in the absence of air yields red phosphorus [Fig. 21.11(b)]. Red phosphorus is more dense, has a higher melting point ($\sim$600°C), is much less reactive, is essentially nontoxic, and is easier and safer to handle than white phosphorus. Its structure is highly polymeric and appears to contain three-dimensional networks of P_4 tetrahedra joined by P–P single bonds [Fig. 21.12(b)]. Red phosphorus is insoluble in solvents that dissolve white phosphorus. When red phosphorus is heated, P_4 molecules sublime from the solid. This accounts for the fact that the products of the reactions of red phosphorus are usually the same as those produced when the white form reacts.

Black phosphorus is prepared by heating white phosphorus under high pressure (12,000 atm). The structure of black phosphorus contains puckered sheets of phosphorus atoms, each atom joined by single bonds to three other atoms [Fig. 21.12(c)]. As in red phosphorus, this interconnected structure gives black phosphorus a higher melting point, a higher boiling point, and lower reactivity than white phosphorus.

Arsenic. Arsenic also exists in several allotropic forms, the most stable of which is the gray, "metallic" form. This allotrope has a structure that contains sheets of arsenic atoms, each atom joined by single bonds to three other atoms within the sheet, a structure similar to that of black phosphorus.

Sulfur. The allotropy of sulfur is far greater and more complex than that of any other element. Sulfur is the "brimstone" referred to in the Bible, and references to sulfur occur throughout recorded history—right up to the relatively recent discovery that it is

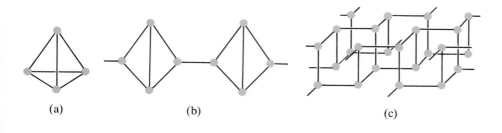

(a)   **(b)**   **(c)**

Figure 21.12

(a) The P_4 molecule found in white phosphorus. (b) The chain structure of red phosphorus. (c) The sheet structure of black phosphorus.

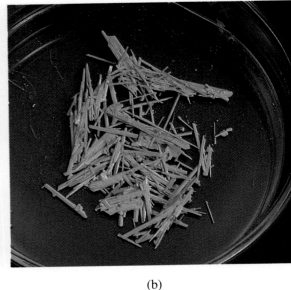

(a)

(b)

Figure 21.13

(a) Crystals of rhombic sulfur.
(b) Crystals of monoclinic sulfur.

a component of the atmosphere of Venus and Io, a moon of Jupiter. The most common and most stable allotrope of sulfur is yellow, **rhombic sulfur,** so named because of the shape of its crystals [Fig. 21.13(a)]. Rhombic sulfur is the form to which all other allotropes revert at room temperature. Crystals of rhombic sulfur melt at 113°C and form a straw-colored liquid. When this liquid cools and crystallizes, long needles of **monoclinic sulfur** are formed [Fig. 21.13(b)]. This is the stable form above 96°C. It melts at 119°C and is soluble in carbon disulfide. At room temperature it gradually reverts to the rhombic form.

Solid rhombic sulfur, rhombic sulfur at its melting point, solutions of rhombic sulfur in carbon disulfide, and monoclinic sulfur all contain S_8 molecules in which the atoms form eight-membered puckered rings that resemble crowns [Fig. 21.14(a)]. Each sulfur atom is bonded to each of its two neighbors in the ring by covalent S–S single bonds.

When rhombic sulfur melts, the straw-colored liquid is quite mobile [Fig. 21.15(a)]; its viscosity is low because S_8 molecules are essentially spherical and offer relatively little resistance as they move past each other. As the temperature rises, S–S bonds in the rings break, and polymeric chains of sulfur atoms result [Fig. 21.14(b)]. These chains combine end to end, forming still longer chains that become entangled with one another. The liquid gradually darkens in color and becomes so viscous that finally (at about 230°C) it does not pour easily [Fig. 21.15(b)]. The unpaired electrons at the ends of the chains of sulfur atoms are responsible for the dark red color. When the liquid is cooled rapidly, a rubberlike amorphous mass, called **plastic sulfur,** results [Fig. 21.15(c)].

Figure 21.14

(a) An S_8 molecule and (b) a chain
of sulfur atoms.

(a)

(b)

(a)

(b)

(c)

Figure 21.15

(a) Straw-colored, liquid rhombic sulfur. (b) Sulfur at about 230°C. (c) Formation of plastic sulfur.

Sulfur boils at 445°C and forms a vapor consisting of S_2, S_6, and S_8 molecules; at about 1000°C the vapor density corresponds to the formula S_2, which is a paramagnetic molecule like O_2 with a similar electronic structure and a sulfur–sulfur double bond.

Selenium. The structural behavior of selenium is somewhat less complicated than that of sulfur. Red **monoclinic selenium** consists of Se_8 rings, whereas gray, "metallic," **hexagonal selenium** comprises helical, polymeric chains of selenium atoms. **Black selenium,** which is the commercial form of the element, has a complex structure of large, polymeric rings of selenium.

An important feature of the structural behavior of the nonmetals is that the elements are usually found naturally with eight electrons in their valence shells. If necessary, the elements form enough covalent bonds to supplement the electrons already present in order to possess an octet. For example, in both diamond and graphite, carbon forms four covalent bonds and thus supplements its four valence electrons. The members of Group VA have five valence electrons and require only three additional electrons to fill their valence shells. These elements form three covalent bonds in their free state: triple bonds in the N_2 molecule and three single bonds to three different atoms in arsenic and in each of the allotropes of phosphorus that contains the P_4 unit. The elements of Group VIA require only two additional electrons. Oxygen forms a double bond in the O_2 molecule, and sulfur, selenium, and tellurium form two single bonds in various rings and chains. The halogens form diatomic molecules in which each atom is involved in only one bond. This provides the one electron required to supplement the seven electrons in the valence shells of the individual atoms. An atom of a noble gas contains eight electrons in its valence shell, and noble gases do not form covalent bonds to other noble gas atoms.

Finally, note again that only elements that are filling their second principal quantum shell ($n = 2$) consistently form strong multiple bonds. Larger elements have covalent radii that are not conducive to effective overlap of their *p* orbitals.

Chemical Behavior of the Nonmetals

Before we examine the chemical behavior of the nonmetals in this chapter and in Chapters 22 and 23 (as well as the chemistry of the semi-metals in Chapter 25), it will be helpful to review Lewis structures (originally discussed in Section 7.6) and the Lewis concept of acids and bases (originally discussed in Section 16.14). Briefly, a Lewis acid is any species that contains an empty valence shell orbital that can accept a pair of electrons, and a Lewis base is any species that has an unshared pair of electrons to donate. We can predict and understand many chemical reactions if we examine the electronic structures of the reactants to ascertain their Lewis acid–base characteristics. For example, the simplest Lewis acid is the proton, H^+, which contains an empty valence shell ($1s$) orbital, and the simplest Lewis base is the hydride ion, H^-, which has an unshared pair of electrons in its valence shell (also $1s$). Anytime a source of protons and a hydride ion are in proximity to one another, we can predict that hydrogen gas will be produced (Fig. 21.16).

$$H_3O^+ + H^- \longrightarrow H_2 + H_2O$$

Understanding this Lewis acid–base reaction enables us to predict that when a metal hydride is added to an acid or to water, hydrogen gas should be evolved.

$$CaH_2 + H_2O \longrightarrow Ca(OH)_2 + H_2(g)$$

This concept also makes it easy to understand why water can be formed when a proton source encounters the hydroxide ion, another Lewis base.

$$H_3O^+ + :\overset{..}{\underset{..}{O}}{-}H^- \longrightarrow 2 \quad \overset{..}{\underset{H \quad H}{O}}$$

We also recognize this reaction as a Brønsted acid–Brønsted base reaction (see Section 16.1).

Many molecules of the nonmetals and the semi-metals contain empty valence orbitals or unshared electron pairs. Here again, their Lewis structures account for much of their chemical behavior. For example, using Lewis acid–base concepts we can explain why water, a Lewis base with two unshared electron pairs on oxygen, does not react with carbon tetrachloride, CCl_4, but does react with silicon tetrachloride, $SiCl_4$. The Lewis structures of CCl_4 and $SiCl_4$ are identical, because carbon and silicon both belong to Group IVA and have the same number of valence electrons.

$$\begin{array}{cc} :\overset{..}{Cl}: & :\overset{..}{Cl}: \\ | & | \\ :\overset{..}{Cl}{-}\overset{..}{\underset{|}{C}}{-}\overset{..}{Cl}: \quad & :\overset{..}{Cl}{-}\overset{..}{\underset{|}{Si}}{-}\overset{..}{Cl}: \\ :\overset{..}{Cl}: & :\overset{..}{Cl}: \end{array}$$

However, these two molecules differ in that carbon is using all of its valence orbitals (a $2s$ orbital and three $2p$ orbitals) for bonding, whereas silicon uses its $3s$ orbital and its three $3p$ orbitals but still has five empty $3d$ orbitals. Thus, whereas the carbon atom in CCl_4 can be considered neither a Lewis acid nor a Lewis base, the silicon atom in $SiCl_4$ (with empty valence shell orbitals) is a Lewis acid and should react with the Lewis base H_2O.

Figure 21.16

Calcium hydride reacts rapidly with water, producing $H_2(g)$ and $Ca(OH)_2$.

The initial step in the reaction of $SiCl_4$ with H_2O is the formation of an unstable Lewis acid–Lewis base adduct (a compound that contains a coordinate covalent bond) to form $SiCl_4 \cdot H_2O$. A molecule of hydrogen chloride then leaves.

Unstable

This happens four times, producing $Si(OH)_4$, which is unstable and decomposes to SiO_2 and two molecules of water.

㉑.4   Hydrogen

An uncombined hydrogen atom consists of one proton in the nucleus and one valence electron in the $1s$ orbital. The $n = 1$ valence shell has a capacity of two electrons, and hydrogen can rightfully occupy two locations in the periodic table. It can be considered a Group IA element because it has only one valence electron, and it can be considered a Group VIIA element because it needs only one additional electron to fill its valence shell. Thus hydrogen can lose an electron to form the proton, H^+, it can gain an electron to form a hydride ion, H^-, or it can share an electron to form a single, covalent bond. In reality, hydrogen is a unique element that almost deserves its own location in the periodic table.

Hydrogen has two additional isotopes (see Section 3.3 and Table 3.1). **Deuterium,** which contains one proton and one neutron in the nucleus, accounts for 0.0156% of naturally occurring hydrogen. **Tritium,** whose nucleus contains one proton and two neutrons, exists naturally in only trace quantities and is radioactive.

Hydrogen (H_2) is a colorless, tasteless, odorless gas that is relatively unreactive at ordinary temperatures due, in part, to the relatively high hydrogen–hydrogen bond strength. At higher temperatures, it enters into many chemical reactions. It directly reacts with many nonmetals (such as the halogens, oxygen, and nitrogen), producing covalent hydrides. These hydrides (as well as hydrides of nonmetals that do not react *directly* with hydrogen) can also be prepared by the reaction of an anion of the nonmetal with an acid. For example, phosphine, PH_3, can easily be prepared by adding acid to magnesium phosphide, Mg_3P_2, or aluminum phosphide, AlP. Again, this illustrates the fact that the phosphide ion, P^{3-}, is a good Lewis base (and Brønsted base) that readily combines with H^+, a Lewis acid.

The active metals in Groups IA and IIA react directly with hydrogen to form white, crystalline ionic hydrides of the formulas MH and MH_2 that contain the hydride anion, H^-. Hydrogen is absorbed by many transition metals as well as by the lanthanide and actinide metals.

Hydrogen gas, H_2, is a reducing agent. That is, the hydrogen loses electrons and its oxidation number increases from 0 to $+1$. It reacts with many heated metal oxides to reduce the metal and form water. For example, copper and water are formed when hydrogen gas is passed over heated copper(II) oxide, CuO (Fig. 21.17).

Figure 21.17
Copper is produced from CuO by
heating in an atmosphere of H_2.

㉑.5 Carbon

Carbon, the first element of Group IVA, is the only nonmetal in this group. Of the other members, silicon and germanium are semi-metals (Chapter 25), and tin and lead are post-transition metals (Chapter 28). Even though their properties are quite different, gaseous atoms of all these elements have the same ns^2np^2 valence shell electron configuration.

Almost all compounds of carbon are covalent. Exceptions occur in the case of very electropositive metals; with these, carbon forms **carbides,** in which carbon anions exist. Like the first element in every other group, carbon has no d orbitals in its valence shell, so it cannot exceed an octet of bonding electrons. Generally all four of its valence electrons are used in bonding, and its hybridization can be sp, sp^2, or sp^3. Thus the coordination number of carbon can be 2, 3, or 4, and its molecular geometry can be linear, trigonal planar, or tetrahedral (see Sections 8.5–8.8 and Fig. 30.1 for depiction of geometry).

Carbon in the form of diamond is very unreactive at room temperature, although it will burn in air at high temperatures. Graphite, because of its layer structure, is more reactive, although carbon is not considered a very reactive element. Graphite is oxidized by hot oxyacids such as HNO_3 and reacts with other elements at high temperatures. It burns in the presence of oxygen to form carbon monoxide, CO, or carbon dioxide, CO_2, depending on the amount of oxygen present. It is also a relatively good reducing agent, reacting with many oxides to form the element or a carbide and CO or CO_2.

$$SiO_2 + C \xrightarrow{\Delta} Si + CO_2$$
$$CaO + 3C \xrightarrow{\Delta} CaC_2 + CO$$

21.6 Nitrogen, Phosphorus, and Arsenic

The nonmetals in Group VA are nitrogen, phosphorus, and arsenic. Antimony is a semi-metal and bismuth is a metal. As we consistently find with the first element in a group, some of the chemical properties of nitrogen are anomalous. Other family members follow the expected trends.

The valence shell electron configuration of the gaseous atoms of Group VA elements is ns^2np^3, and the three p electrons are unpaired in accordance with Hund's rule (every orbital in a subshell is singly occupied before any orbital in that subshell is doubly occupied; Section 5.11). Nitrogen has no d orbitals, so it cannot exceed an octet; all other members of the group have empty valence shell d orbitals. In their covalent compounds, all three elements can form sp, sp^2, and sp^3 hybrid orbitals, and phosphorus and arsenic can also form sp^3d and sp^3d^2 hybrid orbitals. Nitrogen is the only member of the group that readily forms multiple bonds. Nitrogen has an electronegativity value of 3.0 (Table 7.2), which is higher than that of every other element except oxygen and fluorine.

The three Group VA nonmetals fill their valence shells by gaining electrons to form anions or by sharing their electrons to form covalent molecules. Compounds of nitrogen, phosphorus, and arsenic with the electropositive metals of Groups IA and IIA contain the strong Lewis bases nitride ion, N^{3-}, phosphide ion, P^{3-}, and arsenide ion, As^{3-}. Covalent compounds of nitrogen, phosphorus, and arsenic are generally trigonal pyramidal with an unshared pair of electrons, and in the case of nitrogen, multiply bonded molecules or ions are possible.

In these Lewis structures and those in the remainder of the chapter, the three unshared pairs of electrons on halogen atoms bonded to a central atom have been omitted for clarity.

Because of the great strength of the $N\equiv N$ bond, gaseous nitrogen is relatively inert at room temperature, whereas phosphorus and arsenic are reactive even at low temperatures. Further differences between nitrogen and other group members are apparent in their chemistry. Nitrogen and oxygen react in an endothermic reaction to yield either NO or NO_2, depending on the amount of oxygen present (Fig. 21.18). In excess oxygen, nitrogen dioxide is the product. An examination of the Lewis resonance structures of this molecule shows that it is paramagnetic with an unpaired electron on nitrogen.

Because of the unpaired electron, it should not be surprising that NO_2 exists in equilibrium with its dimer, N_2O_4. A **dimer** is a molecule consisting of two identical, simpler units that are sometimes called **monomers.**

Phosphorus and arsenic, in contrast to nitrogen, react with oxygen to yield P_4O_6 and As_4O_6 or P_4O_{10} and As_4O_{10}, depending on whether an excess of oxygen is present. (See

Figure 21.18

Lightning provides the energy necessary for the reaction of nitrogen with oxygen in the atmosphere. Each year lightning converts about 40 million tons of N_2 to NO.

Fig. 23.29 for the structures of P_4O_6 and P_4O_{10}.) These molecules preserve the basic tetrahedral structure found in elemental phosphorus and elemental arsenic (at elevated temperatures). Phosphorus and arsenic react readily with the halogens, yielding the trihalide or the pentahalide; nitrogen does not react directly with chlorine, bromine, or iodine.

$$P_4(xs) + 6F_2 \longrightarrow 4PF_3$$

$$P_4 + 10F_2(xs) \longrightarrow 4PF_5$$

Whereas phosphorus and arsenic react with other nonmetals and with many metals, nitrogen is generally unreactive.

21.7 Oxygen, Sulfur, and Selenium

Group VIA is made up of the nonmetals oxygen, sulfur, and selenium, the semi-metal tellurium, and the metal polonium. The gaseous atoms of these elements have valence shell electron configurations of ns^2np^4. The three nonmetals in this group fill their valence shells by gaining two electrons to form the divalent anions O^{2-}, S^{2-}, and Se^{2-} or by sharing electrons in covalent bonds.

Oxygen is the second most electronegative element in the periodic table—it is exceeded only by fluorine. Because it is so electronegative, oxygen almost always has a negative oxidation number. But sulfur and selenium, which have very similar electronegativity values, display common oxidation numbers of -2, $+2$, $+4$, and $+6$. In its covalent compounds, oxygen is the central atom only when it is combined with hydrogen or fluorine; in these compounds the hybridization of oxygen is generally regarded as sp^3. Examples include water, H_2O, hydrogen peroxide, H_2O_2, oxygen difluoride, OF_2, and dioxygen difluoride, O_2F_2. Oxygen readily forms multiple bonds with itself and with other elements.

Sulfur and selenium also form multiple bonds with other elements and are involved in covalent bonds in which their hybridizations can be sp^2, sp^3, sp^3d, or sp^3d^2. Again we see that oxygen cannot exceed an octet in its bonding, whereas the heavier elements are able to do so.

Elemental oxygen, O_2, is notable for its paramagnetism (Section 9.11). It contains two unpaired electrons—a characteristic that is not predicted by its Lewis structure. It is a strong oxidizing agent and forms compounds with every element in the periodic table except the first four noble gases, He, Ne, Ar, and Kr. Sulfur and selenium are also reactive elements, though less so than oxygen. Sulfur combines directly with all elements except iodine, nitrogen, tellurium, the noble gases, and a few transition metals. Selenium is only slightly less reactive.

Figure 21.19
Zinc reacts with sulfur in a vigorous exothermic reaction.

As we noted in Chapter 13, in addition to forming the oxide ion, O^{2-}, oxygen can also form the peroxide ion, O_2^{2-}, and the superoxide ion, O_2^-. Sulfur and selenium oxidize most metals to form sulfide, S^{2-}, and selenide, Se^{2-}, ions (Fig. 21.19). They also form disulfide and diselenide ions, S_2^{2-} and Se_2^{2-}, respectively, as well as larger polysulfide and polyselenide ions, S_n^{2-} and Se_n^{2-}. For example, sodium and sulfur react as follows:

$$2Na + S \longrightarrow Na_2S$$

$$Na_2S + S \longrightarrow Na_2S_2$$

$$Na_2S + 4S \longrightarrow Na_2S_5$$

Sulfur and selenium are oxidized by nonmetals that are more electronegative, such as oxygen and the halogens. The reduced stability of the highest oxidation number of the heavier members of a group is illustrated by the reactions of sulfur and selenium with oxygen. When sulfur burns in air, it forms sulfur dioxide and a little sulfur trioxide. More sulfur trioxide forms when sulfur or sulfur dioxide is heated with oxygen in the presence of a catalyst. The heavier element selenium forms selenium dioxide when heated in air or oxygen, but selenium trioxide cannot be made by heating selenium or selenium dioxide with oxygen, because it is unstable and decomposes above 180°C.

㉑.8 Fluorine, Chlorine, Bromine, and Iodine

The nonmetals fluorine, chlorine, bromine, iodine, and astatine constitute Group VIIA of the periodic table (the halogens). Astatine is a very radioactive element that decays rapidly; it will not be considered in this chapter.

The valence shell of a gaseous halogen atom has the electron configuration ns^2np^5. A halogen can complete its octet by gaining an electron to form a halide ion, X^-, or by sharing an electron to form a covalent compound. Because fluorine has no d orbitals and is the most electronegative element, it forms only one single covalent bond with less electronegative nonmetals. In any Lewis structure, fluorine is *always* a terminal atom, never a central atom. Other halogens may form several bonds with nonmetal atoms that are more electronegative.

All of the halogens are oxidizing agents. Fluorine is the strongest oxidizing agent of all the elements. Because of its very large first ionization energy, it is never oxidized, and there is no evidence of a positive oxidation state for fluorine. Halogens become progressively weaker oxidizing agents as their ionization energies—and hence their nonmetallic character—decrease down the group.

An elemental halogen oxidizes less electronegative halogens (poorer oxidizing agents) and halide ions that are formed from less electronegative halogens. For example, fluorine oxidizes chlorine, bromine, and iodine (or their anions), whereas chlorine oxidizes only bromine and iodine (or their anions).

All of the halogens except fluorine form some compounds in which they exhibit a positive oxidation number. With the one exception of fluorine, the chemical properties of the halogens differ in degree rather than in kind. The high ionization energies make the formation of positive halogen ions most unlikely, except possibly for iodine. On the other hand, positive oxidation numbers of +1, +3, +5, and +7 (and sometimes other oxidation numbers) are observed in covalent compounds of the halogens with oxygen in oxides, oxyacids, and salts of these oxyacids, or in compounds with more electronegative halogens, such as ICl_3 and BrF_5.

21 .9 Helium, Neon, Argon, Krypton, Xenon, and Radon

Because the noble gases have valence shell electron configurations of ns^2 (He) or ns^2np^6 (all others), we would expect them not to be very reactive. Also, because ionization energy decreases down a group, we would expect that only the heavier noble gases might react—and then only with strong oxidizing agents. With the exception of a few krypton compounds (for example, KrF_2), all noble gas compounds are xenon compounds. They are xenon–fluorine, xenon–oxygen, xenon–nitrogen, xenon–oxyfluorine, and xenon–carbon–fluorine compounds. Xenon fluorides (XeF_2, XeF_4, and XeF_6) are prepared by direct reaction of xenon and fluorine in different ratios. The hybridizations of xenon in the three fluorides are sp^3d, sp^3d^2, and sp^3d^3. Oxygen-containing xenon compounds come from reactions of the fluorides with water. For example, xenon hexafluoride reacts with water to form either $XeOF_4$ or XeO_3, depending on the amount of water present.

$$XeF_6 + H_2O \longrightarrow XeOF_4 + 2HF$$

$$XeF_6 + 3H_2O \longrightarrow XeO_3 + 6HF$$

All the compounds of xenon are strong oxidizing agents in which xenon is reduced to xenon gas in oxidation–reduction reactions.

㉑.10 Compounds of the Nonmetals

The nonmetals form binary ionic compounds with the active metals (Chapter 13) and with most other metals with oxidation numbers of +1, +2, and +3. With metals of oxidation number +4 or higher, the nonmetals form covalent compounds or compounds with a substantial amount of covalent behavior. The nonmetals form covalent binary compounds with other nonmetals and with semi-metals.

Hydrides. Hydrogen compounds of the Group IA metals and of Ca, Sr, and Ba in Group IIA are ionic compounds that contain hydrogen as the hydride anion, H^-. The hydride ion is a strong Lewis base and it is a strong reducing agent. As we noted earlier, H^- reacts vigorously with any source of the Lewis acid H^+ to form hydrogen gas.

Hydrogen is absorbed by many transition metals, lanthanide metals, and actinide metals, producing materials that are called **metallic hydrides** because they exhibit many metallic properties. For example, they are electrical conductors. These hydrides do not contain hydride ions; instead, hydrogen atoms are located in the spaces between the metal atoms, and the compounds are generally nonreactive.

Most hydrides of the nonmetals exhibit acidic behavior. The compounds HCl, HBr, and HI are strong Brønsted acids (see Section 16.5); HF, H_2O, H_2S, and H_2Se are weak Brønsted acids. Ammonia, NH_3, and phosphine, PH_3, are not acidic and instead function as Lewis bases (and Brønsted bases), reacting with the Lewis acid H^+, from water in aqueous solution, to yield basic solutions.

$$\overset{..}{\underset{H\ \overset{|}{\underset{H}{}}\ H}{N}} + H_2O \rightleftharpoons NH_4{}^+ + OH^-$$

Most binary hydrides of carbon are neither acidic nor basic in water.

Chloride, bromide, and iodide ions are weak Lewis and Brønsted bases, and fluoride ion is moderately weak. All other monatomic negative ions, such as the hydride ion, H^-, the nitride ion, N^{3-}, and the sulfide ion, S^{2-}, are very strong bases and pick up hydrogen ions from acids (even weak acids such as water), forming the hydrides.

Oxides. Oxygen forms binary compounds with all of the elements except He, Ne, Ar, and Kr. Metals and nonmetals can exhibit their highest oxidation numbers in compounds with oxygen (and fluorine; see the following discussion of halides). The oxides of the alkali metals, of the alkaline earth metals, and of the transition metals and post-transition metals in their lower oxidation states (+1, +2, +3) are ionic in their behavior; they contain the oxide ion, O^{2-}. The oxides of the metals with high oxidation numbers are covalent in character. Nonmetal oxides are also covalent (and usually molecular).

The oxide ion is strongly basic, and all soluble and most insoluble *ionic* oxides react with acids, giving water and a salt of the metal. Ionic metal oxides that are soluble react with water to form metal hydroxides (see Section 13.5). The soluble ionic oxides include most of the oxides of the active metals. Ionic transition metal oxides and post-transition metal oxides are generally not soluble in water.

Most nonmetal oxides are acidic and react with water to form oxyacids (Section 21.2).

$$SO_2 + H_2O \longrightarrow H_2SO_3$$

A few nonmetal oxides, such as CO and N_2O, do not react with water. Covalent oxides of the transition metals and post-transition metals with higher oxidation numbers also exhibit acidic behavior. These either react with water and form acids or neutralize bases and form salts.

$$CrO_3 + H_2O \longrightarrow H_2CrO_4$$

$$SnO_2 + Ca(OH)_2 \longrightarrow CaSnO_3 + H_2O$$

The ease with which elemental oxygen picks up electrons is mirrored by the difficulty of removing electrons from oxygen in most oxides. Of all the elements, only the very reactive fluorine molecule oxidizes oxides to form oxygen.

Halides. Halogens form compounds with almost all of the other elements, including other halogens. Metals and nonmetals with their highest oxidation numbers are usually found as fluorides (or oxides). For example, sulfur exhibits an oxidation number of +6 in sulfur(VI) fluoride, SF_6, but the highest oxidation number for sulfur in a binary chloride is +4, found in sulfur(IV) chloride, SCl_4. The only bromide is sulfur(I) bromide, S_2Br_2, and sulfur iodides are not known. The halides become progressively better reducing agents as they become heavier, reflecting the increasing ease of removing electrons from larger atoms or ions. The iodide ion is a better reducing agent than the bromide ion, which in turn is a better reducing agent than the chloride ion. Thus the heavier a halide ion, the more likely it is to reduce a metal or nonmetal with a high oxidation number, and the less stable are halides of the heavier halogens with other elements with higher oxidation numbers.

The variation in properties among the halides ranges from those of ionic species to those of covalent molecules (Fig. 21.20). The halides of the alkali metals, of the alkaline earth metals, and of the transition metals in their lower oxidation states (+1, +2, +3) are ionic in their behavior. These ionic compounds tend to have high melting points (above 400°C) and high electrical conductivities in the molten state. Those that are soluble in water form hydrated metal ions and halide ions.

The halides of the nonmetals, as well as those of the metals with high charges and small sizes and/or high oxidation states, are covalent in character. In the covalent metal halides, the attraction of the metal for the valence electrons of the halide ion produces the covalent behavior. These halides are characterized by low melting points, by volatility, by solubility in nonpolar solvents, and by lack of electrical conductivity in the molten state.

Except for the halides of carbon and nitrogen, most covalent halides react with water to form a covalent oxide or hydroxide and the corresponding hydrohalic acid, as indicated by the reactions of PI_3 and WCl_6 with water.

$$PI_3 + 3H_2O \longrightarrow P(OH)_3 + 3HI$$

$$WCl_6 + 3H_2O \longrightarrow WO_3 + 6HCl$$

The formula of $P(OH)_3$ is usually written as H_3PO_3 because the compound is an acid, the weak acid called phosphorous acid.

As might be expected, some metal halides are intermediate in character between the ionic and covalent ones. For example, iron(III) chloride, $FeCl_3$, is volatile and has a low

F⁻ Sr^{2+}

SrF_2, a solid

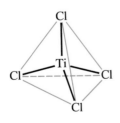

$TiCl_4$, a liquid

Figure 21.20

The structures of SrF_2, an ionic solid, and $TiCl_4$, a covalent liquid.

melting point. It also reacts with water, giving an acid solution; however, it is a good conductor of electricity in the molten state.

For Review

Summary

The noble gases and those elements with electronegativities greater than or equal to that of hydrogen are considered nonmetals. These elements are hydrogen (Group IA or VIIA); carbon (Group IVA); nitrogen and phosphorus (Group VA); oxygen, sulfur, and selenium (Group VIA); fluorine, chlorine, bromine, iodine, and astatine (Group VIIA); and helium, neon, argon, krypton, xenon, and radon (Group VIIIA). Compounds of the nonmetals with active metals, or with most other metals with oxidation numbers of $+1$, $+2$, and $+3$, are ionic and contain the nonmetal as a negative ion. Nonmetals form covalent compounds with other nonmetals and with metals with large charges and small sizes or high oxidation numbers. With the exception of the hydrides of C, N, and P, the hydrides of the nonmetals generally are acidic, as are the oxides. The nonmetals become progressively better oxidizing agents as their electronegativity increases (except for nitrogen, which is an anomalously weak oxidizing agent).

Hydrogen has the chemical properties of a nonmetal with a relatively low electronegativity. It forms ionic hydrides with active metals, covalent compounds in which it has an oxidation number of -1 with less electronegative elements, and covalent compounds in which it has an oxidation number of $+1$ with more electronegative nonmetals. It reacts with oxygen, sulfur, nitrogen, and the halogens. Hydrogen reduces the oxides of many metals, forming the metal and water.

Carbon (Group IVA) exhibits oxidation numbers ranging from -4 to $+4$. It is covalently bonded in the vast majority of its compounds. The only nonmetals that oxidize carbon are oxygen, sulfur, and fluorine; carbon is a relatively nonreactive nonmetal.

Nitrogen (Group VA) exhibits all oxidation numbers from -3 to $+5$. Phosphorus and arsenic commonly exhibit an oxidation number of -3 with active metals and of $+3$ and $+5$ with more electronegative nonmetals. Phosphorus and arsenic are oxidized by halogens and by oxygen. Elemental nitrogen is not very reactive.

The nonmetals of Group VIA (O, S, and Se) form compounds with almost all of the elements. Oxygen is a strong oxidizing agent, and sulfur and selenium are good oxidizing agents. Except in a few compounds with fluorine, oxygen exhibits negative oxidation numbers in all of its compounds; the most common is -2, in ionic and covalent oxides. Other oxidation numbers are found in peroxides (O_2^{2-}) and superoxides (O_2^-), compounds which contain O–O bonds. Sulfur and selenium exhibit oxidation numbers of -2, $+2$, $+4$, and $+6$ in their compounds.

The halogens are members of Group VIIA. The heavier halogens form compounds in which they have oxidation numbers of -1, $+1$, $+3$, $+5$, and $+7$, although they sometimes exhibit other oxidation numbers. Fluorine is a very potent oxidizing agent and forms compounds in which it always exhibits an oxidation number of -1. The oxidizing ability of the elemental halogens and the resistance of halide anions to oxidation decrease as halogen size increases.

The noble gas elements exhibit a very limited chemistry. Krypton and xenon react with fluorine, forming KrF_2 and the xenon fluorides XeF_2, XeF_4, and XeF_6. Xenon oxides may be prepared by the reaction of water with the fluorides.

Key Terms and Concepts

acid anhydride (21.2)
allotrope (21.3)
carbide (21.5)
catenation (21.1)
deuterium (21.4)
dimer (21.6)
diselenide (21.7)
disproportionation reaction (21.2)

disulfide (21.7)
halide (21.10)
hydride (21.10)
Lewis acid–Lewis base behavior
  (21.2)
metalloid (21.1)
monomer (21.6)

oxide (21.10)
peroxide (21.7)
polyselenide (21.7)
polysulfide (21.7)
semi-metal (21.1)
sulfide (21.7)
tritium (21.4)

Exercises

Answers for selected even-numbered exercises marked by red numbers appear at the end of the book. The worked-out solutions to all even-numbered exercises appear in the *Solutions Guide*.

1. Both nitrogen and oxygen are colorless, odorless, and tasteless gases. How can we distinguish between them using chemical properties?
2. Both N_2 and F_2 are diatomic molecules. How do the chemical bonds in the molecules differ, and how are they similar?
3. Describe five chemical properties of phosphorus, or of compounds of phosphorus, that characterize it as a nonmetal.
4. Compare and contrast the chemical properties of elemental oxygen and sulfur.
5. With what element(s) can bromine form binary compounds in which it exhibits a positive oxidation number?
6. Carbon monoxide, CO, and nitrogen, N_2, are isoelectronic gases, both of which have triple bonds. Would you consider these molecules Lewis acids or Lewis bases?
7. Which of the following elements exhibit a positive oxidation number when combined with selenium? With phosphorus?
   (a) Ga   (d) I   (f) N
   (b) Cl   (e) F   (g) Si
   (c) Mg
8. Why does carbon form a maximum of four single covalent bonds?
9. From the positions of the elements in the periodic table, answer the following:
   (a) Does Cl_2 or C reduce S?
   (b) Does Li_2O or ClO_2 neutralize H_2SO_4?
   (c) Does P_4 or Cl_2 oxide S?
   (d) Does Al or Cl_2 oxidize P_4?
   (e) Does Zn or O_2 reduce Se?
   (f) Does Li_2O or SO_2 neutralize $NH_3(aq)$?
10. Classify each of the following as a Lewis acid or a Lewis base.
    (a) HS^- (d) CO   (g) F^-
    (b) P_4 (e) As^{3-} (h) H^+
    (c) PH_3 (f) H^- (i) Se^{2-}
11. Which anion in each of the following groups is most difficult to oxidize?

(a) I^-, Cl^-, F^- (c) As^{3-}, P^{3-}, N^{3-}
(b) O^{2-}, S^{2-}, Se^{2-} (d) N^{3-}, O^{2-}, F^-

12. Write a complete and balanced equation for the reaction of each of the following compounds with water.
    (a) XeF_6 (d) P_4O_6 (g) N_2O_3
    (b) SO_3 (e) Cl_2O_3 (h) NO_2
    (c) SeO_2 (f) SeO_3 (i) Mg_3P_2

13. Arrange the members of each of the following groups in order of decreasing acid strength. (You may need to refer to Section 16.3.)
    (a) HF, HCl, HBr, HI   (c) H_2O, H_2S, H_2Se, H_2Te
    (b) HF, H_2O, NH_3, CH_4 (d) NH_3, PH_3, AsH_3

Hydrogen

14. Why does hydrogen not exhibit an oxidation number of -1 when bonded to nonmetals?
15. Which of the binary hydrogen compounds of the nonmetals is the strongest acid? Which is the weakest acid?
16. The reaction of calcium hydride, CaH_2, with water can be characterized as a Lewis acid–base reaction.

$$CaH_2 + 2H_2O \longrightarrow Ca(OH)_2 + 2H_2$$

Identify the Lewis acid and the Lewis base among the reactants. The reaction is also an oxidation–reduction reaction. Identify the oxidizing agent, the reducing agent, and the changes in oxidation number that occur in the reaction.
17. In drawing Lewis structures, we learn that hydrogen forms only one single bond in covalent compounds. Why?
18. What mass of CaH_2 is required to react with water to provide enough hydrogen gas to fill a balloon at 20°C and 0.8 atm pressure with a volume of 4.5 L? (For the balanced equation, see Exercise 16.)
19. What mass of hydrogen gas results from the reaction of 8.5 g of KH with water?

$$KH + H_2O \longrightarrow KOH + H_2$$

Carbon

20. Write the Lewis structure for carbon monoxide, and explain how it can act as a Lewis base.

21. What are the four quantum numbers for each electron in a carbon atom?

22. Write the Lewis structures for ethane, C_2H_6, ethylene, C_2H_4, and acetylene, C_2H_2. What is the geometry around each carbon atom? What is the hybridization of carbon in each molecule?

23. Describe the crystal structures of graphite and diamond, and relate the physical properties of each to its structure.

24. Calculate ΔG°_{298} for the following reaction.

$$C(s, \textit{diamond}) \longrightarrow C(s, \textit{graphite})$$

Is the reaction spontaneous?

25. Predict whether each of the following molecules is polar or nonpolar. (*Hint:* You may want to review Section 8.3.)
   (a) HCN   (c) H_2CO (e) CH_3OH
   (b) CH_2F_2 (d) C_2H_2 (f) CCl_4

Nitrogen, Phosphorus, and Arsenic

26. Draw the Lewis structures of NO_2, NO_2^-, and NO_2^+. Predict the ONO bond angle in each species, and give the hybridization of the nitrogen in each species.

27. Predict whether each of the following molecules is a Lewis acid or a Lewis base or could act as either.
   (a) PF_3 (d) AsH_3 (f) P_4
   (b) PH_4^+ (e) NH_2^- (g) N_2H_4
   (c) AsF_5

28. What mass of gaseous ammonia can be produced from the reaction of 3.0 g of hydrogen gas and 3.0 g of nitrogen gas?

29. Although PF_5 and AsF_5 are stable, nitrogen does not form NF_5 molecules. Explain this difference among members of the same group.

30. The phosphorus–phosphorus triple bond energy is 490 kJ/mol. Refer to Table 7.3 to obtain the bond energy of a phosphorus–phosphorus single bond, and calculate the approximate value of ΔH for the following reaction.

$$P_4(g) \longrightarrow 2P_2(g)$$

31. Use Table 7.3 to compare the strength of a nitrogen–nitrogen single bond and a nitrogen–nitrogen triple bond. Is the triple bond stronger or weaker than three single bonds?

32. Complete and balance each of the following equations (*xs* indicates that the reactant is present in excess).
   (a) $P_4 + xsS \longrightarrow$ (d) $P_4 + Mg \longrightarrow$
   (b) $P_4 + Li \longrightarrow$ (e) $P_4 + xsF_2 \longrightarrow$
   (c) $P_4 + xsO_2 \longrightarrow$

Oxygen, Sulfur, and Selenium

33. Classify each of the following molecules as a Lewis acid, a Lewis base, or a molecule that could function as either.
   (a) H_2Se (c) H_3O^+ (e) SF_4
   (b) S^{2-} (d) O_2 (f) O_2^{2-}

34. Write Lewis structures for the two allotropes of oxygen. What is wrong with the Lewis structure for O_2?

35. Determine the oxidation number of selenium in each of the following species.
   (a) HSe^- (c) SeO_2 (e) Se_2^{2-}
   (b) $SeCl_2$ (d) SeF_6 (f) H_2SeO_4

36. Write chemical equations describing three chemical reactions in which elemental selenium acts as an oxidizing agent and three chemical reactions in which it acts as a reducing agent.

37. Refer to Table 6.4. Do the first ionization energies of oxygen, sulfur, and selenium indicate the correct order of increasing metallic character?

38. Predict the product when elemental sulfur reacts with a large excess of fluorine gas. If 5.75 g of sulfur is used in this reaction, what mass of the predicted product is formed?

39. Write a balanced equation for the reaction that occurs when each of the following is burned in excess oxygen.
   (a) C   (c) As   (e) Li
   (b) Al   (d) Ca   (f) P_4

40. What mass of oxygen gas is required to prepare 32.7 g of Na_2O? What is the volume of the gas at STP?

41. Sulfur can form SF_2, SF_4, and SF_6, whereas oxygen forms only OF_2. Explain.

42. Describe the different structures that are found when elemental sulfur is heated beginning with the solid through the formation of sulfur vapor.

43. What is the hybridization of selenium and the molecular geometry of each of the following compounds: SeF_2, SeF_4, and SeF_6?

44. Which is the stronger acid, H_2SO_4 or H_2SeO_4? Why?

Halogens

45. Which is the strongest acid, HOF, HOCl, HOBr, or HOI? Explain your choice.

46. Which of the following is the strongest acid: HOCl, $HClO_2$, $HClO_3$, or $HClO_4$? Explain your choice.

47. Write the Lewis structure for each of the following species.
   (a) HF   (c) PBr_3 (e) IF_7
   (b) I_3^- (d) HOI   (f) ClF_3

48. Does an examination of the first ionization energies of the halogens support the generalization that electropositive character increases down the group? Explain.

49. Write a balanced chemical equation describing the reaction that occurs in each of the following cases.
   (a) Magnesium is added to hydrochloric acid.
   (b) Sodium hydroxide is added to hydrobromic acid.
   (c) Ammonia gas is bubbled through hydroiodic acid.
   (d) Bromine is bubbled through hydroiodic acid.

50. Elemental chlorine can be prepared by adding dilute hydrochloric acid slowly to solid manganese dioxide, MnO_2. The manganese is reduced in this reaction to aqueous Mn^{2+} (as $MnCl_2$), and water is also produced. How many milliliters of 2.25 M HCl is needed to completely react with 14.5 g of MnO_2?

$$MnO_2 + 4HCl \longrightarrow MnCl_2 + 2H_2O + Cl_2$$

51. Excess fluorine reacts with elemental phosphorus to form phosphorus pentafluoride, PF_5. How many grams of PF_5 can be prepared from 8.25 g of phosphorus?

52. From the data given in Appendix I, calculate the free energy change for the reaction of hydrogen with each of the halogens. Determine which of these reactions is not spontaneous at 25°C.

53. Obtain the bond energies of the F–F, Cl–Cl, Br–Br, and I–I bonds from the data given in Appendix I, and arrange these molecules in increasing order of their X–X bond energies.

Noble Gases

54. Draw the molecular orbital diagram for He_2. What is the He–He bond order? Would this same bond order be calculated for the other noble gases? Does this explain why the noble gas elements exist as monatomic elements? Explain.

55. Draw the Lewis structure, and give the hybridization, of xenon in each of the following molecules:
    (a) XeF_2 (c) XeF_6 (e) XeO_4
    (b) XeF_4 (d) XeO_3 (f) $XeOF_4$

56. What is the molecular geometry of each of the following compounds: XeF_2, XeF_4, and XeO_4?

57. Iodide ion in acid reacts with XeO_3 to produce xenon gas, water, and the triiodide ion (I_3^-). Write a balanced equation for this reaction.

58. A 0.492-g sample of a xenon–fluorine compound exerts a pressure of 47.8 torr at 127°C in a bulb with a volume of 1238 mL. What is the molecular formula of this xenon–fluorine compound?

Additional Exercises

59. Refer to Table 6.5. Why do you suppose phosphorus, sulfur, and chlorine have greater electron affinities than nitrogen, oxygen, and fluorine, respectively?

60. Which of the following compounds react with water to give an acid solution? Which give a basic solution? Write a balanced equation for the reaction of each with water.

(a) NaH   (d) SO_3 (g) PCl_3
(b) H_2S (e) CaO   (h) N_2O_5
(c) HCl   (f) Na_3P (i) SF_4

61. Which is a stronger acid, H_2S or H_2Se? Explain your answer.

62. Air contains 20.99% oxygen by volume. Find what volume of air, in cubic meters, at 27.0°C and 0.9868 atm is required to oxidize 1.00 metric ton (1000 kg) of sulfur to sulfur dioxide, assuming that all of the oxygen reacts with sulfur.

63. The bond length in the O_2 molecule is 1.209 Å; that in the O_3 molecule is 1.278 Å. Why does ozone have a longer bond?

64. Iodine reacts with liquid chlorine at −40°C to give an orange compound containing 54.3% iodine and 45.7% chlorine. Write the balanced equation for the reaction.

65. The combustion of 9.180 g of sodium to sodium oxide is exothermic; 100.74 kJ of heat is evolved. What is the enthalpy of formation of sodium oxide?

66. The enthalpy of formation of $CS_2(l)$ is +89.54 kJ mol^{-1}. How much heat is required for the reaction of 10.00 g of S_8 with carbon according to the following equation? Is the reaction exothermic or endothermic?

$$4C(s) + S_8(s) \longrightarrow 4CS_2(l)$$

67. When phosphorus burns to give $P_4O_{10}(s)$, an unusually large amount of energy is involved. Determine ΔH_{298}° for the reaction of exactly 1 mol of P_4, using the data given in Appendix I. Determine ΔG_{298}° for the reaction.

68. At 422 K the partial pressures of gaseous PCl_5, PCl_3, and Cl_2 in a closed system were found to be 0.453 atm, 6.08×10^{-2} atm, and 6.08×10^{-2} atm, respectively. Determine K_p for the oxidation

$$PCl_3(g) + Cl_2(g) \longrightarrow PCl_5(g)$$

69. Thallium(I) chloride is one of the few insoluble chlorides. What is the molar solubility of T1Cl, the solubility product of which is 1.8×10^{-4}?

The Nonmetals, Part 1: Hydrogen, Oxygen, Sulfur, and the Halogens

The sun consists mainly of hydrogen.

In Chapter 21 we discussed the general behavior of the nonmetals as a group. In this chapter and the next we shall examine the chemical behavior of some of these elements in more detail. This chapter treats hydrogen, oxygen, sulfur, and the halogens. The next chapter will treat carbon, nitrogen, phosphorus, and the noble gases.

Hydrogen

Early in the sixteenth century, the Swiss–German physician Paracelsus noticed that the action of dilute sulfuric acid on iron produced a flammable gas. Boyle (of Boyle's law fame; see Section 10.3) made the same observation in 1671, but it was not until 1766 that Cavendish, an Englishman, recognized this gas as a distinct substance and prepared it by the action of various acids on iron, zinc, and tin and by the novel method of passing steam through a red-hot gun barrel (which yielded hydrogen and Fe_3O_4). Lavoisier, a French chemist, proposed the name *hydrogen,* derived from Greek words meaning "water former," because water was produced when the gas burned in air.

22.1 Occurrence and Preparation of Hydrogen

Hydrogen is the most abundant element in the universe, and it is the third most abundant element (after oxygen and silicon) on the earth's surface. The sun and other stars are composed largely of hydrogen, as are the gases found in interstellar space. It is estimated that 90% of the atoms in the universe are hydrogen atoms.

Hydrogen accounts for nearly 11% of the mass of water, its most abundant compound on earth. It is an important part of the tissues of all plants and animals, petroleum, many minerals, cellulose and starch, sugar, fats, oils, alcohols, acids, and thousands of other substances. Hydrogen is a component of more compounds than any other element.

At ordinary temperatures, hydrogen is a colorless, odorless, tasteless, and nonpoisonous gas consisting of diatomic molecules, H_2. It is the lightest known substance at STP. When cooled and compressed, hydrogen changes to a liquid that boils at $-253°C$ (20 K) and freezes at $-259°C$ (14 K).

Hydrogen is more expensive to isolate than elements such as oxygen and nitrogen that are found in the air in an uncombined state. Hydrogen must be prepared from compounds by breaking chemical bonds, and this requires much more energy than simply condensing an element to separate it from other substances found in air. The most common methods of preparing hydrogen follow.

1. From Steam and Carbon or Hydrocarbons. Water is the cheapest and most abundant source of hydrogen. Passing steam over coke (an impure form of carbon) at 1000°C produces a mixture of carbon monoxide and hydrogen.

$$C(s) + H_2O(g) \xrightarrow{1000°C} CO(g) + H_2(g)$$
Water gas

This gaseous mixture is known as **water gas** and is used as an industrial fuel. Pure hydrogen can be obtained by mixing the water gas with steam in the presence of a catalyst to convert the CO to CO_2, which is much more soluble in water than is hydrogen.

$$CO(g) + H_2O(g) \xrightleftharpoons{\text{Catalyst}} H_2(g) + CO_2(g)$$

This reaction is sometimes called the **water gas shift reaction.**

Hydrocarbons are compounds that contain only carbon and hydrogen. Hydrocarbons from natural gas or petroleum can be mixed with steam and passed over a

Figure 22.1

The electrolysis of water produces hydrogen and oxygen.

nickel-based catalyst to produce carbon monoxide and hydrogen. Propane is an example of a hydrocarbon reactant.

$$C_3H_8(g) + 3H_2O(g) \xrightarrow[\text{Catalyst}]{900°C} 3CO(g) + 7H_2(g)$$

2. Electrolysis. Hydrogen is liberated when a direct current of electricity is passed through water containing a small amount of an electrolyte such as H_2SO_4, NaOH, or Na_2SO_4 (Fig. 22.1). Bubbles of hydrogen are formed at the cathode, and oxygen is evolved at the anode. The net reaction can be summarized by the equation

$$2H_2O(l) + \text{electrical energy} \longrightarrow 2H_2(g) + O_2(g)$$

Because electricity is so expensive, electrolytic hydrogen is produced in large quantities only when very pure gas is needed. Hydrogen is also a product of the electrolytic production of sodium hydroxide and chlorine (Sections 13.3 and 20.13).

$$[2Na^+(aq)] + 2Cl^-(aq) + 2H_2O(l) + \text{electrical energy} \longrightarrow$$
$$[2Na^+(aq)] + 2OH^-(aq) + Cl_2(g) + H_2(g)$$

3. Reaction of Metals with Acids or Water. This is the most convenient laboratory method of producing hydrogen. Electropositive metals reduce the hydrogen ion in dilute acids or water to produce hydrogen gas and metal salts. For example, iron in dilute hydrochloric acid produces hydrogen gas and iron(II) chloride (Fig. 22.2), and zinc in dilute hydrochloric acid produces hydrogen gas and zinc(II) chloride.

$$Fe(s) + 2H_3O^+(aq) + [2Cl^-(aq)] \longrightarrow Fe^{2+}(aq) + [2Cl^-(aq)] + H_2(g) + 2H_2O(l)$$

As we noted in Chapter 13, the alkali metals (such as sodium and lithium) react rapidly with water to produce hydrogen gas and the metal hydroxide (see Fig. 13.3 for the reaction with lithium).

$$2Na(s) + 2H_2O(l) \longrightarrow 2Na^+(aq) + 2OH^-(aq) + H_2(g)$$

This reaction is too vigorous to use for the laboratory production of hydrogen. Sometimes it gets hot enough to ignite the metal as well as the hydrogen as it is produced.

Iron and other less active metals displace hydrogen from water at elevated temperatures. When steam is passed over magnesium, for example, hydrogen is produced rapidly.

$$Mg(s) + H_2O(g) \longrightarrow H_2(g) + MgO(s)$$

4. Reaction of Certain Elements with Strong Bases. Aluminum and many post-transition metals and semi-metals such as silicon react with concentrated solutions of strong bases, with the liberation of hydrogen gas (Fig. 22.3).

$$2Al(s) + 2OH^-(aq) + 6H_2O(l) \longrightarrow 2Al(OH)_4^-(aq) + 3H_2(g)$$

5. Reaction of Ionic Metal Hydrides with Water. Hydrogen can also be produced by the reaction of hydrides of the active metals, which contain the very strongly basic H^- anion, with water (see Section 21.10 and Fig. 22.4).

$$CaH_2(s) + 2H_2O(l) \longrightarrow Ca^{2+}(aq) + 2OH^-(aq) + 2H_2(g)$$

Metal hydrides are expensive but convenient sources of hydrogen, especially where space and weight are important factors, as they are in the inflation of life jackets, life rafts, and military balloons.

Figure 22.2

The reaction of iron with an acid produces hydrogen. Here iron reacts with hydrochloric acid.

Figure 22.3

Hydrogen is produced when aluminum dissolves in a basic solution.

Figure 22.4

Hydrogen is produced when an ionic hydride reacts with water. The example shows the reaction of calcium hydride with water.

22.2 Chemical Properties of Hydrogen

At ordinary temperatures hydrogen is relatively inactive chemically, but when heated, it enters into many chemical reactions.

1. Reaction with Elements. When heated, hydrogen reacts with the metals of Group IA and with Ca, Sr, and Ba (the more active metals in Group IIA). The compounds formed are crystalline **ionic hydrides** that contain the hydride anion (H^-), a strong reducing agent and a strong base, which reacts vigorously with water and other acids to form hydrogen gas (see Section 22.1).

The reactions of hydrogen with the nonmetals generally produce *acidic* hydrogen compounds with hydrogen in the +1 oxidation state. The reactions become more exothermic and vigorous as the electronegativity of the nonmetal increases. Hydrogen reacts with nitrogen and sulfur only when heated, but it reacts explosively with fluorine (producing gaseous HF) and, under some conditions, with chlorine (producing gaseous HCl). A mixture of hydrogen and oxygen explodes if ignited (Fig. 22.5). Because of the explosive nature of the reaction, caution must be exercised in handling hydrogen (or any other combustible gas) in order to avoid the formation of an explosive mixture in a confined space. Although most hydrides of the nonmetals are acidic (see Section 16.5), ammonia and phosphine (PH_3) are very, very weak acids and generally function as bases. The reactions of hydrogen with the elements are summarized in Table 22.1.

Figure 22.5

Explosion of hydrogen on the airship *Hindenburg* while it was landing at Lakehurst, New Jersey, May 6, 1937. Following the ignition of hydrogen in one compartment, ignition of the other compartments took place within seconds, resulting in the complete destruction of the giant airliner. This one event essentially ended the use of hydrogen in lighter-than-air craft and has even produced what is termed the Hindenburg syndrome, reluctance to use hydrogen as a fuel.

Table 22.1	Chemical Reactions of Hydrogen with Other Elements
General Equation	**Comments**
$\frac{n}{2}H_2 + M \longrightarrow MH_n$	Ionic hydrides with Group IA and Ca, Sr, Ba; metallic hydrides with transition metals
$H_2 + C \longrightarrow$ (no reaction)	
$3H_2 + N_2 \longrightarrow 2NH_3$	Requires high pressure and temperature; low yield
$2H_2 + O_2 \longrightarrow 2H_2O$	Exothermic and potentially explosive
$H_2 + S \longrightarrow H_2S$	Requires heating; low yield
$H_2 + X_2 \longrightarrow 2HX$	X = F, Cl, Br, I; explosive with F_2; low yield with I_2

2. Reaction with Compounds. Hydrogen reduces the heated oxides of many metals, with the formation of the metal and water (Fig. 21.17). For example, when hydrogen is passed over heated CuO, copper and water are formed.

$$H_2(g) + CuO(s) \xrightarrow{\Delta} Cu(s) + H_2O(g)$$

Hydrogen may also reduce some metal oxides to lower oxides.

$$H_2(g) + MnO_2(s) \xrightarrow{\Delta} MnO(s) + H_2O(g)$$

22.3 Isotopes of Hydrogen; Heavy Water

Hydrogen is composed of three isotopes: (1) ordinary hydrogen, ^1_1H; (2) **deuterium, ^2_1H**; and (3) **tritium, ^3_1H**. In a naturally occurring sample of hydrogen, there is one atom of deuterium for every 7000 ^1_1H atoms and one atom of tritium for every 10^{18} ^1_1H atoms. The chemical properties of the different isotopes are very similar, because they have identical electron structures, but they differ in some physical properties because of their differing atomic masses. Elemental deuterium and tritium have lower vapor pressures than ordinary hydrogen. Consequently, when liquid hydrogen evaporates, the heavier isotopes are somewhat concentrated in the last portions to evaporate. Deuterium is isolated by the electrolysis of heavy water, D_2O. Tritium is made by a nuclear reaction (see Section 24.13).

Water composed of deuterium and oxygen, D_2O, is called **heavy water**, or **deuterium oxide.** Heavy water is produced by an exchange process followed by electrolysis. In the process, liquid water and gaseous hydrogen sulfide are mixed, and the deuterium atoms exchange between sulfur and oxygen. At low temperatures, deuterium preferentially binds to oxygen as D_2O; at high temperatures, it binds to sulfur as D_2S.

$$H_2S + D_2O \underset{\text{Cold}}{\overset{\text{Hot}}{\rightleftharpoons}} D_2S + H_2O$$

Hydrogen sulfide, bubbled through water at an elevated temperature, is enriched with respect to D_2S through exchange. After the enriched hydrogen sulfide is drawn off, the reverse exchange at lower temperatures produces water that contains a larger proportion of D_2O than before. Many repetitions of the process yield water with a D_2O concentration of about 15%, which is then enriched to 99.8% D_2O by electrolysis. During the electrolysis, water molecules containing deuterium migrate to a cathode more slowly than light water molecules, so the heavier water molecules tend to remain behind while the light water is decomposed. Several hundred tons of heavy water are now produced each year.

The slightly different physical properties of D_2O are illustrated by the fact that the density of D_2O is 10% higher than that of H_2O, and the fact that its melting and boiling points are 3.79°C and 101.4°C, respectively. Reactions in D_2O are somewhat slower than in H_2O. Heavy water is one of the moderators used in nuclear reactors to reduce the speed of neutrons so that the fission process can take place (Section 24.11). It is a convenient source of deuterium for preparation of compounds in which all of the hydrogen atoms have been replaced by deuterium. For example, NaOD can be prepared by the reaction of Na or Na_2O with D_2O.

Using mass spectrometry (see Section 5.6) it is possible to detect the presence of as little as 1 part of deuterium in 100,000 parts of hydrogen in a sample. For this reason, heavy water and deuterium serve as valuable tracers in the study of both chemical and physiological changes. For example, by replacing ordinary hydrogen with deuterium in molecules of food, investigators can study the processes of digestion and metabolism in the body.

22.4 Uses of Hydrogen

Two-thirds of the world's hydrogen production is devoted to the manufacture of ammonia, which is used primarily as a fertilizer and in the manufacture of nitric acid. Hydrogen is also used extensively in the process of **hydrogenation,** in which vegetable oils are changed from liquids to solids. Crisco is an example of a hydrogenated oil. The change results from the addition of H_2 to carbon–carbon double bonds to give single bonds (see Section 30.3). Methyl alcohol, an important industrial solvent and raw material, is produced synthetically by the catalyzed reaction of hydrogen with carbon monoxide.

$$2H_2 + CO \xrightarrow{\text{Catalyst}} CH_3OH$$

Hydrogen is currently used in several ways as a fuel, and its potential uses may come to be even more important. The reaction of hydrogen with oxygen is a very exothermic reaction, releasing 286 kJ of energy per mole of water formed. Hydrogen burns without explosion under controlled conditions. As we noted before, water gas (a mixture of hydrogen and carbon monoxide) is an important industrial fuel. The oxygen–hydrogen torch, because of the high heat of combustion of hydrogen, can achieve temperatures up to 2800°C. The hot flame of this torch is used in "cutting" thick sheets of many metals.

Hydrogen is an important rocket fuel. The rocket that launches space shuttles employs liquid hydrogen as a fuel, along with liquid oxygen (Fig. 22.6). Hydrogen also has attributes that make it attractive for more general uses as a fuel in the future. The most attractive aspect of using hydrogen as a fuel is that it can be produced from water. Imagine how nice it would be, in this energy-hungry world, to have a fuel that we could produce from water and that, when we burned it, yielded water again. However, there are many problems that must be solved. A substantial amount of energy must be expended to obtain hydrogen from water. Both sunlight and excess energy from nuclear reactors are being examined as potential sources of this energy. Other problems arise in safely storing, transporting, and distributing this potentially explosive gas.

Figure 22.6

Liquid hydrogen and liquid oxygen are used as fuel in space shuttles.

Oxygen

The discovery of oxygen marked the beginning of modern chemistry. Credit for the discovery of oxygen is usually given to Joseph Priestley, an English clergyman and scientist, who prepared oxygen in 1774 by focusing the sun's rays on mercury(II) oxide by means of a lens (Fig. 22.7). He tested the gaseous product with a burning candle and noted that the candle burned more brightly than in ordinary air. Shortly thereafter, Antoine-Laurent Lavoisier recognized that the products of the combustion of metals weighed more than the pure metals because oxygen combined with the metals during combustion.

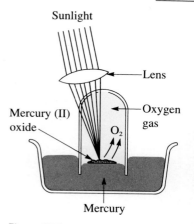

Figure 22.7
The apparatus that Priestley used to prepare oxygen. When HgO is heated, it decomposes, producing gaseous oxygen and mercury.

22.5 Occurrence and Preparation of Oxygen

Oxygen is the most abundant element on the earth's surface, and it forms compounds with most of the other elements. It is essential to combustion and to respiration in most plants and animals. Oxygen occurs as O_2 molecules and, to a limited extent, as O_3 (ozone) molecules in air. It forms about 23% of the mass of the air. About 89% of water by mass consists of combined oxygen. About 50% of the mass and 90% of the volume of the earth's crust consist of oxygen combined with other elements, principally silicon. In combination with carbon, hydrogen, and nitrogen, oxygen is a large part of the weight of the bodies of plants and animals.

In 1989, 18.9 million tons of oxygen were produced in the United States, making it third in production among all chemicals. Approximately 97% of the oxygen produced commercially comes from air and 3% from the electrolysis of water (Fig. 22.1), because air and water are abundant, cheap, and easy to process. Methods for the preparation of oxygen follow.

1. Fractional Evaporation of Liquid Air. Oxygen (boiling point, 90 K) is separated from the air in commercial quantities by cooling and compressing air until it liquefies and then distilling off the lower-boiling nitrogen (boiling point, 77 K) and some other elements.

2. Electrolysis of Water. The electrolysis of water to produce hydrogen and water is described in Section 22.1.

3. Decomposition of Metal Oxides and Peroxides. Small amounts of oxygen are sometimes produced by decomposition reactions. The oxides of metals located near the bottom of the activity series (see Section 13.1) are not thermally stable and lose oxygen when heated. For example, when red mercury(II) oxide, HgO, is heated, metallic mercury and oxygen are formed.

$$2HgO(s) \xrightarrow{\triangle} 2Hg(l) + O_2(g)$$

This is the method of preparing oxygen used by Priestley and Lavoisier (Fig. 22.7).

In some metal oxides in which the metal has a high oxidation number, the metal is a strong enough oxidizing agent to transform oxide ions to oxygen gas when heated. These compounds undergo thermal decomposition reactions in which part of the oxygen is liberated. The remainder is combined in a metal oxide in which the metal has a lower, more stable oxidation number. Examples include the decomposition of lead(IV) oxide to lead(II) oxide and that of chromium(VI) oxide to chromium(III) oxide.

$$2PbO_2 \xrightarrow{\triangle} 2PbO + O_2$$

$$4CrO_3 \xrightarrow{\triangle} 2Cr_2O_3 + 3O_2$$

Ionic peroxides (which contain an O—O bond) decompose to the corresponding oxides, with evolution of oxygen. For example,

$$2BaO_2(s) \longrightarrow 2BaO(s) + O_2(g)$$

4. Heating Certain Salts That Contain Oxygen. The nitrate salts of certain metals yield oxygen when heated.

$$2NaNO_3 \xrightarrow{\triangle} 2NaNO_2 + O_2$$

$$2Cu(NO_3)_2 \xrightarrow{\triangle} 2CuO + 4NO_2 + O_2$$

When a mixture of manganese(IV) oxide and potassium chlorate is heated, the latter decomposes quite rapidly at about 270°C, producing oxygen and potassium chloride. The manganese(IV) oxide is a catalyst for the decomposition.

$$2KClO_3(s) \xrightarrow[\triangle]{MnO_2} 2KCl(s) + 3O_2(g)$$

The laboratory preparation of oxygen by heating potassium chlorate can be dangerous when done carelessly. Explosions can occur when combustible materials such as carbon, sulfur, rubber, or a glowing wood splint come in contact with hot potassium chlorate. The danger involved in this experiment cannot be overemphasized. Proceed with caution when preparing oxygen by this method.

(a)

22.6 Properties of Oxygen

Oxygen is a colorless, odorless, and tasteless gas at ordinary temperatures. It is pale blue in the liquid state and boils at −183°C (90 K). Solid oxygen, also pale blue, melts at −218.4°C (54.8 K). Oxygen is slightly more dense than air. Although it is only slightly soluble in water (49 mL of gas dissolves in 1 L at STP), its solubility is very important to aquatic life.

The oxygen molecule is **paramagnetic;** that is, it contains two unpaired electrons and is attracted by a magnetic field (see photo on page 249).

Because an oxygen atom has six valence electrons, we might expect two pairs of electrons to be shared between the atoms in a diatomic oxygen molecule, with all electrons paired. However, careful measurement of the magnitude of the paramagnetism indicates two unpaired electrons per molecule. Their presence is consistent with the molecular orbital description of the bonding in O_2 (Section 9.11), in which the unpaired electrons are distributed singly in the two π_p^* antibonding molecular orbitals.

Oxygen actively reacts with most other elements and with many compounds.

(b)

Figure 22.8

Reactions of metals and nonmetals with oxygen. (a) Magnesium burns brilliantly in oxygen, forming a white smoke of MgO. (b) Steel wool burns vigorously in oxygen, forming brown solid Fe_2O_3.

1. Reaction with Elements. Oxygen reacts directly at room temperature or at elevated temperatures with all other elements (Fig. 22.8) except the noble gases, the halogens, and a few second- and third-row transition metals of low reactivity [those below copper in the activity series, the oxides of which decompose upon heating (see Section 13.1)]. The more active metals form peroxides or superoxides (see Section 13.5). Less active metals and the nonmetals give oxides. Oxides of the halogens, of at least one of the noble gases, and of the metals at the bottom of the activity series (see Section 13.1) can be prepared, but not by the direct action of the elements with oxygen. The reactions of oxygen with many of the elements are summarized in Table 22.2.

Table 22.2   Chemical Properties of Elemental Oxygen

General Equation	Comments
Reactions with Elements	
$n\text{M} + \dfrac{m}{2}\text{O}_2 \longrightarrow \text{M}_n\text{O}_m$	Oxygen reacts with most metals, M, except those at the bottom of the activity series (Section 13.1)
$2\text{Na} + \text{O}_2 \longrightarrow \text{Na}_2\text{O}_2$	A peroxide forms with Na (Section 13.5)
$\text{M} + \text{O}_2 \longrightarrow \text{MO}_2$	Peroxides form with M = Ca, Sr, Ba (Section 13.5)
$\text{M} + \text{O}_2 \longrightarrow \text{MO}_2$	M = K, Rb, Cs form superoxides (Section 13.5)
$2\text{H}_2 + \text{O}_2 \longrightarrow 2\text{H}_2\text{O}$	Potentially explosive reaction
$2\text{C} + \text{O}_2 \longrightarrow 2\text{CO}$	With a stoichiometric amount of O_2
$\text{E} + \text{O}_2 \longrightarrow \text{EO}_2$	With heating in excess O_2; E = lighter members of Group IVA: C, Si, Ge, Sn
$2\text{Pb} + \text{O}_2 \longrightarrow 2\text{PbO}$	Pb is the heaviest member of Group IVA
$\text{N}_2 + \text{O}_2 \longrightarrow 2\text{NO}$	High temperature required; low yield of product
$\text{E}_4 + 3\text{O}_2 \longrightarrow \text{E}_4\text{O}_6$	Requires a stoichiometric amount of O_2; E = P, As, Sb
$\text{P}_4 + 5\text{O}_2 \longrightarrow \text{P}_4\text{O}_{10}$	Phosphorus burns in air
$4\text{Bi} + 3\text{O}_2 \longrightarrow 2\text{Bi}_2\text{O}_3$	With heating in excess O_2; Bi is the heaviest member of Group VA
$\text{E} + \text{O}_2 \longrightarrow \text{EO}_2$	E = heavier members of Group VIA: S, Se, Te
Reactions with Compounds	
$2\text{CO} + \text{O}_2 \longrightarrow 2\text{CO}_2$	Requires ignition
$2\text{NO} + \text{O}_2 \longrightarrow 2\text{NO}_2$	Spontaneous reaction
$\text{P}_4\text{O}_6 + 2\text{O}_2 \longrightarrow \text{P}_4\text{O}_{10}$	
$2\text{SO}_2 + \text{O}_2 \longrightarrow 2\text{SO}_3$	Requires heat and Pt catalyst; occurs very slowly in the atmosphere
$\text{C}_n\text{H}_m + \left(n + \dfrac{m}{4}\right)\text{O}_2 \longrightarrow n\text{CO}_2 + \dfrac{m}{2}\text{H}_2\text{O}$	This is the general reaction for the burning of a hydrocarbon (a combustion reaction)
(For example, $\text{CH}_4 + 2\text{O}_2 \longrightarrow \text{CO}_2 + 2\text{H}_2\text{O}$)	
$4\text{NH}_3 + 5\text{O}_2 \longrightarrow 4\text{NO} + 6\text{H}_2\text{O}$	Ammonia burns in O_2
$2\text{H}_2\text{S} + 3\text{O}_2 \longrightarrow 2\text{SO}_2 + 2\text{H}_2\text{O}$	
$\text{CS}_2 + 3\text{O}_2 \longrightarrow \text{CO}_2 + 2\text{SO}_2$	
$2\text{MS} + 3\text{O}_2 \longrightarrow 2\text{MO} + 3\text{SO}_2$	Most metal sulfides form metal oxides and SO_2 when heated in air

As we saw in Chapter 13, the formulas of the binary oxides, peroxides, and superoxides can generally be determined from the position of the combining element in the periodic table and the oxidation number of oxygen. Thus the reaction of the Group IA element lithium with oxygen at ordinary pressures gives Li_2O (oxidation number of Li = +1, oxidation number of O = −2), and that of gallium, a Group IIIA element, gives Ga_2O_3 (oxidation number of Ga = +3, oxidation number of O = −2).

2. Reaction with Compounds. Elemental oxygen also reacts with some compounds. A compound made up of elements that combine with oxygen when free may be expected to react with oxygen to form oxides of the constituent elements, when one or more of the atoms in the compound do not exhibit their maximum oxidation number. For example, hydrogen sulfide, H_2S, contains sulfur with an oxidation number of −2. Because the sulfur does not exhibit its maximum oxidation number, and because free sulfur reacts with oxygen, we would expect H_2S to react with oxygen. It does, giving water and sulfur dioxide. Oxides such as CO and P_4O_6 that contain an element with a lower oxidation number than is usually formed when the element combines with an excess of oxygen also react with additional oxygen. Examples are given in Table 22.2.

Elemental oxygen is a strong oxidizing agent. The ease with which elemental oxygen picks up electrons is mirrored by the difficulty of removing electrons from oxygen in most oxides. Of the elements, only the very reactive fluorine molecule oxidizes oxides to form oxygen gas.

22.7 Ozone

When dry oxygen is passed between two electrically charged plates (Fig. 22.9), a decrease in the volume of the gas occurs, and **ozone** (O_3, Fig. 22.10), an allotrope of oxygen possessing a distinctive odor, is formed. The formation of ozone from oxygen is an endothermic reaction, in which the energy is furnished in the form of an electrical discharge, heat, or ultraviolet light.

$$3O_2 \xrightarrow[\text{discharge}]{\text{Electric}} 2O_3 \qquad \Delta H° = 286 \text{ kJ}$$

The sharp odor associated with sparking electrical equipment is due, in part, to ozone.

Ozone is formed naturally in the upper atmosphere by the action of ultraviolet light from the sun on the oxygen there.

Voltage on outer foil

Metal foil on outer tube

O_2 and O_3

Dry O_2

Voltage on inner foil

Parallel glass tubes

Metal foil on inner tube

Figure 22.9

Laboratory apparatus for the preparation of ozone.

$$O_2(g) \xrightarrow{\text{Ultraviolet light}} O(g) + O(g)$$

$$O(g) + O_2(g) \longrightarrow O_3(g)$$

Most atmospheric ozone is found in the stratosphere, a layer of the atmosphere extending from about 10 to 50 kilometers above the earth's surface. This ozone acts as a barrier to harmful ultraviolet light from the sun by absorbing it via a chemical decomposition reaction.

$$O_3(g) \xrightarrow{\text{Ultraviolet light}} O(g) + O_2(g)$$

The reactive oxygen atom recombines with molecular oxygen to complete the ozone cycle. The frequency of skin cancer and other damaging effects of ultraviolet radiation are decreased by the presence of stratospheric ozone. Concern has recently arisen that **chlorofluorocarbons,** CFC's (known commercially as Freons), which are used as aerosol propellants in spray cans and as refrigerants, are causing depletion of ozone in the stratosphere (see photograph on page 447). This occurs because ultraviolet light also causes CFC's to decompose, producing atomic chlorine. The chlorine atoms react with ozone molecules, resulting in a net removal of O_3 molecules from the stratosphere. Freon-11 ($CFCl_3$) offers an example.

$$CFCl_3(g) \xrightarrow{\text{Ultraviolet light}} CFCl_2(g) + Cl(g)$$

$$Cl(g) + O_3(g) \longrightarrow ClO(g) + O_2(g)$$

$$ClO(g) + O(g) \longrightarrow Cl(g) + O_2(g)$$

The oxygen atoms are supplied by the photochemical decomposition of ozone. The chlorine atoms act as catalysts (see Section 14.13), because they are not consumed and—unfortunately—take part in many reactions with ozone.

In recent years, substantial reductions in ozone concentrations over the South Pole have been detected (Fig. 22.11). Whether this ozone hole is due to Freon pollution is

Figure 22.10

The bent O_3 molecule and the resonance structures necessary to describe its bonding.

Figure 22.11

Because of ozone depletion in the stratosphere, it is important to monitor ozone concentrations continually. Stratospheric ozone can be measured in specially equipped aircraft such as this flying laboratory.

Figure 22.12
A mixture of ozone, nitrogen oxides, and unburned hydrocarbons forms smog when exposed to sunlight.

still under debate, and only time will tell how serious this problem is. Significant ozone depletion could have a drastic effect on life on the earth (Section 29.5).

Ozone produced in the lower atmosphere reacts with engine exhaust and contributes to smog (see Fig. 22.12). Much of the deterioration of automobile tires is due to contact with ozone in the air.

Ozone is pale blue as a gas and deep blue as a liquid. It has a sharp, irritating odor, produces headaches, and is poisonous. Energy is absorbed when ozone is formed from molecular oxygen, so ozone is more active chemically than oxygen and decomposes readily into oxygen by the exothermic reaction

$$2O_3 \longrightarrow 3O_2 \qquad \Delta H° = -286 \text{ kJ}$$

As a consequence, it is less stable and more reactive than oxygen.

Ozone is a powerful oxidizing agent and forms oxides with many elements at temperatures at which O_2 will not react. It can be readily detected in a gas by passing the gas through a solution of an iodide containing some starch as an indicator.

$$2I^-(aq) + O_3(g) + H_2O(l) \longrightarrow 2OH^-(aq) + I_2(aq) + O_2(g)$$

The O_3 oxidizes I^- to I_2, elemental iodine, which in combination with excess I^- imparts a blue color to the starch.

22.8 The Importance of Oxygen to Life

The energy required for maintenance of normal body functions in human beings and in other organisms is derived from the slow oxidation of chemical compounds in the body. Oxygen is the final oxidizing agent in these reactions. In humans, oxygen passes from the lungs into the blood, where it combines with hemoglobin, producing oxyhemoglobin. In this form, oxygen is carried by the blood to tissues, where it is released and consumed in reactions with electrons (e^-) and protons (H^+). The ultimate products are carbon dioxide and water. The blood carries the carbon dioxide through the veins to the lungs, where it gives up the carbon dioxide and collects another supply of oxygen. The digestion and assimilation of food regenerate the materials consumed by oxidation in the body; in fact, the same amount of energy is liberated as if the food had been burned outside the body.

The oxygen in the atmosphere is continually replenished through the action of green plants by a process called **photosynthesis.** The products of photosynthesis may vary, but the process can be generalized as the conversion of carbon dioxide and water to glucose (a sugar, see Section 31.7) and oxygen using the energy of light.

$$6CO_2 + 6H_2O \xrightarrow[\text{Light}]{\text{Chlorophyll}} C_6H_{12}O_6 + 6O_2$$

Carbon   Water   Glucose   Oxygen
dioxide

Thus the oxygen that is converted to carbon dioxide and water by the metabolic processes in plants and animals is returned to the atmosphere by these photosynthetic reactions.

22.9   Uses of Oxygen

Oxygen is essential in combustion processes such as the burning of fuels. Oxygen is also required for the decay of organic matter. Plants and animals use the oxygen from the air in respiration. Oxygen-enriched air is administered in medical practice when a patient is receiving an inadequate supply of oxygen as a result of shock, pneumonia, or some other illness. Health services use about 13% of the oxygen produced commercially.

Approximately 30% of all oxygen produced commercially is used to remove carbon from iron during steel production (see Section 27.18). Large quantities of pure oxygen are also consumed in metal fabrication and in the cutting and welding of metals with oxyhydrogen and oxyacetylene torches (see Fig. 4.1). The chemical industry employs oxygen for oxidizing many substances.

Liquid oxygen is used as an oxidizing agent in the space shuttle and other rocket engines. It is also used to provide gaseous oxygen for life support in space.

The uses of the allotrope ozone depend on its reactivity with other substances. As a bleaching agent for oils, waxes, fabrics, and starch, it oxidizes the colored compounds in these substances to colorless compounds. It is sometimes used instead of chlorine to decontaminate water.

Sulfur

Sulfur has been known from very early times, because it occurs free in nature as a solid. In fact, sulfur (or brimstone, as it was sometimes called) and carbon were the only nonmetallic elements known to the ancients. Sulfur, along with sulfuric acid, is a major component of the atmosphere of the planet Venus, and the surface of Io, a moon of Jupiter (Fig. 22.13), is believed to be covered with sulfur.

Figure 22.13

The surface of Io, a moon of Jupiter, is believed to be covered with sulfur.

22.10 Occurrence and Preparation of Sulfur

Sulfur exists as elemental deposits as well as sulfides of iron (Fig. 22.14), zinc, lead, and copper and sulfates of sodium, calcium, barium, and magnesium. Hydrogen sulfide is often a component of natural gas and occurs in many volcanic gases (Fig. 22.15). Sulfur compounds are also found in coal. Sulfur is a constituent of many proteins and therefore exists in the combined state in living matter.

Free sulfur is mined by the **Frasch process** (Fig. 22.16) from enormous underground deposits in Texas and Louisiana. Superheated water (170°C and 10 atmospheres pressure) is forced down the outermost of three concentric pipes to the underground deposit. When the hot water melts the sulfur, compressed air is forced down the inner-

Figure 22.14

Iron(II) disulfide is called pyrite. It is also known as "fool's gold" because it looks like gold.

Figure 22.15

Volcanoes are thought to be the source of two-thirds of the sulfur compounds in the atmosphere through their emission of H_2S. At the high temperatures involved, H_2S reacts with oxygen to produce SO_2.

most pipe. The liquid sulfur mixed with air forms a foam that flows up through the outlet pipe. The emulsified sulfur is conveyed to large settling vats, where it solidifies upon cooling (Fig. 22.17). Sulfur produced by this method is 99.5 to 99.9% pure and requires no purification for most uses.

Sulfur is also obtained, in quantities exceeding that extracted by means of the Frasch process, from hydrogen sulfide recovered during the purification of "sour" natural gas (Section 22.12).

22.11 Properties of Sulfur

Sulfur exists in several allotropic forms (see Section 21.3). The stable form at room temperature contains eight-membered rings and should technically be written as S_8. However, chemists commonly use the symbol S to simplify the coefficients in chemical equations; we will follow this practice in the rest of this book.

Like oxygen, which is also a member of Group VIA, sulfur exhibits distinctly nonmetallic behavior. It oxidizes metals, giving a variety of binary sulfides in which sulfur exhibits a negative oxidation number. Elemental sulfur oxidizes less electronegative nonmetals and is oxidized by more electronegative nonmetals, such as oxygen and the halogens. Sulfur is also oxidized by other strong oxidizing agents. For example, concentrated nitric acid oxidizes sulfur to the sulfate ion, with the concurrent formation of nitrogen(IV) oxide.

$$S + 6HNO_3 \longrightarrow 2H_3O^+ + SO_4^{2-} + 6NO_2$$

Figure 22.16

Diagram of the Frasch process for mining sulfur.

Figure 22.17

Molten sulfur mined by the Frasch process is pumped into large tanks and allowed to solidify.

The products of the reaction with hot, concentrated sulfuric acid are sulfur dioxide and water.

$$S + 2H_2SO_4 \longrightarrow 3SO_2 + 2H_2O$$

The general chemical behavior of sulfur is discussed in Section 21.7. The chemistry of sulfur with an oxidation number of -2 is similar to that of oxygen. Unlike oxygen, however, sulfur forms a variety of compounds in which it exhibits positive oxidation numbers. Some of the general reactions of sulfur and its compounds are summarized in Table 22.3.

Table 22.3   Chemical Properties of Sulfur and Its Compounds

General Equation	Comments
Reactions with Elements	
$nM + mS \longrightarrow M_nS_m$	Most metals combine with sulfur, giving sulfides that contain the S^{2-} ion
$nM + xsS \longrightarrow M_n(S_x)_m$	With excess S, some metals give polysulfides, S_x^{2-}; $x = 2, 3, 4, 5$
$H_2 + S \longrightarrow H_2S$	In low yield; H_2S decomposes at elevated temperatures
$E + 2S \longrightarrow ES_2$	E = C, Si, Ge, the lighter members of Group IVA
$E + S \longrightarrow ES$	E = Sn, Pb, the heavier members of Group IVA
$N_2 + S \longrightarrow$ no reaction	N_2 does not react with S
$P_4 + 10S \longrightarrow P_4S_{10}$	With less S, many other phosphorus sulfides are possible
$2E + 3S \longrightarrow E_2S_3$	E = As, Sb, Bi, the heavier members of Group VA
$S + O_2 \longrightarrow SO_2$	Traces of SO_3 also form when S burns in air
$S + 3F_2 \longrightarrow SF_6$	Other sulfur fluorides can be prepared indirectly
$S + nCl_2 \longrightarrow S_2Cl_2$ or SCl_2	Product depends on the reaction stoichiometry
$2S + Br_2 \longrightarrow S_2Br_2$	I_2 does not react with S
Reactions of Compounds	
$S^{2-} + 2H^+ \longrightarrow H_2S$	S^{2-} is a strongly basic anion
$S^{2-} + \text{oxidant} \longrightarrow S$	S^{2-} can be oxidized to S or to higher oxidation states
$2H_2S + O_2 \longrightarrow 2S + 2H_2O$	Requires a stoichiometric amount of O_2
$2H_2S + 3O_2 \longrightarrow 2SO_2 + 2H_2O$	With excess O_2
$2H_2S + SO_2 \longrightarrow 2H_2O + 3S$	
$CS_2 + 3O_2 \longrightarrow CO_2 + 2SO_2$	
$2SO_2 + O_2 \longrightarrow 2SO_3$	Catalyst required for satisfactory yield
$SO_2 + H_2O \longrightarrow H_2SO_3$	Sulfurous acid
$SO_2 + O^{2-} \longrightarrow SO_3^{2-}$	Sulfite ion
$SO_3 + H_2O \longrightarrow H_2SO_4$	Sulfuric acid
$SO_3 + O^{2-} \longrightarrow SO_4^{2-}$	Sulfate ion

㉒.12 Hydrogen Sulfide and Sulfides

Hydrogen sulfide, H_2S, is a colorless gas that is responsible for the offensive odor of rotten eggs and of many hot springs. Hydrogen sulfide is as toxic as hydrogen cyanide. Great care must be exercised in handling it. Hydrogen sulfide is particularly deceptive because it paralyzes the olfactory nerves; after a short exposure, one does not smell it!

The production of hydrogen sulfide by the direct reaction of the elements ($H_2 + S$) is unsatisfactory, because the reaction is reversible and hydrogen sulfide decomposes upon heating. A more effective preparation is the reaction of a metal sulfide with a dilute strong acid (Fig. 22.18). For example,

$$FeS(s) + 2H_3O^+(aq) \longrightarrow Fe^{2+}(aq) + H_2S(g) + 2H_2O(l)$$

The sulfur in metal sulfides and in hydrogen sulfide is readily oxidized, making metal sulfides and H_2S good reducing agents (Fig. 22.19). In acidic solutions, hydrogen sulfide reduces Fe^{3+} to Fe^{2+}, Br_2 to Br^-, MnO_4^- to Mn^{2+}, $Cr_2O_7^{2-}$ to Cr^{3+}, and HNO_3 to NO_2. The sulfur in the H_2S is usually oxidized to elemental sulfur, unless a large excess of the oxidizing agent is present. In this case the sulfide may be oxidized to SO_3^{2-} or SO_4^{2-} (or to SO_2 or SO_3 in the absence of water).

Hydrogen sulfide burns in air, forming water and sulfur dioxide. When heated with a limited supply of air or with sulfur dioxide (which can be produced by the combustion of H_2S), free sulfur is formed.

$$2H_2S(g) + O_2(g) \longrightarrow 2S(s) + 2H_2O(l)$$

In this way sulfur is recovered from the hydrogen sulfide found in many sources of natural gas. The deposits of sulfur in volcanic regions may be the result of the reaction between H_2S and SO_2, because both are constituents of volcanic gases.

Most of the more reactive metals displace hydrogen from hydrogen sulfide. For example, lead sulfide is formed by the action of hydrogen sulfide on metallic lead, according to the equation

$$Pb(s) + H_2S(g) \longrightarrow PbS(s) + H_2(g)$$

Figure 22.18

The reaction of FeS with H_2SO_4 produces gaseous H_2S.

(a)   (b)

Figure 22.19

When (a) a solution of sodium dichromate, $Na_2Cr_2O_7$ (red), is added to a solution of sodium sulfide, Na_2S (colorless), (b) the sulfide ions are oxidized to elemental sulfur, which is insoluble in water.

Figure 22.20

Molecular structures and Lewis structures of S_2^{2-}, S_5^{2-}, and H_2S_5.

Silver tableware tarnishes, via the formation of black silver sulfide, when used with eggs and other foods that contain certain sulfur compounds.

$$4Ag(s) + 2H_2S(g) + O_2(g) \longrightarrow 2Ag_2S(s) + 2H_2O(l)$$

Hydrogen sulfide is a weak diprotic acid. An aqueous solution of hydrogen sulfide is called **hydrosulfuric acid.** The acid ionizes in two stages, giving hydrogen sulfide ions, HS^-, in the first stage and sulfide ions, S^{2-}, in the second (see Section 17.4). Salts of both the HS^- and S^{2-} ions are known. For example, passing an excess of hydrogen sulfide into a solution of sodium hydroxide yields **sodium hydrogen sulfide.**

$$H_2S + [Na^+] + OH^- \rightleftharpoons [Na^+] + HS^- + H_2O$$

Adding a stoichiometric amount of sodium hydroxide to a solution of sodium hydrogen sulfide gives **sodium sulfide,** Na_2S, upon evaporation.

$$[Na^+] + OH^- + [Na^+] + HS^- \rightleftharpoons [2Na^+] + S^{2-} + H_2O$$

Hydrogen sulfide is a weak acid, so the sulfide ion and the hydrogen sulfide ion are strong bases. Aqueous solutions of soluble sulfides and hydrogen sulfides are basic.

$$S^{2-} + H_2O \rightleftharpoons HS^- + OH^-$$

$$HS^- + H_2O \rightleftharpoons H_2S + OH^-$$

The sulfide ion is slowly oxidized by oxygen, so sulfur precipitates when a solution of hydrogen sulfide or a sulfide salt is exposed to the air for a time.

When elemental sulfur is added to a solution of a soluble metal sulfide, the sulfur dissolves by combining with the sulfide ion to form complex **polysulfide ions,** S_n^{2-} ($n = 2$ to 5). The sulfur atoms of these complex ions are linked by covalent bonds (Fig. 22.20). Disulfide ions, S_2^{2-}, are analogous to peroxide ions, O_2^{2-}. The polysulfide ions, like the peroxide ion and free sulfur, are oxidizing agents.

When solutions containing polysulfide ions are acidified, a white, very finely divided form of free sulfur (milk of sulfur) and hydrogen sulfide are produced (Fig. 22.21).

$$S_2^{2-} + 2H_3O^+ \longrightarrow H_2S(g) + S(s) + 2H_2O$$

Figure 22.21

Addition of acid to a solution of a polysulfide produces finely divided sulfur.

22.13 Oxides of Sulfur

The two common oxides of sulfur are **sulfur dioxide,** SO_2, and **sulfur trioxide,** SO_3. The odor of burning sulfur is due to sulfur dioxide. Sulfur dioxide occurs in volcanic gases and in the atmosphere near industrial plants that burn coal or oil that contains sulfur compounds. The oxide forms when these sulfur compounds react with oxygen during combustion.

Sulfur dioxide is produced commercially by burning free sulfur and by roasting (heating in air) sulfide ores such as ZnS, FeS_2, and Cu_2S (Section 27.2). (Roasting, which forms the metal oxide, is the first step in the separation of the metals from the ores.) Sulfur dioxide is prepared conveniently in the laboratory by the action of sulfuric acid on either sulfite salts, containing the SO_3^{2-} ion, or hydrogen sulfite salts, containing HSO_3^-. Sulfurous acid, H_2SO_3, is formed first, but it quickly decomposes into sulfur dioxide and water. Sulfur dioxide is also formed when many reducing agents react with hot concentrated sulfuric acid. **Sulfur trioxide** forms slowly when sulfur dioxide and oxygen are heated together; the reaction is exothermic.

$$2SO_2 + O_2 \longrightarrow 2SO_3 \qquad \Delta H° = -197.8 \text{ kJ}$$

Sulfur dioxide is a gas at room temperature, and the SO_2 molecule is bent (Fig. 22.22). Sulfur trioxide melts at 17°C and boils at 43°C. In the vapor state its molecules are single SO_3 units (Fig. 22.23), but in the solid state SO_3 exists in several polymeric forms.

Sulfur dioxide and sulfur trioxide are acidic oxides. Both react with water to give oxyacids; SO_2 produces the moderately strong acid **sulfurous acid,** H_2SO_3, and SO_3 produces the strong acid **sulfuric acid,** H_2SO_4. Sulfur trioxide dissolves readily in concentrated sulfuric acid and forms **pyrosulfuric acid,** $H_2S_2O_7$, also known as **fuming sulfuric acid** or **oleum.**

The sulfur oxides react as Lewis acids with many oxides and hydroxides in Lewis acid-base reactions (Section 16.14), with the formation of **sulfites** or **hydrogen sulfites** and **sulfates** or **hydrogen sulfates,** respectively.

$$BaO + SO_2 \longrightarrow BaSO_3 \text{ (a sulfite)}$$

$$KOH + SO_2 \longrightarrow KHSO_3 \text{ (a hydrogen sulfite)}$$

$$BaO + SO_3 \longrightarrow BaSO_4 \text{ (a sulfate)}$$

$$KOH + SO_3 \longrightarrow KHSO_4 \text{ (a hydrogen sulfate)}$$

The sulfur atom in sulfur trioxide exhibits its maximum oxidation number, so SO_3 cannot be oxidized. It can act as an oxidizing agent, however. Sulfur dioxide can be both oxidized and reduced. It is slowly oxidized by oxygen to sulfur trioxide. Chlorine oxidizes SO_2 to **sulfuryl chloride,** SO_2Cl_2 [Fig. 22.24(a)]. A related compound, **thionyl**

Figure 22.22

The molecular structure and resonance forms of sulfur dioxide.

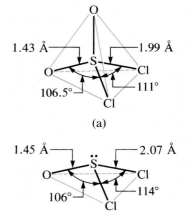

Figure 22.24

The molecular structures of (a) sulfuryl chloride (tetrahedral) and (b) thionyl chloride (trigonal pyramidal).

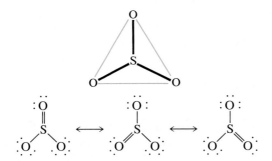

Figure 22.23

The structure of sulfur trioxide in the gas phase and its resonance forms.

chloride, $SOCl_2$ [Fig. 22.24(b)], is formed by the metathesis reaction of sulfur dioxide with phosphorus(V) chloride.

$$SO_2(g) + PCl_5(s) \longrightarrow SOCl_2(l) + POCl_3(l)$$

Like most nonmetal halides, $SOCl_2$ and SO_2Cl_2 react with water, giving hydrogen chloride and sulfur dioxide or sulfur trioxide (or the acids), respectively.

$$SOCl_2(l) + H_2O(l) \longrightarrow SO_2(g) + 2HCl(g)$$

$$SO_2Cl_2(l) + H_2O(l) \longrightarrow SO_3(l) + 2HCl(g)$$

Air pollution by sulfur oxides is a major pollution problem. It is estimated that 30–40 million tons of sulfur dioxide are emitted into the atmosphere of the United States each year. This material itself is very harmful to plant and animal life, as well as to many materials, but a problem of even greater concern is **acid rain.** Sulfur dioxide and sulfur trioxide both dissolve in atmospheric water droplets to form acidic solutions that can be very damaging when distributed in the form of rain. It is thought that sulfuric acid is the major cause of the acidity in acid rain, which is damaging forests in the northern hemisphere and is resulting in declining numbers of fish in many northern lakes. Acid rain is also very corrosive to metals, limestone, and other materials. This problem can be solved, but addressing it will be extremely expensive. It is very difficult to remove sulfur from oil and coal before it is burned. Chapter 29 discusses in detail the problem of acid rain and other airborne pollution, as well as possible solutions.

㉒.14 Sulfurous Acid and Sulfites

Sulfur dioxide dissolves in water to form a solution of sulfurous acid, as expected for the oxide of a nonmetal. **Sulfurous acid** is unstable, and anhydrous H_2SO_3 cannot be isolated. Boiling a solution of sulfurous acid expels the sulfur dioxide. Like other diprotic acids, sulfurous acid ionizes in two steps; the **hydrogen sulfite ion,** HSO_3^-, and the **sulfite ion,** SO_3^{2-}, are formed. Sulfurous acid is a moderately strong acid. Ionization is about 25% in the first stage, but it is much less in the second ($K_{a_1} = 1.2 \times 10^{-2}$ and $K_{a_2} = 6.2 \times 10^{-8}$).

Solid sulfite and hydrogen sulfite salts can be prepared by adding a stoichiometric amount of a base to a sulfurous acid solution and then evaporating the water. These salts are also formed by the reaction of SO_2 with oxides and hydroxides (Section 22.13). Solid sodium hydrogen sulfite forms sodium sulfite, sulfur dioxide, and water when heated.

$$2NaHSO_3(s) \xrightarrow{\Delta} Na_2SO_3(s) + SO_2(g) + H_2O(l)$$

Sulfurous acid can be oxidized by strong oxidizing agents. Oxygen in the air oxidizes it slowly to the more stable sulfuric acid.

$$2H_2SO_3 + O_2 + 4H_2O \longrightarrow 4H_3O^+ + 2SO_4^{2-}$$

Solutions containing the purple permanganate ion rapidly turn colorless when sulfurous acid is added; the MnO_4^- ion is reduced to the colorless Mn^{2+} ion as sulfurous acid is oxidized to sulfate ion.

$$2MnO_4^- + 5H_2SO_3 + 4H_2O \longrightarrow 2Mn^{2+} + 4H_3O^+ + 5SO_4^{2-} + 3H_2O$$

Solutions of sulfites are also very susceptible to air oxidation, whereby sulfates are formed. Thus solutions of sulfites always contain sulfates after standing exposed to air.

22.15 Sulfuric Acid and Sulfates

Sulfuric acid, H_2SO_4 (Fig. 22.25), is prepared by oxidizing sulfur to sulfur trioxide and then converting the trioxide to sulfuric acid (see Section 2.12). Pure sulfuric acid is a colorless, oily liquid that freezes at 10.5°C. It fumes when heated because the acid decomposes to water and sulfur trioxide. More sulfur trioxide than water is lost during the heating, until a concentration of 98.33% acid is reached. Acid of this concentration boils at 338°C without further change in concentration (a constant boiling solution, Section 12.16) and is sold as concentrated H_2SO_4.

Concentrated sulfuric acid dissolves in water with the evolution of a large amount of heat. **Caution! Adding water to the concentrated acid may cause dangerous spattering of the acid. Do not add water to concentrated sulfuric acid; add the acid slowly to water, while stirring the solution to distribute the heat of dilution.** The large heat of dilution of sulfuric acid is caused by hydrate and hydronium ion formation. The hydrates $H_2SO_4 \cdot H_2O$, $H_2SO_4 \cdot 2H_2O$, and $H_2SO_4 \cdot 4H_2O$ are known.

The strong affinity of concentrated sulfuric acid for water makes it a good dehydrating agent. Gases that do not react with the acid can be dried by passing them through it. So great is the affinity of concentrated sulfuric acid for water that it removes hydrogen and oxygen, in the form of water, from many organic compounds containing these elements in a 2-to-1 ratio. For example, cane sugar, $C_{12}H_{22}O_{11}$, is charred by concentrated sulfuric acid (Fig. 22.26).

$$C_{12}H_{22}O_{11} \longrightarrow 12C + 11H_2O$$

Concentrated sulfuric acid can cause serious burns, because it reacts with organic compounds in the skin.

Sulfuric acid is a strong diprotic acid that ionizes in two stages. In aqueous solution the first stage is essentially complete. The secondary ionization is less nearly complete, but even so HSO_4^- is a moderately strong acid (about 25% ionized in solution; $K_a = 1.2 \times 10^{-2}$).

Being a diprotic acid, sulfuric acid forms both **sulfates,** such as Na_2SO_4, and **hydrogen sulfates,** such as $NaHSO_4$. The sulfates of barium, strontium, calcium, and lead

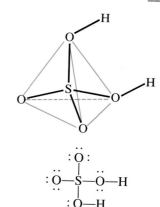

Figure 22.25

The tetrahedral molecular structure and the Lewis structure of sulfuric acid.

Figure 22.26

When (a) concentrated sulfuric acid is added to cane sugar, $C_{12}H_{22}O_{11}$, (b) the sulfuric acid begins to remove the elements of water from the sugar (dehydrating), leaving (c) elemental carbon.

(a)

(b)

(c)

are only slightly soluble in water. These salts occur in nature as the minerals **barite,** $BaSO_4$; **celestite,** $SrSO_4$; **gypsum,** $CaSO_4 \cdot 2H_2O$; and **anglesite,** $PbSO_4$. They can be prepared in the laboratory by metathesis reactions. For example, adding barium nitrate to a solution of sodium sulfate causes the precipitation of white barium sulfate:

$$Ba^{2+} + [2NO_3^-] + [2Na^+] + SO_4^{2-} \longrightarrow BaSO_4(s) + [2Na^+] + [2NO_3^-]$$

This reaction is the basis of a qualitative and quantitative test for the sulfate ion and the barium ion.

Among the important soluble sulfates are Glauber's salt, $Na_2SO_4 \cdot 10H_2O$; Epsom salts, $MgSO_4 \cdot 7H_2O$; blue vitriol, $CuSO_4 \cdot 5H_2O$; green vitriol, $FeSO_4 \cdot 7H_2O$; and white vitriol, $ZnSO_4 \cdot 7H_2O$. Because the HSO_4^- ion is an acid, hydrogen sulfates, such as $NaHSO_4$, exhibit acidic behavior. Sodium hydrogen sulfate is the primary ingredient in some household cleansers.

Hot, concentrated sulfuric acid is an oxidizing agent. Depending on its concentration, the temperature, and the strength of the reducing agent, sulfuric acid oxidizes many compounds and, in the process, undergoes reduction to either SO_2, HSO_3^-, SO_3^{2-}, S, H_2S, or S^{2-}. The displacement of volatile acids from their salts by concentrated sulfuric acid is described in Section 16.7.

The amount of sulfuric acid used in industry exceeds that of any other manufactured compound. During 1989, 43.4 million tons were produced in the United States alone.

The major uses of sulfuric acid are based largely on its strongly acidic character. It is used to produce ammonium sulfate (4.7 million tons in the United States in 1989) and soluble phosphate fertilizers; to refine petroleum and to remove impurities from such products as gasoline and kerosene; to pickle steel (clean its surface of rust); to produce dyes, drugs, and disinfectants from coal tar; to serve as an electrolyte itself or to produce metal sulfates for electrolytes; to manufacture other chemicals, such as hydrochloric and nitric acids; and to produce textiles, paints, plastics, explosives, and lead storage batteries.

The Halogens

The elements of Group VIIA of the periodic table are known as the **halogens,** a term derived from Greek words meaning "sea salt producer." The term *halogen* was originally given only to chlorine, but its application was later extended to cover all Group VIIA elements. The binary compounds of the halogens are called **halides.** The first four halogens—fluorine, chlorine, bromine, and iodine—were first isolated between 1774 and 1886. Salts of these elements are common in nature. Astatine, the fifth halogen, was first prepared artificially in 1940. It is a radioactive element of limited stability.

㉒.16 Occurrence and Preparation of the Halogens

The halogens are too reactive to occur free in nature, but their compounds are widely distributed. Chlorides are the most abundant, and although fluorides, bromides, and iodides are less common, they are reasonably available.

All of the halogens occur in sea water as halide ions. The concentration of the chloride ion is 0.54 M; that of the other halides is less than 10^{-4} M. Fluorine is also found in the minerals **fluorite**, CaF_2, **fluoroapatite**, $Ca_5(PO_4)_3F$, and **cryolite**, Na_3AlF_6, and in small amounts in teeth, bone, and the blood. Chlorine is found in high concentrations in the Great Salt Lake and the Dead Sea and in extensive salt beds (Fig. 22.27) that contain NaCl, $MgCl_2$, or $CaCl_2$. It is a component of stomach acid, which is hydrochloric acid. Bromine occurs in the Dead Sea and in underground brines. Iodine is found in small quantities in Chile saltpeter, in underground brines, and in sea kelp. Iodine is an essential component of the thyroid gland.

The best sources of the halogens (except iodine) are halide salts. The halide ions can be oxidized to free diatomic halogen molecules by various methods, depending on the ease of oxidation of the halide ion. This increases with increasing atomic size, in the order $F^- < Cl^- < Br^- < I^-$.

Fluorine is the most powerful oxidizing agent of the known elements; it spontaneously oxidizes most other elements. The reverse reaction, the oxidation of fluorides, is very difficult to accomplish; electrolytic oxidation is needed to prepare elemental fluorine. Electrolysis is often used to accomplish oxidation–reduction reactions with species that are oxidized or reduced with difficulty. The electrolysis is commonly performed in a molten mixture of potassium hydrogen fluoride, KHF_2, and anhydrous hydrogen fluoride (melting point 72°C). When electrolysis begins, HF is decomposed to form fluorine gas at the anode and hydrogen at the cathode. The two gases are kept separated to prevent their recombination to form hydrogen fluoride.

Most commercial **chlorine** is produced by electrolysis of the chloride ion in aqueous solutions of sodium chloride. Other products of the electrolysis are hydrogen and sodium hydroxide (see Sections 13.3 and 20.13). Chlorine is also a product when metals such as sodium, calcium, and magnesium are produced by the electrolysis of their fused chlorides (see Sections 13.3 and 20.12).

Figure 22.27

An underground salt mine in a bed of essentially pure salt.

Chloride, bromide, and iodide ions are easier to oxidize than fluoride ions. Thus chlorine, bromine, and iodine also can be prepared by the chemical oxidation of the respective halides. Small quantities of chlorine are sometimes prepared by oxidation of the chloride ion in acid solution with strong oxidizing agents such as manganese dioxide (MnO_2), potassium permanganate ($KMnO_4$), or sodium dichromate ($Na_2Cr_2O_7$). The reaction with manganese dioxide is

$$MnO_2(s) + 2Cl^-(aq) + 4H_3O^+(aq) \longrightarrow Mn^{2+}(aq) + Cl_2(g) + 6H_2O(l)$$

The methods for small-scale oxidation of bromides to bromine are like those used for the oxidation of chlorides.

Bromine is prepared commercially by the oxidation of bromide ion by chlorine.

$$2Br^-(aq) + Cl_2(g) \longrightarrow Br_2(l) + 2Cl^-(aq)$$

Chlorine is a stronger oxidizing agent than bromine, and the equilibrium for this reaction lies well to the right. Essentially all domestic bromine is produced by chlorine oxidation of bromide ions obtained from underground brines found in Arkansas.

Elemental **iodine** is sometimes produced by the oxidation of iodide ion with chlorine. An excess of chlorine must be avoided; it forms iodine monochloride, ICl, and iodic acid, HIO_3. Iodine is produced commercially by the reduction of sodium iodate, $NaIO_3$, an impurity in deposits of Chile saltpeter, with sodium hydrogen sulfite.

$$2IO_3^- + 5HSO_3^- \longrightarrow 3HSO_4^- + 2SO_4^{2-} + H_2O + I_2(s)$$

22.17 Uses of the Halogens

Fluorine gas has been used to fluorinate organic compounds (to replace hydrogen with fluorine) since its initial discovery by Moissan in 1886. The resulting **fluorocarbon** compounds are quite stable and nonflammable. **Freon-12**, CCl_2F_2, is widely used as a refrigerant (Section 29.5). Teflon is a polymer composed of $-CF_2CF_2-$ units. **Perfluorodecalin**, $C_{10}F_{18}$ (Fig. 22.28), is useful as a blood substitute, in part because oxygen is very soluble in this chemically inert substance. Fluorine gas is used in the production of **uranium hexafluoride**, UF_6, which is used in the separation of isotopes for the production of atomic energy. Fluoride ion is added to water supplies and to some toothpastes as SnF_2 or NaF to fight tooth decay. Some evidence exists that fluoride ion may be harmful to the body. There is still some controversy.

Chlorine is used to bleach wood pulp and cotton cloth. The chlorine reacts with water to form hypochlorous acid, which oxidizes colored substances to colorless ones. Large quantities of chlorine are used in chlorinating hydrocarbons (replacing hydrogen with chlorine) to produce compounds such as carbon tetrachloride (CCl_4), chloroform ($CHCl_3$), and ethyl chloride (C_2H_5Cl) and in the production of polyvinyl chloride (PVC) and other polymers. Chlorine is also used to kill the bacteria in community water supplies.

Bromine is used to produce certain dyes, light-sensitive silver bromide for photographic film, and sodium and potassium bromides for sedatives.

Iodine in alcohol solution with potassium iodide is used as an antiseptic (tincture of iodine). Iodide salts are essential for the proper functioning of the thyroid gland; an iodine deficiency may lead to the development of goiter. Iodized table salt contains 0.023% potassium iodide. Silver iodide is used in photographic film and in the seeding of clouds to induce rain. Iodoform, CHI_3, is an antiseptic.

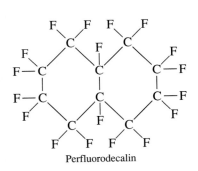

Perfluorodecalin

Figure 22.28

Perfluorodecalin is used as a blood substitute.

22.18 Properties of the Halogens

Fluorine is a pale yellow gas, chlorine is a greenish-yellow gas, bromine is a deep reddish-brown liquid three times as dense as water, and iodine is a grayish-black crystalline solid with a low melting point (Fig. 22.29). Liquid bromine has a high vapor pressure, and the reddish vapor can easily be seen in a bottle containing the liquid. Iodine crystals have a high vapor pressure. When gently heated, these crystals sublime and form a beautiful deep violet vapor (see photo on page 237).

Bromine is only slightly soluble in water, but it is miscible in all proportions in less polar (or nonpolar) solvents such as alcohol, ether, chloroform, carbon tetrachloride, and carbon disulfide, forming solutions that vary in color from yellow to reddish-brown, depending on the concentration.

Iodine is soluble in chloroform, carbon tetrachloride, carbon disulfide, and many hydrocarbons, giving violet solutions of I_2 molecules. The solutions have the same color as I_2 molecules in the gas phase. Iodine dissolves only slightly in water, giving brown solutions. It is quite soluble in alcohol, ether, and aqueous solutions of iodides, with which it also forms brown solutions. These brown solutions result because iodine molecules have empty valence shell d orbitals and can act as weak Lewis acids (see Section 16.14). They can form Lewis acid–base complexes with solvent molecules that can function as Lewis bases or with the iodide ion, which can also act as a Lewis base. The equation for the reversible reaction of iodine with the iodide ion to give the triiodide ion, $I_3{}^-$, is

$$:\!\ddot{I}\!:^- + \; :\!\ddot{I}\!-\!\ddot{I}\!: \;\rightleftharpoons\; :\!\ddot{I}\!-\!\ddot{I}\!-\!\ddot{I}\!:^-$$

The elemental (free) halogens are oxidizing agents with strengths decreasing in the order $F_2 > Cl_2 > Br_2 > I_2$. In general, as the ionization energy of a halogen decreases, its strength as an oxidizing agent also decreases. The easier it is to oxidize the halogen—that is, as the electropositive character increases—the more difficult it is for the halogen to act as an oxidizing agent. Fluorine generally oxidizes an element to its highest oxidation number, whereas the heavier halogens may not. For example, when fluorine reacts with sulfur, SF_6 is formed. Chlorine gives SCl_2 and bromine, S_2Br_2. Iodine does not react with sulfur.

Figure 22.29

Chlorine is a pale yellow-green gas, gaseous bromine is deep orange, and gaseous iodine (produced by warming the solid) is purple. (Fluorine is so reactive that it is too dangerous for the photographer to handle.)

The general chemical behavior of the halogens is discussed in Section 21.8. The reactions of elemental halogens with a variety of substances are summarized in Table 22.4.

Fluorine reacts directly and forms binary fluorides with all of the elements except the lighter noble gases (He, Ne, and Ar). Fluorine is such a strong oxidizing agent that many substances ignite on contact with it. Drops of water inflame in fluorine and form O_2, OF_2, H_2O_2, O_3, and HF. Wood and asbestos ignite and burn in fluorine gas. Most hot metals burn vigorously in fluorine. However, fluorine can be handled in copper, iron, magnesium, or nickel containers, because an adherent film of the fluoride salt protects their surfaces from further attack.

Fluorine readily displaces chlorine and the other halogens from solid metal halides; in an excess of fluorine, halogen fluorides are formed. Fluorine and hydrogen react explosively. Fluorine is the only element that reacts directly with the noble gas xenon.

Although it is a strong oxidizing agent, chlorine is less active than fluorine. For example, fluorine and hydrogen react explosively, but when chlorine and hydrogen are mixed in the dark, the reaction between them is so slow as to be imperceptible. When the mixture is exposed to light, the reaction is explosive. Chlorine is less active toward

---

Table 22.4   Chemical Properties of the Elemental Halogens

General Equation	Comments
Reactions with Elements	
$2M + nX_2 \longrightarrow 2MX_n$	With almost all metals
$H_2 + X_2 \longrightarrow 2HX$	With decreasing reactivity in the order $F_2 > Cl_2 > Br_2 > I_2$
$Xe + \dfrac{n}{2}F_2 \longrightarrow XeF_n$	$n = 2, 4,$ or 6
$nX_2 + X_2' \longrightarrow 2X'X_n$	X' heavier than X; n an odd integer
$S + 3F_2 \longrightarrow SF_6$	Se and Te can replace S
$S + Cl_2 \longrightarrow SCl_2$	
$2S + X_2 \longrightarrow S_2X_2$	With Cl_2 or Br_2
$2P + 3X_2 \longrightarrow 2PX_3$	With excess P; also with As, Sb, or Bi
$2P + 5X_2 \longrightarrow 2PX_5$	With excess halogen, except I_2
Reactions with Compounds	
$X_2 + 2X'^- \longrightarrow 2X^- + X_2'$	X' heavier than X
$F_2 + H_2O \longrightarrow$ $O_2 + O_3 + OF_2 + H_2O_2 + HF$	Unbalanced; actual distribution of products depends on reaction conditions
$X_2 + 2H_2O \longrightarrow H_3O^+ + X^- + HOX$	Not with F_2
$X_2 + H_2S \longrightarrow 2HX + S$	With Cl_2 or Br_2
$X_2 + CO \longrightarrow COX_2$	With Cl_2 or Br_2
$X_2 + SO_2 \longrightarrow SO_2X_2$	With F_2 or Cl_2
$X_2 + PX_3 \longrightarrow PX_5$	Not with I_2
$-\overset{|}{\underset{|}{C}}-H + X_2 \longrightarrow -\overset{|}{\underset{|}{C}}-X + HX$	With F_2, Cl_2 or Br_2 and many hydrocarbons
$\underset{/}{\overset{\backslash}{}}C=C\underset{\backslash}{\overset{/}{}} + X_2 \longrightarrow -\overset{X}{\underset{|}{C}}-\overset{X}{\underset{|}{C}}-$	With Cl_2, Br_2, or I_2 and many hydrocarbons containing C=C double bonds

metals than fluorine, and oxidation reactions usually require higher temperatures. Molten sodium ignites in chlorine (Fig. 22.30). Chlorine attacks most nonmetals (C, N_2, and O_2 are notable exceptions), forming covalent molecular compounds. Chlorine generally reacts with compounds that contain only carbon and hydrogen (hydrocarbons) by adding to multiple bonds or by substitution (Table 22.4).

When chlorine is added to water, it is both oxidized and reduced in a **disproportionation** reaction (Section 21.2).

$$Cl_2 + 2H_2O \rightleftharpoons HOCl + H_3O^+ + Cl^-$$

Half the chlorine atoms oxidize to the $+1$ oxidation state (in hypochlorous acid), and the other half reduce to the -1 oxidation state (in chloride ion). This disproportionation is incomplete, so chlorine water is a solution of chlorine molecules, hypochlorous acid molecules, hydronium ions, and chloride ions. When exposed to light, this solution undergoes a photochemical decomposition.

$$2HOCl + 2H_2O \xrightarrow{\text{Sunlight}} 2H_3O^+ + 2Cl^- + O_2(g)$$

The chemical properties of bromine are similar to those of chlorine, although bromine is the weaker oxidizing agent and its reactivity is less than that of chlorine.

Iodine is the least reactive of the four naturally occurring halogens. It is the weakest oxidizing agent, and its ion is the most easily oxidized. Iodine reacts with metals, but heating is often required. It does not oxidize other halide ions but does oxidize some other nonmetal anions such as sulfide ion, S^{2-}.

$$S^{2-} + I_2 \longrightarrow S + 2I^-$$

Compared with the other halogens, iodine reacts only slightly with water. Traces of iodine in water react with a mixture of starch and iodide ion, forming a deep blue color. This reaction is used as a very sensitive test for the presence of iodine in water.

Figure 22.30
Molten sodium (mp 97.8°C) inflames in an atmosphere of chlorine.

22.19 Interhalogens

Compounds formed from two different halogens are called **interhalogens.** Interhalogen molecules consist of one atom of the heavier halogen bonded by single bonds to an odd number of atoms of the lighter halogen. The structures of IF_3, IF_5, and IF_7 are shown in Fig. 22.31. Formulas for other interhalogens, each of which can be prepared by the reaction of the respective halogens, are given in Table 22.5.

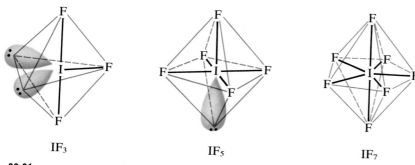

Figure 22.31
Structures of IF_3 (T-shaped), IF_5 (square pyramidal), and IF_7 (pentagonal bipyramidal).

Table 22.5
Interhalogens[a]

XX′	XX′$_3$	XX′$_5$	XX′$_7$
ClF(g)	ClF$_3$(g)	ClF$_5$(g)	
BrF(g)	BrF$_3$(l)	BrF$_5$(l)	
BrCl(g)			
IF(s)	IF$_3$(s)	IF$_5$(l)	IF$_7$(g)
ICl(l)	ICl$_3$(s)		
IBr(s)			

[a]The physical states shown are those at STP.

$$ICl_2^-$$

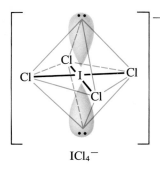

$$ICl_4^-$$

Figure 22.32

Structures of the ions ICl_2^- (linear) and ICl_4^- (square planar).

Note from Table 22.5 that fluorine is able to oxidize iodine to its maximum oxidation number, +7, whereas bromine and chlorine, which are more difficult to oxidize, achieve only the +5 oxidation state. Because smaller halogens are grouped about a larger one, the maximum number of smaller atoms possible increases as the radius of the larger atom increases. Many of these compounds are unstable, and most are extremely reactive. The interhalogens react like their component halides; halogen fluorides, for example, are stronger oxidizing agents than halogen chlorides.

The ionic **polyhalides** of the alkali metals, compounds such as KI_3, $KICl_2$, $KICl_4$, $CsIBr_2$, and $CsBrCl_2$ that contain an anion composed of at least three halogen atoms, are closely related to the interhalogens (Fig. 22.32). The formation of the polyhalide anion I_3^- is responsible for the solubility of iodine in aqueous solutions containing iodide ion.

$$I_2(s) + I^-(aq) \longrightarrow I_3^-(aq)$$

22.20 Hydrogen Halides

Binary compounds containing only hydrogen and a halogen are called **hydrogen halides.** At room temperature the pure hydrogen halides HF, HCl, HBr, and HI are gases.

The anhydrous hydrogen halides are rather inactive chemically and do not attack dry metals at room temperature. However, they react with many metals at elevated temperatures, forming metal halides and hydrogen. These reactions are sometimes used to prepare anhydrous metal halides.

$$Fe(s) + 2HCl(g) \xrightarrow{300°C} FeCl_2(s) + H_2(g)$$

The hydrogen halides can be prepared by the general techniques used to prepare other acids (see Section 16.7), although each technique is not suitable for every hydrogen halide. As indicated in Table 22.4, fluorine, chlorine, and bromine react directly with hydrogen to form the respective hydrogen halide. This reaction is used to prepare hydrogen chloride and hydrogen bromide commercially. Bromine reacts much less vigorously with hydrogen than does chlorine. The direct reaction of hydrogen and iodine is unsatisfactory for the preparation of hydrogen iodide, because the reaction is slow and the equilibrium yield is low. Heat decomposes HI, so the rate of reaction cannot be increased by heating. Hydrogen fluoride can be prepared by the direct reaction of the elements, but elemental fluorine is expensive and the reaction is violent; other means are used to prepare HF.

Hydrogen halides can be prepared by acid–base reactions between a nonvolatile strong acid and a metal halide. The escape of the gaseous hydrogen halide drives the reaction to completion. For example, hydrogen fluoride is usually prepared by heating a mixture of calcium fluoride, CaF_2, and concentrated sulfuric acid.

$$CaF_2(s) + H_2SO_4(aq) \longrightarrow CaSO_4(s) + 2HF(g)$$

Gaseous hydrogen fluoride is also a by-product in the preparation of phosphate fertilizers by the reaction of fluoroapatite, $Ca_5(PO_4)_3F$, with sulfuric acid (see Section 2.12). Hydrogen chloride is prepared, both in the laboratory and commercially, by the reaction of concentrated sulfuric acid with a chloride salt [Fig. 22.33(a)]. Sodium chloride is generally used, because it is the least expensive chloride. Hydrogen bromide and hydrogen iodide cannot be prepared in similar reactions, because sulfuric acid is such a strong oxidizing agent that it oxidizes both bromide and iodide ions [Fig. 22.33(b)].

(a)

(b)

Figure 22.33

(a) The reaction of sulfuric acid with NaCl produces gaseous HCl.
(b) With NaI, sulfuric acid oxidizes the iodide ion and produces I_2.

The reaction of a covalent nonmetal bromide with water and that of a covalent nonmetal iodide with water produce hydrogen bromide and hydrogen iodide, respectively.

$$PBr_3(l) + 3H_2O(l) \longrightarrow 3HBr(g) + H_3PO_3(aq)$$

$$PI_3(s) + 3H_2O(l) \longrightarrow 3HI(g) + H_3PO_3(aq)$$

This method is rarely used to prepare hydrogen chloride; the method (discussed above) wherein sodium chloride is used is much less expensive.

About two-thirds of the hydrogen chloride produced commercially in the United States (2.6 million tons in 1989) is a by-product of the reactions used to prepare chlorinated hydrocarbons. For example, the reaction used to manufacture ethyl chloride from ethane (C_2H_6) and chlorine also yields hydrogen chloride.

$$C_2H_6(g) + Cl_2(g) \longrightarrow C_2H_5Cl(g) + HCl(g)$$

Figure 22.34

Hydrochloric acid is usually supplied as a 36.5–38.0% solution of HCl in water.

Hydrogen bromide is a by-product of the manufacture of brominated hydrocarbons by a similar reaction involving bromine and hydrocarbons.

All of the hydrogen halides are very soluble in water (Fig. 22.34). With the exception of hydrogen fluoride, which has a strong hydrogen–fluorine bond, they are strong acids. Reactions of the hydrohalic acids with metals or with metal hydroxides, oxides, and carbonates are often used to prepare soluble salts of the halides. Most chloride salts are soluble (AgCl, $PbCl_2$, and Hg_2Cl_2 are the commonly encountered exceptions).

The halide ions in hydrohalic acids give these substances the properties associated with $X^-(aq)$. The heavier halide ions (Cl^-, Br^-, I^-) can act as reducing agents and are oxidized by lighter halogens or other oxidizing agents. They also serve as precipitating agents for insoluble metal halides.

Pure hydrogen fluoride differs from the other hydrogen halides because it forms strong intermolecular hydrogen bonds (see Section 11.4). This gives liquid hydrogen fluoride an anomalously high boiling point for a hydrogen halide (see Fig. 11.7). Hydrogen-bonded dimers, $(HF)_2$, are observed in the vapor. Only very weak hydrogen bonds can occur in hydrogen chloride, hydrogen bromide, and hydrogen iodide, because the electronegativities of the halogen atoms in these molecules are lower, and consequently the polarities of the bonds are smaller.

1.405 Å →

103.2°

1.405 Å →

OF_2

1.70 Å →

110.8°

1.70 Å →

Cl_2O

Figure 22.35

Angular structures of the OF_2 and Cl_2O molecules (drawn approximately to scale). Bond distances are measured between the nuclei of the atoms.

Hydrofluoric acid is unique in its reactions with sand (silicon dioxide) and with glass, which is a mixture of silicates (mainly calcium silicate).

$$SiO_2 + 4HF \longrightarrow SiF_4(g) + 2H_2O$$

$$CaSiO_3 + 6HF \longrightarrow CaF_2 + SiF_4(g) + 3H_2O$$

The silicon escapes from these reactions as silicon tetrafluoride, a volatile compound. Because hydrogen fluoride attacks glass, it is used to frost or etch glass. Light bulbs are frosted with hydrogen fluoride, and markings on thermometers, burets, and other glassware are made with it.

The largest use for hydrogen fluoride is in the production of fluorocarbons for refrigerants such as the Freons, plastics, and propellants. The second largest use is in the manufacture of cryolite, Na_3AlF_6, which is important in the production of aluminum (Section 13.3). The acid is also used in the production of other inorganic fluorides (such as BF_3), which serve as catalysts in the industrial synthesis of certain organic compounds.

Extreme care should be taken when handling hydrofluoric acid, for it causes painful and slow-healing burns. It is a local anesthetic, and its presence may not be noticed until much damage has been done.

Hydrochloric acid is inexpensive. It is an important and versatile acid in industry and is used in the manufacture of metal chlorides, dyes, glue, glucose, and various other chemicals. A considerable amount is also used in the activation of oil wells and as a pickle liquor—an acid used to remove oxide coatings from iron or steel that is to be galvanized, tinned, or enameled. The amounts of hydrobromic acid and hydroiodic acid used commercially are insignificant by comparison.

22.21 Binary Oxygen–Halogen Compounds

The halogens do not react directly with oxygen, but binary oxygen–halogen compounds can be prepared by the reactions of the halogens with oxygen-containing compounds. Oxygen compounds with chlorine, bromine, and iodine are called oxides because oxygen is the more electronegative element in these compounds. On the other hand, fluorine compounds with oxygen are called fluorides because fluorine is the more electronegative element.

As a class, the oxides are extremely reactive and unstable, and their chemistry has little practical importance. Dichlorine monoxide (Fig. 22.35) and chlorine dioxide (Fig. 22.36) are the only commercially important compounds. They are employed as bleaching agents (for use with wood pulp and flour) and for water treatment.

1.47 →

117.6°

1.47 →

Figure 22.36

Structure of the ClO_2 molecule.

22.22 Oxyacids of the Halogens and Their Salts

The compounds HXO, HXO_2, HXO_3, and HXO_4, where X represents Cl, Br, or I, are called **hypohalous, halous, halic,** and **perhalic** acids, respectively. The strengths of these acids increase from the hypohalous acids, which are very weak acids, to the perhalic acids, which are very strong. The known acids are listed in Table 22.6.

Name	Fluorine	Chlorine	Bromine	Iodine
Table 22.6	**Oxyacids of the Halogens**			
Hypohalous	HOF	HOCl	HOBr	HOI
Halous		$HClO_2$		
Halic		$HClO_3$	$HBrO_3$	HIO_3
Perhalic		$HClO_4$	$HBrO_4$	HIO_4
Paraperhalic				H_5IO_6

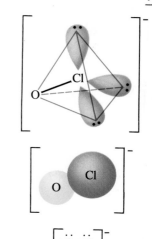

Figure 22.37

Structure of the hypochlorite ion, ClO^-.

The only known oxyacid of fluorine is the very unstable **hypofluorous acid,** HOF, which is prepared by the reaction of gaseous fluorine with ice.

$$F_2(g) + H_2O(s) \longrightarrow HOF(g) + HF(g)$$

This compound does not ionize in water, and no salts are known.

The reactions of chlorine and bromine with water are analogous to that of fluorine with ice, but these reactions do not go to completion, and mixtures of the halogen and the respective hypohalous and hydrohalic acids result. The reaction of the halogen with mercury(II) oxide is used to prepare a solution of the pure **hypohalous acid** (X = Cl, Br, I).

$$2X_2 + 3HgO + H_2O \longrightarrow HgX_2 \cdot 2HgO + 2HOX(aq)$$

None of the hypohalous acids except HOF has been isolated in the free state. Because of their thermal instability, they are stable only in solution. The hypohalous acids are all very weak acids; however, HOCl is a stronger acid than HOBr, which in turn is stronger than HOI.

Solutions of salts containing the basic **hypohalite** ions, OX^- (Fig. 22.37), can be prepared by adding base to solutions of hypohalous acids. The salts have been isolated as solids. All of the hypohalites are unstable with respect to disproportionation in solution, but the reaction is slow for hypochlorite. Hypobromite and hypoiodite disproportionate rapidly, even in the cold.

$$3XO^- \longrightarrow 2X^- + XO_3^-$$

Sodium hypochlorite is used as an inexpensive bleach (Clorox®) and germicide. It is produced commercially by the electrolysis of cold, dilute aqueous sodium chloride solutions under conditions where the resulting chlorine and hydroxide ion can react. The net reaction is

$$Cl^- + H_2O \xrightarrow[\text{energy}]{\text{Electrical}} ClO^- + H_2$$

The only definitely known halous acid is **chlorous acid,** $HClO_2$, obtained by the reaction of barium chlorite with dilute sulfuric acid.

$$Ba(ClO_2)_2(aq) + H_2SO_4(aq) \longrightarrow BaSO_4(s) + 2HClO_2(aq)$$

A solution of $HClO_2$ is obtained by filtering off the barium sulfate. Chlorous acid is not stable; it slowly decomposes in solution to give chlorine dioxide, hydrochloric acid, and water. Chlorous acid reacts with bases to give salts containing the **chlorite ion** (Fig.

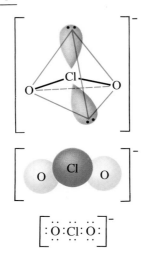

Figure 22.38

Structure of the chlorite ion, ClO_2^-.

22.38). Metal chlorite salts can also be prepared by the action of chlorine dioxide on a metal peroxide. For example, sodium peroxide reacts as follows:

$$2ClO_2(g) + Na_2O_2(s) \longrightarrow 2NaClO_2(s) + O_2(g)$$

Sodium chlorite is used extensively in the bleaching of paper, because it is a strong oxidizing agent that does not damage the paper.

Chloric acid, $HClO_3$, and **bromic acid,** $HBrO_3$, are stable only in solution, but **iodic acid,** HIO_3, can be isolated as a stable white solid from the reaction of iodine with concentrated nitric acid.

$$I_2(s) + 10HNO_3(aq) \longrightarrow 2HIO_3(s) + 10NO_2(g) + 4H_2O(l)$$

The lighter halic acids can be obtained from their barium salts by reaction with dilute sulfuric acid. The reaction is analogous to that used to prepare chlorous acid. All of the halic acids are strong acids and very active oxidizing agents. Salts containing **halate** ions (Fig. 22.39) can be prepared by reaction of the acids with bases. Metal chlorates are also prepared by electrochemical oxidation of a hot solution of a metal halide. Bromates can be produced by the oxidation of bromides with hypochlorite ion; oxidation of iodides with chlorates gives iodates. Sodium chlorate is used as a weed killer; potassium chlorate is used in some matches and in a method for the laboratory preparation of oxygen (Section 22.5).

Perchloric acid, $HClO_4$, can be obtained by treating a perchlorate, such as potassium perchlorate, with sulfuric acid under reduced pressure. The $HClO_4$ distills from the mixture.

$$KClO_4(s) + H_2SO_4(aq) \longrightarrow HClO_4(l) + KHSO_4(s)$$

Perchloric acid explodes above 92°C, but it distills at temperatures below 92° at reduced pressures. Dilute aqueous solutions of perchloric acid are quite stable thermally, but concentrations above 60% are unstable and dangerous. Perchloric acid and its salts are powerful oxidizing agents. Serious explosions have occurred when concentrated solutions were heated with easily oxidized substances. However, its reactions as an oxidizing agent are slow when perchloric acid is cold and dilute. The acid is among the strongest of all acids. Most salts containing the **perchlorate ion** (Fig. 22.40) are soluble. They are prepared by reactions of bases with perchloric acid and, commercially, by the electrolysis of hot solutions of their chlorides.

An account of the search for perbromic acid and perbromates and of the various reasons for their supposed nonexistence is an interesting chemical story. The perbromate ion was first prepared in 1968 by an esoteric radiochemical synthesis,

$$^{83}_{34}SeO_4^{2-} \longrightarrow {}^{83}_{35}BrO_4^- + \beta^-$$

which stimulated the search for chemical syntheses. The first isolation of a perbromate salt was accomplished by oxidation of the bromate ion, BrO_3^-, with aqueous xenon difluoride.

$$BrO_3^- + XeF_2 + H_2O \longrightarrow BrO_4^- + Xe + 2HF$$

Perbromate salts are difficult to prepare, and currently the best syntheses involve the oxidation of bromates in basic solution with fluorine gas. Perbromic acid, $HBrO_4$, is prepared by the acidification of perbromate salts.

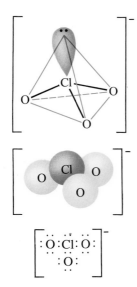

Figure 22.39

Structure of the chlorate ion, ClO_3^-.

Several different acids containing iodine in the +7 oxidation state are known; they include **metaperiodic acid,** HIO_4, and **paraperiodic acid,** H_5IO_6. Salts of these acids can be readily prepared by reactions with bases.

For Review

Summary

Hydrogen has the chemical properties of a nonmetal with a relatively low electronegativity. It forms ionic hydrides with active metals, covalent compounds in which it has an oxidation number of −1 with less electronegative elements, and covalent compounds in which it has an oxidation number of +1 with more electronegative nonmetals. It reacts explosively with oxygen, fluorine, and chlorine; less readily with bromine; and much less readily with iodine, sulfur, and nitrogen. Hydrogen reduces the oxides of those metals lying below chromium in the activity series to form the metal and water.

Oxygen (Group VIA) forms compounds with almost all of the elements. Except in a few compounds with fluorine, oxygen exhibits negative oxidation numbers in its compounds. The most common oxidation number is −2, in **oxides.** The −1 oxidation number is found in compounds that contain O—O bonds, **peroxides.** Oxygen is a strong oxidizing agent. **Ozone,** O_3, is an allotrope of oxygen, O_2. Ozone forms from oxygen in an endothermic reaction and is a stronger oxidizing agent than O_2.

Sulfur (Group VIA) reacts with almost all metals and readily forms the **sulfide ion,** S^{2-}, in which it has an oxidation number of −2, or **polysulfides,** S_n^{2-}. Sulfur also reacts with most nonmetals. It exhibits an oxidation number of −2 in covalent compounds with less electronegative elements. With more electronegative elements it exhibits oxidation numbers of +4 and +6 (commonly) and +1 and +2 (occasionally).

Sulfur burns in air and forms sulfur dioxide, which reacts with water to form the weak, unstable **sulfurous acid.** Neutralization of sulfurous acid and reactions of sulfur dioxide with metal oxides produce **sulfites.** The slow reaction of sulfur dioxide with oxygen produces sulfur trioxide. Sulfur trioxide is used to prepare **sulfuric acid,** a strong acid and an oxidizing agent. Neutralization of sulfuric acid and reactions of sulfur trioxide with metal oxides produce **sulfates.** Replacement of an OH group or an oxygen atom in a sulfuric acid molecule or a sulfate ion produces derivatives of sulfuric acid and of the sulfate ion.

The **halogens** are members of Group VIIA. The heavier halogens form compounds in which they have oxidation numbers of −1, +1, +3, +5, and +7, although they sometimes exhibit other oxidation numbers. Fluorine always exhibits an oxidation number of −1 in compounds.

The oxidizing ability of the elemental halogens and the resistance of the halides to oxidation decrease as halogen size increases. This is reflected in the ease of preparation of the elements from their halide salts. The gaseous **hydrogen halides** form from the direct reaction of halogens and hydrogen and from the other general techniques used to make acids. They dissolve in water to give solutions of **hydrohalic acids.**

The halogens form **halides** with less electronegative elements. Halides of the metals vary from ionic to covalent; halides of nonmetals are covalent. **Interhalogens** are formed by the combination of two different halogens. Binary oxygen–halogen compounds, generally of low stability, are known, as are **hypohalous, halous, halic,** and **perhalic** acids and their salts.

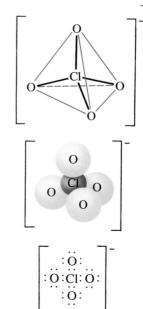

Figure 22.40

Structure of the perchlorate ion, ClO_4^-.

Key Terms and Concepts

acid rain (22.13)
deuterium (22.3)
disproportionation (22.18)
disulfide (22.12)
Frasch process (22.10)
halic acid (22.22)
halides (22.20)
halous acid (22.22)
hydrocarbon (22.1)

hydrogen halide (22.20)
hydrohalic acid (22.20)
hydrosulfuric acid (22.12)
hypohalous acid (22.22)
interhalogen (22.19)
ionic hydrides (22.2)
oxide (22.6)
ozone depletion (22.7)
paramagnetic (22.6)

perhalic acid (22.22)
peroxide (22.6)
photosynthesis (22.8)
polyhalide ion (22.19)
polysulfide (22.12)
sulfate (22.15)
sulfide (22.12)
sulfite (22.14)
tritium (22.3)

Exercises

Answers for selected even-numbered exercises marked by red numbers appear at the end of the book. The worked-out solutions to all even-numbered exercises appear in the *Solutions Guide*.

1. Both fluorine and chlorine are gases that contain diatomic molecules and have a yellowish color. How can we distinguish between them by using physical properties? By using chemical properties?

2. Why is it easier and cheaper to prepare commercial quantities of liquid oxygen than of liquid hydrogen?

3. Arrange the halogens in order of decreasing:
   (a) reducing activity
   (b) ionization energy
   (c) atomic radius
   (d) strength of intermolecular forces
   (You may need to refer to Section 11.3.)

4. From the positions of the elements in the periodic table, predict which of the following pairs:
   (a) reduces H_2; Na or F_2 (c) reduces S; I_2 or Al
   (b) oxidizes S; H_2 or Cl_2 (d) oxidizes O; F_2 or H_2

Hydrogen

5. Write the chemical equation that describes the preparation of hydrogen when steam is passed through a red-hot gun barrel.

6. Write balanced chemical equations for the preparation of hydrogen from:
   (a) Zn + HCl   (c) C + H_2O
   (b) CaH_2 + H_2O (d) H_2O + electrical energy

7. Write a balanced chemical equation for the reaction, if any, of each of the following metals with water and with hydrochloric acid: Na, Ca, Al, Pb, Fe, Pt. Also name the compounds formed in each reaction.

8. Explain: "Metal hydrides are convenient and portable sources of hydrogen."

9. Write a balanced chemical equation that serves as an example of hydrogen acting as (a) an oxidizing agent and (b) a reducing agent. Identify the changes in oxidation number that occur in each reaction.

10. The reaction of KH with H_2O to produce potassium hydroxide and hydrogen gas may be characterized as an oxidation–reduction reaction. Identify the oxidizing agent, the reducing agent, and the changes in oxidation number that occur in the reaction.

11. What mass of hydrogen gas results from the reaction of 15.5 g of NaH with water?

12. Hydrogen gas is not very soluble in water. At 25°C a saturated solution of H_2 in water is 7.86×10^{-5} M. How many liters of H_2 at 1.00 atm and 25°C are dissolved in exactly 1 L of solution?

13. How many grams of hydrogen and of zinc sulfate, $ZnSO_4$, can be prepared by the reaction of 20.5 g of zinc with sulfuric acid, H_2SO_4?

14. Give the name of an ionic hydride and a covalent hydride. Write a balanced equation showing the preparation of each compound, and draw the Lewis structure of each compound.

15. A sample of hydrogen gas has a pressure of 0.75 atm in a bulb with a volume of 2.50 L. This bulb is connected to another bulb that has been completely evacuated and has a volume of 4.00 L. What will be the final pressure in the two bulbs when the gas has been allowed to expand into the second bulb?

16. Using Graham's law (see Section 10.12), calculate the ratio of the rates of diffusion of hydrogen gas, H_2, and deuterium gas, D_2.

Oxygen

17. Refer to Fig. 22.7 and write a balanced equation for the reaction that Priestley used to prepare oxygen.

18. Write balanced equations for the preparation of oxygen from (a) CaO_2, (b) H_2O, (c) KNO_3, and (d) PbO_2.

19. Draw a molecular orbital diagram for O_2, for O_2^-, and for O_2^{2-} (see Chapter 9).

20. What is the oxidation number of oxygen in HOF?
21. Cite three industrial uses of O_2.
22. Cite two industrial uses of O_3.
23. Why is the O—O bond longer in ozone than in oxygen?
24. How many moles of oxygen are contained in a 50.0-L cylinder at 22.0°C if the pressure gauge indicates 2000 lb/in^2?
25. Which of the following materials do you think burns in oxygen: $GeH_4(g)$, GeO_2, SiO_2, CO, CO_2, Ca, MgO? Why don't some of these materials burn in oxygen?
26. Write a balanced chemical equation for the reaction of an excess of oxygen with each of the following. Remember that oxygen is a strong oxidizing agent and tends to oxidize an element to its maximum oxidation state.
    (a) Mg (d) Ga (g) C_2H_2
    (b) Rb (e) Na_2SO_3 (h) CO
    (c) Bi (f) AlN
27. What volume of oxygen at STP can be formed from 0.500 mol of $KClO_3$?
28. How many liters of oxygen gas are produced at 20°C and 750 torr when 10.0 g of sodium peroxide reacts with water to produce sodium hydroxide and oxygen?

Sulfur

29. Write a balanced chemical equation for the reaction of sulfur with each of the following.
    (a) Br_2 (c) Al (e) Zn
    (b) Na (d) Se (f) Ba
30. Explain why hydrogen sulfide is a gas at room temperature, whereas water, which has a lower molecular mass, is a liquid.
31. Give the hybridization and oxidation number for sulfur in SO_2, in SO_3, and in H_2SO_4.
32. Which is the stronger acid, $NaHSO_3$ or $NaHSO_4$?
33. Determine the oxidation number of sulfur in SF_6, SO_2F_2, and KHS.
34. Which is a stronger acid, sulfurous acid or sulfuric acid? Why?
35. Oxygen forms double bonds in O_2, but sulfur forms single bonds in S_8. Why?
36. Give the Lewis structure of each of the following.
    (a) SF_4 (d) SO_2Cl_2 (g) $O_3SSSSO_3{}^{2-}$
    (b) K_2SO_4 (e) H_2SO_3 $(S_4O_6)^{2-}$
    (c) H_2S_3 (f) SO_3
37. Write two balanced chemical equations in which sulfuric acid acts as an oxidizing agent.
38. The molecules SCl_6, SBr_6, and SI_6 cannot be prepared by the reaction of sulfur and elemental halogen. Why?
39. Explain how you would dilute concentrated sulfuric acid with water. Why would you follow this procedure?
40. Some natural waters contain small amounts of hydrogen sulfide, which causes a bad smell. Treating this water with

chlorine oxidizes the H_2S to elemental sulfur. Write a balanced chemical equation for this reaction.
41. Why do solutions of sulfites usually contain sulfate ions?
42. Show by means of balanced chemical equations why solutions of sulfides and hydrogen sulfides are basic.
43. Designate each of the following compounds as polar or nonpolar.
    (a) SO_2Cl_2 (c) SO_2 (e) H_2S
    (b) SO_3 (d) SF_4 (f) Cl_3PS
44. A volume of 28.92 mL of a 0.08099 M standard sulfuric acid solution is required to titrate a 30.00-mL sample of sodium hydroxide. If H_2SO_4 acts as a diprotic acid, what is the molarity of the sodium hydroxide solution?
45. On the basis of the position of sulfur in the periodic table, predict the products of, and write a balanced chemical equation for, each of the following reactions. (There may be more than one correct answer, depending on your choice of stoichiometries.)
    (a) $Cl_2 + SO_2$ (d) $H_2S + S^{2-}$
    (b) $Li_2O + SO_2$ (e) $F_2 + H_2S$
    (c) $NaOCl + Na_2S$ (f) $Br^- + SO_2$
46. What volume of hydrogen sulfide gas at STP can be produced by the reaction of 57.8 g of aluminum sulfide, Al_2S_3, with an excess of phosphoric acid?

Halogens

47. Which is the stronger acid, $HClO_3$ or $HBrO_3$? Why?
48. Which is the stronger acid, $HClO_4$ or $HBrO_4$? Why?
49. What is the hybridization of iodine in each of the iodine fluorides (Table 22.5)?
50. Why is iodine monochloride more polar than iodine monobromide?
51. How is iodine produced from sodium iodate?
52. Suggest two reasons why fluorine is not used in the extraction of bromine from brine.
53. Describe an industrial preparation for each of the halogens.
54. Predict the molecular geometries of each of the following.
    (a) IF_5 (c) PCl_5 (e) SeF_4
    (b) $I_3{}^-$ (d) $SiBr_4$ (f) ClF_3
55. Which halogen has the highest ionization energy? Is this what you would predict on the basis of what you have learned about periodic properties?
56. Name each of the following compounds.
    (a) $Fe(BrO_4)_3$ (c) $NaBrO_3$ (e) $NaClO_4$
    (b) BrF_3 (d) PBr_5 (f) KClO
57. Explain why at room temperature fluorine and chlorine are gases, bromine is a liquid, and iodine is a solid. (You may need to refer to Section 11.3.)
58. What is the oxidation state of the halogen in each of the following?
    (a) H_5IO_6 (c) ClO_2 (e) ICl_3
    (b) $IO_4{}^-$ (d) ICl_2 (f) F_2

59. Write a balanced chemical equation for the reaction that occurs in each of the following cases.
    (a) Potassium hydroxide is added to a solution of bromic acid.
    (b) Metallic zinc is added to a solution of perchloric acid.
    (c) Chlorine is added to a solution of sodium hydroxide.
    (d) Paraperiodic acid reacts with an excess of barium hydroxide. (Assume paraperiodic acid is a diprotic acid.)

60. Why is iodine more soluble in a solution of potassium iodide than in water?

61. Write a balanced chemical equation for each of the following.
    (a) Chlorine gas reacts with aqueous potassium iodide.
    (b) Iodine reacts with aqueous sodium chloride.
    (c) Fluorine gas is bubbled into water.
    (d) Liquid bromine is added to aqueous sodium iodide.

62. Give the empirical formula of the ionic compound formed by each of the following pairs of elements.
    (a) Ba, I   (c) Sr, I   (e) Al, I
    (b) Mg, Cl   (d) Na, F   (f) Rb, Br

63. Using the reactions of the halogens with sulfur, show that the oxidizing abilities of the halogens decrease as their size increases.

64. Write the Lewis structure of each of the oxyacids of bromine (Table 22.6). Designate the oxidation number of bromine in each of these acids.

65. Write a balanced chemical equation describing a laboratory preparation of each of the hydrogen halides.

66. Write a balanced chemical equation that describes the reaction of bromine with each of the following.
    (a) sodium   (c) hydrogen   (e) excess chlorine
    (b) calcium   (d) excess phosphorus (f) sulfur

67. Write balanced chemical equations demonstrating that Cl_2O and I_2O_5 are acid anhydrides.

68. By considering the changes in oxidation number that occur, show that the reaction of chlorine with water is a disproportionation reaction.

Additional Exercises

69. Which of the following compounds react with water to give an acid solution? Which give a basic solution? Write a balanced chemical equation for the reaction of each with water.
    (a) CaH_2 (c) HF   (e) Na_2O
    (b) HS^- (d) SO_3 (f) I_2O_5

70. A gas mixture at equilibrium at 1375 K exhibits a partial pressure of HBr of 0.998 atm, a partial pressure of H_2 of 3.82×10^{-3} atm, and a partial pressure of Br_2 of 3.82×10^{-3} atm. What is K_p for the decomposition of HBr to H_2 and Br_2?

71. The combustion of 9.180 g of sodium to sodium oxide is exothermic; 100.74 kJ of heat is evolved. What is the enthalpy of formation of sodium oxide?

72. The density of HF(g), 0.991 g/L at 19°C and 1.00 atm, is unexpectedly high. Calculate the apparent molecular mass of HF from these data, and explain this result.

73. How many grams of sodium iodate are required to prepare 0.100 kg of iodine by reduction with sodium hydrogen sulfite?

74. A sample of cadmium chloride with a mass of 1.766 g gave 1.089 g of cadmium upon electrolysis. Determine the formula of cadmium chloride.

75. Which of the following compounds or ions have the same structure: I_3^-, Cl_2O, HOF, ClF_3, ICl_4^-, IF_4^+, ClO_4^-, XeF_2?

76. Write the balanced chemical equation for the reaction that occurs when BrCl dissolves in water.

77. What mass of PCl_3 can be prepared by the reaction of chlorine with 13.55 g of phosphorus?

78. The reactions involved in the preparation of sulfuric acid are highly exothermic. Using the data given in Appendix I, calculate the enthalpy changes for each of the following reactions.
    (a) $S(s) + O_2(g) \longrightarrow SO_2(g)$
    (b) $2SO_2(g) + O_2(g) \longrightarrow 2SO_3(g)$
    (c) $SO_3(g) + H_2O(l) \longrightarrow H_2SO_4(l)$

The Nonmetals, Part 2: Carbon, Nitrogen, Phosphorus, and the Noble Gases

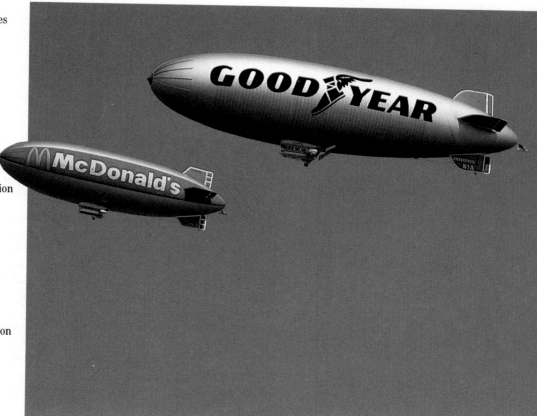

These lighter-than-air craft use helium for its lifting power and because it is not flammable.

This chapter continues the more detailed discussion (begun in Chapter 22) of the chemistry of certain specific nonmetals. In this chapter we shall consider the behavior of carbon, nitrogen, phosphorus, and the noble gases (helium, neon, argon, krypton, xenon, and radon).

Carbon

Figure 23.1

Samples of diamond and graphite, two forms of carbon.

Living matter is composed almost entirely of water and compounds of carbon, but this element is not very abundant in the earth's crust. Although estimates of its crustal abundance vary, it is no more than 0.1% by mass.

Chemists have identified several million carbon compounds that are either found in or produced by living organisms, and they have synthesized hundreds of thousands of other carbon compounds. Most of these compounds are classified as **organic compounds** because at one time chemists believed that most carbon compounds could be obtained only from living organisms.

The organic chemistry of carbon is introduced in Chapter 30, and the role of carbon compounds in living systems is discussed in Chapter 31. The unique feature of the chemistry of carbon that gives rise to so many compounds is its ability to undergo **catenation**—that is, to form chains and rings by bonding to itself. Not only does it form single carbon-to-carbon bonds (for example, H_3C-CH_3) but it also forms multiple (double and triple) bonds (for example, $H_2C=CH_2$ and $HC\equiv CH$). Sulfur (Sections 21.3 and 22.12) and silicon (Section 25.10) also catenate, but not nearly as much as carbon.

㉓.1 Occurrence and Allotropes of Carbon

Approximately half of the carbon in the earth's crust occurs in the form of the carbonate anion, CO_3^{2-}. The most common metal carbonates are calcium carbonate (chalk, limestone, coral, and marble), magnesium carbonate, and dolomite ($CaCO_3 \cdot MgCO_3$). The remaining carbon is found combined in living and dead organic matter; in natural gas, petroleum, and coal; in the air as carbon dioxide; and in natural waters as dissolved carbon dioxide and carbonic acid, H_2CO_3. Carbon is also found in the free state as diamond and graphite (Figs. 21.6 and 23.1).

Several other forms of elemental carbon also exist. **Carbon black, charcoal,** and **coke** appear to be amorphous forms of carbon, but they consist of very small microcrystals of graphite. Carbon black is soot that is formed when compounds of carbon and

Figure 23.2

Activated charcoal is used as an adsorbent in the purification of water.

hydrogen (hydrocarbons) are burned in a minimum amount of air. It is used in the rubber industry to strengthen and reinforce rubber and as a pigment in inks, paints, paper, and plastics.

Charcoal results from heating wood, sawdust, peat, or other organic matter at high temperatures in the absence of air. Charcoal is extremely porous, having a large surface area relative to its volume. Activated charcoal can be produced by heating charcoal with steam or carbon dioxide at high temperature. Activated charcoal finds extensive use as a decolorizing agent in the sugar industry, and it reduces pollution as a purification material in the treatment of water and air. Charcoal can be used in these ways because of its adsorbing ability (Fig. 23.2). **Adsorption** is a surface phenomenon in which the surface forces of the adsorbing agent attract and hold molecules of the substance being adsorbed.

Coke is produced by heating coal at high temperature in the absence of air. It is used extensively in the metallurgy of iron in blast furnaces (Section 27.2).

㉓.2 Chemical Properties of Carbon

At ordinary temperatures, all forms of elemental carbon are almost inert toward most reagents. Graphite, with its layered structure [Fig. 21.7(b)], undergoes some reactions in which atoms, molecules, or ions penetrate between the layers. The products are called **intercalation** compounds of graphite. The reactivity of carbon increases rapidly with rising temperatures, and at elevated temperatures it is very reactive. Hot carbon is a reducing agent. It reduces oxygen, forming either carbon monoxide, CO, or carbon dioxide, CO_2, depending on the amount of oxygen present. With sulfur it forms carbon disulfide, CS_2, and with fluorine it forms carbon tetrafluoride, CF_4. Hot carbon reduces many metal oxides, forming carbon monoxide or carbon dioxide and the elemental metal (Fig 23.3). With certain metals it forms carbides, such as iron carbide, Fe_3C, which have metallic properties. Some of the general reactions of carbon and its compounds are summarized in Table 23.1.

Figure 23.3

A mixture of copper oxide and carbon (left) produces copper metal (right) upon heating. The carbon reduces the CuO to free Cu.

Figure 23.4

Graphite composites are used in sports equipment for their high strength and light weight.

Figure 23.5

Industrial diamonds are arranged in a mold used to cast a diamond-studded bit for drilling through very hard rock formations.

Table 23.1	Chemical Properties of Carbon and Its Compounds
General Reaction	Comments

Reactions with Elements

$2C + O_2 \longrightarrow 2CO$	With heat and a stoichiometric amount of O_2
$C + O_2 \longrightarrow CO_2$	With heat and excess O_2
$C + 2S \longrightarrow CS_2$	With heat in an inert atmosphere
$C + 2F_2 \longrightarrow CF_4$	
$C + CuO \longrightarrow Cu + CO$	Many metal oxides react similarly
$3C + CaO \longrightarrow CaC_2 + CO$	Product contains C_2^{2-} ion

Reactions of Compounds

$2CO + O_2 \longrightarrow 2CO_2$	
$CO_2 + H_2O \rightleftharpoons H_2CO_3$	CO_2 is an acidic oxide
$MO + CO \longrightarrow M + CO_2$	Many metal oxides are reduced by CO
$CH_4 + 2O_2 \longrightarrow CO_2 + 2H_2O$	Most hydrocarbons burn, producing CO_2 and H_2O
$CaCO_3 \longrightarrow CaO + CO_2$	Many carbonates decompose upon heating
$CO_2 + O^{2-} \longrightarrow CO_3^{2-}$	CO_2 is a Lewis acid
$CS_2 + S^{2-} \longrightarrow CS_3^{2-}$	CS_2 is a Lewis acid

Because of its resistance to heat and other chemicals and because it is a good conductor of electricity, graphite is used to make electrodes, high-temperature crucibles, motor brushes, and electrical contacts. It is also used in lead pencils and in the manufacture of paint. A more recent application is in the high-strength composites used in tennis rackets, fishing rods, and golf clubs (Fig. 23.4).

The chemical reactivity of diamond is much lower than that of other forms of carbon. Diamond can be produced from graphite under conditions of high pressure (above 125,000 atmospheres) and high temperature (about 3300°C). It is denser than graphite and is the hardest known substance. Because of their hardness, synthetic diamonds are used in many industrial settings for cutting, grinding, and drilling (Fig. 23.5).

㉓.3 Carbon Monoxide

Carbon monoxide, CO [Fig. 23.6(a)], is produced when carbon is heated or burned in a limited amount of oxygen. The reaction of steam with red-hot coke also produces carbon monoxide, along with hydrogen in the mixture called water gas, as described in Section 22.1.

Carbon monoxide is prepared in the laboratory by heating formic acid, HCOOH, or oxalic acid, $H_2C_2O_4$, with concentrated sulfuric acid, which removes the elements of water from the acid and absorbs the water produced (see Section 22.15). For example, with oxalic acid,

$$H_2C_2O_4(s) \xrightarrow{\text{Conc. } H_2SO_4} H_2O(l) + CO(g) + CO_2(g)$$

The carbon dioxide in the resulting mixture can be removed by passing the mixture through solid sodium hydroxide, which absorbs the carbon dioxide, leaving pure carbon monoxide.

Carbon monoxide burns readily in oxygen, forming carbon dioxide.

$$2CO(g) + O_2(g) \longrightarrow 2CO_2(g) \qquad \Delta H° = -566 \text{ kJ}$$

This reaction makes carbon monoxide useful as a gaseous fuel. At high temperatures carbon monoxide reduces many metal oxides, so it is an important reducing agent in metallurgical processes. Copper(II) oxide, CuO, and iron(III) oxide, Fe_2O_3, are two oxides that are reduced to the metal with formation of carbon dioxide.

Carbon monoxide is a very dangerous poison; it is an odorless and tasteless gas and therefore gives no warning of its presence. It combines with the hemoglobin (see Section 26.1) in blood to form a compound that is too stable to be broken down by body processes. When the hemoglobin is combined with CO, it cannot combine with oxygen; this destroys the hemoglobin's ability to carry oxygen.

Figure 23.6

The molecular and electronic structures of (a) CO and (b) CO_2.

23.4 Carbon Dioxide

Carbon dioxide, CO_2 [Fig. 23.6(b)], is produced when any form of carbon or almost any carbon compound is burned in an excess of oxygen. Many carbonates liberate carbon dioxide when they are heated. Heating calcium carbonate, $CaCO_3$, produces carbon dioxide and calcium oxide, CaO (see Section 13.7).

Large quantities of industrial carbon dioxide are obtained as a by-product of the fermentation of glucose (a sugar) during the preparation of alcohol and alcoholic beverages. The net reaction is

$$C_6H_{12}O_6(aq) \xrightarrow{\text{Yeast}} 2C_2H_5OH(aq) + 2CO_2(g)$$
$$\text{Glucose} \qquad\qquad \text{Ethanol}$$

Carbon dioxide can be made in the laboratory by the reaction of acids with carbonates.

$$CaCO_3(s) + 2H_3O^+(aq) \longrightarrow Ca^{2+}(aq) + 3H_2O(l) + CO_2(g)$$

Carbon dioxide is a colorless and odorless gas that is 1.5 times as dense as air. It is not toxic, although a large concentration can cause suffocation (lack of oxygen). Carbon dioxide is a component of all carbonated beverages. One liter of water at 20°C dissolves 0.9 liter of carbon dioxide at 1 atmosphere, forming carbonic acid, which has a mildly acid taste. The gas is easily liquefied by compression, because its critical temperature (see Section 11.9) is relatively high (31.1°C). Solid carbon dioxide sublimes at normal atmospheric pressure. Its vapor pressure is 1 atmosphere at −78.5°C. Thus solid carbon dioxide, **dry ice,** is a valuable refrigerant that is always free of the liquid.

Carbon dioxide is used as a fire extinguisher because most substances do not burn in it, it is easily generated, and it is cheap. Air containing as little as 2.5% carbon dioxide extinguishes a flame.

The atmosphere contains about 0.04% by volume of carbon dioxide and serves as a huge reservoir of this compound. The carbon dioxide content of the atmosphere has increased significantly in the last few years because of the burning of fossil fuels (Fig. 23.7). A "greenhouse effect" can result when increased carbon dioxide and water vapor in the atmosphere absorb infrared radiation from the sun and do not allow it to escape back into space (see Section 29.7). Some researchers feel that the resulting increased heat in the atmosphere could cause the earth's average temperature to increase 2–3°C. This change would have serious effects on climate, ocean levels, and agriculture.

The solubility of carbon dioxide in water makes oceans and lakes significant reservoirs of this gas. Atmospheric carbon dioxide is in equilibrium with that dissolved in water and with that bound (as carbonate) in the earth's crust.

With the help of sunlight and chlorophyll (as a catalyst), green plants convert carbon dioxide and water into sugar and oxygen (see Section 22.8). Conversely, carbon dioxide is a product of respiration and is returned to the air by plants and animals.

Figure 23.7

Ice cores from a Yukon glacier contain bubbles of air that were trapped over 140 years ago. Analysis of this trapped air shows that carbon dioxide levels in today's air are 27% higher than the air in those samples.

23.5 Carbonic Acid and Carbonates

Carbon dioxide is the anhydride of **carbonic acid,** H_2CO_3, which forms in small amounts when carbon dioxide dissolves in water. Carbonic acid is a diprotic acid.

$$H_2CO_3 + H_2O \rightleftharpoons H_3O^+ + HCO_3^-$$

$$HCO_3^- + H_2O \rightleftharpoons H_3O^+ + CO_3^{2-}$$

When carbon dioxide dissolves in water, most of it is present as CO_2 molecules rather than H_2CO_3 molecules. The first ionization constant for carbonic acid is about 2×10^{-4}. However, in considering equilibria involving carbonic acid, it is convenient to assume that all of the carbon dioxide in solution is present as carbonic acid, and thus the value of 4.3×10^{-7} is commonly used for K_a in such calculations. This leads to correct values for the concentration of hydronium ion and hydrogen carbonate ion in solution. It does, however, give the impression that carbonic acid is a weaker acid than it actually is.

The carbon-oxygen bonds in carbon dioxide are polar covalent bonds (Section 7.5). The high electronegativity of oxygen makes it negative with respect to carbon, which becomes the positive end of the bond.

$$O^- \!\!=\!\! \overset{+\,+}{C} \!\!=\!\! {}^-O$$

Thus carbon is susceptible to attack by negative species, and it reacts with Lewis bases such as the oxide ion and the hydroxide ion to form carbonate ions and hydrogen carbonate ions, respectively, in Lewis acid–base reactions.

$$CO_2 + O^{2-} \longrightarrow CO_3^{2-}$$

$$CO_2 + OH^- \longrightarrow HCO_3^-$$

When a solution of sodium hydroxide is saturated with carbon dioxide, **sodium hydrogen carbonate,** $NaHCO_3$, is formed.

$$Na^+ + OH^- + CO_2 \longrightarrow Na^+ + HCO_3^-$$

This compound is also called sodium bicarbonate, or baking soda. The action of baking soda (for example, it causes bread and cake to rise) is due to the reaction of the basic hydrogen carbonate anion with an acid, producing gaseous carbon dioxide and water (Fig. 23.8).

$$HCO_3^- + H_3O^+ \longrightarrow H_2CO_3 + H_2O \longrightarrow CO_2 + 2H_2O$$

Because the hydrogen carbonate anion is stronger as a base than it is as an acid, solutions of salts of hydrogen carbonate are weakly alkaline.

$$HCO_3^- + H_2O \rightleftharpoons H_2CO_3 + OH^-$$

When equivalent amounts of sodium hydroxide and a solution of sodium hydrogen carbonate are combined, crystals of the 10-hydrate of **sodium carbonate,** $Na_2CO_3 \cdot 10H_2O$, form upon evaporation. This hydrate, also called washing soda, is commonly used as a water softener (Section 29.13) in the home. If heated gently, it forms anhydrous sodium carbonate, Na_2CO_3, called soda ash in industry. Solutions of sodium carbonate are basic because the carbonate anion is a moderately strong base.

$$CO_3^{2-} + H_2O \rightleftharpoons HCO_3^- + OH^- \qquad K_b = 1.4 \times 10^{-4}$$

Figure 23.8

The reaction of baking soda, $NaHCO_3$, with an acid produces CO_2, a sodium salt of the acid, and water.

23.6   Carbon Disulfide

At high temperatures carbon is oxidized by sulfur to **carbon disulfide,** CS_2 (Fig. 23.9). Air must be excluded because the volatile carbon disulfide is highly flammable and burns to form CO_2 and SO_2.

Pure carbon disulfide is a colorless, very volatile liquid with a disagreeable odor. The liquid is dense (1.28 g/mL) and is immiscible with water. The vapor is denser than air and very poisonous.

Like carbon dioxide, carbon disulfide is a Lewis acid. Carbon disulfide reacts with the sulfide ion, S^{2-}, giving the thiocarbonate ion, CS_3^{2-} [Fig. 23.10(a)], and with the amide ion, NH_2^-, giving the dithiocarbamate ion, $H_2NCS_2^-$ [Fig. 23.10(b)].

When sulfur replaces part or all of the oxygen in a molecule or ion, the prefix *thio* is used. Thus CO_3^{2-} is the carbonate ion, whereas CS_3^{2-} is the thiocarbonate ion.

Large quantities of carbon disulfide are used in making rayon by the viscose process and in the manufacture of cellophane.

Figure 23.9

The molecular and electronic structures of CS_2.

Figure 23.10

(a) One of three resonance structures of the thiocarbonate ion. (b) One of two resonance structures of the dithiocarbamate ion.

23.7   Carbon Tetrachloride

Carbon tetrachloride, CCl_4, is produced by the reaction of chlorine with methane, CH_4.

$$CH_4 + 4Cl_2 \xrightarrow{\triangle} CCl_4 + 4HCl$$

Because this is a tetrahedral, nonpolar molecule, it is an excellent solvent for other nonpolar substances such as fats, oils, and greases. It once was used for dry cleaning fabric. Because its vapor is about five times as heavy as air and it does not burn, it was also used as a fire extinguisher. However, because carbon tetrachloride has been recognized as a carcinogen, its use has been sharply reduced.

23.8   Carbides and Cyanides

Calcium carbide, CaC_2, is an important commercial product made by heating calcium oxide with carbon (coke). It reacts with water (Fig. 23.11), forming acetylene, $HC{\equiv}CH$.

$$CaC_2 + 2H_2O \longrightarrow Ca(OH)_2 + C_2H_2(g)$$

The reaction of calcium carbide with nitrogen at about 1100°C gives **calcium cyanamide,** $CaCN_2$.

$$CaC_2 + N_2 \xrightarrow{1100°C} CaCN_2 + C$$

The linear cyanamide ion, NCN^{2-}, is isoelectronic and isostructural with carbon dioxide and carbon disulfide [compare Fig. 23.12 with Figs. 23.6(b) and 23.9].

The fusion of calcium cyanamide with carbon and sodium carbonate produces **sodium cyanide,** $NaCN$.

$$CaCN_2 + C + Na_2CO_3 \xrightarrow{\triangle} CaCO_3 + 2NaCN$$

The sodium cyanide is separated from the insoluble calcium carbonate by dissolving it in water. Sodium cyanide can also be prepared by the reaction of sodium amide with carbon at 500 to 600°C.

Figure 23.11

The reaction of solid calcium carbide with water produces acetylene, C_2H_2, a flammable gas.

$$\ddot{N} = C = \ddot{N}^{2-}$$

Figure 23.12

The structure of the cyanamide ion. Note the similarity to the isoelectronic molecules CO_2 [Fig. 23.6(b)] and CS_2 (Fig. 23.9).

$$:C \equiv N:^{-}$$

Figure 23.13

Structure of the cyanide ion. Note the similarity to the isoelectronic molecule CO [Fig. 23.6(a)].

$$NaNH_2 + C \xrightarrow{500-600°C} NaCN + H_2$$

The cyanide ion, CN^-, is isoelectronic and isostructural with carbon monoxide [compare Fig. 23.13 with Fig. 23.6(a)]. It is both a Lewis base and a Brønsted base, and, as such, it combines with acid to form the very weak acid **hydrogen cyanide,** HCN.

$$H_3O^+(aq) + CN^-(aq) \longrightarrow HCN(g) + H_2O(l)$$

Hydrogen cyanide is a gas that smells like bitter almonds. Like carbon monoxide, it is very poisonous; a dose of about 0.05 gram is fatal to humans.

Both cyanamides and cyanides find extensive use in the plastics and polymer industries. Calcium cyanamide is used to prepare melamine, a raw material for the production of plastics such as Melmac. Hydrogen cyanide is used in the preparation of acrylonitrile polymers used in synthetic fibers such as Dynel and Orlon.

Nitrogen

Compounds of nitrogen have an extensive history; the first historical record of ammonium chloride is from the fifth century B.C. Ammonium salts, nitric acid, nitrates, and aqua regia (a mixture of nitric acid and hydrochloric acid; Section 23.14) were well known to the alchemists. Elemental nitrogen was first recognized as an element by the Scotch botanist Daniel Rutherford in 1772. He demonstrated that this gas supports neither life nor combustion.

23.9 Occurrence and Preparation of Nitrogen

The atmosphere consists of 78% nitrogen by volume and 75% nitrogen by mass. There are more than 20 million tons of nitrogen over every square mile of the earth's surface. Nitrogen is a component of proteins and of the genetic material of all plants and animals. The most important mineral sources of nitrogen in combined form are deposits of saltpeter, KNO_3, in India and other countries of the Far East and deposits of Chile saltpeter, $NaNO_3$, in South America.

Nitrogen is obtained industrially by the fractional distillation of liquid air. Nitrogen is prepared in the laboratory by heating a solution of ammonium nitrite.

$$NH_4NO_2(aq) \longrightarrow 2H_2O(l) + N_2(g) \qquad \Delta H° = -305.1 \text{ kJ}$$

In actual practice, a mixture of sodium nitrite and ammonium chloride is used to furnish the ions of ammonium nitrite, because NH_4NO_2 is so unstable that it cannot be safely stored. Atmospheric nitrogen (nitrogen plus the noble gases) can be isolated in the laboratory by burning phosphorus in air that is confined over water. The P_4O_{10} formed dissolves in the water, and the residual gas is primarily nitrogen.

Large volumes of atmospheric nitrogen are used for making ammonia (Section 23.11), the principal starting material used for preparation of large quantities of other nitrogen-containing compounds. Most other uses of elemental nitrogen are based on its inactivity. It is used when a chemical process requires an inert atmosphere. Canned foods and luncheon meats cannot oxidize in a pure nitrogen atmosphere, so they retain a better flavor and color and spoil less rapidly when sealed with nitrogen instead of air.

23.10 Properties of Nitrogen

Under ordinary conditions, nitrogen is a colorless, odorless, and tasteless gas. It boils at $-195.8°C$ (77.4 K) and freezes at $-210.0°C$ (63 K). It is slightly less dense than air, for air contains the heavier molecules of oxygen and argon as well as molecules of nitrogen. Because the nitrogen molecule contains a nitrogen–nitrogen triple bond ($:N\equiv N:$), it is very unreactive (Section 9.10). The only common reactions of N_2 at room temperature occur with lithium to give Li_3N, with certain transition metal complexes, and with hydrogen or oxygen in certain bacteria known as nitrogen-fixing bacteria. Nitrogen forms nitrides upon heating with active metals and gives low yields of ammonia upon heating with hydrogen. Heating with oxygen followed by rapid cooling (quenching) produces nitric oxide, NO. The general unreactivity of nitrogen makes the remarkable ability of some bacteria to synthesize nitrogen compounds, using atmospheric nitrogen gas as the source, one of the exciting chemical events on our planet.

Compounds of nitrogen in all of the possible oxidation states from -3 to $+5$ are known. Much of the chemistry of nitrogen involves oxidation–reduction reactions. The general chemical behavior of nitrogen is discussed in Section 21.6. Some of the reactions of nitrogen and its compounds are summarized in Table 23.2.

Unshared pair

Figure 23.14

Structure of an ammonia molecule.

23.11 Ammonia

Ammonia, NH_3, is produced in nature when any nitrogen-containing organic material decomposes in the absence of air. Its odor is common in decaying organic matter. Ammonia is usually prepared in the laboratory by the reaction of an ammonium salt with a strong base such as sodium hydroxide. The acid–base reaction with the weakly acidic ammonium ion gives ammonia (Fig. 23.14). Ammonia also forms when ionic nitrides react with water. The nitride ion is a much stronger base than the hydroxide ion.

$$Mg_3N_2(s) + 6H_2O(l) \longrightarrow 3Mg(OH)_2(s) + 2NH_3(g)$$

Ammonia is produced commercially by the direct combination of the elements in the **Haber process.**

$$N_2(g) + 3H_2(g) \overset{\text{Catalyst}}{\rightleftharpoons} 2NH_3(g) \qquad \Delta H° = -92 \text{ kJ}$$

This reaction is very slow at room temperature; it is carried out at an elevated temperature and pressure with a catalyst so that the rate is fast enough for the reaction to be practical. Because the reaction is exothermic, the yield decreases as the temperature is raised. However, four volumes of reactants ($1N_2$ and $3H_2$) give two volumes of product ($2NH_3$), so high pressure increases the yield (see Section 15.9). Thus the process is carried out at the lowest temperatures and highest pressures practicable: 400–600°C and 200–600 atmospheres. The most efficient catalyst is a mixture of iron oxide and potassium aluminate. Nitrogen for the process is obtained from liquid air, and much of the hydrogen is obtained from water gas (Section 22.1). The mixture of hydrogen and nitrogen is compressed, heated, and passed over the catalyst. The ammonia is removed by liquefaction, and the residual hydrogen and nitrogen are recycled through the process. Fritz Haber, a German chemist, received the 1918 Nobel prize in chemistry for his success in developing the direct synthesis of ammonia on a commercial scale.

Ammonia is a colorless gas with a sharp, pungent odor. Smelling salts utilize this powerful odor (Fig. 23.15). Gaseous ammonia is readily liquefied, giving a colorless

Figure 23.15

Smelling salts contain ammonium carbonate, which is in equilibrium with ammonia, carbon dioxide, and water. When a tube of smelling salts is broken, the ammonia is released and inhaled. The effect of this olfactory irritant is to shock a fainting person into normal awareness.

Table 23.2	Chemical Properties of Nitrogen and Its Compounds

General Equation	Comments
Reactions with Elements	
$N_2 + 6Li \longrightarrow 2Li_3N$	N^{3-} forms with active metals
$N_2 + 3Mg \xrightarrow{\Delta} Mg_3N_2$	
$N_2 + 3H_2 \rightleftharpoons 2NH_3$	Reversible, slow reaction; low yield at elevated temperatures
$N_2 + O_2 \xrightarrow{\Delta} 2NO$	Low-yield, endothermic reaction; requires heating
Reactions of Compounds	
$NH_3 + H^+ \longrightarrow NH_4^+$	NH_3 acts both as a weak base
$NH_3 + LiCH_3 \longrightarrow LiNH_2 + CH_4$	and as a very weak acid
$NH_4^+ + OH^- \longrightarrow NH_3 + H_2O$	NH_4^+ is a weak acid
$4NH_3 + 5O_2 \xrightarrow{\Delta} 4NO + 6H_2O$	
$NH_4NO_2 \longrightarrow N_2 + 2H_2O$	The NH_4^+ ion is oxidized by NO_2^-
$NH_4NO_3 \xrightarrow{\Delta} N_2O + 2H_2O$	Potentially explosive reaction
$2NH_3 + 3CuO \xrightarrow{\Delta} N_2 + 3Cu + 3H_2O$	
$NH_3 + OCl^- \longrightarrow NH_2Cl + OH^-$	
$NH_2Cl + NH_3 + OH^- \longrightarrow N_2H_4 + Cl^- + H_2O$	
$Cu + HNO_3 \longrightarrow NO_2$ or NO, $Cu(NO_3)_2$, and H_2O	Concentrated HNO_3 gives NO_2; dilute HNO_3 gives NO
$2NO + O_2 \longrightarrow 2NO_2$	
$NO + NO_2 \rightleftharpoons N_2O_3$	
$2NO_2 \rightleftharpoons N_2O_4$	
$2NO_2 + H_2O \longrightarrow HNO_3 + HNO_2$	NO_2 disproportionates in water
$3NO_2 + H_2O \longrightarrow 2HNO_3 + NO$	
$4HNO_3 + P_4O_{10} \longrightarrow 2N_2O_5 + 4HPO_3$	

liquid that boils at $-33°C$. Liquid ammonia has a vapor pressure of only about 10 atmospheres at $25°C$; it is readily handled in steel cylinders. Solid ammonia is white and crystalline; it melts at $-78°C$. Because of intermolecular hydrogen bonding (see Section 11.4), the enthalpy of vaporization of liquid ammonia is higher than that of any other liquid except water, so ammonia is used as a refrigerant. Ammonia is quite soluble in alcohol, ether, and water (1180 L at STP dissolves in 1 L of H_2O).

The chemical properties of ammonia are as follows:

1. Ammonia acts as a Brønsted base, because it readily accepts protons, and as a Lewis base, in that it can be an electron-pair donor (Section 16.14). When ammonia dissolves in water, only about 1% reacts to form ammonium and hydroxide ions; the remainder is present as unreacted NH_3 molecules. Although it is a weak base, ammonia readily accepts protons from acids and hydronium ions, forming salts of the **ammonium ion,** NH_4^+. The ammonium ion is similar in size to the potassium ion, and ionic compounds of the two ions exhibit many similarities in their structures and solubilities.

Ammonia forms **ammines** by sharing electrons with metal ions, which act as Lewis acids (Section 26.1). The diammine silver ion forms by the reaction

$$Ag^+ + 2\,NH_3 \longrightarrow [H_3N-Ag-NH_3]^+$$

In these species, ammonia functions as a Lewis base.

2. Ammonia can display acidic behavior, although it is a much weaker acid than water. It reacts with very strong bases, such as the CH_3^- ion. Like other acids, ammonia reacts with metals, although it is so weak that high temperatures are often required. Hydrogen and (depending on the stoichiometry) **amides** (salts of NH_2^-), **imides** (salts of NH^{2-}), or **nitrides** (salts of N^{3-}) are formed.

3. The nitrogen atom in ammonia has its lowest possible oxidation number (-3) and thus is not susceptible to reduction. However, it can be oxidized. Ammonia burns in air, giving NO and water. Hot ammonia and the ammonium ion are active reducing agents. Of particular interest are the oxidations of ammonium ion by nitrite ion, NO_2^-, to give pure nitrogen and by nitrate ion to give nitrous oxide, N_2O.

About three-fourths of the 33.8 billion pounds of ammonia produced in the United States during 1989 was used in fertilizers, either as the compound or as an ammonium salt such as the sulfate, nitrate, or dihydrogen phosphate. The application of anhydrous ammonia (Fig. 23.16) or of solutions of ammonium compounds is standard farm procedure. Large quantities of ammonia are used in the production of nitric acid, urea, and other nitrogen compounds. Household ammonia is an aqueous solution of ammonia that is generally used as a cleanser.

Figure 23.16

Anhydrous ammonia, stored under pressure as a liquid in the tank, is applied as a fertilizer on this Iowa farm.

23.12 Derivatives of Ammonia

There are a number of compounds that can be considered derivatives of ammonia, in that one or more of the hydrogen atoms in the ammonia molecule have been replaced by some other atom or group of atoms, bonded to the nitrogen atom by a single bond. Inorganic derivatives include chloramine, NH_2Cl, hydrazine, N_2H_4, and hydroxylamine NH_2OH.

Ammonia   Chloramine   Hydrazine   Hydroxylamine

Organic analogs that contain nitrogen–carbon bonds are called *amines* (for example, methylamine is H_3C-NH_2); they are discussed in Chapter 30.

Chloramine, NH_2Cl, results from the reaction of sodium hypochlorite, NaOCl, with ammonia in basic solution. In the presence of a large excess of ammonia at low temperature, the chloramine reacts further to produce **hydrazine,** N_2H_4.

$$NH_3(aq) + OCl^-(aq) \longrightarrow NH_2Cl(aq) + OH^-(aq)$$

$$NH_2Cl(aq) + NH_3(aq) + OH^-(aq) \longrightarrow N_2H_4(aq) + Cl^-(aq) + H_2O(l)$$

Anhydrous hydrazine is relatively stable, both thermally and kinetically, despite its positive enthalpy and free energy of formation.

$$N_2(g) + 2H_2(g) \longrightarrow N_2H_4(l) \qquad \Delta H_f^\circ = 50.6 \text{ kJ mol}^{-1}; \ \Delta G_f^\circ = 149.2 \text{ kJ mol}^{-1}$$

It is a fuming, colorless liquid that has some physical properties remarkably similar to those of H_2O (it melts at 2°C, boils at 113.5°C, and has a density at 25°C of 1.00 g/mL). It burns rapidly and completely in air with substantial evolution of heat.

$$N_2H_4(l) + O_2(g) \longrightarrow N_2(g) + 2H_2O(l) \qquad \Delta H^\circ = -621.5 \text{ kJ mol}^{-1}$$

1.126 Å

1.186 Å

$$N{=}N{=}\ddot{O} \longleftrightarrow :N{\equiv}N{-}\ddot{\ddot{O}}:$$

Figure 23.17

The molecular and resonance structures of a molecule of nitrous oxide, N_2O.

Figure 23.18

The reaction of copper metal with dilute nitric acid (top) produces a solution of $Cu(NO_3)_2$ and NO (bottom). The colorless NO is oxidized by the oxygen in the air to NO_2, which is yellow to brown depending on its concentration.

Like ammonia, hydrazine is both a Brønsted base and a Lewis base, although it is weaker than ammonia. It reacts with strong acids and forms two series of salts that contain the $N_2H_5^+$ and $N_2H_6^{2+}$ ions, respectively.

Hydrazine is readily oxidized by hydrogen peroxide; nitrogen and water are the products. The reaction products are both gases at the temperature of the reaction, and the reaction is highly exothermic. Hydrazine and hydrogen peroxide have therefore been used as rocket propellants.

Pure **hydroxylamine,** NH_2OH, is an unstable white solid that decomposes to ammonia, water, nitrogen, and nitrous oxide at about 15°C. The decomposition can be explosive at elevated temperatures. Aqueous solutions are more stable. Hydroxylamine is a base with a strength somewhat less than that of ammonia. It is an active reducing agent. It is usually prepared and handled as a hydroxylammonium salt, such as the chloride, $[NH_3OH]^+Cl^-$.

㉓.13 Oxides of Nitrogen

Nitrogen oxides in which nitrogen exhibits each of its positive oxidation numbers from +1 to +5 are well characterized. They are listed in Table 23.3.

When ammonium nitrate is heated, **nitrous oxide** (dinitrogen oxide), N_2O (Fig. 23.17), is formed. In this oxidation–reduction reaction, the nitrogen in the ammonium ion is oxidized by the nitrogen in the nitrate ion. Nitrous oxide is a colorless gas possessing a mild, pleasing odor and a sweet taste. It is used as an anesthetic for minor operations, especially in dentistry, under the name of laughing gas.

Low yields of **nitric oxide,** NO, are produced when nitrogen and oxygen are heated together. It also forms by direct union of nitrogen and oxygen in the air brought about by lightning during thunderstorms. Nitric oxide is produced commercially by burning ammonia. In the laboratory, nitric oxide is produced by reduction of nitric acid. When copper reacts with dilute nitric acid (Fig. 23.18), nitric oxide is the principal reduction product.

$$3Cu + 8HNO_3 \longrightarrow 2NO(g) + 3Cu(NO_3)_2 + 4H_2O$$

Pure nitric oxide can be obtained by reducing nitric acid with an iron(II) salt in dilute acid solution.

$$3Fe^{2+} + NO_3^- + 4H_3O^+ \longrightarrow 3Fe^{3+} + NO(g) + 6H_2O$$

Gaseous nitric oxide is the most thermally stable of the nitrogen oxides and is also the simplest known thermally stable molecule with an unpaired electron. It is one of the

Table 23.3	The Oxides of Nitrogen	
Formula	Oxidation Number of Nitrogen	Common Name
N_2O	+1	Nitrous oxide
NO	+2	Nitric oxide
N_2O_3	+3	Dinitrogen trioxide
NO_2	+4	Nitrogen dioxide
N_2O_4	+4	Dinitrogen tetraoxide
N_2O_5	+5	Dinitrogen pentaoxide

air pollutants generated by internal combustion engines, resulting from the reaction of nitrogen and oxygen from the air during the combustion process (see Section 29.3).

At room temperature nitric oxide is a slightly soluble, colorless gas consisting of diatomic molecules. As is often the case with molecules that contain an unpaired electron, two molecules combine to form a dimer by pairing their unpaired electrons. Liquid NO is partially dimerized, and solid NO contains dimers.

When a mixture of equal parts of nitric oxide and nitrogen dioxide is cooled to $-21°C$, the gases form **dinitrogen trioxide,** a blue liquid consisting of N_2O_3 molecules (Fig. 23.19). Dinitrogen trioxide exists only in liquid and solid states. When heated, it forms a mixture of NO and NO_2.

Nitrogen dioxide is prepared in the laboratory by heating the nitrate of a heavy metal,

$$2Pb(NO_3)_2(s) \xrightarrow{\triangle} 2PbO(s) + 4NO_2(g) + O_2(g)$$

or by the reduction of concentrated nitric acid with copper metal (Fig. 23.20). Nitrogen dioxide is prepared commercially by oxidizing nitric oxide with air.

The nitrogen dioxide molecule (Fig. 23.21) contains an unpaired electron, which is responsible for its color and paramagnetism. It is also responsible for the dimerization of NO_2. At low pressures or at high temperatures, nitrogen dioxide has a deep brown color that is due to the presence of the NO_2 molecule. At low temperatures the color almost entirely disappears as **dinitrogen tetraoxide,** N_2O_4, is formed (see Figs. 15.8 and 23.21). At room temperature an equilibrium exists.

$$2NO_2(g) \rightleftharpoons N_2O_4(g) \qquad K_p = 6.86$$

Dinitrogen pentaoxide, N_2O_5 (Fig. 23.22), is a white solid formed by the dehydration of nitric acid by phosphorus(V) oxide.

$$P_4O_{10} + 4HNO_3 \longrightarrow 4HPO_3 + 2N_2O_5$$

Above room temperature it is unstable both as a solid and as a gas, decomposing to N_2O_4 and O_2.

$$2N_2O_5(g) \longrightarrow 2N_2O_4(g) + O_2(g)$$

Figure 23.19

The molecular and resonance structures of a molecule of dinitrogen trioxide, N_2O_3.

Figure 23.20

The reaction of copper metal with concentrated HNO_3 produces a solution of $Cu(NO_3)_2$ and brown fumes of NO_2.

Nitrogen dioxide, NO_2

Dinitrogen tetraoxide (nitrogen dioxide dimer), N_2O_4

Figure 23.21

The molecular structures of molecules of nitrogen dioxide, NO_2, and dinitrogen tetraoxide, N_2O_4, and the resonance structures of nitrogen dioxide.

Figure 23.22

The molecular structure of a molecule of dinitrogen pentaoxide, N_2O_5.

The oxides of nitrogen(III), nitrogen(IV), and nitrogen(V) react with water and form nitrogen-containing oxyacids. Nitrogen(III) oxide, N_2O_3, is the anhydride of nitrous acid; HNO_2 forms when N_2O_3 reacts with water. There are no stable oxyacids containing nitrogen with an oxidation number of +4. Nitrogen(IV) oxide, NO_2, disproportionates in one of two ways when it reacts with water. In cold water a mixture of HNO_2 and HNO_3 is formed. At higher temperatures HNO_3 and NO form. Nitrogen(V) oxide, N_2O_5, is the anhydride of nitric acid; HNO_3 is produced when N_2O_5 reacts with water.

$$N_2O_5 + H_2O \longrightarrow 2HNO_3$$

The nitrogen oxides exhibit extensive oxidation–reduction behavior. Nitrous oxide, nitrogen(I) oxide, resembles oxygen in its behavior when heated with combustible substances. It is a strong oxidizing agent that decomposes when heated to form nitrogen and oxygen. Because one-third of the gas liberated is oxygen, nitrous oxide supports combustion better than air. A glowing splint bursts into flame when thrust into a bottle of this gas. Nitric oxide acts both as an oxidizing agent and as a reducing agent. For example,

Oxidizing agent: $P_4 + 6NO \longrightarrow P_4O_6 + 3N_2$

Reducing agent: $Cl_2 + 2NO \longrightarrow 2ClNO$

Nitrogen dioxide (or dinitrogen tetraoxide) is a good oxidizing agent. For example,

$$NO_2 + CO \longrightarrow NO + CO_2$$

$$NO_2 + 2HCl \longrightarrow NO + Cl_2 + H_2O$$

Dinitrogen pentaoxide reacts violently with metals, with nonmetals, and with organic materials, serving as an oxidizing agent. For example,

$$N_2O_5 + Na \longrightarrow NaNO_3 + NO_2$$

$$N_2O_5 + I_2 \longrightarrow I_2O_5 + N_2$$

㉓.14 Nitric Acid and Nitrates

Figure 23.23

The molecular and resonance structures of a molecule of nitric acid, HNO_3. N—O distances are (a) 1.41 Å and (b) 1.22 Å.

Both N_2O_5 and NO_2 react with water to form **nitric acid,** HNO_3. Nitric acid (Fig. 23.23) was known to the alchemists of the eighth century as *aqua fortis* (meaning "strong water"). It was prepared from KNO_3 and was used in the separation of gold from silver; it dissolves silver but not gold. Traces of nitric acid occur in the atmosphere after thunderstorms, and its salts are widely distributed in nature. Chile saltpeter, $NaNO_3$, is found in tremendous deposits (3 kilometers wide by 300 kilometers long, and up to 2 meters thick) in the desert region near the boundary of Chile and Peru. Bengal saltpeter, KNO_3, is found in India and in other countries of the Far East.

Nitric acid can be prepared in the laboratory by heating a nitrate salt (such as sodium or potassium nitrate) with concentrated sulfuric acid.

$$NaNO_3(s) + H_2SO_4(l) \xrightarrow{\Delta} NaHSO_4(s) + HNO_3(g)$$

Nitric acid boils at 86°C, whereas sulfuric acid boils at 338° ($NaNO_3$ and $NaHSO_4$ are nonvolatile), and nitric acid is readily removed by distillation.

Nitric acid is produced commercially by the **Ostwald process:** oxidation of ammonia to nitric oxide, NO; oxidation of nitric oxide to nitrogen dioxide, NO_2; and conversion of nitrogen dioxide to nitric acid. A mixture of ammonia and excess air, heated to

600–700°C, literally burns with a flame when passed through a platinum–rhodium catalyst. Admission of additional air oxidizes the nitric oxide to nitrogen dioxide. The nitrogen dioxide, excess oxygen, and the unreactive nitrogen from the air are passed through a water spray, and nitric acid and nitric oxide form as the nitrogen dioxide disproportionates. The nitric oxide is combined with more air and recycled through the process. The nitric acid is drawn off and concentrated. Most of the 16.0 billion pounds of nitric acid produced in the United States in 1989 came from the Ostwald process.

Pure nitric acid is a colorless liquid that boils at 86°C and freezes at −42°C. It decomposes when exposed to light or when heated, producing a mixture of oxygen, water, and nitrogen oxides, among which nitrogen dioxide is predominant.

$$4HNO_3 \xrightarrow{\triangle} 4NO_2 + 2H_2O + O_2$$

Consequently, pure nitric acid fumes in moist air, forming a cloud of very small droplets of aqueous nitric acid as the NO_2 reacts with water in the air. It is often yellow or brown in color because of the NO_2 formed as it decomposes. Nitric acid is stable in aqueous solution; solutions containing 68% of the acid are sold as concentrated nitric acid. It is both a strong oxidizing agent and a strong acid.

The action of nitric acid on a metal rarely produces H_2 (by reduction of H^+) in more than small amounts. Instead, the acid is reduced. The products formed depend on the concentration of the acid, the activity of the metal, and the temperature. A mixture of nitrogen oxides, nitrates, and other reduction products is usually produced. Less active metals such as copper, silver, and lead reduce concentrated nitric acid primarily to nitrogen dioxide (Fig. 23.20). The reaction of dilute nitric acid with copper gives NO (Fig. 23.18). The more active metals, such as zinc and iron, give nitrous oxide with dilute nitric acid. With zinc, we have

$$4Zn + 10H_3O^+ + 2NO_3^- \longrightarrow 4Zn^{2+} + N_2O(g) + 15H_2O$$

When the acid is very dilute, either nitrogen gas or ammonium ions may be formed, depending on the conditions. In each case, the nitrate salts of the metals crystallize when the resulting solutions are evaporated.

Nonmetallic elements, such as sulfur, carbon, iodine, and phosphorus, are oxidized by concentrated nitric acid to their oxides or oxyacids, with the formation of NO_2.

$$S(s) + 6HNO_3(aq) \longrightarrow H_2SO_4(aq) + 6NO_2(g) + 2H_2O(l)$$

$$C(s) + 4HNO_3(aq) \longrightarrow CO_2(g) + 4NO_2(g) + 2H_2O(l)$$

Many compounds are oxidized by nitric acid. Hydrochloric acid is readily oxidized by concentrated nitric acid to chlorine and chlorine dioxide. A mixture of 1 part concentrated nitric acid and 3 parts concentrated hydrochloric acid (called *aqua regia*, which means "royal water") reacts vigorously with metals. This mixture is particularly useful in dissolving gold and platinum and other metals that lie below hydrogen in the activity series. The action of aqua regia on gold can be represented, in a somewhat simplified form, by the equation

$$Au(s) + 4HCl(aq) + 3HNO_3(aq) \longrightarrow HAuCl_4(aq) + 3NO_2(g) + 3H_2O(l)$$

Nitric acid reacts with proteins, such as those in the skin, to give a yellow material called xanthoprotein. You may have noticed that if you get nitric acid on your fingers, they turn yellow.

Nitrates, salts of nitric acid, form when metals or their oxides, hydroxides, or carbonates react with nitric acid. Most nitrates are soluble in water; indeed, one of the significant uses of nitric acid is to prepare soluble metal nitrates.

Figure 23.24

The molecular structure of a molecule of nitrous acid, HNO_2.

All nitrates decompose when heated. When sodium or potassium nitrate is heated, a nitrite is formed and oxygen is evolved.

$$2NaNO_3(s) \xrightarrow{\triangle} 2NaNO_2(s) + O_2(g)$$

A nitrate of a heavy metal produces the oxide of the metal when heated. With copper(II) nitrate, the equation is

$$2Cu(NO_3)_2(s) \xrightarrow{\triangle} 2CuO(s) + 4NO_2(g) + O_2(g)$$

Ammonium nitrate produces nitrous oxide. The nitrates, especially ammonium nitrate, can explode when heated or detonated.

Nitric acid is used extensively in the laboratory and in chemical industries as a strong acid and as an active oxidizing agent. It is used in the manufacture of explosives, dyes, plastics, and drugs. Salts of nitric acid (nitrates) are valuable as fertilizers. Gunpowder is a mixture of potassium nitrate, sulfur, and charcoal. Ammonal, an explosive, is a mixture of ammonium nitrate and aluminum powder.

㉓.15 Nitrous Acid and Nitrites

The reaction of N_2O_3 with water gives a pale blue solution of **nitrous acid,** HNO_2 (Fig. 23.24). However, HNO_2 is easier to prepare by addition of an acid to a solution of a nitrite; nitrous acid is a weak acid, so the nitrite ion is basic.

$$NO_2^- + H_3O^+ \longrightarrow HNO_2 + H_2O$$

Nitrous acid is very unstable and exists only in solution. It disproportionates slowly at room temperature (rapidly when heated) into nitric acid and nitric oxide. Nitrous acid is an active oxidizing agent with strong reducing agents, and it is oxidized to nitric acid by active oxidizing agents.

Sodium nitrite, $NaNO_2$, is the most important salt of nitrous acid. It is usually made by reducing molten sodium nitrate with lead.

$$NaNO_3 + Pb \longrightarrow NaNO_2 + PbO$$

Sodium nitrite is added to meats such as hot dogs and cold cuts. The nitrite ion has two functions. It limits the growth of bacteria that can cause food poisoning, and it prolongs the meat's retention of its red color. The addition of sodium nitrite to meat products is now controversial, because nitrous acid is known to react with certain organic compounds to form a class of compounds known as nitrosoamines. Nitrosoamines produce cancer in laboratory animals. This has prompted the U.S. Food and Drug Administration (FDA) to limit the amount of $NaNO_2$ that can legally be added to foods.

The nitrites are much more stable than the acid (the salts of all oxyacids are more stable than the acids themselves), but nitrites, like nitrates, can explode. Nitrites are soluble in water ($AgNO_2$ is only slightly soluble).

When nitrous acid is reduced by hydrazine, **hydrazoic acid,** HN_3 (Fig. 23.25), is formed.

$$N_2H_4(aq) + HNO_2(aq) \longrightarrow HN_3(aq) + 2H_2O(l)$$

Figure 23.25

The molecular structure and resonance forms of a molecule of hydrazoic acid, HN_3.

It is a weak acid and reacts with both oxidizing and reducing agents. Its salts are called **azides;** like the acid, the azides are unstable. Azides of electropositive metals decompose smoothly to nitrogen and the metal when heated; other metal azides (and the acid itself) explode. Lead azide, $Pb(N_3)_2$, is used as a detonator for explosives.

㉓.16 The Nitrogen Cycle

Nitrogen is an essential constituent of all plants and animals; it is present principally in proteins and in the nucleic acids that make up genetic material—complex organic materials that contain carbon, hydrogen, and oxygen as well (see Sections 31.3 and 31.10). Most plants obtain the nitrogen necessary for growth by absorbing nitrogen compounds, primarily ammonium and nitrate salts, through their roots. However, some legumes, such as clover, alfalfa, peas, and beans, are able to obtain their nitrogen from the air by means of nitrogen-fixing bacteria, which live in nodules on their roots. These bacteria convert atmospheric nitrogen into nitrites and nitrates, which are assimilated by the host plant. Generally, the bacteria fix more nitrogen than is used by the plant; when the legume dies, the unused nitrogen remains in the soil and is available for other plants. Animals obtain their nitrogenous compounds by eating plants and other animals.

Tremendous quantities of nitrogen are fixed as nitric oxide by lightning (Fig. 21.18). The nitric oxide is then oxidized to nitrogen dioxide by atmospheric oxygen, and reaction with water forms nitrous and nitric acids by the same reactions as in the Ostwald process (Section 23.14). These acids are carried by rain to the soil, where they react with oxides and carbonates of metals to form nitrites and nitrates, respectively. Some soil bacteria oxidize nitrites to nitrates, a process called **nitrification.** Other bacteria change ammonia into nitrites. Denitrifying bacteria decompose nitrates and other nitrogen compounds to free nitrogen.

The decay of both plant and animal matter returns nitrogen to the soil in the form of nitrates, and either ammonia or free nitrogen is produced. Thus nitrogen passes through a cycle of fundamental importance to all plants and animals.

Phosphorus

Phosphorus is too active a nonmetal to exist free in nature. It is found in many minerals and is a component of both plants and animals. Bones, teeth, and nerve and muscle tissue contain combined phosphorus. The nucleic acids DNA and RNA, molecules that carry an organism's genetic information, contain phosphorus. The metabolism of foods and the production of energy in the body require phosphorus compounds. Such foods as eggs, beans, peas, and milk furnish phosphorus for our body requirements. Plants obtain it from soluble phosphates in the soil, so phosphates are important fertilizers. Phosphorus forms compounds that are used in foodstuffs, explosives, matches, agricultural chemicals (including insecticides, herbicides, and fertilizers), soaps and detergents, and special metal alloys.

㉓.17 Occurrence and Preparation of Phosphorus

Phosphorus is produced commercially by heating calcium phosphate, obtained from phosphate rock (Section 2.12), with sand and coke.

$$2Ca_3(PO_4)_2 + 6SiO_2 + 10C \xrightarrow{\Delta} 6CaSiO_3 + 10CO + P_4(g)$$

Figure 23.26
The molecular structure of P_4S_3 (top), which is used in the heads of "strike-anywhere" matches (bottom).

The phosphorus distills out of the furnace and is condensed to a solid or burned to form P_4O_{10}, from which other phosphorus compounds are manufactured. Elemental phosphorus is shipped to plants where it is converted into phosphoric acid and phosphates. This strategem makes it unnecessary to pay freight costs for transporting the oxygen and water used in the manufacture of phosphorus compounds.

Large quantities of phosphorus compounds are converted into acids and salts to be used in fertilizers and in the chemical industries. Other uses are in the manufacture of special alloys such as ferrophosphorus and phosphor bronze. Considerable quantities of phosphorus are used in making fireworks, bombs, and rat poisons.

White phosphorus once was used in the manufacture of matches. Because the workers who were exposed to the fumes suffered from severe bone disease, it was replaced in the heads of "strike-anywhere" matches by tetraphosphorus trisulfide, P_4S_3 (Fig. 23.26).

㉓.18 Properties of Phosphorus

Phosphorus is an active nonmetal. In compounds, phosphorus is most commonly observed with oxidation numbers of -3, $+3$, and $+5$. Phosphorus exhibits oxidation numbers that are unusual for a Group VA element in compounds that contain phosphorus–phosphorus bonds; examples include diphosphorus tetrahydride, H_2P—PH_2, and tetraphosphorus trisulfide, P_4S_3 (Fig. 23.26).

The most important chemical property of elemental phosphorus is its reactivity with oxygen. Slow oxidation of white phosphorus causes it to get warm, and it spontaneously inflames when it reaches 35–45°C. Because of this, white phosphorus must be stored under water (see Fig. 21.11). Burns caused by phosphorus are very painful and slow to heal. *White phosphorus should be handled only with forceps and should be put in water immediately after use.* Red phosphorus is less active than the white form; it does not ignite in air unless it is heated to about 250°C. However, the products of the reactions of red phosphorus are the same as those of the white form.

Phosphorus is one of the least electronegative of the nonmetals. It reacts with active metals, forming salts that contain the very basic **phosphide ion, P^{3-}**. With transition metals it forms phosphides that are not ionic. Phosphorus is oxidized by the nonmetals oxygen, sulfur, and the halogens. The general chemical behavior of phosphorus is discussed in Section 21.6. Some of the reactions of phosphorus and its compounds are summarized in Table 23.4.

㉓.19 Phosphine

The most important hydride of phosphorus is **phosphine,** PH_3, a gaseous analog of ammonia in formula and structure. Unlike ammonia, phosphine cannot be made by the direct union of the elements. It is prepared by the reaction of an ionic phosphide with acid or is a byproduct of the disproportionation of white phosphorus in a hot concentrated solution of sodium hydroxide.

$$AlP + 3H_2O \xrightarrow{H_3O^+} PH_3 + Al(OH)_3$$

$$P_4 + 4OH^- + 2H_2O \longrightarrow 2HPO_3^{2-} + 2PH_3$$

Table 23.4 Chemical Properties of Phosphorus and Its Compounds

General Equation	Comments
Reactions of Phosphorus	
$P_4 + 12Na \longrightarrow 4Na_3P$	Active metals reduce P to P^{3-}
$P_4 + 6Mg \longrightarrow 2Mg_3P_2$	
$P_4 + 3O_2 \longrightarrow P_4O_6$	In about 50% yield; requires a stoichiometric amount of O_2
$P_4 + 5O_2 \longrightarrow P_4O_{10}$	Very exothermic reaction
$P_4 + S \longrightarrow P_4S_{10}, P_4S_3,$ and others	A variety of phosphorus sulfides form, depending on the stoichiometry
$P_4 + 6X_2 \longrightarrow 4PX_3$	X = F, Cl, Br, I
$P_4 + 10X_2 \longrightarrow 4PX_5$	X = F, Cl, Br
$P_4 + 3NaOH + 3H_2O \longrightarrow$ $3NaH_2PO_2 + PH_3$	P disproportionates in base
Reactions of Compounds	
$P^{3-} + 3H_3O^+ \longrightarrow PH_3 + 3H_2O$	
$PX_3 + 3H_2O \longrightarrow H_3PO_3 + 3HX$	Forms phosphorous acid; X = halogen
$PX_5 + H_2O \longrightarrow POX_3 + 2HX$	X = halogen
$PX_5 + 4H_2O \longrightarrow H_3PO_4 + 5HX$	Forms phosphoric acid; X = halogen
$P_4O_6 + 6H_2O \longrightarrow 4H_3PO_3$ $\left.\right\}$	The oxides of phosphorus are acidic
$P_4O_{10} + 6H_2O \longrightarrow 4H_3PO_4$	
$H_3PO_4 + OH^- \longrightarrow$ $H_2PO_4^-, HPO_4^{2-},$ or PO_4^{3-}	Product depends on stoichiometry

The disproportionation reaction produces phosphine and sodium hydrogen phosphite, Na_2HPO_3. Pure phosphine is not spontaneously flammable. However, diphosphorus tetrahydride (or diphosphine), P_2H_4, a by-product of the disproportionation, is spontaneously flammable and ignites the phosphine on contact with air. Consequently, phosphine is best prepared and handled under an atmosphere of nitrogen or some other inert gas.

Phosphine is a colorless, very poisonous gas, which has an odor like that of decaying fish. It is easily decomposed by heat ($4PH_3 \longrightarrow P_4 + 6H_2$). Like ammonia, gaseous phosphine unites with gaseous hydrogen halides, forming the phosphonium compounds, PH_4Cl, PH_4Br, and PH_4I. However, phosphine is a much weaker base than ammonia; these compounds decompose in water, and the insoluble PH_3 escapes from solution.

23 .20 Phosphorus Halides

Phosphorus reacts directly with the halogens, forming **trihalides**, PX_3, and **pentahalides**, PX_5. The trihalides are much more stable than the corresponding nitrogen trihalides; nitrogen pentahalides do not form because of nitrogen's inability to form more than four bonds.

The chlorides PCl_3 and PCl_5 (Fig. 23.27) are the most important halides of phosphorus. The colorless, liquid **phosphorus trichloride** is prepared by passing chlorine over molten phosphorus. Solid **phosphorus pentachloride** is prepared by oxidizing the trichloride with excess chlorine. The pentachloride is an off-white solid that sublimes when warmed and decomposes reversibly into the trichloride and chlorine when heated.

Unshared pair

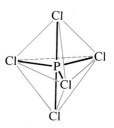

Figure 23.27

The molecular structure of PCl_3 and of PCl_5 in the gas phase.

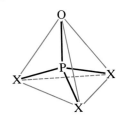

Figure 23.28

The molecular structure of a phosphorus oxyhalide, POX_3.

Like most other nonmetal halides, both phosphorus chlorides react with an excess of water and form hydrogen chloride and an oxyacid; PCl_3 gives phosphorous acid, H_3PO_3, and PCl_5 gives phosphoric acid, H_3PO_4. All the halides of phosphorus fume in moist air because they react with water vapor. Partial reaction produces **phosphorus(V) oxyhalides,** POX_3, which have tetrahedral structures (Fig. 23.28).

The pentahalides of phosphorus are Lewis acids because of the empty valence shell d orbitals of phosphorus. They readily react with halide ions that are Lewis bases to give the anion PX_6^-. Whereas phosphorus pentafluoride is a molecular compound in all states, X-ray studies show that solid phosphorus pentachloride is an ionic compound, $[PCl_4^+][PCl_6^-]$, as are phosphorus pentabromide, $[PBr_4^+][Br^-]$, and phosphorus pentaiodide, $[PI_4^+][I^-]$.

㉓.21 Phosphorus Oxides

Phosphorus forms two common oxides, **phosphorus(III) oxide** (or tetraphosphorus hexaoxide), P_4O_6, and **phosphorus(V) oxide** (or tetraphosphorus decaoxide), P_4O_{10} (Fig. 23.29). Phosphorus(III) oxide is a white crystalline solid with a garliclike odor. Its vapor is very poisonous. It oxidizes slowly in air and inflames when heated to 70°C, forming P_4O_{10}. Phosphorus(III) oxide dissolves slowly in cold water to form phosphorous acid, H_3PO_3.

Phosphorus(V) oxide, P_4O_{10}, is a white flocculent powder that is prepared by burning phosphorus in excess oxygen. Its enthalpy of formation is very high (-2984 kJ), and it is quite stable and a very poor oxidizing agent. When P_4O_{10} is dropped into water, it reacts with a hissing sound, and heat is liberated as orthophosphoric acid is formed.

$$P_4O_{10}(s) + 6H_2O(l) \longrightarrow 4H_3PO_4(aq)$$

Because of its great affinity for water, phosphorus(V) oxide is used extensively for drying gases and removing water from many compounds.

㉓.22 Orthophosphoric Acid

Pure **orthophosphoric acid,** H_3PO_4 (Fig. 23.30), forms colorless, deliquescent crystals that melt at 42°C. It is commonly called phosphoric acid and is commercially available as an 82% solution known as "syrupy phosphoric acid."

Figure 23.29

The molecular structures of P_4O_6 and P_4O_{10}.

One commercial method of preparing orthophosphoric acid is to treat calcium phosphate with concentrated sulfuric acid.

$$Ca_3(PO_4)_2(s) + 3H_2SO_4(aq) \longrightarrow 2H_3PO_4(aq) + 3CaSO_4(s)$$

The products are diluted with water, and the calcium sulfate is removed by filtration. This method gives a dilute acid that is contaminated with calcium dihydrogen phosphate, $Ca(H_2PO_4)_2$, and other compounds associated with native calcium phosphate. Pure orthophosphoric acid is manufactured by dissolving P_4O_{10} in water.

Orthophosphoric acid is a triprotic acid and forms three series of salts: **dihydrogen phosphates,** containing the $H_2PO_4^-$ ion; **hydrogen phosphates,** containing the HPO_4^{2-} ion; and **orthophosphates** (or simply phosphates), containing the PO_4^{3-} ion. Soluble dihydrogen phosphate salts form aqueous solutions that are weakly acidic, because $H_2PO_4^-$ is a weak acid. Solutions of hydrogen phosphates are basic, because the monohydrogen phosphate ion is stronger as a base than as an acid. Solutions of orthophosphates are strongly basic, because the PO_4^{3-} ion is a relatively strong base.

Orthophosphoric acid, dihydrogen phosphate salts, and hydrogen phosphate salts decompose when heated, and water is given off. The resulting phosphorus-containing products have P—O—P bonds.

23.23 Phosphorous Acid

The action of water on P_4O_6, PCl_3, PBr_3, or PI_3 forms **phosphorous acid,** H_3PO_3 (Fig. 23.31). Pure phosphorous acid is most readily obtained by hydrolyzing phosphorus trichloride,

$$PCl_3(l) + 3H_2O(l) \longrightarrow H_3PO_3(aq) + 3HCl(g)$$

heating the resulting solution to expel the hydrogen chloride, and evaporating the water until white crystals of phosphorous acid appear upon cooling. The crystals are deliquescent, very soluble in water, and have an odor like that of garlic. The solid melts at 70.1°C and decomposes at about 200°C by disproportionation into phosphine and orthophosphoric acid.

$$4H_3PO_3(l) \longrightarrow PH_3(g) + 3H_3PO_4(l)$$

Phosphorous acid and its salts are active reducing agents, because they are readily oxidized to phosphoric acid and phosphates, respectively. Phosphorous acid reduces the silver ion to free silver, mercury(II) salts to mercury(I) salts, and sulfurous acid to sulfur.

Phosphorous acid forms only two series of salts, which contain the **dihydrogen phosphite ion,** $H_2PO_3^-$, and the **hydrogen phosphite ion,** HPO_3^{2-}, respectively. The third atom of hydrogen cannot be replaced; it is bonded to the phosphorus atom rather than to an oxygen atom, and like the hydrogen atoms in phosphine, it is not very acidic.

23.24 Hypophosphorous Acid

The solution remaining from the preparation of phosphine from white phosphorus and a base contains the **hypophosphite ion,** $H_2PO_2^-$. The barium salt can be obtained by using barium hydroxide in the preparation. When barium hypophosphite is treated with

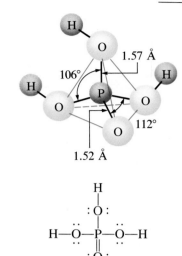

Figure 23.30

The molecular and electronic structures of orthophosphoric acid, H_3PO_4.

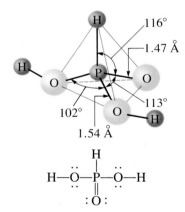

Figure 23.31

Phosphorous acid, H_3PO_3. Note that one hydrogen atom is bonded directly to the phosphorus atom. The other two hydrogen atoms are bonded to oxygen atoms. Only those hydrogen atoms that are bonded through an oxygen atom are acidic.

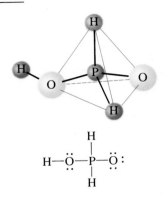

$$H-\overset{..}{\underset{..}{O}}-\overset{\underset{H}{|}}{\underset{H}{P}}-\overset{..}{\underset{..}{O}}:$$

Figure 23.32
Hypophosphorous acid, H_3PO_2. Note that two of the three hydrogen atoms are attached directly to the phosphorus atom. Hence only one hydrogen atom is acidic, the one bonded through an oxygen atom.

sulfuric acid, barium sulfate precipitates and **hypophosphorous acid,** H_3PO_2 (Fig. 23.32), forms in solution.

$$Ba^{2+} + 2H_2PO_2^- + 2H_3O^+ + SO_4^{2-} \longrightarrow BaSO_4(s) + 2H_3PO_2 + 2H_2O$$

The acid is weak and monoprotic, forming only one series of salts. Two nonacidic hydrogen atoms are bonded directly to the phosphorus atom. Hypophosphorous acid and its salts are strong reducing agents because phosphorus is in the unusually low oxidation state of +1.

The Noble Gases

No compounds of the elements of Group VIIIA of the periodic table were known for many years, so these elements were called the *inert* gases. However, when it was discovered that some of these gases form a limited range of compounds, the name *noble* gases was adopted. They are sometimes called the *rare* gases.

23.25 Discovery and Production of the Noble Gases

Although all the noble gases are present in the atmosphere in small amounts, the first was discovered in the sun. In 1868, the French astronomer Pierre-Jules-César Janssen went to India to study a total eclipse of the sun. Using a spectroscope, he found one new yellow line in its spectrum. The English chemist Edward Frankland and the English astronomer Sir Norman Lockyer concluded that the sun contained a previously undiscovered element, which they jointly named **helium,** from the Greek word *helios,* meaning "the sun." Twenty-seven years later the Scottish chemist Sir William Ramsay detected helium on the earth for the first time. He showed that the traces of gas present in the uranium mineral cleveite have a spectrum identical to that of helium.

In 1905 Professor Hamilton P. Cady and D. F. McFarland of the University of Kansas discovered that a sample of natural gas contained 1.84% helium by mass. Helium is now isolated from certain natural gases by liquefying the condensable components, leaving only helium as a gas. The United States has most of the world's commercial supply of this element in its helium-bearing gas fields.

In 1894 the British physicist Lord Rayleigh observed that a sample of nitrogen prepared by removing the oxygen, carbon dioxide, and water vapor from air had a density of 1.2572 grams per liter, whereas a liter of nitrogen prepared from ammonia had a density of only 1.2506 grams per liter under the same conditions. This difference caused Rayleigh to suspect a previously undiscovered element in the atmosphere. About the same time, by passing nitrogen obtained from the air over red-hot magnesium, Sir William Ramsay isolated a small amount of gas that would not combine with any other element.

$$3Mg(s) + N_2(g) \longrightarrow Mg_3N_2(s)$$

Rayleigh and Ramsay both found that the residual gases showed spectral lines never before observed. In 1894 they announced the *isolation* of a noble gas for the first time.

They called this gas **argon,** meaning "the lazy one." It was later found that this residual gas also contained traces of the other noble gases: helium, neon, krypton, and xenon.

In 1898 Ramsay and his assistant Morris W. Travers isolated **neon** (meaning "the new element") by the fractional distillation of impure liquid oxygen. Shortly thereafter they showed that the less volatile fractions from liquid air contain two other new elements, **krypton** ("the hidden element") and **xenon** ("the stranger").

In 1900 the German physicist Friedrich E. Dorn discovered that one of the disintegration products of radium is a gas similar in chemical properties to the noble gases. At first this gas was called *radium emanation,* but later its name was changed to **radon.**

Argon, neon, krypton, and xenon are produced by the fractional distillation of liquid air. Radon is collected from radium salts. More recently it has been observed that this radioactive gas is present in very small amounts in many different soils and minerals. Its accumulation in well-insulated, tightly sealed buildings constitutes a health hazard (Section 24.16). Commercial kits designed to detect small amounts of radon are now available (Fig. 23.33).

Figure 23.33

Kits designed to detect radon in buildings and homes can be purchased.

㉓.26 Properties of the Noble Gases

The boiling points and melting points of the noble gases are extremely low compared to those of other substances of comparable atomic or molecular masses. This is because no strong chemical bonds hold the atoms together in the liquid or solid states. Only weak London dispersion forces (see Section 11.3) are present, and these forces can hold the atoms together only when molecular motion is very slight, as it is at very low temperatures. Helium is the only substance known that does not solidify on cooling at normal pressure. It remains liquid close to absolute zero (0.001 K) at ordinary pressures, but it solidifies under elevated pressure.

Almost from the time of their discovery, chemists tried to combine the noble gases with other elements, but until 1962 no covalently bonded compounds of these nonmetals had been prepared. In 1962 Neil Bartlett, then in Canada, reported the preparation of a yellow compound of xenon, which he formulated as $Xe[PtF_6]$. This discovery led a group of chemists at the Argonne National Laboratory to think that xenon might be oxidized by the highly electronegative element fluorine, and they prepared XeF_4. Since that time a number of additional compounds have been reported, and the chemistry of xenon is rather extensive. Krypton forms a difluoride, KrF_2, which is thermally unstable at room temperature. Radon apparently forms RnF_2, but the evidence is based solely on radiochemical tracer techniques because radon has no stable isotopes. Stable compounds of helium, neon, and argon are not known.

㉓.27 Noble Gas Compounds

Stable compounds of xenon form when xenon reacts with fluorine. **Xenon difluoride,** XeF_2, is prepared by heating an excess of xenon gas with fluorine gas at 400°C and cooling. The material forms colorless crystals, which are stable at room temperature in a dry atmosphere. **Xenon tetrafluoride,** XeF_4 (Fig. 23.34), and **xenon hexafluoride,** XeF_6, are prepared in an analogous manner, with a stoichiometric amount of fluorine and an excess of fluorine, respectively. Compounds with oxygen are prepared by replacing fluorine atoms in the xenon fluorides with oxygen.

Figure 23.34

Crystals of xenon tetrafluoride, XeF_4.

Xenon compounds are very strong oxidizing agents. They may disproportionate in water, and they react with strong Lewis acids by donating a fluoride ion. The reaction with AsF_5 is

$$XeF_2(s) + AsF_5(s) \longrightarrow [XeF]^+[AsF_6]^-$$

Xenon difluoride is quite soluble in water. It dissolves as undissociated molecules that soon oxidize the water to produce xenon, hydrogen fluoride, and oxygen.

$$2XeF_2(s) + 2H_2O(l) \longrightarrow 2Xe(g) + 4HF(aq) + O_2(g)$$

The reaction of xenon tetrafluoride is more complicated because it is accompanied by disproportionation of the xenon(IV). With a stoichiometric amount of water, $XeOF_4$ is formed, but with excess water the covalent Xe—F bonds in the oxyfluoride hydrolyze and the oxide, XeO_3, forms.

$$6XeF_4(s) + 8H_2O(l) \longrightarrow 4Xe(g) + 2XeOF_4(l) + 16HF(g) + 3O_2(g)$$

$$XeOF_4(l) + 2H_2O(aq) \longrightarrow XeO_3(aq) + 4HF(aq)$$

Dry, solid **xenon trioxide,** XeO_3, is an extremely sensitive explosive that must be handled with care. When XeF_6 reacts with water, the +6 oxidation state for the xenon is retained.

$$XeF_6(s) + 3H_2O(l) \longrightarrow XeO_3(aq) + 6HF(aq)$$

Both XeF_6 and XeO_3 disproportionate in basic solution, producing xenon, oxygen, and salts of the **perxenate ion,** XeO_6^{4-}, in which xenon reaches its maximum oxidation number of +8.

Xenon difluoride reacts with acids such as HSO_3F, F_5TeOH, and $HClO_4$, which are resistant to oxidation, with evolution of hydrogen fluoride and formation of one or two Xe—O bonds, depending on the stoichiometry of the reaction. Compounds formed this way include $FXeOSO_2F$, $FXeOTeF_5$, and $Xe(OTeF_5)_2$.

Although most of the chemistry of xenon involves Xe—F and Xe—O bonds, chemists have also been successful in preparing compounds containing Xe—N and Xe—C bonds. Compounds of this type that have been reported include $FXeN(SO_2F)_2$ and $Xe(CF_3)_2$.

㉓.28 Uses of the Noble Gases

Helium is used for filling balloons and lighter-than-air craft; because it does not burn, it is safer to use than hydrogen. Helium at high pressures is not a narcotic; nitrogen is. Thus mixtures of oxygen and helium are used by divers working under high pressures in order to avoid the disoriented mental state known as nitrogen narcosis, the so-called rapture of the deep, that can result from breathing air. Mixtures of helium and oxygen are also beneficial in the treatment of certain respiratory diseases such as asthma. The lightness and rapid diffusion of helium decrease the muscular effort involved in breathing. Helium is used as an inert atmosphere for the melting and welding of easily oxidizable metals and for many chemical processes that are sensitive to air.

Liquid helium (boiling point 4.2 K) is used to reach low temperatures for cryogenic research, and it is essential for achieving the low temperatures necessary to produce superconduction in traditional superconducting materials.

Neon is used in neon lamps and signs. When an electric spark is passed through a tube containing neon at low pressure, the familiar glow of the neon sign is emitted (Fig.

23.35). The color of the light given off by a neon tube can be changed by mixing argon or mercury vapor with the neon and by utilizing tubes made of glasses of special color. Neon lamps cost less to operate than ordinary electric lamps, and their light penetrates fog better.

Argon is used in gas-filled electric light bulbs, where its lower heat conductivity and chemical inertness make it preferable to nitrogen for inhibiting vaporization of the tungsten filament and prolonging the life of the bulb. Fluorescent tubes commonly contain a mixture of argon and mercury vapor. Many Geiger-counter tubes are filled with argon.

Krypton–xenon flash tubes are used for taking high-speed photographs. An electric discharge through such a tube gives a very intense light that lasts only 1/50,000 of a second.

For Review

Summary

Figure 23.35

Neon signs are ubiquitous in Las Vegas.

Carbon (Group IVA) exhibits oxidation numbers ranging from -4 to $+4$. It is covalently bonded in the vast majority of its compounds. The immense number and variety of carbon compounds are due to the ability of carbon atoms to bond together and form chains and rings of atoms. These compounds are also discussed in Chapters 30 and 31, which describe the organic and biochemical behavior of carbon, respectively. This chapter describes the inorganic chemistry of carbon.

Carbon is relatively nonreactive as an element; the only nonmetals that oxidize it are oxygen, sulfur, and fluorine. **Carbon monoxide** forms when carbon and oxygen react in stoichiometric amounts. **Carbon dioxide** forms when carbon or carbon monoxide reacts with an excess of oxygen. Carbon dioxide is a weakly acidic nonmetal oxide. It acts as a Lewis acid toward oxide ion (forming the carbonate ion) and other Lewis bases, and it gives a low yield of **carbonic acid** when it dissolves in water. Carbonic acid is a weak acid that is a source of the weakly basic **hydrogen carbonate ion,** HCO_3^-, and the more strongly basic **carbonate ion,** CO_3^{2-}. Other anions that contain carbon include the **acetylide ion,** C_2^{2-}, the **cyanide ion, CN^-,** and the **cyanamide ion, CN_2^{2-}.**

Nitrogen (Group VA) is not very reactive. At room temperature it reacts with lithium. At elevated temperatures it reacts with active metals, forming **nitrides,** N^{3-}, and with hydrogen and with oxygen in reversible low-yield reactions, forming ammonia and nitric oxide, respectively.

Ammonia exhibits both Brønsted and Lewis base behavior, and it undergoes oxidation. **Hydrazine, hydroxylamine, nitric oxide,** and **ammonium salts** are prepared from ammonia. Ammonia is prepared by the direct reaction of hydrogen and nitrogen by the **Haber process.** Because the rate of reaction is slow at low temperatures, high pressures, elevated temperatures, and a catalyst are required.

Nitrogen exhibits oxidation states ranging from -3 to $+5$. The most important oxides are **nitric oxide** and **nitrogen dioxide,** because they are intermediates in the preparation of nitric acid by oxidation of ammonia. These two oxides can also be prepared by reduction of nitric acid. Dinitrogen trioxide is the anhydride of nitrous acid; dinitrogen pentaoxide is the anhydride of nitric acid.

Nitric acid is one of the important strong acids of commerce. It is also a strong oxidizing agent. Metals dissolve in nitric acid by reduction of the nitrate ion, generally with formation of nitrogen dioxide or nitric oxide, rather than by reduction of hydrogen ion with the production of hydrogen gas. **Nitrous acid,** a weak acid, can be prepared by the acidification of a solution of a nitrite salt.

Phosphorus (Group VA) commonly exhibits an oxidation number of -3 with active metals and of $+3$ and $+5$ with more electronegative nonmetals. Hydrolysis of **phosphides** or disproportionation of phosphorus in base produces **phosphine, PH_3**. Phosphorus is oxidized by halogens and by oxygen. The oxides are phosphorus(V) oxide, P_4O_{10}, and phosphorus(III) oxide, P_4O_6.

Orthophosphoric acid, H_3PO_4, is prepared by the reaction of phosphates with sulfuric acid or of water with phosphorus(V) oxide. Orthophosphoric acid is a triprotic acid that forms three types of salts. Upon heating, orthophosphoric acid loses water and forms condensed phosphoric acids.

The reaction of PCl_3 with water produces **phosphorous acid, H_3PO_3**. One hydrogen atom is bonded directly to the phosphorus atom, so this acid contains only two acidic hydrogen atoms. **Hypophosphorous acid, H_3PO_2**, contains two hydrogen atoms bonded directly to the phosphorus atom and one acidic hydrogen.

The noble gas elements exhibit a very limited chemistry. Xenon reacts directly with fluorine, forming the xenon fluorides XeF_2, XeF_4, and XeF_6. Xenon oxides can be prepared by the reaction of water with the fluorides, and the reaction of certain acids with XeF_2 forms derivatives containing Xe—O bonds.

Key Terms and Concepts

adsorption (23.1)
amide (23.11)
carbonate (23.4)
carbon black (23.1)
carbonic acid (23.5)
catenation (introduction)
charcoal (23.1)
coke (23.1)

cyanamide (23.8)
cyanide (23.8)
derivatives of ammonia (23.12)
Haber process (23.11)
hypophosphite (23.24)
imide (23.11)
intercalation compounds (23.2)
nitrate (23.14)

nitride (23.11)
nitrite (23.15)
nitrogen cycle (23.16)
noble gas (23.25)
Ostwald process (23.14)
phosphate (23.22)
phosphide (23.18)
phosphite (23.23)

Exercises

Answers for selected even-numbered exercises marked by red numbers appear at the end of the book. The worked-out solutions to all even-numbered exercises appear in the *Solutions Guide*.

1. Complete and balance the chemical equation for each of the following oxidation–reduction reactions. In some cases there may be more than one correct answer, depending on the amounts of reactants used.
   (a) $Mg + P_4 \longrightarrow$
   (b) $Li + N_2 \longrightarrow$
   (c) $Na + P_4 \longrightarrow$
   (d) $C + S \longrightarrow$
   (e) $C + F_2 \longrightarrow$
   (f) $P_4 + xsO_2 \longrightarrow$
   (g) $Xe + xsF_2 \longrightarrow$
   (h) $N_2 + H_2 \longrightarrow$
   (i) $NO + NO_2 \longrightarrow$

2. Compare and contrast the chemical properties of the two naturally occurring allotropes of carbon, of carbon dioxide and carbon disulfide, and of phosphorous acid and nitrous acid.

3. Give the name and formula of a nitrogen compound that illustrates each of the different oxidation states that nitrogen can display.

4. In general, with which elements does phosphorus react to form compounds in which it has a negative oxidation number?

Nitrogen

5. Write the Lewis structure for each of the following.
   (a) NH^{2-}
   (b) N^{3-}
   (c) N_2F_4
   (d) NH_2^-
   (e) NF_3
   (f) N_3^-

6. For species (c) through (f) listed in Exercise 5, indicate the hybridization of the nitrogen atom (for N_3^-, the central nitrogen).

7. Explain how ammonia can function both as a Brønsted base and as a Lewis base.

8. Determine the oxidation number of nitrogen in each of the following.
   (a) NCl_3
   (b) $ClNO$
   (c) N_2O_5
   (d) N_2O_3
   (e) NO_2^-
   (f) N_2O_4
   (g) N_2O
   (h) NO_3^-
   (i) HNO_2
   (j) HNO_3

9. Predict whether each neutral molecule listed in Exercise 8 is polar or nonpolar.

10. Explain why ammonia gives basic solutions in water.

11. What is the molarity of a solution prepared by adding 0.38 g of sodium nitrate to enough water to make 50.0 mL of solution?

12. How many ammonia molecules are there in 43 g of ammonia?

13. What is the mass in grams of an NO_2 molecule?

14. A certain fertilizer contains 15.8% nitrogen by mass. How much nitrogen is there in 2.75 kg of the fertilizer?

15. What volume of ammonia measured at 1.20 atm and 77°F is required to react with 800 mL of 0.510 M HCl solution?

16. Write an equation for the reaction of concentrated HNO_3 with each of the following. (In some cases there may be more than one correct answer.)
   (a) K_2CO_3 (d) K_2SO_3 (f) C
   (b) $Ba(OH)_2$ (e) P_4 (g) SO_2
   (c) Ag

17. Nitric oxide can be produced by the combustion of ammonia in the presence of a catalyst. How many grams of nitric oxide can be produced when 0.120 mol of ammonia is burned in the presence of 0.140 mol of oxygen gas?

18. The oxidation of ammonia and that of nitric oxide are exothermic reactions. Using Appendix I, calculate ΔH°_{298} for each of these reactions.

19. What mass of ammonia is produced when water is added to the product of the reaction of 93.0 g of lithium with excess elemental nitrogen?

Phosphorus

20. Write the Lewis structure for each of the following.
   (a) HCP   (c) PH_4^+ (e) PO_4^{3-}
   (b) PH_3 (d) P_2H_4 (f) PF_5

21. Describe the molecular structure of each of the molecules listed in Exercise 20.

22. Complete and balance each of the following chemical equations. (In some cases there may be more than one correct answer.)
   (a) $P_4 + Al \longrightarrow$ (e) $P_4 + xsSe \longrightarrow$
   (b) $P_4 + Na \longrightarrow$ (f) $P_4 + O_2 \longrightarrow$
   (c) $P_4 + F_2 \longrightarrow$ (g) $P_4O_6 + O_2 \longrightarrow$
   (d) $P_4 + xsCl_2 \longrightarrow$

23. Describe the hybridization of phosphorus in each of the following.
   (a) P_4O_{10} (e) H_3PO_4
   (b) P_4O_6 (f) H_3PO_3
   (c) PH_4I (an ionic (g) PH_3
       compound)   (h) P_2H_4
   (d) PBr_3

24. What volume of 0.200 M NaOH is required to neutralize the solution produced by dissolving 2.00 g of PCl_3 in an excess of water? Note that when H_3PO_3 is titrated under these conditions, only one proton of the acid molecule reacts.

25. How much $POCl_3$ can be produced from 25.0 g of PCl_5 and the appropriate amount of H_2O?

26. How many tons of $Ca_3(PO_4)_2$ are needed to prepare 5.0 tons of phosphorus if a yield of 90% is obtained?

27. Write equations showing the stepwise ionization of phosphorous acid.

28. Compare the structures of PF_4^+, PF_5, PF_6^-, and POF_3.

29. Why does phosphorous acid form only two series of salts, even though the molecule contains three hydrogen atoms?

30. Assign an oxidation number to phosphorus in each of the following.
   (a) NaH_2PO_4 (d) K_3PO_4
   (b) PF_5 (e) Na_3P
   (c) P_4O_{10} (f) $Na_4P_2O_7$

31. Show that the decomposition of phosphorous acid by heat involves a disproportionation reaction.

32. Write a balanced chemical equation for each of the following preparations.
   (a) H_3PO_4 from P_4O_{10} (d) PH_3 from AlP
   (b) P_4O_6 from P_4 (e) PCl_5 from P_4
   (c) P_4 from $Ca_3(PO_4)_2$

33. Write balanced chemical equations for the preparation and hydrolysis of aluminum phosphide.

34. What structural feature do P_4, P_4O_6, and P_4O_{10} have in common? How do they differ?

Carbon

35. Write the Lewis structure, including resonance forms where necessary, for each of the following.
   (a) CO_3^{2-} (c) C_2H_4 (e) COS
   (b) CO_2S^{2-} (d) CF_2Br_2 (f) $H_2NCS_2^-$

36. Indicate the hybridization of carbon in each of the molecules and ions listed in Exercise 35.

37. Why is carbon monoxide toxic?

38. Write a balanced chemical equation for the complete combustion of each of the following.
   (a) C_3H_8 (c) C_2H_4
   (b) C_2H_5OH (d) CH_3CO_2H

39. Indicate whether each of the following molecules is polar or nonpolar.
   (a) HCN   (c) CO   (e) CH_2Cl_2
   (b) CS_2 (d) C_2H_2 (f) CBr_4

40. Write a chemical equation for the synthesis of each of the following.
   (a) calcium cyanamide   (e) coke
   (b) calcium carbide   (f) ethanol
   (c) carbon dioxide   (g) carbonic acid
   (d) carbon monoxide

41. A 2.358-g sample of coal contains 1.987 g of carbon. Calculate the percentage by mass of carbon in the coal.

42. Gold mining involves the use of potassium cyanide to separate gold as a complex ion from other materials. The reaction is

$$4Au + 8KCN + O_2 + 2H_2O \longrightarrow 4KAu(CN)_2 + 4KOH$$

How many grams of potassium cyanide are required to separate exactly 1 oz of gold?

The Noble Gases

43. Give the hybridization of xenon in each of the following.

(a) XeF_2 (c) XeO_2F_2 (e) XeO_4

(b) XeF_4 (d) XeO_3 (f) $XeOF_4$

44. What is the molecular structure of each of the molecules listed in Exercise 43?

45. Indicate whether each molecule listed in Exercise 43 is polar or nonpolar.

46. What is the oxidation number of xenon in each of the following?

(a) XeO_2F_2 (c) XeF_3^+ (e) XeO_3

(b) XeF^+ (d) XeO_6^{4-} (f) XeO_3F_2

47. A mixture of xenon and fluorine was heated. A sample of the white solid that formed reacted with hydrogen to give 81 mL of xenon at STP and hydrogen fluoride, which was collected in water, giving a solution of hydrofluoric acid. The hydrofluoric acid solution was titrated, and 68.43 mL of 0.3172 M sodium hydroxide was required to reach the equivalence point. Determine the empirical formula for the white solid, and write balanced chemical equations for the reactions involving xenon.

48. Basic solutions of Na_4XeO_6 are powerful oxidants. What mass of $Mn(NO_3)_2 \cdot 6H_2O$ reacts with 125.0 mL of a 0.1717 M basic solution of Na_4XeO_6 that contains an excess of sodium hydroxide if the products include Xe and a solution of sodium permanganate?

Additional Exercises

49. Write the balanced chemical equation or equations necessary to carry out the following transformations. (Use H_2O, H_2, and/or O_2, as needed.)

(a) P_4 from Na_3PO_4 and any other necessary reagents

(b) K_2CO_3 from K_2O and C

(c) $Mg(NO_3)_2$ from Mg and N_2

(d) H_3PO_4 from P_4 and Cl_2

50. The solubility product of $Ca_3(PO_4)_2$ is 1×10^{-25}. What is the concentration of $Ca_3(PO_4)_2$ in a saturated solution of $Ca_3(PO_4)_2$ if you disregard hydrolysis of the PO_4^{3-} ion?

51. For each of the following, give an answer and an explanation.

(a) Which is a stronger base, HPO_4^{2-} or PO_4^{3-}?

(b) Which is a stronger acid, NH_3 or PH_3?

(c) Which is a stronger base, N^{3-} or P^{3-}?

52. At a certain temperature and 1.0 atm, a mixture of $N_2O_4(g)$ and $NO_2(g)$ contains 30.0% $NO_2(g)$ by volume. Calculate the partial pressures of the two gases when they are at equilibrium at the same temperature with a total pressure of 9.0 atm.

53. (a) When phosphine burns to give liquid orthophosphoric acid, an unusually large amount of energy is involved. Calculate ΔH_{298}° for the reaction, using the data given in Appendix I.

(b) Calculate the value of ΔH_{298}° for the production of solid orthophosphoric acid by this reaction.

54. What mass of phosphorus is required to prepare 60.08 g of PCl_3 by the reaction of chlorine with phosphorus?

55. Determine what quantity of nitric acid can be prepared by the Ostwald process from 300 ft^3 of ammonia, measured at 4.00 atm and 250°C, if a 93.0% yield is obtained (based on the original quantity of ammonia).

56. At 422 K the partial pressures of gaseous PCl_5, PCl_3, and Cl_2 in a closed system are 0.453 atm, 6.08×10^{-2} atm, and 6.08×10^{-2} atm, respectively. Determine K_p for the dissociation reaction.

$$PCl_5(g) \longrightarrow PCl_3(g) + Cl_2(g)$$

57. Increases in the price of petroleum result in increases in the price of ammonia. Why?

58. Which is the stronger oxidizing agent, hydrazine or hydrogen peroxide? Give evidence supporting your answer.

24 Nuclear Chemistry

Uranium oxide is used as the fuel in many nuclear reactors.

The chemical changes (transformations of one form of matter into another) that we have studied so far have involved only the electrons in atoms. When we discussed changes in atoms during reactions, we focused on changes in the electron structures of the atoms. However, there is a branch of chemistry called **nuclear chemistry** that considers changes and differences in atomic nuclei. This branch is on the borderline between physics and chemistry. It began with the discovery of radioactivity in 1896 by Antoine Becquerel, a French physicist, and has become increasingly important during the twentieth century.

The Stability of Nuclei

24.1 The Nucleus

The nucleus of an atom is composed of protons and, with the exception of $_1^1H$, neutrons (Sections 2.3 and 3.3). The number of protons in the nucleus is called the **atomic number, Z,** of the element, and the sum of the number of protons and the number of neutrons is the **mass number, A.** Atoms with the same atomic number but different mass numbers are **isotopes** of the same element. When talking about a single type of nucleus, we often use the term **nuclide** and identify it by the notation $_Z^AX$, where X is the symbol for the element, A is the mass number, and Z is the atomic number (for example, $_6^{14}C$). Sometimes a nuclide is referred to by the name of the element followed by a hyphen and the mass number; for example, $_6^{14}C$ may be called carbon-14.

Protons and neutrons, collectively called **nucleons,** are packed together tightly in a nucleus. A nucleus is quite small (about 10^{-13} cm) compared to the entire atom (about 10^{-8} cm). Nuclei are extremely dense; they average 1.8×10^{14} grams per cubic centimeter. This density is very large compared to the densities of familiar materials. Water, for example, has a density of 1 gram per cubic centimeter. Osmium, the densest element known, has a density of 22.5 grams per cubic centimeter. If the earth's density were equal to the average nuclear density, the earth's radius would be only about 200 meters. (The actual radius of the earth is approximately 6.37×10^6 meters.)

To hold positively charged protons together in the very small volume of a nucleus requires tremendous force, because the positive charges repel one another strongly at such short distances. The **nuclear force** is the force of attraction between nucleons that holds the nucleus together. This force acts between protons, between neutrons, and between protons and neutrons. The nuclear force is very different from and much stronger than the electrostatic force that holds negatively charged electrons around a positively charged nucleus. In fact, the nuclear force is the strongest force known; it is about 30–40 times stronger than electrostatic repulsions between protons in a nucleus. Although the exact nature of the nuclear force is unknown, it is known that it is a short-range force, effective only within distances of about 10^{-13} centimeter.

24.2 Nuclear Binding Energy

Although the nature of the nuclear force is unknown, the magnitude of the energy changes associated with its action can be determined. As an example, let us consider the nucleus of the helium atom, $_2^4He$, which consists of two protons and two neutrons. If a helium nucleus were to be formed by the combination of two protons and two neutrons without any change of mass, the mass of the helium atom (including the mass of the two electrons outside the nucleus) would be

$$(2 \times 1.0073) + (2 \times 1.0087) + (2 \times 0.00055) = 4.0331 \text{ amu}$$
$$\underset{\text{protons}}{} \qquad \underset{\text{neutrons}}{} \qquad \underset{\text{electrons}}{}$$

However, the mass is only 4.0026 amu. This difference between the calculated and experimental masses, the **mass defect** of the atom, indicates a loss in mass of 0.0305 amu. The loss in mass accompanying the formation of an atom from protons, neutrons, and electrons is due to conversion of that much mass to **nuclear binding**

energy. Such conversions are extremely exothermic; thus the reverse reaction, decomposition of an atom to protons, neutrons, and electrons is extremely endothermic—and very difficult to accomplish.

The nuclear binding energy can be calculated from the mass defect by the **Einstein equation**

$$E = mc^2$$

where E represents energy in joules, m stands for mass in kilograms, and c is the speed of light in meters per second. A tremendous quantity of energy results from the conversion of even a very small quantity of matter to energy.

Example 24.1

Calculate the binding energy for the nuclide $^4_2$He in joules per mole and in millions of electron-volts (MeV) per nucleus.

The difference in mass between a $^4_2$He nucleus and two protons plus two neutrons is 0.0305 amu. In order to use the Einstein equation to convert this mass defect into the equivalent energy in joules, we must express the mass defect in kilograms (1 amu = 1.6605×10^{-27} kg).

$$0.0305 \text{ amu} \times \frac{1.6605 \times 10^{-27} \text{ kg}}{1 \text{ amu}} = 5.06 \times 10^{-29} \text{ kg}$$

The nuclear binding energy in *one* nucleus is found from the Einstein equation ($E = mc^2$).

$$E = 5.06 \times 10^{-29} \text{ kg} \times (3.00 \times 10^8 \text{ m s}^{-1})^2$$
$$= 4.54 \times 10^{-12} \text{ kg m}^2 \text{ s}^{-2}$$
$$= 4.54 \times 10^{-12} \text{ J}$$

Units of kg m^2 s^{-2} are equivalent to J (see Section 4.1). The binding energy in 1 mol of helium nuclei is

$$4.54 \times 10^{-12} \text{ J/nucleus} \times 6.022 \times 10^{23} \text{ nuclei/mol} = 2.73 \times 10^{12} \text{ J mol}^{-1}$$
$$= 2.73 \times 10^9 \text{ kJ mol}^{-1}$$

Binding energies are often expressed in millions of electron-volts (MeV) per nucleus rather than in joules. The conversion factor is

$$1 \text{ MeV} = 1.602189 \times 10^{-13} \text{ J}$$

giving

$$4.54 \times 10^{-12} \text{ J/nucleus} \times \frac{1 \text{ MeV}}{1.602189 \times 10^{-13} \text{ J}} = 28.3 \text{ MeV/nucleus}$$

The changes in mass in all ordinary chemical reactions are negligible, because only chemical bonds change—that is, they form or break. On the other hand, the changes in mass in nuclear reactions are very significant. If the nuclear reaction of 2 moles of neutrons with 2 moles of hydrogen atoms to give 1 mole of helium atoms could be made to occur, 2.73×10^9 kilojoules of energy would be released (Example 24.1). For comparison, burning 1 mole of methane (an ordinary chemical reaction) releases only 8.9×10^2 kilojoules, about three million times less energy.

The **binding energy per nucleon** (that is, the total binding energy for the nucleus divided by the sum of the numbers of protons and neutrons present in the nucleus) is greatest for the nuclei of elements with mass numbers between 40 and 100 and decreases with mass numbers less than 40 or greater than 100 (Fig. 24.1). The most stable nuclei are those with the largest binding energy per nucleon—those in the vicinity of iron, cobalt, and nickel in the periodic table. The binding energy per nucleon in helium is

$$\frac{28.3}{4} = 7.08 \text{ MeV/nucleon}$$

The binding energy per nucleon in $^{56}_{26}\text{Fe}$ is almost 25% larger than in ^4_2He, as shown in the following example.

Example 24.2

Calculate the binding energy per nucleon in MeV for the iron isotope with an atomic number of 26 and a mass number of 56, $^{56}_{26}\text{Fe}$, which has an atomic mass of 55.9349 amu.

To determine the binding energy per nucleon, we must first determine the nuclear binding energy from the mass defect of the nucleus. The mass defect is the difference between the mass of 26 protons, 30 neutrons, and 26 electrons and the observed mass of a $^{56}_{26}\text{Fe}$ atom.

$$\text{Mass defect} = [(26 \times 1.0073) + (30 \times 1.0087) + (26 \times 0.00055)] - 55.9349$$

$$= 56.4651 - 55.9349$$

$$= 0.5302 \text{ amu}$$

Now we can calculate the nuclear binding energy in millions of electron-volts.

$$E = mc^2$$

$$= 0.5302 \text{ amu} \times \frac{1.6605 \times 10^{-27} \text{ kg}}{1 \text{ amu}} \times (3.00 \times 10^8 \text{ m s}^{-1})^2$$

$$= 7.92 \times 10^{-11} \text{ kg m}^2 \text{ s}^{-2}$$

$$= 7.92 \times 10^{-11} \text{ J}$$

$$7.92 \times 10^{-11} \text{ J} \times \frac{1 \text{ MeV}}{1.602189 \times 10^{-13} \text{ J}} = 494 \text{ MeV}$$

The binding energy per nucleon is found by dividing the total nuclear binding energy by 56, the number of nucleons in the atom.

$$\text{Binding energy per nucleon} = \frac{494 \text{ MeV}}{56}$$

$$= 8.82 \text{ MeV}$$

The iron-56 nucleus is one of the more stable nuclei (Fig. 24.1); it has one of the highest binding energies.

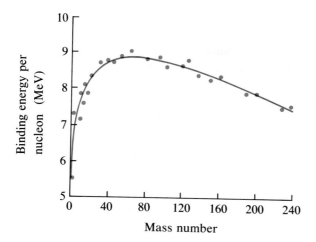

Figure 24.1
Binding energy curve for the elements.

24.3 Nuclear Stability

A nucleus is stable if it cannot be transformed into another configuration without adding energy from the outside. A plot of the number of neutrons versus the number of protons for stable nuclei (the curve shown in Fig. 24.2) shows that the stable isotopes fall into a narrow band, which is called the **band of stability.** The straight line in Fig. 24.2

Figure 24.2

A plot of number of neutrons versus number of protons for naturally occurring nuclei. Each dot shows the number of protons and neutrons in a known stable nucleus. All isotopes of elements with atomic numbers greater than 83 are unstable.

represents equal numbers of protons and neutrons for comparison. The figure indicates that the lighter stable nuclei, in general, have equal numbers of protons and neutrons. For example, nitrogen-14 has 7 protons and 7 neutrons. Heavier stable nuclei, however, have slightly more neutrons than protons, as the curve shows. For example, iron-56 has 30 neutrons and 26 protons, a neutron-to-proton ratio of 1.15. Lead-207 has 125 neutrons and 82 protons, a neutron-to-proton ratio equal to 1.52.

The isotopes that are to the left or to the right of the band of stability have unstable nuclei and are **radioactive.** All isotopes with atomic numbers above 83 are radioactive. Radioactive nuclei change spontaneously (decay) to other nuclei that are either in or closer to the band of stability. We will discuss the nature of these changes toward more stable nuclei in subsequent sections.

24.4 The Half-Life

The number of atoms of a radioactive element that disintegrate per unit of time is a constant fraction of the total number of atoms present. The time required for $\frac{1}{2}$ of the atoms in a sample to decay is called its **half-life.** The half-lives of radioactive nuclides vary widely. For example, the half-life of $^{142}_{58}Ce$ is 5×10^{15} years, that of $^{226}_{88}Ra$ is 1590 years, that of $^{222}_{86}Rn$ is 3.82 days, and that of $^{216}_{84}Po$ is 0.16 second. Only $\frac{1}{2}$ of a sample of radium-226 remains unchanged after 1590 years, and at the end of another 1590 years the sample will have decayed to $\frac{1}{4}$ of its initial mass, and so on. The half-lives of a number of nuclides are listed in Appendix K.

Radioactive decay is a first-order process (see Sections 14.4 and 14.5). The rate constant k for a radioactive disintegration can be expressed in terms of the half-life, $t_{1/2}$, by the following equation (which applies to all first-order reactions; see Section 14.5):

$$k = \frac{0.693}{t_{1/2}}$$

The relationship between the initial amount of a radioactive isotope and the amount remaining after a given period of time is expressed by the logarithmic relationship that applies to all other first-order reactions (see Section 14.5).

$$\ln \frac{c_0}{c_t} = kt$$

where c_0 is the initial mass or number of moles and c_t is the mass or number of moles remaining at time t.

Example 24.3 Calculate the rate constant for the radioactive disintegration of cobalt-60, an isotope used in cancer therapy. $^{60}_{27}Co$ decays with a half-life of 5.2 years to produce $^{60}_{28}Ni$.

$$k = \frac{0.693}{t_{1/2}}$$

$$= \frac{0.693}{5.2 \text{ yr}} = 0.13 \text{ yr}^{-1}$$

Example 24.4 Calculate the fraction and the percentage of a sample of the $^{60}_{27}Co$ isotope that will remain after 15 years.

$$\ln \frac{c_0}{c_t} = kt$$

$$= (0.13 \text{ yr}^{-1})(15 \text{ yr}) = 1.95$$

$$\frac{c_0}{c_t} = \text{antiln } 1.95 = 7.03$$

The fraction that will remain is equal to the amount at time t divided by the initial amount, or c_t/c_0.

$$\frac{c_t}{c_0} = \frac{1}{7.03} = 0.14$$

The fraction of $^{60}_{27}\text{Co}$ remaining after 15 years is 0.14. Thus 14% of the $^{60}_{27}\text{Co}$ originally present will remain after 15 years.

How long does it take for a sample of $^{60}_{27}\text{Co}$ to disintegrate to the extent that only 2.0% of the original amount remains?

Example 24.5

$$c_t = 0.020 \times c_0$$

Therefore

$$\frac{c_0}{c_t} = \frac{1}{0.020} = 50$$

$$\ln 50 = kt = (0.13 \text{ yr}^{-1})t$$

$$t = \frac{\ln 50}{0.13 \text{ yr}^{-1}} = 30 \text{ yr}$$

The half-life of $^{216}_{84}\text{Po}$ is 0.16 s. How long does it take to reduce a sample of it to the negligible amount of 0.000010% of the original amount (1.0×10^{-7} times the original amount)?

Example 24.6

$$k = \frac{0.693}{0.16 \text{ s}} = 4.33 \text{ s}^{-1}$$

$$c_t = 1.0 \times 10^{-7} \times c_0$$

Hence

$$\frac{c_0}{c_t} = 1.0 \times 10^7$$

$$\ln(1.0 \times 10^7) = (4.33 \text{ s}^{-1})t$$

$$t = \frac{\ln(1.0 \times 10^7)}{4.33 \text{ s}^{-1}} = 3.7 \text{ s}$$

These examples indicate part of the problem that arises in the disposal of radioactive isotopes. In 3.7 seconds any reasonable quantity of $^{216}_{84}\text{Po}$ would be reduced to a negligible quantity and would itself no longer be a problem. However, the burst of radiation during the first second or so would be extremely intense and very hazardous. Furthermore, $^{216}_{84}\text{Po}$ is a part of a series (see Table 24.1, page 786). It decays into $^{212}_{82}\text{Pb}$, which is itself radioactive with a half-life of 10.6 hours, producing $^{212}_{83}\text{Bi}$, which has a half-life of 60.5 minutes, and so on, until finally the stable isotope $^{208}_{82}\text{Pb}$ is reached. Hence, in coping with radiation effects and isotope disposal, we must take into account all steps in the decay of the material. In contrast to the few seconds required for the decay of $^{216}_{84}Po$, it takes 30 years for 98% of a sample of $^{60}_{27}Co$ to disintegrate. Radium-226, an isotope with a half-life of 1590 years, takes even longer to decay. Even after 200 years, 91.6% of the original quantity of $^{226}_{88}Ra$ would still be present. Obviously we cannot simply leave radium-226 or other radioactive isotopes lying around on the assumption that the radiation danger will disappear within a short period.

Nuclear Reactions

The following sections describe reactions of nuclei that result in changes in their atomic numbers, mass numbers, and energy states. Such reactions are called **nuclear reactions.** Nuclear reactions result (1) from the spontaneous decay of naturally occurring or artificially produced radioactive nuclei, (2) from the fission of unstable heavy nuclei, (3) from the fusion of light nuclei, and (4) from the bombardment of nuclei with other nuclei or with other particles.

㉔.5   Equations for Nuclear Reactions

An equation that describes a nuclear reaction identifies the nuclides involved in the reaction, their mass numbers and atomic numbers, and the other particles involved in the reaction. These particles include:

1. **alpha particles (^4_2He, or α),** helium nuclei, consisting of two neutrons and two protons
2. **beta particles ($_{-1}^{0}e$, or β),** electrons
3. **positrons ($_{+1}^{0}e$, or β^+),** particles with the same mass as an electron but with 1 unit of *positive* charge
4. **protons (^1_1H, or p),** nuclei of hydrogen atoms
5. **neutrons (^1_0n, or n),** particles with a mass approximately equal to that of a proton but with no charge

Nuclear reactions also often involve **gamma rays (γ).** Gamma rays are electromagnetic radiation, somewhat like X rays in character but with higher energies and shorter wavelengths.

A correctly written nuclear reaction is balanced; that is, the sum of the mass numbers of the reactants equals the sum of the mass numbers of the products, and the sum of the atomic numbers of the reactants equals the sum of the atomic numbers of the products. If the atomic number and the mass number of all but one of the particles in a nuclear reaction are known, we can identify the particle by balancing the reaction.

Examples of equations of some types of nuclear reactions of historical interest follow.

1. The first radioactive element that was found, naturally occurring polonium, was discovered by the Polish scientist Marie Curie and her husband, Pierre, in 1898. It decays by alpha emission.

$$^{212}_{84}Po \longrightarrow {}^{208}_{82}Pb + {}^4_2He \tag{1}$$

With the loss of an alpha particle (which is composed of 2 neutrons and 2 protons), the mass number decreases by 4 and the atomic number decreases by 2 in going from $^{212}_{84}\text{Po}$ to $^{208}_{82}\text{Pb}$.

2. Technetium, a radioactive element that does not occur naturally on the earth and was first prepared in 1937, decays by beta emission.

$$^{98}_{43}\text{Tc} \longrightarrow {}^{98}_{44}\text{Ru} + {}^{0}_{-1}\text{e} \qquad (2)$$

In beta emission, a neutron in the nucleus changes into a proton (that remains in the nucleus) and an electron that is ejected.

$$^{1}_{0}\text{n} \longrightarrow {}^{1}_{1}\text{H} + {}^{0}_{-1}\text{e}$$

The mass number remains the same because a proton has replaced a neutron in the nucleus; the atomic number increases by 1 because of the extra proton in the nucleus.

3. One of the many fission reactions of uranium in the first nuclear reactor (1942) is

$$^{235}_{92}\text{U} + {}^{1}_{0}\text{n} \longrightarrow {}^{87}_{35}\text{Br} + {}^{146}_{57}\text{La} + 3\,{}^{1}_{0}\text{n} \qquad (3)$$

With the addition of 1 neutron and the subsequent loss of 3 neutrons, the mass number decreases from 235 for $^{235}_{92}\text{U}$ to a total of 233 for $^{87}_{35}\text{Br}$ and $^{146}_{57}\text{La}$ together; the atomic number for U-235 is the same as the total of the atomic numbers of Br-87 and La-146 (that is, 92).

4. One of the fusion reactions present during the detonation of a hydrogen bomb is

$$^{3}_{1}\text{H} + {}^{2}_{1}\text{H} \longrightarrow {}^{4}_{2}\text{He} + {}^{1}_{0}\text{n} \qquad (4)$$

The total number of neutrons in $^{3}_{1}\text{H}$ and $^{2}_{1}\text{H}$ is 3, and the total number of protons is 2. With the loss of 1 neutron in forming $^{4}_{2}\text{He}$, the number of neutrons decreases to 2 for $^{4}_{2}\text{He}$ and the number of protons remains 2; thus the mass number is 4 for $^{4}_{2}\text{He}$ and the atomic number is 2.

5. The first element prepared by artificial means was prepared in 1919 by bombarding nitrogen atoms with α particles.

$$^{14}_{7}\text{N} + {}^{4}_{2}\text{He} \longrightarrow {}^{17}_{8}\text{O} + {}^{1}_{1}\text{H} \qquad (5)$$

$^{14}_{7}\text{N}$ and $^{4}_{2}\text{He}$ together have a total of 9 neutrons and 9 protons. With the loss of a proton in forming $^{17}_{8}\text{O}$, the number of neutrons remains 9 and the number of protons decreases to 8. Thus for oxygen-17, the mass number is 17 and the atomic number is 8.

Example 24.7

The reaction of an α particle with magnesium-25 ($^{25}_{12}\text{Mg}$) produces a proton ($^{1}_{1}\text{H}$) and a nuclide of another element. Identify the new nuclide produced.

The nuclear reaction can be written as

$$^{25}_{12}\text{Mg} + {}^{4}_{2}\text{He} \longrightarrow {}^{A}_{Z}\text{X} + {}^{1}_{1}\text{H}$$

where A is the mass number and Z is the atomic number of the new nuclide, X. Because the sum of the mass numbers of the reactants must equal the sum of the mass numbers of the products, $25 + 4 = A + 1$, or $A = 28$. Similarly, the atomic numbers must balance, so $12 + 2 = Z + 1$, and $Z = 13$. The element with atomic number 13 is aluminum. Thus the product is $^{28}_{13}\text{Al}$ [an unstable nuclide with a half-life of 2.3 min that decays by β emission (Section 24.6) to $^{28}_{14}\text{Si}$].

24 .6 Radioactive Decay

The spontaneous change of an unstable nuclide into another is called **radioactive decay.** The unstable nuclide is often called the **parent nuclide;** the nuclide that results from the decay, the **daughter nuclide.** The daughter nuclide may be stable, or it may decay further. Different types of radioactive decay can be classified by the radiation produced.

1. The loss of an α particle (which contains two neutrons and two protons), $\boldsymbol{\alpha}$ **decay,** occurs primarily in heavy nuclei ($A \geq 200$, $Z > 83$). Because loss of an α particle gives a daughter nuclide with a mass number 4 units smaller and an atomic number 2 units smaller than those of the parent nuclide, the daughter nuclide has a larger neutron-to-proton ratio than the parent nuclide; and, if the parent nuclide undergoing α decay lies below the band of stability (Fig. 24.2), the daughter nuclide will lie closer to the band.

2. A nuclide with a large neutron-to-proton ratio (one that lies above the band of stability in Fig. 24.2) can reduce this ratio by electron emission, or $\boldsymbol{\beta}$ **decay,** in which a neutron in the nucleus decays into a proton that remains in the nucleus and an electron that is emitted.

$$\,_0^1 n \longrightarrow \,_1^1 H + \,_{-1}^{0} e$$

Emission of an electron does not change the mass number of the nuclide but does increase the number of its protons and decrease the number of its neutrons. Consequently, the neutron-to-proton ratio is decreased, and the daughter nuclide lies closer to the band of stability than did the parent nuclide.

3. Certain artificially produced nuclides in which the neutron-to-proton ratio is low (nuclides that lie below the band of stability in Fig. 24.2) undergo $\boldsymbol{\beta^+}$ **decay,** the emission of a positron. During the course of β^+ decay, a proton is converted into a neutron with the emission of a positron.

$$\,_1^1 H \longrightarrow \,_0^1 n + \,_{+1}^{0} e \; (\beta^+)$$

The neutron-to-proton ratio increases, and the daughter nuclide lies closer to the band of stability than did the parent nuclide.

When a positron and an electron interact, they annihilate each other. All of their mass is converted into energy—two 0.511-MeV γ rays are produced.

$$\underset{\text{Electron}}{\,_{-1}^{0} e} + \underset{\text{Positron}}{\,_{+1}^{0} e} \longrightarrow 2\gamma \qquad (0.511 \text{ MeV each})$$

4. A proton is converted to a neutron when one of the electrons in an atom is captured by the nucleus (this capture is called **electron capture**).

$$\,_1^1 H + \,_{-1}^{0} e \longrightarrow \,_0^1 n$$

Like β^+ decay, electron capture occurs when the neutron-to-proton ratio is low (the nuclide lies below the band of stability). Electron capture has the same effect on the nucleus as positron emission; the atomic number is decreased by 1 as a proton is converted into a neutron. This increases the neutron-to-proton ratio, and the daughter nuclide lies closer to the band of stability than did the parent nuclide.

5. A daughter nuclide may be formed in an excited state and then decay to its ground state with the emission of a γ ray, high-energy electromagnetic radiation. Figure 24.3 illustrates the relationships for the decay of uranium-233 to thorium-229. There is no change of mass number or atomic number during emission of a γ ray. Such $\boldsymbol{\gamma}$**-ray**

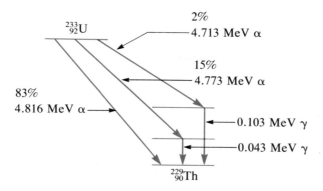

Figure 24.3

The decay of $^{233}_{92}$U to $^{229}_{90}$Th. The decay can occur by three paths. Two paths give excited states of the $^{229}_{90}$Th nuclide, which decay to the ground state by emission of γ rays.

emission is observed only when a nuclear reaction produces a daughter nuclide that is in an excited state.

The naturally occurring radioactive isotopes of the heavier elements fall into chains of successive disintegrations, or decays, and all the species in one chain constitute a radioactive family, or series. Three of these series include most of the naturally radioactive elements of the periodic table. They are the **uranium series,** the **actinium series,** and the **thorium series.** Each series is characterized by a parent (first member) with a long half-life and a series of decay processes that ultimately leads to a stable end-product—that is, an isotope on the band of stability (Fig. 24.2). In all three series the end-product is an isotope of lead: $^{206}_{82}$Pb in the uranium series, $^{207}_{82}$Pb in the actinium series, and $^{208}_{82}$Pb in the thorium series.

The steps in the thorium decay series are given in Table 24.1 as an illustration of one natural chain of successive decays.

24 .7 Radioactive Dating

Radioactive Dating Using Carbon-14. The radioactivity of carbon-14 provides a method for dating objects that have been living matter. Carbon-14 is produced in the upper atmosphere by the reaction of nitrogen atoms with neutrons from cosmic rays in space.

$$^{14}_{7}\text{N} + ^{1}_{0}\text{n} \longrightarrow ^{14}_{6}\text{C} + ^{1}_{1}\text{H}$$

The $^{14}_{6}$C then reacts with oxygen molecules to form $^{14}_{6}\text{CO}_2$. Other isotopes of carbon (principally carbon-12) also react with oxygen to produce CO_2 molecules, each containing the requisite carbon isotope.

Plants and other organisms remove CO_2 from the atmosphere during photosynthesis, producing oxygen and incorporating into their tissues substances called carbohydrates that include glucose, $C_6H_{12}O_6$ (see Section 31.7).

$$6CO_2 + 6H_2O \longrightarrow C_6H_{12}O_6 + 6O_2 \tag{1}$$

A variety of oxidation–reduction reactions of oxygen with glucose and other organic substances then once again produce carbon dioxide and water. The carbon dioxide and water are returned to the atmosphere. For glucose, the reaction is the reverse of Equation (1).

$$C_6H_{12}O_6 + 6O_2 \longrightarrow 6CO_2 + 6H_2O \tag{2}$$

Table 24.1   **The Thorium Decay Series**

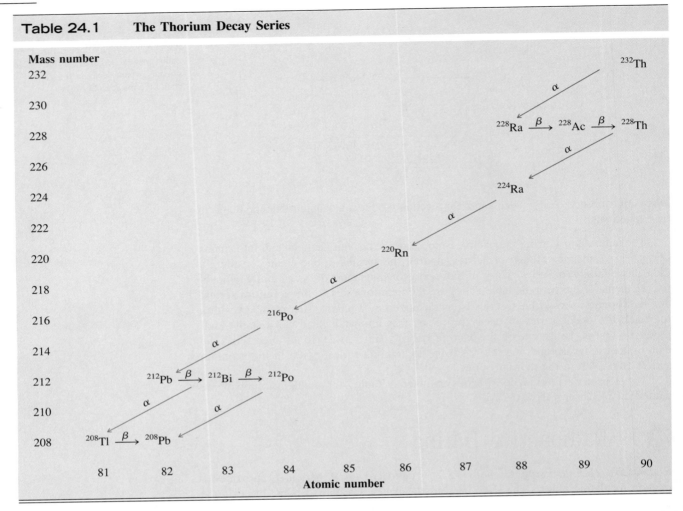

An equilibrium is thus established in the atmosphere and in the organism so that the concentrations of $^{14}_6CO_2$ and $^{12}_6CO_2$, and also the ratio of $^{14}_6C$ to $^{12}_6C$ ($^{14}_6C/^{12}_6C$), remain constant in the atmosphere and in plants and other organisms.

The incorporation of $^{14}_6CO_2$ and $^{12}_6CO_2$ into plants and other organisms is a regular part of the photosynthesis life cycle (Sections 22.8 and 31.14). The $^{14}_6C/^{12}_6C$ ratio found in the living portion of a plant is the same as the $^{14}_6C/^{12}_6C$ ratio in the atmosphere.

When the plant dies, it no longer participates in the photosynthesis life cycle. Because $^{12}_6C$ is a stable isotope and does not decay radioactively, its concentration does not change. Carbon-14 decays by β emission with a half-life of 5730 years (Appendix K).

$$^{14}_6C \longrightarrow {}^{14}_7N + {}^{\;\;0}_{-1}e$$

Thus the $^{14}_6C/^{12}_6C$ ratio begins to decrease, after the plant dies, with the gradual disappearance of $^{14}_6C$ by radioactive decay without its being replaced. This decrease in the ratio with time provides a measure of the time that has elapsed since the death of the plant (or other organism). For example, with the half-life of $^{14}_6C$ being 5730 years, if the $^{14}_6C/^{12}_6C$ ratio in a wooden object found in an archaeological dig is half what it is in a living tree, this indicates that the wooden object is 5730 years old.

The accuracy of this technique depends on the $^{14}_{6}CO_2/^{12}_{6}CO_2$ ratio in a living plant being the same now as it was in an earlier era, but this assumption is not strictly valid. Due to the increasing accumulation of CO_2 molecules (largely $^{12}_{6}CO_2$) in the atmosphere caused by combustion and other man-made processes on earth, the ratio of $^{14}_{6}CO_2$ to $^{12}_{6}CO_2$ in the atmosphere has changed significantly since 1945. This man-made increase in $^{12}_{6}CO_2$ in the atmosphere causes the $^{14}_{6}CO_2/^{12}_{6}CO_2$ ratio to decrease, and this in turn affects the ratio in currently living organisms on the earth. Fortunately, however, accurate correction factors have been determined from other data, such as tree dating via examination of annual growth rings. With these correction factors, accurate dates can be determined. Furthermore, highly accurate determinations of $^{14}_{6}C/^{12}_{6}C$ ratios can be obtained from very small samples (as little as a milligram) by the use of a mass spectrometer (see Section 5.6).

Radioactive Dating Using Nuclides Other than Carbon-14. Radioactive dating can also utilize other radioactive nuclides, such as $^{238}_{92}U$ (which decays in a series of steps to the stable isotope $^{206}_{82}Pb$) and $^{87}_{37}Rb$ (which decays to the stable isotope $^{87}_{38}Sr$ in one β-emission step). Both uranium-238 and rubidium-87 can be used for establishing the age of rocks and the approximate age of the earth from the ages of the oldest rocks.

To estimate the lower limit for the earth's age, scientists determine the age of various rocks and minerals, assuming that the earth must be at least as old as the rocks and minerals in its crust. One method, using rubidium-87 dating, is to measure the relative amounts of $^{87}_{37}Rb$ and $^{87}_{38}Sr$ in rock. $^{87}_{37}Rb$ decays to $^{87}_{38}Sr$ with a half-life of 4.7×10^{10} years. Thus 1 gram of $^{87}_{37}Rb$ would produce 0.5000 gram of $^{87}_{38}Sr$ and leave 0.5000 gram of $^{87}_{37}Rb$ after decaying for 47 billion years. Such a radioactive dating method in a rock formation in southwestern Greenland has shown this formation to have an age of nearly 3.8 billion years. This is one of the oldest known rocks on earth. The following example illustrates this type of determination.

One of the oldest known rock formations on earth (about 3.8 billion years old, from Greenland). The pocket knife is used to indicate scale.

A sample of a rock was found to contain 8.23 mg of $^{87}_{37}Rb$ and 0.47 mg of $^{87}_{38}Sr$. Calculate the age of the rock. The half-life of $^{87}_{37}Rb$ is 4.7×10^{10} yr.

Example 24.8

$$^{87}_{37}Rb \longrightarrow ^{87}_{38}Sr + ^{0}_{-1}e$$

Calculate the value of the decay rate constant for $^{87}_{37}Rb$, remembering that all radioactive decay is first-order.

$$k = \frac{0.693}{t_{1/2}} = \frac{0.693}{4.7 \times 10^{10} \text{ yr}} = 1.47 \times 10^{-11} \text{ yr}^{-1}$$

Calculate the number of moles of $^{87}_{37}Rb$ and $^{87}_{38}Sr$ found in the sample at time t.

$$8.23 \text{ mg} \times \frac{1 \text{ g}}{1000 \text{ mg}} \times \frac{1 \text{ mol}}{87 \text{ g}} = 9.46 \times 10^{-5} \text{ mol of } ^{87}_{37}Rb$$

$$0.47 \text{ mg} \times \frac{1 \text{ g}}{1000 \text{ mg}} \times \frac{1 \text{ mol}}{87 \text{ g}} = 5.40 \times 10^{-6} \text{ mol of } ^{87}_{38}Sr$$

Each mole of $^{87}_{37}Rb$ that disappeared (by radioactive decay of the $^{87}_{37}Rb$ that was initially present in the rock) produced 1 mol of $^{87}_{38}Sr$. Hence the number of moles of $^{87}_{37}Rb$ that disappeared by radioactive decay is equal to the number of moles of $^{87}_{38}Sr$ that was produced. This amount is the 5.40×10^{-6} mol of $^{87}_{38}Sr$ found in the rock at time t *if* all of the $^{87}_{38}Sr$ present at time t resulted from radioactive decay of $^{87}_{37}Rb$ and *no stron-*

Example 24.8 continued

tium-87 was present initially in the rock. If we are willing to make this assumption, we can calculate the total number of moles of rubidium-87 initially present in the rock:

Total number of moles of $^{87}_{37}Rb$ *initially present* in the rock at time t_0

= number of moles of $^{87}_{37}Rb$ at time t + number of moles
  of $^{87}_{37}Rb$ that decayed during the time interval $t - t_0$
= number of moles of $^{87}_{37}Rb$ measured at time t + number of moles
  of $^{87}_{38}Sr$ measured at time t
= 9.46×10^{-5} mol + 5.40×10^{-6} mol = 1.00×10^{-4} mol

The number of moles can be substituted for concentrations in the expression

$$\ln \frac{c_0}{c_t} = kt$$

Thus

$$\ln \frac{1.00 \times 10^{-4} \text{ mol}}{9.46 \times 10^{-5} \text{ mol}} = 1.47 \times 10^{-11} \, t$$

$$t = \left(\ln \frac{1.00 \times 10^{-4}}{9.46 \times 10^{-5}} \right) \left(\frac{1}{1.47 \times 10^{-11} \text{ yr}^{-1}} \right)$$

$$= 3.8 \times 10^9 \text{ yr} = 3.8 \text{ billion years} = \text{age of the rock sample}$$

Because this is the oldest rock known on earth, its age also provides an estimate for the age of the earth of about 4 billion years. Some other methods of determining the age of the earth similarly indicate an age of about 4 billion years.

It is important to remember that in performing the above calculation, we assumed that *all* of the stable isotope $^{87}_{38}Sr$ found in the rock at time t was due to radioactive decay of $^{87}_{37}Rb$. It is possible, however, that some of the $^{87}_{38}Sr$ measured in the rock at time t existed initially in the rock, at time t_0. If this were the case, it would introduce an error into the calculation. This is one of the reasons why experimental determinations of the age of various objects by radioactive dating may not be as accurate as the data imply. Furthermore, to justify extrapolating such calculations for the age of a rock in order to estimate the age of the earth, it is very important to have good reason to believe that the rock under investigation is one of the oldest rocks on earth. Therefore, any calculation such as the above (indicating the age of a rock as 3.8×10^9 years, for example) leads to rounded values such as "nearly 4 billion years" for the estimated age of the earth.

24.8 Synthesis of Nuclides

Atoms with stable nuclei can be converted to other atoms (**transmuted**) by bombardment with other nuclei or with high-speed particles. The first artificial nucleus was made in Lord Rutherford's laboratory in 1919. He bombarded nitrogen atoms with high-speed α particles emanating from a naturally radioactive isotope of radium and observed the reaction

$$^{14}_{7}N + ^{4}_{2}He \longrightarrow ^{17}_{8}O + ^{1}_{1}H \tag{1}$$

The $^{17}_8O$ and ^1_1H nuclei are stable, so this nuclear reaction does not lead to further changes.

Many artificially induced nuclear reactions produce unstable nuclei that then undergo radioactive decay, referred to as **artificial radioactivity.** For example, boron-10 reacts with an α particle to form nitrogen-13 and a neutron.

$$^{10}_5B + ^4_2He \longrightarrow ^{13}_7N + ^1_0n \qquad (2)$$

Nitrogen-13 is radioactive and decays by β^+ decay.

$$^{13}_7N \longrightarrow ^{13}_6C + \beta^+$$

In an abbreviated notation for **transmutation reactions,** the bombarding particle and the product particle are written in parentheses between the symbols for the reactant and product nuclides. Thus Equations (1) and (2) can be written as

$$^{14}_7N(\alpha, p)^{17}_8O \qquad and \qquad ^{10}_5B(\alpha, n)^{13}_7N$$

respectively, where α, p, and n are symbols for an α particle, a proton, and a neutron; $^{14}_7N$ and $^{10}_5B$ are symbols for the reactants; and $^{17}_8O$ and $^{13}_7N$ are symbols for the products.

Generally, the charged particles used to cause transmutation reactions are accelerated to the kinetic energies that will produce reactions by machines (**accelerators**) that use magnetic and electric fields to accelerate the particles. In all accelerators the particles move in a vacuum to avoid collisions with gas molecules.

Because neutrons are not charged, they cannot be accelerated in accelerators to the velocities necessary for many nuclear transmutations. When **high-speed neutrons** (neutrons that contain high kinetic energies) are required, they are usually obtained from radioactive decay reactions or from various nuclear reactions occurring in nuclear reactors (Section 24.11). Neutrons emitted in nuclear reactions usually have sufficiently high kinetic energies for transmutation reactions. In some applications, **low-speed neutrons** (referred to as **thermal neutrons**) are better than high-speed neutrons. An example is the use of thermal neutrons to initiate fission reactions in nuclear reactors (Sections 24.9 and 24.11).

Many known elements have been transmuted into other known elements. Also, a considerable number of new elements have been synthesized. Examples of these include element 43, technetium (Tc); element 85, astatine (At); element 87, francium (Fr); and element 61, promethium (Pm).

Prior to 1940 the heaviest known element was uranium, whose atomic number is 92. In 1940 McMillan and Abelson were able to make element 93, neptunium (Np), by bombarding uranium-238 with high-velocity neutrons. The nuclear reactions are

$$^{238}_{92}U + ^1_0n \longrightarrow ^{239}_{92}U$$

$$^{239}_{92}U \xrightarrow{23\ min} ^{239}_{93}Np + ^0_{-1}e$$

Neptunium-239 is also radioactive, with a half-life of 2.3 days, and decays to plutonium (Pu), whose atomic number is 94.

$$^{239}_{93}Np \longrightarrow ^{239}_{94}Pu + ^0_{-1}e$$

Elements 95 through 109 have also been prepared artificially. The elements beyond element 92 (uranium) are called **transuranium elements.** Elements 89 through 103 make up the **actinide series.** Element 109 was prepared in 1982 by a West German group who bombarded a target of bismuth-209 with accelerated nuclei of iron-58.

$$^{209}_{83}Bi + ^{58}_{26}Fe \longrightarrow ^{266}_{109}Une + ^1_0n$$

The researchers identified the element even though they made only one atom of it! The decay products of the atom are characteristic of those expected for element 109. It began to decay about 5×10^{-3} second after its formation, with the emission of an α particle and the formation of an isotope of element 107 that the same research team had first produced the preceding year.

$$^{266}_{109}\text{Une} \longrightarrow ^{262}_{107}\text{Uns} + ^{4}_{2}\text{He}$$

$$\searrow ^{258}_{105}\text{Unp} + ^{4}_{2}\text{He}$$

$$\downarrow \text{Electron capture}$$

$$^{258}_{104}\text{Unq} \longrightarrow \text{Smaller nuclei}$$

Equations describing the preparation of some other isotopes of the transuranium elements are given in Table 24.2.

The name *rutherfordium,* with the symbol Rf, has been suggested for element 104 by American scientists who synthesized the element. Soviet scientists, who also worked out the synthesis of the element, have suggested the name *kurchatovium.* It has been proposed that element 105 be named *hahnium,* with the symbol Ha, to honor Otto Hahn, the late German scientist who won the Nobel prize for the discovery of nuclear fission.

Both a Soviet and an American group have announced the synthesis of element 106, by quite different methods. The two groups have agreed not to propose any name for the element until it has been decided who will get credit for being the first to synthesize it. The failure of these two groups to reach agreement is responsible, in part, for the

Table 24.2		**Preparation of Some of the Transuranium Elements**	
Name	Symbol	Atomic Number	Reaction
Neptunium	Np	93	$^{238}_{92}\text{U} + ^{1}_{0}\text{n} \longrightarrow ^{239}_{93}\text{Np} + ^{0}_{-1}\text{e}$
Plutonium	Pu	94	$^{238}_{92}\text{U} + ^{2}_{1}\text{H} \longrightarrow ^{238}_{93}\text{Np} + 2\,^{1}_{0}\text{n}$
			$^{238}_{93}\text{Np} \longrightarrow ^{238}_{94}\text{Pu} + ^{0}_{-1}\text{e}$
Americium	Am	95	$^{239}_{94}\text{Pu} + ^{1}_{0}\text{n} \longrightarrow ^{240}_{95}\text{Am} + ^{0}_{-1}\text{e}$
Curium	Cm	96	$^{239}_{94}\text{Pu} + ^{4}_{2}\text{He} \longrightarrow ^{242}_{96}\text{Cm} + ^{1}_{0}\text{n}$
Berkelium	Bk	97	$^{241}_{95}\text{Am} + ^{4}_{2}\text{He} \longrightarrow ^{243}_{97}\text{Bk} + 2\,^{1}_{0}\text{n}$
Californium	Cf	98	$^{242}_{96}\text{Cm} + ^{4}_{2}\text{He} \longrightarrow ^{245}_{98}\text{Cf} + ^{1}_{0}\text{n}$
Einsteinium	Es	99	$^{238}_{92}\text{U} + 15^{1}_{0}\text{n} \longrightarrow ^{253}_{99}\text{Es} + 7\,^{0}_{-1}\text{e}$
Fermium	Fm	100	$^{239}_{94}\text{Pu} + 15^{1}_{0}\text{n} \longrightarrow ^{254}_{100}\text{Fm} + 6\,^{0}_{-1}\text{e}$
Mendelevium	Md	101	$^{253}_{99}\text{Es} + ^{4}_{2}\text{He} \longrightarrow ^{256}_{101}\text{Md} + ^{1}_{0}\text{n}$
Nobelium	No	102	$^{246}_{96}\text{Cm} + ^{12}_{6}\text{C} \longrightarrow ^{254}_{102}\text{No} + 4\,^{1}_{0}\text{n}$
Lawrencium	Lr	103	$^{250}_{98}\text{Cf} + ^{11}_{5}\text{B} \longrightarrow ^{257}_{103}\text{Lr} + 4\,^{1}_{0}\text{n}$
Unnilquadium	Unq	104	$^{249}_{98}\text{Cf} + ^{12}_{6}\text{C} \longrightarrow ^{257}_{104}\text{Unq} + 4\,^{1}_{0}\text{n}$
Unnilpentium	Unp	105	$^{249}_{98}\text{Cf} + ^{15}_{7}\text{N} \longrightarrow ^{260}_{105}\text{Unp} + 4\,^{1}_{0}\text{n}$
Unnilhexium	Unh	106	$^{206}_{82}\text{Pb} + ^{54}_{24}\text{Cr} \longrightarrow ^{257}_{106}\text{Unh} + 3\,^{1}_{0}\text{n}$
			$^{249}_{98}\text{Cf} + ^{18}_{8}\text{O} \longrightarrow ^{263}_{106}\text{Unh} + 4\,^{1}_{0}\text{n}$

systematic names suggested by the International Union of Pure and Applied Chemistry (see Section 6.1 and Table 24.2) for the elements beyond element 103.

Elements 106, 107, 108, and 109 are very unstable. Whether or not additional elements can be made cannot be predicted at this time, but there is reason to hope that some can be, particularly within the range of elements 110–115.

Glenn Seaborg, an eminent American chemist and Nobel prize winner, has suggested extending the periodic table to include new elements for which the synthesis might be possible (Table 24.3). (It may be helpful at this point to review the material in

Table 24.3   Predicted Locations of New Elements in the Periodic Table

																	s
																1 H	2 He

s

									d					*p*			
1 H																	
3 Li	4 Be											5 B	6 C	7 N	8 O	9 F	10 Ne
11 Na	12 Mg											13 Al	14 Si	15 P	16 S	17 Cl	18 Ar
19 K	20 Ca	21 Sc	22 Ti	23 V	24 Cr	25 Mn	26 Fe	27 Co	28 Ni	29 Cu	30 Zn	31 Ga	32 Ge	33 As	34 Se	35 Br	36 Kr
37 Rb	38 Sr	39 Y	40 Zr	41 Nb	42 Mo	43 Tc	44 Ru	45 Rh	46 Pd	47 Ag	48 Cd	49 In	50 Sn	51 Sb	52 Te	53 I	54 Xe
55 Ca	56 Ba	[57–71] *	72 Hf	73 Ta	74 W	75 Re	76 Os	77 Ir	78 Pt	79 Au	80 Hg	81 Tl	82 Pb	83 Bi	84 Po	85 At	86 Rn
87 Fr	88 Ra	[89–103] †	104 Unq	105 Unp	106 Unh	107 Uns	108 Uno	109 Une	110	111	112	113	114	115	116	117	118
119	120	[121–153] ‡	154	155	156	157	158	159	160	161	162	163	164	165	166	167	168

f

	57 La	58 Ce	59 Pr	60 Nd	61 Pm	62 Sm	63 Eu	64 Gd	65 Tb	66 Dy	67 Ho	68 Er	69 Tm	70 Yb	71 Lu
*Lanthanide series															
†Actinide series	89 Ac	90 Th	91 Pa	92 U	93 Np	94 Pu	95 Am	96 Cm	97 Bk	98 Cf	99 Es	100 Fm	101 Md	102 No	103 Lr

g   *f*

	121	122	123	124	137	138	139	140	141	150	151	152	153
‡Super actinides													

Chapter 5 on the filling of shells and subshells by electrons.) Element 104 is the first element of the **transactinide series** (that is, the elements beyond the actinide series). The chemical properties of these elements can be predicted by the method of Mendeleev—comparison with their lighter analogs in the table. Element 104 should be an analog of hafnium; 105 an analog of tantalum; and so on to element 118, a noble gas analogous to radon.

The most striking feature of Seaborg's extension of the periodic table is the addition of another inner transition series of elements starting with atomic number 121 and extending through atomic number 153. He calls this grouping the **superactinide series.** This series would include elements, after element 121, in which the $5g$ orbitals fill (see Table 5.2). Element 121 would receive the first $7d$ electron (the $n = 7$ major shell being the second from the outside) and would be analogous to scandium, yttrium, lanthanum, and actinium. The first of eighteen $5g$ electrons could enter at element 122, for which the $n = 5$ shell is the fourth from the outside; the eighteenth $5g$ electron would enter at element 139. This would presumably be followed by the addition of fourteen $6f$ electrons (the third major shell from the outside) for elements 140 through 153, making this latter series an inner transition series analogous to the lanthanide and actinide series. Following the superactinide inner transition series, elements 154 through 168 would be analogous to elements 104 through 118, with the addition of the remaining ten $7d$ electrons in the second major shell from the outside and the $6p$ electrons in the outermost major shell. Element 168 would be another noble gas—or should we expect a noble liquid?

Although the foregoing proposals by Seaborg on possible electron configurations for elements not yet synthesized are speculative, they do represent a logical extrapolation from the electron configurations for elements that are now known.

Nuclear Energy and Other Applications

24.9 Nuclear Fission

The greater stability of the nuclei of elements with mass numbers of intermediate values suggested the possibility of spontaneous decomposition of the less stable nuclei of the heavy elements into more stable fragments of approximately half their sizes. Two German scientists, Hahn and Strassman, reported in 1939 that uranium-235 atoms bombarded with slow-moving neutrons split into smaller fragments, consisting of elements near the middle of the periodic table, and several neutrons. This process is called fission. Among the fission products (often referred to as "fission fragments") were barium, krypton, lanthanum, and cerium, all of which have more stable nuclei than uranium-235.

$$^{235}_{92}\text{U} + {}^{1}_{0}\text{n} \longrightarrow \quad \text{fission fragments} \ + \text{neutrons} + \text{energy}$$
$$\text{Isotopes of Ba, Kr, etc.}$$

The sum of the atomic numbers of the fission products is 92, the atomic number of the original uranium nucleus. A loss of mass of about 0.2 amu per uranium atom occurs in these fission reactions. This mass is converted into a fantastic quantity of energy, which can be calculated from the Einstein equation $E = mc^2$ (Section 24.2). The fission of 1 pound of uranium-235, for example, produces about 2.5 million times as much energy as is produced by burning 1 pound of coal.

Fission of a uranium-235 nucleus produces, on the average, 2.5 neutrons as well as fission fragments. These neutrons may cause the fission of other uranium-235 atoms, which in turn provide more neutrons, setting up a **chain reaction.** Nuclear fission becomes self-sustaining when the number of neutrons produced by fission equals or exceeds the number of neutrons absorbed by splitting nuclei plus the number lost to the surroundings. The amount of a fissionable material that will support a self-sustaining chain reaction is called a **critical mass.** The critical mass of a fissionable material depends on the shape of the sample as well as on the type of material.

An atomic bomb contains several pounds of fissionable material, $^{235}_{92}$U or $^{239}_{94}$Pu, and an explosive device for compressing it quickly into a small volume. When fissionable material is in small pieces, the proportion of neutrons that escape at the relatively large surface area is great, and a chain reaction does not take place. When the small pieces of fissionable material are brought together quickly to form a body with a mass larger than the critical mass, the relative number of escaping neutrons decreases, and a chain reaction and explosion result. The explosion of an atomic bomb can release more energy than the explosion of thousands of tons of TNT.

Chain reactions of fissionable materials can be controlled without explosion in a nuclear reactor for the production of energy (Fig. 24.4 and Section 24.11).

㉔.10 Nuclear Fusion

The process of combining very light nuclei into heavier nuclei is also accompanied by the conversion of mass into large amounts of energy. The process is called **fusion** and is the focus of an intensive research effort to develop a practical thermonuclear reactor

Figure 24.4

The core of a research reactor at Sandia National Laboratories, seen looking down through shielding water. The characteristic blue glow is Cerenkov radiation, which is light produced by rapidly moving charged particles.

The lab setup used by Drs. Pons and Fleischmann at the University of Utah for their experiments in cold fusion.

(Section 24.13). The principal source of energy in the sun is the fusion reaction in which four hydrogen nuclei are fused into one helium nucleus.

$$4\ {}^1_1\text{H} \longrightarrow {}^4_2\text{He} + 2\ {}^0_{+1}\text{e}\ (\beta^+)$$

Four hydrogen nuclei have a mass that is 0.7% greater than that of a helium nucleus; this extra matter is converted into energy during atomic fusion. By contrast, only about 0.1% of the mass of the fuel is converted into energy during atomic fission.

It has been found that a deuteron, ${}^2_1\text{H}$, and a triton, ${}^3_1\text{H}$, which are the nuclei of the heavy isotopes of hydrogen, undergo fusion at extremely high temperatures (**thermonuclear fusion**) to form a helium nucleus and a neutron.

$$^2_1\text{H} + {}^3_1\text{H} \longrightarrow {}^4_2\text{He} + {}^1_0\text{n}$$

This change is accompanied by a conversion of a portion of the mass into energy and is one of the nuclear reactions of the hydrogen bomb. In a hydrogen bomb, a fission bomb (uranium or plutonium) is exploded inside a charge of deuterium and tritium to provide the temperature of many millions of degrees required for the fusion of the deuterium and tritium.

If the fusion of heavy isotopes of hydrogen could be controlled at reasonably low temperatures, hydrogen from the water of the oceans could supply immense amounts of energy for future generations. Thus a great deal of excitement followed the announcement in early 1989 that such ''cold fusion'' had been accomplished via electrolysis of deuterium oxide (D_2O, heavy water) in the presence of a palladium cathode at room temperature.

In the experiments that led to the announcement, the researchers filled a large glass tube with heavy water and dissolved lithium metal in it to produce an electrolytic solution of lithium deuteroxide, LiOD. Within this solution, they placed a platinum wire anode coiled around a palladium cathode. An electric current was applied between the two electrodes, bringing about electrolytic decomposition of the water into deuterium gas, D_2, and oxygen gas, O_2. In addition, production of heat and (in some experiments) radiation were observed. The deuterium, which formed at the cathode, was thought to diffuse into the palladium rod, gradually filling vacant sites in the palladium lattice over a period of days or weeks. The researchers proposed that the resulting compression of the deuterium atoms tightly within the lattice led to their fusing, with a resultant energy release that appeared to be greater than could be explained if only ordinary chemical reactions were occurring.

The announcement excited scientists and others because of the potential importance of the procedure as a simple, inexpensive method for producing clean energy in large quantities at low temperatures without significant radiation problems; but at the same time, skepticism arose. Prior accomplishments of nuclear fusion had required difficult and expensive conditions that involved temperatures of millions of degrees brought about by nuclear fission or laser techniques (Section 24.13).

Immediately following the announcement, attempts were made to replicate (reproduce) cold fusion in other laboratories, and many of these attempts were unsuccessful. Several seemed to indicate some excess energy production, but it was not clear that the excess energy was the result of nuclear fusion. Laboratories also could not agree whether the expected radiation products of tritium (${}^3_1\text{H}$), helium-4, and neutrons were produced in sufficient quantity to justify concluding that fusion had occurred. At the time of this writing, the source of any excess energy is not understood. Many scientists still doubt that fusion occurred and question whether the process can lead to feasible commercial energy production, but a consensus seems to be developing that *something* interesting is going on that warrants further investigation.

24.11 Nuclear Power Reactors

Any **nuclear reactor** (Fig. 24.5) that produces power via the fission of uranium or plutonium by bombardment with slow neutrons must have at least five components (Fig. 24.6).

1. A Nuclear Fuel. A fissionable isotope (commonly $^{235}_{92}U$, $^{233}_{92}U$, or $^{239}_{94}Pu$) must be present in sufficient quantity to provide a self-sustaining chain reaction. Most reactors in the United States use pellets of the uranium oxide U_3O_8, in which the concentration of uranium-235 has been increased (enriched) from its natural level to about 3%. The U_3O_8 pellets are contained in a tube (a fuel rod) of a protective material, usually a zirconium alloy. The core of a typical nuclear power reactor in the United States has about 40,000 kilograms of enriched U_3O_8 contained in several hundred fuel rods.

Naturally occurring uranium is a mixture of several isotopes; uranium-238 is the most abundant. About 1 in every 140 uranium atoms is the uranium-235 isotope. To obtain a higher concentration of uranium-235, it is necessary to separate uranium-235. The most successful method separates $^{235}_{92}UF_6$ from $^{238}_{92}UF_6$ by fractional diffusion of large volumes of gaseous UF_6 at low pressure through porous barriers. This method is based on the fact that the lighter $^{235}_{92}UF_6$ molecules diffuse through a porous barrier faster than the heavier $^{238}_{92}UF_6$ molecules (Graham's Law, Sections 10.12 and 10.14). The enriched UF_6 is then chemically converted to U_3O_8.

2. A Moderator. Neutrons produced by nuclear reactions move too fast to cause fission. They must be slowed down before they will be absorbed by the fuel and produce additional nuclear reactions. In a reactor, neutrons are slowed by collision with the

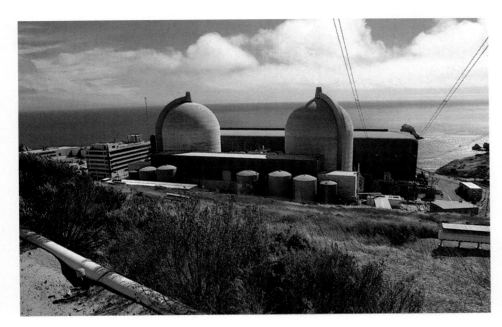

Figure 24.5

A commercial nuclear plant for generating electricity. The two large, domed structures are the containment buildings that house the reactors.

Figure 24.6

A light-water nuclear reactor. This reactor uses pressurized liquid water at 280°C and 150 atm as both a coolant and a moderator.

Cover (removable for refueling)

Control rods

Water outlet (320°C)

Fuel rods

Steel shield

Water inlet (280°C)

Concrete shield

Coolant water and moderator

nuclei of a moderator such as heavy water (D$_2$O; see Section 22.3), graphite, carbon dioxide, or light (ordinary) water. These materials are used because they do not react with or absorb neutrons. Most reactors in operation in the United States use light water as the moderator. Graphite is used in reactors in many other countries.

3. A Coolant. The coolant carries the heat from the fission reaction to an external boiler and turbine, where it is transformed into electricity (Fig. 24.7). The coolant is a gas or liquid that is pumped through the reactor core. Some coolants also serve as moderators.

Figure 24.7

A power-generating plant employing a nuclear power reactor. In a coal-fired power plant the steam is generated in a boiler. Note that the reactor coolant is contained in a closed system and does not come in contact with outside cooling water. The reactor shielding has been omitted for clarity.

Containment vessel

Generator

Steam

Turbine

Coolant

Coolant

Hot water (waste heat)

Outside cooling water

Water

Condenser

Pump

Pump

Reactor

Heat exchanger

Electricity generation

4. A Control System. A nuclear reactor is controlled by adjusting the number of slow neutrons present to keep the rate of the chain reaction at a safe level. Control is maintained by control rods that absorb neutrons. Rods containing cadmium or boron-10 are often used. Boron-10, for example, absorbs neutrons by the reaction $^{10}_{5}B(n, \alpha)^{7}_{3}Li$. The chain reaction can be completely stopped by inserting all of the control rods into the core between the fuel rods.

5. A Shield and Containment System. A nuclear reactor produces neutrons and other particles by radioactive decay of the products resulting from fusion. In addition, a reactor is very hot, and high pressures result from the circulation of water or another coolant through it. A reactor must withstand high temperatures and pressures and must protect operating personnel from the radiation. A reactor container often consists of three parts: (1) the reactor vessel, a steel shell that is 3–20 centimeters thick and absorbs much of the radiation produced by the reactor; (2) a main shield of 1–3 meters of high-density concrete; and (3) a personnel shield of lighter materials to absorb γ rays and X rays for the protection of the operators. In addition, reactors are often covered with a steel or concrete dome designed to contain any radioactive materials released by a reactor accident (Fig. 24.5).

The importance of a containment vessel is amply illustrated by two accidents at nuclear reactors. In March 1979, the cooling system of one of the reactors at the Three Mile Island plant in Pennsylvania failed, and the cooling water spilled from the reactor onto the floor of the containment building. The temperature of the core climbed to at least 2200°C, and the upper portion of the core began to melt. In addition, the zirconium alloy cladding of the fuel rods began to react with steam and produced hydrogen.

$$Zr(s) + 2H_2O(g) \longrightarrow ZrO_2(s) + 2H_2(g)$$

The hydrogen accumulated in the confinement building and it was feared that there was danger of an explosion of a mixture of hydrogen and air in the building. Consequently, hydrogen gas and radioactive gases (primarily krypton and xenon) were vented from the building. Within a week, cooling water circulation was restored and the core began to cool. The plant was closed for nearly 10 years during the cleanup process.

Although no discharge of radioactive material is desirable, the discharge of radioactive krypton and xenon, such as occurred at the Three Mile Island plant, is among the most tolerable. These gases readily disperse in the atmosphere and thus do not produce highly radioactive areas. Moreover, they are noble gases and are not absorbed into plant and animal matter in the food chain. Effectively none of the heavy elements of the core of the reactor were released into the environment, and no cleanup of the area outside of the containment building was necessary.

A second major nuclear accident occurred in April 1986 at the V. I. Lenin power plant near Chernobyl in the Ukraine. While operating at low power during an unauthorized experiment with some of its safety devices shut off, one of the reactors at the plant became unstable. Its chain reaction became uncontrollable and increased to a level far beyond that for which the reactor was designed. The steam pressure in the reactor went to between 100 and 500 times the full power pressure and ruptured the reactor. Because the reactor was not enclosed in a containment building, the hot core was exposed to the environment. In the initial burst, a large amount of radioactive material spewed out, and additional fission products were released as the graphite moderator of the core continued to burn. The fire was controlled, but a total of 203 plant workers and firemen developed acute radiation sickness, and 32 died. The reactor has since been encapsulated in concrete, and, after a year of decontamination of the reactor site and surrounding countryside, other reactors at the plant were restarted and residents began returning to towns and villages in the area. However, in 1989 significant radiation problems were still found to persist in the area, and in 1990 area residents were again evacuated.

It should be noted that the reactors used in some places in the Soviet Union, including Chernobyl, are unique. They are the only reactors that are designed with potential low power instability. These reactors have been modified since the accident to reduce the risk of a recurrence.

The energy produced by a reactor fueled with enriched uranium results from the fission of $^{235}_{92}U$ (Section 24.9) as well as from the fission of $^{239}_{94}Pu$. Plutonium-239 forms from $^{238}_{92}U$ present in the fuel (Section 24.8). In any nuclear reactor, only about 0.1% of the mass of the fuel is converted into energy. The other 99.9% remains in the fuel rods as fission products and unused fuel. All of the fission products absorb neutrons, and after a period of several months to a year, depending on the reactor, the fission products must be removed by changing the fuel rods. Otherwise, the concentration of these fission products would increase until the reactor could no longer operate because of their absorption of neutrons.

Spent fuel rods contain a variety of products, consisting of unstable nuclei ranging in atomic number from 25 to 60, some transuranium elements, including $^{239}_{94}Pu$ and $^{241}_{95}Am$, and unreacted $^{235}_{92}U$ and $^{238}_{92}U$. The unstable nuclei and the transuranium elements give the spent fuel a dangerously high level of radioactivity. The long-lived isotopes $^{90}_{38}Sr$ and $^{137}_{55}Cs$ and the shorter-lived isotope $^{131}_{53}I$ are particularly dangerous because they can be incorporated into human bodies if the radioactive material is dispersed in the environment. Consequently, it is absolutely essential that this material never be released into the biosphere. It takes about 400 years for the radioactivity of $^{90}_{38}Sr$ and $^{137}_{55}Cs$ to decrease to a reasonably safe level. Other nuclides such as $^{241}_{95}Am$ and $^{239}_{94}Pu$ have much longer half-lives and require thousands of years to decay to a safe level. The ultimate fate of the nuclear reactor as a significant source of energy in the United States probably rests on whether or not a scientifically and politically satisfactory technique for processing and storing the components of spent fuel rods can be developed.

24.12 Breeder Reactors

A **breeder reactor** is a nuclear reactor that produces more fissionable material than it consumes. Because the supply of naturally occurring uranium is limited (some estimates suggest that the known reserves will last for only another 50 years of full-scale use), the conversion of nonfissionable material to nuclear fuel in a breeder reactor may provide a long-term energy supply. The breeder reactor is constructed with a blanket of $^{238}_{92}U$ or $^{232}_{90}Th$, each of which is much more plentiful than $^{235}_{92}U$, surrounding the core of fissionable material. Extra neutrons produced by the fission in the core are captured by the blanket to form (breed) more fissionable atoms.

$^{238}_{92}U$ produces the fissionable nuclide $^{239}_{94}Pu$ according to the reactions described in Section 24.8. $^{232}_{90}Th$ produces the fissionable nuclide $^{233}_{92}U$ by the following series of reactions:

$$^{232}_{90}Th + ^{1}_{0}n \longrightarrow ^{233}_{90}Th$$

$$^{233}_{90}Th \xrightarrow{23 \text{ min}} ^{233}_{91}Pa + ^{0}_{-1}e$$

$$^{233}_{91}Pa \xrightarrow{27 \text{ days}} ^{233}_{92}U + ^{0}_{-1}e$$

Experimental breeder reactors are in operation in the United States, Great Britain, the Soviet Union, and France.

Breeder reactors present challenges in addition to those outlined in Section 24.11. Not only must spent fuel be stored, but the blanket of fertile material must be processed (by remote control) to separate the radioactive fuel from other radioactive by-products, and the large amounts of plutonium produced must be safely stored. Plutonium-239 decays with a half-life of 24,000 years by α emission; thus it will remain in the biosphere for a very long time if it is dispersed. Plutonium is one of the most toxic substances known; estimates of a fatal dose are as low as 1 microgram (10^{-6} g).

24.13 Fusion Reactors

A fusion reactor is a nuclear reactor in which fusion reactions of light nuclei (Section 24.10) are controlled. At the time of this writing, there are no self-sustaining fusion reactors operating in the world, although small-scale fusion reactions have been run for very brief periods.

Fusion reactions thus far require very high temperatures—about 10^8 K. At these temperatures all molecules dissociate into atoms, and the atoms ionize, forming a new state of matter called a **plasma.** Because no solid materials are stable at 10^8 K, a plasma cannot be contained by mechanical devices. Two techniques to contain a plasma at the density and temperature necessary for a fusion reaction to occur are currently under study. The techniques involve containment by a magnetic field (Fig. 24.8) and by the use of focused laser beams (Fig. 24.9).

After a plasma of hydrogen isotopes is generated and contained, it undergoes fusion reactions when the temperature exceeds about 10^8 K. One such reaction is

$$\ce{^2_1H + ^3_1H \longrightarrow ^4_2He + ^1_0n} \tag{1}$$

which proceeds with a mass loss of 0.0188 amu, corresponding to the release of 1.69×10^9 kilojoules per mole of $\ce{^4_2He}$ formed. Deuterium ($\ce{^2_1H}$) is available from heavy water.

Figure 24.8

The experimental fusion reactor at Princeton. The plasma in this device is contained by a magnetic field.

Figure 24.9

This bank of lasers produces the very intense light necessary to induce fusion.

Tritium ($^3_1$H) can be prepared by reaction of lithium with the neutrons from the fusion reaction.

$$^1_0n + ^6_3Li \longrightarrow ^3_1H + ^4_2He \tag{2}$$

㉔.14 Additional Applications of Radioisotopes

Radioactive isotopes have the same chemical properties as stable isotopes of the same element, so we can use them as a label to track compounds containing them by monitoring their radioactive emissions. When used in this way, they are referred to as **radioactive tracers.** Radioactive isotopes are also used in many other applications when a source of radiation is needed. In this section we will discuss selected uses of radioactive tracers and number of other applications of radioactive materials, including treatment of cancer and study of the mechanisms and kinetics of chemical reactions.

Applications in Medicine. Many radioactive isotopes are used as diagnostic tracers in medicine. Four typical examples are technetium-99 ($^{99}_{43}$Tc), thallium-201 ($^{201}_{81}$Tl), iodine-131 ($^{131}_{53}$I), and sodium-24 ($^{24}_{11}$Na). After injection, technetium-99 is absorbed preferentially by certain damaged tissues, such as those in the heart, liver, and lungs. The location of the technetium, and hence the damaged tissue, can be determined by detecting the γ rays emitted by the technetium isotope. Thallium-201 becomes concentrated in healthy heart tissue, so the two isotopes, $^{99}_{43}$Tc and $^{201}_{81}$Tl, are used together to study damage in heart tissue. Iodine-131 becomes concentrated in the thyroid gland, the liver, and some parts of the brain. It can therefore be used to monitor goiter and other thyroid problems and liver and brain tumors. Salt solutions containing sodium-24 are injected into the bloodstream to help physicians follow the flow of blood and locate obstructions in the circulatory system. Other radioisotopes used as tracers in medicine are $^{133}_{54}$Xe (lungs), $^{32}_{15}$P (eyes, tumors, liver), and $^{51}_{24}$Cr and $^{59}_{26}$Fe (red blood cells).

In some cases, the same isotope used as a tracer can also be used, in higher doses, as treatment. For example, iodine-131 is effective in the treatment of thyroid cancer when it arrives at the site, as well as in its diagnostic use as a tracer. The radiation from the decay of iodine-131 destroys cancer cells at a faster rate than healthy cells. The treatment of cancer by injected radioisotopes is one form of **chemotherapy.** An example of

A radioisotopic tracer scan used in medicine.

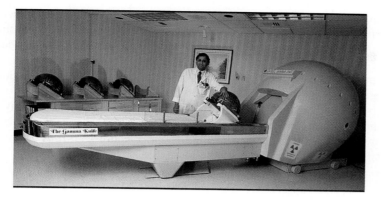

A cobalt-60 machine used in treatment of cancer.

radiation therapy (wherein the isotope is not injected into the body but radiation from it is delivered externally) is the use of γ-ray radiation from $^{60}_{27}Co$ for the treatment of various forms of cancer, including leukemia. Cobalt-60 has replaced X rays in many cases in the treatment of cancer.

Applications in Agriculture. Radioisotopes are used in such diverse ways as to label fertilizers in studies of nutrient uptake by plants and crop growth, to facilitate investigations of digestive and milk-producing processes in cows, and to make possible many other agricultural studies on the growth and metabolism of animals and plants.

Radioisotopes are also used in agriculture to determine the mechanisms of reactions. An example is the study of photosynthesis. The overall reaction (Section 24.7) is

$$6CO_2(g) + 6H_2O(l) \longrightarrow C_6H_{12}O_6(s) + 6O_2(g)$$

but the reaction is more complex, proceeding through a series of steps in which various organic compounds are produced. In studies of the pathway of this reaction, plants were exposed to CO_2 containing $^{14}_6C$. At regular intervals, the plants were analyzed to determine which organic compounds contained $^{14}_6C$ and how much of each compound was present. From the time sequence in which the compounds appeared and the amount of each present at given time intervals, scientists learned more about the pathway of the reaction.

Applications in Industry. Industrial applications of radioactive materials are diverse. They include determining the thickness of films and thin metal sheets by exploiting the penetration abilities of various types of radiation. Tracers are used in determining the effects of oils and oil additives on engine wear during actual engine operation. The metal in pistons, piston rings, bearings, and other engine parts is labeled with radioactive isotopes of the metal. As the metal wears off, it goes into the oil and the additives, where the radioactive emission is continuously monitored. Flaws in metals either intended for structural purposes or already in place in bridges or other structures can be detected by using high-energy gamma rays from cobalt-60 in a fashion similar to the way X rays are used to examine the human body.

Applications in Research. A number of research applications in medicine, agriculture, and industry have already been mentioned. In research laboratories, one of the most active pursuits is the study of mechanisms and kinetics of reactions. In these investigations, an element is labeled and its path traced from reactant to products during the course of a reaction.

Miscellaneous Applications. Gamma radiation of foods can kill larvae, insects, and the parasites that cause trichinosis in pork. It also helps in the preservation of foods for storage. Some chemicals used to preserve foods in the past have been shown to have adverse effects. Thus irradiation may prove to be a better method. Many studies are under way to determine whether the method is safe and whether it has any deleterious effects on food.

One method of controlling flies is to sterilize male flies by γ-ray radiation so that females breeding with those flies do not produce offspring.

Americium-241, an α emitter with a half-life of 458 years, is used in tiny amounts in ionization-type smoke detectors. The α emissions from the $^{241}_{95}$Am ionize the air between two electrode plates in the ionizing chamber (Section 24.15). A battery supplies a potential that causes movement of the ions, thus creating a small electric current. When enough smoke enters the chamber, the movement of the ions is impeded, reducing the conductivity of the air. This causes a marked drop in the current, triggering an alarm.

A somewhat different use of radioisotopes is in the conversion of heat produced by the radioactive decay of the plutonium isotope, $^{238}_{94}$Pu, to electrical energy in long-lived batteries, such as those used in long space fights to other planets.

Radioactive Emissions and the Environment

㉔.15 Ionization of Matter by Radiation

The increased use of radioisotopes has led to increased concern over the effects of these materials on matter, especially in biological systems. Some radioactive elements are sources of high-energy particles. Energy transferred to biological cells can break chemical bonds and ionize molecules, thereby causing malfunctions in the normal processes occurring in the cells. The most serious biological damage from radioactive emissions results from the ability of some of these emissions to ionize and fragment molecules. For example, alpha and beta particles emitted from nuclear decay reactions possess much higher energies than ordinary chemical bond energies. When these particles strike and penetrate matter, they give energy to molecules, removing electrons and producing ions and molecular fragments that are extremely reactive. In a biological system, this can seriously disrupt the normal operations of the cells.

The ability of various kinds of emissions to cause ionization varies greatly, and some particles have almost no tendency to produce ionization. Alpha particles have about 2 times the ionizing power of fast-moving neutrons, about 10 times that of β particles, and about 20 times that of γ rays and X rays.

The magnitude of the difference is very large between the biological effects of nonionizing radiation (for example, light and microwaves) and ionizing radiation (for example, α and β particles, γ rays, X rays, and high-energy ultraviolet radiation). The effect of energy absorbed from nonionizing radiation is principally an increase in the temperature of the system. Such radiation speeds up the movement of atoms and molecules, which is equivalent to heating the sample. Biological systems are sensitive to heat, as we all know from touching hot surfaces or spending a day at the beach in the sun. Nevertheless, a large amount of nonionizing radiation is necessary before dangerous levels are reached. Ionizing radiation is between 10 thousand and 10 billion times more dangerous than nonionizing radiation. Thus the most serious biological damage from radiation in a biological system comes from ionizing radiation.

24.16 Radiation Dosage

It is impossible to avoid exposure to ionizing radiation. Radiation is emitted both from natural sources and as a result of human activities. Two common units for measuring radiation doses are the **rad** (**r**adiation **a**bsorbed **d**ose) and the **rem** (**r**oentgen **e**quivalent in **m**an). The rad is the amount of radiation that results in absorption of 1×10^2 joules of energy per kilogram of tissue. The rem includes a biological factor referred to as the **RBE** (**r**elative **b**iological **e**ffectiveness).

$$\text{Number of rems} = \text{RBE} \times \text{number of rads}$$

Thus the rad indicates the specific energy of the radiation dose, whereas the rem takes into account both the energy and the biological effects of the type of radiation involved in the radiation dose.

We can compare the RBE values for particles when they are emitted by typical nuclear reactions (emission-level energy). The approximate values are listed below.

	RBE
X rays (photons)	1
Gamma rays	1
Beta particles	1
Neutrons	2.0–2.3
Protons	2.0–2.3
Alpha particles	10

The rad is the primary dosage unit in X-ray therapy, where the specific amount of radiation energy is the important factor. The rem is used for all particles, not just X rays. It is the primary dosage unit used in assessing biological damage from radiation encountered both from natural sources and as a result of human activities, ranging from normal exposures in our everyday lives to exposures from accidents in nuclear plants.

In the United States, the average annual dose of radiation received by one man or woman is about 0.100 rems from natural sources; an additional, more variable amount ranging from about 0.050 to 0.100 rems per person is attributable to human activities. The average, taking into account all sources, is about 0.190 rems. Natural sources include cosmic rays from the sun and a variety of radionuclides that enter our bodies when we breathe (for example, $^{14}_{6}C$, $^{85}_{36}Kr$, and $^{222}_{86}Rn$) or through the food chain (for example, $^{40}_{19}K$, $^{90}_{38}Sr$, and $^{131}_{53}I$). Radon-222 results from the $^{238}_{92}U$ decay series, in which $^{238}_{92}U$ (half-life 4.51×10^9 years) decays in a series of 14 steps ending in the stable

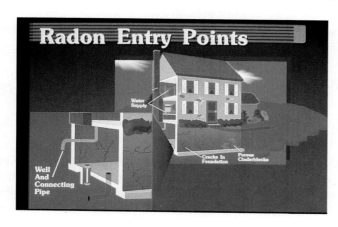

Radon-222 seeps into houses and other buildings from rocks below that contain uranium-238, a radon emitter. The radon enters through cracks in concrete foundations and basement floors, stone or porous cinderblock foundations, and openings for water and gas pipes.

Table 24.4	Estimated Annual Per Capita Exposure from Several Sources	
Emission Source	Annual Per Capita Exposure, in Rems
Cosmic radiation	0.050
Diagnostic X rays	0.050
Radiation from the earth	0.047
Radiotherapy (X rays, radioisotopes)	0.010
Radiation from the air	0.005
Consumer products and industry (color TV, industrial wastes, etc.)	0.005
Radioactive fallout	0.004
Building materials	0.003
Human tissues in the body (mainly $^{40}_{19}K$ and $^{90}_{38}Sr$)	0.001
Nuclear power plants	0.0002

isotope $^{206}_{82}Pb$. The product from the sixth step in the series is $^{222}_{86}Rn$, which is an α emitter with a half-life of 3.82 days. Radon-222 continually seeps into many homes and other structures from rocks below that contain uranium-238. This is an especially troubling problem in buildings so tightly insulated that radon is trapped inside the structure. Sources of radiation derived from human activities include dental and medical X rays, airplane flights (which are bombarded by increased concentrations of cosmic rays in the upper atmosphere), industrial and mining activities, and color TV. Table 24.4 gives the estimated average annual exposure per person from several sources.

Although properly operating nuclear plants contribute only a very small percentage of the total annual average per capita exposure, the potential for accidents releasing large quantities of radioactive materials and for the improper disposal of radioactive products from spent fuel elements must be addressed with care. Accordingly, significant and increasing efforts are devoted to ensuring that completely adequate safeguards are developed and utilized in all nuclear plants.

A short-term sudden dose of about 470 rems is estimated to have a 50% probability of causing the death of the victim within 30 days of exposure. Exposure to radioactive emissions has a cumulative effect in the body during a person's lifetime—another reason why it is important to avoid any unnecessary exposure to radiation.

24.17 Factors Involved in Radiation Damage

The extent of damage from radiation that can occur in a biological system depends upon not only the type of radiation, but also on the following factors.

1. **The Ability of Radiation to Penetrate into the Biological System.** Low-energy alpha particles are stopped by the skin and do not penetrate it, but they can cause great damage to the skin at the point of contact. With higher energies, alpha particles can depending on their energy, penetrate through the skin to the internal organs at any depth,

causing significant damage to the sensitive internal tissue. Similar damage occurs from alpha particles that are ingested into the body by inhalation or in other ways.

The extent of penetration of beta particles also depends on the amount of energy. Low-energy beta particles penetrate about 1 centimeter of tissue for each 3 million electron-volts (MeV) of energy. At comparable energies, the penetration of positrons is similar to that of beta particles. X rays (photons) and gamma rays at comparable energies penetrate to a greater extent than beta particles, and neutrons penetrate to a still greater extent. All particles, depending on their penetration, can severely damage both skin and internal tissue. Table 24.5 compares the penetrating abilities of some of the common types of radioactive emissions at comparable energies.

2. **The Energy of the Radiation.** The primary effect of the energy of a particle is to change the depth of penetration. Once a particle enters a site, the important issue becomes the ability of the particle to disseminate its energy. The extent of damage depends on the RBE (relative biological effectiveness—Section 24.16). Alpha and beta particles, though not as penetrating at low energies as most other particles at comparable

(left) A PET (positron emission tomography) machine. (right) A PET scan of the brain. Unlike conventional X rays, PET scans are not distorted by bone, and they have the additional advantage of being able to define very slight distinctions between tissues.

Table 24.5	Relative Penetration Abilities of Some Common Types of Radioactive Emissions[a]
Type of Particle	Penetration
Alpha (α)	Low
Beta (β)	Low to moderate
Positron (β^+)	Low to moderate
Proton	Low to moderate
X rays (photons)	High
Gamma (γ)	High
Neutron	Very high

[a] At comparable energies

The lead shielding used to protect operators of X-ray machines in hospitals.

energies, are extremely effective in causing ionization and can do immense damage. For example, people who work with plutonium-239, which is an α emitter, must have complete protection against inhaling even the tiniest amounts of the substance. Gamma rays, on the other hand, are deeply penetrating but are not as effective as alpha and beta particles in causing ionization.

3. Residence Time of the Radioactive Substance. How long a radioactive substance resides in a biological system can have a significant effect on the extent of the damage it causes. For example, the unreactive noble gas krypton-85 passes through the body so quickly that it has little time to cause damage by its beta emission. Strontium-90, on the other hand, being an alkaline earth metal similar to calcium, collects in the bone structure of the body, where it remains for a long time; its beta emission can cause bone cancer. X rays pass through the body in about a millionth of a second, and in the process they collide with a few cells. The principal effect of the X rays is on water molecules, to which the X rays transmit their energy, causing chemical reactions that produce unstable transition-state substances (see Section 14.7) known as free radicals. The free radicals then produce peroxides, which are lethal to cells.

24.18 Somatic and Genetic Radiation Damage

Radiation damage to organisms is classified as either somatic or genetic. **Somatic damage** affects the organism during its lifetime; for example, this damage killed the victims of the accident at Chernobyl (Section 24.11). With massive doses of radiation, the symptoms of somatic damage can appear immediately; with small doses, they may first appear years later.

Some cancer is brought about by damage to the mechanisms that control growth in cells, causing them to reproduce at an uncontrolled rate. The tissues most likely to be damaged by radiation are those that reproduce at a rapid rate, including cells of the gastrointestinal tract, bone marrow, and other blood-forming tissues. Damage to blood-forming tissues may result in the blood diseases called the *leukemias,* some of the major cancers resulting from radiation.

Short-term somatic effects after radiation often produce a decrease in the number of white blood cells, fatigue, nausea, and diarrhea. Large exposures can result in death from gastrointestinal failure, damage to the nervous system, or blood disorders.

Genetic damage harms offspring by damaging genes and chromosomes. Genetic damage, then, has longer-term effects than somatic damage, and in some cases it may take several generations for the genetic damage to become apparent.

For Review

Summary

Protons and neutrons, collectively called **nucleons,** are held together by a short-range, but very strong, force called the **nuclear force.** The **nuclear binding energy** can be calculated from the **mass defect** (the difference in mass between a nucleus and the nucleons of which it is composed) by the **Einstein equation,**

$$E = mc^2$$

The binding energy per nucleon is largest for the elements with mass numbers between 40 and 100; these are the most stable nuclei.

Stable nuclei have equal numbers of neutrons and protons or a few more neutrons than protons. Nuclei that deviate from stable neutron-to-proton ratios are radioactive, and they decay by losing one of several different kinds of particles. These include α **particles,** ^4_2He; β **particles,** $^0_{-1}e$; **positrons,** $^0_{+1}e$ (β^+); and **neutrons,** ^1_0n. Nuclear reactions also often involve γ **rays,** and some nuclei decay by **electron capture.** Each of these modes of decay leads to a new nucleus with a more stable neutron-to-proton ratio. The kinetics of the decay process are first-order. The **half-life** of a radioactive isotope is the time that is required for $\frac{1}{2}$ of the atoms in a sample to decay. Each radioactive nuclide has its own characteristic half-life.

The ages of various objects from earlier times can be determined by a process called **radioactive dating.**

New atoms can be produced by bombarding other atoms with nuclei or high-speed particles. The products of these **transmutation reactions** can be stable or radioactive. A number of artificial elements, including technetium, astatine, and the transuranium elements, have been produced in this way.

Nuclear power can be generated through **fission** (reactions in which a heavy nucleus breaks up into two or more lighter nuclei and several neutrons). Because the neutrons may induce additional fission reactions when they combine with other heavy nuclei, a **chain reaction** can result. Useful power is obtained if the fission process is carried out in a **nuclear reactor.** The conversion of light nuclei into heavier nuclei **(fusion)** also produces energy. At present, this energy has not been contained adequately and is too expensive to be feasible for commercial energy production.

Radioactive isotopes have many other practical uses in a wide variety of fields, including medicine, agriculture, industry, and research. In medicine, radioisotopes can be used as tracers in the diagnosis of disease or as therapy. The use, as treatment, of isotopes that are delivered from an external source is called radiation therapy; injecting isotopes into the body is one form of chemotherapy.

Key Terms and Concepts

alpha (α) decay (24.6)
α particle (24.5)
artificial radioactivity (24.8)
atomic number (24.1)
band of stability (24.3)
beta (β) decay (24.6)
β particle (24.5)
breeder reactor (24.12)
chain reaction (24.9)
chemotherapy (24.14)
critical mass (24.9)
daughter nuclide (24.6)
Einstein equation (24.2)
electron capture (24.6)
fission (24.9)

fusion (24.10)
fusion reactor (24.13)
gamma (γ) ray (24.5)
genetic damage (24.18)
half-life (24.4)
ionization by radioactive emissions (24.15)
mass defect (24.2)
mass number (24.1)
neutron (24.5)
nuclear binding energy (24.2)
nuclear force (24.1)
nuclear reactor (24.11)
nucleon (24.1)

nuclide (24.1)
parent nuclide (24.6)
positron (β^+) emission (24.5)
proton (24.5)
radiation damage (24.15–24.18)
radiation dosage (24.16)
radiation energy (24.17)
radiation penetration (24.17)
radiation therapy (24.14)
radioactive dating (24.7)
radioactive decay (24.6)
radioactive tracers (24.14)
somatic damage (24.18)
transmutation reaction (24.8)

Exercises

Answers for selected even-numbered exercises marked by red numbers appear at the end of the book. The worked-out solutions to all even-numbered exercises appear in the *Solutions Guide*.

1. Write a brief description or definition of each of the following.
   (a) nucleon   (f) nuclide
   (b) α particle   (g) mass number
   (c) β particle   (h) atomic number
   (d) positron   (i) electron capture
   (e) γ ray

2. Indicate the number of protons and neutrons in each of the following nuclei.
   (a) $^{14}_{7}N$ (d) $^{3}_{1}H$ (g) uranium-235
   (b) $^{1}_{1}H$ (e) neon-20   (h) ^{12}C
   (c) $^{2}_{1}H$ (f) lead-206   (i) ^{14}C

Nuclear Stability

3. Which of the following nuclei lie within the band of stability shown in Fig. 24.2?
   (a) chlorine-37   (e) ^{206}Pb
   (b) calcium-40   (f) ^{211}Pb
   (c) ^{204}Bi (g) ^{222}Rn
   (d) ^{56}Fe (h) carbon-14

4. Which of the following nuclei would you expect to be unstable because they do not lie in the band of stability?
   (a) $^{34}_{15}P$ (d) $^{3}_{1}H$
   (b) $^{238}_{92}U$ (e) $^{245}_{94}Pu$
   (c) $^{42}_{20}Ca$

5. Define and illustrate the term *half-life*.

6. A $^{7}_{4}Be$ atom (mass = 7.0169 amu) decays to a $^{7}_{3}Li$ atom (mass = 7.0160 amu) by electron capture. How much energy (in millions of electron-volts) is produced by this reaction?

7. The mass of the atom $^{19}_{9}F$ is 18.99840 amu.
   (a) Calculate its binding energy per atom in millions of electron-volts.
   (b) Calculate its binding energy per nucleon.

8. What percentage of a 0.100-g sample of $^{254}_{102}No$ remains 5.0 min after it is formed (half-life of 55 s)? 1.0 h after it is formed?

9. The isotope ^{208}Tl undergoes β decay with a half-life of 3.1 min.
   (a) What isotope is the product of the decay?
   (b) Is ^{208}Tl more stable or less stable than an isotope with a half-life of 54.5 s?
   (c) How long will it take for 99.0% of a sample of pure ^{208}Tl to decay?
   (d) What percentage of a sample of pure ^{208}Tl remains undecayed after 1.0 h?

10. The half-life of ^{239}Pu is 24,000 yr. What fraction of the ^{239}Pu present in nuclear wastes generated today will be present in 1000 yr?

11. The mass of a hydrogen atom ($^{1}_{1}H$) is 1.007825 amu; that of a tritium atom ($^{3}_{1}H$) is 3.01605 amu; and that of an α particle is 4.00150 amu. How much energy in kilojoules per mole of $^{4}_{2}He$ produced is released by the following fusion reaction?
$$^{1}_{1}H + ^{3}_{1}H \longrightarrow ^{4}_{2}He$$

12. If 1.000 g of $^{226}_{88}Ra$ produces 0.0001 mL of the gas $^{222}_{86}Rn$ at STP in 24 h, what is the half-life of ^{226}Ra in years?

13. Calculate the time required for 99.999% of each of the following radioactive isotopes to decay.
   (a) $^{240}_{94}Pu$ (half-life = 6580 yr)
   (b) $^{13}_{5}B$ (half-life = 1.9×10^{-2} s)
   (c) $^{233}_{92}U$ (half-life = 1.62×10^{5} yr)

14. The isotope $^{90}_{38}Sr$ is one of the extremely hazardous species in the fallout from a nuclear fission explosion. A 0.500-g sample diminishes to 0.393 g in 10.0 yr. Calculate the half-life.

15. Calculate the density of the $^{24}_{12}Mg$ nucleus in g mL^{-1}, assuming that it has a typical nuclear diameter of 1×10^{-13} cm and is spherical in shape.

Nuclear Decay

16. How do nuclear reactions differ from ordinary chemical changes?

17. Describe the types of radiation emitted from the nuclei of naturally radioactive elements.

18. The loss of an α particle by a nucleus causes what change in the atomic number and the mass of the nucleus? What change occurs in the atomic number and mass when a β particle is emitted?

19. What is the change in the nucleus that gives rise to a β particle? To a β^{+} particle?

20. Many nuclides with atomic numbers greater than 83 decay by processes such as electron emission. Explain the observation that the emissions from these unstable nuclides normally include α particles also.

21. Identify the various particles that may be produced in a nuclear reaction.

22. Write a balanced equation for each of the following nuclear reactions.
   (a) Uranium-230 undergoes α decay.
   (b) Bismuth-212 decays to polonium-212.
   (c) Beryllium-8 and a positron are produced by the decay of an unstable nucleus.
   (d) Neptunium-239 forms from the reaction of uranium-238 with a neutron and then spontaneously converts to plutonium-239.
   (e) Strontium-90 decays to yttrium-90.

23. Write a nuclear reaction for each step in the formation of $^{218}_{84}Po$ from $^{238}_{92}U$, which proceeds by a series of decay reac-

tions involving stepwise emission of α, β, β, α, α, α, α particles, in that order.

24. Complete each of the following equations.
    (a) $^{27}_{13}Al + ^4_2He \longrightarrow ? + ^1_0n$
    (b) $^7_3Li + ? \longrightarrow 2\,^4_2He$
    (c) $^{239}_{94}Pu + ? \longrightarrow ^{242}_{96}Cm + ^1_0n$
    (d) $^{14}_6C \longrightarrow ^{14}_7N + ?$
    (e) $^{14}_7N + ^4_2He \longrightarrow ? + ^1_1H$

25. Fill in the atomic number of the initial nucleus, and write out the complete nuclear symbol for the product of each of the following nuclear reactions.
    (a) $^9Be(\alpha, n)$
    (b) $^{23}Na(^2H, p)$
    (c) $^{33}S(n, p)$
    (d) $^{33}S(p, n)$
    (e) $^{10}B(\alpha, p)$
    (f) $^{27}Al(\alpha, n)$
    (g) $^{63}Cu(p, n)$

26. Complete the following notations by filling in the missing parts.
    (a) $(n, 2n)^{66}Cu$
    (b) $(\alpha, n)^{30}P$
    (c) $(^2H, n)^{238}Np$
    (d) $^{10}B(\alpha,)^{13}C$
    (e) $^{232}Th(, n)^{235}U$
    (f) $^2H(^{12}C,)^{10}B$
    (g) $^{24}Mg(\alpha, n)$
    (h) $^{238}U(^{12}_6C, 4n)$

27. Use the abbreviated system of notation, as in Exercise 26, to describe:
    (a) the production of ^{17}O from ^{14}N by α-particle bombardment
    (b) the production of ^{14}C from ^{14}N by neutron bombardment
    (c) the production of ^{233}Th from ^{232}Th by neutron bombardment
    (d) the production of ^{239}U from ^{238}U by ^2_1H bombardment

28. Which of the following nuclei is most likely to decay by positron emission: chromium-53, manganese-51, or iron-59? Explain your choice.

29. For each of the following unstable isotopes, predict by what mode(s) spontaneous radioactive decay might proceed.
    (a) ^6_2He (n/p ratio too large)
    (b) $^{60}_{30}Zn$ (n/p ratio too small)
    (c) ^{235}Pa (too much mass, n/p ratio too large)
    (d) $^{241}_{94}Np$
    (e) ^{18}F
    (f) ^{129}Ba
    (g) ^{237}Pu

30. Explain in terms of Fig. 24.2 how unstable heavy nuclides (atomic number greater than 83) may decompose to form nuclides of greater stability (a) if they are below the band of stability and (b) if they are above the band of stability.

31. Technetium-99 (which is often used as a radioactive tracer

for the assessment of heart, liver, and lung damage because it is absorbed by damaged tissues) has a half-life of 6.0 h. Calculate the rate constant for the decay of $^{99}_{43}Tc$. (Recall that radioactive decay is a first-order process.)

32. Technetium-99 is prepared from ^{98}Mo. Molybdenum-98 combines with a neutron to give molybdenum-99, an unstable isotope that decays by β emission to give an excited form of ^{99}Tc. This excited nucleus relaxes to the ground state by emission of a γ ray. The ground state of ^{99}Tc decays by β emission. Write the equation for each of these nuclear reactions.

Radioactive Dating

33. (a) If for Example 24.8 of Section 24.7, some $^{87}_{38}Sr$ was initially present in the rock, would the rock be younger, older, or the same age as the age calculated in the example? Explain your answer.
    (b) If the rock was not as old as the earth, would the age of the earth be less, more, or the same as the age of the earth estimated from the calculation in the example? Explain your answer.

34. A laboratory investigation shows that a sample of uranium ore contains 5.37 mg of $^{238}_{92}U$ and 2.52 mg of $^{206}_{82}Pb$. Calculate the age of the ore. The half-life of $^{238}_{92}U$ is 4.5×10^9 yr.

Nuclear Power

35. How does nuclear fission differ from nuclear fusion? Why are both of these processes exothermic?

36. Describe the components of a nuclear reactor.

37. Cite the conditions necessary for a nuclear chain reaction to take place, and explain how it can be controlled for the purpose of energy production without an explosion occurring.

38. In usual practice, both a moderator and control rods are needed to operate a nuclear chain reaction safely for the purpose of energy production. Cite the function of each, and explain why both are necessary.

39. Describe how the potential energy of uranium is converted into electrical energy in a nuclear power plant. What is a breeder reactor?

40. List the advantages and disadvantages of nuclear energy (compared to coal, fuel oil, natural gas, and water) as a source of electrical power.

41. Discuss and compare the problems posed by radioactive wastes for radioactive substances of short half-life and for those of long half-life.

The Semi-Metals

Emeralds, like the lava shown on page 297, are composed of natural silicates.

A series of five elements called the **semi-metals,** sometimes referred to as the **metalloids,** separate the metals from the nonmetals in the periodic table. These elements look metallic, but they conduct electricity poorly. They are semiconductors. Their chemical behavior is intermediate between that of metals and nonmetals; for example, the pure semi-metal elements form covalent crystals like the nonmetals, but like the metals, they generally do not form monatomic anions.

In this chapter we shall discuss the chemical behavior of semi-metals. The chapter begins with an overview of these elements; sections dealing with the chemistry of two of the semi-metals—boron and silicon—follow.

㉕.1 The Chemical Behavior of the Semi-Metals

The semi-metals are boron, silicon, germanium, antimony, and tellurium (Fig. 25.1). They include certain members of Groups IIIA, IVA, VA, and VIA. Semi-metals are fairly nonreactive elements, having electronegativities slightly lower than that of hydrogen.

Crystalline elemental **boron** is, in general, chemically inert at room temperature, reacting only with fluorine and oxygen. With fluorine, boron trifluoride, BF_3, is formed. With oxygen, a layer of boric oxide, B_2O_3, is formed on the surface of the boron, which does not react further. At higher temperatures, boron reacts with all of the nonmetals except hydrogen and the noble gases and with all of the semi-metals except germanium and tellurium. It also reacts at high temperatures with almost all metals, except for some heavy metals such as cadmium, mercury, and lead. Boron reacts with carbon at very high temperatures to form boron carbide, B_4C, which is second only to diamond in hardness.

Boron is oxidized when heated with water, sulfur dioxide, nitric oxide, carbon dioxide, and many other oxides. It is also oxidized to B_2O_3 at elevated temperatures by both concentrated nitric acid and sulfuric acid, but it does not react with nonoxidizing acids. Boron resists attack by boiling concentrated aqueous sodium hydroxide and by molten sodium hydroxide at 500°C. In general, boron compounds react readily with water to give boric acid, $B(OH)_3$ (sometimes written as H_3BO_3), and with air to give boric oxide.

Figure 25.1

The location of the semi-metals, shown in yellow, in the periodic table. Nonmetals are shown in green; the metals in red.

Boron has a $2s^2 2p^1$ electron structure; in its stable compounds it exhibits an oxidation number of +3. In most of its chemical properties, boron behaves as a nonmetal. Its compounds are covalent. In most covalent compounds [for example, in BF_3 (Fig. 25.2) and B_2O_3 (Fig. 11.21)], the boron is sp^2 hybridized with trigonal planar molecular geometry and bond angles of 120° (see Sections 8.1, 8.2, and 8.7). The p orbital that is not hybridized is empty; consequently, boron compounds with three covalent bonds are strong Lewis acids (see Section 16.14). The addition of a fourth group in a Lewis acid–base reaction gives a four-coordinate boron atom with a tetrahedral geometry and sp^3 hybridization (see Sections 8.1, 8.2, and 8.8). For example, the reaction of BF_3 with NaF produces the tetrahedral BF_4^- ion by the reaction

$$BF_3(g) + NaF(s) \longrightarrow NaBF_4(s)$$

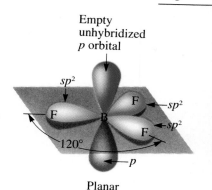

Empty
unhybridized
p orbital

Planar

Figure 25.2

In most covalent compounds of boron, such as BF_3, boron is sp^2 hybridized with trigonal planar molecular geometry. The empty p orbital makes these compounds good Lewis acids.

In addition to compounds in which it exhibits an oxidation number of +3, as expected for a member of Group IIIA, boron forms an extensive variety of compounds in which it has other, sometimes fractional, oxidation numbers. These include some of the boron hydrides (Section 25.4), a class of boron–hydrogen–carbon compounds called carboranes; and compounds such as BO, BF, and B_4Cl_4.

Silicon, like boron, is unreactive at low temperatures and resists attack by air, water, and acids. A very thin film of silicon dioxide, SiO_2, protects the surface from significant attack. This film dissolves in base and exposes the surface, so silicon dissolves in hot sodium hydroxide or potassium hydroxide solutions, forming anions of silicon and oxygen called silicates (Section 25.14) and hydrogen gas. For example,

$$Si(s) + 2OH^-(aq) + H_2O(l) \longrightarrow SiO_3^{2-}(aq) + 2H_2(g)$$

Silicon reacts with the halogens at high temperatures, forming volatile tetrahalides, such as SiF_4. Silicon oxidizes in air at elevated temperatures to give silicon dioxide, SiO_2, a solid. In the majority of its compounds, silicon exhibits an oxidation number of +4.

Unlike carbon, the first member of Group IVA, silicon does not readily form double or triple bonds. It normally forms compounds in which it is either sp^3 hybridized, exhibiting tetrahedral molecular geometry and four single covalent bonds, or sp^3d^2 hybridized, exhibiting octahedral molecular geometry and six single covalent bonds. Silicon compounds of the general formula SiX_4, where X is a highly electronegative group, can act as Lewis acids and form six-coordinate silicon. For example, silicon tetrafluoride, SiF_4, reacts with sodium fluoride to give $Na_2[SiF_6]$, which contains the octahedral $[SiF_6]^{2-}$ ion.

$$2NaF(s) + SiF_4(g) \longrightarrow Na_2SiF_6(s)$$

Except for silicon tetrafluoride, silicon halides are extremely sensitive to water. For example, when $SiCl_4$ is exposed to water, it reacts rapidly and all four chlorine atoms are replaced by hydroxide groups. The overall reaction is

$$SiCl_4(l) + 4H_2O(l) \longrightarrow Si(OH)_4(s) + 4HCl(aq)$$

Orthosilicic acid, $Si(OH)_4$ or H_4SiO_4, is unstable and gradually dehydrates to SiO_2.

$$Si(OH)_4(s) \longrightarrow SiO_2(s) + 2H_2O(l)$$

Germanium is very similar to silicon in its chemical behavior. However, it also forms a series of compounds, such as GeO and $GeCl_2$ that react with air or water, in which it exhibits an oxidation number of +2.

Antimony generally forms compounds in which it exhibits an oxidation number of +3 or +5. The element tarnishes only slightly in dry air but is readily oxidized when warmed, giving antimony(III) oxide, Sb_4O_6. Antimony(V) oxide must be prepared by indirect means, such as the dehydration of the product of the reaction of antimony(V) chloride with water. The element reacts readily with stoichiometric amounts of fluorine, chlorine, bromine, or iodine, giving trihalides or, with excess fluorine or chlorine, forming the pentahalides SbF_5 and $SbCl_5$. Depending on the stoichiometry, it forms antimony(III) sulfide, Sb_2S_3, or antimony(V) sulfide, Sb_2S_5, when heated with sulfur. It is oxidized, but not dissolved, by hot nitric acid, forming Sb_4O_6. It is slowly dissolved by hot concentrated sulfuric acid, forming $Sb_2(SO_4)_3$ and evolving SO_2. The fact that neither the element nor its oxides react with nitric acid to give the nitrate indicates that antimony is not very metallic. However, as would be expected, the metallic nature of the element is more pronounced than that of arsenic, which lies immediately above it in Group VA.

Tellurium combines directly with most elements, although less readily than the lighter members of Group VIA (oxygen, sulfur, and selenium). The most stable tellurium compounds are the tellurides, salts of Te^{2-} formed with the active metals and the lanthanides, and compounds with oxygen, fluorine, and chlorine, in which tellurium normally exhibits an oxidation number of +2 or +4. Although tellurium(VI) compounds are known, there is a marked resistance to oxidation to this maximum group oxidation number. The oxidation of tellurium in air gives TeO_2 rather than TeO_3, for example. Tellurium(VI) compounds are good oxidizing agents.

25.2 Structures of the Semi-Metals

The crystal structures of the semi-metals are characterized by covalent bonding. In this regard, these elements resemble nonmetals in their behavior.

Elemental silicon, germanium, antimony, and tellurium are lustrous, metallic-looking solids. Silicon and germanium crystallize with a diamondlike structure [Fig. 21.7(a)]. Each atom within the crystal is covalently bonded to four neighboring atoms at the corners of a regular tetrahedron. Single crystals of silicon and germanium are giant three-dimensional molecules. The crystal structure of antimony is layerlike and is similar to that of black phosphorus [Fig. 21.12(c)]. Each antimony atom forms covalent bonds to three adjacent atoms in the layer. Tellurium forms crystals that contain infinite spiral chains of tellurium atoms. Each atom in the chain is bonded to two other atoms.

Figure 25.3

An icosahedron, a symmetrical solid shape with 20 faces each of which is an equilateral triangle. The faces meet at 12 corners.

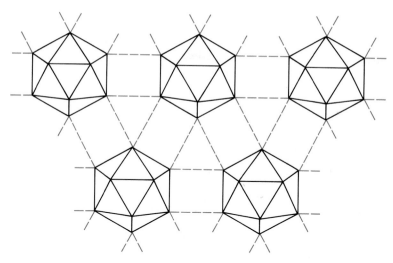

Figure 25.4

The structure of boron. Each icosahedron contains twelve boron atoms. Each of six of these is bonded to a boron atom in another icosahedron by a two-center bond (1.71Å), and each of the other six is bonded to two boron atoms, each in a separate icosahedron, by a three-center bond (2.03Å). Only the three-center bonds between icosahedra are shown here.

Pure crystalline boron is transparent. The crystals have a rather unusual structure; they consist of icosahedra (Fig. 25.3) with a boron atom at each corner. In the most common form of boron, the icosahedra are packed together in a manner similar to cubic closest packing of spheres (Figure 25.4; also see Section 11.14). All boron–boron bonds within each icosahedron are identical and are approximately 1.76 Å in length. However, there are two kinds of boron–boron bonds between the icosahedra. Each of six of the twelve boron atoms of an icosahedron is joined to a boron atom in adjacent icosahedra by a regular covalent bond between the two atoms, which is 1.71Å long. (These bonds are not shown in Fig. 25.4.) Each of the other six atoms is bonded to *two* other atoms, one in each of two other icosahedra, by a bond in which two electrons bond three atoms, forming a bond that is 2.03Å long.

In Chapters 7 and 8, we discussed bonds in which two atoms are bonded together by one pair of electrons in a bond that results from the overlap of two atomic orbitals. These bonds are called **two-center two-electron bonds.** However, in some situations three atoms are bonded together by one pair of electrons in a bond formed from the overlap of three atomic orbitals. These bonds are called **three-center two-electron bonds.** As was pointed out in Chapter 9, in a two-center two-electron bond, one bonding molecular orbital and one antibonding molecular orbital result from the overlap of two atomic orbitals (see Section 9.1). In a three-center two-electron bond, one bonding molecular orbital and two antibonding molecular orbitals (or one bonding orbital, one nonbonding orbital, and one antibonding orbital) result from the overlap of three atomic orbitals. The two electrons occupy the bonding molecular orbital. The formation of the bonding orbital in elemental boron is shown in Fig. 25.5.

The three-center two-electron bond is found with atoms that do not have enough electrons to satisfy ordinary two-center bond requirements. Boron makes the greatest use of the three-center bond; it exhibits this type of bond not only in elemental boron but also in boron hydrides (Section 25.4) and carboranes.

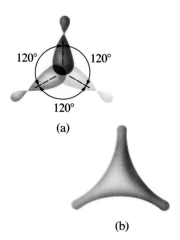

(a)

(b)

Figure 25.5

The three-center B—B—B bond involving the overlap of three sp^3 hybrid orbitals, which share one pair of electrons. (a) The overlap diagram for the hybrid orbitals. (b) The overall outline of the bonding molecular orbital.

Boron

Boron and its compounds have been known for a long time. The boron-containing compound borax is mentioned in early Latin works on chemistry. Gay-Lussac and Thénard in France and Davy in England first prepared impure elemental boron in 1808 by reducing boric acid with potassium.

25.3 Occurrence and Preparation of Boron

Boron constitutes less than 0.001% by weight of the earth's crust. It does not occur in the free state in nature but rather is found in compounds with oxygen. Boron is widely distributed in volcanic regions as boric acid, $B(OH)_3$, and in dry lake regions, including the desert areas of California (Fig. 25.6), as **borates,** salts of boron oxyacids, such as **borax,** $Na_2B_4O_7 \cdot 10H_2O$, and **kernite,** $Na_2B_4O_7 \cdot 4H_2O$.

Reduction of boric oxide with powdered magnesium forms boron (95–98% pure) as a brown amorphous powder.

$$B_2O_3 + 3Mg \longrightarrow 2B + 3MgO$$

The magnesium oxide is removed by dissolving it in hydrochloric acid. Pure boron can be obtained by passing a mixture of the trichloride and hydrogen either through an electric arc or over a hot tungsten filament.

$$2BCl_3(g) + 3H_2(g) \xrightarrow{\text{1500°C}} 2B(s) + 6HCl(g) \qquad \Delta H° = 253.7 \text{ kJ}$$

25.4 Boron Hydrides

Boron forms a series of volatile hydrides that are quite different from the hydrides of carbon and silicon. The hydride BH_3 does not exist as the monomer at room temperature, although Lewis acid–base adducts, such as $H_3B–CO$ and $H_3B–PH_3$, are known.

Figure 25.6

An open-pit borate mine and processing plant in Boron, California.

Instead, BH_3 dimerizes and the simplest stable boron hydride is **diborane,** $(BH_3)_2$, more commonly written as B_2H_6. An electronic structure cannot be written for B_2H_6 that is consistent with the theory of regular covalent bonds outlined in Chapter 7 and with the properties of the compound. It would require 14 valence electrons (7 electron pairs) to form the covalent structure

$$
\begin{array}{cc}
\text{H} & \text{H} \\
| & | \\
\text{H}-\text{B}-\text{B}-\text{H} \\
| & | \\
\text{H} & \text{H}
\end{array}
$$

but only 12 electrons are available for bond formation. (Compounds of this sort are sometimes called electron-deficient.) The structure most in keeping with the properties of diborane is one with two different kinds of hydrogen atoms (Fig. 25.7).

Four of the six hydrogen atoms in B_2H_6 are involved in two-center two-electron bonds, but the other two are bonded to the boron atoms in three-center two-electron bonds. The four regular two-center B—H bonds are all in the same plane and use eight of the 12 valence electrons. A hydrogen above and below the plane is connected to the two boron atoms by a three-center two-electron B—H—B bond. The three atoms are bonded by a bond that contains one pair of electrons, analogous to the B—B—B three-center bond in elemental boron (Section 25.2). The two three-center bonds hold the remaining four electrons.

The reaction of lithium aluminum hydride with boron trifluoride in diethyl ether solution yields diborane.

$$4BF_3 + 3LiAlH_4 \longrightarrow 2B_2H_6(g) + 3LiF + 3AlF_3$$

Above 300°C, diborane rapidly decomposes into boron and hydrogen. It is also spontaneously flammable, having a higher enthalpy of combustion per gram than all but a few substances.

$$B_2H_6(g) + 3O_2(g) \longrightarrow B_2O_3(s) + 3H_2O(l) \qquad \Delta H° = -2165 \text{ kJ}$$

Diborane is not acidic; it reacts with water, forming boric acid and hydrogen.

$$B_2H_6(g) + 6H_2O(l) \longrightarrow 2B(OH)_3(s) + 6H_2(g) \qquad \Delta H° = -509 \text{ kJ}$$

Heating diborane above 100°C in a seated vessel (a pyrolysis reaction) results in the formation of boron hydrides of higher molecular mass, as do the pyrolysis reactions of other boron hydrides. Over 25 neutral boron hydrides and an even larger number of boron hydride anions have been characterized. Examples include B_4H_{10}, $B_{10}H_{14}$, $B_3H_8^-$, and $B_{10}H_{10}^{2-}$. In all these compounds, boron uses all four of its valence orbitals and its three valence electrons, necessitating three-center two-electron bonding.

(a)

The structure of B_2H_6

(b)

Figure 25.7

The structure of the diborane molecule, B_2H_6. (a) The molecular structure. (b) The spatial arrangement of the bonding orbitals.

When an excess of sodium hydride reacts with boron trifluoride, **sodium borohydride,** $NaBH_4$, is formed. The four hydrogen atoms in the tetrahedral anion $[BH_4]^-$ are covalently bonded to the boron atom.

$$Na^+ \left[\begin{array}{c} H \\ | \\ H-B-H \\ | \\ H \end{array} \right]^-$$

Sodium borohydride

The oxidation number of the hydrogen atoms in the BH_4^- ion is -1. Salts containing the borohydride ion or other similar complex hydrides, such as the aluminum hydride ion, AlH_4^-, are very useful reducing agents, particularly for organic compounds. This is consistent with the presence of hydrogen with a negative oxidation number and the fact that it is a strong reducing agent as discussed in Section 21.10.

25.5 Boron Halides

Boron trihalides—BF_3, BCl_3, BBr_3, and BI_3—can be prepared by direct union of the elements. These nonpolar molecules contain boron that exhibits sp^2 hybridization, and a trigonal planar molecular geometry. The fluoride and chloride compounds are colorless gases, the bromide is liquid, and the iodide is a white crystalline solid.

The heavier boron trihalides readily hydrolyze in water to form the products boric acid and the corresponding hydrohalic acid. Boron trichloride reacts according to the equation

$$BCl_3(g) + 3H_2O(l) \longrightarrow B(OH)_3(aq) + 3HCl(aq)$$

When boron trifluoride is added to hydrofluoric acid, it reacts to give **fluoroboric acid,** HBF_4.

$$BF_3(aq) + HF(aq) + H_2O(l) \longrightarrow H_3O^+(aq) + BF_4^-(aq)$$

In the latter reaction, the BF_3 molecule acts as a Lewis acid (electron-pair acceptor) and accepts a pair of electrons from a fluoride ion, as shown by the equation

$$:\ddot{F}:^- + \begin{array}{c} :\ddot{F}: \\ B:\ddot{F}: \\ :\ddot{F}: \end{array} \longrightarrow \left[\begin{array}{c} :\ddot{F}: \\ :\ddot{F}:B:\ddot{F}: \\ :\ddot{F}: \end{array} \right]^-$$

Fluoroboric acid is a strong acid that is stable only in solution.

25.6 Boron Oxide and Oxyacids of Boron

Boron burns at 700°C in oxygen, forming **boric oxide,** B_2O_3. Boric oxide can be obtained as crystals, but when melted and allowed to solidify it forms a glass (Fig. 11.21). Boric oxide is used in the production of heat-resistant borosilicate glass (Fig. 25.8) and certain optical glasses. It dissolves in hot water to form **boric acid,** $B(OH)_3$.

$$B_2O_3(s) + 3H_2O(l) \longrightarrow 2B(OH)_3(aq)$$

The boron atom in B(OH)$_3$ is sp^2-hybridized and is at the center of an equilateral triangle with oxygen atoms at the corners.

$$
\begin{array}{c}
\text{O---H} \\
120°\nwarrow | \nearrow 120° \\
\text{H---O---B---O} \\
120° \\
|
\text{H}
\end{array}
$$

In solid B(OH)$_3$ these triangular units are held together by hydrogen bonding. Boric acid is a very weak acid that does not act as a proton donor but rather as a Lewis acid accepting an unshared pair of electrons from the Lewis base OH$^-$.

$$B(OH)_3 + 2H_2O \rightleftharpoons B(OH)_4^- + H_3O^+ \qquad K_a = 5.8 \times 10^{-10}$$

When boric acid is heated to 100°C, molecules of water are eliminated between pairs of adjacent OH groups to form **metaboric acid,** HBO$_2$. With further heating at about 150°, additional B—O—B linkages form, connecting the BO$_3$ groups together with shared oxygen atoms to form **tetraboric acid,** H$_2$B$_4$O$_7$. At still higher temperatures, boric oxide is formed.

$$B(OH)_3 \xrightarrow{\triangle} HBO_2 + H_2O$$

$$4HBO_2 \xrightarrow{\triangle} H_2B_4O_7 + H_2O$$

$$H_2B_4O_7 \xrightarrow{\triangle} 2B_2O_3 + H_2O$$

The formation of acids and oxyanions with bridging oxygen atoms is one of the characteristic properties of the chemistry of the semi-metals. Silicon forms an extensive array of bridged oxyanions (Section 25.14).

㉕.7 Borates

Borates are salts of the oxyacids of boron. Borates result from the reaction of a base with an oxyacid or from the fusion of boric acid or boric oxide with a metal oxide or hydroxide. Borate anions range from the simple trigonal planar BO$_3^{3-}$ ion to complex

Figure 25.8

Borosilicate glass is prepared from silicon dioxide and boric oxide. Laboratory glassware, such as Pyrex and Kimax, is made of borosilicate glass because it does not break when heated.

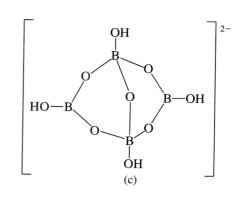

Figure 25.9

The borate anions found in (a) CaB_2O_4, (b) $KB_5O_8 \cdot 4H_2O$, and (c) $Na_2B_4O_7 \cdot 10H_2O$. The anion in CaB_2O_4 is an infinite chain.

species containing chains and rings of three- and four-coordinated boron atoms. The structures of the anions found in CaB_2O_4, $K[B_5O_6(OH)_4] \cdot 2H_2O$ (commonly written $KB_5O_8 \cdot 4H_2O$), and $Na_2[B_4O_5(OH)_4] \cdot 8H_2O$ (commonly written $Na_2B_4O_7 \cdot 10H_2O$) are shown in Fig. 25.9.

Commercially, the most important borate is **borax**, or **sodium tetraborate 10-hydrate**, $Na_2B_4O_7 \cdot 10H_2O$. Most of the supply of borax comes directly from dry lakes, such as Searles Lake in California, or is prepared from kernite, $Na_2B_4O_7 \cdot 4H_2O$. Borax is a salt of a strong base and a weak acid, so its aqueous solutions are basic as a result of the hydrolysis of the tetraborate ion.

$$B_4O_7{}^{2-} + 7H_2O \rightleftharpoons 4B(OH)_3 + 2OH^-$$

Borax is used to soften water and to make washing compounds. These uses depend on the alkaline character of its solutions and the insolubility of the borates of calcium and magnesium.

When heated, borax melts and forms a glass that dissolves metal oxides. An example is given by the equation

$$Na_2B_4O_7 + CuO \longrightarrow 2NaBO_2 + Cu(BO_2)_2$$

Because of this property, borax is used as a flux to remove oxides from metal surfaces in soldering and welding. Different metals form borax glasses of different colors—a fact applied in detecting certain metals. Cobalt borax glass is blue, for example.

25.8 Boron–Nitrogen Compounds

A number of compounds containing boron–nitrogen bonds have been prepared and studied. Two of particular interest are **boron nitride**, BN, and **borazine**, $B_3N_3H_6$.

Boron nitride is the final product of the thermal decomposition of many boron–nitrogen compounds, such as $B(NH_2)_3$ and F_3BNH_3. It can also be prepared by heating boron with nitrogen or ammonia or by heating borax with ammonium chloride. Crystalline boron nitride is a white solid that sublimes somewhat below 3000°C; it melts at this temperature under pressure. It is inert to most reagents but can be decomposed by reaction with molten hydroxides. The structure of one form of boron nitride is analogous to that of graphite [see Section 21.3 and Fig. 21.7(b)]; layers of atoms in both are made up of hexagonal rings. We might have predicted this similarity between boron nitride and graphite had we remembered that boron immediately precedes carbon in the periodic table and has one less valence electron, whereas nitrogen immediately follows carbon and has one more valence electron. The combination of boron and nitrogen has the same number of valence electrons as two carbon atoms(that is, B—N is isoelectronic with C—C); an extended number of boron and nitrogen atoms have the same number of valence electrons as the same number of carbon atoms. Also, the sizes of these atoms are similar and the average of the electronegativities of boron (2.0) and nitrogen (3.0) equals the electronegativity of carbon (2.5).

Boron nitride
layer

Graphite
layer

This form of boron nitride is sometimes called **inorganic graphite.**

A second form of boron nitride, Borazon, is produced just as diamond is produced from graphite—by heating the layer form of BN to high temperature under high pressure with a catalyst. Borazon has the same structure as diamond [see Section 21.3 and Fig. 21.7(a)] and is almost as hard as diamond. It is now produced commercially.

Borazine, $B_3N_3H_6$, and hydrogen are formed when ammoniates of the boron hydrides, such as H_3BNH_3, are heated at 180–200°C. Borazine has been called **inorganic benzene,** because its structure and physical properties are similar to those of benzene. However, its chemistry is different, because the B—N bonds are polar and the C—C bonds are not.

Borazine

Benzene

Silicon

Both carbon and silicon are members of Group IVA. The nonmetal carbon, with its ability to form compounds containing carbon–carbon bonds, plays the dominant structural role in the plant and animal worlds, and the semi-metal silicon, which readily forms compounds containing Si—O—Si bonds, is of prime importance in the mineral world. The name *silicon* is derived from the Latin word for flint, *silex*.

Silicon has the valence shell electron configuration $3s^23p^23d^0$, and it commonly forms tetrahedral compounds in which it is sp^3 hybridized with an oxidation number of +4. The major differences between the chemistry of carbon and that of silicon are due to the relative strength of the carbon–carbon bond, the relative weakness of the silicon–

silicon bond, carbon's ability to undergo catenation (Chapter 23), and the presence of the empty $3d$ valence shell orbitals in silicon, which enables tetrahedral silicon compounds to act as Lewis acids. Tetrahedral carbon compounds cannot act as Lewis acids.

25.9 Occurrence and Preparation of Silicon

Silicon comprises nearly one-fourth of the mass of the earth's crust—second in abundance there only to oxygen. The crust is composed almost entirely of minerals in which silicon atoms are connected by oxygen atoms in complex structures involving chains, layers, and three-dimensional frameworks. These minerals constitute the bulk of most common rocks (except limestone and dolomite), soils, clays, and sands. Sand and sandstone are forms of impure silicon dioxide, as are quartz, amethyst, agate, and flint. Most rocks are built up of the common metal cations and silicate anions. Materials such as granite, bricks, cement, mortar, ceramics, and glasses are composed of silicon compounds. A great variety of silicates exists in nature, and many of these have important specific uses. However, they are so stable that it is not economical to use them as sources of metals (except for beryl, $Be_3Al_2Si_6O_{18}$, from which beryllium is obtained).

Berzelius first prepared elemental silicon in an impure form in 1823 by heating silicon tetrafluoride with potassium. It can also be obtained by the reduction of silicon dioxide with strong reducing agents at high temperatures. With carbon and magnesium as the reducing agents, the equations are

$$SiO_2(s) + 2C(s) \longrightarrow Si(s) + 2CO(g)$$

$$SiO_2(s) + 2Mg(s) \longrightarrow Si(s) + 2MgO(s)$$

Extremely pure silicon, such as that required for the manufacture of semiconductor electronic devices, is prepared by the decomposition of silicon tetrahalides or silane, SiH_4, at high temperatures, followed by a purification method known as **zone refining.** In this method a rod of silicon is heated at one end by a heat source that produces a thin cross section of molten silicon. The heat source is moved slowly from one end of the rod to the other. As this thin, molten region moves, impurities in the silicon dissolve in the liquid silicon and move with the molten region. Ultimately they are concentrated in the other end of the silicon rod, which can be removed (Fig. 25.10). This highly purified silicon, containing no more than one part impurity per million parts of silicon, is the most important element in the computer industry (Fig. 25.11). It is used in semiconductor electronic devices such as transistors, microcomputers, and solar cells (see Section 9.16 and Fig. 9.19). Elemental silicon is also used as a deoxidizer in the production of steel, copper, and bronze and in the manufacture of acid-resistant iron alloys.

25.10 Silicon Hydrides

Silicon forms a series of hydrides, including SiH_4, Si_2H_6, Si_3H_8, Si_4H_{10}, and Si_6H_{14}. These compounds contain Si—H and Si—Si single bonds. Because of the presence of the silicon empty d orbitals, the chemical behavior of these silicon hydrides is decidedly

Inert atmosphere

Solidifying silicon

Moving heat source

Molten silicon

Melting silicon

Silicon rod

Eventual layer of impurities

(a)

(b)

Figure 25.10

(a) Zone refining apparatus that results in ultrapure elemental silicon. (b) These ultrapure silicon rods can be cut into thin slices to obtain the silicon wafers used in semiconductor devices. (The rainbow colors in this photograph result from reflections of the fluorescent lights from the room.)

different from that of the hydrocarbons (compounds of carbon and hydrogen) of similar formulas. For example, the silicon hydrides inflame spontaneously in air, whereas the hydrocarbons do not.

Acids react with magnesium silicide to form **silane**, SiH_4, which has a structure and formula analogous to methane, CH_4.

$$Mg_2Si(s) + 4H_3O^+(aq) \longrightarrow 2Mg^{2+}(aq) + SiH_4(g) + 4H_2O(l)$$

Silane, a colorless gas, is thermally stable at ordinary temperatures but spontaneously inflames when exposed to air. The products of its oxidation are silicon dioxide and water.

$$SiH_4(g) + 2O_2(g) \longrightarrow SiO_2(s) + 2H_2O(g) \qquad \Delta H° = -1429 \text{ kJ}$$

The hydrogen atoms in silane can be replaced one at a time by halogen atoms via reaction of silane with hydrogen halides, using the corresponding aluminum halide as a catalyst. With HBr, using $AlBr_3$ as the catalyst, the reactions are given by the following equations:

$$SiH_4(g) + HBr(g) \longrightarrow SiH_3Br(g) + H_2(g)$$
$$SiH_3Br(g) + HBr(g) \longrightarrow SiH_2Br_2(l) + H_2(g)$$
$$SiH_2Br_2(l) + HBr(g) \longrightarrow SiHBr_3(l) + H_2(g)$$
$$SiHBr_3(l) + HBr(g) \longrightarrow SiBr_4(l) + H_2(g)$$

Figure 25.11

Silicon computer chips are vital to the computer industry. Their small size (as compared to matchheads here) aids in the manufacture of small, lightweight, but very powerful computers.

Silane is extremely sensitive to hydroxides, reacting readily as a Lewis acid to give silicates and hydrogen.

$$SiH_4(aq) + 2OH^-(aq) + H_2O(l) \longrightarrow SiO_3^{2-}(aq) + 4H_2(g)$$

In contrast, methane, CH_4, is unreactive to hydroxides.

Perhaps the most important reaction of compounds containing an Si—H bond, at least from a commercial standpoint, is the reaction with hydrocarbons such as propene, $CH_3CH{=}CH_2$, that contain carbon–carbon double bonds.

$$CH_3CH{=}CH_2 + H_2SiCl_2 \longrightarrow CH_3CH_2CH_2SiHCl_2$$

$$CH_3CH{=}CH_2 + CH_3CH_2CH_2SiHCl_2 \longrightarrow (CH_3CH_2CH_2)_2SiCl_2$$

These reactions are used in the preparation of silicones (Section 25.15).

25.11 Silicon Carbide

When a mixture of sand and a large excess of coke is heated in an electric furnace, **silicon carbide (carborundum),** SiC, is produced according to the equation

$$SiO_2(s) + 3C(s) \longrightarrow SiC(s) + 2CO(g) \qquad \Delta H° = 624.7 \text{ kJ}$$

The product is blue-black, iridescent crystals (Fig. 25.12) nearly as hard as diamonds and very stable at high temperatures. The crystals are crushed, and the particles are screened to uniform size, mixed with a binder of clay or sodium silicate, molded into various shapes such as grinding wheels, and fired. Silicon carbide is used as an abrasive for cutting, grinding, and polishing and is used on sandpaper.

Silicon carbide exists in many different crystalline forms; in all of these forms each atom is surrounded tetrahedrally by four of the other kind [see Fig. 11.23(c)]. One crystalline form has a structure like that of diamond [see Section 21.3 and Fig. 21.7(a)]. To rupture a crystal of silicon carbide, a number of very strong covalent bonds must be broken. The high decomposition temperature (above 2200°C), the extreme hardness, the brittleness, and the chemical inactivity of silicon carbide are due to these strong covalent bonds.

25.12 Silicon Halides

All the tetrahalides of silicon, SiX_4, and several mixed halides of the type $SiCl_2F_2$ have been prepared. **Silicon tetrachloride** can be prepared by direct chlorination at elevated temperatures or by heating silicon dioxide with chlorine and carbon. The equations are

$$Si(s) + 2Cl_2(g) \longrightarrow SiCl_4(g)$$

$$SiO_2(s) + 2C(s) + 2Cl_2(g) \longrightarrow SiCl_4(g) + 2CO(g)$$

Silicon tetrachloride is a covalent tetrahedral molecule containing four covalent Si—Cl bonds. It is a nonpolar, low-boiling (57°C) colorless liquid that fumes strongly in moist air to produce a dense smoke of finely divided silica as the Si—Cl bonds are replaced by Si—O bonds.

$$SiCl_4(l) + 2H_2O(g) \longrightarrow SiO_2(s) + 4HCl(g)$$

Figure 25.12

Silicon carbide, nearly as hard as diamond, is used as an industrial abrasive.

The Si—Cl bonds in silicon tetrachloride can be replaced by Si—C bonds in a stepwise fashion by reaction with a stoichiometric amount of $Li^+CH_3^-$ or other compounds that contain carbon anions.

$$SiCl_4 + Li^+CH_3^- \longrightarrow Cl_3SiCH_3 + LiCl$$

$$SiCl_4 + 2ClMgC_2H_5 \longrightarrow Cl_2Si(CH_2CH_3)_2 + 2MgCl_2$$

Elemental silicon ignites spontaneously in an atmosphere of fluorine, forming gaseous **silicon tetrafluoride,** SiF_4. The reaction of hydrofluoric acid with silica or a silicate also produces SiF_4.

$$SiO_2(s) + 4HF(g) \longrightarrow SiF_4(g) + 2H_2O(l) \qquad \Delta H° = -191.2 \text{ kJ}$$

$$CaSiO_3(s) + 6HF(g) \longrightarrow SiF_4(g) + CaF_2(s) + 3H_2O(l)$$

Silicon tetrafluoride hydrolyzes in water, producing **fluorosilicic acid,** H_2SiF_6, as well as **orthosilicic acid.**

$$3SiF_4(g) + 8H_2O(l) \longrightarrow \underset{\substack{\text{Orthosilicic} \\ \text{acid}}}{H_4SiO_4(s)} + 4H_3O^+(aq) + \underset{\substack{\text{Fluorosilicic} \\ \text{acid}}}{2SiF_6^{2-}(aq)}$$

Fluorosilicic acid is a stronger acid than sulfuric acid. It is stable only in solution, however, and upon evaporation of the water decomposes according to the equation

$$H_2SiF_6(s) \longrightarrow 2HF(g) + SiF_4(g)$$

The difference in the reactivity of SiF_4 and $SiCl_4$ with water can be attributed to the great strengths of Si—O, Si—C, and Si—F bonds. Exposure of $SiCl_4$ and most other silicon compounds to water or oxygen results in their decomposition to compounds containing Si—O bonds, unless the compounds are stabilized by the presence of Si—O, Si—C, or Si—F bonds.

25.13 Silicon Dioxide (Silica)

Silicon dioxide, silica, is found in both crystalline and amorphous forms. The usual crystalline form of silicon dioxide is **quartz,** a hard, brittle, clear, colorless solid. It is used in many ways—for architectural decorations, semiprecious jewels, optical instruments, and frequency control in radio transmitters.

The contrast in structure and physical properties between silicon dioxide and its carbon analog, carbon dioxide, is interesting. Solid carbon dioxide (dry ice) contains single CO_2 molecules with very weak intermolecular forces holding them together in the crystal. The low melting point and volatility of dry ice reflect these weak forces between molecules. Each of the two oxygen atoms is attached to the central carbon atom by double bonds. In contrast, silicon in silicon dioxide does not form double bonds. In silicon dioxide each silicon atom is linked to four oxygen atoms by single bonds directed toward the corners of a regular tetrahedron, and SiO_4 tetrahedra share oxygen atoms. This structure gives a three-dimensional, continuous silicon–oxygen network. A quartz crystal is a macromolecule of silicon dioxide [see Fig. 11.23(b)].

At 1600°C, quartz melts to give a viscous liquid with a random internal structure. When the liquid is cooled, it does not crystallize readily but usually supercools and forms a glass, also called *silica*. The SiO_4 tetrahedra in glassy silica have the random

Figure 25.13

The tetrahedral structure of the SiO_4^{4-} ion. (Only the oxygen atoms are shown; the silicon atom, not shown, is at the center.)

arrangement characteristic of supercooled liquids, and the glass has some very useful properties. Silica is highly transparent to both visible and ultraviolet light. It is used in lamps that give radiation rich in ultraviolet light and in certain optical instruments that operate with ultraviolet light. The coefficient of expansion of silica glass is very low, so it is not easily fractured by sudden changes in temperature. It is insoluble in water and inert toward all acids except hydrofluoric acid.

$$SiO_2(s) + 4HF(aq) \longrightarrow SiF_4(g) + 2H_2O(l)$$

This reaction is used in the quantitative separation of silica from other oxides, because both products are volatile. Hot solutions of metal hydroxides and fused metal carbonates convert silica into soluble silicates (SiO_4^{4-} and SiO_3^{2-}). Typical examples are

$$SiO_2 + 4OH^- \xrightarrow{\Delta} SiO_4^{4-} + 2H_2O$$
$$SiO_2 + Na_2CO_3 \xrightarrow{\Delta} Na_2SiO_3 + CO_2$$

The latter reaction is employed in the conversion of silicate rocks to soluble forms for analysis and is part of the glassmaking process (Section 25.16).

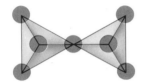

Figure 25.14

The structure of the $Si_2O_7^{6-}$ ion. (A silicon atom, not shown, is at the center of each tetrahedron.)

㉕.14 Natural Silicates

Silicates are salts containing anions composed of silicon and oxygen. There are many types of silicates, because the silicon-to-oxygen ratio can vary widely. In all silicates, however, sp^3 hybridized silicon atoms are found at the centers of tetrahedra with oxygen at the corners, and silicon is tetravalent. The variation in the silicon-to-oxygen ratio occurs because the silicon–oxygen tetrahedra may exist as discrete, independent units or may share oxygen atoms at corners, edges, or (more rarely) faces, in a variety of ways. The silicon-to-oxygen ratio varies according to the extent of sharing of oxygen atoms by silicon atoms in the linking together of the tetrahedra.

It is convenient to classify the silicates into groups on the basis of the way the silicon–oxygen tetrahedra are linked.

1. Individual SiO_4^{4-} tetrahedra exist as independent groups in some minerals. Examples include **olivine**, Mg_2SiO_4, and **zircon**, $ZrSiO_4$. Positively charged metallic ions (Mg^{2+}, Zr^{4+}) bind together the negatively charged SiO_4^{4-} ions, which have the tetrahedral structure shown in Fig. 25.13. (Note that only the oxygen atoms are shown in the figure; a silicon atom is in the center of each tetrahedron but is not shown.)

2. Two SiO_4 tetrahedra share one corner oxygen and form discrete $Si_2O_7^{6-}$ ions (Fig. 25.14) in **hardystonite**, $Ca_2ZnSi_2O_7$, and **hemimorphite**, $Zn_4(OH)_2Si_2O_7 \cdot H_2O$, for example. The cations are between the $Si_2O_7^{6-}$ ions and bind them together.

3. Three SiO_4 tetrahedra share corners and form closed rings in **benitoite**, $BaTiSi_3O_9$. The $Si_3O_9^{6-}$ ions (Fig. 25.15) are held together by the metal cations. The rings are arranged in sheets with their planes parallel. Six SiO_4 tetrahedra share corners to form a closed ring in **beryl (emerald)**, $Be_3Al_2Si_6O_{18}$.

4. Chains of SiO_4 tetrahedra in which each tetrahedron shares two oxygen atoms are present in **diopside**, $CaMg(SiO_3)_2$, and other minerals. Such a chain (Fig. 25.16) has an empirical formula of SiO_3^{2-}, but no SiO_3^{2-} ions are present as independent entities. Parallel chains extend the full length of the crystal and are held together by the positively charged metal ions lying between them.

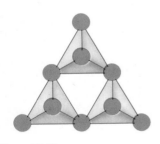

Figure 25.15

The structure of the $Si_3O_9^{6-}$ ion. (A silicon atom, not shown, is at the center of each tetrahedron.)

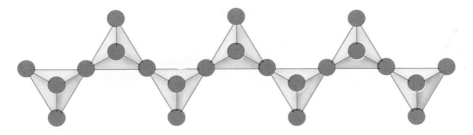

Figure 25.16

A portion of a SiO_3^{2-} chain. (A silicon atom, not shown, is at the center of each tetrahedron.)

5. Double silicon–oxygen chains form when SiO_4 tetrahedra in single chains share oxygen atoms (Fig. 25.17). Metal cations link the parallel chains together. The fact that these ionic bonds are not as strong as the silicon–oxygen bonds within the chains accounts for the fibrous nature of many of these minerals. Belonging to this group are a class of fibrous silicate minerals collectively called **asbestos.** The most abundant kind of asbestos is **chrysotile,** $Mg_3(Si_2O_5)(OH)_4$ (Fig. 25.18). Chrysotile, which has fibers longer than 20 mm, has been used in numerous fire-proofing and insulating applications. Unfortunately, prolonged exposure to airborne asbestos fiber dust can be dangerous and may cause cancer of the lungs and chest wall (pleura); its use as insulation has therefore been banned.

6. Silicon–oxygen sheets are formed by sharing of oxygen atoms between double chains. Metal ions form ionic bonds between the sheets. These ionic bonds are weaker than the silicon bonds within the sheets; thus minerals with this structure cleave into thin layers. Some examples include the micas **talc,** $Mg_3Si_4O_{10}(OH)_2$, and **muscovite,** $KAl_2(AlSi_3O_{10})(OH,F)_2$. Note the aluminum atoms can substitute for silicon atoms, as in muscovite. When this occurs, a larger charge on the cations is required to produce a neutral entity.

7. Three-dimensional silicon–oxygen networks with some of the tetravalent silicon replaced by trivalent aluminum are also observed. The negative charge that results is neutralized by a distribution of positive ions throughout the network. Examples include **feldspar,** $K(AlSi_3O_8)$, and the **zeolites,** such as $Na_2(Al_2Si_3O_{10}) \cdot 2H_2O$. There is currently great interest in zeolites because of the presence of tunnels and systems of inter-

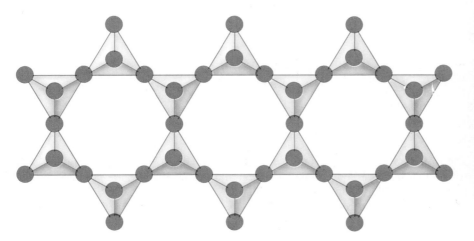

Figure 25.17

A portion of a double silicon–oxygen chain. (A silicon atom, not shown, is at the center of each tetrahedron.)

Figure 25.18

Chrysotile asbestos, shown here magnified 45 times, is the most common form of the mineral.

Figure 25.19

Model of a zeolite. Zeolites find many uses because of the cavities in their structures.

connected cavities in their structures (Fig. 25.19). These materials, which are sometimes called molecular sieves, are used to remove water and other small molecules from mixtures, to separate molecules for which the molecular masses are the same or similar but the molecular structures are different, to contain highly dispersed catalysts, and to promote specific size-dependent chemical reactions.

25.15 Silicones

Polymeric organosilicon compounds containing Si—O—Si linkages and Si—C bonds are known as **silicones**. Because these compounds contain strong Si—O and Si—C bonds, they are generally very stable. Silicones have the general formula $(R_2SiO)_x$ and may be linear, cyclic, or cross-linked polymers of the types shown.

Linear silicone   Cyclic silicone   Cross-linked silicone

The R in the formulas represents methyl ($—CH_3$), ethyl ($—C_2H_5$), phenyl ($—C_6H_5$), or some other hydrocarbon group. The linear and cyclic silicones are produced by hydrolyzing organochlorosilanes of the type R_2SiCl_2, followed by polymerization through the elimination of a molecule of water from two hydroxyl groups of adjacent $R_2Si(OH)_2$ molecules.

$$R_2SiCl_2 + 2H_2O \longrightarrow R_2Si(OH)_2 + 2HCl$$

Organosilicon polymers incorporate some of the properties of both hydrocarbons and oxysilicon compounds. They are remarkably stable toward heat and chemical reagents and are water-repellent. Depending on the extent of polymerization and the molecular complexity, silicones may be oils, greases, rubberlike substances, or resins. They are used as lubricants, hydraulic fluids, electrical insulators, and moisture-proofing agents. The viscosity of silicone oils changes so little as the temperature changes that they can be employed as lubricants where there are extreme variations in temperature.

Paper, wool, silk, and other fabrics can be coated with a water-repellent film by exposing them for a second or two to the vapor of **trimethylchlorosilane**, $(CH_3)_3SiCl$. The —OH groups on the surface of the materials react, and the surface becomes coated with a thin film (monolayer) of $(CH_3)_3Si$—O— groups. This layer repels water.

$$\text{(Surface)—OH} + \text{Cl—Si}(CH_3)_3 \longrightarrow \text{(Surface)—O—Si}(CH_3)_3 + HCl$$

25.16 Glass

Glass is a supercooled liquid consisting of a complex mixture of silicates. It is transparent, brittle, and entirely lacking in the ordered internal structure characteristic of crystals. When heated, it does not melt sharply. Instead it gradually softens until it becomes liquid.

The glass used for windowpanes, bottles, dishes, and so forth is a mixture of sodium silicates and calcium silicates with an excess of silica. It is made by heating together sand, sodium carbonate (or sodium sulfate), and calcium carbonate.

$$Na_2CO_3 + SiO_2 \xrightarrow{\Delta} Na_2SiO_3 + CO_2(g)$$

$$Na_2SO_4 + SiO_2 \xrightarrow{\Delta} Na_2SiO_3 + SO_3(g)$$

$$CaCO_3 + SiO_2 \xrightarrow{\Delta} CaSiO_3 + CO_2(g)$$

After the bubbles of gas have been expelled, a clear viscous melt results. This is poured into molds or stamped with dies to produce pressed glassware. Articles such as bottles, flasks, and beakers are formed by taking a lump of molten glass on a hollow tube, inserting it into a mold, and blowing with compressed air until the glass assumes the outline of the mold. Plate glass (float glass) is made by pouring molten glass on a layer of very pure molten tin. Because the molten tin surface is perfectly smooth, the glass floating on it is also perfectly smooth and does not need to be ground and polished after hardening.

Glassware is annealed by heating it for a time just below its softening temperature and then cooling slowly. Annealing lessens internal strains and thereby reduces the chances of breakage from shock or temperature change.

If sodium is replaced by potassium in a glass melt, a higher-melting, harder, and less-soluble glass is obtained. If part of the calcium is replaced by lead, a glass of high density and high refractive index is formed. This variety of glass is called **flint glass** and is used in making lenses and cut-glass articles. Borosilicate glass (with some silicon atoms replaced by boron atoms; brand names Pyrex or Kimax) is used for test tubes, flasks, and other laboratory glassware because it is resistant to sudden changes in temperature and to chemical action.

One form of **safety glass** used in automobiles contains a thin layer of plastic held between two pieces of thin plate glass. Adhesion of the glass to the flexible plastic reduces the danger from flying glass and jagged edges if it is broken.

Enamels on kitchen utensils, sinks, and bathtubs and glazes on pottery are made of easily melted glass containing agents such as titanium dioxide and tin(IV) oxide that make the glass opaque.

25.17 Cement

Portland cement is essentially powdered calcium aluminosilicate, which sets to a hard mass when treated with water. It is made by pulverizing a mixture of limestone ($CaCO_3$) and clay (an aluminosilicate) and then roasting the powder in a rotary kiln at about 1500°C. This treatment yields marble-sized lumps called *clinker,* which are ground with a little gypsum, $CaSO_4 \cdot 2H_2O$, to a very fine powder.

Concrete is made by adding water to a mixture of Portland cement, sand, and stone or gravel. The complex reactions that take place as the Portland cement mixture sets (starts to harden to form concrete) are not completely understood. It is known that calcium aluminate hydrolyzes, forming calcium hydroxide and aluminum hydroxide. These compounds then react with calcium silicates, yielding calcium aluminosilicate in the form of interlocking crystals. Portland cement sets rapidly (within 24 hours) and then hardens slowly over a period of years.

For Review

Summary

The elements boron, silicon, germanium, antimony, and tellurium separate the metals from the nonmetals in the periodic table. These elements, called **semi-metals** or sometimes **metalloids,** exhibit properties characteristic of both metals and nonmetals. Their electronegativities are less than that of hydrogen, but they do not form positive ions. The structures of these elements are similar to those of nonmetals, but the elements are electrical semiconductors.

Boron exhibits some metallic characteristics, but the great majority of its chemical behavior is that of a nonmetal that exhibits an oxidation state of $+3$ in its compounds (although other oxidation states are known). Its valence shell configuration is $2s^2 2p^1$, so it forms trigonal planar compounds with three single covalent bonds. The resulting compounds are Lewis acids, because the unhybridized p orbital does not contain an electron pair. The most stable boron compounds are those containing oxygen and fluorine. Diborane, the simplest stable boron hydride, contains **three-center two-electron bonds,** as does elemental boron.

Silicon is a semi-metal with a valence shell configuration of $3s^2 3p^2 3d^0$. It commonly forms tetrahedral compounds in which silicon exhibits an oxidation state of $+4$. Although the d orbital is unfilled in four-coordinate silicon compounds, its presence makes silicon compounds much more reactive than the corresponding carbon compounds. Silicon forms strong single bonds with carbon, giving rise to the stability of silicon carbide and **silicones.** Silicon also forms strong bonds to oxygen and fluorine. **Silicates** contain oxyanions of silicon and are important components of minerals and glass.

Key Terms and Concepts

asbestos (25.14)
borates (25.7)
borazine (25.8)
boric acid (25.6)
borohydride ion (25.4)
boron nitride (25.8)

diborane (25.4)
Portland cement (25.17)
silane (25.10)
silica (25.13)
silicates (25.14)

silicon carbide (25.11)
silicones (25.15)
three-center bond (25.2)
two-center bond (25.2)
zeolites (25.14)

Exercises

Answers for selected even-numbered exercises marked with red numbers appear at the end of the book. The worked-out solutions to all even-numbered exercises appear in the *Solutions Guide*.

1. Write a balanced equation for the reaction of germanium with an excess of each of the following: Cl_2, Se, HCl, F_2.
2. Write a balanced equation for the reaction of antimony with an excess of each of the following: heated O_2, Cl_2, I_2, concentrated HNO_3.
3. Write a balanced equation for the reaction of tellurium with an excess of each of the following: Cl_2, K, O_2, Al.
4. Compare the physical properties of the oxides, halides, and hydrides of the semi-metals to those of the oxides, halides, and hydrides of the metals.
5. Trigonal planar boron compounds and tetrahedral silicon compounds can both function as Lewis acids. How do they differ in their Lewis acid behavior?
6. Give the hybridization of the semi-metal and the molecular geometry for each of the following compounds.
   (a) GeH_4 (d) H_2Te (g) SiF_6^{2-}
   (b) SbF_3 (e) GeF_2 (h) $SbCl_5$
   (c) $Te(OH)_6$ (f) $TeCl_4$ (i) TeF_6
7. Name each of the following compounds.
   (a) TeO_2 (c) GeF_4 (e) GeH_4
   (b) Sb_2S_3 (d) SiH_4 (f) $NaBH_4$
8. The bonding in crystalline boron is more like that of a metal than that of a nonmetal, whereas the bonding in crystalline tellurium is more like that of a nonmetal than that of a metal. Explain this statement.
9. Which would you expect to be a better Lewis base: the carbide ion, C^{4-}, or the silicide ion, Si^{4-}? Why?
10. List the common oxidation numbers exhibited by each of the semi-metals.

Boron

11. Using only the periodic table, write the complete electron configuration of a boron atom and a B^{3+} cation.
12. Why are the compounds known as boron hydrides said to exhibit electron-deficient bonding?
13. Write a Lewis structure for each of the following molecules or ions.

(a) H_3BPH_3 (c) BBr_3 (e) $B(OH)_3$
(b) BF_4^- (d) $B(CH_3)_3$ (f) H_3BCN^-

14. Describe the hybridization of boron and the molecular structure of each molecule and ion listed in Exercise 13.
15. Write a balanced equation for the reaction of elemental boron with F_2, O_2, S, Se, and Br_2, respectively. (Most of these reactions require high temperature.)
16. Why is borazine, $B_3N_3H_6$, sometimes referred to as inorganic benzene?
17. Why should the physical properties of the two forms of boron nitride resemble those of graphite and diamond?
18. Why is boron limited to a maximum coordination number of 4 in its compounds?
19. A 0.7849-g sample of elemental boron was heated in the presence of oxygen gas and gave 2.5274 g of boric oxide, B_2O_3. From this information and the atomic mass of oxygen, calculate the atomic mass of boron. (Show your work.)
20. Write two equations in which the semi-metal boron acts as a metal and two equations in which it acts as a nonmetal.
21. Write balanced chemical equations for the conversion of boric oxide to (a) boric acid and (b) impure boron.
22. How might one prepare boron from boron tribromide?
23. Show by equations the relationship between boric oxide and the boric acids.
24. Is the solution that results when you add borax to water acidic or basic? Why?
25. Identify the oxidizing agent and the reducing agent in the chemical reaction of boron trichloride with hydrogen gas.
26. From the data given in Appendix I, determine the standard enthalpy change and the standard free energy change for each of the following reactions.
   (a) $BF_3(g) + 3H_2O(l) \longrightarrow B(OH)_3(s) + 3HF(g)$
   (b) $BCl_3(g) + 3H_2O(l) \longrightarrow B(OH)_3(s) + 3HCl(g)$
   (c) $B_2H_6(g) + 6H_2O(l) \longrightarrow 2B(OH)_3(s) + 6H_2(g)$

Silicon

27. Write a formula for each of the following compounds.
   (a) silicon dioxide   (d) carborundum
   (b) silicon tetraiodide   (e) magnesium silicide
   (c) silane   (f) fluorosilicic acid

28. Using only the periodic table, write the complete electron configuration for silicon, including any empty orbitals in the valence shell.

29. Write a Lewis structure for each of the following molecules and ions.
    (a) $(CH_3)_3SiH$ (c) Si_2H_6 (e) SiH_2F_2
    (b) SiO_4^{4-} (d) $Si(OH)_4$ (f) SiF_6^{2-}

30. Describe the hybridization of silicon and the molecular structure of the molecules and ions listed in Exercise 29.

31. Write two equations in which the semi-metal silicon acts as a metal and two equations in which it acts as a nonmetal.

32. Describe the hybridization and the bonding of a silicon atom in elemental silicon.

33. Classify each of the following molecules as polar or nonpolar.
    (a) SiH_4 (c) $SiCl_3H$ (e) SiF_4
    (b) Si_2H_6 (d) $(CH_3)_2SiH_2$ (f) $SiCl_2F_2$

34. How does the following reaction show the acidic character of SiO_2? Which acid–base theory applies?

$$CaO + SiO_2 \xrightarrow{\Delta} CaSiO_3$$

35. Account, in terms of molecular and crystal structure, for the low melting point of dry ice (solid CO_2) and the high melting point of SiO_2.

36. A hydride of silicon prepared by the reaction of Mg_2Si with acid exerted a pressure of 306 torr at 26°C in a bulb with a volume of 57.0 mL. If the mass of the hydride was 0.0861 g, what is its molecular mass? What is the molecular formula of the hydride?

37. Explain, in terms of their Lewis structures, why carbon forms carbonic acid, H_2CO_3, whereas silicon forms silicic acid, H_4SiO_4.

38. Using periodic properties such as ionization energies, sizes, and electronegativities, explain what similarities and differences you might expect between the chemistry of silicon and that of germanium.

39. Write an equation for the combustion reactions of SiH_4 and Si_2H_6.

40. Heating a mixture of sand and coke in an electric furnace produces either silicon or silicon carbide. What determines which is formed?

41. Account for the fact that although a carbon atom readily forms stable double bonds with another carbon atom, silicon–silicon double bonds are not formed as readily and are not as stable.

Additional Exercises

42. (a) From the table of bond energies given in Section 7.9 (Table 7.3), calculate the approximate enthalpy change for the reaction:

$$SiH_4(g) + 4HF(g) \longrightarrow SiF_4(g) + 4H_2(g)$$

(b) Using bond energy data, calculate the approximate enthalpy change for the corresponding reaction with methane:

$$CH_4(g) + 4HF(g) \longrightarrow CF_4(g) + 4H_2(g)$$

(c) Why do the two enthalpy changes differ so greatly?

(d) Which reaction is more likely to proceed spontaneously?

43. Boron monofluoride, BF, is an unstable molecule. Draw the Lewis structure of BF, and compare it to the Lewis structure of carbon monoxide, CO.

44. Silicon reacts with sulfur at elevated temperatures. If 0.0923 g of silicon reacts with sulfur to give 0.3030 g of silicon sulfide, determine the empirical formula of silicon sulfide.

45. The experimentally determined ratio of hydrogen atoms to boron atoms in a gas is 2.5 to 1. How could it be proved that the gas actually consists of B_4H_{10} molecules?

46. A hydride of boron contains 88.5% boron and 11.5% hydrogen by mass. The density of the hydride at 125°C and 450 torr is 2.21 g/L. A 5.0-mL gaseous sample of this hydride at 125°C and 450 torr decomposes to the elements, giving 35 mL of H_2 under the same conditions. Determine the molecular formula of the hydride, and show that all data are consistent with that formula.

47. Using the combustion reaction for Si_2H_6 that you found in Exercise 39, calculate how many grams of silica, SiO_2, are produced when 25.0 mL of gaseous Si_2H_6 reacts with excess oxygen gas at STP.

Coordination Compounds

The color of malachite, a copper-bearing mineral, is due to crystal field splitting of the copper ions' d-orbitals.

The hemoglobin in your blood, the blue dye in the ink in your ballpoint pen and in your blue jeans, chlorophyll, vitamin B-12, and the catalyst used in the manufacture of polyethylene all contain **coordination compounds,** or **complexes**—compounds in which neutral molecules and/or negative ions are bonded to metal ions. Such complexes are Lewis acid–base adducts (Section 16.14). The neutral molecules or negative ions are Lewis bases, each having at least one pair of electrons available for coordinate covalent bonding to the metal ion. The metal ions are Lewis acids, which can accept the pairs of electrons from the Lewis bases.

Ions of the transition metals, of the inner transition metals, and of a few metals near these series in the periodic table are especially likely to form complexes. Some examples of complexes include $[Ag(NH_3)_2]^+$, $[Cu(NH_3)_4]^{2+}$, $[Fe(CN)_6]^{3-}$, $[Co(NH_3)_6]^{3+}$, $[Pt(NH_3)_2Cl_2]$, $[Al(H_2O)_6]^{3+}$, and $[Zn(OH)_4]^{2-}$. Many of these complexes are highly colored (Fig. 26.1). In this chapter we shall consider the structures and properties of such complexes as these.

Introduction to Coordination Compounds

26.1 Basic Concepts

The **central metal ion** or **central metal atom** in a complex is a metal ion or atom that functions as a Lewis acid (Section 16.14) and that accepts electron pairs from groups attached to it. The attached groups are called **ligands.** Ligands are the Lewis bases (Section 16.14) in the complex; they can be either ions or neutral molecules. Within a ligand, the atom attached directly to the metal through a coordinate covalent bond (Section 7.4) is called the **donor atom.**

The **coordination sphere** consists of the central metal ion plus its attached ligands. It is usually enclosed in brackets when written in a formula. The **coordination number** of the central metal ion is the number of donor atoms bonded to it. The coordination number for the silver ion in $[Ag(NH_3)_2]^+$ is 2; that for the copper(II) ion in $[Cu(NH_3)_4]^{2+}$ is 4; and that for the cobalt(III) ion in $[Co(NH_3)_6]^{3+}$ is 6 [Fig. 26.2(a)]. In each of these examples, the coordination number is also equal to the number of ligands in the coordination sphere, but that is not always the case. Some ligands, such as ethylenediamine, $H_2NCH_2CH_2NH_2$,

$$H-\overset{\displaystyle H}{\underset{\displaystyle H}{N}}-\overset{\displaystyle H}{\underset{\displaystyle H}{C}}-\overset{\displaystyle H}{\underset{\displaystyle H}{C}}-\overset{\displaystyle H}{\underset{\displaystyle }{N}}-H$$

(a)   (b)

Figure 26.2

Two complexes with a coordination number of 6. The six donor atoms are shown in color. (a) $[Co(NH_3)_6]^{3+}$ is formed from a Co^{3+} ion and six NH_3 molecules as ligands. (b) $[Co(en)_3]^{3+}$ is formed from a Co^{3+} ion and three $H_2NCH_2CH_2NH_2$ (ethylenediamine) molecules as ligands (the latter is abbreviated as en in the formula). Two N atoms from each en molecule bond to the Co^{3+} ion, giving it a coordination number of 6.

contain two donor atoms (shown in color). The coordination number for cobalt in $[Co(H_2NCH_2CH_2NH_2)_3]^{3+}$ is 6 [Fig. 26.2(b)]. The coordination sphere of this complex contains only three ligands, but six nitrogen atoms are bonded to the cobalt. The most common coordination numbers are 2, 4, and 6, but examples of all coordination numbers from 2 to 12 are known.

When a ligand bonds to a central metal ion by several donor atoms, it is called a **polydentate ligand,** or a **chelating ligand.** These names are based on the Greek words for *tooth* and *claw,* respectively. A polydentate ligand "bites" the metal ion with more than one tooth (hence *poly,* for *many*). A chelate holds the metal ion rather like a crab's claw would hold a marble. A complex with a chelating ligand is called a **metal chelate;** examples include $[Co(H_2NCH_2CH_2NH_2)_3]^{3+}$ [Fig. 26.2(b)] and the heme complex in hemoglobin (Fig. 26.3), which contains a polydentate ligand with four donor atoms.

Ligands are sometimes identified with prefixes that indicate the number of donor atoms in the ligand. Ligands with one donor atom are called **monodentate ligands** ("one-tooth" ligands); examples are Cl^-, OH^-, and NH_3. Ligands with two donor groups are called **bidentate ligands** ("two-tooth" ligands); examples are ethylenediamine, $H_2NCH_2CH_2NH_2$, and the anion of the amino acid glycine, $NH_2CH_2CO_2^-$ (Fig. 26.4). **Tridentate ligands, tetradentate ligands, pentadentate ligands,** and **hexadentate ligands** contain three, four, five, and six donor atoms, respectively. The ligand in heme (Fig. 26.3) is a tetradentate ligand.

Figure 26.3

Heme, the square planar complex of iron found in hemoglobin. The donor atoms are shown in color.

Figure 26.4

A complex composed of a Pt^{2+} ion and two anions of the amino acid glycine. The Pt^{2+} ion and the donor oxygen and nitrogen atoms (in color) are planar.

26.2 The Naming of Complexes

The nomenclature of complexes is patterned after a system suggested by Alfred Werner, a Swiss chemist and Nobel laureate, whose outstanding work more than 90 years ago laid the foundation for a clearer understanding of these compounds. The following five rules are used for naming complexes.

1. If a coordination compound is ionic, name the cation first and the anion second, in accordance with usual nomenclature.

2. Name the ligands first, followed by the central metal.

3. Name the ligands alphabetically. Negative ligands (anions) have names formed by adding *-o* to the stem name of the group; for example,

F^-	fluoro	NO_3^-	nitrato
Cl^-	chloro	OH^-	hydroxo
Br^-	bromo	O^{2-}	oxo
I^-	iodo	NH_2^-	amido
CN^-	cyano	$C_2O_4^-$	oxalato
NO_2^-	nitro (M—N bond)	CO_3^{2-}	carbonato
ONO^-	nitrito (M—O bond)		

For most neutral ligands the name of the molecule is used. The four common exceptions are *aqua* (H_2O), *ammine* (NH_3), *carbonyl* (CO), and *nitrosyl* (NO).

4. If more than one ligand of a given type is present, the number is indicated by the prefixes *di-* (for two), *tri-* (for three), *tetra-* (for four), *penta-* (for five), and *hexa-* (for six). Sometimes the prefixes *bis-* (for two), *tris-* (for three), and *tetrakis-* (for four) are used when the name of the ligand already includes *di-*, *tri-*, or *tetra-*, contains numbers, begins with a vowel, or is for a polydentate ligand.

5. When the complex is either a cation or a neutral molecule, the name of the central metal atom is spelled exactly like the name of the element and is followed by a Roman numeral in parentheses to indicate its oxidation number. When the complex is an anion, the suffix *-ate* is added to the stem for the name of the metal, followed by the Roman numeral designation of its oxidation number. Sometimes the Latin name of the metal is used when the English name is clumsy. For example, *ferrate* is used instead of *ironate*, *plumbate* instead of *leadate*, and *stannate* instead of *tinate*. Examples in which the complex is a cation (shown in color) are as follows:

$[Co(NH_3)_6]Cl_3$	Hexaamminecobalt(III) chloride
$[Pt(NH_3)_4Cl_2]^{2+}$	Tetraamminedichloroplatinum(IV) ion
$[Ag(NH_3)_2]^+$	Diamminesilver(I) ion
$[Cr(H_2O)_4Cl_2]Cl$	Tetraaquadichlorochromium(III) chloride
$[Co(H_2NCH_2CH_2NH_2)_3]_2(SO_4)_3$	Tris(ethylenediamine)cobalt(III) sulfate

Examples in which the complex is neutral:

$[Pt(NH_3)_2Cl_4]$	Diamminetetrachloroplatinum(IV)
$[Co(NH_3)_3(NO_2)_3]$	Triamminetrinitrocobalt(III)
$[Ni(H_2NCH_2CH_2NH_2)_2Cl_2]$	Dichlorobis(ethylenediamine)nickel(II)

Examples in which the complex is an anion (shown in color):

$K_3[Co(NO_2)_6]$	Potassium hexanitrocobaltate(III)
$[PtCl_6]^{2-}$	Hexachloroplatinate(IV) ion
$Na_2[SnCl_6]$	Sodium hexachlorostannate(IV)

Figure 26.5

Octahedral structures of the complex ions in (left to right) [Co(H₂O)₆]Cl₂, K₂[PtCl₆], and [Cr(en)₃](NO₃)₃. Here again, en is the abbreviation for the ethylenediamine molecule, H₂NCH₂CH₂NH₂.

26.3 The Structures of Complexes

The structures of many compounds and ions were discussed in Chapter 8. Now we extend our study to coordination compounds with many of these same structures.

The most common structures of the complexes in coordination compounds are octahedral, tetrahedral, and square planar. Octahedral complexes have a coordination number of 6, and the six donor atoms are arranged at the corners of an octahedron around the central metal ion. Examples are shown in Fig. 26.5. The chloride and nitrate anions in [Co(H₂O)₆]Cl₂ and [Cr(en)₃](NO₃)₃ and the potassium cations in K₂[PtCl₆] are not bonded to the metal ion. Ions outside the brackets in the formula of a coordination compound do not form coordinate covalent bonds to the central metal atom but instead are bonded by ionic bonds.

Many chemists use an abbreviated drawing of an octahedron [Fig. 26.6(a)] when describing the geometry about a metal ion. However, one can draw a more realistic octahedron by following the steps outlined in Fig. 26.6(b).

Complexes in which the metal shows a coordination number of 4 exist in one of two different geometric arrangements: square planar or tetrahedral. Examples of four-coordinate complexes with a square planar geometry include [Pt(NH₃)₂Cl₂] [Fig. 26.7(a)] and [Cu(NH₃)₄]²⁺; examples of four-coordinate complexes with a tetrahedral geometry include [Zn(CN)₄]²⁻ [Fig. 26.7(b)] and [NiBr₄]²⁻.

Many other geometries are also possible. Table 26.1 shows several known types.

(a)

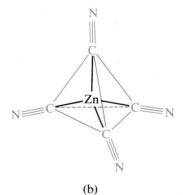

(b)

Figure 26.7

(a) The square planar configuration of [Pt(NH₃)₂Cl₂], and (b) the tetrahedral configuration of the [Zn(CN)₄]²⁻ ion.

(1)   (2)   (3)   (4)

(a) An abbreviated drawing of an octahedron.

(b) To construct a complete octahedron quickly and simply: (1) Draw a regular hexagon. (2) Draw a triangle inside the hexagon. (3) Draw another triangle with dashed lines upside-down inside the hexagon. (4) Add symbols for central metal (black) and ligands (red).

Figure 26.6

Steps in drawing an octahedron.

Table 26.1   **Geometric Shapes and Corresponding Hybridization of Metal Orbitals for Several Complexes**

Geometric Shape	Diagram of Shape	Coordination Number	Hybridization of Metal	Examples
Linear		2	sp	$[Ag(NH_3)_2]^+$, $[Cu(CN)_2]^-$
Trigonal planar		3	sp^2	$[HgCl_3]^-$
Tetrahedral		4	sp^3	$[Zn(CN)_4]^{2-}$, $[FeCl_4]^-$, $[CoBr_4]^{2-}$
Square planar		4	dsp^2	$[Ni(CN)_4]^{2-}$, $[Cu(NH_3)_4]^{2+}$
Square pyramidal		5	d^2sp^2	$[VOCl_4]^{2-}$, $[Ni(Br)_3\{(C_2H_5)_3P\}_2]$
Trigonal bipyramidal		5	dsp^3	$[Fe(CO)_5]$, $[Mn(CO)_4NO]$
Octahedral		6	d^2sp^3 or sp^3d^2	$[Co(NH_3)_6]^{3+}$, $[PtCl_6]^{2-}$, $[MoF_6]^-$

Violet, *cis* form

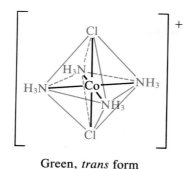

Green, *trans* form

Figure 26.8

The *cis* and *trans* isomers of [Co(NH₃)₄Cl₂]⁺.

26 .4 Isomerism in Complexes

Certain complexes, such as the [Co(NH₃)₄Cl₂]⁺ ion in [Co(NH₃)₄Cl₂]NO₃ and the Pt(NH₃)₂Cl₂ molecule, have more than one form. Different chemical species that have the same chemical formula are called **isomers.** The octahedral [Co(NH₃)₄Cl₂]⁺ ion has two isomers. Crystal structure analysis, performed by using X-ray methods and other experimental techniques, shows that one form has a *cis* **configuration** (chloride ions occupy adjacent corners of the octahedron) and the other form has a ***trans* configuration** (chloride ions occupy opposite corners), as shown in Fig. 26.8. The square planar [Pt(NH₃)₂Cl₂] molecule also exists in *cis* and *trans* forms (Fig. 26.9). Isomers such as these, which differ only in the way the atoms are oriented in space relative to each other, are called **geometric isomers, or stereoisomers.**

Different geometric isomers of a substance are distinct chemical compounds. They exhibit different properties even though they have the same formula. For example, the two isomers of [Co(NH₃)₄Cl₂]NO₃ differ in color; the *cis* form is violet and the *trans* form is green. Furthermore, these isomers have different dipole moments, infrared spectra, solubilities, and reactivities. The isomers of [Pt(NH₃)₂Cl₂] also differ in behavior. Perhaps the most interesting difference is that *cis*-[Pt(NH₃)₂Cl₂] exhibits antitumor activity whereas *trans*-[Pt(NH₃)₂Cl₂] does not.

Increasing the variety of ligands around a metal can increase the possible number of isomers. The [Co(NH₃)₄Cl₂]⁺ ion can form two isomers; the more complicated [Cr(NH₃)₂(H₂O)₂(Br)₂]⁺ ion has a variety of different geometric isomers. Each ligand can be *trans* to one like it (as shown in the figure on the left below), or the ammonia molecules can be *trans* to each other while the water molecules and bromine atoms are *cis* to their counterparts (figure on the right).

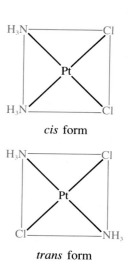

cis form

trans form

Figure 26.9

The *cis* and *trans* isomers of Pt(NH₃)₂Cl₂.

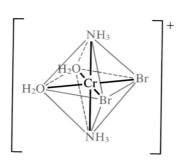

Similarly, the water molecules or the bromine atoms can be *trans* to each other while the other ligands are *cis* to ones like themselves.

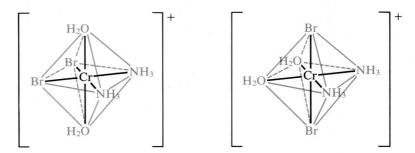

Finally, each group can be *cis* to one like itself; in this case two different arrangements are possible:

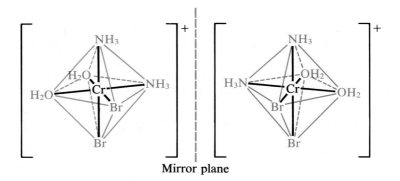

Mirror plane

These last two geometrical isomers have the same arrangement of ligands in the coordination sphere (*cis*-H_2O, *cis*-Br, *cis*-NH_3), but they are mirror images of each other and are not superimposable. Therefore they are not geometrically identical. Isomers that are mirror images of each other but not identical are called **optical isomers.** (See Section 30.6 for a discussion of nonsuperimposable mirror images.) Mirror images of the other geometrical isomers of [Cr(NH$_3$)$_2$(H$_2$O)$_2$(Br)$_2$]$^+$ can be drawn, but these mirror images can be superimposed and so are identical. For example, the following mirror images are identical to each other; either may be turned 90° on an axis through the two corners occupied by the ammonia molecules and superimposed on the other.

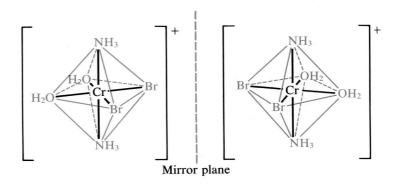

Mirror plane

As demonstrated in the diagrams, the $[Cr(NH_3)_2(H_2O)_2(Br)_2]^+$ complex has a total of six geometrical isomers, two of which are a pair of optical isomers.

The tris(ethylenediamine)cobalt(III) ion, $[Co(H_2NCH_2CH_2NH_2)_3]^{3+}$, has two optical isomers, as shown in Fig. 26.10.

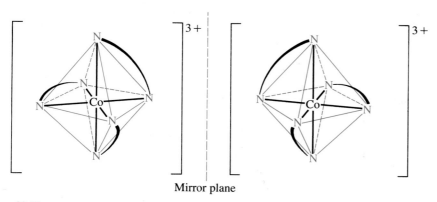

Mirror plane

Figure 26.10

Optical isomers of $[Co(H_2NCH_2CH_2NH_2)_3]^{3+}$. In these abbreviated formulas, N⌒N stands for $H_2NCH_2CH_2NH_2$.

The $[Co(en)_2Cl_2]^+$ ion has two *cis* isomers, which are a pair of optical isomers, and one *trans* isomer. The *trans* configuration has no optical isomerism. Its mirror image is superimposable on it and is therefore identical to it. The three isomers are shown in Fig. 26.11.

26.5 Uses of Complexes

Chlorophyll (Fig. 26.12), the green pigment in plants, is a complex that contains magnesium. Plants appear green because chlorophyll absorbs red and purple light; the reflected light consequently appears green (Section 26.10). The energy resulting from the absorption of light is used in photosynthesis (Section 31.14). The square planar copper(II)

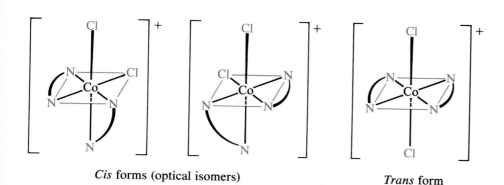

Cis forms (optical isomers)   *Trans* form

Figure 26.11

The three isomeric forms of $[Co(en)_2Cl_2]^+$. In these abbreviated formulas, N⌒N stands for $H_2NCH_2CH_2NH_2$.

Figure 26.12

Chlorophyll, a square planar magnesium complex found in plants.

Figure 26.13

Copper phthalocyanine blue, a square planar copper complex found in some blue dyes.

complex phthalocyanine blue (Fig. 26.13) is one of many complexes used as pigments or dyes. This complex is used in blue ink, blue jeans, and certain blue paints.

The structure of heme (Fig. 26.3), the iron-containing complex in hemoglobin, is very similar to that of chlorophyll. In hemoglobin the red heme complex is bonded to a large protein molecule (globin) by coordination of the protein to a position above the plane of the heme molecule. Oxygen molecules are transported by hemoglobin in the blood by being bound to the coordination site opposite the binding site of the globin molecule (Fig. 26.14).

Complexing agents are often used for water softening because they tie up such ions as Ca^{2+}, Mg^{2+}, and Fe^{2+}, which make water hard (Section 29.12). Complexing agents that tie up metal ions are also used as drugs. British Anti-Lewisite, $HSCH_2CH(SH)CH_2OH$, a drug developed during World War I as an antidote for the arsenic-based war gas Lewisite, is now used to treat poisoning by heavy metals such as arsenic, mercury, thallium, and chromium. The drug (abbreviated as BAL) is a ligand and functions by making a water-soluble chelate of the metal; this metal chelate is eliminated by the kidneys. Another polydentate ligand, enterobactin, which is isolated from certain bacteria, is used to form complexes of iron and thereby to control the severe iron build-up found in patients suffering from blood diseases such as Cooley's anemia, who require frequent transfusions. As the transfused blood breaks down, the usual metabolic processes that remove iron are overloaded, and excess iron can build up to fatal levels. Enterobactin forms a water-soluble complex with the excess iron, and this complex can be safely eliminated by the body.

The anticancer drug *cis*-platin is *cis*-[Pt(NH_3)_2Cl_2], a square planar platinum(II) complex [Fig. 26.7(a)]. This substance, the biological activity of which was first observed by scientists at Michigan State University in 1969, is believed to cross-link DNA strands (Section 31.10) and thereby interfere with mitosis (cell division).

Some complexing groups, when coordinated to certain metals, make the metal more easily assimilated by plants; in other cases, they keep the metal from being effectively utilized by the plant. Hence complexes can be effective in soil treatment. An example is the tris(ethylenediamine)iron(III) ion, $[Fe(en)_3]^{3+}$, which is the active agent in a substance that is added to the soil to provide iron to pin oak trees.

Figure 26.14

A representation of the hemoglobin structure. The red units are the heme groups (Fig. 26.3) in the structure. The blue chains are the protein globin chains that combine with the heme groups. The molecule transports oxygen because each Fe atom in a heme group forms a complex containing one O_2 molecule. Adapted from R. E. Dickerson and I. Geis from *The Structure and Action of Proteins,* Benjamin/Cummings Publisher, Menlo Park, CA. Illustration © 1969 by Dickerson and Geis.

In the electroplating industry it has been found that many metals plate out as a smoother, more uniform, better-looking, and more adherent surface when plated from a bath containing the metal as a complex ion. Thus complexes such as $[Ag(CN)_2]^-$ and $[Au(CN)_2]^-$ are used extensively in the electroplating industry.

Bonding and Electron Behavior in Coordination Compounds

Any theory of the arrangement of electrons in coordination compounds must explain four important properties of the compounds: their stabilities, their structures, their colors, and their magnetic properties. The first modern attempt to explain the properties of complex compounds invoked the concepts of valence bond theory (Section 8.4) and hybridization (Section 8.5) to describe the formation of bonds in these compounds. A later model relies on crystal field theory; it focuses on the electrostatic repulsions between the electrons of the central metal ion and the ligands to describe the behavior of the electrons that gives rise to the color and magnetic properties of the compounds. Molecular orbital theory combines features of both of these models and explains all of these properties of the complexes in coordination compounds.

26.6 Valence Bond Theory

Valence bond theory treats a metal–ligand bond as a coordinate covalent bond (Section 7.4) formed when a filled orbital on the donor atom overlaps a hybrid orbital on the central metal atom. The electron pair from the ligand is shared with the metal, and this electron pair occupies both an atomic orbital on the ligand and one of several equivalent hybrid orbitals on the metal. The ligand is a Lewis base; the metal, a Lewis acid.

In a tetrahedral complex such as $[FeCl_4]^-$, a total of four electron pairs from the four ligands occupy hybrid orbitals on the metal ion. As we noted in Section 8.8, four equivalent hybrid orbitals on the metal result from the hybridization of one s and three p orbitals, giving sp^3 hybridization. Tetrahedral complexes can be described as sp^3 hybridized.

Let us look more closely at the tetrahedral $[FeCl_4]^-$ ion. An isolated iron atom in its ground state has the electron configuration $1s^2 2s^2 2p^6 3s^2 3p^6 3d^6 4s^2$ (Section 5.12). Each atomic orbital can accommodate two electrons of opposing spin. The electrons enter each orbital of a given type singly before any pairing of electrons occurs within those orbitals—Hund's rule (Section 5.11). The valence shell of an iron atom includes the partially filled $3d$ orbitals, the filled $4s$ orbital, and empty $4p$ and $4d$ orbitals. Each orbital in the valence shell can be represented by a circle as follows:

Fe atom

When the iron(III) ion, Fe^{3+}, is formed, the atom loses the two electrons in the $4s$ orbital and one of the electrons from the pair of electrons in a $3d$ orbital, giving an electron configuration with a half-filled $3d$ subshell and empty $4s$, $4p$, and $4d$ subshells.

Fe^{3+} ion

The $4s$ and $4p$ orbitals of the iron(III) ion can hybridize to form a set of sp^3 hybrid orbitals that are directed toward the corners of a tetrahedron. These hybrid orbitals accept the electrons in a tetrahedral complex such as $[FeCl_4]^-$. This bonding is analogous to that in methane (Section 8.8), except that in this case, coordinate covalent bonds are formed with both electrons of each bond coming from a ligand. The distribution of electrons on iron in the $[FeCl_4]^-$ ion is

$[FeCl_4]^-$

Tetrahedral hybrid orbitals

In an octahedral complex such as $[Co(NH_3)_6]^{3+}$, a total of six electron pairs from the six ligands enter hybrid orbitals on the metal ion. As we noted in Section 8.9, six equivalent hybrid orbitals on the metal result from the hybridization of two d, one s, and three p orbitals. However, two different types of hybridization must be invoked to describe the bonding in octahedral complexes: inner-shell (d^2sp^3) hybridization and outer-shell (sp^3d^2) hybridization. The formation of a set of hybrid orbitals from two d orbitals of the inner d subshell and orbitals from the outer s and p subshells is called **inner-shell hybridization.** Hybridization of two 3d orbitals, a 4s orbital, and three 4p orbitals to give a set of d^2sp^3 hybrid orbitals on a cobalt ion is an inner-shell hybridization. The d orbitals come from an inner shell (the shell with $n = 3$), and the s and p orbitals come from the outer shell (the shell with $n = 4$). Hybridization of a 4s orbital, 4p orbitals, and 4d orbitals to give a set of sp^3d^2 hybrid orbitals on a cobalt ion is an **outer-shell hybridization.** The d orbitals come from the outer shell of the atom, the same shell that contains the s and p orbitals.

Whether an atom in an octahedral complex undergoes inner-shell hybridization or outer-shell hybridization must be determined experimentally. This is done by measuring the atom's magnetic moment (Section 26.9)—or by using some other experimental measurement—in order to determine the number of unpaired electrons on the atom. Let us consider as examples the hybridization in $[Fe(H_2O)_6]^{2+}$, which contains four unpaired electrons, and that in $[Fe(CN)_6]^{4-}$, which contains no unpaired electrons. Both of these ions are complexes of a Fe^{2+} ion. The electron configuration of a free Fe^{2+} ion is

The Fe^{2+} ion contains four unpaired electrons. If the hybridization in the octahedral $[Fe(H_2O)_6]^{2+}$ ion is described as a sp^3d^2 outer-shell hybridization that involves the 4d orbitals, the four unpaired electrons of the free Fe^{2+} ion can be accommodated in the unhybridized 3d orbitals in the complex and remain unpaired, as is observed. The hybrid orbitals used in bonding must be formed from the 4s, the three 4p, and two of the 4d orbitals of the iron(II) ion. The distribution of electrons on Fe^{2+} in the $[Fe(H_2O)_6]^{2+}$ ion is

The magnetic moment of $[Fe(CN)_6]^{4-}$ indicates that it has no unpaired electrons. The hybridization in this complex is an inner-shell hybridization. The 3d orbitals (rather than the 4d orbitals) appear to be involved in the inner-shell d^2sp^3 hybridization of the Fe^{2+} ion in this octahedral complex ion. This must force the unpaired electrons from the 3d orbitals used in the hybridization into the unhybridized 3d orbitals and results in the pairing of all electrons.

In the case of four-coordinate structures with a square planar configuration, the four bonds of the central atom arise from dsp^2 hybridization, as illustrated here for $[Ni(CN)_4]^{2-}$.

$[Ni(CN)_4]^{2-}$ (no unpaired electrons)

Square planar hybrid orbitals

Table 26.1 notes other types of hybridization in coordination compounds.

26.7 Crystal Field Theory

The valence bond model of bonding in a complex attributes the formation of bonds to the overlap of ligand orbitals with metal orbitals and the sharing of electrons *from the ligands* between the ligands and the central metal in the complex. In each of the complexes discussed in Section 26.6, the hybrid orbitals were occupied by electrons from the ligands; the electrons from the metal were not involved in the formation of bonds.

The colors of complexes and their magnetic properties can be considered to result from the electrons that are not involved in the covalent bonding between the metal ion

Colors of various compounds of chromium, with different oxidation states and ligands. From left to right, solutions of K_2CrO_4, $CrCl_3 \cdot 6H_2O$, $Cr(NO_3)_3$, $K_2Cr_2O_7$, and $[Cr(H_2O)_4Cl_2]Cl$.

and the ligands. It is possible to use a model involving simple electrostatic interactions between the ligands and the electrons in the unhybridized orbitals of the central metal atom to understand, interpret, and predict the colors, magnetic behavior, and some structures of coordination compounds of transition metals. This electrostatic model of the properties of complexes is called **crystal field theory.**

Crystal field theory does not explain the bonding in complexes; it describes only behavior that can be attributed to electrons on the metal atom in the complex. Like valence bond theory, crystal field theory tells only part of the story of the behavior of complexes. However, it tells the part that valence bond theory does not. In its pure form, crystal field theory ignores any covalent bonding between ligands and metal ions. Both the ligand and the metal are treated as infinitesimally small point charges. The effect of ligands on the electrons of a metal results from the electrostatic repulsions between the negative charge on the ligands and the electrons of the central metal.

Let us consider the behavior of the electrons in the unhybridized d orbitals in an octahedral complex. In Section 5.10 the shapes of the s, p, and d orbitals were given. An s orbital is spherical. A p orbital has a dumbbell shape, and the three p orbitals for a given level are oriented at right angles to one another along the x, y, and z axes (Fig. 5.18). The d orbitals, which occur in sets of five, consist of lobe-shaped regions and are arranged in space as shown in Fig. 26.15, reproduced within an octahedral structure.

The lobes in two of the five d orbitals, the d_{z^2} and $d_{x^2-y^2}$ orbitals, point toward the ligands on the corners of the octahedron around the metal (Fig. 26.15). These two orbitals are called the e_g **orbitals** (the symbol actually refers to the symmetry of the

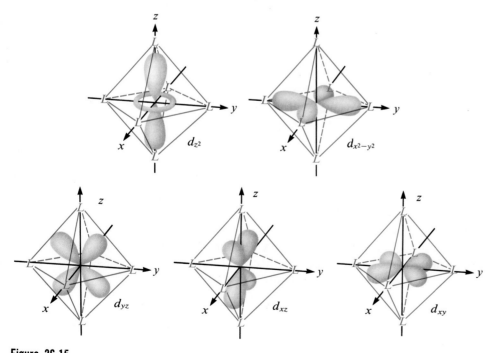

Figure 26.15

Diagrams showing the directional characteristics of the five d orbitals. L indicates a ligand at each corner of the octahedron.

orbitals, but we will use it as a convenient name for these two orbitals in an octahedral complex). The other three orbitals, the d_{xy}, d_{xz}, and d_{yz} orbitals, the lobes of which point between the ligands on the corners of the octahedron, are called the **t_{2g} orbitals** (again the symbol really refers to the symmetry of the orbitals). As six ligands approach the metal ion along the axes of the octahedron, their point charges repel the electrons in the d orbitals of the metal ion. However, the repulsions between the electrons in the e_g orbitals (the d_{z^2} and $d_{x^2-y^2}$ orbitals) and the ligands are greater than the repulsions between the electrons in the t_{2g} orbitals (the d_{xy}, d_{xz}, and d_{yz} orbitals) and the ligands because the lobes of the e_g orbitals point directly at the ligands, whereas the lobes of the t_{2g} orbitals point between them. Thus electrons in e_g orbitals of a metal ion in an octahedral complex have higher potential energies than those of electrons in t_{2g} orbitals. The difference in energy may be represented as follows:

The difference in energy between the e_g and the t_{2g} orbitals is called the **crystal field splitting** and is symbolized by **10Dq.**

The size of the crystal field splitting (10Dq) depends on the nature of the six ligands located around the central metal ion. Different ligands produce different crystal field splittings. The increasing crystal field splitting produced by ligands is expressed in the **spectrochemical series,** a short version of which is given here.

$$I^- < Br^- < Cl^- < F^- < H_2O < C_2O_4^{2-} < NH_3 < en < NO_2^- < CN^-$$

A few ligands of the spectrochemical series, in order of increasing field strength of the ligand

In this series the ligands on the left have a low field strength, and those on the right have a high field strength. Thus the crystal field splitting produced by an iodide ion (I^-) as a ligand is much smaller than that produced by a cyanide ion (CN^-) as a ligand.

In a simple metal ion in the gas phase, the electrons are distributed among the five $3d$ orbitals in accord with Hund's rule (Section 5.11), because the orbitals all have the same energy. However, if the metal ion lies in an octahedron formed by six ligands, the energies of the d orbitals are no longer the same, and two opposing forces are set up. One force tends to keep the electrons of the metal ion distributed with unpaired spins within all of the d orbitals. It requires energy to pair up electrons in an orbital; this energy is called the **pairing energy, P.** The other force tends to reduce the average energy of the d electrons by placing as many of them as possible in the lower-energy t_{2g} orbitals. The d electrons end up with the lowest possible total energy. If it requires less energy for the d electrons to be excited to the upper e_g orbitals than to pair in the lower t_{2g} orbitals (10Dq < P), then they will remain unpaired. If it requires less energy to pair d electrons in the lower t_{2g} orbitals than to put them in the upper e_g orbitals (10Dq > P), then they will pair.

In $[Fe(CN)_6]^{4-}$ the strong field of six cyanide ions produces a large crystal field splitting. Under these conditions the electrons require less energy to pair than to be excited to the e_g orbitals (10Dq > P). The six $3d$ electrons of the Fe^{2+} ion pair in the three t_{2g} orbitals. The result is in agreement with the experimentally measured magnetic moment of $[Fe(CN)_6]^{4-}$ (no unpaired electrons).

In $[Fe(H_2O)_6]^{2+}$, on the other hand, the weak field of the water molecules produces only a small crystal field splitting. Because it requires less energy to excite electrons to the e_g orbitals than to pair them ($10Dq < P$), they remain distributed in all five $3d$ orbitals.

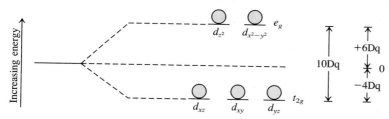

Four unpaired electrons should be present, as is verified by measuring the magnetic moment of $[Fe(H_2O)_6]^{2+}$. A similar line of reasoning can be followed for complexes of iron(III) to show why $[Fe(CN)_6]^{3-}$ has only one unpaired electron, whereas $[Fe(H_2O)_6]^{3+}$ and $[FeF_6]^{3-}$ both have five unpaired electrons.

26.8 Crystal Field Stabilization Energy

As indicated earlier, the difference in energy between the e_g and t_{2g} orbitals in an octahedral complex is commonly symbolized by 10Dq.

Because the splitting of the five d orbitals into two energy levels does not change the total energy, the zero line on the energy axis is the weighted average energy of these orbitals. Thus the e_g and t_{2g} energies are $+6Dq$ and $-4Dq$, respectively. Hence

$$2\left(\frac{3}{5} \times 10Dq\right) + 3\left(-\frac{2}{5} \times 10Dq\right) = 2(+6Dq) + 3(-4Dq) = 0$$

A value for each complex, called the **crystal field stabilization energy (CFSE)**, can be calculated. The crystal field stabilization energy is a measure of how much more stable a complex is than a hypothetical complex that is identical in every way except that it shows no crystal field splitting. Consider, for example, an octahedral complex of the vanadium(III) ion, which has two d electrons (referred to as d^2). The two unpaired electrons occupy two of the lower-energy t_{2g} orbitals. In calculating the crystal field stabilization energy, we take into account the fact that there are two electrons, each with an energy of $-4Dq$ relative to the zero-energy line.

V^{3+} with weak-field or strong-field ligands
CFSE $= 2(-4Dq) = -8Dq$

Now consider another metal ion, the manganese(II) ion, which has five d electrons (d^5). In the free ion these electrons are distributed evenly throughout the five d orbitals in accordance with Hund's rule. If the ion is coordinated to ligands that produce a weak field ($10Dq < P$), the five electrons remain evenly distributed; that is, there are three unpaired electrons in the t_{2g} level and two in the e_g level.

Mn^{2+} with weak-field ligands
CFSE $= 2(+6Dq) + 3(-4Dq) = 0$

The two electrons in the e_g orbitals are in the higher energy level, corresponding to $+6Dq$, and the three electrons in the t_{2g} orbitals are in the lower energy level, corresponding to $-4Dq$. Hence the crystal field stabilization energy is zero in this weak-field case.

$$CFSE = 2(+6Dq) + 3(-4Dq) = 0$$

If, however, the Mn^{2+} ion is coordinated to ligands that produce a strong field ($10Dq > P$), all five electrons fall into the lower-energy nonbonding t_{2g} orbitals, and none are in the higher-energy e_g orbitals.

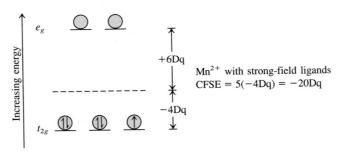

Mn^{2+} with strong-field ligands
CFSE $= 5(-4Dq) = -20Dq$

The crystal field stabilization energy for Mn^{2+} in this strong-field case is $-20Dq$.

$$CFSE = 5(-4Dq) + 0(+6Dq) = -20Dq$$

In the weak-field case for Mn^{2+}, the splitting of the two energy levels (the 10Dq value) is much smaller than it is for the strong-field case. The possible gain in energy that would result if the fourth and fifth electrons occupied the lower-energy t_{2g} orbitals is not large enough to overcome the repulsion of the electrons for each other and to pair them up. Hence the fourth and fifth electrons go singly into the higher-energy e_g orbitals.

Sometimes the term **low-spin complex,** or **spin-paired complex,** is applied to complexes of a given metal with ligands of high field strength; the term **high-spin complex,** or **spin-free complex,** is sometimes used for complexes with ligands of low field strength.

Table 26.2 shows the crystal field stabilization energy for a variety of octahedral complexes with weak and strong fields. The calculated CFSE values in the table have been experimentally verified by spectroscopic methods. A relatively large negative number indicates that more energy is evolved in the formation of the complex and that, in general, the complex is more stable for a given ligand. Remember, however, that each 10Dq value varies with the ligand, and we must take this into account when considering the stabilities of complexes with different ligands. Weak-field ligands cause less splitting between the energy levels for a given metal ion and have smaller 10Dq values, in general, than do strong-field ligands attached to the same metal ion.

Table 26.2 Crystal Field Stabilization Energy (CFSE) of Octahedral Complexes

Configuration	Weak Field (high spin)				Strong Field (low spin)				Examples
	t_{2g}	e_g	Number of Unpaired Electrons	CFSE (Dq)	t_{2g}	e_g	Number of Unpaired Electrons	CFSE (Dq)	
d^0	0	0	0	0	0	0	0	0	Ca^{2+}, Sc^{3+}
d^1	1	0	1	-4	1	0	1	-4	Ti^{3+}
d^2	2	0	2	-8	2	0	2	-8	V^{3+}
d^3	3	0	3	-12	3	0	3	-12	Cr^{3+}, V^{2+}
d^4	3	1	4	-6	4	0	2	-16	Cr^{2+}, Mn^{3+}
d^5	3	2	5	0	5	0	1	-20	Mn^{2+}, Fe^{3+}
d^6	4	2	4	-4	6	0	0	-24	Fe^{2+}, Co^{3+}
d^7	5	2	3	-8	6	1	1	-18	Co^{2+}
d^8	6	2	2	-12	6	2	2	-12	Ni^{2+}
d^9	6	3	1	-6	6	3	1	-6	Cu^{2+}
d^{10}	6	4	0	0	6	4	0	0	Cu^+, Zn^{2+}

Used by permission from *Concepts and Models of Inorganic Chemistry*, B. E. Douglas, D. H. McDaniel, and J. J. Alexander (2nd ed.). John Wiley and Sons Inc., New York, 1983, p. 270.

🔢.9 Magnetic Moments of Molecules and Ions

Molecules such as O_2 (Section 9.11) and NO (Section 9.14) and ions such as $[Fe(H_2O)_6]^{2+}$ (Section 26.7) that contain unpaired electrons are **paramagnetic.** As shown in the photograph of liquid oxygen on page 249, paramagnetic substances tend to be attracted into a magnetic field, such as that between the poles of a magnet. Many transition metal complexes have unpaired electrons and hence are paramagnetic. Molecules such as N_2 (Section 9.10) and ions such as Na^+ and $[Fe(CN)_6]^{4-}$ (Section 26.7) that contain no unpaired electrons are **diamagnetic.** Diamagnetic substances have a slight tendency to be repelled by a magnetic field.

An electron in an atom spins about its own axis. Because the electron is electrically charged, this spin gives it the properties of a small magnet, with north and south poles. Two electrons in the same orbital spin in opposite directions, and their magnetic moments cancel because their north and south poles are opposed. When an electron in an atom or ion is unpaired, the magnetic moment due to its spin makes the entire atom or ion paramagnetic. Thus a sample containing such atoms or ions is paramagnetic. The size of the magnetic moment of a system containing unpaired electrons is related directly to the number of such electrons; the greater the number of unpaired electrons, the larger the magnetic moment. Therefore, the observed magnetic moment is used to determine the number of unpaired electrons present.

🔢.10 Colors of Transition Metal Complexes

When atoms absorb light of the proper frequency, their electrons are excited to higher energy levels (Chapter 5). The same thing can happen in coordination compounds. Electrons can be excited from the lower-energy t_{2g} to the next higher-energy e_g orbitals, provided that the latter are not already filled with paired electrons.

Figure 26.16

Passing white light through a prism shows that it is actually a mixture of all colors of visible light (red, orange, yellow, green, blue, indigo, and violet).

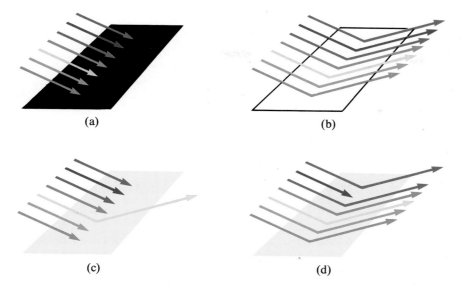

Figure 26.17

(a) An object is black if it absorbs all colors of light. (b) If it reflects all colors of light, it is white. (c) An object (such as this yellow strip) has a color if it absorbs all colors except one (yellow in this case). (d) The strip also appears yellow if it absorbs the complementary color from white light (the complementary color of yellow is indigo).

The human eye perceives a mixture of all the colors, in the proportions present in sunlight, as white light (Fig. 26.16). The eye also utilizes complementary colors in color vision and perceives a mixture of two complementary colors, in the proper proportions, as white light. Likewise, when a color is missing from white light, the eye sees its complement (Fig. 26.17). For example, as shown in Table 26.3, when red light is removed from white light, the eye sees the color blue-green; when violet is removed from white light, the eye sees lemon yellow; when green light is removed, the eye sees purple. The blue color of the $[Cu(NH_3)_4]^{2+}$ ion (Fig. 26.18) results because this ion absorbs orange and red light, leaving the complementary colors of blue and blue-green (Fig. 26.19).

Consider $[Fe(CN)_6]^{4-}$ (Section 26.7). The electrons in the t_{2g} orbitals can absorb energy and be excited to the next higher energy level. The necessary energy corresponds to photons of violet light. When white light impinges on $[Fe(CN)_6]^{4-}$, violet light is absorbed (to accomplish the excitation), and the eye sees the unabsorbed complement,

Figure 26.18
A solution of $[Cu(NH_3)_4]^{2+}$

Table 26.3	Complementary Colors	
Wavelength, Å	Spectral Color	Complementary Color[a]
4100	Violet	Lemon yellow
4300	Indigo	Yellow
4800	Blue	Orange
5000	Blue-green	Red
5300	Green	Purple
5600	Lemon yellow	Violet
5800	Yellow	Indigo
6100	Orange	Blue
6800	Red	Blue-green

[a]The complementary color is seen when the spectral color is removed from white light.

Figure 26.19

A solution of $[Cu(NH_3)_4]^{2+}$ is blue because the ion absorbs orange light and red light, the complementary colors of blue and blue-green, respectively.

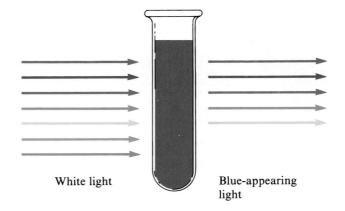

White light   Blue-appearing light

lemon yellow. $K_4[Fe(CN)_6]$ is lemon yellow (Fig. 26.20). In contrast, when white light strikes $[Fe(H_2O)_6]^{2+}$, red light (longer wavelength, lower energy) is absorbed. The eye sees its complement, blue-green. $[Fe(H_2O)_6]SO_4$, for example, is therefore blue-green.

A coordination compound of the Cu^+ ion has a d^{10} configuration, and all the e_g orbitals are filled. In order to excite an electron to a higher level, such as the $4p$ orbital, photons of very high energy are needed. This energy corresponds to very short wavelengths in the ultraviolet region of the spectrum. No visible light is absorbed, so the eye sees no change and the compound appears white or colorless. A solution containing $[Cu(CN)_2]^-$, for example, is colorless (Fig. 26.21). On the other hand, Cu^{2+} complexes have a vacancy in the e_g orbitals, and electrons can be excited to this level. The wavelength (energy) of the light absorbed corresponds to the visible part of the spectrum, and Cu^{2+} complexes are almost always colored—blue, blue-green, violet, or yellow (Fig. 26.21).

As we noted earlier, strong-field ligands cause a large split in the energies of the d orbitals of the central metal atom (significantly negative 10Dq value). Transition metal coordination compounds with these ligands are yellow, orange, or red because they

Figure 26.20

A solution of $K_4[Fe(CN)_6]$.

Figure 26.21

From left to right, solutions of the colorless Cu^+ complex $[Cu(CN)_2]^-$ and the colored Cu^{2+} complexes, $[Cu(H_2O)_4]^{2+}$, $[Cu(en)_2]^{2+}$, and $[CuBr_4]^{2-}$.

absorb higher-energy violet or blue light. On the other hand, coordination compounds of transition metals with weak-field ligands are blue-green, blue, or indigo because they absorb lower-energy yellow, orange, or red light.

26 .11 Molecular Orbital Theory

We have seen that valence bond theory is especially useful in explaining the bonding in complexes and that a theory based primarily on electrostatic interactions is particularly useful in explaining the magnetic properties and the energies involved in the electron transitions that give rise to the colors of complexes. However, neither of these theories can explain certain other properties of complexes. Because most bonds have both ionic and covalent character, the theory of bonding in complexes can be improved by using molecular orbital concepts to introduce some contribution due to covalent bonding into the crystal field theory. In Chapter 9 we discussed the molecular orbital theory. Now we can use it to understand the nature of the bonding in coordination compounds.

Molecular orbital energy diagrams for complexes are the same in principle as those for diatomic species (Chapter 9) but are, of course, more complicated because several atoms are involved, instead of just two, and a large number of electrons must be considered. The molecular orbital energy diagrams for $[CoF_6]^{3-}$, possessing weak-field ligands, and for $[Co(NH_3)_6]^{3+}$, possessing strong-field ligands, are shown in Fig. 26.22.

Figure 26.22

Molecular orbital energy diagrams for $[CoF_6]^{3-}$ and $[Co(NH_3)_6]^{3+}$.

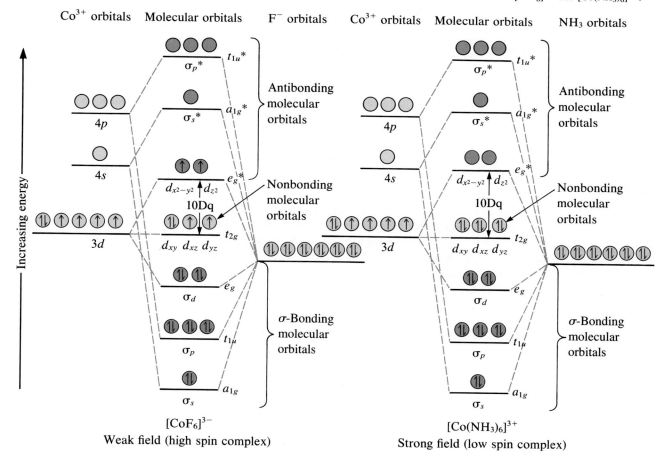

Only the six d electrons of the Co^{3+} ion and the unshared pair of electrons of each of the six ligands (a total of 18 electrons) are included.

The arrangement and symbols shown in Fig. 26.22 are, in general, those described in Chapter 9. In addition, t_{1u}, a_{1g}, e_g, and t_{2g} are used to label the various energy levels. In some cases the molecular orbital is also labeled $d_{x^2-y^2}$, d_{z^2}, or d_{xy}, etc., corresponding to a d orbital. The antibonding and nonbonding energy levels use the e_g* and t_{2g} designations, respectively, in the molecular orbital energy level diagram. The energy difference between them is 10Dq (Sections 26.7 and 26.8).

Figure 26.22 shows that the ligand atomic orbitals are lower in energy than the corresponding metal atomic orbitals. This is indicative of some ionic character (see Section 9.14); that is, the electrons in these orbitals spend more time near the ligands than near the metal ions.

Two of the d orbitals (the e_g orbitals: $d_{x^2-y^2}$ and d_{z^2}), are directed, as indicated in Section 26.7, toward the corners of the octahedron, where the ligands are located. In addition, the one 4s atomic orbital and three 4p atomic orbitals of the metal are also so oriented with respect to the octahedron corners. Hence these metal atomic orbitals overlap with ligand orbitals, and six antibonding and six bonding molecular orbitals are formed. The other three d orbitals (the t_{2g} orbitals: d_{xy}, d_{xz}, and d_{yz}) do not point toward the ligand orbitals and hence are not involved in σ bonding; these molecular orbitals are called nonbonding orbitals. In complexes, therefore, the t_{2g} orbitals are unaffected by σ bonding, whereas each of the e_g orbitals combines with a ligand orbital to give an antibonding molecular orbital and a bonding molecular orbital.

Note in Fig. 26.22 that the 10Dq value is larger for the low-spin complex $[Co(NH_3)_6]^{3+}$. Measurements show the 10Dq value to be approximately 290 kilojoules per mole. Note also that the electrons in the t_{2g} orbitals are paired. For the high-spin complex $[CoF_6]^{3-}$ the 10Dq value is smaller (approximately 150 kilojoules per mole), and two unpaired electrons are in the antibonding molecular orbitals labeled e_g*.

Analogous molecular orbital energy diagrams can be constructed for complexes that have geometrical structures other than octahedral, such as square planar and tetrahedral.

For Review

Summary

Metal ions can form **coordination compounds,** or **complexes,** in which a **central metal atom or ion** is bonded to two or more **ligands** by coordinate covalent bonds. Ligands with more than one donor atom are called **polydentate ligands** and form **chelates.** The common geometries found in complexes are tetrahedral and square planar (both with a **coordination number** of 4) and octahedral (with a coordination number of 6). *Cis* and *trans* **configurations** are possible in some octahedral and square planar complexes. In addition to these geometrical isomers, **optical isomers** (molecules or ions that are mirror images but not identical) are possible in certain octahedral complexes.

The bonding in coordination compounds can be described in terms of valence bond theory, although this model of bonding does not explain the magnetic properties and colors very well. In the valence bond model, the bonds are regarded as normal coordinate covalent bonds between a ligand, which acts as a Lewis base, and an empty hybrid metal atomic orbital.

The **crystal field theory** treats interactions between the electrons on the metal and the ligands as a simple electrostatic effect. The presence of the ligands near the metal ion changes the energies of the metal d orbitals relative to their energies in the free ion. Both the color and the magnetic properties of a complex can be attributed to this **crystal field splitting. Crystal field stabilization energy,** which also results from the crystal field splitting, can enhance the stability of a complex. The magnitude of the splitting (**10Dq**) depends on the nature of the ligands bonded to the metal. Strong-field ligands produce large splittings and favor formation of **low-spin complexes,** in which the t_{2g} orbitals are completely filled before any electrons occupy the e_g orbitals. Weak-field ligands favor formation of **high-spin complexes.** Both the t_{2g} and the e_g orbitals are singly occupied before any are doubly occupied.

The **molecular orbital theory** can describe both the bonding in coordination compounds and the colors and magnetic properties of such complexes.

Key Terms and Concepts

central metal atom or ion (26.1)
chelating ligand (26.1)
cis configuration (26.4)
color (26.10)
coordination number (26.1)
coordination sphere (26.1)
crystal field splitting (26.7)
crystal field stabilization energy,
  CFSE (26.8)

crystal field theory (26.7)
diamagnetic (26.9)
donor atom (26.1)
e_g orbitals (26.7)
geometric isomers (26.4)
high-spin complex (26.8)
hybridization of orbitals (26.6)
inner-shell hybridization (26.6)
isomerism (26.4)

ligands (26.1)
low-spin complex (26.8)
optical isomers (26.4)
outer-shell hybridization (26.6)
paramagnetic (26.9)
polydentate ligand (26.1)
structure of complexes (26.3)
t_{2g} orbitals (26.7)
trans configuration (26.4)

Exercises

Answers for selected even-numbered exercises marked by red numbers appear at the end of the book. The worked-out solutions to all even-numbered exercises appear in the *Solutions Guide*.

Structure and Nomenclature

1. Explain what is meant by: (a) coordination sphere, (b) ligand, (c) donor atom, (d) coordination number, (e) coordination compound, and (f) chelating ligand.
2. Indicate the coordination number for the central metal atom in each of the following coordination compounds.
   (a) $[Pt(H_2O)_2Br_2]$
   (b) $[Pt(NH_3)(py)(Cl)(Br)]$
     (py = pyridine, C_5H_5N)
   (c) $[Zn(NH_3)_2Cl_2]$
   (d) $[Zn(NH_3)(py)(Cl)(Br)]$
   (e) $[Ni(H_2O)_4Cl_2]$
   (f) $[Fe(en)_2(CN)_2]^+$
     (en is ethylenediamine)
3. Using the ligands NH_3 and Cl^-, construct two examples each of square planar complexes with Pt^{2+}, tetrahedral complexes with Zn^{2+}, and octahedral complexes with Co^{3+}. Do not count isomers.
4. Give the coordination number for each coordinated metal ion in the following compounds.
   (a) $[Co(CO_3)_3]^{3-}$
     (CO_3^{2-} is bidentate
     in this complex.)
   (b) $[Cu(NH_3)_4]^{2+}$
   (c) $[Co(NH_3)_4Br_2]_2SO_4$
   (d) $[Pt(NH_3)_4][PtCl_4]$
   (e) $[Cr(en)_3](NO_3)_3$
   (f) $[Pd(NH_3)_2Br_2]$
     (square planar)
   (g) $K_3[Fe(CN)_6]$
   (h) $[Zn(NH_3)_2Cl_2]$
5. Give the coordination numbers and write the formulas for the following, including all isomers where appropriate.

   (a) tetrahydroxozincate(II) ion (tetrahedral)
   (b) hexacyanopalladate(IV) ion
   (c) dichloroaurate(I) ion (*aurum* is Latin for gold)
   (d) diamminedichloroplatinum(II)
   (e) potassium diamminetetrachlorochromate(III)
   (f) hexaamminecobalt(III) hexacyanochromate(III)
   (g) dibromobis(ethylenediamine)cobalt(III) nitrate
6. Name each of the compounds or ions given in Exercise 4.
7. Sketch the structures of the following complexes. Indicate any *cis, trans,* and optical isomers.
   (a) $[Pt(H_2O)_2Br_2]$ (square planar)
   (b) $[Pt(NH_3)(py)(Cl)(Br)]$ (square planar, py = pyridine, C_5H_5N)
   (c) $[Zn(NH_3)_3Cl]^+$ (tetrahedral)
   (d) $[Pt(NH_3)_3Cl]^+$ (square planar)
   (e) $[Ni(H_2O)_4Cl_2]$
   (f) $[Co(C_2O_4)_2Cl_2]^{3-}$ ($C_2O_4^{2-}$ is the bidentate oxalate ion, $^-O_2CCO_2^-$)
8. Draw diagrams for any *cis, trans,* and optical isomers that could exist for the following (en is ethylenediamine).
   (a) $[Co(en)_2(NO_2)Cl]^+$
   (b) $[Co(en)_2Cl_2]^+$
   (c) $[Cr(NH_3)_2(H_2O)_2Br_2]^+$
   (d) $[Pt(NH_3)_2Cl_4]$
   (e) $[Cr(en)_3]^{3+}$
   (f) $[Pt(NH_3)_2Cl_2]$
9. Name each of the compounds or ions given in Exercise 8.
10. Using NH_3 and Br^- as ligands, (a) give the formula of a six-coordinated chromium(III) complex that would not give ions when dissolved in water; (b) give the formula of a complex containing one six-coordinated chromium(III) ion that

would give two ions when dissolved in water; and (c) sketch the isomers of the compounds you formulated in (a) and (b).

11. Sketch each of the isomers for the ion $[Pt(en)(NH_3)_2Br_2]^{2+}$.

12. In this and other chapters we have discussed substances the structures of which encompass a considerable variety of geometric shapes. (a) Name each shape. (b) Draw a diagram of each. (c) Give a specific example of each. (d) Indicate the relationship of atomic orbitals to each of the geometric shapes. (e) Discuss the realtionship of the geometric shape to the number of groups attached to the central element. (*Hint:* It might be helpful to use coordination compounds in your answer, but do not confine your answer to coordination compounds or the material in this chapter alone.)

Bonding in Complexes

13. Draw orbital diagrams and indiate what type of hybridization you would expect for each of the following.
    (a) $[Co(NH_3)_6]^{3+}$
    (b) $[Zn(NH_3)_4]^{2+}$
    (c) $[Cd(CN)_4]^{2-}$
    (d) $[Fe(en)_3]^{3+}$
    (e) $[Fe(CN)_6]^{4-}$

14. Show by means of orbital diagrams the hybridization for each of the examples given in Table 26.1.

15. Determine the number of unpaired electrons expected for $[Fe(CN)_6]^{3-}$ and for $[Fe(H_2O)_6]^{3+}$ in terms of crystal field theory.

16. Verify, by calculation, the crystal field stabilization energies listed in Table 26.2.

17. How many unpaired electrons are present in each of the following?
    (a) $[CoF_6]^{3-}$ (high-spin)
    (b) $[Co(en)_3]^{3+}$ (low-spin)
    (c) $[Mn(CN)_6]^{3-}$ (low-spin)
    (d) $[Mn(CN)_6]^{4-}$ (low-spin)
    (e) $[MnCl_6]^{4-}$ (high-spin)
    (f) $[RhCl_6]^{3-}$ (low-spin)

18. Is it possible for a complex of a metal of the first transition series to have six or seven unpaired electrons? Explain.

19. The crystal field splitting in a tetrahedral complex is

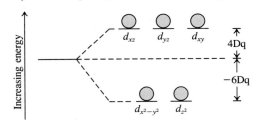

    (a) Show that the crystal field stabilization energy for a tetrahedral complex such as VCl_4 with a d^1 configuration is $-6Dq$.
    (b) All known tetrahedral complexes are high-spin. For what electron configurations is the value of the crystal field stabilization energy the greatest?
    (c) Calculate the CFSE value for each of the following tetrahedral complexes: $[NiCl_4]^{2-}$, $[FeCl_4]^{-}$, $[CoBr_4]^{2-}$, $[Zn(OH)_4]^{2-}$, $[MnCl_4]^{2-}$.

20. What is the significance of the relative energy values of ligand atomic orbitals, metal atomic orbitals, and the corresponding molecular orbitals for $[CoF_6]^{3-}$ and $[Co(NH_3)_6]^{3+}$?

21. For complexes of the same metal ion with no change in oxidation number, the stability increases as the CFSE of the complex increases. Which complex in each of the following pairs of complexes is the more stable? $[Fe(H_2O)_6]^{2+}$ or $[Fe(CN)_6]^{4-}$; $[Co(NH_3)_6]^{3+}$ or $[CoF_6]^{3-}$; $[Mn(H_2O)_6]^{2+}$ or $[MnCl_6]^{4-}$.

22. Explain how the diphosphate ion, $O_3POPO_3^{4-}$, can function as a water softener by complexing Fe^{2+} and preventing the precipitation of an insoluble iron salt.

23. Assume that you have a complex of a transition metal ion with a d^6 configuration. Can you tell whether the complex is octahedral or tetrahedral if measuring the magnetic moment establishes that it has no unpaired electrons? (See Exercise 19 for the crystal field splitting in a tetrahedral complex.)

Additional Exercises

24. Determine the crystal field splitting of the d orbitals in a two-coordinated complex as the two ligands approach the metal along the z axis.

25. What is the crystal field splitting of the nickel ion in NiO? Of the Mn^{2+} ion in MnF_2? (See Section 11.15.)

26. The formation constant for $[Fe(CN)_6]^{3-}$ is 1×10^{44}; that for $[Fe(CN)_6]^{4-}$ is 1×10^{37}. Is this consistent with the difference in CFSE between the two complexes? CN^- is a strong-field ligand in both complexes.

27. Calculate the concentration of free copper ion that is present in equilibrium with 1.0×10^{-3} M $[Cu(NH_3)_4]^{2+}$ and 1.0×10^{-1} M NH_3.

28. Trimethylphosphine, $:P(CH_3)_3$, can act as a ligand by donating the lone pair of electrons on the phosphorus atom. If trimethylphosphine is added to a solution of nickel(II) chloride in acetone, a blue compound that has a molecular mass of approximately 270 and contains 21.5% Ni, 26.0% Cl, and 52.5% $P(CH_3)_3$ can be isolated. This blue compound does not have any isomeric forms. What are the geometry and molecular formula of the blue compound?

29. The standard reduction potential for the reaction

    $$[Co(H_2O)_6]^{3+} + e^- \longrightarrow [Co(H_2O)_6]^{2+}$$

    is about 1.8 V. The reduction potential for the reaction

    $$[Co(NH_3)_6]^{3+} + e^- \longrightarrow [Co(NH_3)_6]^{2+}$$

    is $+0.1$ V. Calculate the cell potentials to show which of the complex ions, $[Co(H_2O)_6]^{2+}$ or $[Co(NH_3)_6]^{2+}$, can be oxidized to the corresponding cobalt(III) complex by oxygen.

30. Using the radius ratio rule and the ionic radii given inside the back cover, predict whether complexes of Ni^{2+}, Mn^{2+}, and Sc^{3+} with Cl^- will be tetrahedral or octahedral. Write the formulas for these complexes.

31. The complex ion $[Co(en)_3]^{3+}$ is diamagnetic. Would you expect the $[Co(en)_3]^{2+}$ ion to be diamagnetic or paramagnetic? The $[Co(CN)_6]^{3-}$ ion? Explain your reasoning in each case.

The Transition Elements

Gold medal (front) from the 1988 Winter Olympics in Calgary, Alberta, Canada.

We have daily contact with several of the transition elements. Iron, copper, nickel, chromium, silver, and gold are the transition metals that are most often encountered. Iron is used in the manufacture of many metal items, ranging from the rings in your notebook and the cutlery in your kitchen to automobiles, ships, and buildings. Copper is used in electrical wiring and coins, nickel in coins, chromium as a protective plating on automobile bumpers and plumbing fixtures, and silver and gold in jewelry.

The outermost s orbital and the first inner d orbitals counting from the outside [the ns and $(n-1)d$ orbitals] make up the valence shells of the transition elements. Some or all of the electrons in these two subshells are used when these elements form compounds. Because a given element can often exhibit several different oxidation numbers and because the presence of a partially filled *d* subshell leads to colored compounds, these elements exhibit a rich and fascinating chemistry.

Periodic Relationships of the Transition Elements

㉗.1 The Transition Metals

Two sets of metallic elements that include a total of 62 elements may be identified as transition metals (Fig. 27.1): the ***d*-block elements,** which are usually called the transition elements (yellow in the periodic table), and the ***f*-block elements,** usually called the inner transition elements (orange in the periodic table). The *d*-block elements are those elements in which the second shell, counting in from the outside is filling from 8 to 18 electrons as its *d* orbitals [the $(n-1)d$ subshell] fill. The *f*-block elements are those elements in which the third shell, counting in from the outside is filling from 18 to 32 electrons as its *f* orbitals [the $(n-2)f$ subshell] fill. Table 5.3 lists the electron configurations of the elements.

Figure 27.1

The location of the *d*-block elements (highlighted in yellow) and the *f*-block elements, the inner transition metals (highlighted in orange), in the periodic table. Nonmetals are shown in green; semi-metals in blue; and the remaining metals in red.

1 IA	2 IIA	3 IIIB	4 IVB	5 VB	6 VIB	7 VIIB	8	9 VIIIB	10	11 IB	12 IIB	13 IIIA	14 IVA	15 VA	16 VIA	17 VIIA	18 VIIIA
H																H	He
Li	Be											B	C	N	O	F	Ne
Na	Mg											Al	Si	P	S	Cl	Ar
K	Ca	Sc	Ti	V	Cr	Mn	Fe	Co	Ni	Cu	Zn	Ga	Ge	As	Se	Br	Kr
Rb	Sr	Y	Zr	Nb	Mo	Tc	Ru	Rh	Pd	Ag	Cd	In	Sn	Sb	Te	I	Xe
Cs	Ba		Hf	Ta	W	Re	Os	Ir	Pt	Au	Hg	Tl	Pb	Bi	Po	At	Rn
Fr	Ra		Unq	Unp	Unh	Uns	Uno	Une									

	La	Ce	Pr	Nd	Pm	Sm	Eu	Gd	Tb	Dy	Ho	Er	Tm	Yb	Lu
	Ac	Th	Pa	U	Np	Pu	Am	Cm	Bk	Cf	Es	Fm	Md	No	Lr

(a)

(b)

Figure 27.2
Examples of transition metals that are used in the fabrication of durable items. (a) Earrings made of titanium; (b) chromium-plated socket wrenches.

The *d*-block elements are divided into the **first transition series** (the elements Sc through Cu in the fourth period of the periodic table), the **second transition series** (the elements Y through Ag in the fifth period), and the **third transition series** (the element La and the elements Hf through Au in the sixth period). Actinium, Ac, is the first member of the **fourth transition series,** which also includes Unq through Une, all in the seventh period. The fourth transition series is incomplete at present. The *f*-block elements are the elements Ce through Lu, which constitute the **lanthanide series** or **rare earth elements,** and the elements Th through Lr, which constitute the **actinide series.**

Because lanthanum behaves very much like the lanthanide elements, it is often considered a lanthanide element, even though its electron configuration makes it the first member of the third transition series. (Examine the placement and color of lanthanum in the periodic table.) Similarly, the behavior of actinium often causes it to be considered with the actinide series, although its electron configuration makes it the first member of the fourth transition series.

The transition elements have common properties. They are almost all hard, strong, high-melting metals (Fig. 27.2) that conduct heat and electricity well. They readily form alloys with one another and with other metallic elements. The elements of the *f*-block, of Group IIIB, and of the first transition series are sufficiently active that they react with acids. Both the *d*-block and the *f*-block elements form a vast array of coordination compounds (see Chapter 26).

In this chapter we shall focus primarily on the chemical behavior of the elements of the first transition series, although we shall occasionally compare these elements with the other elements in the same group.

㉗.2 Preparation of the Transition Metals

Iron, copper, silver, and gold were known to the ancients because these metals occur free in nature (Fig. 27.3). Elemental iron resulting from meteorite falls is found in small quantities; free copper, silver, and gold occur in larger amounts. The largest known deposit of free copper is in the upper peninsula of Michigan, near the border between Canada and the United States. The largest single mass of elemental copper yet found, weighing 420 tons, is on display in the Smithsonian Institution in Washington, D.C.

Most metals are extracted from compounds found in a variety of ores. The ease of recovery varies widely, depending on how difficult it is to separate the metal compound from other compounds in the ore and to reduce the combined element to the metal. The majority of ores contain metal sulfides or metal oxides. We shall discuss the isolation of iron, copper, and silver from their ores in detail because those three specific processes

(b)

(c)

(a)

Figure 27.3

Transition metals occur in nature in various forms. Examples are (a) a nugget of copper, (b) iron in the form of red hematite (Fe_2O_3), and (c) gold.

illustrate the principal means of isolating most metals. First, however, let us look at the general procedures, known as **extractive metallurgy,** for producing metals from their ores. Most such processes include three principal steps: preliminary treatment, smelting, and refining.

1. Preliminary Treatment. Generally, ores must be subjected first to processing to make them suitable for chemical extraction of the metals. This usually involves pulverizing the ore by crushing and grinding, concentrating the metal-bearing portions by removing most of the **gangue** (materials of very little commercial value that are associated with the economically valuable metallic minerals), and sometimes treating the metal compounds chemically to convert them into substances that are more readily reduced to the metal.

2. Smelting. The next step is extraction of the metal in the molten state, a process called **smelting** that includes reduction of the metallic compound to the metal. The remaining gangue is removed by addition of a **flux,** a chemical that reacts with the gangue to form a substance with a low melting point—a **slag.** When the gangue is silica or a silicate (an acidic gangue), a basic flux such as lime or limestone is used. At the high temperature of the furnace in which the reduction occurs, the lime reacts with the silica by a Lewis acid–base reaction to produce fused (molten) calcium silicate. The molten slag is easily separated from the fused metal because of the difference in their densities and because they are insoluble in each other. Sometimes the gangue is a basic gangue, in which case an acidic flux is used.

3. Refining. The final step in the metallurgical process is refining the metal. The low-boiling metals, such as zinc and mercury, can be purified from less volatile metals by distillation. When fused on an inclined table, low-melting metals such as tin flow away from higher-melting impurities. The most common method for refining many metals is by electrolysis.

As illustrations of metallurgy of the transition elements, we shall consider in detail the metallurgy of iron, copper, and silver. Then we shall present several brief vignettes of the metallurgy of other metals of the first transition series, Sc through Cu. (Scandium will not be included because it is of little technological importance and very little of it is produced.)

Metallurgy of Iron

The early application of iron to the manufacture of tools and weapons was possible because of the wide distribution of iron ores and the ease with which the iron compounds in the ores could be reduced by carbon. For a long time charcoal was the form of carbon used in the reduction process. The production and use of iron on a large scale began about 1620, when coal was introduced as the reducing agent.

The important iron oxide ores are **hematite, Fe_2O_3**, and **magnetite, Fe_3O_4**. The presence of Fe_2O_3 accounts largely for the red color of many rocks and soils. Hematite often occurs as the reddish-brown hydrate $2Fe_2O_3 \cdot 3H_2O$, which is called **limonite. Siderite** is a white or brownish carbonate, **$FeCO_3$**. Pyrite, FeS_2 (see Fig. 22.14), occurs as pale yellow crystals with a metallic luster, which are easily mistaken for gold and are therefore called fool's gold.

Taconite, a hard rock composed of crystals of magnetite interlocked with crystals of silica, makes up some 95% of the iron-bearing deposits of the famous Mesabi Range in upper Minnesota. Once regarded as useless for steel production, the taconite ores are now used extensively as a result of the development of satisfactory techniques for mining and concentrating them.

The first step in the metallurgy of iron is usually roasting the ore (heating the ore in air) in order to remove water, decompose carbonates to the oxides, and convert sulfides to the oxides. The oxides are then reduced in a blast furnace 80–100 feet high and about 25 feet in diameter (Fig. 27.4). The charge of roasted ore and coke, along with limestone as a flux, is introduced continuously into the top of the furnace. Molten iron and slag are withdrawn at the bottom. The entire stock in a furnace may weigh several hundred tons.

Near the bottom of a furnace are nozzles through which preheated air (500°C) is blown into the furnace. As soon as the air enters, the coke in the region of the nozzles is oxidized to carbon dioxide with the liberation of a great deal of heat, which raises the temperature to about 1500°C. As the carbon dioxide passes upward through the overlying layer of white-hot coke, it is reduced to carbon monoxide.

$$CO_2 + C \longrightarrow 2CO$$

The carbon monoxide serves as the reducing agent in the upper regions of the furnace. The individual reactions are indicated in Fig. 27.4.

75 ft, 230°C	$3Fe_2O_3 + CO \rightarrow 2Fe_3O_4 + CO_2$
65 ft, 410°C	$Fe_3O_4 + CO \rightarrow 3FeO + CO_2$
55 ft, 525°C	$FeO + CO \rightarrow Fe + CO_2$
45 ft, 865°C	$C + CO_2 \rightarrow 2CO$
35 ft, 945°C	$CaCO_3 \rightarrow CaO + CO_2; \ C + CO_2 \rightarrow 2CO$
25 ft, 1125°C	$CaO + SiO_2 \rightarrow CaSiO_3; \ C + CO_2 \rightarrow 2CO$
15 ft, 1300°C	$C + O_2 \rightarrow CO_2$
5 ft, 1510°C	

CO, CO_2, N_2

Iron ore, coke, limestone

Air inlet

Slag

Molten iron   Outlet

Figure 27.4

Reactions that occur at different levels within a blast furnace. Heights of the levels are designated in feet.

The iron oxides are completely reduced in the upper region of the furnace. In the middle region, limestone (calcium carbonate) decomposes, and the resulting calcium oxide combines with silica and silicates in the ore to form slag.

$$CaO + SiO_2 \longrightarrow CaSiO_3$$

Just below the middle of the furnace, the temperature is high enough to melt both the iron and the slag. They collect in layers at the bottom of the furnace; the less dense slag floats on the iron and protects it from oxidation. Several times a day, the slag and molten iron are withdrawn from the furnace. The iron is transferred to casting machines or to a steelmaking plant (Fig. 27.5). The slag is often used in the manufacture of Portland cement (Section 25.17). A modern blast furnace can produce as much as 3000 tons of iron daily.

The hot exhaust gases, which issue from the top of the blast furnace, contain some unoxidized carbon monoxide and are mixed with air and burned to preheat the air used in the operation of the blast furnace.

The manufacture of steel will be discussed in Section 27.18.

Metallurgy of Copper

The most important copper ores are sulfides such as **chalcocite, Cu_2S,** and **chalcopyrite, $CuFeS_2$.** Other ores are **cuprite, Cu_2O, melaconite, CuO,** and **malachite, $Cu_2(OH)_2CO_3$.** (Malachite is the green ore shown on our book cover.)

Ores that contain elemental (free) copper are pulverized, the unwanted rock material (gangue) is washed away, and the copper is melted and poured into molds to cool. Oxide and carbonate ores are often leached (dissolved out using a solvent) with sulfuric acid to produce copper(II) sulfate solutions, from which copper metal may be obtained by electrodeposition (see Chapter 20). High-grade oxide and carbonate ores are reduced by heating them with coke mixed with a suitable flux, which removes impurities by combining with them.

Sulfide ores usually contain less than 10% copper. These ores are first concentrated by **flotation.** In this process the pulverized ore is mixed with water to which a carefully selected oil has been added. A froth is produced by blowing air through the mixture. The metal sulfide particles have little or no attraction for water, but their surfaces are preferentially coated by the oil. The oily particles adhere to the air bubbles in the froth, which floats on the surface. The particles of sand, rock, clay, etc., are wetted by water and sink to the bottom of the flotation vat. The froth containing the metal-bearing particles is removed, and the ore is recovered in a highly concentrated form.

The concentrate is then roasted in a furnace, at a temperature below its melting point, to drive off the moisture and remove part of the sulfur as sulfur dioxide. The remaining mixture, which consists of Cu_2S, FeS, FeO, and SiO_2, is smelted (extracted in the molten state) by mixing it with limestone, which serves as a flux, and heating the mixture so that it melts. The reactions that take place during the formation of the slag are

$$CaCO_3 + SiO_2 \longrightarrow CaSiO_3 + CO_2$$

$$FeO + SiO_2 \longrightarrow FeSiO_3$$

Reduction of the Cu_2S that remains after smelting is accomplished by blowing air through the molten material. The air converts part of the Cu_2S to Cu_2O. As soon as copper(I) oxide is formed, it is reduced by the remaining copper(I) sulfide to metallic copper.

Figure 27.5
Casting molten iron.

$$2Cu_2S + 3O_2 \longrightarrow 2Cu_2O + 2SO_2$$

$$2Cu_2O + Cu_2S \longrightarrow 6Cu + SO_2$$

The last traces of copper oxide are removed by reduction with H_2 and CO produced from natural gas. The copper obtained in this way is called **blister copper** because of its characteristic appearance, which is due to the air blisters it contains (Fig. 27.6).

The impure copper is cast into large plates, which are used as anodes in the electrolytic refining of the metal (see Section 20.14). Thin sheets of pure copper serve as the cathodes; copper(II) sulfate, in a solution of sulfuric acid, is used as the electrolyte. The impure copper passes into solution from the anodes, and pure copper plates out onto the cathodes as electrolysis proceeds. The copper deposited on the cathode has an average purity of 99.95%. Inert metals in the anodes do not oxidize but fall to the bottom of the electrolytic cell as anode mud, along with bits of slag and Cu_2O. Silver, gold, and the platinum metals are recovered from the anode mud. The value of the precious metals recovered from the anode mud is often sufficient to pay the cost of the electrolytic refining. Metals more active than copper, such as zinc and iron, are oxidized at the anode, and their cations pass into solution, where they remain.

Figure 27.6

Blister copper.

Metallurgy of Silver

Silver is found sometimes in large nuggets (Fig. 27.7) but more frequently in veins and related deposits. It is frequently found alloyed with gold, copper, or mercury. It occurs combined as the chloride, **AgCl (horn silver),** and as the sulfide, **Ag_2S,** which is usually mixed with the sulfides of lead, copper, nickel, arsenic, and antimony. Most silver produced is a by-product of the mining of other metals such as lead and copper. Another source of silver is the anode mud formed during the electrolytic refining of copper (as discussed above).

When lead is obtained from lead sulfide ore, it is usually mixed with some silver. The silver is extracted by the use of zinc, in which silver is about 3000 times more soluble than it is in lead. The lead is melted and thoroughly mixed with a small quantity of zinc. Lead and zinc are immiscible. Most of the silver leaves the lead and dissolves in the zinc. When mixing is stopped, the zinc rises to the surface of the lead and solidifies. The zinc–silver alloy is removed from the lead, and the more volatile zinc is separated from the silver by distillation. This extraction procedure is known as the **Parkes process.**

The extraction of silver from its ores is often accomplished by a process called **hydrometallurgy,** the general separation of a metal from other metals by causing it to go into aqueous solution as a soluble complex ion and then precipitating it as the free metal via a suitable reducing agent. In the presence of air, alkali metal cyanides readily form the soluble dicyanoargentate(I) ion, $[Ag(CN)_2]^-$, from silver metal and all of its compounds. Representative equations are

$$4Ag + 8CN^- + O_2 + 2H_2O \longrightarrow 4[Ag(CN)_2]^- + 4OH^-$$

$$2Ag_2S + 8CN^- + O_2 + 2H_2O \longrightarrow 4[Ag(CN)_2]^- + 2S + 4OH^-$$

$$AgCl + 2CN^- \rightleftharpoons [Ag(CN)_2]^- + Cl^-$$

The silver is precipitated from the cyanide solution by addition of either zinc or aluminum, which serves as a reducing agent.

$$2[Ag(CN)_2]^- + Zn \longrightarrow 2Ag + [Zn(CN)_4]^{2-}$$

Figure 27.7

Naturally occurring free silver may be found as nuggets or in veins.

Hydrometallurgy is also used in the extraction of other precious metals. An example is the extraction of gold through the formation of the $[Au(CN)_2]^-$ ion.

Vignettes of Metallurgy of Other Members of the First Transition Series

As with iron, most ores of titanium, vanadium, chromium, and manganese contain these elements as oxides. The metals are recovered by reduction after the oxides have been separated from other minerals in the ores. As with copper, the common ores of cobalt and nickel contain these elements as mixtures of sulfides that often include iron sulfides.

Titanium and Vanadium. Titanium is recovered by reaction of titanium(IV) oxide with carbon and chlorine at red heat, forming titanium(IV) chloride.

$$TiO_2 + C + 2Cl_2 \xrightarrow{\Delta} TiCl_4 + CO_2$$

The $TiCl_4$ is then reduced with magnesium metal at about 1000°C. At the temperatures of the reaction, magnesium metal is a liquid (melting point 651°C); the magnesium chloride is volatile and sublimes away, leaving solid titanium metal (melting point 1675°C).

$$TiCl_4(g) + 2Mg(l) \xrightarrow{\Delta} Ti(s) + 2MgCl_2(g)$$

An inert atmosphere (one without possible reactants) is used to prevent oxidation of the titanium metal. The process by which **vanadium** is produced is similar; in it, calcium metal is used to reduce vanadium(V) oxide, V_2O_5, to vanadium metal.

Chromium and Manganese. These elements are produced by the high-temperature reduction of the oxides Cr_2O_3 and MnO_2, respectively, with aluminum metal.

$$Cr_2O_3 + 2Al \longrightarrow 2Cr + Al_2O_3$$

$$3MnO_2 + 4Al \longrightarrow 3Mn + 2Al_2O_3$$

Chromium is also produced by the electrolytic reduction of its compounds from aqueous solution, a process used in chromium plating.

Cobalt and Nickel. These elements are more difficult to recover than iron because of the need to separate the various metal sulfides and the difficulty of reducing some of the metal ions. Seventeenth-century metallurgists thought that nickel ores were copper ores because of the similarity in appearance, but when the ores failed to yield copper, they were called *kupfernickel*. In German *kupfer* means copper, and *nickel* means a devil, one of which was thought to prevent the extraction of copper from the ores. The name *cobalt* is derived from the German word *kobold*, which means goblin. Early metallurgists believed that goblins carefully guarded the cobalt ores to prevent human beings from liberating the metal.

The metallurgy of cobalt involves the separation of cobalt sulfide from the nickel, copper, and iron sulfides, its conversion to Co_3O_4, and the reduction of this oxide with aluminum or hydrogen.

$$3Co_3O_4 + 8Al \longrightarrow 9Co + 4Al_2O_3$$

$$Co_3O_4 + 4H_2 \longrightarrow 3Co + 4H_2O$$

The impure metal is purified by electrolytic deposition on a rotating stainless steel cathode.

Nickel is recovered by roasting the ore in air or pure oxygen to convert the sulfide to the oxide. The oxide is then reduced by carbon, giving a metal that is approximately 96% pure. It is purified electrolytically to 99.98% nickel. Any gold, silver, or platinum that may be present is not affected by the electrolysis and is recovered from the residues at the anode.

㉗.3 Properties of the Transition Elements

Figure 27.8
Solutions containing $Cr^{3+}(aq)$, $Fe^{3+}(aq)$, and $Co^{2+}(aq)$ (left, center, and right, respectively) are stable.

Both the *d*-block (transition) and *f*-block (inner transition) elements are metals and generally have the usual physical properties of metals. However, these elements vary from active to very inactive metals.

The elements of the first transition series (Sc through Cu) form ionic compounds that dissolve in water giving stable solvated cations. The heavier *d*-block elements usually do not form simple positive ions that are stable in water. Thus the Cr^{3+}, Fe^{3+}, and Co^{2+} ions are stable in aqueous solutions (Fig. 27.8), whereas the Mo^{3+}, Ru^{2+}, and Ir^{2+} ions are not. The majority of simple water-stable ions formed by the heavier *d*-block elements are oxyanions such as MoO_4^{2-} and ReO_4^{-}.

The heavier elements of Group VIIIB (ruthenium, osmium, rhodium, iridium, palladium, and platinum) are sometimes called the **platinum metals.** These elements and gold are particularly nonreactive. They do not form simple cations that are stable in water, and, unlike the earlier elements in the second and third transition series, they do not form stable oxyanions.

The inner transition elements, the *f*-block elements, are among the most active of the transition elements.

The transition elements (here we use the term broadly to refer to both the *d*-block elements and the *f*-block elements) react with nonmetals to form binary compounds; heating is usually required. Both the *d*-block and the *f*-block elements react with halogens to form a variety of halides ranging in oxidation number from +1 to +6. With the exception of palladium, platinum, and gold, they react with sulfur to form sulfides. On heating, oxygen reacts with all of the transition elements except palladium, platinum, silver, and gold; the oxides of these, even if formed, decompose upon heating. The *f*-block elements, the elements of Group IIIB, and the elements of the first transition series (except copper) are sufficiently active to react with aqueous solutions of strong acids, forming hydrogen and solutions of the corresponding salts.

As we cross the three series of the *d*-block elements from left to right on the periodic table, we find that each successive element through the manganese family can form compounds with a wider range of oxidation numbers. The oxidation numbers of the elements of the first transition series are listed in Table 27.1.

The elements at the beginning of the first transition series exhibit a highest oxidation number that corresponds to the loss of all of the electrons in both the *s* and *d* orbitals of their valence shell. The titanium(IV) ion, for example, is formed when the titanium atom loses its two 3*d* and two 4*s* electrons. These group oxidation numbers are the most stable oxidation numbers for scandium, titanium, and vanadium. Moving across the series, it becomes progressively more difficult to form these highest oxidation numbers. Scandium, like aluminum, exhibits no lower oxidation numbers in its compounds. Compounds of titanium(IV) are harder to reduce than those of vanadium(V), which in turn are harder to reduce than those of chromium(VI) or manganese(VII). No compounds of iron(VIII) are known. Beyond manganese, the elements are stable with oxidation numbers of +1, +2, or +3. All the elements of the first transition series form ions with a

Table 27.1		Oxidation Numbers of the Elements of the First Transition Series							
Sc	Ti	V	Cr	Mn	Fe	Co	Ni	Cu	
								+1	
	+2	+2	+2	+2	+2	+2	+2	+2	
+3	+3	+3	+3	+3	+3	+3		+3	
	+4	+4	+4	+4					
		+5	+5						
			+6	+6					
				+7					

charge of $+2$ or $+3$ that are stable in water, although those of the early members of the series can be readily oxidized by air.

The elements of the second and third transition series generally are more stable with higher oxidation numbers than are the elements of the first series. For example, the simple chemistry of molybdenum and tungsten, members of Group VIB, is limited to an oxidation number of $+6$ in aqueous solution. Chromium, the lightest member of the group, forms stable Cr^{3+} ions in water and, in the absence of air, stable Cr^{2+} ions in water. The sulfide with the highest oxidation number for chromium is Cr_2S_3, which contains the Cr^{3+} ion. Molybdenum and tungsten form sulfides in which the metal exhibits oxidation numbers of $+4$ and $+6$.

27.4 The Lanthanide Contraction

Much of the similarity of the chemistry of the elements of the second and third transition series can be attributed to the similar sizes of these elements within each group, in addition to their similarity in valence electron structure. As the table of atomic and ionic radii on the inside back cover of this book shows, the expected increase in radii of the atoms or ions occurs in going down a group from the first d-block transition series to the second series. However, within a given group of d-block transition elements, the radii of the elements of the second and third series are almost the same. This is because the lanthanide elements (f-block), which are between lanthanum in Group IIIB (atomic number 57) and hafnium in Group IVB (atomic number 72) exhibit decreasing size with increasing atomic number, as is shown by the ionic radii ($+3$ ion) listed in Table 27.2. This size decrease, referred to as the **lanthanide contraction,** results in an expected regular gradation in properties through the series, including a decrease in the basicity of the hydroxides, $M(OH)_3$, with increasing atomic number of the elements.

Also as a result of the lanthanide contraction, and illustrative of the foregoing statement about similarities in sizes of corresponding d-block transition elements of the second and third series in a given group, zirconium and hafnium are the same size (atomic radius, 1.57 Å); hafnium is smaller than expected because of the contraction in size through the lanthanide elements immediately preceding it. Zirconium and hafnium, because they are not only in the same family but also of the same size, are similar in chemical properties, occur together in nature, and are difficult to separate (Section 27.10). The pairs niobium and tantalum, and molybdenum and tungsten, are also more similar in size than expected and, accordingly, more similar in properties. The lantha-

Table 27.2		Electron Configurations and Ionic Radii of the Lanthanide Elements (Rare Earth Elements)	
Atomic Number	Element	Electron Configuration	Ionic (M^{3+}) Radius, Å
57	La	$[Xe]4f^05d^16s^2$	1.15
58	Ce	$[Xe]4f^25d^06s^2$	1.034
59	Pr	$[Xe]4f^35d^06s^2$	1.013
60	Nd	$[Xe]4f^45d^06s^2$	0.995
61	Pm	$[Xe]4f^55d^06s^2$	0.979
62	Sm	$[Xe]4f^65d^06s^2$	0.964
63	Eu	$[Xe]4f^75d^06s^2$	0.950
64	Gd	$[Xe]4f^75d^16s^2$	0.938
65	Tb	$[Xe]4f^95d^06s^2$	0.923
66	Dy	$[Xe]4f^{10}5d^06s^2$	0.908
67	Ho	$[Xe]4f^{11}5d^06s^2$	0.894
68	Er	$[Xe]4f^{12}5d^06s^2$	0.881
69	Tm	$[Xe]4f^{13}5d^06s^2$	0.869
70	Yb	$[Xe]4f^{14}5d^06s^2$	0.858
71	Lu	$[Xe]4f^{14}5d^16s^2$	0.848

nide contraction also accounts for the fact that yttrium has nearly the same radius as gadolinium, which is about midway through the lanthanide series. Being very similar to the lanthanide elements in charge and size characteristics, yttrium has very similar properties and occurs with those elements in nature.

Figure 27.9 illustrates the effect of the lanthanide contraction on sizes of the elements in the third transition series. Whereas the elements of the second transition series, as expected, have larger atomic radii than the corresponding elements of the first transition series, the elements of the third transition series have about the same atomic radii as the corresponding elements of the second transition series. A similar graph of ionic radii of ions of the same charge would show the same effect. (See the table on the inside back cover for atomic and ionic radii.)

It is also interesting to note that the lanthanide contraction has an effect on the ionization energies of elements in the third transition series. Whereas, in general, ionization energies decrease from top to bottom within periodic table groups, the elements of the third transition series (which follow the lanthanide contraction) are *higher* than the corresponding elements in the second transition series (see Table 6.4). This occurs because both the larger nuclear charge and the smaller size work to require more energy to remove an electron from the atom. This effect on ionization energy persists throughout the elements in the third transition series and even throughout the representative elements mercury, thallium and lead.

27.5 Compounds of the Transition Metals

The simple compounds of the transition metals range from ionic to covalent. In their lower oxidation states, the transition metals form ionic compounds; in their higher oxidation states, they form covalent compounds. Unlike the active metals, the variation in

Figure 27.9

The effect of the lanthanide contraction on size (atomic radius) of the elements of the third transition series. As a result of the contraction, the elements of the third transition series are close to the same size as those of the second transition series.

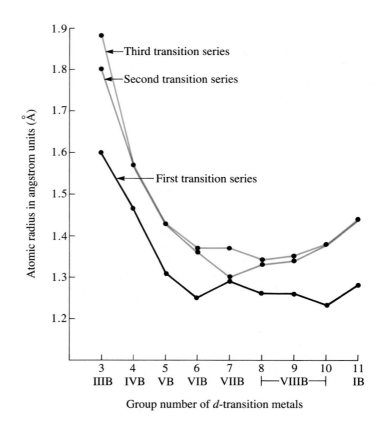

Group number of d-transition metals

oxidation states of the transition metals gives these compounds a metal-based oxidation–reduction chemistry. The chemistry of several classes of compounds containing the transition metals follows.

Halides

Anhydrous halides of each of the transition elements can be prepared by the direct reaction of the metal with halogens. For example,

$$2Fe + 3Cl_2 \longrightarrow 2FeCl_3$$

Heating a metal halide with additional metal can be used to form a halide of the metal with a lower oxidation number.

$$Fe + 2FeCl_3 \longrightarrow 3FeCl_2$$

The stoichiometry of the metal halide that results from the reaction of a metal with a halogen is determined by the relative amounts of metal and halogen and by the strength of the halogen as an oxidizing agent. Generally fluorine forms fluorides containing metals in their highest oxidation numbers. The other halogens may not form analogous compounds. In fact, the iodide ion is a sufficiently good reducing agent that the iodides of some metals are limited to compounds containing the metal in its lowest oxidation number. The oxidation numbers of the first transition series metals in their halides are given in Table 27.3.

Table 27.3   **Oxidation Numbers of the First Transition Series Metals in Their Halides**

	Sc	Ti	V	Cr	Mn	Fe	Co	Ni	Cu
F	3	3,4	3,4,5	2,3,4,5	2,3,4	2,3	2,3	2	2
Cl	3	2,3,4	2,3,4	2,3	2	2,3	2	2	1,2
Br	3	2,3,4	2,3,4	2,3	2	2,3	2	2	1,2
I	3	2,3,4	2,3	2,3	2	2	2	2	1

The nature of the bonding in the anhydrous halides of the elements of the first transition series varies with the oxidation number of the metal. Halides of metals with lower oxidation numbers are ionic; halides of metals with higher oxidation numbers are covalent. For example, the titanium chlorides $TiCl_2$ and $TiCl_3$ are ionic compounds with high melting points, whereas $TiCl_4$ is a volatile liquid with covalent titanium–chlorine bonds. All halides of the heavier d-block elements have significant covalent character.

Stable water solutions of the halides of the metals of the first transition series, the lanthanide elements, and of the actinides are generally prepared by addition of a hydrohalic acid to carbonates, hydroxides, oxides, or other compounds containing basic anions. Sample reactions are

$$NiCO_3(s) + 2H_3O^+(aq) + [2F^-(aq)] \longrightarrow$$
$$Ni^{2+}(aq) + [2F^-(aq)] + 3H_2O(l) + CO_2(g)$$

$$Co(OH)_2(s) + 2H_3O^+(aq) + [2Br^-(aq)] \longrightarrow Co^{2+}(aq) + [2Br^-(aq)] + 4H_2O(l)$$

$$La_2O_3(s) + 6H_3O^+(aq) + [6I^-(aq)] \longrightarrow 2La^{3+}(aq) + [6I^-(aq)] + 9H_2O(l)$$

Many of these metals also dissolve in these acids, forming a solution of the salt and hydrogen gas. Evaporation of the water gives hydrated halides such as $NiF_2 \cdot 6H_2O$, $CoBr_2 \cdot 7H_2O$, and $LaI_3 \cdot 9H_2O$, where the centered dots in the formulas indicate that the water is present in the solids as water of hydration (that is, as identifiable molecules; see Section 13.3, Part 3). The metals of the second and third transition series are generally not soluble in acids.

The reaction of water with the anhydrous halides of the elements of the first transition series depends on the oxidation number of the transition metal. Compounds with metal oxidation numbers of $+1$, $+2$, and $+3$, if soluble, dissolve to form solutions containing metal ions and the respective halide ions. Those transition metal ions that are not stable in water react with it or disproportionate (see Section 21.2); Ti^{2+} is oxidized by water, Co^{3+} is reduced by water, and Cu^+ disproportionates by the reaction

$$2Cu^+ \longrightarrow Cu + Cu^{2+}$$

A majority of the halides of the elements of the second and third transition series either are not soluble or react with water.

The covalent behavior of the transition metals with higher oxidation numbers is exemplified by the reaction of the metal tetrahalides with water. Both the covalent titanium and vanadium tetrahalides react with water to give solutions containing the corresponding hydrohalic acids and the covalent oxyions TiO^{2+} and VO^{2+}, respectively.

$$TiCl_4(l) + 3H_2O(l) \longrightarrow TiO^{2+}(aq) + 2H_3O^+(aq) + 4Cl^-(aq)$$

$$VBr_4(l) + 3H_2O(l) \longrightarrow VO^{2+}(aq) + 2H_3O^+(aq) + 4Br^-(aq)$$

The tetrafluorides of chromium and manganese react with water, forming hydrofluoric acid and precipitates of the dioxides. Vanadium(V) fluoride reacts with water and forms hydrofluoric acid and vanadium(V) oxide.

Oxides

Oxides of the transition metals with oxidation numbers of $+1$, $+2$, and $+3$ behave as ionic compounds that contain metal ions and oxide ions, whereas those with oxidation numbers of $+4$, $+5$, $+6$, and $+7$ contain covalent metal–oxygen bonds. Table 27.4 lists the common oxides of the metals of the first transition series. The oxides indicated in boldface in Table 27.4 are stable when heated in air and form when the metals are oxidized by heating in air. They also form when hydroxides, carbonates, oxalates, and certain other oxides of these metals are heated in air.

Oxides of the metals of the first transition series with lower metal oxidation numbers can be prepared by heating an oxide containing the metal in a higher oxidation number with a reducing agent such as hydrogen or the metal. For example, **vanadium(III) oxide, V_2O_3,** can be prepared by heating vanadium(V) oxide in an atmosphere of hydrogen; **titanium(II) oxide, TiO,** can be prepared from titanium(IV) oxide and titanium metal.

$$V_2O_5 + 2H_2(g) \xrightarrow{800°C} V_2O_3 + 2H_2O(g)$$

$$TiO_2 + Ti \xrightarrow{1200°C} 2TiO$$

Alternatively, many of these compounds can be produced by heating the corresponding hydroxides, carbonates, or oxalates in an inert atmosphere. **Iron(II) oxide** can be made by heating iron(II) oxalate, and **cobalt(II) oxide** by heating cobalt(II) hydroxide.

$$FeC_2O_4 \longrightarrow FeO + CO + CO_2$$

$$Co(OH)_2 \longrightarrow CoO + H_2O(g)$$

Oxides of the transition metals with higher oxidation numbers are formed by precipitation from acidic solution or by oxidation under special conditions. For example, **chromium(VI) oxide, CrO_3,** is produced as scarlet crystals when concentrated sulfuric acid is added to a concentrated solution of potassium dichromate. **Cobalt(III) oxide, Co_2O_3,** can be produced by gently heating cobalt(II) nitrate.

Table 27.4   Oxides of the Metals of the First Transition Series[a]

Sc	Ti	V	Cr	Mn	Fe	Co	Ni	Cu
								Cu_2O
	TiO	VO		MnO	FeO	CoO	**NiO**	**CuO**
				Mn_3O_4	**Fe_3O_4**	**Co_3O_4**		
Sc_2O_3	**Ti_2O_3**	V_2O_3	**Cr_2O_3**	Mn_2O_3	Fe_2O_3	Co_2O_3		
	TiO_2	VO_2	CrO_2	MnO_2				
		V_2O_5						
			CrO_3					
				Mn_2O_7				

[a]The oxides in boldface form when the metal is heated in air.

The elements of the early portion of the second and third transition series are generally oxidized to their highest oxidation numbers when heated in air. The oxides of the platinum metals are unstable at elevated temperatures and must be prepared by indirect methods, such as the careful dehydration of the hydroxides or precipitation.

Ionic oxides crystallize with the metal ions occupying holes in an array of oxide ions. In such structures, one metal ion can substitute for another of about the same size. As can be seen in the table of ionic radii (inside back cover of this book), the radii of the transition metal ions are similar, so substituting one transition metal ion for another is easy. Thus oxides that contain mixtures of the same metal ions with different oxidation numbers or mixtures of two or more types of metal ions are well known. For example, Mn_3O_4, Fe_3O_4, and Co_3O_4 all contain one M^{2+} ion and two M^{3+} ions for every four O^{2-} ions. Some of the metal ions can be replaced by other divalent metal ions. For example, the Mn^{2+} ion in Mn_3O_4 can be replaced by Mg^{2+} or by Fe^{2+}, giving $MgMn_2O_4$ or $FeMn_2O_4$, respectively. The trivalent ions can also be replaced; $MnAl_2O_4$, $MnCo_2O_4$, and $MnCr_2O_4$ are examples.

With the exception of CrO_3 and Mn_2O_7, transition metal oxides are not soluble in water. They exhibit their acid–base properties by reacting with acids or bases. Trends in acidity are as we would expect from the principles enumerated in Section 16.5 regarding size and oxidation number of the central element.

Overall, oxides of transition metals with the lowest oxidation numbers are basic, the intermediate ones are amphoteric, and the highest ones are primarily acidic. The oxides of metals with oxidation numbers of +1, +2, and +3 are basic; they react with aqueous acids to form solutions of salts and water. Examples include

$$CoO(s) + 2H_3O^+(aq) + [2NO_3^-(aq)] \longrightarrow Co^{2+}(aq) + [2NO_3^-(aq)] + 3H_2O(l)$$

$$NiO(s) + 2H_3O^+(aq) + [SO_4^{2-}(aq)] \longrightarrow Ni^{2+}(aq) + [SO_4^{2-}(aq)] + 3H_2O(l)$$

$$Sc_2O_3(s) + 6H_3O^+(aq) + [6Cl^-(aq)] \longrightarrow 2Sc^{3+}(aq) + [6Cl^-(aq)] + 9H_2O(l)$$

The oxides of metals with oxidation numbers of +4 are amphoteric, and most are not soluble in either acids or bases. **Vanadium(V) oxide, chromium(VI) oxide,** and **manganese(VII) oxide** are acidic. They react with solutions of hydroxides to form salts of the oxyanions VO_4^{3-}, CrO_4^{2-}, and MnO_4^-. For example,

$$CrO_3(s) + [2Na^{2+}(aq)] + 2OH^-(aq) \longrightarrow [2Na^+(aq)] + CrO_4^{2-}(aq) + H_2O(l)$$

Chromium(VI) oxide and manganese(VII) oxide react with water to form the acids H_2CrO_4 and $HMnO_4$, respectively.

Hydroxides

When a hydroxide solution of an active metal is added to an aqueous solution of a salt of a transition metal of the first transition series, a gelatinous precipitate forms. For example, adding a solution of sodium hydroxide to a solution of cobalt sulfate produces a gelatinous blue precipitate of **cobalt(II) hydroxide.**

$$Co^{2+}(aq) + [SO_4^{2-}(aq)] + [2Na^+(aq)] + 2OH^-(aq) \longrightarrow$$
$$Co(OH)_2(s) + [2Na^+(aq)] + [SO_4^{2-}(aq)]$$

In this and many other cases these precipitates are hydroxides containing the transition metal ion, hydroxide ions, and water coordinated to the transition metal. Upon gentle warming, the anhydrous hydroxides can be obtained from these precipitates, but if the precipitates are heated too strongly, they may decompose to oxides. In other cases the precipitates are hydrated oxides composed of the metal ion, oxide ions, and water of hydration. These substances do not contain hydroxide ions. Both the hydroxides and the hydrated oxides either react with acids to form salts and water or react with many of the oxides of the nonmetals to form salts with oxyanions such as those shown in Table 13.5.

Carbonates

Many of the elements of the first transition series form insoluble carbonates. Thus these carbonates can be prepared by the addition of a soluble carbonate salt to a solution of a transition metal salt. For example, **nickel carbonate** can be prepared from solutions of nickel nitrate and sodium carbonate.

$$Ni^{2+}(aq) + [2NO_3^-(aq)] + [2Na^+(aq)] + CO_3^{2-}(aq) \longrightarrow$$
$$NiCO_3(s) + [2Na^+(aq)] + [2NO_3^-(aq)]$$

Solutions of the carbonate ion contain hydroxide ion as a result of the basic character of the carbonate ion, which is the anion of the weak polyprotic acid H_2CO_3 (see Section 17.11).

$$CO_3^{2-} + H_2O \rightleftharpoons HCO_3^- + OH^-$$

$$HCO_3^- + H_2O \rightleftharpoons H_2CO_3 + OH^-$$

If a transition metal forms a hydroxide or a hydrated oxide that is less soluble than the transition metal carbonate, the hydroxide or hydrated oxide forms in preference to the carbonate; precipitation of the less soluble substance is a driving force for the metathesis reaction (Section 2.11, Part 3a).

The reactions of the transition metal carbonates are similar to those of the active metal carbonates (see Section 13.7). They react with acids to form metal salts, carbon dioxide, and water. Upon heating, they decompose, forming the transition metal oxides.

Sulfides

Transition metal sulfides can be prepared by heating the metals with sulfur; by heating gaseous hydrogen sulfide with the metals or with certain metal oxides, hydroxides, or carbonates; and because most transition metal sulfides are insoluble, they can be prepared by adding a solution of a soluble sulfide to aqueous solutions of transition metal salts.

$$Fe + S \longrightarrow FeS$$

$$Mo + 2H_2S \longrightarrow MoS_2 + 2H_2$$

$$Cu^{2+}(aq) + S^{2-}(aq) \longrightarrow CuS(s)$$

Precipitation reactions and the reactions with hydrogen sulfide usually give compounds in which the metal exhibits a single oxidation number. The stoichiometry of the direct reaction of sulfur with a metal can be adjusted so that the product contains mixed oxidation states. This is observed in V_5S_8, for example, which contains V^{3+} and V^{4+} ions.

The sulfide ion is a stronger reducing agent than the oxide ion, so many sulfides in which the metal exhibits a high oxidation number are not stable; the metal is reduced by the sulfide ion. With the exception of TiS_2 and VS_2, sulfides of the first transition series are limited to those in which the metals have oxidation numbers of +1, +2, or +3.

Metals of the second and third transition series form sulfides with higher oxidation numbers, because these elements are more stable with higher oxidation numbers.

Other Salts

A wide variety of salts containing transition metals have been prepared. Simple salts of oxyanions such as the nitrate, sulfate, and perchlorate ions are usually stable only with metals of the first transition series. Soluble salts of the heavier transition metals are generally found only as the oxyanions of these metals. A variety of salts can be prepared from the metals or from the common compounds that we have just discussed. Examples of these preparations include the following:

1. **Reactions of Acids with Basic Metal Compounds.** Oxides, hydroxides, and carbonates of the elements of the first transition series react with solutions of most acids to form solutions of salts, which can be isolated by evaporation of the solvent. Like the halides, the solid compounds usually contain water of hydration. The reaction of nickel carbonate with nitric acid is an example; hydrated nickel nitrate forms when the resulting solution is evaporated.

$$NiCO_3(s) + 2H_3O^+(aq) + [2NO_3^-(aq)] \longrightarrow$$
$$Ni^{2+}(aq) + [2NO_3^-(aq)] + CO_2(g) + 3H_2O(l)$$

$$Ni^{2+}(aq) + 2NO_3^-(aq) + 6H_2O(l) \xrightarrow{\text{Evaporation}} Ni(NO_3)_2 \cdot 6H_2O(aq)$$

2. **Oxidation–Reduction Reactions.** With the exception of copper, the elements of the first transition series are more active than hydrogen and react with acids, liberating hydrogen gas. The reaction of these metals with acids is a second source for their salts. A solution of **iron(II) perchlorate,** for example, can be prepared by the reaction of metallic iron with an aqueous solution of perchloric acid.

$$Fe(s) + 2H_3O^+(aq) + [2ClO_4^-(aq)] \longrightarrow$$
$$Fe^{2+}(aq) + [2ClO_4^-(aq)] + H_2(g) + 2H_2O(l)$$

Copper and the other elements react with nitric acid and with concentrated sulfuric acid by oxidation–reduction reactions involving the oxyanion of the acid.

3. **Metathesis Reactions.** Insoluble salts can be prepared by mixing solutions of two soluble compounds. **Barium chromate** is prepared in this way from the soluble salts barium chloride and potassium chromate.

$$Ba^{2+}(aq) + [2Cl^-(aq)] + [2K^+(aq)] + CrO_4^{2-}(aq) \longrightarrow$$
$$BaCrO_4(s) + [2K^+(aq)] + [2Cl^-(aq)]$$

4. **Preparation of Oxyanions.** Salts containing transition metal oxyanions such as VO_4^{3-}, CrO_4^{2-}, MoO_4^{2-}, and WO_4^{2-} can be prepared by heating active metal oxides or hydroxides with the corresponding oxides of the transition metals, or by the reaction of solutions of hydroxides with the oxides. These reactions generally occur without a change in the oxidation number of the transition metal. For example,

$$V_2O_5 + 3Li_2O \xrightarrow{\Delta} 2Li_3VO_4$$

$$MoO_3(s) + 2NaOH(s) \xrightarrow{\Delta} Na_2MoO_4(s) + H_2O(g)$$

$$CrO_3(s) + [2K^+(aq)] + 2OH^-(aq) \longrightarrow [2K^+(aq)] + CrO_4^{2-}(aq) + H_2O(l)$$

The Elements of Group IIIB

The elements of Group IIIB include scandium, yttrium, lanthanum, and actinium. Because the lanthanide (rare earth) elements and the actinide elements resemble lanthanum and actinium, respectively, in many of their properties (due to similar sizes and valence subshell electron configurations), we will also consider the *f*-block elements in this section.

27.6 Scandium, Yttrium, Lanthanum, and Actinium

Scandium, yttrium, lanthanum, and actinium are similar to active metals in some of their reactions. These elements form ionic compounds containing trivalent ions, M^{3+}. The free metals are sufficiently active that they react with the oxygen of the air at room temperature. All burn readily, giving the oxides M_2O_3. They react with halogens at room temperature and with most nonmetals upon warming. The metals react readily with acids, producing salts and hydrogen gas.

The chemistry of scandium resembles that of aluminum. As we noted in Section 27.2, very little scandium is commercially produced because it is of little technological importance. Yttrium and lanthanum are isolated during the separation of the rare earths (Section 27.7). Actinium is a product of the radioactive decay of ^{235}U, and it can also be produced artificially. Only trace amounts of actinium are available.

Yttrium is used in the electronics industry. Yttrium compounds are used in the phosphors that produce the red color on color television tubes. **Yttrium iron garnet, $Y_3Fe_5O_{12}$,** is used in microwave devices, and **yttrium aluminum garnet (YAG), $Y_3Al_5O_{12}$,** is used in lasers and as an artificial gemstone. Yttrium is also a component of a new high-temperature superconductor (Section 27.22).

Lanthanum oxide is used in some kinds of glass. The metal is a component of misch metal (Section 27.7).

27.7 The Lanthanide Series (Rare Earth Elements)

The **lanthanide series (rare earth elements),** beginning with cerium (element 58) and extending through lutetium (element 71), are very similar in chemical and physical properties to each other and to lanthanum. This is attributed to their similarity in size and to the fact that the electron configurations of the atoms differ principally in the number of electrons in the inner 4*f* and 5*d* subshells rather than in their outer 6*s* subshell (see Table 27.2). The electron configurations of the trivalent ions differ only in the 4*f* subshell. These ions have the configuration $[Xe]4f^n5d^06s^0$.

The rare earth elements are active metals that form oxides with the general formula M_2O_3 upon exposure to air. Their usual oxidation number is $+3$; except for cerium, this is the only oxidation number of these elements that is stable in water. Cerium also forms salts in which it exhibits an oxidation number of +4. All cerium(IV) salts are quite strong oxidizing agents.

The rare earths are found in many minerals, and some of the rare earths are actually more common than several of the most familiar elements. **Monazite sand** is the most important source of these minerals; it contains, in the form of phosphates, all elements of the lanthanide series (including lanthanum) except promethium (atomic number 61), which does not occur in nature at all. [Promethium isotopes are made synthetically by nuclear transmutation reactions (see Section 24.8) and are radioactive.]

The rare earth elements resemble each other so closely that their chemical separation has been an exceedingly difficult task. Formerly the only effective method of separation was fractional crystallization of certain of their salts, involving many hundreds of successive crystallizations. Now ion-exchange liquid chromatography techniques provide a much more rapid and effective separation. This method employs the selective adsorption of the ions of the various rare earths on a chromatographic column containing an ion-exchange resin (see Section 29.13), followed by fractional elution of the adsorbed material by a suitable solvent.

An alloy of iron with a mixture of the rare earth metals, known commercially as **misch metal,** is used in making the flints in cigarette lighters. A mixture of the fluorides of these metals forms the core of the carbon arcs used in motion picture projectors. Recently the rare earths have been found to have great catalytic power in some important industrial reactions such as petroleum cracking and reforming. Some of the rare earth elements are used in color television tubes to improve the color rendition (especially of reds).

27.8 The Actinide Series

The series of elements beginning with thorium (element 90) and extending through lawrencium (element 103) is called the **actinide series.** All the elements of this series are radioactive. They are analogous to the rare earths in that the electron configurations of succeeding elements in the series differ by one electron—in this case in either the $5f$ or $6d$ subshell. The properties of the actinide elements are similar to those of the rare earths. The actinide elements have a characteristic oxidation number of +3 but show a much wider variation in oxidation number than the elements of the lanthanide series. Thorium resembles cerium in that it also has an oxidation number of +4.

Elements 93 through 103 do not occur naturally and have been prepared synthetically by nuclear reactions (see Section 24.8). The most important elements in the actinide series are thorium, uranium, and plutonium; the importance of the latter two is related to their use in atomic energy (see Sections 24.9 and 24.11).

Thorium occurs as the dioxide in monazite sand, in some cases to the extent of 10%, along with the rare earths. Elemental thorium is obtained by reducing **thorium(IV) chloride, ThCl$_4$,** with sodium; thorium(IV) chloride is prepared by the reaction of chlorine and a heated mixture of the dioxide and carbon. Thorium is very similar to the elements of Group IVB. It exhibits an oxidation number of +4 in its compounds. **Thorium hydroxide, Th(OH)$_4$,** is highly basic, and its salts react to a limited extent with water. Tungsten filaments for electric lamps are thoriated to increase their efficiency and retard their disintegration.

Uranium, the first radioactive element to be discovered, is found in the minerals **pitchblende, U$_3$O$_8$,** and **carnotite, K$_2$(UO$_2$)$_2$(VO$_4$)$_2 \cdot$8H$_2$O.** The principal sources of uranium minerals are in Colorado, Utah, the Congo, and the Great Bear Lake region of

Canada. The metal can be obtained by reduction of the oxide with carbon, calcium, or aluminum. Uranium is a white, lustrous metal of high density (18.9 g/cm³), and it melts at 1132°C. The metal is moderately active and forms compounds in which it shows oxidation numbers of +2, +3, +4, +5, and +6. The uranium salts that are important industrially contain the dipositive uranyl ion, UO_2^{2+}. These include **uranyl nitrate, $UO_2(NO_3)_2 \cdot 6H_2O$,** and **uranyl acetate, $UO_2(CH_3CO_2)_2 \cdot 2H_2O$.** There are several series of uranates, the most important of which are the diuranates, such as **sodium diuranate, $Na_2U_2O_7 \cdot 6H_2O$.** Uranium compounds are used for producing yellow glazes on ceramic ware, as mordants, and in the dye industry. The chief interest in uranium at present involves its release of nuclear energy and its conversion to elements that release nuclear energy (see Sections 24.9 and 24.11).

With increasing atomic number, the actinide elements exhibit a contraction in size (the **actinide contraction**) that is analogous to the lanthanide contraction discussed in Section 27.4.

The Elements of Group IVB

The elements of Group IVB [titanium, zirconium, hafnium, and element 104 (unnilquadium)], all of which have $ns^2(n-1)d^2$ electron configurations, commonly exhibit the oxidation number of +4; the two d electrons of the incomplete inner subshell and the two s electrons of the outer shell are used in bonding. These elements, however, also show oxidation numbers of +2 and +3. Zirconium and hafnium are even more similar in chemical properties than their being in the same family would lead us to expect. This similarity results from their similarity in size, which arises because of the lanthanide contraction (Section 27.4).

27.9 Titanium

Titanium is one of the more abundant elements. It is tenth among the elements in abundance in the earth's crust, ranking above such useful metals as nickel, copper, zinc, lead, tin, and mercury.

The most important ores of titanium from the commercial standpoint are **ilmenite, $FeTiO_3$,** and **rutile, TiO_2.** The dioxide is an excellent white pigment for paints and is used in the preparation of white rubber and white leather. In the production of chemicals in the United States, titanium dioxide ranks 44th; 1,110,000 tons were produced in 1989. **Titanium(IV) chloride, $TiCl_4$,** is a liquid that reacts quickly with the water in moist air, producing a dense white smoke containing finely divided TiO_2. Titanium(IV) chloride is used in producing smoke screens and in skywriting.

$$TiCl_4(l) + 2H_2O(l \text{ or } g) \longrightarrow TiO_2(s) + 4HCl(g)$$

Titanium metal is very strong, light (density = 4.49 g/cm³), high-melting, and corrosion-resistant. These properties make the metal and its alloys valuable in the production of jet engines and high-speed aircraft. An alloy, ferrotitanium, is used in making special steels of great strength and toughness, in which the titanium acts as a "scavenger" to remove nitrogen and other undesirable impurities.

Titanium forms three oxides—TiO, Ti_2O_3, and TiO_2—and their corresponding hydroxides.

㉗.10 Zirconium and Hafnium

Zirconium is not as abundant as titanium but is far more abundant than such familiar metals as lead, copper, nickel, zinc, mercury, and tin. Its chief ores are **zircon, $ZrSiO_4$,** and **baddeleyite, ZrO_2.** The metal is obtained by converting the $ZrSiO_4$ and the ZrO_2 to K_2ZrF_6, then heating it with sodium, potassium, or aluminum. Ferrozirconium has been used with some success in the production of a tough steel.

Zirconium dioxide, ZrO_2, which is called **zirconia,** is the most important compound of the element because of its excellent refractory qualities. These include a high melting point (about 2700°C), a low coefficient of expansion, and a high resistance to corrosion.

Zircon, the naturally occurring silicate, $ZrSiO_4$, is found in a variety of colors and, because of its beauty and hardness, is used as a semiprecious stone in jewelry.

Hafnium was discovered in 1923 by Coster and Hevesy in zircon from Norway by means of spectroscopic analysis. Because it is similar in size to zirconium (as a result of the lanthanide contraction, Section 27.4), it is found in nearly all zirconium minerals, most of which contain about 5% hafnium. The fact that hafnium has chemical properties very similar to those of zirconium makes separation of the two elements difficult.

The Elements of Group VB

Vanadium, niobium, and tantalum are typical transition metals; they exhibit a wide range of oxidation numbers and form highly colored compounds. Table 27.5 lists some of the physical properties of the metals. The lanthanide contraction (Section 27.4) contributes to the similarity in size and properties of niobium and tantalum.

㉗.11 Vanadium

Vanadium is the most important element of Group VB. Its importance lies in the fact that addition of **ferrovanadium** to steel removes impurities and forms an alloy steel of special properties. Vanadium steel is tough and strong, and it is used wherever a steel is

Table 27.5		Some Physical Properties of the Metals of Group VB					
	Atomic Number	Atomic Mass, amu	Atomic Radius, Å	Ionic (M^{5+}) Radius, Å	Density at 20°C, g/cm^3	Melting Point, °C	Boiling Point, °C
Vanadium	23	50.942	1.31	0.40	5.96	1730	3375
Niobium	41	92.906	1.43	0.69	8.57	2487	4930
Tantalum	73	180.948	1.43	0.68	16.6	2997	5425

needed that will withstand strain, vibration, and shock, such as in automobile crank-shafts and heavy machinery. The principal ores of vanadium are **vanadinite, $Pb_5(VO_4)_3Cl$,** and **carnotite, $K_2(UO_2)_2(VO_4)_2 \cdot 8H_2O$.** Most of the vanadium consumed in the United States comes from Colorado and other western states and from Peruvian coal, the ashes of which may contain up to 48% V_2O_5.

Vanadium forms compounds in which it shows oxidation states of +2, +3, +4, and +5. As might be expected, the oxides VO and V_2O_3 are basic, whereas VO_2 is amphoteric and V_2O_5 is acidic. The compounds of vanadium in its different oxidation states exhibit strikingly varied colors. Compounds of V^{2+} are lavender; V^{3+}, green; V^{4+}, blue; and V^{5+}, orange.

Vanadium(V) oxide, V_2O_5, is the most important of the vanadium compounds. It is used as a catalyst in a variety of industrial processes, including the contact process for making sulfuric acid (Section 2.12, Part 1).

🔴.12 Niobium and Tantalum

The principal mineral of niobium is **columbite, $Fe(NbO_3)_2$,** which usually occurs associated with the tantalum mineral known as **tantalite, $Fe(TaO_3)_2$.** Fusion of the mixture of pulverized columbite and tantalite with potassium fluoride, followed by extraction of the melt with water, gives a solution containing complex fluorides of niobium and tantalum. Potassium heptafluorotantalate(V), K_2TaF_7, forms crystals that are less soluble than those of the niobium salt, K_2NbOF_5, thus permitting the two compounds to be separated by fractional crystallization. The metals are obtained by electrolysis of the fused complex fluorides.

Stainless steel containing a fraction of a percent of niobium resists corrosion at high temperatures, making it possible for the steel to be welded. Other niobium alloys are used in the manufacture of motors for jet airplanes. Tantalum confers the same resistance to corrosion on steel as does niobium. Tantalum alloys are used for making tools and dental and surgical instruments so corrosion-resistant that they can be sterilized in a flame without dulling their cutting edges. Tantalum forms an extremely hard carbide, Ta_4C_5, which is employed as an abrasive and as a cutting tool for machining steel.

In most of their compounds, niobium and tantalum have an oxidation state of +5. In fact, only a few compounds appear to exist in which they show a lower oxidation number. The pentaoxides, Nb_2O_5 and Ta_2O_5, are formed by heating the corresponding acids or by burning the metals in air.

The Elements of Group VIB

Figure 27.10

Colors of three compounds of chromium, each with a chromium oxidation number of +6. The compounds are, from the top, potassium dichromate ($K_2Cr_2O_7$), chromium(VI) oxide (CrO_3), and sodium chromate (Na_2CrO_4).

The elements that constitute Group VIB of the periodic table are chromium, molybdenum, tungsten, and element 106 (unnilhexium). These metals are typical transition metals; they show a variety of oxidation numbers, form highly colored compounds (Fig. 27.10), and form stable complex ions. Chromium exhibits behavior that is characteristic of the more active metals of the first transition series. The behavior of molybdenum and tungsten is characteristic of the early members of the second and third transition series.

Simple salts containing chromium with oxidation numbers of +2, +3, and +6 are stable in water. The stable water-soluble salts of molybdenum and tungsten are generally limited to those containing oxyanions in which the metals exhibit oxidation numbers of +6 (MoO_4^{2-} and WO_4^{2-}).

㉗.13 Properties of Chromium

Chromium is the lightest member of Group VIB. Elemental chromium does not occur in nature; its most important ore is **chromite, $FeCr_2O_4$.** Practically all of the chromium used in the United States is imported.

Reduction of chromite by carbon yields carbon monoxide and an alloy of iron and chromium called ferrochrome, which is used in making chromium steels. Pure chromium is prepared by reducing chromium(III) oxide with aluminum. It can also be produced by the electrolytic reduction of its compounds from aqueous solution, a process used in chromium plating.

Chromium is a very hard, silvery white, crystalline metal. It becomes passive when coated with a thin layer of oxide, which protects it against further corrosive attack. This property, along with its metallic luster, accounts for its extensive use in the plating of iron and copper objects. Passivity is produced by treatment with concentrated nitric acid or chromic acid or by exposure of the metal to air. When not in the passive state, chromium dissolves readily in dilute acids, with the evolution of hydrogen gas.

Chromium exhibits several oxidation numbers; the principal ones are +2, +3, and +6. The compounds of chromium are highly colored. The particular color exhibited depends on the oxidation number and on the structure of the compound. Chromium(III) compounds tend to be more stable than chromium(II) compounds. Chromium(III) forms alums of the type $KCr(SO_4)_2 \cdot 12H_2O$, solutions of which are bluish-violet when cold and green when hot (Fig. 27.11). This alum is used in the tanning of leather, the printing of calico, the waterproofing of fabrics, and as a mordant. It is the most important of the soluble chromium salts.

(a)

(b)

Figure 27.11

Solutions of the chromium(III) alum, $KCr(SO_4)_2 \cdot 12H_2O$, are (a) bluish-violet when cold and (b) green when hot.

27.14 Uses of Chromium

A large portion of the chromium produced goes into steel alloys, which are very hard and strong. **Stainless steel,** which generally contains chromium and some nickel, is used because of its corrosion resistance. Nonferrous chromium alloys include **nichrome** and **chromel** (Ni and Cr), which are used in the wires of heating elements because of their high electrical resistance. Chromium is widely used as a protective and decorative coating for other metals, such as plumbing fixtures and automobile trim.

The compounds of chromium have many uses, including applications as paint pigments and mordants and in the tanning of leather. Certain refractories used as linings for high-temperature furnaces are made by mixing pulverized chromite ore with clay or magnesia (MgO).

Manganese (Group VIIB)

Manganese is the lightest member of Group VIIB. In nature it is found principally as **pyrolusite, MnO$_2$.** Nearly pure manganese can be prepared by the high-temperature reduction of the dioxide by aluminum (Section 27.2). However, because alloys of manganese and iron are used extensively in the production of steel, such alloys are usually produced instead of pure manganese.

Manganese is a gray-white metal with a slightly reddish tinge. It is brittle and looks like cast iron. It is readily oxidized by moist air and reacts slowly with water, forming manganese(II) hydroxide and hydrogen. It dissolves readily in dilute acids, forming manganese(II) salts.

27.15 Compounds of Manganese

Manganese exhibits an unusually large number of oxidation states in its compounds: +2, +3, +4, +6, and +7. It forms five oxides and five corresponding series of salts (Table 27.6).

Although manganese forms compounds in which it exhibits oxidation numbers of +2, +3, +4, +6, and +7, the only stable cation is the dipositive manganese ion, Mn^{2+}. The common soluble manganese(II) salts are the chloride, sulfate, and nitrate. Each imparts a faint pink color to its solutions. A majority of the manganese compounds

Table 27.6   Classes of Manganese Compounds

Oxidation Number	Oxide	Hydroxide	Character	Derivative	Name	Color
+2	MnO	Mn(OH)$_2$	Moderately basic	MnCl$_2$	Manganese(II) chloride	Pink
+3	Mn$_2$O$_3$	Mn(OH)$_3$	Weakly basic	MnCl$_3$	Manganese(III) chloride	Violet
+4	MnO$_2$	H$_2$MnO$_3$	Weakly acidic	CaMnO$_3$	Calcium manganite	Brown
+6	MnO$_3$	H$_2$MnO$_4$	Moderately acidic	K$_2$MnO$_4$	Potassium manganate	Green
+7	Mn$_2$O$_7$	HMnO$_4$	Strongly acidic	KMnO$_4$	Potassium permanganate	Purple

Figure 27.12
The oxidation of glycerol by potassium permanganate is sufficiently exothermic that the glycerol inflames.

in which manganese has oxidation numbers of +3, +4, +6, or +7 are relatively unstable. Exceptions are the stable MnO_2, a highly insoluble compound in which manganese has an oxidation number of +4, and the permanganate salts, in which it has an oxidation number of +7. Potassium permanganate is a valuable laboratory reagent because it is a strong oxidizing agent (Fig. 27.12). It is used, for example, in the titration of oxalic acid and of other reducing agents.

27.16 Uses of Manganese and Its Compounds

Manganese forms a number of alloys used in making very hard steels for the manufacture of rails, safes, and heavy machinery. About 12.5 pounds of manganese metal are used in the production of every ton of steel to remove oxygen, nitrogen, and sulfur. An alloy called **manganin** (Cu, 84%; Mn, 12%; Ni, 4%) is used in instruments for making electrical measurements, because its electrical resistance does not change significantly with changes in temperature.

Manganese dioxide is used to correct the green color produced in glass by iron(II) compounds, to color glass and enamels black, as an oxidizing agent or dryer in black paints, and as a depolarizer in dry cells. Potassium permanganate is used as a disinfectant, a deodorant, and a germicide.

Iron (Group VIIIB)

Iron was known at least as early as 4000 B.C. and was probably used to some extent during prehistoric times. Free iron is not commonly found in nature, so the iron used in prehistoric times may well have been of meteoric origin. The early use of iron to manufacture tools and weapons was possible because of its wide distribution in ores and the ease with which the iron compounds in the ores can be reduced by charcoal. The production and use of iron on a large scale began when coal was introduced as the reducing agent in 1620.

Iron is the most widely used of all metals. (The amount used is 14 times the amount of all other metals combined.) The reasons for this are that its ores are abundant and widely distributed, the metal is easily and cheaply produced from the ores, and its properties can be varied over a wide range by the addition of other substances and by different methods of treatment, such as tempering (heating and cooling quickly) and annealing (heating and cooling slowly).

Iron ranks second in abundance among the metals (aluminum is first) and fourth among all elements in the earth's crust. The central core of the earth is largely iron. Metallic meteorites are usually about 90% iron, and the remainder is principally nickel. Practically all rocks, minerals, and soils, as well as plants, contain some iron. Iron is present in hemoglobin, which acts as the carrier of oxygen in our blood (Fig. 26.3).

㉗.17 Properties of Iron

Pure iron is silvery-white, ductile, relatively soft, high in tensile strength, and capable of taking a high polish. These properties are greatly modified by impurities, especially carbon. Pure iron is attracted by a magnet but does not retain magnetism. Iron dissolves in hydrochloric acid and dilute sulfuric acid, forming hydrogen and iron(II) ions, Fe^{2+}. Hot concentrated sulfuric acid forms Fe^{3+}, and SO_2 is evolved. Cold concentrated nitric acid induces **passivity** in iron. When passive, a metal does not react with dilute acids that otherwise would readily dissolve it. The passivity is easily destroyed by a scratch or by shock. Hot dilute nitric acid oxidizes iron to Fe^{3+} with the evolution of nitric oxide. When heated to redness, iron reduces steam to produce hydrogen and iron(II,III) oxide, Fe_3O_4, which is the same oxide that is produced when iron burns in oxygen. When exposed to moist air at ordinary temperatures, iron becomes oxidized, with a loose coating of partially hydrated iron(III) oxide, $Fe_2O_3 \cdot nH_2O$, rust (see Section 20.11).

Iron forms two principal series of compounds in which its oxidation numbers are +2 and +3. The +2 and +3 series are called iron(II) or ferrous compounds and iron(III) or ferric compounds, respectively. The oxides and hydroxides of iron(II) and iron(III) are basic, with little or no acidic character.

㉗.18 The Manufacture of Steel

The term *steel* is applied to many widely different alloys of iron. **Steel** is made from iron by removing impurities and adding substances such as manganese, chromium, nickel, tungsten, molybdenum, and vanadium to produce alloys with properties that make the material suitable for specific uses. Most steels also contain small but definite percentages of carbon (0.04–2.5%). Thus a large part of the carbon contained in iron must be removed in the manufacture of steel.

Steels can be classified in three main categories: (1) **carbon steels,** which are primarily iron and carbon; (2) **stainless steels,** low-carbon steels containing about 12% chromium; and (3) **alloy steels,** specialty steels that contain large amounts of other elements to impart special properties for specific uses. Of the approximately 141 million tons of steel produced yearly in the United States, about 124.6 million tons (88.4%) are carbon steels, 14.8 million tons (10.5%) are stainless steels, and 1.6 million tons (1.1%) are alloy steels.

The principal process used in the production of steel is the **basic oxygen process,** which utilizes a cylindrical furnace with a basic lining, such as magnesium oxides and calcium oxides (Fig. 27.13). A typical charge is 80 tons of scrap iron, 200 tons of molten iron, and 18 tons of limestone (to form slag). A jet of high-purity (99.5%) oxygen is directed into the white-hot molten charge through a water-cooled lance. The

Figure 27.13

Molten steel being poured from a basic oxygen furnace.

oxygen produces a vigorous reaction that oxidizes the impurities in the charge. In the central reaction zone, temperatures reach a level close to the boiling point of iron. The entire steelmaking cycle is completed in one hour or less. Electrostatic precipitators (see Section 12.27) clean the gases resulting from the furnace reactions and make the furnaces virtually smokeless. The steel produced is of extremely high and uniform quality.

Carbon is the most important alloying element in steel. It may be present either in combination with iron as **cementite, Fe_3C,** or as crystals of graphite (free carbon, C). The reaction of iron with carbon is reversible, and cementite is stable only at elevated temperatures. If cementite is cooled slowly, it decomposes to iron and graphite.

$$Fe_3C \rightleftharpoons 3Fe + C$$

Steel containing cementite in solid solution in iron must be made by quenching (quickly cooling) the hot metal in water or oil. The rate of decomposition of cementite is very slow at lower temperatures, so quick cooling does not provide enough time for the decomposition to occur. This steel is hard, brittle, and light-colored. If the metal is cooled slowly, the cementite decomposes and the carbon is deposited largely as separate crystals of graphite; the product is softer and more pliable and has a much higher tensile strength than steel that has been cooled rapidly.

Certain materials called **scavengers** are added to iron in the manufacture of steel to remove impurities, especially oxygen and nitrogen, and thus improve the quality of the product. The most important scavengers are aluminum, ferrosilicon, ferromanganese, and ferrotitanium. They react with dissolved oxygen and nitrogen, forming oxides and nitrides, respectively, which are removed with the slag.

For every ton of steel produced, about 25–30 pounds of nonferrous metals are added or used as coatings. By the appropriate choice of the number and percentages of these elements, alloy steel of widely varying properties can be manufactured. Some of the important alloy steels and their features are given in Table 27.7.

Cobalt (Group VIIIB)

㉗.19 Properties of Cobalt

Cobalt is similar to iron in appearance but has a faint tinge of pink. Like iron and nickel, it is magnetic. Almost all cobalt produced is a by-product of the extraction of nickel, copper, silver, and other metals. Cobalt dissolves slowly in warm dilute hydrochloric or sulfuric acid and more rapidly in dilute nitric acid, forming salts of cobalt(II). The Co^{2+} ion is the only simple hydrated ion of cobalt that is stable in aqueous solution. Like iron and nickel, cobalt is rendered passive (unreactive) by contact with concentrated nitric acid. It is not oxidized when exposed to air, but at red heat it reduces hydrogen in steam, with the evolution of hydrogen gas. The halogens, except fluorine, convert the metal to cobalt(II) halides.

Cobalt is alloyed with iron and small percentages of other metals for use in high-speed cutting tools and surgical instruments. Permanent magnets are made from the alloys **Alnico** (Al, Ni, Co, and Fe), **Hiperco** (Co, Fe, and Cr), and **Vicalloy** (Co, Fe, and V).

Cobalt(II) hydroxide, $Co(OH)_2$, is formed as a blue flocculent precipitate ($K_{sp} = 2 \times 10^{-16}$) when an alkali metal hydroxide is added to a solution of a cobalt(II)

Table 27.7 **Alloy Steels**

Name	Composition	Characteristic Properties	Uses
Manganese steel	10–18% Mn	Hard, tough, resistant to wear	Railroad rails, safes, armor plate, rock-crushing machinery
Silicon steel	1–5% Si	Hard, strong, highly magnetic	Magnets
Duriron	12–15% Si	Resistant to corrosion, acids	Pipes, kettles, condensers, etc.
Invar	36% Ni	Low coefficient of expansion	Meter scales, measuring tapes, pendulum rods
Chrome–vanadium	1–10% Cr, 0.15% V	Strong, resistant to strains	Axles
Stainless steel	14–18% Cr, 7–9% Ni	Resistant to corrosion	Cutlery, instruments
Permalloy	78% Ni	High magnetic susceptibility	Ocean cables
High-speed steels	14–20% W or 6–12% Mo	Retain temper at high temperatures	High-speed cutting tools
Nickel steel	2–4% Ni	Hard and elastic, resistant to corrosion	Drive shafts, gears, cables

salt (Fig. 27.14). The blue color of the precipitate changes to violet and then to pink, probably as a result of hydration.

When cobalt(II) hydroxide is heated in the absence of air, **cobalt(II) oxide, CoO,** results. This oxide is a black substance, but when dissolved in molten glass, it gives the glass a blue color. Such glass is called cobalt glass and contains **cobalt(II) silicate.** Ignition of cobalt(II) hydroxide or oxide in air gives rise to **cobalt(II,III) oxide, Co_3O_4. Cobalt(III) oxide, Co_2O_3,** can be produced by gently heating **cobalt(II) nitrate, $Co(NO_3)_2$.**

$$4Co(NO_3)_2 \xrightarrow{\triangle} 2Co_2O_3 + 8NO_2 + O_2$$

Note that three elements in this reaction change their oxidation numbers. (You will find balancing this equation by the oxidation–reduction method a real challenge.)

Cobalt(II) oxide and hydroxide readily dissolve in hydrochloric acid. Concentration of the resulting solution causes crystallization of **cobalt(II) chloride 6-hydrate, $CoCl_2 \cdot 6H_2O$,** which is red. The hydrated cobalt(II) ion, $[Co(H_2O)_6]^{2+}$, exhibits a pink color in solution. When partially dehydrated, cobalt(II) chloride changes to a deep blue color. This is believed to result from a change in the coordination number of the cobalt(II) ion from 6 to 4.

$$[Co(H_2O)_6]Cl_2 \longrightarrow [Co(H_2O)_4]Cl_2 + 2H_2O$$
$$\text{Pink} \qquad\qquad\qquad \text{Blue}$$

The same change in color is effected by dissolving $CoCl_2 \cdot 6H_2O$ in alcohol. Writing made on paper with a dilute solution of the hydrated salt is almost invisible, but when the

Figure 27.14

A precipitate of $Co(OH)_2$ forms when NaOH is added to a solution of a salt of cobalt(II).

paper is warmed, dehydration of the salt occurs and the writing becomes blue. It fades again as hydration takes place from moisture of the air. This is the chemistry of one kind of "invisible" ink.

In addition to the simple salts, oxides, and hydroxides, cobalt forms a large number of coordination compounds (Chapter 26). Cobalt(II) simple salts are more stable than are those of cobalt(III); cobalt(III) coordination compounds, in contrast, are much more stable than the corresponding cobalt(II) ones. Thus the majority of the more stable coordination compounds of cobalt contain the metal with the +3 oxidation number. Some of the more important cobalt(III) coordination compounds are **hexaamminecobalt(III) chloride, $[Co(NH_3)_6]Cl_3$, potassium hexacyanocobaltate(III), $K_3[Co(CN)_6]$,** and **sodium hexanitrocobaltate(III), $Na_3[Co(NO_2)_6]$.** In these compounds the six ligands, such as NH_3, CN^-, and NO_2^-, occupy the corners of a regular octahedron with the cobalt at the center, d^2sp^3 hybridization (Sections 26.3 and 26.6).

Nickel (Group VIIIB)

㉗.20 Properties of Nickel

Nickel is a silvery-white metal that is hard, malleable, and ductile. Like iron and cobalt, it is highly magnetic. It is not oxidized by air under ordinary conditions, and it is resistant to the action of bases. Dilute acids slowly dissolve nickel; hydrogen is evolved. Nickel is made passive by treatment with concentrated nitric acid; nickel so treated no longer displaces hydrogen from dilute acids.

Because of its hardness, resistance to corrosion, and high reflectivity when polished, nickel is widely used in the plating of iron, steel, and copper. It is also a constituent of many important alloys, such as **Monel metal** (Ni, Cu, and a little Fe) and **Permalloy** (Ni and Fe), used in instruments for electrical transmission and reproduction of sound. **German silver** is a nickel–copper–zinc alloy. **Nichrome** and **Chromel** contain nickel, iron, and chromium. **Alnico** contains aluminum, nickel, iron, and cobalt; it is highly magnetic, able to lift 4000 times its own weight of iron. **Platinite** and **Invar** are nickel alloys that have the same coefficient of expansion as that of glass and are therefore used for "seal-in" wires through glass, such as those in electric light bulbs. Finely divided nickel is used as a catalyst in the hydrogenation of oils.

In its compounds, nickel exhibits an oxidation number of +2 almost exclusively. One notable exception is the +4 oxidation number in **nickel(IV) oxide, NiO_2,** a black substance formed by the oxidation of nickel(II) salts in alkaline solution. This oxide forms one of the electrodes in the nickel–cadmium cell (Section 20.9).

The Elements of Group IB

Copper, silver, and gold, which are sometimes called the **coinage metals,** are members of Group IB of the periodic table. Copper exhibits behavior similar to that of the other elements of the latter half of the first transition series. Silver and gold are relatively inactive transition metals with behavior that is characteristic of the platinum metals.

Each element exhibits multiple oxidation numbers of $+1$, $+2$, and $+3$. However, the most common oxidation number for copper is $+2$; for silver, $+1$; and for gold, $+3$.

These metals were the first to be used by humans, because they are found in the free state, they tarnish slowly, and their appearance is pleasing to the eye. Ornaments of gold have been found in Egyptian tombs constructed in the prehistoric Stone Age. Gold and silver coins were used as a medium of exchange in India and Egypt thousands of years ago. It is believed that copper was the first metal to be fashioned into utensils, instruments, and weapons; its use for such purposes began sometime during the Stone Age. The practice of alloying copper with tin and the use of the resulting bronze in place of stone introduced the Bronze Age.

27.21 Properties of Copper

Copper is a reddish-yellow metal. It is ductile and malleable, so it is readily fashioned into wire, tubing, and sheets. Copper is the best electrical conductor among the cheaper metals, but when used for this purpose it must be quite pure, because small amounts of impurities greatly reduce its conductivity.

The extensive uses of copper make it the metal second in commercial importance to iron. The chief use of copper is in the production of all types of electrical wiring. Copper is also used in the production of a great many alloys. Among the most important ones are **brass** (Cu, 60–82%; Zn, 18–40%), **bronze** (Cu, 70–95%; Zn, 1–25%; Sn, 1–18%), **aluminum bronze** (Cu, 90–98%; Al, 2–10%), and **German silver** (Cu, 50–60%; Zn, 20%; Ni, 20–25%).

Copper is relatively inactive chemically. In moist air it first turns brown as a result of the formation of a very thin, adherent film of either copper oxide or copper sulfide (from SO_2 or other sulfur substances that are sometimes present in the air). Prolonged weathering causes copper to become coated with a green film of the hydroxycarbonate $Cu_2(OH)_2CO_3$. This compound or the hydroxysulfate is responsible for the green color of well-weathered copper (Fig. 27.15).

When heated in air, copper oxidizes, forming copper(II) oxide along with some copper(I) oxide. Oxidizing acids, and nonoxidizing acids in the presence of air, convert copper to the corresponding copper(II) salts. Aqueous ammonia in the presence of air dissolves copper, producing a blue solution containing $[Cu(NH_3)_4]^{2+}$. Alkali metal hydroxides have no effect on the metal. Sulfur vapor reacts with hot copper to give both Cu_2S and CuS. Hot copper burns in chlorine to give $CuCl_2$.

Copper forms two chief series of compounds, in which it has the oxidation numbers of $+1$ and $+2$. Copper also exhibits an oxidation number of $+3$, but copper(III) compounds are rare. Copper(I) forms a complete series of binary compounds, such as halide and oxide, but oxysalts of copper(I) are few in number and are readily decomposed by water. In contrast, copper(II) forms a complete series of oxysalts, but some of its binary compounds are unstable and decompose spontaneously.

Copper(II) sulfate, $CuSO_4$, is the most important of the copper salts. The anhydrous salt is colorless, but when it is crystallized from aqueous solution, the blue pentahydrate **$[Cu(H_2O)_4]SO_4 \cdot H_2O$,** known as **blue vitriol,** is formed. As indicated by the formula, one of the five water molecules is attached in a different way; four of the water molecules are coordinated to the copper(II) ion, and the fifth is attached to the sulfate ion and two of the coordinated water molecules by hydrogen bonds. The structure of the pentahydrate may be represented as follows:

Figure 27.15

The light green color of the Statue of Liberty is due to a coating of $Cu_2(OH)_2CO_3$ produced by the weathering of its copper covering. In the extensive repair project completed in 1986, care was taken to preserve the green patina in order to retain the statue's traditional appearance.

$$\left[\begin{array}{c} \text{H} \qquad \text{H} \\ \text{H---O} \qquad \text{O---H} \\ \qquad \text{Cu} \\ \text{H---O} \qquad \text{O---H} \\ \text{H} \qquad \text{H} \end{array} \right]$$

The coordination sphere has a planar structure, dsp^2 hybridization (see Sections 26.3 and 26.6).

Copper(II) sulfate is produced commercially by oxidizing copper(II) sulfide either directly to the sulfate or to the oxide, which is then converted to the sulfate by reaction with sulfuric acid. In the laboratory the anhydrous sulfate may be prepared by oxidizing copper with hot concentrated sulfuric acid.

$$Cu(s) + 2H_2SO_4(l) \longrightarrow CuSO_4(s) + SO_2(g) + 2H_2O(l) \qquad \Delta H° = -11.9 \text{ kJ}$$

Copper(II) sulfate is used in the electrolytic refining of copper, in electroplating, in the Daniell cell (see Section 20.8 and Fig. 20.6), in the manufacture of pigments, as a color-fixing agent in the textile industry, and in the prevention of algae in reservoirs and swimming pools.

Anhydrous **copper(II) chloride, CuCl$_2$,** can be prepared as a yellow crystalline salt by direct union of the elements. The blue-green hydrated salt $Cu(H_2O)_2Cl_2$ can be obtained by treating either the carbonate or the hydroxide of copper(II) with hydrochloric acid and evaporating the solution. Concentrated solutions of copper(II) chloride are green, because they contain both the hydrated copper(II) ion $[Cu(H_2O)_4]^{2+}$, which is blue, and the tetrachlorocuprate(II) ion $[CuCl_4]^{2-}$, which is yellow. The combination of blue and yellow looks green to the eye (Fig. 27.16). When such a solution is diluted, water molecules replace the chloride ions of the $[CuCl_4]^{2-}$ ion, and the solution turns blue.

Copper and the reactions it undergoes provided the inspiration for the cover of this text. The background photograph is of solid malachite ore. The inset on the front cover shows liquid (molten) copper. One of the photographs on the back cover shows sheets of oxidized solid copper, and the other shows raw ore tailings produced at a mine.

Figure 27.16

A sample of hydrated copper(II) chloride.

Oxygen
Yttrium
Copper
Barium

Figure 27.17

The unit cell of the superconductor $YBa_2Cu_3O_7$.

Figure 27.18

A graph of the relationship between resistance and temperature for the high-temperature superconductor $YBa_2Cu_3O_{6.5}$. This substance is a superconductor below 92 K. Note how the resistance falls to zero upon cooling.

27.22 Copper Oxide Superconductors

One of the most potentially exciting scientific discoveries of the 1980s was the characterization of new materials, referred to as "high-temperature superconductors," that exhibit superconductivity at temperatures above 90 K. **Superconductors** conduct electricity with no resistance. They also possess unusual magnetic properties.

Typical among the high-temperature superconducting materials are ternary oxides containing yttrium (or one of several rare earth elements), barium, and copper in a $1:2:3$ ratio. The formula of the yttrium compound is $YBa_2Cu_3O_x$, where x ranges from about 6.5 to 7 depending on the conditions under which the compound was prepared. The variable amount of oxygen reflects the fact that some of the copper in these compounds can be oxidized from copper(II) to copper(III). For $x = 6.5$, all of the copper is present as copper(II); for $x = 7$, one-third of the copper is oxidized to copper(III).

The superconducting copper oxides are ionic compounds. The structure of a unit cell of $YBa_2Cu_3O_7$ is illustrated in Fig. 27.17. The copper(II) and copper(III) ions cannot be distinguished in the structure because the compound is a solid solution (see Section 12.6) containing copper(II) and copper(III) ions.

Because these oxides are ionic compounds and are ceramics (glasslike in character), they are brittle and fragile and cannot be drawn out to form wires, as can a metal such as copper itself. However, ceramic wires and other shapes can be formed by mixing the ceramic powder or its ingredients with an organic binder (a glue) and then extruding a thin strip through a press. (This works just like squeezing a fine strip of toothpaste out of a tube.) The sample is then heated to burn off the binder and annealed, giving a current-carrying ceramic strip.

Most currently used commercial superconducting materials, niobium alloys such as NbTi and Nb_3Sn, do not become superconducting until they are cooled below 23 K ($-250°C$). This requires the use of liquid helium, which has a boiling temperature of 4 K and is expensive and difficult to handle. The new materials become superconducting at temperatures close to 90 K (Fig. 27.18), temperatures that can be reached by cooling with liquid nitrogen (boiling temperature 77 K). A sample immersed in boiling liquid nitrogen is cooled to 77 K. Not only are liquid-nitrogen-cooled materials easier to handle, but the cooling costs are also about 1000 times less than for liquid helium.

Liquid-nitrogen-cooled superconductors could revolutionize society. Power companies, for example, could use underground superconducting transmission lines that would carry current for hundreds of miles with no loss of power due to resistance in the wires. This would allow generating stations to be located in areas remote from population centers and near to the natural resources necessary for power production.

Superconducting microchips could lead to more powerful supercomputers. Present chips produce waste heat as a result of the resistance of the electric current as it flows through the chip, so the chips have to be spaced in such a way as to allow a coolant to flow through them. Superconducting chips would produce no waste heat because they would have no resistance. Thus chips could be packed closer together and the signals would require less time to travel from chip to chip. This would make possible smaller computers that work faster.

Superconducting materials are particularly useful for generating very strong magnetic fields. Because they have no resistance, superconducting coils can carry very large currents without melting, and these large currents can be used to generate very strong magnetic fields.

The Japanese National Railways has already built an experimental train that is levitated above the tracks via frictionless magnetic force generated by superconducting

Figure 27.19
Experimental magnetic levitation train on the test track in Myazaki, Japan. It uses repulsion forces between superconducting electromagnets in the train and ferromagnets attached to the guideway for levitation, guidance, and propulsion or deceleration. At about 100 miles per hour, the superconducting magnets on the train raise it about 4 inches above the guideway, eliminating essentially all friction and enabling it to achieve speeds of approximately 300 miles per hour.

magnets cooled by liquid helium (Fig. 27.19). This train can travel up to 300 miles an hour, but the expense and difficulty of carrying liquid helium have so far prevented any practical routine use. Approval has been granted for installation in the 1990s of a German ''levitated'' train, using conventional magnets, to run between the Orlando, Florida, airport and Walt Disney World. Other such projects are under serious consideration. *If* the new high-temperature superconductors become adaptable for practical use, rendering cooling by liquid nitrogen feasible, they could make such trains commonplace.

The medical application of magnetic resonance imaging (MRI) devices [a form of nuclear magnetic resonance (NMR, Section 8.12)] requires the use of superconducting magnets to image tissues inside the body. Today's superconducting magnets are cooled by liquid helium, making existing scanners complex and expensive. The new superconductors could lower the price of these instruments and increase their power. The development of nuclear fusion (Sections 24.10 and 24.13) would be enhanced if these materials could be used to produce magnetic fields strong enough to contain the hot plasma in which the nuclear reactions take place.

If high-temperature superconductors can be converted from laboratory to practical technology, it will require a tremendous amount of research and development. In particular, shaping the superconducting ceramics into useful shapes with the right physical and electrical properties presents a large challenge. Work in this area is under way, and experimental superconducting rods, rings, wires, tapes, and thin films have been fabricated.

27.23 Properties of Silver

Silver is a white, lustrous metal, the polished surface of which is an excellent reflector of light. As a conductor of heat and electricity it is second only to gold. Silver is noted for its ductility and malleability.

Silver is not attacked by oxygen in the air under ordinary conditions but tarnishes quickly in the presence of hydrogen sulfide or on contact with sulfur-containing foods such as eggs and mustard. Its reaction with hydrogen sulfide in the presence of air is

$$4Ag(s) + 2H_2S(g) + O_2(g) \longrightarrow 2Ag_2S(s) + 2H_2O(l) \qquad \Delta H° = -595.59 \text{ kJ}$$

Silver tarnish is a thin film of silver sulfide.

The halogens react with silver, forming the halides, and the metal is soluble in oxidizing acids such as nitric acid and hot sulfuric acid.

$$3Ag + 4H_3O^+ + NO_3^- \longrightarrow 3Ag^+ + NO(g) + 6H_2O$$

Because silver lies below hydrogen in the activity series (Section 13.1), it is not soluble in nonoxidizing acids such as hydrochloric acid. The common oxidation number exhibited by silver is +1.

A large amount of silver is used for the making of coins, silverware, and ornaments. For most of its uses silver is too soft to wear well, and it is therefore hardened by alloying it with other metals, particularly copper. **Sterling silver** contains 7.5% copper, and jewelry silver contains 20% copper. Large amounts of silver are used in the preparation of dental alloys, photographic films, and mirrors.

The electroplating industry uses a large percentage of the silver produced. The object to be plated with silver is made the cathode in an electrolytic cell containing a solution of $Na[Ag(CN)_2]$ as the electrolyte. The anode is a bar of pure silver, which dissolves to replace the silver ions removed from the solution as plating proceeds. The electrode reactions are

Cathodic reduction: $[Ag(CN)_2]^- + e^- \longrightarrow Ag + 2CN^-$

Anodic oxidation: $\qquad Ag + 2CN^- \longrightarrow [Ag(CN)_2]^- + e^-$

The film of deposited silver has a flat white appearance but burnishing (polishing) can give it a brilliant luster.

The characteristic luster can be restored to tarnished silverware by the following application of the activity series. The tarnished silver object is immersed in a solution of a teaspoonful of baking soda and a teaspoonful of salt in a liter of water, held in an aluminum vessel. (A piece of aluminum metal foil in a glass vessel serves equally well.) The aluminum and the silver must be in contact. After the tarnish is removed, the silver object should be thoroughly washed. The chemistry involved may be explained as follows: The more active aluminum displaces the silver from the tarnish, causing it to plate out on the silver object, according to the equation

$$3Ag^+ + Al \longrightarrow 3Ag + Al^{3+}$$

The tarnish is removed with little loss of silver. However, the "antiquing" that develops over time (actually silver sulfide tarnish), which often gives a desirable appearance by defining the crevices of the design, is removed also. Silver polish can be used to remove tarnish, but in this case the silver in the tarnish is lost.

Silver mirrors are formed by depositing a thin layer of silver on glass. This is accomplished by reducing a solution of silver nitrate in ammonia with some mild reducing agent, such as glucose or formaldehyde.

The insoluble silver halides are formed as curdy precipitates when halide ions are added to solutions of silver salts. Silver chloride ($K_{sp} = 1.8 \times 10^{-10}$) is white; silver bromide ($K_{sp} = 3.3 \times 10^{-13}$) is pale yellow; silver iodide ($K_{sp} = 1.5 \times 10^{-16}$) is yellow. When exposed to light, the halides of silver turn violet at first and finally black; during this process, they are decomposed into the elements. This is the basis for the heavy use of silver halides in photographic films.

$$2AgX + \text{light} \longrightarrow 2Ag + X_2 \qquad (X = \text{halogen})$$

27.24 Properties of Gold

Gold is a soft yellow metal and is the most malleable and ductile of all metals. Gold foil can be made by hammering the metal into sheets so thin that 300,000 of them make a pile only 1 inch thick; 1 gram of gold can be drawn into a wire more than a mile and a half in length. Pure gold is too soft to be used for jewelry and coinage; for such purposes it is always alloyed with copper, silver, or some other metal. The purity of gold is expressed in **carats,** a designation that indicates the number of parts by mass of gold in 24 parts of alloy. Thus 24-carat gold is the pure metal, and a 10-carat alloy is $\frac{10}{24}$ gold by mass. Red or yellow gold alloys contain copper, and white gold alloys contain palladium, nickel, or zinc.

Gold is a very inactive metal. It neither combines directly with oxygen nor corrodes in the atmosphere. The metal is not affected by any single common acid or by bases. It does, however, dissolve readily in aqua regia (see Section 23.14).

$$Au + 6H_3O^+ + 3NO_3^- + 4Cl^- \longrightarrow [AuCl_4]^- + 3NO_2(g) + 9H_2O$$

It is also dissolved by a solution of chlorine and by cyanide in the presence of air; the latter reaction is used to separate gold from its ores.

In most of its compounds gold has an oxidation number of +1 or +3.

For Review

Summary

The transition elements are the elements with partially filled d orbitals (d-block elements) or f orbitals (f-block elements) in their valence shells. The d-block elements are further classified into the first, second, third, and fourth transition series; the f-block is divided into the lanthanide series and the actinide series.

Extractive metallurgy, the general procedure for producing metals from their ores, usually involves three main steps: (1) **preliminary treatment** of the ores to make them suitable for chemical extraction of the metals, (2) **smelting,** which extracts the metals in the molten state and includes reduction of the metallic compounds in the ores to the metals, and (3) **refining,** which is the purification of the metals.

Superconductors, including **high-temperature superconductors,** are the subject of extensive research efforts today. If their use becomes practical, many exciting applications will follow.

Key Terms and Concepts

actinide contraction (27.8)
actinide series (27.1, 27.8)
basic oxygen process (27.18)
blast furnace (27.2)
blister copper (27.2)
cementite (27.18)
d-block elements (27.1, 27.3)
extractive metallurgy (27.2)
f-block elements (27.1, 27.3)
flotation process (27.2)

flux (27.2)
gangue (27.2)
high-temperature superconductor (27.22)
hydrometallurgy (27.2)
inner transition elements (27.1, 27.3)
lanthanide contraction (27.4)
lanthanide series (27.7)
Parkes process (27.2)
platinum metals (27.3)

rare earth elements (27.7)
refining process (27.2)
roasting process (27.2)
scavenger (27.18)
slag (27.2)
smelting process (27.2)
stainless steel (27.14, 27.18)
steel (27.18)
superconductor (27.22)
transition elements (27.1, 27.3)

Exercises

Answers for selected even-numbered exercises marked by red numbers appear at the end of the book. The worked-out solutions to all even-numbered exercises appear in the *Solutions Guide*.

1. Which of the elements of the first transition series are reduced to the elemental state by carbon during their isolation?
2. What are the various reducing agents used to isolate the elements of the first transition series?
3. Describe the electrolytic process for refining copper.
4. What reactions occur in a blast furnace? Which of these are oxidation–reduction reactions?
5. Describe the Parkes process for extracting silver from lead.
6. Write the electron configurations for the following elements: Sc, Ti, Cr, Fe, Mo, Ru.
7. Write the electron configurations for Ti and the Ti^{2+}, Ti^{3+}, and Ti^{4+} ions.
8. Write the electron configurations for the following elements and their 3+ ions: La, Sm, and Lu.
9. Why are the elemental (free) rare earth elements not found in nature?
10. Why are the rare earths found associated with one another in nature?
11. Which of the following elements is most likely to be used to prepare La by the reduction of La_2O_3: Al, C, or Fe? Why?
12. Describe the lanthanide contraction.
13. What is the effect of the lanthanide contraction on the chemistry of the elements of the second and third transition series?
14. Which of the following ions are not stable in water: Sc^{3+}, Ti^{2+}, Cr^{2+}, Fe^{4+}, Co^{3+}, Ni^{2+}, Cu^+?
15. Which of the following is the strongest oxidizing agent: VO_4^{3-}, CrO_4^{2-}, or WO_4^{2-}?
16. Which of the following elements is most likely to form an oxide with the formula MO_3: Zr, Nb, Mo?
17. In what ways are the Group VIIIB metals Fe, Co, and Ni typical of transition metals in general?
18. In what ways are the Group VIB metals typical of transition metals in general?
19. Predict the products of the following reactions. *Note:* In addition to using the information in this chapter, also use the knowledge you have accumulated at this stage of your study, including information on the prediction of reaction products (see Section 7.14).
    (a) $CuCO_3 + HI(aq) \longrightarrow$
    (b) $TiBr_4 + H_2O \longrightarrow$
    (c) $CoO + O_2 \xrightarrow{\Delta}$
    (d) $La + O_2 \xrightarrow{\Delta}$
    (e) $V + VCl_3 \xrightarrow{\Delta}$
    (f) $Co + xsF_2 \longrightarrow$
    (g) $CrO_3 + CsOH(aq) \longrightarrow$
    (h) $Fe + H_2SO_4 \longrightarrow$
    (i) $LaCl_3(aq) + NaOH(aq) \longrightarrow$
    (j) $W + O_2 \xrightarrow{\Delta}$
    (k) $Mn(OH)_2 + HBr(aq) \longrightarrow$
    (l) $Cr + O_2 \xrightarrow{\Delta}$
    (m) $Mn_2O_3 + HCl(aq) \longrightarrow$
    (n) $Ti + xsF_2 \xrightarrow{\Delta}$

Chromium

20. Account for the extensive use of chromium in the plating of iron and copper objects, such as the trim on automobiles.
21. What is the reaction between hydrogen ions and chromate ions? This is called a condensation reaction. Explain.
22. Write the Lewis structure of chromic acid.
23. Write an equation to illustrate the action of the dichromate ion as an oxidizing agent.
24. Reduction of chromite ore by carbon yields an alloy of iron and chromium. How would you separate the two components of this alloy into solutions of their respective cations, if necessary?
25. Write a balanced chemical equation describing the oxidation of aqueous chromium(II) to chromium(III) in air.
26. Predict the products of the following reactions. (See the note in Exercise 19.)
    (a) $Cr_2(SO_4)_3 + Zn$ in acid.
    (b) $TiCl_2$ is added to a solution containing an excess of CrO_4^{2-} ion.
    (c) $Cr^{2+} + CrO_4^{2-}$ in acid solution.
    (d) Mn is heated with CrO_3.
    (e) $CrO + 2HNO_3$ in water.
    (f) $CrCl_3$ is added to an aqueous solution of NaOH.

Manganese

27. Write a balanced equation for the reaction of manganese dioxide and hydrochloric acid.
28. Identify two uses of manganese dioxide.
29. How is potassium permanganate prepared commercially?
30. How are the ferromanganese alloys produced?
31. Explain the dissolution of manganese(II) hydroxide in aqueous ammonium chloride in terms of an acid–base reaction.
32. Write the names and formulas for compounds in which manganese exhibits each of the following oxidation numbers: +2, +3, +4, +6, +7.
33. How can the insolubility of barium sulfate be applied to the preparation of free permanganic acid?
34. Would you expect a manganese(VII) oxide solution to have a pH greater or less than 7.0? Justify your answer.
35. Predict the products of the following reactions. (See the note in Exercise 19.)
    (a) MnO_2 is warmed in a solution of HBr.
    (b) An excess of Mn metal is added to a solution of $KMnO_4$.

(c) A mixture of MnO_2 and BaO is heated in air.

(d) VCl_3 is added to a solution of $KMnO_4$.

(e) $MnCO_3$ is added to a solution of HNO_3.

(f) MnO is heated in air.

Iron

36. Identify each of the following: hematite, magnetite, cementite, stainless steel, alloy steel.

37. Write the names and formulas of the principal ores of iron.

38. Describe the effect of cementite in the manufacture of steel from iron.

39. Give the general equation for the reaction of iron(III) salts with water. Write equations showing the steps in the reactions of iron(III) chloride to produce a precipitate of hydrated $Fe(OH)_3$, $[Fe(H_2O)_3(OH)_3]$.

40. Iron(II) can be titrated to iron(III) by dichromate ion, which is reduced to chromium(III) in acid solution. A 4.600-g sample of iron ore is dissolved and the iron converted to iron(II). Exactly 23.52 mL of 0.0150 M $Na_2Cr_2O_7$ is required in the titration. What percentage of the ore sample was iron?

41. What is the composition of iron rust?

42. How many cubic feet of air at STP is required per ton of Fe_2O_3 to convert that Fe_2O_3 into iron in a blast furnace? Assume air is 19% oxygen by volume (see Section 27.2).

43. What is the gas produced when iron(II) sulfide is treated with a nonoxidizing acid?

44. Predict the products of the following reactions. (See the note in Exercise 19.)

(a) Fe is heated in an atmosphere of steam.

(b) $NaOH$ is added to a solution of $Fe(NO_3)_3$.

(c) $FeSO_4$ is added to an acidic solution of K_2CrO_4.

(d) Fe is added to a dilute solution of H_2SO_4.

(e) A solution of $Fe(NO_3)_2$ and HNO_3 is allowed to stand in air.

(f) $FeCO_3$ is added to a solution of $HClO_4$.

(g) Fe is heated in air.

Cobalt

45. On the basis of the reactions of elemental fluorine, chlorine, and oxygen with metallic cobalt, predict which is the strongest oxidizing agent.

46. Why does cobalt precede nickel in the periodic table when cobalt has a higher atomic mass than nickel?

47. Sketch the geometrical structure of $[Co(CN)_6]^{3-}$.

48. What is the percent by mass of cobalt in sodium hexanitrocobaltate(III)?

49. Predict the products of the following reactions. (See the note in Exercise 19.)

(a) $NaOH$ is added to a solution of $Co(NO_3)_2$.

(b) $NaOH$ and Na_2S are added to a solution of $Co(NO_3)_2$.

(c) $CoSO_4$ is added to a solution of NH_3.

(d) $CoCO_3$ is added to a solution of $HClO_4$.

(e) Co is heated with I_2.

(f) Co is added to a dilute solution of H_2SO_4.

(g) Co is heated in air.

50. (a) Balance the following equation by oxidation–reduction methods, noting that *three* elements change oxidation numbers.

$$Co(NO_3)_2 \longrightarrow Co_2O_3 + NO_2 + O_2$$

(b) Now balance the same equation by inspection.

(c) Which method do you prefer for balancing this oxidation–reduction equation?

Nickel

51. What is the composition of Alnico? What use is made of it?

52. List the composition (in terms of metals that are present) and key properties of several nickel alloys.

53. Find the potential of the following electrochemical cell.

$$Cd \,|\, Cd^{2+}, \; M = 0.10 \quad \overset{e^-}{\longrightarrow} \quad Ni^{2+}, \; M = 0.50 \,|\, Ni$$

54. What is meant by *passivity*?

55. How is nickel rendered passive?

56. Write the equation for the dissolution of nickel(II) hydroxide in aqueous ammonia.

57. Predict the products of the following reactions. (See the note in Exercise 19.)

(a) KOH is added to a solution of $NiCl_2$.

(b) NH_3 and Na_2S are added to a solution of $Ni(NO_3)_2$.

(c) $NiSO_4$ is added to a solution of NH_3.

(d) $NiCO_3$ is added to a solution of $HClO_4$.

(e) Ni is heated with Cl_2.

(f) Ni is added to a dilute solution of H_2SO_4

(g) Ni is heated in air.

Copper

58. Explain the three oxidation numbers of copper in terms of electronic structure.

59. A white precipitate forms when copper metal is added to a solution of copper(II) chloride and hydrochloric acid. The white precipitate dissolves in excess concentrated hydrochloric acid. Dilution with water causes the white precipitate to reappear. Write equations for the reactions involved.

60. Why are most slightly soluble copper salts readily dissolved by aqueous ammonia?

61. Explain the Daniell cell and the use of copper(II) sulfate in it.

62. Sketch the structure of $Cu(H_2O)_4SO_4 \cdot H_2O$.

63. Copper plate makes up the surface of the Statue of Liberty in New York harbor. Why does it appear green?

64. Compare the stability of copper(I) halides to that of copper(II) halides.

65. Would you expect CuS to dissolve in a 1 M NH_3 solution?

66. How many grams of $CuCl_2$ contain the same mass of copper as 100 g of CuCl?

67. A 1.008-g sample of a silver–copper alloy is dissolved and treated with excess iodide ion. The liberated I_2 is titrated with a 0.1052 M $S_2O_3^{2-}$ solution. If 29.84 mL of this solution is required, what is the percentage of Cu in the alloy?

68. The formation constant of $[Cu(NH_3)_4]^{2+}$ is 1.2×10^{12}. What will be the equilibrium concentration of Cu^{2+} if 1.0 g of Cu is oxidized and put into 1.0 L of 0.25 M NH_3 solution?

Silver

69. Compare the solubilities of silver halides in water and in aqueous ammonia.

70. Why does silver dissolve in nitric acid but not in hydrochloric acid?

71. Explain the tarnishing of silver in the presence of sulfur-containing substances.

72. What properties of silver have made it valuable as a coinage metal? As an element used extensively in the photographic film industry?

73. Dilute sodium cyanide solution is slowly dripped into a slowly stirred silver nitrate solution. A white precipitate forms temporarily but dissolves as the addition of sodium cyanide continues. Use chemical equations to explain this observation.

74. Write equations for the electrode reactions when $Na[Ag(CN)_2]$ is used as the electrolyte in silver plating.

75. Show several ways in which coordination compounds play an important part in the chemistry of silver.

76. A 2.5624-g sample of a pure solid alkali metal chloride is dissolved in water and treated with excess silver nitrate. The resulting precipitate, filtered and dried, weighs 3.03707 g. What was the percent by mass of chloride ion in the original compound? What is the identity of the salt?

77. The formation constant of $[Ag(CN)_2]^-$ is 1.0×10^{20}. What will be the equilibrium concentration of Ag^+ if 1.0 g of Ag is oxidized and put into 1 L of 1.0×10^{-1} M CN^- solution?

Gold

78. Write balanced half-reactions for the following changes, which occur during the recovery of gold from an ore.

$$Au \longrightarrow [Au(CN)_2]^- \longrightarrow Au$$

79. Account for the variable oxidation number of gold in terms of electronic structure.

80. Would you expect salts of the gold(I) ion, Au^+, to be colored? Explain. (See Section 26.10.)

81. How many gold atoms are there in 3.0 g of 18-carat gold?

$\mathscr{28}$ The Post-Transition Metals

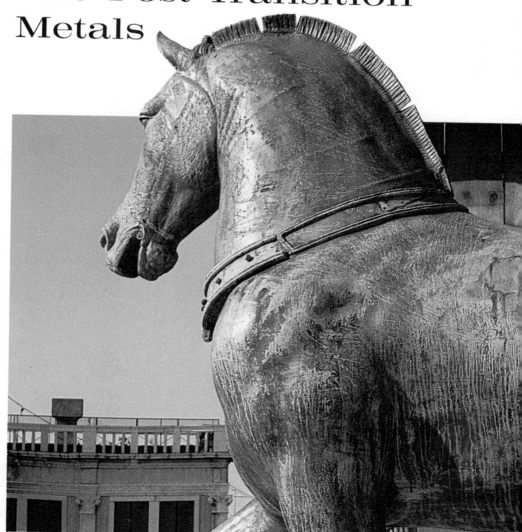

This bronze horse was cast in the third century B.C.

Ten metals in the periodic table that are known as the post-transition metals form cations with pseudo noble gas electron configurations. That is, the valence (outer) shell of each loses all its electrons, and the underlying shell (the $n - 1$ shell) is completely filled with an electron configuration of $(n - 1)s^2$, $(n - 1)p^6$, and $(n - 1)d^{10}$, giving a pseudo noble gas configuration (see Section 7.2). These elements are zinc, cadmium, and mercury from Group IIB, gallium, indium, and thallium from Group IIIA, tin and lead from Group IVA, bismuth from Group VA, and polonium from Group VIA (Fig. 28.1). The reactivities of these elements range from those of fairly active metals (zinc, cadmium, and gallium) to those of much less active metals (lead and

Figure 28.1

The location of the post-transition metals, shown in yellow, in the periodic table. Nonmetals are shown in green, semi-metals in blue, and the remaining metals in red.

mercury). All of the post-transition metals form ionic compounds, expected for metallic elements, but they also form a variety of covalent compounds.

Several of these elements were known in ancient times, because they are easily extracted from their ores. Mercury was known to the Greek philosopher Aristotle, who referred to it as quicksilver (living silver) because of its appearance and liquid state. The alchemists named the element after Mercury, the swift messenger of the gods in Roman mythology. One of the early uses of mercury was in the alchemists' attempts to transmute common metals into gold. They assumed that mercury had unusual powers because it is a liquid and because it dissolves other metals, forming amalgams.

Lead was known to the early Egyptians and Babylonians, and it is mentioned in the Old Testament. Lead pipes were commonly used by the Romans for conveying water, and in the Middle Ages lead was used as a roofing material. The stained glass windows of the great cathedrals of that age are set in lead.

Tin is an essential component of the alloy that gave its name to the Bronze Age.

28.1 The Chemical Behavior of the Post-Transition Metals

Zinc, cadmium, and **mercury** (Fig. 28.2) are the three elements in Group IIB in the periodic table. Each of these elements has two electrons in its outer shell and 18 in the underlying shell $[(n - 1)s^2, (n - 1)p^6, (n - 1)d^{10}, ns^2]$ (see Section 5.12). When these

Figure 28.2

(left to right) Zinc, cadmium, and mercury.

metals form ions with a charge of $+2$, the two outer s electrons are lost, giving pseudo-noble gas electron configurations $[(n-1)s^2,(n-1)p^6,(n-1)d^{10}]$ (see Section 7.2).

Zinc, cadmium, and mercury are representative metals that commonly exhibit the group oxidation number of $+2$, although mercury also exhibits an oxidation number of $+1$ in compounds that contain the diatomic Hg_2^{2+} group. The melting points, boiling points, and heats of vaporization for the Group IIB metals are lower than those for any other group of metals except the alkali metals (Group IA). Of the three elements, zinc is the most reactive and mercury the least. Both cadmium and mercury compounds are toxic.

The chemical behaviors of zinc and cadmium are quite similar. Both elements lie above hydrogen in the activity series (see Section 13.1). They react with oxygen, sulfur, phosphorus, and the halogens to form compounds containing the metals with the group oxidation number of $+2$. For example,

$$Zn + Cl_2 \longrightarrow ZnCl_2$$

$$Cd + I_2 \longrightarrow CdI_2$$

$$2Zn + O_2 \longrightarrow 2ZnO$$

$$Cd + S \longrightarrow CdS$$

$$6Zn + P_4 \longrightarrow 2Zn_3P_2$$

They also react with solutions of acids, resulting in the liberation of hydrogen gas and the formation of salts that generally are soluble. The reaction of zinc with hydrochloric acid (Fig. 28.3) is

$$Zn(s) + 2H_3O^+(aq) + 2Cl^-(aq) \longrightarrow H_2(g) + Zn^{2+}(aq) + 2Cl^-(aq) + 2H_2O(l)$$

Mercury is very different from zinc and cadmium. It is a liquid at 25°C, and many metals dissolve in it, forming **amalgams.** Mercury is a nonreactive element that lies well below hydrogen in the activity series. Thus it does not displace hydrogen from acids, and it dissolves only in oxidizing acids such as nitric acid (Fig. 28.4).

$$Hg(l) + HCl(aq) \longrightarrow \text{no reaction}$$

$$3Hg(l) + 8HNO_3(aq) \longrightarrow 3Hg(NO_3)_2(aq) + 4H_2O(l) + 2NO(g)$$

Mercury compounds decompose when they are heated, so elemental mercury reacts to form compounds only at relatively low temperatures—and then only with oxygen, sulfur, and the halogens.

Figure 28.3

Zinc is an active post-transition metal. It dissolves in hydrochloric acid, forming a solution of colorless Zn^{2+} ions, Cl^- ions, and hydrogen gas.

Figure 28.4

Mercury is an inactive post-transition metal. It does not react with hydrochloric acid (left). It dissolves in nitric acid (right) because this acid is a strong oxidizing agent. (The brown fumes of NO_2 result from atmospheric oxidation of the NO produced from the reaction of Hg with HNO_3.)

$$2Hg + O_2 \xrightarrow{300°} 2HgO$$

$$Hg + S \longrightarrow HgS$$

$$Hg + I_2 \longrightarrow HgI_2$$

Mercury exhibits an oxidation number of +2 in these compounds.

Mercury exhibits an oxidation number of +1 in covalent compounds containing X—Hg—Hg—X groups, such as Hg_2Cl_2, and in solutions containing salts of the Hg_2^{2+} ion. The Hg_2^{2+} ion is a diatomic species formed by one valence electron of each mercury atom combining to form a covalent single bond between the two mercury atoms.

The +2 ions of all three of the elements of Group IIB are small in relation to their charges, so they show strong tendencies toward the formation of covalent compounds and complex ions. The simplest complex ions containing these elements are those with halides, cyanide, and ammonia. Coordination numbers of 4 and 6 are usual in the complexes of these elements. The four-coordinated complexes are tetrahedral. The six-coordinated complexes have octahedral structures (see Section 26.3).

Gallium, indium, and **thallium** (Fig. 28.5) are members of Group IIIA. Each of these elements has three electrons in its outer shell and 18 in the underlying shell $[(n-1)s^2,(n-1)p^6,(n-1)d^{10},ns^2,np^1]$ (see Section 5.12). As described in Section 13.2, these elements form compounds in which they exhibit the group oxidation number of +3. Their +3 ions exhibit a pseudo noble gas electron configuration $[(n-1)s^2, (n-1)p^6,(n-1)d^{10}]$. In addition, gallium and indium exhibit oxidation numbers of +1

Figure 28.5

(left to right) Gallium, indium, and thallium. Gallium has a low melting temperature (29.8°C) and melts when held in the hand (body temperature is 37°C). Compare this photograph with the photograph of solid gallium on page 159. The dull color of the thallium is due to a layer of thallium(I) oxide and hydroxide resulting from the reaction of the metal with the atmosphere.

Figure 28.6
Tin (left) and lead (right).

Figure 28.7
Tin(II) chloride is an ionic solid; tin(IV) chloride is a covalent liquid.

in certain unstable compounds, and thallium readily forms compounds with an oxidation number of +1. All of these elements lie above hydrogen in the activity series and react with acids, liberating hydrogen gas. Gallium and indium are oxidized to the +3 ion, but thallium is oxidized only to the Tl^+ ion, the stable oxidation number for thallium in water. Gallium, indium, and thallium react with nonmetals to form salts. Thallium(III) salts form only with strong oxidizing agents.

Thallium is an example of an element that exhibits the so-called **inert pair effect.** The stability of an oxidation number that is two below the group oxidation number is a result of the resistance of the pair of *s* electrons in the valence shell to being lost during formation of an ion or to participation in the formation of a covalent bond. The *s* electrons are, in effect, an inert pair of electrons. The electron configuration of the thallium atom is $[Xe]4f^{14}5d^{10}6s^26p^1$, and that of the Tl^+ ion is $[Xe]4f^{14}5d^{10}6s^2$, showing that the 6*s* electrons are not lost when this ion forms. The stability of the *s* electrons in the valence shells of the post-transition metals increases down a group in the periodic table, so the heaviest member of a group exhibits the most pronounced inert pair effect.

Tin and **lead** (Fig. 28.6) are the heavy members of Group IVA of the periodic table. The light elements in this group, carbon, silicon, and germanium, are primarily nonmetallic in character, whereas tin and lead become increasingly metallic in their properties with increasing atomic mass and decreasing ionization energy. Tin and lead form stable dipositive cations, Sn^{2+} and Pb^{2+}, with oxidation numbers two below the group oxidation number of +4. The stability of this oxidation state can also be attributed to the inert pair effect. The fact that the hydroxides of these ions are amphoteric is an indication of some nonmetallic character. Tin and lead also form covalent compounds in which the +4 oxidation number is exhibited; for example, $SnCl_4$ and $PbCl_4$ are low-boiling covalent liquids (Fig. 28.7).

Tin is a moderately active metal. It reacts with acids to form tin(II) compounds and with nonmetals to form either tin(II) or tin(IV) compounds, depending on the stoichiometry. Lead is less reactive. It lies just above hydrogen in the activity series and is attacked only by hot concentrated acids.

Bismuth, the heaviest member of Group VA, is a typical metal (Fig. 28.8). It readily gives up three of its five valence electrons to active nonmetals to form the tripositive ion, Bi^{3+}. It forms compounds with the group oxidation number of +5 only when treated with strong oxidizing agents.

Polonium is a member of Group VIA. It is an intensely radioactive element that results from the radioactive decay of uranium and thorium (see Section 24.6). Its chemical behavior is similar to the metallic behavior of tellurium (see Section 25.1). We will not consider polonium further in this chapter.

Figure 28.8
Bismuth.

㉘.2 Occurrence and Isolation of the Post-Transition Metals

Ores of the post-transition metals usually contain mixtures of these elements as oxides or sulfides. Some ores also contain certain transition elements. Thus isolation of a post-transition metal often requires reduction of a mixture of metal oxides or sulfides to the metals, followed by separation of two or more metals.

Because the activities of the post-transition metals are lower than those of the transition metals and much lower than those of the active metals, compounds of the post-transition metals are readily reduced. Carbon is sufficient to reduce most of their ores. The post-transition metals have low melting points and low boiling points, compared to those of the transition metals. Thus, unlike the transition metals, they can be separated by fractional distillation. Electrolysis is sometimes used for separation; careful control of the applied voltage makes possible the deposition of one metal at a potential that is too low to deposit a second.

Zinc is usually obtained from **sphalerite**, or **zinc blende**, ZnS, the principal ore of zinc. Less important ores include **zincite**, ZnO; **smithsonite**, $ZnCO_3$; franklinite, a mixture of oxides of zinc, iron, and manganese; and **willemite**, Zn_2SiO_4. Sulfide ores are first concentrated by flotation (see Section 27.2) and then roasted to convert zinc sulfide to zinc oxide. Carbonate ores that contain zinc are converted to the oxide simply by heating.

$$2ZnS + 3O_2 \xrightarrow{\triangle} 2ZnO + 2SO_2 \qquad \Delta H° = -878.3 \text{ kJ}$$
$$ZnCO_3 \xrightarrow{\triangle} ZnO + CO_2 \qquad \Delta H° = 71.0 \text{ kJ}$$

Zinc oxide is reduced by heating it with coal in a fire-clay vessel.

$$ZnO + C \xrightarrow{\triangle} Zn + CO$$

As rapidly as zinc is produced, it distills out and is condensed. It contains impurities of cadmium, iron, lead, and arsenic, but it can be purified by careful redistillation.

An electrolytic process is also employed to produce zinc. Roasted ore is treated with dilute sulfuric acid, giving a solution of zinc sulfate and the sulfates of other metals. Silver sulfate and lead sulfate remain in the residue because they are insoluble. The resulting solution is treated with powdered zinc to reduce the less active metals, such as copper, arsenic, and antimony, to the elemental state. Any iron(II) present is oxidized by passing air through the solution. Manganese and iron are precipitated as hydroxides by adding a calculated amount of slaked lime (calcium hydroxide). After the solution is thus purified, it is electrolyzed, and zinc is deposited on aluminum cathodes. Sulfuric acid is regenerated as electrolysis proceeds; it is used in the leaching of additional roasted ore. At intervals the cathodes are removed, and the zinc is scraped off, melted, and cast into ingots. Electrolytic zinc has a purity of 99.95%.

Cadmium is found in the rare mineral **greenockite**, CdS, and in small amounts (less than 1%) in several zinc ores. Most cadmium comes from zinc smelters and from the sludge obtained from the electrolytic refining of zinc.

In the smelting of cadmium-containing zinc ores, the two metals are reduced together. Because cadmium is more volatile (bp = 767°C) than zinc (bp = 907°C), their separation can be accomplished by fractional distillation. Separation of the two metals is also possible by selective electrolytic deposition. Cadmium is less active than zinc and is deposited at a lower voltage.

Cadmium is a silvery, crystalline metal that is only slightly tarnished by air or water at ordinary temperatures. A large part of the cadmium produced is used in the electronics industry and as an anticorrosion coating on such metals as iron and steel. The electrolyte solution used to deposit cadmium contains tetracyanocadmate ions, $[Cd(CN)_4]^{2-}$, made by mixing cadmium chloride and sodium cyanide. The equation for the cathodic reduction is

$$[Cd(CN)_4]^{2-} + 2e^- \longrightarrow Cd + 4CN^-$$

The most important commercial source of **mercury** is the dark red sulfide, HgS, known as **cinnabar** (Fig. 28.9). When cinnabar is roasted, metallic mercury distills from the furnace and is condensed to the liquid. Ordinarily the roasting of a mineral in air results in the oxidation of the metal to an oxide. However, the mercury oxides are thermally unstable and decompose to the elements at the temperature of the furnace. Mercury can be purified by washing it with dilute nitric acid to oxidize the metallic impurities or by distilling it in an atmosphere of oxygen to remove the more active metals.

Figure 28.9

A sample of the mineral cinnabar, HgS.

No ores contain large fractions of **gallium, indium,** or **thallium.** Gallium is present in aluminum ores in small amounts and is recovered as a by-product during the refining of aluminum. Because of the tremendous scale of the aluminum industry, gallium is readily available. Indium occurs in small amounts in zinc ores, particularly zinc sulfide ores. Indium is recovered from the flue dust produced when ZnS is roasted during the metallurgy of zinc. Thallium occurs along with lead. It is recovered during the smelting of lead.

Tin is obtained from **cassiterite,** or **tinstone,** SnO_2, the most abundant tin ore. Roasting of the ore removes arsenic and sulfur as volatile oxides. Oxides of other metals are extracted by means of hydrochloric acid. The purified ore is reduced by carbon.

$$SnO_2(s) + 2C(s) \xrightarrow{\Delta} Sn(l) + 2CO(g) \qquad \Delta H° = 360 \text{ kJ}$$

The molten tin, which collects on the bottom of the furnace, is drawn off and cast into blocks **(block tin)**. The crude tin is remelted and permitted to flow away from the higher-melting impurities (chiefly compounds of iron and arsenic). Further purification of the tin is accomplished by electrolysis, using impure tin anodes, pure tin cathodes, and an electrolyte of hexafluorosilicic acid (H_2SiF_6) and sulfuric acid.

Lead is obtained principally from lead sulfide, PbS, commonly called **galena.** Other common ores are lead carbonate, $PbCO_3$, called **cerrusite,** and lead sulfate, $PbSO_4$, called **anglesite.** These ores are first concentrated by flotation to remove unwanted materials and a large part of the zinc sulfide usually associated with lead ores. The concentrated ore is then roasted in air to convert most of the sulfide to the oxide.

$$2PbS(s) + 3O_2(g) \xrightarrow{\Delta} 2PbO(s) + 2SO_2(g) \qquad \Delta H° = -710.4 \text{ kJ}$$

The roasted product is reduced in a blast furnace (see Section 27.2) with coke and scrap iron.

$$PbO(s) + C(s) \xrightarrow{\Delta} Pb(l) + CO(g)$$

$$PbO(s) + CO(g) \xrightarrow{\Delta} Pb(l) + CO_2(g)$$

$$PbS(s) + Fe(s) \xrightarrow{\Delta} Pb(l) + FeS(s)$$

The molten lead obtained from a blast furnace generally contains copper, antimony, arsenic, bismuth, gold, and silver. If this crude lead is stirred in air, antimony, arsenic, and bismuth are oxidized. The oxides of these metals rise to the surface, and the molten lead can be drained off for further refining. Gold and silver can be extracted from the lead by the Parkes process (see Section 27.2) or by the electrolytic **Betts process.** In the Betts process thin sheets of pure lead are used as cathodes, and plates of impure lead are used as anodes. The electrolyte is a solution containing lead hexafluorosilicate, $PbSiF_6$, and hexafluorosilicic acid, H_2SiF_6.

Bismuth is most often found in nature in the free state. It sometimes occurs in compounds such as bismuth(III) oxide, Bi_2O_3 (called **bismuth ocher**), or bismuth(III) sulfide, Bi_2S_3 (called **bismuth glance**). Ores containing the free metal are treated by heating them in inclined iron pipes. The metal melts and flows away from the remaining materials. The oxide and sulfide ores are roasted and then heated with charcoal. As the elemental bismuth forms, it melts and collects beneath the less dense material. Bismuth is produced in the United States as a by-product of the refining of other metals, particularly lead.

28.3 Uses of the Post-Transition Metals

Zinc is a silvery metal that quickly tarnishes to a blue-gray appearance. This color is due to an adherent coating of a basic carbonate, $Zn_2(OH)_2CO_3$, which protects the underlying metal from further corrosion. The metal is hard and brittle at ordinary temperatures but ductile and malleable at 100–150°C. When molten zinc is poured into cold water, it solidifies in irregular masses called **granulated,** or **mossy, zinc.**

A large amount of zinc is used in the manufacture of dry cells (see Section 20.8) for flashlight batteries and portable radios; in the manufacture of the small button-shaped alkaline dry cell batteries used in some cameras, calculators, and watches; and in the production of alloys such as **brass** (Cu and Zn) and **bronze** (Cu, Sn, and Zn). About half of the zinc metal produced is used to protect iron and other metals from corrosion by air and water. Its protective action results from the basic carbonate film on its surface. Furthermore, it protects a less active metal such as iron, because it forms an electrochemical cell in which zinc serves as the anode and iron as the cathode (see Section 20.11). The zinc coating on iron may be applied in several ways, and the product is called **galvanized iron.**

Cadmium is a silvery, crystalline metal that resembles zinc. It is only lightly tarnished by air or water at ordinary temperatures. Cadmium can be used in electroplating metals, such as iron and steel, to protect them from corrosion. Cadmium-plated metals are more resistant to corrosion, more easily soldered, and more attractive in appearance than galvanized (zinc-coated) metals, but their use has been restricted because of the toxicity of cadmium (Section 28.4).

Several alloys of cadmium are easily fusible; these include **Woods' metal** (12.5% Cd), melting at 65.5°C, and **Lipowitz alloy** (10% cadmium), melting at 70°C. Because these alloys melt from the heat produced by the first stages of a fire, they are used in fire-alert devices. Some antifriction alloys used for bearings contain cadmium. Rods of cadmium are used in nuclear reactors (see Section 24.11) to absorb neutrons and thus control the chain reaction.

Mercury is the only metal that is a liquid below 25°C. Its low freezing point (−38.87°C), its high boiling point (356.6°C), its uniform coefficient of expansion, and the fact that it does not wet glass make mercury an excellent thermometric substance. Because of its chemical inactivity, mobility, high density, and electrical conductivity, it is used extensively in barometers, vacuum pumps, and liquid seals and for electrical contacts. Except for iron and platinum, all metals readily dissolve in (or are wetted by) mercury to form amalgams. Sodium amalgam is used as a reducing agent because it is less active than sodium metal alone. Amalgams of tin, silver, and gold are used in dentistry.

Gallium is seeing increasing use in gallium arsenide (GaAs) semiconductors.

Tin exists as three allotropic solids: **gray tin** (cubic crystals), **white tin** (tetragonal crystals), and **brittle tin** (rhombic crystals). The white form is malleable. When a rod of it is bent, the crystals slip over one another, producing a sound described as tin cry. When white tin is heated, it changes to the brittle form. At temperatures below 13.2°C, white tin slowly changes into gray tin, which is powdery. Consequently, articles made of tin are likely to disintegrate in cold weather, particularly if the cold spell is lengthy (Fig. 28.10). The change progresses slowly from the spot of origin, and the gray tin that is first formed catalyzes further change. In a way, this effect is similar to the spread of an infection in a plant or animal body. For this reason, it is called tin disease or tin pest.

The principal use of tin is in the electrolytic production of tin plate—sheet iron coated with tin to protect it from corrosion. However, when a scratch through the tin exposes the iron, corrosion sets in rapidly. Iron is more active than tin and corrodes more rapidly when in contact with tin than otherwise. This is because iron and tin in contact with each other, when both are in contact with moist air, constitute an electrolytic cell that promotes corrosion (see Section 20.11). Tin is also used in making alloys such as **bronze** (Cu, Sn, and Zn) and **solder** (Sn and Pb).

Lead is a soft metal that has little tensile strength and the greatest density of the common metals (except for gold and mercury). Lead has a metallic luster when freshly cut but quickly acquires a dull gray color when exposed to moist air. It becomes oxidized on its surface, forming a protective layer that is both compact and adherent; this film is probably lead hydroxycarbonate, $Pb_3(OH)_2(CO_3)_2$.

The major uses of lead exploit the ease with which it is worked, its low melting point, its great density, and its resistance to corrosion. Lead is a principal constituent of the lead storage battery (see Section 20.9). It is an important component of solder (Sn and Pb).

Bismuth is a lustrous, hard, and brittle metal with a reddish tint. Like antimony, melted bismuth expands when it solidifies—a most unusual property. Because of this, it is used in the formation of alloys to prevent them from shrinking on solidification. This is particularly important in alloys used in casting, which must expand to fill all of the space in the mold.

Alloys of bismuth, tin, and lead have low melting points, which make them useful for electrical fuses, safety plugs for boilers, and automatic sprinkler systems. Some of these alloys melt even in hot water. For example, **Rose's metal** (Bi, 50%; Pb, 25%; Sn, 25%) melts at 94°C, and **Wood's metal** (Bi, 50%; Pb, 25%; Sn, 12.5%; Cd, 12.5%) melts at 65.5°C.

Figure 28.10

Disintegration due to the cold is evident in this tin object.

28.4 Physiological Action of the Post-Transition Metals

Zinc is one of the most important metals in biological processes, and it appears to be necessary to all forms of life. It is a key component of more than 80 enzymes, which are the catalysts of biochemical reactions in living organisms (see Section 31.5). The body of an adult human contains about 2 grams of zinc. Interestingly, cadmium and mercury, which are members of the same group as zinc, have no known biological function and are, in fact, among the most toxic of elements.

Metallic mercury is a cumulative poison; the breathing of air containing mercury vapor and contact with the liquid metal should be avoided. Mercury compounds are also poisonous. The fatal dose of mercury(II) chloride is 0.2–0.4 gram. The mercury(II) ions combine with the proteins in the kidneys and destroy their ability to remove waste products from the blood. Mercury also has a permanent effect on the brain and central nervous system. Antidotes for mercury poisoning are egg white and milk; the proteins in these substances precipitate the mercury in the stomach before it can be absorbed into the body. Mercury poisoning is treated with chelates such as BAL, British Anti-Lewisite (see Section 26.5).

Cadmium is extremely toxic. Its effects on the liver and nervous system are similar to those of mercury. As a consequence, the use of cadmium is significantly limited.

Thallium is the heaviest member of Group IIIA. Both thallium metal and its compounds are very toxic. However, an isotope of thallium, ^{201}Tl, is useful in trace amounts in medical tests of the heart (see Section 24.14).

Tin is nontoxic, but lead is a heavy-metal poison. It interferes with the catalytic ability of enzymes in various metabolic processes. Typical symptoms of lead poisoning include anemia, headaches, convulsions, and kidney, brain, and nervous-system disorders. Lead poisoning, like mercury poisoning, is treated with chelating agents.

At one time lead hydroxycarbonate, $Pb_3(OH)_2(CO_3)_2$, was used extensively as the paint pigment **white lead.** Many people, particularly children, have suffered lead poisoning because of its extensive use as a house paint. Because of the danger of poisoning, it has been largely replaced as a paint pigment by titanium dioxide, zinc oxide, and lithopone (a mixture of barium sulfate and zinc sulfide), especially on objects used by children.

Compounds of the Post-Transition Metals

28.5 Oxides of the Post-Transition Metals

The common oxides of the post-transition metals are shown in Table 28.1.

1. **Preparation of the Oxides.** The oxides of the post-transition metals can be prepared by reactions of the metals with oxygen, by thermal decomposition of hydroxides or other salts, or by oxidation of oxides or other compounds.

(a) **Zinc oxide, cadmium oxide, gallium oxide, indium oxide, thallium(I) oxide, tin(IV) oxide, lead(II) oxide,** and **bismuth(III) oxide** form when the corresponding metals burn in air. Examples of the reactions involved are

$$4Tl + O_2 \longrightarrow 2Tl_2O$$
$$2Cd + O_2 \longrightarrow 2CdO$$
$$4In + 3O_2 \longrightarrow 2In_2O_3$$
$$Sn + O_2 \longrightarrow SnO_2$$

Under these conditions, thallium, lead, and bismuth, the heaviest elements in their respective groups and the elements for which the inert pair effect is most pronounced, form oxides in which they exhibit oxidation numbers two less than the group oxidation number.

Table 28.1	Common Oxides of the Post-Transition Metals[a]		
Group IIB	Group IIIA	Group IVA	Group VA
ZnO	Ga_2O_3		
CdO	In_2O_3	SnO	
		SnO_2	
HgO	Tl_2O	PbO	Bi_2O_3
	Tl_2O_3	Pb_3O_4	Bi_2O_5
		PbO_2	

[a] Oxides for which formulas are printed in red are formed when the corresponding metal burns in air.

Mercury(II) oxide forms slowly when mercury is warmed below 500°C in oxygen; it decomposes above this temperature.

(b) Tin(II) oxide and the oxides that result from burning the metal can also be prepared by the thermal decomposition of the corresponding metal hydroxides and carbonates, as well as certain of their other salts. In some cases the thermal decomposition occurs at room temperature. For example, mercury(II) oxide can be prepared by adding a solution of a strong base to a solution of a mercury(II) salt; $Hg(OH)_2$ is unstable, and HgO precipitates from the mixture.

Tin(II) oxide, SnO, can be prepared by treating a hot solution of a tin(II) compound with an alkali metal carbonate or by heating tin(II) oxalate in the absence of air. The equations are

$$Sn^{2+}(aq) + CO_3^{2-}(aq) \longrightarrow SnO(s) + CO_2(g)$$

$$SnC_2O_4(s) \xrightarrow[\text{Inert atm.}]{\text{Heat}} SnO(s) + CO_2(g) + CO(g)$$

(c) Formation of the oxides that contain thallium(III), lead(IV), or bismuth(V) may require stronger oxidizing agents than the oxygen present in air. Oxides containing the metal with a lower oxidation number are often used as starting materials in these reactions. **Lead dioxide,** PbO_2, is a black powder (Fig. 28.11) formed by oxidizing lead(II) compounds in alkaline solution. The equation for the oxidation with sodium hypochlorite as the oxidizing agent is

$$PbO(s) + Na^+(aq) + ClO^-(aq) \longrightarrow PbO_2(s) + Na^+(aq) + Cl^-(aq)$$

Bismuth(V) oxide, Bi_2O_5, is produced by the action of very strong oxidizing agents on the trioxide.

Trilead tetraoxide, Pb_3O_4, called red lead (Fig. 28.11), is prepared by carefully heating the monoxide in air at temperatures of 400–500°C. Red lead contains lead with two oxidation numbers; when it is treated with nitric acid, two-thirds of the lead dissolves as lead nitrate (oxidation number = +2), and the other third remains as insoluble lead dioxide (oxidation number = +4). The equation for the reaction is

$$Pb_3O_4 + 4HNO_3 \longrightarrow PbO_2 + 2Pb(NO_3)_2 + 2H_2O$$

Figure 28.11

Black PbO_2, red Pb_3O_4, and yellow PbO.

2. Reactions and Uses of the Oxides. Zinc oxide, ZnO, is used as a paint pigment called **zinc white,** or **Chinese white.** Unlike white lead, it does not blacken with hydrogen sulfide, because zinc sulfide is white. Zinc oxide is also used in the manufacture of automobile tires and other rubber goods and in the preparation of medicinal ointments. It is used in zinc-oxide-based sun screens to prevent sunburn (Fig. 28.12).

When a strong base is added to a cold solution of mercury(II) compound, mercury(II) oxide forms as a yellow precipitate, but when precipitated from hot solutions, it is red. Because the crystal structure is the same in both cases, this difference in color has been attributed to a difference in the size of the HgO particles.

Lead dioxide is the principal constituent of the cathode of the charged lead storage battery (Section 20.9). Lead(IV) tends to revert to the more stable lead(II) ion by gaining two electrons, so lead dioxide is a powerful oxidizing agent.

㉘.6 Hydroxides of the Post-Transition Metals

With the exception of thallium(I) hydroxide, the known hydroxides of the post-transition metals are insoluble. They can be prepared by adding soluble hydroxides, such as the alkali metal hydroxides, to solutions of their salts. For example, one reaction for the formation of zinc hydroxide (Fig. 28.13) is

$$Zn^{2+}(aq) + 2NO_3^-(aq) + 2Na^+(aq) + 2OH^-(aq) \longrightarrow$$
$$Zn(OH)_2(s) + 2Na^+(aq) + 2NO_3^-(aq)$$

An excess of the soluble hydroxide should be avoided, because many of the hydroxides of the post-transition elements are amphoteric and dissolve in an excess of base. Zinc hydroxide, for example, dissolves in a solution of sodium hydroxide (Fig. 28.13).

$$Zn(OH)_2(s) + 2Na^+(aq) + 2OH^-(aq) \longrightarrow 2Na^+(aq) + [Zn(OH)_4]^{2-}(aq)$$

An excess of base causes **tin(II) hydroxide** to dissolve, with the formation of the soluble **stannite ion.**

$$Sn(OH)_2(s) + OH^-(aq) \longrightarrow [Sn(OH)_3]^-(aq)$$

Figure 28.12

Zinc oxide protects this sailor from sunburn.

(a)   (b)

Figure 28.13

(a) Mixing solutions of NaOH and $Zn(NO_3)_2$ produces a white precipitate of $Zn(OH)_2$. (b) Addition of an excess of NaOH results in dissolution of the precipitate.

The stannite ion is an active reducing agent. It is used in qualitative analysis to test for bismuth because it reduces white bismuth(III) hydroxide to black metallic bismuth.

$$2Bi(OH)_3(s) + 3[Sn(OH)_3]^-(aq) + 3OH^-(aq) \longrightarrow 2Bi(s) + 3[Sn(OH)_6]^{2-}(aq)$$

Thallium(I) hydroxide is soluble. It forms when thallium(I) oxide is added to water.

$$Tl_2O(s) + H_2O(l) \longrightarrow 2TlOH(aq)$$

Mercury(I) hydroxide is unstable. Addition of a strong base to a mercury(I) salt produces a mixture of mercury metal and mercury(II) oxide. **Mercury(II) hydroxide** is also unstable; it immediately decomposes to mercury(II) oxide and water.

$$Hg(OH)_2 \longrightarrow HgO + H_2O$$

Addition of a strong base to a solution of a salt of thallium(III), tin(IV), lead(IV), or bismuth(V) does not produce hydroxides. Instead, oxides containing water of hydration (see Section 13.5), called hydrated oxides, are formed.

The hydrated oxide of tin(IV) has the formula $SnO_2 \cdot H_2O$. When this hydrated oxide is melted with sodium hydroxide, **sodium metastannate,** Na_2SnO_3, and water are formed. Because sodium metastannate can be regarded as a salt, $SnO_2 \cdot H_2O$ has been called **metastannic acid,** or sometimes **alpha-stannic acid** to distinguish it from **beta-stannic acid,** which is the hydrated oxide formed when hot concentrated nitric acid reacts with tin. Beta-stannic acid has the same composition as the alpha form, but it is insoluble in acids and only very slightly soluble in strongly alkaline solutions.

Some other alkali metal stannates appear to be derived from **orthostannic acid,** which is unknown but can be represented by the formula $H_2[Sn(OH)_6]$. The sodium salt, for example, is known; it is $Na_2[Sn(OH)_6]$.

When a suspension of **bismuth hydroxide** is boiled, the hydroxide decomposes to **bismuth oxyhydroxide,** BiO(OH), and water.

28.7 Halides of the Post-Transition Metals

Halides of the post-transition metals can be prepared by the techniques used to prepare halides of other metals (see Sections 13.8 and 27.5). However, complications result from the varying stabilities of the oxidation numbers of these elements and the relative nonreactivity of mercury and lead.

1. **Preparation of the Halides.** These compounds can be prepared by a variety of methods.

   (a) The direct reaction of a post-transition metal and a halogen produces the anhydrous halide of the metal. If the post-transition metal exhibits two oxidation numbers, it may be necessary to control the stoichiometry in order to obtain the halide with the lower oxidation number. For example, preparation of tin(II) chloride requires a one-to-one mole ratio of Sn to Cl_2, whereas preparation of tin(IV) chloride requires a one-to-two ratio.

$$Sn + Cl_2 \longrightarrow SnCl_2$$
$$Sn + 2Cl_2 \longrightarrow SnCl_4$$

   (b) The active post-transition metals (zinc, cadmium, gallium, indium, thallium, tin, and bismuth) dissolve in solutions of the hydrogen halides, producing hydrogen and generally forming solutions of halide salts that can be evaporated to produce hydrated metal halides. Zinc, cadmium, gallium, and indium exhibit their respective group oxidation numbers; thallium forms thallium(I) salts, tin forms tin(II) salts, and bismuth forms bismuth(III) salts. The heavier halides of thallium(I) (the chloride, bromide, and iodide) are insoluble and precipitate. Sample reactions include

$$2Tl(s) + 2HCl(aq) \longrightarrow 2TlCl(s) + H_2(g)$$
$$Cd(s) + 2HBr(aq) \longrightarrow CdBr_2(aq) + H_2(g)$$
$$Sn(s) + 2HCl(aq) \longrightarrow SnCl_2(aq) + H_2(g)$$
$$2Ga(s) + 6HI(aq) \longrightarrow 2GaI_3(aq) + 3H_2(g)$$

   (c) Hydroxides, carbonates, and some oxides dissolve in solutions of the hydrohalic acids, forming solutions of halide salts.

   (d) Several of the post-transition metals form insoluble halides. The heavier mercury(I) halides, mercury(II) iodide, the heavier thallium(I) halides, and the heavier lead(II) halides are insoluble. Hence halides such as Hg_2Cl_2, HgI_2, TlBr, and PbI_2 can be prepared by metathesis reactions between soluble salts of these metals and soluble halide salts (Fig. 28.14). For example,

$$Hg^{2+}(aq) + 2I^-(aq) \longrightarrow HgI_2(s)$$

2. **Reactions and Uses of the Halides.** Anhydrous **zinc chloride**, $ZnCl_2$, is a white, very deliquescent solid. It is made by the reaction of zinc with chlorine or by fusing hydrated zinc chloride to drive off the water of hydration. The product, which melts at 262°C, is cast into sticks.

The anhydrous salt is used as a caustic in surgery and as a dehydrating agent in certain organic reactions. Aqueous solutions of zinc chloride are acidic because the **hexaaquozinc(II) ion** is acidic (see Section 17.14).

$$[Zn(H_2O)_6]^{2+} + H_2O \longrightarrow [Zn(H_2O)_5OH]^+ + H_3O^+$$

(a)   (b)

Figure 28.14

(a) HgI_2 forms when solutions of KI and $Hg(NO_3)_2$ are mixed. (b) The precipitate redissolves in excess KI because of the formation of $[HgI_4]^{2-}$.

Because of its acidic nature, a solution of zinc chloride (with ammonium chloride) is used as a **flux** to dissolve the oxides on metal surfaces before soldering.

Concentrated solutions of zinc chloride dissolve cellulose, forming a gelatinous mass that can be molded into various shapes. Fiberboard is made from this material (Fig. 28.15). Zinc oxide dissolves in concentrated solutions of zinc chloride, producing **zinc oxychloride**, Zn_2OCl_2, which sets to a hard mass and is used as a cement.

Cadmium chloride, $CdCl_2$, is converted almost completely into $[CdCl_4]^{2-}$ by high concentrations of the chloride ion. Most cadmium compounds are soluble in an excess of sodium iodide because of the formation of the tetraiodocadmate(II) ion $[CdI_4]^{2-}$.

$$Cd(OH)_2(s) + 4I^-(aq) \longrightarrow [CdI_4]^{2-}(aq) + 2OH^-(aq)$$

Mercury(I) chloride, Hg_2Cl_2 (commonly called mercurous chloride), is a white, insoluble crystalline compound ($K_{sp} = 1.1 \times 10^{-18}$), which is of analytical importance because its insolubility serves to precipitate the mercury(I) ion. Mercury(I) chloride is manufactured on a commercial scale by heating a mixture of mercury(II) sulfate, mercury, and sodium chloride.

$$HgSO_4 + Hg + 2NaCl \longrightarrow Hg_2Cl_2 + Na_2SO_4$$

Mercury(I) chloride is volatile and sublimes from the reaction mixture. It was once commonly used in medicine under the name calomel as a cathartic and a diuretic (a stimulant for the large intestine and the kidneys).

When exposed to light, mercury(I) chloride slowly decomposes.

$$Hg_2Cl_2 \longrightarrow HgCl_2 + Hg$$

Hence it is usually stored in amber-colored bottles.

Reducing agents, such as tetrachlorostannate(II) ion, readily reduce mercury(I) compounds to metallic mercury. This reaction is used in qualitative tests for the ion.

Figure 28.15

This closeup view of fiberboard shows the random arrangement of fibers caused by dissolving cellulose in zinc chloride.

Mercury(II) chloride, $HgCl_2$, is prepared commercially by heating mercury(II) sulfate with sodium chloride; the $HgCl_2$ sublimes from the reaction mixture.

$$HgSO_4 + 2NaCl \xrightarrow{\Delta} HgCl_2 + Na_2SO_4$$

The compound $HgCl_2$ is also called **corrosive sublimate.** In dilute solutions it is used as an antiseptic. It is moderately soluble in water but only slightly ionized, as indicated by the low electrical conductivity of its aqueous solutions. Its solubility can be increased by adding an excess of chloride ions, which cause the formation of the complex **tetrachloromercurate(II) ion** according to the equation

$$HgCl_2 + 2Cl^- \rightleftharpoons [HgCl_4]^{2-}$$

Iodide ions precipitate mercury(II) ions from solution as HgI_2, which is red. **Mercury(II) iodide** is soluble in a solution containing an excess of iodide ions (Fig. 28.14); **tetraiodomercurate(II) ions** are formed according to the equation

$$HgI_2 + 2I^- \rightleftharpoons [HgI_4]^{2-}$$

Tin(II) chloride is obtained as the dihydrate ($SnCl_2 \cdot 2H_2O$) by evaporating a solution of $SnCl_2$ in hydrochloric acid. When dissolved in neutral water, tin(II) chloride reacts with the water, forming **tin hydroxychloride,** $Sn(OH)Cl$.

$$SnCl_2 + 2H_2O \rightleftharpoons Sn(OH)Cl + H_3O^+ + Cl^-$$

Tin(II) chloride is widely used as a reducing agent because of the ease with which it is oxidized to tin(IV) compounds. Aqueous solutions of tin(II) compounds must be protected against oxidation by air.

Tin(IV) chloride is a colorless liquid that is soluble in organic solvents such as carbon tetrachloride and is a nonconductor of electricity. These properties are typical of covalent compounds. When dissolved in water, the tetrachloride reacts with water, but in hydrochloric acid, hexachlorostannic acid is produced.

$$SnCl_4(l) + 2H_3O^+(aq) + 2Cl^-(aq) \longrightarrow 2H_3O^+(aq) + [SnCl_6]^{2-}(aq)$$

28.8 Oxysalts of the Post-Transition Metals

A wide variety of salts of the post-transition metals with oxyacids have been characterized.

1. **Preparation of Oxysalts.** Post-transition metal salts of the oxyacids can be prepared by methods that are similar to those used to prepare halides of these metals.
   (a) Active post-transition metals dissolve in solutions of oxyacids, producing hydrogen and solutions of salts of the acids. For example, the reaction of zinc with sulfuric acid is

$$Zn + H_2SO_4 \longrightarrow ZnSO_4 + H_2$$

These salts can be recovered by evaporation of the solutions. The oxidation numbers of the metals are the same as those produced when the metals dissolve in hydrohalic acids (Section 28.7).
   (b) Hydroxides and some oxides dissolve in solutions of oxyacids, forming solutions of salts of these acids. For example,

$$Cd(OH)_2 + 2HClO_4 \longrightarrow Cd(ClO_4)_2 + 2H_2O$$

$$Tl_2O + 2HNO_3 \longrightarrow 2TlNO_3 + H_2O$$

The oxides of tin(IV), lead(IV), and bismuth(V) are not soluble in acids.

(c) The less active post-transition metals dissolve in hot concentrated oxidizing acids such as nitric acid and sulfuric acid. For example, the reaction of lead and hot sulfuric acid produces lead(II) sulfate.

$$Pb + 2H_2SO_4 \longrightarrow PbSO_4(s) + SO_2(g) + 2H_2O$$

Mercury(II) nitrate is formed by the reaction of mercury with an excess of concentrated nitric acid. With an excess of mercury, mercury(I) nitrate is formed.

$$3Hg + 8HNO_3 \longrightarrow 3Hg(NO_3)_2 + 2NO(g) + 4H_2O$$

$$6Hg + 8HNO_3 \longrightarrow 3Hg_2(NO_3)_2 + 2NO(g) + 4H_2O$$

2. Reactions and Uses of the Oxysalts. Zinc sulfate, $ZnSO_4$, is produced commercially in large quantities by roasting **zinc blende,** ZnS, at low red heat.

$$ZnS(s) + 2O_2(g) \xrightarrow{\triangle} ZnSO_4(s) \qquad \Delta H° = -777.0 \text{ kJ}$$

The product is extracted with water and recovered by recrystallization to form crystals of **zinc sulfate 7-hydrate,** $ZnSO_4 \cdot 7H_2O$, which is called **white vitriol.** It is used principally in the production of the white paint pigment **lithopone,** which is a mixture of barium sulfate and zinc sulfide formed by the reaction

$$Ba^{2+}(aq) + S^{2-}(aq) + Zn^{2+}(aq) + SO_4{}^{2-}(aq) \longrightarrow BaSO_4(s) + ZnS(s)$$

When either metallic lead or lead monoxide, PbO, is dissolved in nitric acid, **lead(II) nitrate,** $Pb(NO_3)_2$, is formed. This salt is readily soluble in water, but unless the solution is made slightly acidic with nitric acid, reaction with water occurs and **lead(II) hydroxynitrate** precipitates.

$$Pb^{2+} + 2NO_3{}^- + 2H_2O \longrightarrow Pb(OH)NO_3(s) + H_3O^+ + NO_3{}^-$$

Lead nitrate is unstable at moderately high temperatures and decomposes in the same manner as the nitrates of other heavy metals.

$$2Pb(NO_3)_2 \longrightarrow 2PbO(s) + 4NO_2 + O_2$$

Lead carbonate, $PbCO_3$, can be prepared by the action of sodium hydrogen carbonate on lead chloride. **Lead hydroxycarbonate,** $Pb_3(OH)_2(CO_3)_2$, is formed when alkali metal carbonates are added to solutions containing the lead ion. This compound is the paint pigment white lead; because of the danger of lead poisoning, its use has been largely eliminated.

Lead sulfate, $PbSO_4$, forms when solutions of a soluble lead salt and a soluble sulfate are mixed. It is insoluble in water ($K_{sp} = 1.8 \times 10^{-8}$) but readily dissolves in solutions containing an excess of alkali metal halide or acetate ions. **Lead acetate,** $Pb(CH_3CO_2)_2$, is one of the few soluble compounds of lead; it is a weak electrolyte, indicating that it dissolves mainly as a covalent compound rather than as an ionic one. It is extremely toxic. **Lead chromate,** $PbCrO_4$, is used as a yellow art pigment. It is insoluble in water but dissolves readily in acids and alkali metal hydroxides.

Bismuth(III) nitrate, $Bi(NO_3)_3$, reacts with water, forming **bismuth hydroxynitrate,** $Bi(OH)_2NO_3$.

$$Bi(NO_3)_3 + 4H_2O \longrightarrow Bi(OH)_2NO_3 + 2H_3O^+ + 2NO_3^-$$

When dried, bismuth hydroxynitrate forms **bismuth oxynitrate,** $BiONO_3$. Bismuth oxynitrate and bismuth oxycarbonate, $(BiO)_2CO_3$ (under the names bismuth subnitrate and bismuth subcarbonate), are used in medicine for the treatment of stomach disorders such as gastritis and ulcers and of skin diseases such as eczema.

28.9 Sulfides of the Post-Transition Metals

Sulfides of the post-transition metals occur commonly in nature. The sources of many of these metals are sulfide ores.

There are a wide variety of post-transition metal sulfides that contain metal ions with two different oxidation numbers. We will not consider these compounds; instead, we will consider only those sulfides that contain the metal with a single oxidation number.

1. **Preparation of the Sulfides.** Post-transition metal sulfides can be prepared by the direct reaction of sulfur with a metal or by precipitation from a solution of a metal salt by the addition of hydrogen sulfide or a sulfide salt.

(a) The reaction of sulfur and a metal usually requires warming in order to form the sulfide. Mercury(II) sulfide slowly forms at room temperature, however.

$$2Tl + S \xrightarrow{\triangle} Tl_2S$$

$$Zn + S \xrightarrow{\triangle} ZnS$$

$$Hg + S \longrightarrow HgS$$

$$2Ga + 3S \xrightarrow{\triangle} Ga_2S_3$$

Tin forms one of two sulfides, depending on the stoichiometry of the reaction.

$$Sn + S \xrightarrow{\triangle} SnS$$

$$Sn + 2S \xrightarrow{\triangle} SnS_2$$

The sulfides of the heavy elements thallium, lead, and bismuth (Tl_2S, PbS, and Bi_2S_3) form with the metals exhibiting oxidation numbers two less than the group oxidation number, even when an excess of sulfur is used in their preparation. Sulfide ions are good enough reducing agents to reduce these metal ions when they exhibit their group oxidation numbers.

(b) The sulfides of cadmium(II), mercury(II), tin(II), tin(IV), lead(II), and bismuth(III) precipitate when hydrogen sulfide or a soluble sulfide salt is added to solutions of the metal salts. Examples include the following reactions:

$$Cd^{2+}(aq) + H_2S + 2H_2O \longrightarrow CdS(s) + 2H_3O^+$$

$$Sn^{2+}(aq) + S^{2-} \longrightarrow SnS(s)$$

$$Sn^{4+}(aq) + 2H_2S + 4H_2O \longrightarrow SnS_2(s) + 4H_3O^+$$

$$2Bi^{3+}(aq) + 3S^{2-} \longrightarrow Bi_2S_3(s)$$

Zinc sulfide is soluble in acids; it precipitates only from basic solution.

The sulfides of the post-transition metals of Group IIIA react with water and form the metal hydroxides and hydrogen sulfide; they cannot be prepared from aqueous solution.

2. Reactions and Uses of the Sulfides. Zinc sulfide, ZnS, is insoluble in water ($K_{sp} = 1 \times 10^{-27}$) and in acetic acid but dissolves readily in stronger acids such as hydrochloric acid and sulfuric acid.

$$ZnS + 2H_3O^+ \longrightarrow Zn^{2+} + H_2S + 2H_2O$$

Zinc sulfide is used as a white paint pigment, either alone or mixed with zinc oxide or barium sulfate.

Cadmium sulfide, CdS, is an insoluble bright yellow solid ($K_{sp} = 2.8 \times 10^{-35}$) (Fig. 28.16). It is used as a paint pigment called **cadmium yellow.**

Mercury(I) sulfide, Hg_2S, is unstable and immediately decomposes into mercury and mercury(II) sulfide when it is formed by passing hydrogen sulfide into a solution containing mercury(I) ions.

$$Hg_2^{2+} + H_2S + 2H_2O \longrightarrow HgS + Hg + 2H_3O^+$$

Hydrogen sulfide precipitates black **mercury(II) sulfide,** HgS ($K_{sp} = 2 \times 10^{-59}$), from solutions of mercury(II) salts, even from strongly acidic solutions. The precipitate formed by the interaction of $HgCl_2$ in solution with H_2S is first white, then yellow, then red, and finally black. The white compound has the formula $HgCl_2 \cdot 3HgS$. When heated, HgS becomes bright red; the red sulfide is isomeric with the black and has in the past been used in the pigment **vermilion.**

Mercury(II) sulfide dissolves in solutions of soluble sulfides in the presence of an excess of hydroxide ions and forms the **thiomercurate ion.**

$$HgS + S^{2-} \rightleftharpoons [HgS_2]^{2-}$$

Dark brown **tin(II) sulfide,** SnS ($K_{sp} = 6 \times 10^{-35}$), is not dissolved by alkali metal sulfides or by alkaline polysulfides. However, **tin(IV) sulfide** dissolves in alkali metal sulfides, with the formation of **thiostannate ions,** $[SnS_3]^{2-}$. The addition of acid reprecipitates SnS_2.

$$[SnS_3]^{2-} + 2H_3O^+ \longrightarrow SnS_2(s) + H_2S + 2H_2O$$

Concentrated hydrochloric acid dissolves tin(IV) sulfide, because the complex ion $[SnCl_6]^{2-}$ is formed.

$$SnS_2 + 4H_3O^+ + 6Cl^- \longrightarrow [SnCl_6]^{2-} + 2H_2S + 4H_2O$$

Lead sulfide, PbS, is a black solid ($K_{sp} = 6.5 \times 10^{-34}$), which is insoluble in solutions of dilute acids and soluble metal sulfides.

Figure 28.16

CdS forms when solutions of $CdCl_2$ and Na_2S are mixed.

For Review

Summary

The post-transition metals are zinc, cadmium, and mercury from Group IIB, gallium, indium, and thallium from Group IIIA, tin and lead from Group IVA, bismuth from Group VA, and polonium from Group VIA. The reactivities of these elements range from those of fairly active metals (zinc, cadmium, and gallium) to those of much less active metals (lead and mercury). All of the post-transition metals form ionic compounds, as expected for metallic elements, but they also form a variety of covalent compounds.

Each of the post-transition elements can potentially form an ion with a pseudo noble gas electron configuration $[(n-1)s^2, (n-1)p^6, (n-1)d^{10}]$ by the loss of all of its valence electrons. However, ions with this configuration become more difficult to form down a group and from left to right across a period. Thus the heaviest post-transition elements exhibit the group oxidation number only under strongly oxidizing conditions and generally only in covalent compounds.

Zinc, cadmium, and mercury commonly exhibit the group oxidation number of +2, although mercury also exhibits an oxidation number of +1 in compounds that contain the Hg_2^{2+} group. The chemical behaviors of zinc and cadmium are quite similar. Both elements lie above hydrogen in the activity series. Mercury is very different from zinc and cadmium. It is a nonreactive element that lies well below hydrogen in the activity series.

Gallium, indium, and thallium lie above hydrogen in the activity series and react with acids, liberating hydrogen. Gallium and indium are commonly found with an oxidation number of +3, but thallium is also commonly found as the Tl^+ ion, the stability of which is attributable to the **inert pair effect.**

Tin and lead form stable dipositive cations, Sn^{2+} and Pb^{2+}, with oxidation numbers two below the group oxidation number of +4. This is another example of stability that can be attributed to the inert pair effect. Tin and lead also form covalent compounds in which the +4 oxidation number is exhibited. Tin is a moderately active metal. Lead is less reactive; it lies just above hydrogen in the activity series and is attacked only by hot concentrated acids.

Bismuth readily gives up three of its five valence electrons to active nonmetals to form the tripositive ion, Bi^{3+}. It forms compounds with the group oxidation number of +5 only when treated with strong oxidizing agents.

Polonium is a member of Group VIA. It is an intensely radioactive element that results from the radioactive decay of uranium and thorium.

Techniques for the preparation of compounds for the post-transition metals are similar to those used for the preparation of compounds of other metals of varying activity.

Key Terms and Concepts

allotropic forms of tin (28.3)
alloys (28.3)
amalgam (28.1)
Betts process (28.2)
corrosion (28.3)
galvanized iron (28.3)

halides (28.7)
hydroxides (28.6)
inert pair effect (28.1)
ores (28.2)
oxides (28.5)
oxysalts (28.8)

physiological effects (28.4)
pseudo noble gas electron configuration (28.1)
sulfides (28.9)
tin plate (28.3)

Exercises

Answers for selected even-numbered exercises marked by red numbers appear at the end of the book. The worked-out solutions to all even-numbered exercises appear in the *Solutions Guide.*

Periodic Properties

1. Identify the group oxidation numbers possible for the post-transition metals in their compounds.
2. How do the properties of the post-transition elements gallium, indium, and thallium differ from the properties of the elements boron and aluminum at the top of Group IIIA in the periodic table?

3. Write the electron configurations for an In atom, an In^+ ion, and an In^{3+} ion.
4. Why is +1 found to be a stable oxidation number for thallium when the group oxidation number is +3?
5. Which of the post-transition metals is used to make amalgams?
6. Which post-transition metals form common oxides and halides in which the metal does not exhibit the group oxidation number?
7. Write the chemical formulas for the oxides of each of the post-transition metals with their common oxidation numbers.

8. Which of the post-transition metals do not dissolve readily in acids with the evolution of hydrogen gas? (You may need to refer to Table 13.2 to refresh your memory of the activity series.)

9. Which of the post-transition metals have positive reduction potentials for the reduction of the metal cation to the metal? (You may need to refer to Table 20.1 or Appendix H.)

10. What is the inert pair effect?

Zinc

11. Write balanced chemical equations for the following reactions.
    (a) Zinc sulfide is heated in a stream of oxygen gas.
    (b) Zinc metal is added to a solution of lead(II) nitrate.
    (c) Zinc metal is added to a solution of cadmium nitrate.
    (d) Zinc carbonate is heated until loss of mass stops.
    (e) Zinc carbonate is added to a solution of acetic acid, CH_3CO_2H.
    (f) Mossy zinc is added to a solution of hydrobromic acid.
    (g) Zinc is heated with sulfur.
    (h) An aqueous solution of ammonia is added dropwise to a solution of zinc chloride until $Zn(OH_2)$ has precipitated and then dissolved, the mixture becoming clear again.
    (i) Zinc is burned in air.

12. What is lithopone and how is it produced? How is lithopone superior to white lead as a paint pigment?

13. A dilute solution of perchloric acid is dripped into a solution of sodium zincate, $Na_2[Zn(OH)_4]$. A white gelatinous precipitate is formed; analysis reveals it to be a hydroxide. Upon addition of more acid, a clear solution results. Use chemical equations to explain these observations.

14. What is galvanized iron, how is it produced, and what useful properties does it have?

15. How is zinc metal separated from the impurities cadmium, iron, lead, and arsenic during the refining process?

16. What is the common ore of zinc, and how is zinc extracted from it?

Cadmium

17. How many grams of CdS precipitate when a solution obtained by dissolving 2.5 g of Wood's metal is treated with excess sulfide ion?

18. Write balanced chemical equations for the following reactions.
    (a) Cadmium is burned in air.
    (b) An aqueous solution of ammonia is added dropwise to a solution of cadmium chloride until $Cd(OH)_2$ has precipitated and then dissolved, the mixture becoming clear again.
    (c) Cadmium is heated with sulfur.
    (d) Cadmium is added to a solution of hydrochloric acid.
    (e) Cadmium hydroxide is added to a solution of acetic acid, CH_3CO_2H.
    (f) Cadmium hydroxide is heated until loss of mass stops.

(g) Cadmium metal is added to a solution of mercury(II) nitrate.
    (h) Cadmium metal is added to a solution of lead(II) nitrate.
    (i) Cadmium sulfide is heated in a stream of oxygen gas.

19. How many pounds of cadmium can be obtained from 10.0 tons of ore that is 5.0% greenockite?

20. What is the common source of cadmium, and how is cadmium extracted from it?

21. How is cadmium metal separated from impurities during the refining process?

22. What properties make cadmium effective as a protective coating for other metals?

23. What properties make cadmium unsuitable for general use as a protective coating on car door handles?

Mercury

24. How many pounds of mercury can be obtained from 10 tons of ore that is 7.4% cinnabar?

25. Write balanced chemical equations for the following reactions.
    (a) Mercury(II) oxide is added to a solution of nitric acid.
    (b) Mercury is heated with sulfur.
    (c) Cadmium metal is added to a solution of mercury(II) nitrate.
    (d) Mercury(II) sulfide is heated in a stream of oxygen gas.
    (e) A solution of mercury(II) nitrate is stirred with liquid mercury.
    (f) A solution of mercury(I) nitrate is added to a solution of potassium sulfide.
    (g) An excess of zinc is added to a solution of mercury(II) nitrate.
    (h) Zinc is added to a solution containing an excess of mercury(II) nitrate.

26. What is the common ore of mercury, and how is mercury separated from it?

27. How is mercury metal separated from impurities?

28. The roasting of an ore of a metal usually results in the conversion of the metal to the oxide. Why does the roasting of cinnabar produce metallic mercury rather than an oxide of mercury?

29. Why does mercury dissolve readily in nitric acid or hot sulfuric acid even though it is not attacked by hydrochloric acid?

30. What does it mean to say that mercury(II) halides are weak electrolytes?

31. What properties make mercury valuable as a thermometric substance?

32. Write Lewis structures for $HgCl_2$ and Hg_2Cl_2.

33. Hydrogen sulfide gas is bubbled through a solution marked mercury(I) nitrate. A precipitate forms. Of what substance(s) is the precipitate composed?

34. What is the mass of fish, in kilograms, that one would have to consume to obtain a fatal dose of mercury, if the fish contains 30 parts per million of mercury by weight? (Assume all the mercury from the fish ends up as mercury(II)

chloride in the body and that a fatal dose is 0.20 g of $HgCl_2$.) How many pounds of fish is this?

35. How many moles of ionic species are present in a solution marked 1.0 M mercury(I) nitrate? How would you demonstrate the accuracy of your prediction?

Tin

36. Write balanced chemical equations describing:
    (a) the burning of tin metal
    (b) the dissolution of tin in a solution of hydrochloric acid
    (c) the preparation of sodium metastannate
    (d) the purification of tin by electrolysis
    (e) the reaction of dry bromine with tin (write equations for both possible products)
    (f) the formation of thiostannate ion
    (g) the dissolution of tin oxides by basic solution (two equations)
    (h) the reactions involved when an excess of aqueous NaOH is slowly added to a solution of tin(II) chloride
    (i) the thermal decomposition of tin(II) oxalate
    (j) the reaction of tin with sulfur (write equations for both possible products)

37. Why is $SnCl_4$ not classified as a salt?

38. Why must aqueous solutions of $SnCl_2$ be protected from air?

39. What is the common ore of tin, and how is tin separated from it?

40. A 1.497-g sample of type metal (an alloy of Sn, Pb, Sb, and Cu) is dissolved in nitric acid, and metastannic acid precipitates. This is dehydrated by heating to stannic oxide, which is found to weigh 0.4909 g. What percent tin was in the original type metal sample?

41. How is tin metal separated from impurities during the refining process?

42. Mercury(I) solutions can be protected from oxidizing in air to mercury(II) by keeping them in contact with metallic mercury. Can tin(II) solutions be similarly stabilized against oxidation to tin(IV) by keeping them in contact with metallic tin? [The standard reduction potential for tin(IV) to tin(II) is +0.15 V.]

43. How and why is tin plate applied to the surface of iron?

44. What is tin pest, also known as tin disease?

45. Does metallic tin react with HCl? With HNO_3?

Lead

46. What is the common ore of lead, and how is lead separated from it?

47. How is lead metal separated from impurities during the refining process?

48. A 100-mL volume of a saturated solution of lead(II) iodide contains 0.41 g of solute at 100°C. Calculate the solubility product at this temperature.

49. Describe the Betts process for the refining of lead.

50. When elements in the first transition metal series form dipositive ions, they usually give up their outer shell s electrons. Does this apply to lead when it forms Pb^{2+} ion? Explain your answer.

51. Compare the nature of the bonds in $PbCl_2$ to that of the bonds in $PbCl_4$. Would you expect the existence of Pb^{4+} ions? Explain.

52. Show by suitable equations that lead(II) hydroxide is amphoteric.

53. What is the composition of the tarnish on lead?

54. Why should water to be used for human consumption not be conveyed in lead pipes?

55. Why is $PbCl_2$ somewhat soluble in solutions of high chloride ion concentration?

Bismuth

56. What are the properties of metallic bismuth that make it commercially useful?

57. Compare the basicity and acidity of Bi_2O_3 and Bi_2O_5.

58. Write equations for the reaction of $BiCl_3$ with water.

59. Write balanced chemical equations for the following reactions.
    (a) Bismuth is heated in air.
    (b) An aqueous solution of sodium hydroxide is added dropwise to a solution of bismuth(III) chloride.
    (c) Bismuth is heated with an excess of sulfur.
    (d) Bismuth is added to a solution of hydrobromic acid.
    (e) Bismuth(III) oxide is added to a solution of nitric acid.
    (f) Bismuth(III) hydroxide is heated until loss of mass stops.
    (g) Gallium metal is added to a solution of bismuth(III) nitrate.
    (h) Bismuth metal is added to a solution of lead(II) nitrate.
    (i) Bismuth(III) sulfide is heated in a stream of oxygen gas.

Additional Exercises

60. What is the maximum concentration of S^{2-} possible in a solution that is 0.0010 M in Cd^{2+}?

61. In 1774 Joseph Priestley prepared O_2 by heating red HgO with sunlight focused through a lens. How much heat is required to decompose exactly 1 mol of red HgO(s) to Hg(l) and $O_2(g)$ under standard state conditions?

62. Write balanced chemical equations for the following reactions.
    (a) Gallium is heated in air.
    (b) An aqueous solution of sodium hydroxide is added dropwise to a solution of gallium chloride in water until $Ga(OH)_3$ has precipitated and then dissolved and the solution becomes clear again.
    (c) Indium is heated with an excess of sulfur.
    (d) Indium is added to a solution of hydrobromic acid.
    (e) Gallium(III) hydroxide is added to a solution of nitric acid.
    (f) Indium(III) hydroxide is heated until loss of mass stops.
    (g) Gallium metal is added to a solution of indium nitrate.
    (h) Indium metal is added to a solution of lead(II) nitrate.
    (i) Indium sulfide is heated in a stream of oxygen gas.

63. Write balanced chemical equations for the following reactions.

(a) Thallium is heated in air.

(b) An aqueous solution of sodium hydroxide is added dropwise to a solution of thallium(III) chloride.

(c) Thallium is heated with an excess of sulfur.

(d) Thallium is added to a solution of nitric acid.

(e) Thallium(I) hydroxide is added to a solution of nitric acid.

(f) Thallium(I) carbonate is heated until loss of mass stops.

(g) A solution of thallium(I) hydroxide is added to an aqueous solution of gallium nitrate.

(h) A solution of thallium(I) nitrate is added to an aqueous solution of gallium chloride.

(i) Thallium(I) sulfide is heated in air.

64. Calculate the concentration of $[HgCl_4]^{2-}$ in a solution prepared by adding 4.0×10^{-3} mol of NaCl to 50.0 mL of a 0.040 M $HgCl_2$ solution.

65. Calculate the molar solubilities of AgBr, Hg_2Cl_2, and $PbSO_4$.

66. Calculate the potential of the following electrochemical cell.

$$Cd \,|\, Cd^{2+} \ (0.10 \ M) \,\|\, Ni^{2+} \ (0.50 \ M) \,|\, Ni$$

29

The Atmosphere and Natural Waters

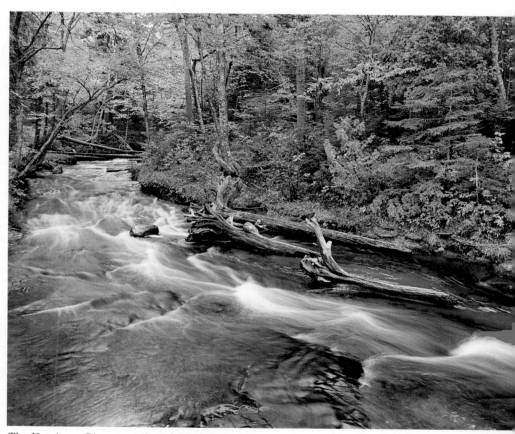

The Hurricane River near Grand Marais, Michigan.

Air and water cover the surface of the earth. The atmosphere is a fluid consisting of a mixture of gases; oceans, rivers, and lakes are fluids consisting of water of varying purity. Air and natural waters serve as sources of raw materials for many chemical processes. Oxygen, nitrogen, and certain noble gases are extracted from the air. The oxygen in air is an essential part of almost all combustion reactions. Water is widely used as a solvent, for producing steam in a variety of different types of power plants, in cooling, and in cleaning. It is a source of hydrogen, and it is used in the manufacture of acids from nonmetal oxides and of bases from metal oxides. The oceans serve as a source of numerous minerals.

Both air and water are essential to our existence. We could live for about five minutes without air and for about seven days without fresh water. However, the quality of air and water has deteriorated as a result of human activities. Both the atmosphere and many bodies of water are used as dumps for a variety of wastes, although increasingly strict regulations are being enacted to control such dumping. In this chapter we will examine the properties of the atmosphere and of naturally occurring waters, some of the sources of their pollution, its effects, and some ways in which this pollution can be reduced.

The Atmosphere

29.1 The Composition of the Atmosphere

The **atmosphere** is the mixture of gaseous substances—the air—that surrounds the earth. For the most part, it consists of almost constant proportions of uncombined nitrogen, oxygen, and the noble gases. The percentage of carbon dioxide varies somewhat, and that of dust and water vapor is widely variable. There are also varying trace amounts of ammonia, hydrogen sulfide, nitrogen oxides, sulfur dioxide, and other gases that are commonly regarded as pollutants. The average composition of unpolluted dry air at sea level is given in Table 29.1.

The chemical behavior of these gases has been described in Chapters 21, 22, and 23.

The percent composition of dry air does not vary much with location or altitude. However, the density of air, as reflected by its pressure, decreases with increasing altitude. The average pressure at sea level is 1.0 atmosphere; at 15,000 feet (almost 3 miles up), 0.53 atmosphere; at 10 miles, about 0.05 atmosphere; and at 30 miles, only about 1×10^{-4} atmosphere.

Table 29.1	Composition of Dry Air at Sea Level		
Component	Percent by Volume	Component	Percent by Volume
Nitrogen	78.03	Helium	0.0005
Oxygen	20.99	Krypton	0.0001
Argon	0.94	Ozone	0.00006
Carbon dioxide	0.035–0.04	Hydrogen	0.00005
Neon	0.0012	Xenon	0.000009

29.2 The Air Pollution Problem

Air pollution is nothing new. In fact, William Shakespeare described the problem in *Hamlet* in about 1601:

This most excellent canopy, the air, look you, this brave o'erhanging firmament, this majestical roof fretted with golden fire, why, it appears no other thing to me than a foul and pestilent congregation of vapors.*

In 1272 Edward I banned the use of smoke-producing coal in an effort to clear the smoky air of London, and the British Parliament ordered a man tortured and hanged for illegally burning coal. Later Richard III imposed a high tax on the use of coal. These efforts accomplished little, however, and London remained smoky. A combination of smoke and fog killed almost 4000 people there during a four-day period in 1952. In Donora, Pennsylvania, in 1948, 20 people died and 5900 became ill during a period of serious air pollution. Less dramatic, but no less tragic for those involved, are the deaths attributable to present-day air pollution (Fig. 29.1). Air pollution alerts and warnings are not uncommon in many cities. Polluted air may ultimately result in shortened lives for all of us, but it is a special problem for those suffering from respiratory diseases such as emphysema and bronchitis. Lung cancer has been found to be significantly more prevalent among people living in air-polluted cities than among those living in rural areas with cleaner air.

The problems due to air pollution reach well beyond those related to human health (Fig. 29.2). It can damage plants, discolor paint, damage textiles, discolor dyes, damage limestone and marble buildings and statues, corrode metals, and damage tires, to name but a few of its harmful effects. In the United States alone, it is estimated that well over 200 million tons of pollutants are emitted into the air annually. Strictly on an economic basis, it has been estimated that air pollution costs the people of the United States several billion dollars per year. Directly or indirectly, air pollution is a major problem. Some progress is being made, but it is essential for us to learn more about the problems and take steps to make further improvements.

In the United States, the Clean Air Act has a toxic chemical provision, but by 1989 the EPA (Environmental Protection Agency) had issued regulations on only seven substances: beryllium, mercury, vinyl chloride, asbestos, benzene, radioactive nuclides, and arsenic. New amendments proposed for the Clean Air Act at the time of this writing list specific additional pollutants, include provisions to prevent accidental release of the listed substances, and require that those responsible for the sources of these materials take precautions to avoid such accidents.

Full enforcement of such regulations would undoubtedly cause a large number of changes, such as closing some sections of large cities to automobile traffic at certain hours, the greater use of public transportation and car pools, and very significant changes in the fuels used by automobiles, electric generating plants, and other industries. Hence, considerable controversy surrounds the proposed amendments.

Figure 29.1

This bicyclist is taking precautions against breathing the exhaust fumes of the cars surrounding him on this busy New York street.

Figure 29.2

The marble of this sculpture has been attacked by airborne sulfur oxides.

㉙.3 The Most Common Air Pollutants

Air pollution results from many causes. Seven of the most common air pollutants, and some of their major effects, follow.

   1. **Sulfur Oxides.** Cause acute leaf injury and attack trees; irritate the human respiratory tract; corrode metals and other building materials; ruin textiles; cause book

*Hamlet, Prince of Denmark, William Shakespeare (1601); Act II, Scene 2.

pages and leather to disintegrate; destroy paint pigments; erode statues. Sulfur dioxide is suspected of being the principal cause of acid rain (Section 29.10).

2. Particulates (Solids). Obscure vision; aggravate lung illnesses; deposit grime on buildings and personal belongings; corrode metals.

3. Carbon Monoxide. Causes headaches, dizziness, and nausea; reduces oxygen content in the blood, impairing mental processes; in sufficient quantity, causes death.

4. Nitrogen Oxides. Cause leaf damage; stunt plant growth; irritate eyes and nasal membranes; cause brown, pungent haze; corrode metals and other building materials; damage rubber. Smog results from the reactions induced by sunlight in a mixture of nitrogen oxides, ozone, and hydrocarbons.

5. Hydrocarbons (Compounds containing only carbon and hydrogen). May be carcinogenic (cancer-producing); retard plant growth and cause abnormal leaf and bud development; produce smog with nitrogen oxides and ozone.

6. Photochemical Oxidants. (a) Ozone and resultant chemical products—discolor leaves of many crops, trees, and shrubs; damage and fade textiles; reduce physical ability, including athletic performance; speed deterioration of rubber; disturb lung function; irritate eyes, nose, and throat; induce coughing; produce smog with nitrogen oxides and hydrocarbons. (b) Peroxyacetyl nitrate (PAN)—discolors leaves; irritates eyes; disturbs lung function.

7. Chlorofluorocarbons (Freons). Deplete the ozone-rich layer in the upper part of the earth's atmosphere, the **stratosphere,** allowing additional ultraviolet radiation from the sun to get through to the earth's surface. There is an actual hole in the ozone layer over the Antarctic and the Arctic (see photo on page 447). This excess ultraviolet radiation can have a variety of harmful effects on people who do not protect themselves from exposure to the sun, including skin cancer and premature aging of the skin.

Over 100 specific polluting compounds fall into these seven categories, and many other materials are contaminants in some specific geographic locations. These include fluorides, lead compounds, beryllium, mercury, pesticides, and radioactive materials. (Radioactive pollutants were discussed in Sections 24.15–24.18.)

We will discuss air pollution in more detail by dividing it into three categories: (1) air pollution from fossil fuels and combustion, (2) air pollution from chlorofluorocarbons, and (3) air pollution from other causes.

29.4 Air Pollution from Fossil Fuels and Combustion

Most air pollution arises from combustion, and much of that is the combustion of fossil fuels such as coal, fuel oils, gasoline, and natural gas. Coal is largely carbon; fuel oils, gasoline, and natural gas are largely hydrocarbons. If combustion occurs with sufficient oxygen to result in complete combustion, carbon produces only carbon dioxide when it burns. With complete combustion, hydrocarbons (for example, methane, CH_4, and octane, C_8H_{18}) produce only carbon dioxide and water.

$$C + O_2 \longrightarrow CO_2$$

$$CH_4 + 2O_2 \longrightarrow CO_2 + 2H_2O$$

$$2C_8H_{18} + 25O_2 \longrightarrow 16CO_2 + 18H_2O$$

However, if combustion is incomplete because of a deficiency of oxygen, carbon monoxide forms.

$$2C + O_2 \longrightarrow 2CO$$

$$2CH_4 + 3O_2 \longrightarrow 2CO + 4H_2O$$

$$2C_8H_{18} + 17O_2 \longrightarrow 16CO + 18H_2O$$

Sulfur dioxide is produced in the burning of coal that contains impurities (Fig. 29.3), such as elemental sulfur or pyrite (FeS_2).

$$S + O_2 \longrightarrow SO_2$$

$$4FeS_2 + 11O_2 \longrightarrow 2Fe_2O_3 + 8SO_2$$

The SO_2 either reacts with water to form sulfurous acid, H_2SO_3 (which is readily oxidized by oxygen to sulfuric acid), or is oxidized by nitrogen oxides or other oxidizing agents to SO_3 (which unites with water to form sulfuric acid; see Section 2.12, Part 1). These acids are among the main substances responsible for acid rain. The catalytic converters of automobile exhaust systems produce small quantities of sulfur dioxide, sulfur trioxide, and sulfuric acid from reactions of the sulfur compounds present in gasoline.

Nitrogen oxides are produced in combustion processes because the nitrogen and oxygen in the air react at high temperatures (Section 23.13).

$$N_2 + O_2 \longrightarrow 2NO \qquad \Delta H° = 180.5 \text{ kJ}$$

$$2NO + O_2 \longrightarrow 2NO_2 \qquad \Delta H° = -114.1 \text{ kJ}$$

The reaction of nitrogen dioxide with water is also believed to be partially responsible for the increased acidity of rain in many parts of the world.

$$2NO_2 + H_2O \longrightarrow HNO_3 + HNO_2$$

Many of the solid pollutants in air are noncombustible or unburned material (ash) from fuels.

Figure 29.3

Reddish spots in this piece of coal are minerals; white spots are voids. (Microtomography was used to make this image of a piece of coal approximately 0.5 mm in diameter.)

Secondary reactions produce additional pollution problems. An example is the photochemical reaction of unburned hydrocarbons and nitrogen oxides from automobile exhausts to form peroxyacetyl nitrate (PAN) and ozone. These compounds are primary constituents of smog, a problem in many of our cities.

The problem of smog is intensified by air inversion. Normally, the layer of air near the earth's surface becomes warmer than the air above and rises, allowing fresh air to take its place. Sometimes, however, a warm layer of air develops above the ground layer and traps the ground layer at the earth's surface. Pollutants from auto exhausts and other sources are also trapped, sometimes for days at a time.

For over 60 years, tetraethyl lead was used in gasoline to provide greater antiknock capability. However, when leaded gasoline is burned in an engine, volatile lead compounds are emitted through the exhaust. Lead compounds are known to have serious physiological effects on humans, and they also render ineffective the catalysts used in catalytic converters. For these reasons, regulations have been imposed that have resulted in unleaded gasoline's replacing almost entirely gasoline containing tetraethyl lead (Fig. 29.4).

Some Solutions to the Problems of Pollution from Fossil Fuels and Combustion
Removing particulate (solid) pollutants from smokestack gases is easily accomplished by the use of electrostatic Cottrell precipitators (see Section 12.27 and Fig. 12.25). Removing gases such as sulfur oxides, however, is more difficult. The wet limestone process for removing sulfur oxides is one that shows promise:

$$SO_2 + CaCO_3 \xrightarrow{H_2O} CaSO_3 + CO_2$$

$$SO_3 + CaCO_3 \xrightarrow{H_2O} CaSO_4 + CO_2$$

The use of low-sulfur coal, natural gas, or fuel oil, instead of high-sulfur coal, reduces the problem, but natural gas and fuel oil are becoming more expensive, and reserves of low-sulfur coal are distant from where they are used.

Removing the sulfur from fossil fuels is another solution. Fuel oil can be fairly readily desulfurized. However, about two-thirds of the sulfur oxides currently emitted by combustion originates in coal, which contains 2.5–3.0% sulfur on the average. Of the coal mined in the United States, about 25% is such that its sulfur can be reduced to 1% by existing processes. It is possible to remove only about half of the sulfur from the other 75% of coal mined.

Over 95% of nitrogen oxide emissions result from combustion; 25% of the emissions come from combustion in steam-electric power plants. Some reduction in nitrogen oxide emissions can be achieved by modifying the combustion process, though there is some loss of efficiency. Development of methods for efficient removal of nitrogen oxides from stack gases is progressing, but more improvement is needed.

Carbon monoxide emission can be lessened by finer control of combustion, better tuning of auto engines, and use of catalytic converters (Fig. 29.5). Catalytic converters reduce carbon monoxide, nitrogen oxides, and unburned hydrocarbon pollutants in automobile exhausts to low levels. One system comprises two converters, each containing a different catalytic material. In the first, oxygen from additional added air reacts with the pollutants on the surface of the solid catalyst. The catalyst in the second converter promotes the spontaneous decomposition of nitrogen oxides to the elements.

$$2NO \longrightarrow N_2 + O_2 \qquad \Delta G° = -173.1 \text{ kJ}$$

$$2NO_2 \longrightarrow N_2 + 2O_2 \qquad \Delta G° = -102.6 \text{ kJ}$$

Figure 29.4

Because of the damaging effects of lead compounds, federal regulations require that cars run on unleaded fuel.

Figure 29.5

Catalytic converters decrease pollutants in the exhaust of automobiles.

Unfortunately, catalytic converters also catalyze reactions involving sulfur compounds in the gasoline. Most serious is the catalysis of the reaction with oxygen to produce sulfur dioxide and sulfur trioxide. These react with water and ultimately form small quantities of sulfuric acid mist, one component of acid rain. Fortunately, technology is available for removing sulfur compounds from gasoline at an earlier stage, during refining.

A three-way catalyst for converters has been developed to remove hydrocarbons, carbon monoxide, nitrogen oxides, and sulfur emissions more thoroughly. Addition of rhodium metal to the catalyst boosts efficiency. Addition of cerium oxide makes it possible for oxygen to be stored in the catalyst during lean fuel operation and released during rich operation. Addition of nickel helps control sulfur emissions.

Catalytic converters have resulted in large decreases in the total amount of pollutants in automobile exhaust emissions. Current projections indicate that, even with the steady increase in numbers of vehicles on our roads, catalytic converters will ultimately eliminate 96% of hydrocarbons and carbon monoxide and 76% of nitrogen oxides from automobile exhausts. However, the high cost of the platinum and rhodium required in the converter catalyst is a major problem. In recent years, the demand for these two metals for use in catalytic converters has been as high as 35% of the total demand for platinum and 73% of the total demand for rhodium. Automobile manufacturers are attempting to find suitable less expensive catalysts.

Alternatives to the internal combustion engine, as well as modifications of existing internal combustion engines, are also under study. Alternatives include electric automobiles with rechargeable batteries. It should be noted, however, that recharging batteries requires electrical power, which in turn requires additional generating facilities. These may cause a subsequent increase in pollution. A change made in order to reduce or avoid one type of pollution often introduces another type. Confronting the pollution dilemma involves solving exceedingly complex, intertwined problems.

A partial answer to our energy crisis may be nuclear energy (see Chapter 24), which can replace large amounts of fossil fuels. It is used in many ways in different countries, including the United States. France is especially committed to nuclear power. But, as we noted in Chapter 24, nuclear energy brings the problems of safeguarding people and the

Figure 29.6

Solar energy panels utilize energy from the sun to supply part of the heat required to warm this building.

environment from radioactive emissions in plant operation and waste disposal. An additional problem that arises in nuclear power plants, as well as conventional power plants, is **thermal discharge,** or **thermal pollution** (Section 29.10), which raises the temperature of lakes, streams, and the surrounding air and can have ill effects on aquatic life and, to a lesser extent, on agriculture and climate.

Using solar energy (energy from the sun; Fig. 29.6) to replace some of the energy otherwise produced from fossil fuels and combustion is in a less advanced state of development, but it holds promise as a clean method for solving some of our power needs. Windmills are used to generate small quantities of electrical power in areas where wind velocities are adequate and reasonably consistent (Fig. 29.7). Meanwhile, we must solve the problems involving combustion of fossil fuels.

29.5 Air Pollution from Chlorofluorocarbons

Figure 29.7

In some areas where wind velocities are dependable and sufficient, large windmills generate a portion of the electrical power.

Compounds containing chlorine, fluorine, and carbon are referred to as **chlorofluorocarbons,** or **CFC's** (also called Freons). They are widely used in applications such as those shown in Table 29.2. The table also shows what percentage of the CFC's used in the United States in 1989 were devoted to each application.

Table 29.2	Use of Chlorofluorocarbons in the United States in 1989 (by Percent)	
Use		**Percent**
Refrigeration and air conditioning		33
Foam blowing for insulation		31
Cleaning agents		23
Other (includes aerosols, sterilization, food freezing, etc.)		13
Total		100

Information from the EPA on five of the most common CFC's and three related compounds containing bromine is given in Table 29.3, which includes the names and abbreviations by which the compounds are identified and some of their properties and uses. The values for "ozone-depletion" are estimates that take into account lifetime in

Table 29.3	Some Compounds Controlled Under the *Montreal Protocol* of 1989[a]		
Substance	Ozone-Depletion Potential	Atmospheric Lifetime, years	Major Uses
Group 1—Production Cuts Mandated			
CCl_3F (CFC-11)	1.0	75	Blowing flexible foam and rigid polyurethane foam, refrigeration, air conditioning
CCl_2F_2 (CFC-12)	1.0	111	Blowing rigid polyurethane and rigid nonpolyurethane foam, refrigeration, air conditioning, aerosols, sterilization, food freezing
$C_2Cl_3F_3$ (CFC-113)	0.8	90	Solvent
$C_2Cl_2F_4$ (CFC-114)	1.0	185	Blowing rigid nonpolyurethane foam, refrigeration, air conditioning
C_2ClF_5 (CFC-115)	0.6	380	Refrigeration, air conditioning
Group 2—Production Freeze Mandated			
$CBrClF_2$ (Halon-1211)	3.0	25	Portable fire extinguishers
$CBrF_3$ (Halon-1301)	10.0	110	Total flooding fire-extinguishing systems
$C_2Br_2F_4$ (Halon-2402)	6.0	na	Fire extinguishers

[a] Selected chlorofluorocarbons are in Group 1; bromine-substituted compounds make up Group 2.
Reprinted with permission from *Chemical and Engineering News*, July 24, 1989, *67*(30) p. 9.
Copyright 1989 by the American Chemical Society.

the atmosphere and the chlorine or bromine content. The values are based on an arbitrary standard of 1.0 assigned to CCl_3F.

As we noted in Section 29.3, chlorofluorocarbons destroy ozone in the stratosphere, (see the discussion of homogeneous catalysts in Section 14.13) where ozone forms a desirable layer that prevents some harmful ultraviolet radiation from the sun from getting through to the earth's surface. Other carbon–halogen compounds, including ones containing bromine such as those listed in Table 29.3, can have the same effect. Ozone itself is a pollutant in the lower part of the earth's atmosphere, the **troposphere** (see the discussion of photochemical oxidants in Section 29.3), but it has historically acted positively in the stratosphere to prevent a significant portion of the sun's ultraviolet radiation from reaching the earth's surface. The destruction of ozone in the stratosphere has given rise to a phenomenon that has been labeled the ''ozone hole'' over the North and South Poles. In 1987, the worst year to date, the stratospheric ozone over Antarctica was decreased by 50% during September and October. Globally, the ozone layer has shrunk an average of 2.5% during the past decade. Consequently, there is rapidly increasing concern about the need for restricting the use of ozone-depleting chemicals.

The release of CCl_2F_2 (CFC-12) from car and truck air conditioners is the largest single source of CFC emissions in the United States. Of the new cars sold in the United States that have air conditioners, approximately 90% use CFC-12.

Possible Solutions to the Problems of Chlorofluorocarbon Pollution. Several states currently require the recycling of CFC-12 during servicing of automobile air conditioners, and other states are considering imposing such a requirement (Fig. 29.8). At the time of this writing, a bill has been submitted in the United States Senate that would make it illegal, after 1993, to sell cars that use CFC's in air conditioners.

The first cap on chlorofluorocarbon production went into effect in 1989 under the terms of the *Montreal Protocol on Substances that Deplete the Ozone Layer,* an international treaty now generally referred to as the *Montreal Protocol.* Producers were required to freeze their production of CFC's at 1986 levels, which represented a cutback of

Figure 29.8

Legislation in several states now mandates the recycling of CCl_2F_2 (CFC-12) during servicing of automobile air conditioners.

about 15% from 1989 output. An additional 20% cutback is called for by 1993, and another of 30% by mid-1998. It is anticipated that CFC's will be completely phased out during the decade of the 1990s.

An intensive critical search is on for chemicals that can replace the chlorofluorocarbons. One possibility is a class of compounds based on chlorofluorocarbons that contain hydrogen atoms (**hydrochlorofluorocarbons, HCFC's**). Examples include $CHCl_2CF_3$ (HCFC-123) and CH_3CCl_2F (HCFC-141b), which are possible substitutes for CCl_3F (CFC-11). Fully halogenated CFC's are so unreactive that essentially all get through the lower-level troposphere to the stratosphere where the ozone layer is. But the hydrogen atoms on the HCFC's make HCFC's susceptible to oxidation in the troposphere; thus they decompose, releasing most of their halogens before they can get to the stratosphere. However, toxicity levels of many of these compounds are not yet well known, and they may, as testing continues, emerge as unacceptably toxic.

29.6 Air Pollution from Other Causes

Other materials that contribute to air pollution result from the vaporization of liquids (or sometimes the sublimation of solids). Additional solid particles are introduced into the air by abrasion or grinding of materials. Examples include metal filings from the polishing or grinding of metals, asbestos loosened by procedures used in its removal from buildings (Figs. 29.9 and 29.10), dust from dust storms or from vehicles moving on dusty roads, and finely divided rubber from wear of automobile tires. Beryllium and its compounds are highly toxic, causing a lung disease called **berylliosis** (similar to tuberculosis) in workers in beryllium plants and laboratories who are not protected adequately against breathing air contaminated with beryllium. The disease causes weakness, shortness of breath, coughing, nervousness, loss of weight, and, ultimately, premature death. The use of pesticides that contain arsenic or other toxic substances can also cause serious air contamination. The use of such pesticides is being increasingly controlled, and several that were once widely used have been banned. Other pollutants that we will not discuss here also contribute to the air pollution problem.

Figure 29.9

Airborne particles of asbestos can be carried into the lungs, increasing a person's chances of developing lung cancer. Workers use extreme caution as they wet, scrape, and bag asbestos for disposal.

Figure 29.10

(left) The arrow pointing to the cloudiness in the lung cavity in this x-ray indicates the accumulation of asbestos fibers, characterizing the condition known as asbestosis. (below) An actual view of asbestos fibers in the lung tissue, magnified ×250.

🔴.7 Global Warming and the Greenhouse Effect

Some of the large amount of energy radiated toward the earth by the sun—perhaps 30% of it—is reflected back into space when it hits the top of the earth's atmosphere. The remainder passes through the atmosphere to the earth's surface, where a portion of it is radiated back through the atmosphere and into space, largely as infrared radiation (Section 5.8).

However, carbon dioxide, water, and some other molecules in the earth's atmosphere strongly absorb infrared radiation. With the increasing accumulation of these molecules in the atmosphere via combustion and other processes, an increasing amount of infrared energy is retained by the earth's atmosphere. This results in a warming effect, referred to as **global warming** or the **greenhouse effect.** This overall warming could significantly affect climate and precipitation patterns.

The molecules that participate in the greenhouse effect by absorbing infrared radiation in the atmosphere are sometimes referred to as **greenhouse gases.** Although carbon dioxide and water are usually predominant among these, a number of other molecules that are being added to the atmosphere in increasing quantities (such as methane and nitrous oxide) can have the same effect and are becoming more and more significant. Some scientists estimate that the combined greenhouse warming by the other gases will soon equal that of carbon dioxide, amounting to a doubling of the greenhouse effect by the year 2030—some 50 years sooner than previously predicted on the basis of carbon dioxide and water alone.

Other phenomena, it should be noted, result in a cooling effect. The greenhouse warming effect and the cooling effect must be kept in balance. A net warming trend would adversely affect many aspects of our lives. It would, for example, lower our fresh-water supplies and undermine agricultural efficiency. A net cooling effect could result in another "little ice age." Scientists who believe that the earth will experience a net warming effect predict a net temperature increase during the next century of 3.5 to 4.5°C, which may seem small. However, an average global temperature change of even 0.4°C in either direction has had drastic consequences in the past. During the major ice age 18,000 years ago, the overall average global temperature was only about 5°C colder than it is now, and during the little ice age that occurred in the years 1550 to 1850, temperatures were only 0.4°C below present levels. A temperature rise of 2°C would be unprecedented in the entire history of human civilization and would make the earth the warmest it has been in 150,000 years (Fig. 29.11).

It is important to realize that scientists disagree about whether the greenhouse effect will actually result in a *long-term* warming of the earth's surface. Some are firmly convinced that this will occur, and they cite impressive evidence of some actual warming in recent years. Others maintain that the warming observed in recent years is within short-term variations that occur regularly, and they cite some net cooling trends in certain geographic areas. Some of the latter scientists believe that we are in fact destined for another little ice age, with global temperatures heading for a net decrease similar to what the earth experienced in the period 1550 to 1850.

The variables being studied are complex. Furthermore, reliable records of temperature, pressure, relative humidity, and concentrations of trace gases have not been kept long enough for us to make long-term predictions with certainty (Fig. 29.12). For example, the first systematic measurements for carbon dioxide levels in the atmosphere were

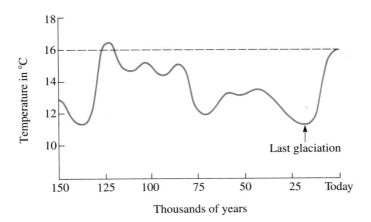

Thousands of years

Figure 29.11
Average global temperatures, in °C, during the last 150,000 years. An increase of less than 1°C over today's average global temperature would make the earth the warmest it has been in 150,000 years. [Reprinted by permission from *Chemical and Engineering News*, March 13, 1989, *67*(11), p. 28. Copyright 1989 by the American Chemical Society.]

made in 1959, and those for methane in 1979. The greenhouse warming effect is probably real and may be increasingly significant. Whether the cooling effects, equally well established, are sufficient to offset the warming effects remains to be seen. In the meantime, if we do not take steps to control the greenhouse effect, much of which has been induced by human carelessness in releasing increased concentrations of greenhouse gases to the atmosphere, the warming effect will almost certainly predominate. An equilibrium between warming factors and cooling factors must be established so that our average global temperature remains at a reasonable level.

Natural Waters

Figure 29.12
A balloon-borne instrument package being released to measure temperature, pressure, and relative humidity at different heights in the atmosphere. Such instruments are sent up from 63 international locations each day.

Water covers nearly three-fourths of the earth's surface. It is present in the atmosphere and the earth's crust, and it comprises a large part of all living plant and animal matter. Nutrients are transported into the roots of plants as solutions in water. Biological reactions occur in aqueous solution in cells. Many industrial reactions are run in water, and much of the chemistry that is discussed in a general chemistry course occurs in aqueous solution. The yearly use of water in the United States averages about 800,000 gallons per person. None of the hundreds of thousands of other chemical substances is more important than water.

Water has its own chemical behavior, and it has been used as a standard for many physical constants and units. Pure water is an odorless, tasteless, and colorless liquid, though large bodies of natural water appear bluish-green. The taste of drinking water is due to dissolved gases and salts.

29.8 Water, an Important Natural Resource

Although there is enough water in the oceans to cover the entire earth to an average depth of 2 miles, human uses generally require fresh water. About a half-gallon of water per day is required to satisfy the biological needs of a human being. About 90 gallons per person per day are used in maintaining cleanliness, cooking food, and heating and air-conditioning homes. These quantities are dwarfed by the 2000 gallons of water used

Figure 29.13
Water is used in many facets of the steel-making industry.

Table 29.4	The Most Abundant Elements in Sea Water[a]	

Element	Concentration, g/L
Cl	18.98
Na	10.56
Mg	1.272
S	0.884
Ca	0.400
K	0.380
Br	0.065
C[b]	0.028
Sr	0.013
B[c]	0.0045
F	0.0014

[a]Excluding dissolved gases
[b]In CO_3^{2-} and HCO_3^-
[c]In H_3BO_3

per person per day by industries in the United States (Fig. 29.13). To produce 1 egg requires 120 gallons of water, 10 gallons are required to produce 1 gallon of gasoline, 80 gallons for 1 kilowatt of electricity, 65,000 gallons for 1 ton of steel, and 3 million gallons for 1 ton of nylon. More water is used for irrigation in the United States than for any other single purpose: over 750 gallons per person per day are consumed.

Unlike most mineral resources, fresh water is renewable, because it is part of a gigantic cycle. Water evaporates from the earth into the atmosphere, is transported in the atmosphere by the winds, and finally falls back to the earth in some form of precipitation. A large part of the water that precipitates is lost to our daily use, however, through evaporation and transpiration by plants.

At the present time, because of recent advances in devising economical and practical desalting processes, the oceans are becoming increasingly important as potential sources of fresh water. It has been estimated that about 2 billion gallons of pure drinking water per day are produced worldwide by desalting water.

29.9 Naturally Occurring Water

All natural waters, even those not polluted by people, are impure because they contain many dissolved substances. Rain water is usually relatively pure (its chief impurities are dust and harmless dissolved gases), but acid rain (Section 29.10) has unfortunately become an increasing problem in recent years. Sea water contains about 3.6% dissolved solids, principally sodium chloride (Table 29.4). Sea water is known to contain at least 72 elements, and it is possible that all naturally occurring elements exist in the sea.

The impurities in the fresh water on the earth's surface vary with the nature of the soil and rocks that it has passed over or through. Increasingly, fresh water also contains impurities added by people. The natural impurities may include dissolved gases such as oxygen, nitrogen, and carbon dioxide (from the air) and ammonia and hydrogen sulfide; dissolved salts; dissolved organic substances from the decay of plant and animal matter; suspended solids such as sand, clay, silt, and organic material; and microorganisms.

During the normal life cycle of a body of fresh water such as a lake, organic sediment slowly accumulates from algae, bacteria, aquatic plants, and animal by-products. Bacteria and other organisms in the lake feed on this sediment and, in the presence of oxygen, decompose the sediment to various molecules and ions, including nitrates and phosphates. This decomposition of organic matter by bacteria in the presence of oxygen is called **aerobic decomposition.** If the supply of oxygen is reduced or if the amount of organic sediment increases to the point where aerobic decomposition cannot keep up with it, the aerobic bacteria die, and other bacteria that live in the absence of oxygen thrive. They, too, decompose the sediment, but the products are much less pleasant. Decomposition of organic matter in the absence of oxygen is called **anaerobic decomposition.** Anaerobic decomposition is accompanied by the smell of rotten eggs because of the presence of hydrogen sulfide (which is the substance responsible for the unpleasant odor of rotten eggs); bubbles of methane are usually visible; and the water is black and often filled with slime.

The process by which a lake grows rich in nutrients (phosphates and nitrates, primarily) and gradually fills with organic sediment and aquatic plants is called **eutrophication,** which can be defined as the biological result of adding substantially to the nutrient base of natural waters.

As a lake ages naturally, it becomes shallower because it fills with sediment, and plant life abounds on the banks and within the lake itself. The lake is slowly transformed into a marsh—and ultimately into dry land—by the processes accompanying eutrophication (Fig. 29.14).

🕮.10 Water Pollution

In addition to the natural contaminants in water, many other pollutants are added to our water supplies by human activities. The very existence of this problem went unrecognized for many years, and its magnitude may not be realized yet. Unfortunately, very little is known about the long-term effects on human health of the many chemical compounds that enter water supplies. A whole new field of chemistry is developing rapidly in which pollutants in our *overall* environment, not just in our water supplies, are studied in connection with their short-range and long-range effects on human health and with their efficient removal.

Several water pollutants are currently causing serious concern. We will consider five of these: (1) phosphates and other nutrients, (2) sewage and other waste materials, (3) toxic pollutants, (4) acid rain, and (5) thermal pollution.

1. **Phosphates and Other Nutrients.** Phosphates have been used widely in laundry detergents and hence have been released in large quantities in municipal wastes into rivers and streams. Furthermore, many fertilizers contain phosphates (Section 2.12, Part 1). A number of phosphate compounds that are present in certain rocks are partially dissolved and reach streams through natural runoff. Phosphate compounds are significant nutrients for algae, bacteria, and aquatic plants. Other nutrients include nitrogen (in the form of ammonia, ammonium salts such as ammonium sulfate, and nitrate salts such as calcium nitrate) and potassium (in potassium salts such as potassium nitrate and potassium sulfate). These are released in municipal wastes, in the runoff from fertilizer application, and in the wastes from animals.

The growth of algae and other aquatic plants is usually controlled by the amount of nutrients available. Excess nutrients lead to rapid plant growth, with a consequent rapid

Figure 29.14
This lake in the Pocono Mountains is well along in the process of natural eutrophication; it is near the end of its conversion to a marsh.

increase in the rate of eutrophication of natural waters. In the worst cases, the deposition of organic sediment can become so extensive that anaerobic bacteria replace the aerobic bacteria and the lake is no longer able to support most forms of life.

Development of effective long-term controls of eutrophication will require a better understanding of the significant nutrients in streams and lakes, the natural plant and animal populations in them, and how these are affected by externally applied factors such as the added nutrients. In the meantime, substitutes for phosphates in detergents are now in use, and methods of removing phosphates from municipal wastes and controlling their undesirable effects in those wastes are increasingly being used.

2. Sewage and Other Waste Materials. In addition to nutrients, municipal sewage contains microorganisms and the by-products from many industrial processes. In some communities, raw sewage used to be dumped directly into natural waters that served as sources of public water supplies. Fortunately, vigorously enforced regulations now prevent most of this, but contamination may also result from breakdowns in sewage treatment plants or from flooding of such plants. Chlorination of municipal water supplies has largely eliminated the danger from bacteria and viruses in drinking water. However, many bodies of natural water are still contaminated with microorganisms and certain chemical by-products, which may pose hazards in domestic water supplies.

The presence of organic matter, nutrients, and microorganisms in water is measured by three tests: **coliform count, algal count,** and **biological oxygen demand (BOD).** A coliform count determines the number of *E. coli* (the characteristic bacteria in animal wastes) present. The algal count is a test for microorganisms other than *E. coli*. The BOD measures the volume of oxygen gas taken up by a given amount of water in five days at 20°C. Because the oxygen is consumed by microorganisms in the water, the BOD is a measure of the total quantity of microorganisms and the nutrients available to them. Pure water has a BOD of 1 part per million (equivalent to 1 milligram of O_2 per liter of water) or less. A BOD of 20 parts per million or less is acceptable for municipal or industrial sewage. Raw sewage exhibits a BOD of 100–400 parts per million.

The coliform count, the algal count, and the BOD do not determine the presence of small amounts of organic compounds (often resulting from industrial wastes), but specialized tests for compounds such as benzene, acetone, toluene, chloroform, and carbon tetrachloride have shown small amounts (1–40 parts per billion) of these materials in the drinking water of cities in industrial areas. The normal water purification procedures do not remove these compounds. In fact, the presence of chloroform, $CHCl_3$, in domestic water supplies may be due to the reaction of chlorine (used in water purification) with naturally occurring organic compounds that result from the decay of plant matter in the soil. Some of these organic pollutants can be removed by filtering domestic water through activated charcoal.

3. Toxic Pollutants. Many waters contain pesticides (organic compounds that are used to kill insects, weeds, and fungi). Pesticides can become concentrated in the food chain of fish and wildlife and kill these species (Fig. 29.15) or decrease their ability to reproduce. Some of these compounds, such as Aldrin, DDT, Dieldrin, and Kepone, have proved so toxic that their manufacture and use have been prohibited.

The very poisonous cation CH_3Hg^+ from the compound methyl mercury, which is more soluble than elemental mercury in water, is produced in inland waters by the action of microorganisms in the bottom mud on mercury that may remain from the prior discharge of waste mercury and mercury compounds. (The discharge of mercury and mercury compounds is now prohibited.) Fish ingest methyl mercury both through their food and through their gills to such an extent that the concentration in their flesh may be

Figure 29.15

A fish kill resulting from a runoff of toxic pollutants.

several thousand times that in the surrounding water. Hence the possibility of humans' getting mercury poisoning from eating some fish (or other animals) is greater than might be expected from the actual concentration of the element in the water.

Considerable attention has recently been devoted to pollution by cadmium, an element in the same periodic group as mercury. The discharge of cadmium, like that of other toxic pollutants such as cyanide, benzidine, and polybromobiphenyl (PBB) compounds, has also been prohibited, but it may be some time before these materials are absent from natural waters.

4. Acid Rain. Rain with an acid concentration of 0.0001–0.001 M has been falling over the eastern United States and in Minnesota, Colorado, Oregon, Washington, southeastern Canada, Scandinavia, Japan, and China. Sulfuric acid appears to be the principal component of this acid rain. Such rain increases the acid content of many lakes to the point where plants and animals cannot live in the water. It also damages vegetation, buildings, and statues (Fig. 29.2) made of limestone or marble (both are $CaCO_3$) and bridges and other structures made of metal.

Natural sources of acid in rain include lightning and volcanic eruptions. Lightning provides the energy to cause the reaction of nitrogen and oxygen in the air, which produces oxides of nitrogen and (subsequently) nitric acid. Volcanic eruptions contain sulfur oxides, leading to production of sulfuric acid in the air. However, many scientists believe that most acid rain is a result of the combustion of fossil fuels such as coal and hydrocarbons, which often contain sulfur and other contaminants (Section 29.4).

It has been suggested that acid rain could be significantly reduced if emission control technology and/or low-sulfur coal were used. However, a switch to low-sulfur coal could depress the midwestern coal mining industry, and consumers of electricity in many states would face substantial rate hikes to pay for the emission control equipment. Some scientists claim that such controls would have very little effect on the acidity of rainfall. The acid rain problem illustrates the conflict between the need to respond promptly to a problem and the responsibility to consider the economic consequences of that response.

5. Thermal Pollution. Discharges that raise the temperature of a body of water may harm fish and increase the growth of algae and other microorganisms. A rise in water temperature of just a few degrees as a result of thermal pollution can decrease the solubility of oxygen in the water to a level too low for many forms of aquatic life to survive. Cooling towers and other facilities to reduce the heat transferred to natural waters are increasingly employed in industrial situations.

It is conceivable that thermal pollution could be beneficial under certain conditions. The Ralston Purina Company and the Florida Power Company, which has replaced a conventional power plant with a nuclear power plant, have cooperated in a study to determine whether selected saltwater fish and shellfish might thrive in warmer water, thereby improving the food supply from the sea.

🅴.11 Purification of Water

Water is purified for city water supplies by first allowing it to stand in large reservoirs where most of the mud, clay, and silt settle out—a process called **sedimentation**—and then filtering it through beds of sand and gravel. Prior to filtration, graphite, lime, and aluminum sulfate are often added to the water. The graphite absorbs organic materials (see Fig. 23.2). The lime and aluminum sulfate react to form aluminum hydroxide as a gelatinous precipitate that settles slowly, carrying with it much of the suspended matter, including most of the bacteria. The bacteria that remain in the water after filtration are killed by adding chlorine.

Relatively pure water for laboratory use is commonly prepared by distillation (Section 11.7). Gases from the air, particularly carbon dioxide, often contaminate distilled water and must be removed for some laboratory operations.

🅴.12 Hard Water

Water containing dissolved calcium, magnesium, and iron salts is known as **hard water.** The anions present in hard water are usually chloride, sulfate, and hydrogen carbonate. Hardness in water is objectionable for two reasons.

1. The calcium, magnesium, and iron ions form insoluble soaps such as calcium stearate, $(C_{17}H_{35}CO_2)_2Ca$, by reaction with soluble soaps such as sodium stearate, $C_{17}H_{35}CO_2Na$ (Section 12.25). Insoluble soaps have no cleansing power, and they adhere to fabrics, giving them a dingy appearance. They also make up the ring in the bathtub. Soap in excess of that needed to precipitate the calcium and magnesium must be added to hard water in order to obtain cleansing action.

2. Hard water is responsible for the formation of scale in boilers, teakettles, and hot water pipes (Fig. 29.16). At high temperatures much of the mineral matter precipitates as scale [insoluble substances such as calcium carbonate, magnesium carbonate, and iron(II) carbonate]. A major component of some scale is calcium sulfate, which is *less* soluble in hot water than in cold and precipitates partly because of that fact. The scale is a poor conductor of heat and thus causes a waste of fuel. Furthermore, scale may cause boiler explosions. Because it is not a good heat conductor, the iron metal under it

(a)

(b)

Figure 29.16

(a) This lengthwise section of a pipe shows the formation of scale.
(b) This cross-section clearly indicates the reduction in pipe diameter for the delivery of water.

must be very hot (often red hot) in order to boil the water in the boiler. If the scale cracks, the water seeps through and comes in contact with the hot metal.

$$4H_2O + 3Fe(hot) \longrightarrow Fe_3O_4 + 4H_2$$

As it is formed, the hydrogen gas breaks the scale loose and more water gets in, producing still more hydrogen and setting the stage for a violent explosion.

29.13 Water-Softening

It is important that the substances responsible for hardness in water be removed before the water is used for washing or in boilers. The removal of the metallic ions responsible for the hardness is called **water-softening.**

Water that contains Ca^{2+}, Mg^{2+}, or Fe^{2+} as hydrogen carbonate salts can be softened by boiling. This drives off carbon dioxide, and the hardness is removed as the metal carbonates precipitate.

$$Ca^{2+} + 2HCO_3^- \xrightarrow{\Delta} CaCO_3(s) + CO_2 + H_2O$$

The hydrogen carbonate ion can also be converted to the carbonate ion by the addition of a base. Commercially, calcium hydroxide is added in the quantity needed to react with the hydrogen carbonate ions to form insoluble calcium carbonate.

$$Ca^{2+} + 2OH^- + Ca^{2+} + 2HCO_3^- \longrightarrow 2CaCO_3(s) + 2H_2O$$

Similar reactions remove Mg^{2+} or Fe^{2+} as insoluble magnesium or iron(II) carbonates. The precipitated carbonates are readily removed from the water by filtration.

Unlike hydrogen carbonate salts, chloride and sulfate salts are not removed by boiling. Crude sodium hydroxide (caustic soda) is often used in large installations to remove both carbonate and noncarbonate salts.

$$Ca^{2+} + 2HCO_3^- + [2Na^+] + 2OH^- \longrightarrow CaCO_3(s) + [2Na^+] + CO_3^{2-} + 2H_2O$$

The sodium carbonate produced then reacts to remove any remaining noncarbonate salts. For example,

$$Ca^{2+} + [SO_4^{2-}] + [2Na^+] + CO_3^{2-} \longrightarrow CaCO_3(s) + [2Na^+] + [SO_4^{2-}]$$

The sodium sulfate or sodium chloride produced is relatively soluble and does not interfere with the cleansing action of soaps or form boiler scale.

Ion exchange provides another useful and highly important means of softening water. When water that contains calcium, magnesium, and iron(II) ions filters slowly through layers of sodium aluminosilicates, those ions are replaced by sodium ions and the water is softened. Aluminosilicates are known as **zeolites.**

$$\underset{\substack{\text{Sodium aluminosilicate} \\ \text{(insoluble)}}}{2NaAlSi_2O_6} + Ca^{2+} \longrightarrow \underset{\substack{\text{Calcium aluminosilicate} \\ \text{(insoluble)}}}{Ca(AlSi_2O_6)_2} + 2Na^+$$

Calcium aluminosilicate can be reconverted into the sodium compound by using a concentrated solution of sodium chloride, thus regenerating the system to remove more calcium ions.

$$Ca(AlSi_2O_6)_2 + 2Na^+ \longrightarrow 2NaAlSi_2O_6 + Ca^{2+}$$

Figure 29.17

Industrial water-softening by ion exchange. When regeneration is necessary, the soft-water outlet valve is closed, and a concentrated NaCl solution is run through the calcium zeolite and out the waste line. Regeneration is complete when the calcium ions are replaced by sodium ions.

This reaction is the reverse of the preceding one, and the direction the reaction takes is controlled by an excess of either Ca^{2+} or Na^+.

$$2NaAlSi_2O_6 + Ca^{2+} \rightleftharpoons Ca(AlSi_2O_6)_2 + 2Na^+$$

After the sodium zeolite is regenerated, it is ready for use again. The ion-exchange method of water-softening is effective for the removal of both carbonate and noncarbonate salts (Fig. 29.17).

Synthetic **ion-exchange resins** have also been developed to soften hard water. These insoluble resins remove both cations and anions from hard water; that is, they demineralize the water completely. Examples of such resins are Amberlite and Zeo-Carb. Metal ions in the hard water displace hydrogen ions from one type of ion-exchange resin, RCO_2H. (R represents a complex hydrocarbon portion of the resin that does not enter into the exchange reaction.)

$$2RCO_2H + Ca^{2+} + [SO_4^{2-}] + 2H_2O \longrightarrow (RCO_2)_2Ca + 2H_3O^+ + [SO_4^{2-}]$$

Another type of ion-exchange resin then removes the ions of the acid from the water.

$$2RNH_2 + 2H_3O^+ + SO_4^{2-} \longrightarrow (RNH_3)_2SO_4(s) + 2H_2O$$

Hence if hard water (or a salt solution) is passed first through a resin that replaces all metal ions with H_3O^+ and then through a resin that combines with the resulting acid, it can be completely demineralized. The result is essentially the same as that achieved through distillation of water. In recent years the use of ion-exchange resins in the treatment of water for industrial, laboratory, and domestic purposes has grown tremendously.

For Review

Summary

The **atmosphere** surrounding the earth is a mixture of gases consisting principally of nitrogen (78%) and oxygen (21%) with smaller amounts of water vapor, carbon dioxide, ozone, and the noble gases (helium, neon, argon, krypton, xenon, radon), but other gases that are usually regarded as air pollutants are also present. The principal pollutants are sulfur oxides, carbon monoxide, nitrogen oxides, hydrocarbons, photochemical oxidants, chlorofluorocarbons, and particulates (which are not gases but suspended solids).

Carbon monoxide and hydrocarbons in the atmosphere generally result from incomplete combustion. Sulfur oxides result from combustion of fuels containing sulfur or from the use of sulfide-containing ores in metallurgical processing. Nitrogen oxides are formed when nitrogen and oxygen in the atmosphere combine under the high-temperature conditions that accompany combustion. Nitrogen oxides and hydrocarbons combine in sunlight to produce photochemical oxidants such as peroxyacetyl nitrate (PAN) and ozone, components of photochemical smog. Each of these air pollutants can adversely affect the health of plants and animals, including humans, and can damage metals, fibers, and building materials.

A number of techniques have been used to reduce the amounts of pollutants released into the atmosphere. These range from relatively simple devices such as gas-tight fuel tank caps, which prevent the evaporation of hydrocarbons, to the use of catalytic converters and the desulfurization of coal.

Whereas ozone is itself a pollutant in the lower part of the earth's atmosphere (the **troposphere**), it acts in the upper part of the earth's atmosphere (the **stratosphere**) to prevent a significant part of the sun's harmful ultraviolet radiation from reaching the earth's surface. Chlorofluorocarbons and other related compounds deplete ozone in the stratosphere, allowing additional ultraviolet radiation from the sun to get through to the earth's surface. A hole in the ozone layer has been found over the South Pole, and there is now some evidence that there is one over the North Pole.

Chlorofluorocarbons are widely used in applications such as refrigeration, air conditioning, blowing polyurethane foams (for insulation), sterilization, food freezing, fire extinguishers, and solvents. It is important to replace them with substances that are not ozone-depleting. Research to discover such substances is under way.

Energy that strikes the earth's surface from the sun is absorbed by plants in photosynthesis, by oceans and other bodies of water, and by soil and rocks. These absorptions cause an increase in temperature, and some of this heat energy is reradiated from the earth's surface, largely as infrared radiation, into the atmosphere. Some of the gases in the atmosphere, such as carbon dioxide, water, and methane, strongly absorb infrared radiation. This causes a portion of the heat energy to be retained by the earth's atmosphere and makes the earth warmer than it otherwise would be. The increase in temperature is referred to as **global warming,** and the effect is called the **greenhouse effect.** Greater amounts of carbon dioxide, from increasing combustion of fossil fuels, and a variety of additional greenhouse gases from industrial processes are increasing the amount of heat retained. Some of this warming is offset by factors that have a cooling effect, but even a small average net increase (or decrease) in the global temperature can have serious consequences. It is extremely important to preserve a favorable equilibrium between the greenhouse effect and the various cooling factors so that the average global temperature will remain at a reasonable level.

Water is a vital natural resource, satisfying both biological and industrial requirements. Natural fresh water from rivers, lakes, and wells usually requires purification to remove sediment and microorganisms. It may also require softening to remove the Ca^{2+}, Mg^{2+}, and Fe^{2+} ions that produce **hard water.** Pollution of natural waters is of great concern. This pollution may be due to excess nutrients finding their way into natural waters (leading to increased rates of **eutrophication**), toxic chemicals from sewage or chemical waste dumps, acid rain, or the discharge of heat into the waters.

Air and water pollution occasion the loss of natural resources, degrade the environment, and undermine health. Current methods of controlling pollution cost money, time, and effort. Development of the new technology necessary for adequate control of pollution carries a high price in dollars and inconvenience. Nevertheless, it appears that we have no choice but to pay that price.

Key Terms and Concepts

acid rain (29.10)
aerobic decomposition (29.9)
air pollution (29.2–29.6)
algal count (29.10)
anaerobic decomposition (29.9)
atmosphere (29.1)
biological oxygen demand, BOD (29.10)
catalytic converter (29.4)

chlorofluorocarbons (29.5)
coliform count (29.10)
eutrophication (29.9)
global warming (29.7)
greenhouse effect (29.7)
hard water (29.12–29.13)
hydrochlorofluorocarbons (29.5)
ion exchange (29.13)

ozone hole (29.5)
stratosphere (29.3)
thermal pollution (29.4, 29.10)
troposphere (29.5)
water pollution (29.10)
water purification (29.11)
water-softening (29.13)
zeolite (29.13)

Exercises

Answers for selected even-numbered exercises marked by red numbers appear at the end of the book. The worked-out solutions to all even-numbered exercises appear in the *Solutions Guide*.

The Atmosphere

1. A concentration of 750 parts per million by volume of carbon monoxide is lethal. What mass of carbon monoxide is required to provide a lethal uniform concentration in a room 6.8 m long, 5.3 m wide, and 2.2 m high if the temperature is 22°C and the atmospheric pressure is 740 torr?

2. Basing your reasoning on the periodic properties of the elements, write balanced chemical equations for the reactions, if any, between the components of air given in Table 29.1 and hot magnesium.

3. Write a balanced equation for each of the following processes.
   (a) The formation of sulfur dioxide from zinc sulfide present in burning coal.
   (b) The formation of nitrogen dioxide in an internal combustion engine.
   (c) The formation of sulfuric acid mist from sulfur dioxide.
   (d) The oxidation of carbon monoxide in an automobile's exhaust by means of a catalytic converter.

4. Name the seven principal air pollutants and identify a source of each. Briefly describe one technique for controlling each of these pollutants.

5. What evidence can you cite to show that air is a mixture rather than a compound?

6. (a) Calculate the density of air, of hydrogen, and of helium at STP in grams per liter. (Assume the average molecular mass of air is 29.10.)
   (b) The lifting power of a gas with a density less than that of air is determined by the difference between its mass and that of an equal volume of air. Calculate the lifting power of hydrogen, the lifting power of helium [which by calculation in part (a) is shown to be approximately twice as heavy as hydrogen for a given volume], and the lifting power of helium as a percentage of that of hydrogen.

7. (a) Why is it important to substitute other kinds of compounds for chlorofluorocarbons (CFC's) in air conditioning and other important practical applications?
   (b) Why are hydrochlorofluorocarbons (HCFC's) thought to be better choices than CFC's?

8. Define the following terms.
   (a) ozone hole   (d) global warming
   (b) greenhouse effect   (e) CFC
   (c) greenhouse gases   (f) HCFC

9. Explain the greenhouse effect. Why is it a problem? What can be done about it?

10. The chlorofluorocarbons CCl_3F (CFC-11) and CCl_2F_2 (CFC-12) have many important practical uses, and in fact CFC-12 is, at the time of this writing, the refrigerant in essentially all automobile air conditioners. The two compounds are prepared by mixing carbon tetrachloride with hydrogen fluoride in the presence of a catalyst. If one exchange of fluorine for chlorine in CCl_4 occurs, CFC-11 is produced. If two such exchanges occur, CFC-12 is produced. Temperature and pressure in the reactor determine whether one or two exchanges occur. The equations for the two processes are

$$CCl_4 + HF \longrightarrow CCl_3F + HCl$$
$$CCl_4 + 2HF \longrightarrow CCl_2F_2 + 2HCl$$

Calculate the number of pounds of carbon tetrachloride and of hydrogen fluoride that are required (a) to produce 125 pounds of CFC-11 and (b) to produce 125 pounds of CFC-12.

Natural Waters

11. What are some of the primary substances responsible for water pollution?

12. Can the purification of water lead to its pollution? Can the pollution of water produce any beneficial results?

13. What is thermal pollution of water? Explain the ways in which it is undesirable. Is it necessarily always undesirable? Explain.

14. Define the following terms:
    (a) BOD
    (b) eutrophication
    (c) aerobic decomposition
    (d) anaerobic decomposition
    (e) hard water
    (f) zeolites

15. What naturally occurring impurities are typically present in unpolluted rain water? In unpolluted river water?

16. What is the effect of excess nutrients in a lake?

17. What metal ions are commonly responsible for the hardness of water?

18. Distinguish between softening and demineralizing of water. Does demineralization soften water?

19. Water that is hard because of the presence of hydrogen carbonate salts may be softened by boiling. Explain, using an equation.

20. One of the reasons why so much slaked lime (calcium hydroxide, Section 13.6) and aluminum sulfate are produced industrially is that these compounds are used in water treatment. Explain how they are used.

21. Assuming 95% recovery, find what volume, in liters, of sea water must be processed to isolate 1.000 metric ton (1000 kg) of magnesium (see Table 29.4).

22. What are the molarities of Na^+ and Cl^- in sea water (see Table 29.4)?

30 Organic Chemistry

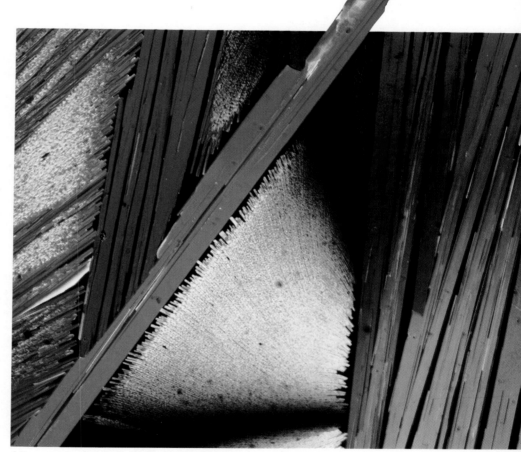

Micrograph of urea crystals, photographed with polarized light.

Organic compounds are compounds of carbon that contain carbon–carbon bonds, carbon–hydrogen bonds, or both. Thousands of carbon compounds have either been found in, or derived from, living organisms, or have been produced by chemists. Altogether about five million natural and synthetic organic compounds have been characterized. That so many organic compounds exist is due primarily to the ability of carbon atoms to combine with other carbon atoms, forming chains of different lengths and rings of different sizes. As pointed out in Chapters 21 and 23, carbon is the first member of Group IVA of the periodic table and has a valence shell electron configuration of $2s^2 2p^2$. Carbon forms covalent bonds in compounds, with all of its four valence electrons generally used in the bonding. Because the valence shell of carbon has only s and p orbitals and thus is limited to eight electrons, carbon exhibits only sp^3, sp^2, or sp hybridization of its atomic orbitals. Carbon thereby displays a coordination number of 4, 3, or 2 with a tetrahedral, trigonal planar, or linear geometry (Sections 8.6–8.8).

Other than carbon, the elements most frequently found in organic compounds are hydrogen, oxygen, nitrogen, sulfur, the halogens, phosphorus, and some of the metals.

The simplest organic compounds contain only carbon and hydrogen and are called **hydrocarbons.** Many hydrocarbons are found in plants, animals, and their fossils; other hydrocarbons have been prepared in the laboratory. Several types of hydrocarbons have been characterized. They are distinguished by the type of bonding and the hybridization of the carbon orbitals.

㉚.1 Saturated Hydrocarbons

Saturated hydrocarbons contain only single covalent bonds. All of the carbon atoms in a saturated hydrocarbon have sp^3 hybridization and are bonded to four other carbon and/or hydrogen atoms. Saturated hydrocarbons of one series have the general molecular formula C_nH_{2n+2}, where n is an integer, and are called **alkanes** (Table 30.1).

In alkanes, all of the carbon atoms are sp^3 hybridized and bonded either to other carbon atoms or to hydrogen atoms by single bonds. All of the C—C bond lengths are about 1.54 Å; all of the C—H bond lengths are about 1.09 Å. The bond angles are close to 109.5° (the tetrahedral angle). Thus, chains of carbon atoms have a staggered, or zig-zag, configuration. The Lewis structures, molecular structures, and models of methane, ethane, and pentane are illustrated in Fig. 30.1. In the molecular structures the bonds shown as striped wedges extend behind the page, and the bonds shown as solid wedges extend in front of the page. Note in the molecular structure and model of pentane that the carbon atoms do not lie in a straight line. For clarity, carbon atoms are usually

Figure 30.1

Models of methane, ethane, and pentane, showing the Lewis structures, the molecular structures, and ball-and-stick models. Striped wedges indicate bonds that extend behind the plane of the paper, and solid wedges indicate bonds that extend in front of the plane of the paper.

Methane
CH_4

Ethane
CH_3CH_3

Pentane
$CH_3CH_2CH_2CH_2CH_3$

					Number of
	Molecular Formula	Melting Point, °C	Boiling Point, °C	Phase at STP[b]	Structural Isomers
Methane	CH_4	−182.5	−161.5	Gas	1
Ethane	C_2H_6	−183.2	−88.6	Gas	1
Propane	C_3H_8	−187.7	−42.1	Gas	1
Butane	C_4H_{10}	−138.3	−0.5	Gas	2
Pentane	C_5H_{12}	−129.7	36.1	Liquid	3
Hexane	C_6H_{14}	−95.3	68.7	Liquid	5
Heptane	C_7H_{16}	−90.6	98.4	Liquid	9
Octane	C_8H_{18}	−56.8	125.7	Liquid	18
Nonane	C_9H_{20}	−53.6	150.8	Liquid	35
Decane	$C_{10}H_{22}$	−29.7	174.0	Liquid	75
Undecane	$C_{11}H_{24}$	−25.6	195.8	Liquid	159
Dodecane	$C_{12}H_{26}$	−9.6	216.3	Liquid	355
Tridecane	$C_{13}H_{28}$	−5.4	235.4	Liquid	802
Tetradecane	$C_{14}H_{30}$	5.9	253.5	Solid	1858
Octadecane	$C_{18}H_{38}$	28.2	316.1	Solid	60,523

Table 30.1   Properties of Some Alkanes[a]

[a] Physical properties for C_4H_{10} and the heavier molecules are those of the *normal* isomer, *n*-butane, *n*-pentane, etc.
[b] STP represents standard temperature and pressure (Section 10.9).

written in straight lines in Lewis structures, but remember that Lewis structures usually show only electron distribution and bonds, not the geometry about each atom. A long chain can twist itself into many different shapes.

Hydrocarbons with the same formula can have different structures. For example, two hydrocarbons have the formula C_4H_{10}; their common names are normal butane (or *n*-butane) and isobutane. These two butanes are **structural isomers.** Such isomers have the same molecular formula but different physical and chemical properties because the arrangement of the atoms in their molecules is different.

The term *normal* refers to a continus chain of carbon atoms with no branching. Normal butane, or *n*-butane, is a continuous-chain molecule and isobutane is a branched-chain molecule.

n-Butane   Isobutane

The number of possible isomers increases with the number of carbon atoms in the hydrocarbon. Hydrocarbons with a large number of carbon atoms have a great many isomers (Table 30.1). The three structural isomers of the hydrocarbon C_5H_{12} have the common names *n*-pentane, isopentane, and neopentane. (See Fig. 11.6 for models of *n*-pentane and neopentane.)

n-Pentane, or
pentane
$CH_3CH_2CH_2CH_2CH_3$

Isopentane, or
2-methylbutane
$CH_3CH_2CH(CH_3)CH_3$

Neopentane, or
2,2-dimethylpropane
$CH_3C(CH_3)_2CH_3$

Note that the following three structures, however, all represent the same molecule, *n*-pentane, and hence are not separate isomers. They are identical—each contains an unbranched chain of five carbon atoms. When you are unsure whether a hydrocarbon is branched, check the carbon backbone. If any specific carbon atom has bonds with more than two other carbons, the molecule is branched.

All of the hydrogen atoms in the —CH_3 groups at the end of *n*-pentane are equivalent, because a carbon atom can rotate freely around a C—C bond.

A few alkanes and some of their properties are listed in Table 30.1. Alkanes possess small or no dipole moments; that is, they are essentially nonpolar. The principal intermolecular forces are London dispersion forces (see Section 11.3), and a smooth increase in boiling point is observed as the molecular mass increases. A transition from the gaseous state to the liquid state and finally to the solid state is also a result of the predominance of dispersion forces.

The members of a second series of saturated hydrocarbons have the general molecular formula C_nH_{2n}, where *n* is an integer, and are called **cycloalkanes.** As the name implies, the molecules of these substances are cyclic (possessing rings). The smallest member of the series is cyclopropane; next are cyclobutane, cyclopentane, etc.

Cyclopropane

Cyclobutane

Cyclopentane

The reactions of alkanes all involve the breaking of C—H or C—C single bonds. In a **substitution reaction,** a typical reaction of alkanes, a second type of atom is substituted for a hydrogen atom.

Ethane   Ethyl chloride

This reaction transforms an alkane molecule into one that contains a more reactive species or group, a **functional group.** The functional group, a halogen in this case, makes it possible for the molecule to take part in many different kinds of reactions.

Alkanes burn in air; the reaction is a highly exothermic oxidation–reduction reaction. Thus they are excellent fuels. A typical combustion reaction is

$$2C_2H_6(g) + 7O_2(g) \longrightarrow 4CO_2(g) + 6H_2O(g) \qquad \Delta H° = -2856 \text{ kJ}$$

Methane is the principal component of natural gas. The butane used in camping stoves and lighters is an alkane. Gasoline is a mixture of continuous- and branched-chain alkanes containing from five to nine carbon atoms plus various additives. Kerosene, diesel oil, and fuel oil are primarily mixtures of alkanes with higher molecular masses.

30.2 The Nomenclature of Saturated Hydrocarbons

The International Union of Pure and Applied Chemistry (IUPAC) has devised a system of nomenclature for the hydrocarbons, their isomers, and their **derivatives** (compounds in which one or more hydrogen atoms have been replaced by other atoms or groups of atoms). The nomenclature for saturated hydrocarbons is based on two rules.

1. To name a hydrocarbon, we must first locate the longest *continuous* chain of carbon atoms. A two-carbon chain is called ethane; a three-carbon chain, propane; and a four-carbon chain, butane. The longest continuous chain of more than four carbon atoms in a saturated hydrocarbon is indicated by one of the following prefixes: five carbons, *penta-;* six carbons, *hexa-;* seven carbons, *hepta-;* eight carbons, *octa-;* nine carbons, *nona-;* and ten carbons, *deca-.* The suffix *-ane* is added at the end (one *a* is dropped when two occur in succession). Thus these names are pentane, hexane, heptane, octane, nonane, and decane, respectively. The names of the hydrocarbons listed in Table 30.1 indicate that these compounds, which are the normal isomers when more than one form exists, contain a single chain of carbon atoms consisting of the same number of carbon atoms as the number of carbon atoms in the molecule. For example, tetradecane in Table 30.1 represents normal tetradecane, n-$C_{14}H_{30}$, which consists of a chain of fourteen (tetradeca) carbon atoms.

2. After finding the longest continuous chain of carbon atoms, we add, as prefixes to the name of the chain, the positions and names of branches that replace hydrogen atoms on this chain (**substituents**). We number the carbon atoms by counting from the end of the chain nearest the substituents. The position of attachment of a substituent or branch is identified by the number of the carbon atom in the chain.

$$\overset{①\ ②\ ③}{CH_3CHCH_3} \qquad \overset{③\ ②\ ①}{CH_3CHCH_3}$$
$$\underset{Cl}{|} \qquad\qquad \underset{CH_3}{|}$$

2-Chloropropane   2-Methylpropane

When more than one substituent is present, either on the same carbon atom or on different carbon atoms, the substituents are usually listed alphabetically. In general, the longest continuous chain of carbon atoms is numbered in such a way as to produce the lowest number for the substituted atom(s) and/or group(s).

$$\overset{⑥\ ⑤\ ④\ ③\ ②\ ①}{CH_3CH_2CHCH_2CHCH_3} \qquad \overset{⑤\ ④\ ③\ ②\ ①}{CH_3CH_2CBr_2CH_2CH_2Cl}$$
$$\underset{F}{|}\quad\ \underset{F}{|}$$

2,4-Difluorohexane   3,3-Dibromo-1-chloropentane
not 3,5-Difluorohexane   *not* 3,3-Dibromo-6-chloropentane

Note that -*o* replaces -*ide* at the end of the name of an electronegative substituent and that the number of substituents of the same type is indicated by the prefixes *di*- (two), *tri*- (three), *tetra*- (four), etc. (for example, *difluoro*- indicates two fluoride substituents).

The longest continuous chain of carbon atoms in *n*-butane is four, but in isobutane the longest continuous chain of carbon atoms is only three, even though there are a total of four carbon atoms in the molecule. Hence, in IUPAC nomenclature, *n*-butane is called butane, but isobutane is 2-methylpropane.

A substituent that contains one less hydrogen than the corresponding alkane is called an **alkyl group.** The name of an alkyl group is obtained by dropping the suffix -*ane* of the alkane name and adding -*yl*. For example, methane becomes *methyl*, and ethane becomes *ethyl*.

Methane   The methyl group   Ethane   The ethyl group

The open bonds in the methyl and ethyl groups indicate that these groups are bonded to another atom.

Removal of any one of the four hydrogen atoms from methane forms a methyl group. These four hydrogen atoms are equivalent. Likewise, removing any one of the six equivalent hydrogen atoms in ethane gives an ethyl group. However, in both propane and 2-methylpropane there are two different types of hydrogen atoms, distinguished by the adjacent atoms or groups of atoms.

Propane   2-Methylpropane

Each of the six equivalent hydrogen atoms of the first type in propane and each of the nine equivalent hydrogen atoms of that type in 2-methylpropane (all shown in black) is

Table 30.2   Some Alkyl Groups

Alkyl Group	Structure
Methyl	CH_3-
Ethyl	CH_3CH_2-
n-Propyl	$CH_3CH_2CH_2-$
Isopropyl	$CH_3\overset{\vert}{C}HCH_3$
n-Butyl	$CH_3CH_2CH_2CH_2-$
sec-Butyl (where sec stands for secondary)	$CH_3CH_2\overset{\vert}{C}HCH_3$
Isobutyl	$CH_3\overset{\vert}{C}HCH_2-$ $\overset{\vert}{C}H_3$
t-Butyl (where t stands for tertiary)	$CH_3\overset{\vert}{\underset{\vert}{C}}CH_3$ CH_3

bonded to a **primary carbon,** a carbon atom bonded to only one other carbon atom. The two red hydrogen atoms in propane are of a second type. They differ from the six hydrogen atoms of the first type in that they are bonded to a **secondary carbon,** a carbon atom bonded to two other carbon atoms. The red hydrogen atom in 2-methylpropane differs from the other nine hydrogen atoms in that molecule; it is bonded to a **tertiary carbon,** a carbon atom bonded to three other carbon atoms. Two different alkyl groups can be formed from each of these molecules, depending on which hydrogen atom is removed. The names and structures of these and several other alkyl groups are listed in Table 30.2. Note that alkyl groups do not exist as stable independent entities. They are always part of some larger molecule. The location of an alkyl group on a hydrocarbon chain is indicated in the same way as any other substituent.

⑦ ⑥ ⑤ ④ ③ ② ①
$CH_3CH_2CH_2CH_2\overset{\vert}{C}HCH_2CH_3$
$\overset{\vert}{C_2H_5}$
3-Ethylheptane

$\overset{CH_3}{\underset{\vert}{\,}}\quad\overset{CH_3}{\underset{\vert}{\,}}$
① ②| ③ |④⑤
$CH_3\overset{\vert}{C}-CH_2\overset{\vert}{C}HCH_3$
$\overset{\vert}{C}H_3$
2,2,4-Trimethylpentane

Cycloalkanes are named in the same way as alkanes. The carbons in the ring are numbered, a substituted carbon being the first.

1-Chloro-2-isobutylcyclohexane

30.3 Alkenes

Organic compounds containing one or more multiple bonds are called **unsaturated** compounds. Hydrocarbon molecules that contain one or more double bonds are members of a series called **alkenes.** The two carbon atoms linked by a double bond are bound together by two bonds, one σ bond and one π bond (Section 8.11). The alkenes have the general molecular formula C_nH_{2n}.

Ethene, C_2H_4, historically called **ethylene,** is the simplest alkene. Each carbon atom in ethene has a trigonal planar structure, as illustrated in Fig. 8.26 in Section 8.11. The second member of the series is **propene (propylene);** the next members are the butene isomers. The series is analogous to the alkane series.

Ethene
(ethylene)

Propene
(propylene)

1-Butene

2-Butene

The IUPAC name of an alkene is derived from that of the alkane with the same number of carbon atoms. The presence of the double bond in the chain is indicated by replacing the suffix -*ane* with the suffix -*ene*. The location of the double bond in the chain is indicated by the lowest number that specifies the position of the first carbon atom in the double bond.

The carbon atoms involved in single bonds in alkenes have sp^3 hybridization, and those in double bonds have sp^2 hybridization. Thus the geometry around the carbon atoms at the double bonds is trigonal planar (Section 8.7). The molecular structure of propene is shown in Fig. 30.2.

Carbon atoms are free to rotate around a single bond but not around a double bond; a double bond is quite rigid. This makes it possible to have two separate isomers of 2-butene, one with both methyl groups on the same side of the double bond and one

Figure 30.2

Models of propene. (a) The molecular structure. (b) A ball-and-stick model. (c) A space-filling model.

(a)

(b)

(c)

Figure 30.3
Molecular models of the *cis* and *trans* isomers of 2-butene.

with the methyl groups on opposite sides (Fig. 30.3). When formulas of butene are written with 120° bond angles around the doubly bonded carbon atoms, the isomers are apparent.

1-Butene

cis isomer   *trans* isomer

2-Butene

The 2-butene isomer in which the two methyl groups are on the same side is called the *cis* isomer; the one in which the two methyl groups are opposite is called the *trans* isomer. In these **geometrical isomers,** the same types of atoms are attached to each other, but the geometries of the two molecules differ. (Recall that in Section 26.4 we discussed geometrical isomers for coordination compounds. It would be a good idea to review that section to see the analogy.) The different geometries produce different properties that make separation of the isomers possible.

Alkenes are much more reactive than alkanes. A π bond, being a weaker bond, is disrupted much more easily than a σ bond. Thus the reaction that is characteristic of alkenes is a type in which the π bond is broken and replaced by two σ bonds. Such a reaction is called an **addition reaction.** Addition reactions to produce saturated molecules are characteristic of unsaturated molecules.

In the presence of a suitable catalyst (Pt, Pd, or Ni, for example), alkenes undergo an addition reaction with hydrogen to form the corresponding alkanes.

Ethene   Ethane

Halogens add to the double bond in an alkene, instead of replacing a hydrogen as occurs in an alkane. For example,

Ethene   1,2-Dichloroethane

Many other reagents react with the double bond in alkenes. An example is the acid-catalyzed addition of water to an alkene to yield an alcohol (Section 30.9).

$$\underset{\text{Ethene}}{\underset{H}{\overset{H}{\diagdown}}C=C\underset{H}{\overset{H}{\diagup}}} + H_2O \xrightarrow{\underset{\text{catalyst}}{\text{Acid,}}} \underset{\text{Ethanol}}{H-\overset{\overset{\displaystyle H}{|}}{\underset{\underset{\displaystyle H}{|}}{C}}-\overset{\overset{\displaystyle H}{|}}{\underset{\underset{\displaystyle OH}{|}}{C}}-H}$$

Alkenes can add to themselves. This very important addition reaction gives polymers (see Section 2.12).

$$n\left(\underset{H}{\overset{H}{\diagdown}}C=C\underset{H}{\overset{H}{\diagup}}\right) \xrightarrow{\text{Catalyst}} \left(\!\!-\overset{\overset{\displaystyle H}{|}}{\underset{\underset{\displaystyle H}{|}}{C}}-\overset{\overset{\displaystyle H}{|}}{\underset{\underset{\displaystyle H}{|}}{C}}-\!\!\right)_{\!n} \qquad \text{(where } n \text{ is large)}$$

Ethene (ethylene) Polyethylene

Ethylene (ethene), a basic raw material used in making polyethylene and in other industrial reactions, is produced from ethane by pyrolysis reactions as described in Section 2.12. Almost 17.5 million tons of ethylene were produced in the United States in 1989 for use in the polymer, petrochemical, and plastics industries.

30.4 Alkynes

Hydrocarbon molecules with one or more triple bonds are called **alkynes;** they make up another series of unsaturated hydrocarbons. Two carbon atoms joined by a triple bond are bound together by one σ bond and two π bonds (Section 8.11). The alkynes have the general molecular formula C_nH_{2n-2}.

The simplest and most important member of the alkyne series is **ethyne, C_2H_2,** commonly called **acetylene.** The Lewis structure for ethyne is

$$H-C\equiv C-H$$

Ethyne (acetylene)

The bonding in the ethyne molecule, which has a linear structure, is illustrated in Fig. 8.29 in Section 8.11 and in Fig. 30.4.

The IUPAC nomenclature for alkynes is similar to that for alkenes except that the suffix *-yne* is used to indicate a triple bond in the chain.

$$\underset{\text{1-Butyne}}{\overset{\text{④ ③ ② ①}}{CH_3CH_2C\equiv CH}} \qquad \underset{\text{2-Methyl-3-hexyne}}{\overset{\text{⑥ ⑤ ④ ③②①}}{CH_3CH_2C\equiv C\underset{\underset{\displaystyle CH_3}{|}}{C}HCH_3}}$$

Chemically, the alkynes are similar to the alkenes except that having two π bonds, they react even more readily, adding twice as much reagent in addition reactions. The reaction of acetylene with bromine is a typical example.

$$H-C\equiv C-H + 2Br_2 \longrightarrow H-\overset{\overset{\displaystyle Br}{|}}{\underset{\underset{\displaystyle Br}{|}}{C}}-\overset{\overset{\displaystyle Br}{|}}{\underset{\underset{\displaystyle Br}{|}}{C}}-H$$

Tetrabromoethane

Figure 30.4

A space-filling model of ethyne.

Acetylene and the other alkynes burn very easily because of the highly exothermic nature of the reaction.

$$2H-C\equiv C-H(g) + 5O_2(g) \longrightarrow 4CO_2(g) + 2H_2O(g) \qquad \Delta H° = -2511.2 \text{ kJ}$$

The flame from burning acetylene is very hot; it is used in welding and cutting metal (see Fig. 4.1). When acetylene burns, some of it breaks down a second way according to the equation

$$2C_2H_2(g) + O_2(g) \longrightarrow 4C(s) + 2H_2O(g)$$

At the temperature of the flame, the particles of carbon give off a brilliant white light. At one time acetylene was used to light homes and in bicycle and automobile lamps; acetylene lamps are still used by some who work in or explore caves.

30.5 Aromatic Hydrocarbons

Benzene, C₆H₆, is the simplest member of a large family of hydrocarbons, called **aromatic hydrocarbons,** that contain ring structures. The benzene molecule contains a hexagonal ring of sp^2-hybridized carbon atoms with the unhybridized p orbital of each one perpendicular to the ring. The electronic structure of benzene can be described as a resonance hybrid of two Lewis structures (see Section 7.8).

Three valence electrons in the sp^2 hybrid orbitals of each carbon atom and the valence electron of each hydrogen atom form the framework of sigma bonds in the benzene molecule (Fig. 30.5). The unhybridized carbon p orbitals, each with one electron, combine to form π bonds. As shown in Figs. 30.6 and 30.7, the electrons in the π bonds are delocalized around the ring, because the electronic structure is the average of the resonance forms. Because the π electrons are delocalized, benzene does not have alkene character. Each bond between two carbon atoms is neither a single nor a double bond but

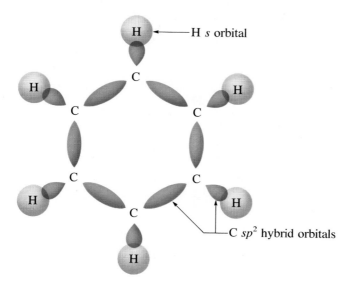

Figure 30.5

The overlapping sp^2 hybrid orbitals of the carbon atoms and s orbitals of the hydrogen atoms that form σ bonds in a benzene ring.

Figure 30.6

The π overlap in a benzene molecule. Hydrogen atoms have been omitted for clarity. The six sp^2-hybridized carbon atoms lie in a plane. The six unhybridized p orbitals, shown in color in (a) and (c), extend above and below the plane and are perpendicular to it. The dashed lines between lobes of p orbitals indicate side-by-side overlap. The overlap occurs in either direction between adjacent lobes, as shown in (a) and (c). The resulting π orbitals are shown in (b) and (d), with the orbital portion of each (in color) lying above and below the hexagonal plane. The resonance forms in (a) and (c) and in (b) and (d) are exactly equivalent. The true structure is an average (hybrid) of the two (see Fig. 30.7).

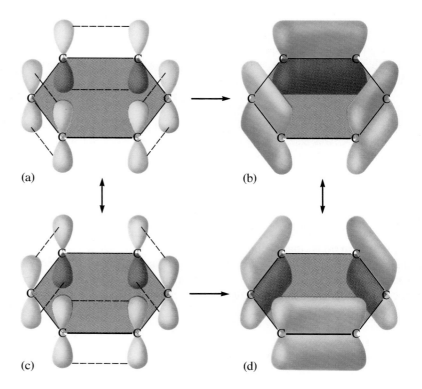

(a)   (b)

(c)   (d)

is intermediate in character (a hybrid). Each bond is equivalent to the others and has a bond order of $1\frac{1}{2}$. Although benzene is often written as one of its resonance forms in chemical formulas, it is important to remember that *all of the carbon–carbon bonds in benzene are equivalent*. The structure of benzene is sometimes written with a circle within the ring (as in the right-hand structure on page 963) to emphasize the fact that the bonds are equivalent and the electrons delocalized.

The π bonding in benzene can be described by the molecular orbital model. The six unhybridized p orbitals can be combined to give three π bonding molecular orbitals and three π antibonding molecular orbitals (Section 9.1). The six electrons (as three pairs) from the unhybridized p orbitals occupy the three π bonding molecular orbitals. These π bonding molecular orbitals are shown in Fig. 30.8.

There are many derivatives of benzene. The hydrogen atoms can be replaced by many different substituents. The following are typical examples.

Toluene   Styrene   Bromobenzene

Figure 30.7

The distribution of π electrons in a benzene molecule.

Xylene is a derivative of benzene in which two hydrogen atoms have been replaced by methyl groups. Xylene has three isomers because the two methyl groups can occupy three different relative positions on the ring.

o-Xylene   *m*-Xylene   *p*-Xylene

Any disubstituted benzene can take one of these three structurally different (isomeric) forms. The relative positions of the two substituents are indicated by the prefixes *o*- (*ortho*-; 1,2 positions), *m*- (*meta*-; 1,3 positions), and *p*- (*para*-; 1,4 positions).

Some important aromatic hydrocarbons and their derivatives contain more than one ring. Examples include naphthalene, $C_{10}H_8$, found in moth balls; anthracene, $C_{14}H_{10}$; and benzpyrene, $C_{20}H_{12}$.

Figure 30.8
The three filled π bonding molecular orbitals in benzene.

Naphthalene   Anthracene   Benzpyrene

Aromatic hydrocarbons are widely used in manufacturing dyes, pharmaceuticals, explosives, and plastics. For example, the important explosive trinitrotoluene (TNT), $C_6H_2(CH_3)(NO_2)_3$, is synthesized from toluene by replacing three hydrogen atoms with nitro groups, —NO_2.

2,4,6-Trinitrotoluene

30.6 Isomerism

Isomers are molecules with identical chemical formulas but different arrangements of the atoms. Thus far we have seen two kinds of isomerism: structural and geometrical. Structural isomers (Section 30.1) are molecules with different arrangements of bonds, such as *n*-butane and 2-methylpropane or the three isomers of xylene (Section 30.5).

Geometrical isomers have the same atoms bonded in the same order, but some parts of the two molecules have different relative spatial arrangements. In *cis* and *trans* isomers of organic compounds, for example, groups are arranged either on the same side (*cis*) or on different sides (*trans*) of bonds that cannot rotate (Section 30.3). Recall, too, that we pointed out in Section 26.4 the existence of geometrical *cis* and *trans* isomers for certain coordination compounds.

Other isomers, called **optical isomers,** make up a category of isomerism that is also characteristic of some coordination compounds (Section 26.4). Optical isomers are detected by their effect on polarized light. Ordinary light is composed of rays that vibrate in all planes parallel to the direction in which the light travels. When ordinary light is passed through a polarizer, such as is used in Polaroid sunglasses or a Nicol prism, only light that vibrates in one plane is transmitted (Fig. 30.9). Such light is called **plane-polarized light.** The direction of the plane in which the light vibrates can be detected by using another polarizer. When a beam of plane-polarized light passes through a solution containing a single form of an optical isomer, the plane of vibration of the light is rotated (Fig. 30.10). Molecules that rotate the plane of vibration of plane-polarized light are **optically active molecules.** The amount of rotation and (thus) the optical activity vary from compound to compound.

A compound that forms optical isomers exists as at least two different forms. One of these isomers rotates plane-polarized light clockwise; such an isomer is called a **dextro-rotatory isomer** or a + isomer. The other isomer rotates plane-polarized light counter-clockwise by an amount exactly equal to the clockwise rotation of the + isomer. The second isomer is called a **levorotatory isomer** or a − isomer. A mixture of equal amounts of a dextrorotatory isomer and a levorotatory isomer of the same substance shows no rotation of plane-polarized light because the effects of the two isomers cancel. In most properties, such as melting point, boiling point, and solubility, optical isomers exhibit identical characteristics. However, optical isomers may exhibit different degrees of reactivity in reactions with other optically active compounds.

Optical isomers of a compound have the same relationship to each other as that of a right hand to a left hand. Both have the same shape and the same order of attachment of

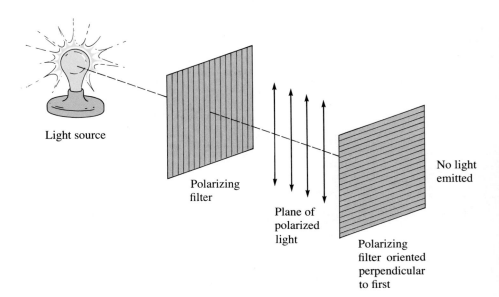

Figure 30.9

When light is passed through a polarizer, only light that vibrates in one plane is transmitted.

Light source

Polarizing filter

Plane of polarized light

Polarizing filter oriented perpendicular to first

No light emitted

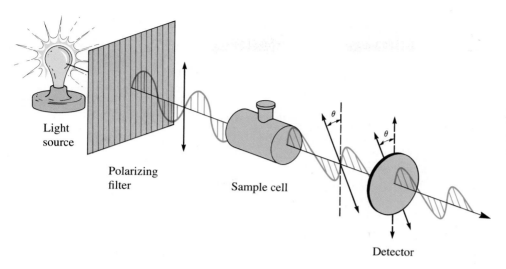

Figure 30.10

When a beam of plane-polarized light passes through a solution containing a single form of an optical isomer, the plane of vibration is rotated by an angle θ that is characteristic for that isomer. The other optical isomer will rotate the plane of vibration of the light by the same angle in the opposite direction $(-\theta)$.

the various parts to one another; they are almost alike. However, they differ in that they are mirror images of each other. Just as your right and left hands cannot be superimposed, two optical isomers of a molecule cannot be superimposed, no matter how they are rotated. Figure 30.11 illustrates the mirror relationship for a hand, for the molecule CHClBrI, and for the amino acid alanine. Note that molecules that contain sp^3-hybrid-

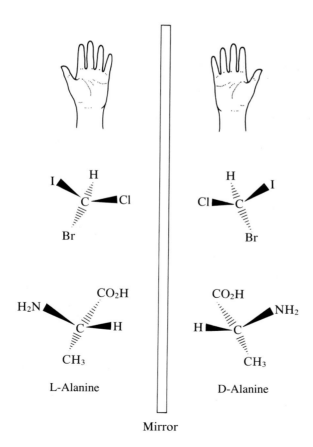

Figure 30.11

Mirror images of a hand, the molecule CHClBrI, and the molecule alanine. Although these objects have the same composition and are the same size and shape, their mirror images cannot be superimposed.

Figure 30.12

The structure of L-cysteine.

ized carbon atoms form optical isomers only when a carbon atom is bonded to four different groups; such a carbon atom within a molecule is referred to as an **asymmetric carbon.**

Practically all optically active molecules found in nature are found as only one of the two possible isomers. For example, the amino acids found in proteins (Section 31.2) are all of the type designated as L (levorotatory). The structure of L-cysteine, one of these amino acids, is shown in Fig. 30.12.

A striking example of the effect of optical activity is found in the oils responsible for the scents of spearmint and caraway seeds. Both oils are composed of a cyclic compound called carvone. However, caraway seed oil contains D-carvone (D stands for dextrorotatory), and spearmint oil contains the other optical isomer, L-carvone.

30 .7 Petroleum

Petroleum is composed chiefly of saturated hydrocarbons, but it may also contain unsaturated hydrocarbons, aromatic hydrocarbons, and their derivatives. The main step in refining petroleum is distilling it into a number of fractions (fractional distillation; Section 12.16), each of which is a complex mixture of hydrocarbons with properties that make it valuable. Additional purification is usually necessary before these fractions can be used. Some of the more important hydrocarbon products derived from the refining of petroleum are listed in Table 30.3.

Gasoline, a mixture of n-hexane, n-heptane, n-octane, and their alkane isomers, is rated on an arbitrary scale in which isooctane (2,2,4-trimethylpentane), once thought to be the ideal fuel for gasoline engines, is given a rating, or octane number, of 100. Gasolines with octane numbers less than 100 are less efficient than isooctane, and those with higher numbers are more efficient.

Derivatives of Hydrocarbons

30 .8 Introduction

Derivatives of hydrocarbons result from the replacement of one or more hydrogen atoms with other atoms, or groups of atoms, called functional groups (Section 30.1). An alcohol is a compound in which an —OH group replaces a hydrogen atom of a hydrocarbon. Methanol, CH_3OH, is related to methane [Fig. 30.13(a)]; ethanol, C_2H_5OH (Section 30.3), is related to ethane [Fig. 30.13(b)]. The general formula for an alcohol is

Figure 30.13

(a) The molecular structures of methane and methanol. (b) The molecular structures of ethane and ethanol.

Methane   Methanol   Ethane   Ethanol

(a)   (b)

Table 30.3	Some Hydrocarbon Products from Petroleum		
	Approximate Composition	Boiling Point Range, °C	Uses
Petroleum ether	C_4 to C_{10}	35–80	Solvent
Gasoline	C_4 to C_{13}	40–225	Motor fuel
Kerosene	C_{10} to C_{16}	175–300	Fuel, lighting
Lubricating oils	C_{20} up	350 up	Lubrication
Paraffin	C_{23} to C_{29}	50–60 (mp)	Candles, waxed paper
Asphalt		Viscous liquids	Paving, roofing
Coke		Solid	Fuel

written R—OH; where R stands for the portion of the molecule other than the functional group; for example, R might represent an alkyl group.

The following sections describe the properties of some specific hydrocarbon derivatives. Take careful note of their functional groups, because many properties of a class of compounds are due to the functional group.

30.9 Alcohols, R—OH

All **alcohols** have one or more hydroxyl (—OH) functional groups, yet they do not behave like bases such as sodium hydroxide and potassium hydroxide. They do not form hydroxide ions in water, nor do they have the other usual properties of bases.

Methanol, or **methyl alcohol, CH₃OH,** is produced commercially from either carbon monoxide or carbon dioxide.

$$CO + 2H_2 \xrightarrow{Ag \text{ or } Cu} CH_3OH$$

$$CO_2 + 3H_2 \longrightarrow CH_3OH + H_2O$$

Methanol is a colorless liquid that boils at 65°C. It smells and tastes like ethyl alcohol. However, methanol is poisonous—breathing the vapor or drinking the liquid may cause blindness or death. Methanol is used in the manufacture of formaldehyde and other organic products; as a solvent for resins, gums, and shellac; and in the denaturing of ethyl alcohol (making it unsafe to drink).

Ethanol, C₂H₅OH, also called **ethyl alcohol, grain alcohol,** or simply **alcohol,** is the most important of the alcohols. It has long been prepared by fermentation of starch, cellulose, and various sugars (Fig. 30.14).

$$C_6H_{12}O_6 \xrightarrow{\text{Enzymes in yeast}} 2C_2H_5OH + 2CO_2(g)$$
Glucose   Ethanol

Large quantities of ethanol are synthesized from ethylene or acetylene. The synthesis from ethylene is summarized by the equation

Figure 30.14

The conversion of sugar in grape juice to alcohol by the enzymes in certain yeasts produces wine.

Ethanol is a colorless liquid with a characteristic and somewhat pleasant odor. It is miscible with water in all proportions. The boiling point of pure ethanol is 78.37°C. It is the least toxic of all the alcohols and is found in all alcoholic beverages. It is used as a solvent in tinctures, essences, and extracts; in the preparation of iodoform, ether, dyes, perfumes, and collodion; as a solvent in the lacquer industry; and to some extent as a motor fuel. It is currently used as an additive in some brands of unleaded gasoline.

The chemistry of alcohols is governed to some degree by whether the hydroxyl group is bonded to a carbon atom that is bonded to one, two, or three other carbon atoms. Alcohols are designated **primary**, **secondary**, or **tertiary**, depending on whether one, two, or three R groups are bonded to the hydroxyl carbon.

$$\begin{array}{ccc}
\overset{\displaystyle H}{\underset{\displaystyle H}{R-C-OH}} & \overset{\displaystyle H}{\underset{\displaystyle R}{R-C-OH}} & \overset{\displaystyle R}{\underset{\displaystyle R}{R-C-OH}} \\[2mm]
\text{Primary} & \text{Secondary} & \text{Tertiary} \\
\text{alcohol} & \text{alcohol} & \text{alcohol}
\end{array}$$

Alcohols containing two or more hydroxyl groups can be made. Important examples are 1,2-ethanediol (ethylene glycol), $C_2H_4(OH)_2$, and 1,2,3-propanetriol (glycerol), $C_3H_5(OH)_3$.

$$\begin{array}{cc}
\overset{\displaystyle H}{\underset{\displaystyle H}{\underset{\displaystyle |}{\overset{\displaystyle |}{H-C-OH}}}} & \overset{\displaystyle H}{\underset{}{H-C-OH}} \\[2mm]
H-C-OH & H-C-OH \\[2mm]
H & H-C-OH \\[2mm]
 & H \\[2mm]
\text{Ethylene glycol} & \text{Glycerol}
\end{array}$$

Ethylene glycol is used as a solvent and as an antifreeze in automobile radiators. Glycerol (also called glycerin) is produced, along with soap, when either fats or oils are heated with an alkali metal hydroxide.

An alcohol's name comes from the hydrocarbon from which it is derived. The hydrocarbon's final -*e* is replaced by -*ol*, and the carbon atom to which the —OH group is bonded is indicated by a number placed before the name.

30.10 Ethers, R—O—R

Ethers are compounds obtained from alcohols by the elimination of a molecule of water from two molecules of the alcohol. For example, when ethanol is treated with a limited amount of sulfuric acid and heated to 140°C, **diethyl ether** and water are formed.

Diethyl ether

In the general formula for ethers, R—O—R, the hydrocarbon groups (R) may be the same or different. Diethyl ether is the most important compound of this class. It is a colorless, volatile liquid (boiling point = 35°C) that is highly flammable. It has been used since 1846 as an anesthetic, though better anesthetics have largely taken its place. Diethyl ether and other ethers are valuable solvents for gums, fats, waxes, and resins.

30.11 Aldehydes, R—C—H

Alcohols represent the first stage of oxidation of hydrocarbons. Further oxidation produces **aldehydes,** compounds containing the group —CHO. Aldehydes are generally made by the oxidation of primary alcohols.

When a mixture of methanol and air is passed through a heated tube containing either silver or a mixture of iron powder and molybdenum oxide, the simplest aldehyde, called **formaldehyde, HCHO,** is formed.

Methanol   Formaldehyde

Formaldehyde is a colorless gas with a pungent and irritating odor; it is soluble in water in all proportions. Formaldehyde is sold in an aqueous solution called **formalin,** which contains about 37% formaldehyde by weight. The solution also contains 7% methanol, which is added to inhibit the formation of an insoluble polymer that occurs when formaldehyde molecules react with one another. In fact, one of the early polymers, Bakelite, a type of plastic having high chemical and electrical resistance, is a formaldehyde polymer that made formaldehyde industrially important. Formaldehyde causes coagulation of proteins, so it is used to preserve tissue specimens and to embalm bodies. It is also useful as a disinfectant and as a reducing agent in the production of silvered mirrors.

Acetaldehyde, CH_3CHO, boils at 20.2°C. It is colorless and water-soluble and smells like freshly cut green apples. It is used in the manufacture of aniline dyes, synthetic rubber, and other organic materials.

The systematic names of aldehydes are formed by replacing the *-e* ending of the parent alkane by *-al*. Acetaldehyde is the common name for ethanal. The chain is numbered with the —CHO group as the first carbon. Thus 3-methyl-butanal is

$$
\overset{④}{CH_3}-\overset{③}{\underset{\underset{CH_3}{|}}{CH}}-\overset{②}{CH_2}-\overset{①}{C}\overset{\displaystyle O}{\underset{\displaystyle H}{\diagup}}
$$

30.12 Ketones, $R-\overset{\displaystyle O}{\overset{\|}{C}}-R$

Ketones, like aldehydes, contain the **carbonyl group,** $C{=}O$. In fact, a ketone may be regarded as an aldehyde in which the hydrogen in the aldehyde group is replaced by a hydrocarbon group. In the general structural formula for ketones (see section heading), the R groups may be the same or different. Ketones are often prepared by the oxidation of secondary alcohols.

Dimethyl ketone, CH_3COCH_3, commonly called **acetone,** is the simplest and most important ketone. It is made commercially by fermenting corn or molasses or by dehydrogenation of 2-propanol (isopropyl alcohol).

$$
\underset{\text{2-Propanol}}{CH_3\overset{\overset{\displaystyle OH}{|}}{C}HCH_3} \xrightarrow[\text{Cu catalyst}]{350°C} \underset{\text{Dimethyl ketone}}{CH_3\overset{\overset{\displaystyle O}{\|}}{C}CH_3} + H_2
$$

It is also a product of the destructive distillation of wood. Acetone is a colorless liquid that boils at 56.5°C and has a characteristic pungent odor and a sweet taste. Among the many uses of acetone are as a solvent for cellulose acetate, cellulose nitrate, acetylene, plastics, and varnishes; as a paint, varnish, and fingernail polish remover; and as a solvent in the manufacture of pharmaceuticals, chemicals, smokeless powder, and the explosive cordite.

30.13 Carboxylic Acids, R—C(=O)—OH

$$R—\overset{\displaystyle O}{\overset{\|}{C}}—OH$$

Carboxylic acids contain the **carboxyl group, —CO₂H.** They are usually weak acids, yet they readily form metal salts. Carboxylic acids may be prepared by the oxidation of primary alcohols or of aldehydes.

$$RCH_2OH \xrightarrow{\text{Oxidation}} R—C\overset{H}{\underset{O}{\big<}} \xrightarrow{\text{Oxidation}} R—C\overset{OH}{\underset{O}{\big<}}$$

| Primary alcohol | Aldehyde | Carboxylic acid |

The simplest carboxylic acid is **formic acid, HCO₂H,** known since 1670. Its name comes from the Latin word *formicus,* which means ''ant''; it was first isolated via the distillation of red ants. It is partially responsible for the irritation of ant bites.

Acetic acid, CH₃CO₂H, constitutes 3–6% of vinegar. Cider vinegar is produced by allowing apple juice to ferment, which changes the sugar present to ethanol, then to acetic acid. Pure, anhydrous acetic acid, sometimes called **glacial acetic acid,** boils at 118.1°C and freezes at 16.6°C. Pure acetic acid has a penetrating odor and produces painful burns. It is an excellent solvent for many organic and some inorganic compounds. Acetic acid is essential in the production of cellulose acetate, a component of many synthetic fibers such as rayon.

Dicarboxylic acids contain two carboxyl groups. Oxalic acid, (CO₂H)₂, consists of two carboxyl groups (dicarboxylic) bonded together.

$$\underset{O}{\overset{HO}{\big>}}C—C\underset{O}{\overset{OH}{\big<}}$$

Oxalic acid

Oxalic acid is a colorless crystalline solid found as a metal hydrogen salt in sorrel, rhubarb, and other plants, to which it imparts a sour taste. In concentrated form it is poisonous.

Benzoic acid, C₆H₅CO₂H, is a colorless crystalline solid with a cyclic structure. It is a monocarboxylic acid that occurs in cranberries and coal tar. The sodium salt of benzoic acid, **sodium benzoate,** is used to preserve foods such as tomato ketchup and fruit juices.

Benzoic acid

30.14 Esters, $R-\overset{\displaystyle O}{\underset{\displaystyle \|}{C}}-OR$

Esters are produced by the reaction of acids with alcohols. For example, the ester **ethyl acetate, $CH_3CO_2C_2H_5$,** is formed when acetic acid reacts with ethanol.

$$CH_3-\overset{\displaystyle O}{\underset{\displaystyle OH}{C}} \;+\; HOC_2H_5 \;\longrightarrow\; CH_3-\overset{\displaystyle O}{\underset{\displaystyle O-C_2H_5}{C}} \;+\; H_2O$$

The distinctive and attractive odors and flavors of many flowers, perfumes, and ripe fruits are due to the presence of one or more esters (Fig. 30.15). Among the most important of the natural esters are fats (such as lard, tallow, and butter) and oils (such as linseed, cottonseed, and olive), which are esters of the trihydroxyl alcohol (triol) glycerol, $C_3H_5(OH)_3$ (Section 30.9) with large carboxylic acids such as palmitic acid, $CH_3(CH_2)_{14}COOH$; stearic acid, $CH_3(CH_2)_{16}COOH$; and oleic acid, $CH_3(CH_2)_7CH{=}CH(CH_2)_7COOH$.

"Fatty acids" are actually esters of organic acids that occur in fats (solids) and oils (liquids). A general formula for fats and oils is

$$\begin{array}{l} R\overset{\displaystyle O}{\underset{\displaystyle \|}{C}}-O-CH_2 \\[6pt] R\overset{\displaystyle O}{\underset{\displaystyle \|}{C}}-O-CH_2 \\[6pt] R\overset{\displaystyle O}{\underset{\displaystyle \|}{C}}-O-CH_2 \end{array}$$

where R may be the same or different in the three locations. In general, when R is saturated the ester is a solid (fat), and when R is unsaturated the ester is a liquid (oil). How much fatty acids we consume and whether they are saturated or unsaturated fatty acids have a significant effect on our health.

Table 30.4 summarizes several important types of hydrocarbon derivatives, the corresponding functional groups, their general formulas and some typical examples.

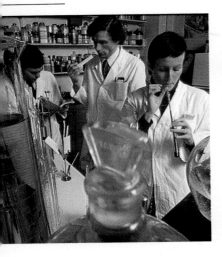

Figure 30.15

Chemists carry out sniff tests on perfumes produced by reactions of organic compounds.

Natural Organic Compounds

30.15 Introduction

Many naturally occurring organic compounds have unique properties and structures. They frequently have potent biological properties and are sometimes important medically. These compounds are often found in nature as a single geometrical or optical isomer (Section 30.6). The strategies that must be employed to duplicate nature's work

Table 30.4   **Several Types of Hydrocarbon Derivatives**

Derivative Type	Functional Group	General Formula	Typical Examples
Alcohols	—OH	R—OH	CH_3CH_2—OH Ethanol (a primary alcohol) $\overset{\displaystyle OH}{\underset{\displaystyle \vert}{CH_3CHCH_3}}$ 2-Propanol (a secondary alcohol) $\overset{\displaystyle OH}{\underset{\displaystyle \vert}{CH_3\underset{\underset{\displaystyle CH_3}{\vert}}{C}CH_3}}$ 2-Methyl-2-propanol (a tertiary alcohol)
Ethers	—O—	R—O—R	CH_3—O—C_2H_5 C_2H_5—O—C_2H_5 Methyl ethyl ether Diethyl ether
Amines	$-N\!\!\big\langle$	$R-N\!\!\big\langle \!\!\begin{array}{c} H \\ H \end{array}$	CH_3—NH_2 Methylamine (a primary amine)
		$\begin{array}{c} R \\ R \end{array}\!\!\big\rangle N-H$	$(C_2H_5)_2$—NH Diethylamine (a secondary amine)
		$\begin{array}{c} R \\ R \end{array}\!\!\big\rangle N-R$	$(C_3H_7)_3N$ Tri-n-propylamine (a tertiary amine)
Thiols	—SH	R—SH	C_2H_5—SH Ethanethiol
Aldehydes	$\overset{\displaystyle O}{\underset{}{-CH}}$ ‖	$\overset{\displaystyle O}{\underset{}{R-CH}}$ ‖	$\overset{\displaystyle O}{\underset{}{H-CH}}$ ‖ $\overset{\displaystyle O}{\underset{}{CH_3-CH}}$ ‖ Formaldehyde Acetaldehyde
Ketones	$\overset{\displaystyle O}{\underset{}{-C-}}$ ‖	$\overset{\displaystyle O}{\underset{}{R-C-R}}$ ‖	$\overset{\displaystyle O}{\underset{}{CH_3-C-CH_3}}$ ‖ $\overset{\displaystyle O}{\underset{}{CH_3-C-C_6H_5}}$ ‖ Dimethyl ketone Methyl phenyl ketone
Acids	$\overset{\displaystyle O}{\underset{}{-COH}}$ ‖	$\overset{\displaystyle O}{\underset{}{R-COH}}$ ‖	$\overset{\displaystyle O}{\underset{}{CH_3COH}}$ ‖ $\overset{\displaystyle O}{\underset{}{C_6H_5COH}}$ ‖ Acetic acid Benzoic acid

(continued)

Table 30.4		(Continued)				
Derivative Type	Functional Group	General Formula	Typical Examples		
Esters	$\overset{O}{\overset{\|}{-C}OR}$	$R-\overset{O}{\overset{\|}{C}OR}$	$CH_3\overset{O}{\overset{\|}{C}OC_2H_5}$ Ethyl acetate	$C_3H_7\overset{O}{\overset{\|}{C}OC_2H_5}$ Ethyl butyrate	
Salts	$\overset{O}{\overset{\|}{-C}O^-M^+}$	$R-\overset{O}{\overset{\|}{C}O^-M^+}$	$CH_3\overset{O}{\overset{\|}{C}O^-Na^+}$ Sodium acetate	$C_2H_5\overset{O}{\overset{\|}{C}O^-K^+}$ Potassium propionate	
Amides	$\overset{O}{\overset{\|}{-C}NH_2}$	$R-\overset{O}{\overset{\|}{C}NH_2}$	$CH_3\overset{O}{\overset{\|}{C}NH_2}$ Acetamide	$C_6H_5\overset{O}{\overset{\|}{C}NH_2}$ Benzamide	

in the laboratory can be very difficult. However, such studies can result in important chemical discoveries and new commercial products. Once a **natural product** is artificially synthesized, variations on the synthesis can be attempted and structural analogs of the natural product prepared. These studies can lead to the production of important pharmaceuticals. There are many different classes of natural products, and we will consider two of those classes.

30.16 Pheromones

Human beings communicate orally, by using sign language, by writing, and by drawing pictures. Some organisms clearly communicate by chemicals. Such chemicals are called pheromones (derived from the Greek *phero,* which means "carrier"). A **pheromone** is a chemical or a mixture of chemicals that is secreted by an individual of a species and elicits a response in another individual of the same species.

Insect pheromones can be classified by their functions. Alarm pheromones signify danger, sex-attractant pheromones help the different sexes of the same species to locate one another, and recruiting pheromones are used to alert other members of the species to the existence of a food source.

It requires only a very small amount of a pheromone to elicit the desired response. It has been reported that a typical female insect may carry only 10^{-8} grams of sex attractant, but that is enough to draw over a billion males from an area of several miles. A male gypsy moth is said to be able to detect sex attractant from a female from as far away as seven miles!

Although many known insect pheromones are not complex in structure, their biological activity is usually dependent on the isomeric form; one geometrical or optical isomer is active and any other isomer is inactive. Pheromone chemistry is an exciting and vigorous field of research, and pheromones are of immediate practical value. For example, sex-attractant pheromones can be used for insect control. Male insects may be drawn by a pheromone to a trap where they can be sterilized and released to mate unproductively with wild females (Fig. 30.16). Three sex-attractant pheromones are shown as follows:

Figure 30.16

A trap for boll weevils that utilizes a sex-attractant pheromone.

$(CH_3)_2CH(CH_2)_4CH{-}CH(CH_2)_9CH_3$

Gypsy moth pheromone

$cis{-}CH_3(CH_2)_{12}CH{=}CH(CH_2)_7CH_3$

House fly pheromone

Boll weevil
pheromone

㉚.17 Alkaloids

Since ancient times, plants have been used for medicinal purposes. The active substances in many of these plants have been isolated and found to contain cyclic molecules
with nitrogen atoms. These nitrogen atoms possess an unshared pair of electrons and are
thus bases. They can react with H_3O^+ in dilute acid to form an ammonium salt, and this
is how they are extracted from the plant.

$$R_3N{:} + H_3O^+ + Cl^- \xrightarrow{H_2O} R_3NH^+Cl^- + H_2O$$

The name **alkaloid** means ''like an alkali''—that is, an alkaloid reacts with acid.
The free compound can then be obtained by reaction with aqueous base.

$$R_3NH^+Cl^- + OH^- \longrightarrow R_3N{:} + H_2O + Cl^-$$

The structures of several naturally occurring alkaloids that have profound physiological
effects in humans are shown below. Carbon atoms in the rings and the hydrogen atoms
bonded to them have been omitted for clarity.

Nicotine

Morphine

Codeine

Heroin

Polymers

㉚.18 Introduction

Polymers and **plastics,** compounds of very high molecular masses, are built up of a
large number of smaller molecules, or **monomers,** that have reacted with one another.
Cellulose, starch, proteins, and rubber are natural polymers (although most rubber in use
is a synthetic polymer). Nylon, rayon, polyethylene, and Dacron are synthetic polymers.

Polymers are used in clothing, fibers, insulation, and construction materials. Recently they have also come to be used in cars (Fig. 2.9) to reduce weight and thus save gasoline. However, these polymers are themselves made from petroleum, which offsets part of the advantage of the lower gasoline consumption.

30.19 Rubber

Natural rubber comes mainly from latex, the sap of the rubber tree. Rubber consists of very long molecules, which are polymers formed by the union of isoprene units, C_5H_8.

$$\underset{\text{Isoprene}}{CH_2{=}\overset{\overset{\displaystyle CH_3}{|}}{C}{-}CH{=}CH_2} + \underset{\text{Isoprene}}{CH_2{=}\overset{\overset{\displaystyle CH_3}{|}}{C}{-}CH{=}CH_2} \longrightarrow$$

$$\underset{\text{Polyisoprene (rubber)}}{\cdots {-}CH_2{-}\overset{\overset{\displaystyle CH_3}{|}}{C}{=}CH{-}CH_2{-}CH_2{-}\overset{\overset{\displaystyle CH_3}{|}}{C}{=}CH{-}CH_2{\cdots}}$$

The number of isoprene units in a rubber molecule is about 2000, so it has a molecular mass of approximately 136,000.

Rubber has the undesirable property of becoming sticky when warmed, but this can be eliminated by **vulcanization.** Rubber is vulcanized by heating it with sulfur to about 140°C. During the process, sulfur atoms add at the double bonds in the linear polymer and form bridges that bind one rubber molecule to another. In this way, a linear polymer is converted into a three-dimensional polymer. During vulcanization, fillers are added to increase the wearing qualities of the rubber and to color it. Among the substances used as fillers are carbon black (black), zinc oxide (white), and titanium dioxide (white).

Synthetic rubbers resemble natural rubber and are often superior to it in certain respects. For example, neoprene is a synthetic polymer with rubberlike properties.

$$n\,CH_2{=}CH{-}\underset{\underset{\displaystyle Cl}{|}}{C}{=}CH_2 \xrightarrow{\text{Polymerization}} \left[{-}CH_2{-}CH{=}\underset{\underset{\displaystyle Cl}{|}}{C}{-}CH_2{-} \right]_n$$

Chloroprene   Neoprene

The monomer chloroprene is similar to isoprene, except that a chlorine atom replaces the methyl group. Neoprene is more elastic than natural rubber, resists abrasion well, and is less affected by oil and gasoline. It is used for making gasoline and oil hoses, automobile and refrigerator parts, electrical insulation, and sports clothing (wet suits). There are many other synthetic elastomers of this type.

Both natural rubber and neoprene are examples of **addition polymers,** polymers that form by addition reactions (Section 30.3).

30.20 Synthetic Fibers

The synthetic fiber nylon is a **condensation polymer.** In a condensation polymerization reaction, some of the atoms of the monomers are lost as water, ammonia, carbon dioxide, and so on. Nylon is made from hexamethylenediamine, which contains an amine

Figure 30.17
A strand of raw nylon may be drawn from the film of nylon that forms at the interface between solutions of the two monomers involved in this synthesis.

group (—NH$_2$) at both ends, and adipic acid, which contains a carboxylic acid group (—CO$_2$H) at both ends (Fig. 30.17). During condensation, linkages of the type R—NH—CO—R are formed and water is eliminated. The part shown in color is an **amide linkage.**

$$NH_2-(CH_2)_6-N\!-\!H + HO\!-\!\overset{\overset{O}{\|}}{C}-(CH_2)_4-\overset{\overset{O}{\|}}{C}OH \longrightarrow NH_2-(CH_2)_6-NH-\overset{\overset{O}{\|}}{C}-(CH_2)_4-\overset{\overset{O}{\|}}{C}OH + H_2O$$

Hexamethylenediamine   Adipic acid

Because the molecule resulting from the condensation has an —NH$_2$ group at one end and a —CO$_2$H group at the other, the condensation process can be repeated many times to form a linear polymer of great length.

$$(n + 1)H_2N(CH_2)_6NH_2 + (n + 1)HO_2C(CH_2)_4CO_2H \longrightarrow$$
Hexamethylenediamine   Adipic acid

$$H_2N(CH_2)_6NH\!-\!\!\left[\overset{\overset{O}{\|}}{C}(CH_2)_4\overset{\overset{O}{\|}}{C}NH(CH_2)_6NH\right]_n\!\!\overset{\overset{O}{\|}}{C}(CH_2)_4CO_2H + 2nH_2O$$
Nylon

Fine threads are produced by extruding melted nylon through tiny holes in a spinneret. Nylon is used in hosiery and other clothing, bristles for toothbrushes, surgical sutures, strings for tennis rackets, fishing line leaders, and many other products.

Dacron is made from ethylene glycol and terephthalic acid by a condensation process that forms an ester linkage. Dacron is one of the family of polyesters.

$$(n + 1)HO\overset{H\ H}{\underset{H\ H}{C\!-\!C}}OH + (n + 1)HO_2C-C\overset{\overset{H\ \ H}{C\!-\!C}}{\underset{\underset{H\ \ H}{C\!=\!C}}{}}C-CO_2H \longrightarrow$$

Ethylene   Terephthalic acid
glycol

$$HO\overset{H\ H}{\underset{H\ H}{C\!-\!C}}O\!-\!\!\left[\overset{\overset{O}{\|}}{C}-C\overset{\overset{H\ \ H}{C\!-\!C}}{\underset{\underset{H\ \ H}{C\!=\!C}}{}}C-\overset{\overset{O}{\|}}{C}-O-\overset{H\ H}{\underset{H\ H}{C\!-\!C}}-O\right]_n\!\!\overset{\overset{O}{\|}}{C}-C\overset{\overset{H\ \ H}{C\!-\!C}}{\underset{\underset{H\ \ H}{C\!=\!C}}{}}C-CO_2H + 2nH_2O$$

Dacron

30 .21 Polyethylene

Polyethylene is widely used and results from the polymerization of ethylene (Section 30.3). It is a flexible, tough polymer that is very water-resistant and has excellent insulating properties. It is used in plastic bottles, bags for fruits and vegetables, and many other items (Fig. 30.18).

If the ethylene molecules contain substituents, the polymer will also contain those substituents.

Figure 30.18

Plastic bags and strips of polymer films such as Saran Wrap® are formed from large continuous tubes blown from the molten polymer.

$$nCH_2\!=\!CHR \xrightarrow{\text{Catalysts}} \left[CH_2\!-\!\underset{R}{\overset{|}{CH}} \right]_n$$

Polypropylene (R = CH_3) is the polymer of propylene, $CH_3CH\!=\!CH_2$. **Polyvinylchloride,** or **PVC** (R = Cl), is the polymer of vinyl chloride, $CH_2\!=\!CHCl$. **Teflon**® results from the polymerization of tetrafluoroethylene, $CF_2\!=\!CF_2$; **polystyrene** (R = C_6H_5) is the polymer of styrene, $C_6H_5CH\!=\!CH_2$. **Saran**® is the polymer of 1,1-dichloroethene, $CH_2\!=\!CCl_2$.

For Review

Summary

With the valence shell electron configuration $2s^2 2p^2$, carbon is the first member of Group IVA of the periodic table. Carbon generally completes its valence shell by sharing electrons in covalent bonds. Because the valence shell of a carbon atom contains only s and p orbitals and thus can contain a maximum of eight electrons, hybridization is limited to sp, sp^2, and sp^3. Strong, stable bonds between carbon atoms produce complex molecules containing chains and rings. The chemistry of these compounds is called **organic chemistry.**

Hydrocarbons are organic compounds composed only of carbon and hydrogen. The **alkanes** are **saturated hydrocarbons**—that is, hydrocarbons that contain only single bonds. **Alkenes** are hydrocarbons that contain one or more carbon–carbon double bonds. **Alkynes** contain one or more carbon–carbon triple bonds. **Aromatic hydrocarbons** contain ring structures with delocalized π-electron systems.

Most hydrocarbons have **structural isomers,** compounds with the same chemical formula but different arrangement of atoms. For example, n-butane and isobutane are structural isomers. Many aromatic hydrocarbons also have structural isomers; o-xylene, m-xylene, and p-xylene are examples. In addition, molecules of the alkenes and alkynes exhibit isomerism based on the position of the multiple bond in the molecule. Most alkenes also exhibit **cis–trans isomerism,** which results from the lack of rotation about a carbon–carbon double bond. Certain organic compounds form **optical isomers,** which contain one or more **asymmetric carbons,** carbon atoms bonded to four different groups.

Alkanes undergo **substitution reactions** in which one of the hydrogen atoms of the alkane is replaced by another type of atom. Alkenes and alkynes undergo **addition reactions** in which a reactant adds to the molecule and converts the carbon–carbon π bond into σ bonds. All hydrocarbons react with oxygen and burn.

Organic compounds that are not hydrocarbons can be considered derivatives of hydrocarbons. A hydrocarbon derivative can be formed by replacing one or more hydrogen atoms of a hydrocarbon by a **functional group,** which contains at least one atom of an element other than carbon or hydrogen. The properties of hydrocarbon derivatives are determined largely by the functional group. The —OH group is the functional group of an **alcohol.** The —O— group is the functional group of an **ether.** Other functional groups include the —CHO group of an **aldehyde,** the —CO— group of a **ketone,** and the —CO_2H group of a **carboxylic acid.** A halogen atom can also act as a functional group.

Many naturally occurring organic compounds or natural products have potent biological properties and are important commercially and medically. Insect **pheromones** are chemicals used for communication among members of species; they may be alarm pheromones, recruiting pheromones, or sex attractants. **Alkaloids** are natural products, often medicinal, that are derived from plants and have a nitrogen atom contained in a cyclic system.

Polymers, compounds of very high molecular masses, form when a large number of smaller molecules (**monomers**) react with one another. **Addition polymers** such as rubber and polyethylene form by addition reactions, whereas **condensation polymers** such as nylon and the polyesters form by condensation reactions.

Key Terms and Concepts

addition polymer (30.19)
addition reaction (30.3)
alcohols (30.9)
aldehydes (30.11)
alkaloids (30.17)
alkanes (30.1)
alkenes (30.3)
alkyl group (30.2)
alkynes (30.4)
aromatic hydrocarbons (30.5)
asymmetric carbon (30.6)
carbonyl group (30.12)

carboxyl group (30.13)
carboxylic acids (30.13)
condensation polymer (30.20)
cycloalkanes (30.1)
derivatives (30.2, 30.8–30.14)
esters (30.14)
ethers (30.10)
functional group (30.1)
geometrical isomers (30.3)
ketones (30.12)
monomers (30.18)

natural products (30.15)
optical isomers (30.6)
optically active molecules (30.6)
pheromones (30.16)
polymers (30.18)
primary carbon (30.2)
secondary carbon (30.2)
structural isomers (30.1)
substituents (30.2)
substitution reaction (30.1)
tertiary carbon (30.2)

Exercises

Answers for selected even-numbered exercises marked by red numbers appear at the end of the book. The worked-out solutions to all even-numbered exercises appear in the *Solutions Guide.*

Hydrocarbons

1. Write the chemical formula and Lewis structure of an alkane, an alkene, an alkyne, and a cyclic hydrocarbon, each of which contains five carbon atoms.
2. Write a Lewis structure for each of the following molecules.
   (a) propene
   (b) *t*-butylthiol
   (c) *sec*-butyl alcohol
   (d) ethyl propyl ether
   (e) *cis*-4-bromo-2-heptene
   (f) 2,2,3-trimethylhexane
   (g) *p*-diiodobenzene
   (h) isopropylcyclopentane
   (i) 3-methyl-1-hexyne
3. What is the difference between the electronic structures of saturated and unsaturated hydrocarbons?
4. Give the complete name for each of the following compounds.
   (a) $(CH_3)_2CHF$

   (b) $CH_3CHClCHClCH_3$

   (c) CH_3CHCH_3
         |
        CH_2CH_3

(d) $CH_3CH{=}CHCH_3$

(e) $CH_3CBrCH_2CH_2CH_2CH_3$
     |
    $CH_2CH{=}CH_2$

(f) $\underset{H}{\overset{F}{\diagdown}}C{=}C\underset{CH_3}{\overset{F}{\diagup}}$

(g) $H_2C\overset{CH_2-CH_2}{\underset{CH_2-CH_2}{\diagup\diagdown}}CHCH(CH_3)CH_3$

(h) $(CH_3)_3CCH_2C{\equiv}CH$

5. Draw a three-dimensional structure for each of the following, using solid and striped wedge-shaped bonds where appropriate (see Fig. 30.1).
   (a) CH_4 (d) t-$(CH_3)_3CH$
   (b) C_2H_4 (e) C_3H_4
   (c) C_3H_6
6. Write Lewis structures for all the isomers of the alkene C_4H_8.
7. Write Lewis structures for all the isomers of the alkyne C_4H_6.
8. Write Lewis structures for all the isomers of C_4H_9Cl. Do any of these isomers exist as optical isomers?

9. Name and write the structures of all isomers of the propyl and butyl groups.

10. Write the structures for all the isomers of the $-C_5H_{11}$ alkyl group.

11. Indicate which of the following molecules can exist as optical isomers.
   (a) *cis*-2-pentene
   (b) dibromodiiodomethane
   (c) 2-methyloctane
   (d) 4-ethyloctane
   (e) isopropyl thiol
   (f) 2-cyanoethanol, $CH_2(CN)CH_2OH$

12. Draw three-dimensional structures, using solid and striped wedge-shaped bonds around the asymmetric carbon atom, for the optical isomers of methionine, $H_2NCH(R)CO_2H$, where R is $-CH_2CH_2SCH_3$.

13. Does the following molecule exist as *cis* and *trans* isomers? As optical isomers?

14. Refer to Appendix I to answer the following questions.
   (a) How much heat is released by the combustion of exactly 5 g of $CH_3OH(l)$? Of $C_2H_5OH(l)$?
   (b) How much heat is released by the combustion of 1 mol of each of the compounds in part (a)?

Derivatives of Hydrocarbons

15. Write the Lewis structure, indicating resonance structures where appropriate, for each of the following molecules or ions.
   (a) ethanol
   (b) acetone
   (c) acetaldehyde
   (d) dimethyl ether
   (e) formic acid
   (f) benzoate ion, the anion of benzoic acid (4 resonance structures)

16. Identify each of the following classes of organic compounds, in which R is an alkyl group.
   (a) RH
   (b) ROH
   (c) RCOR
   (d) RCO_2H
   (e) RNH_2
   (f) ROR
   (g) RCHO

17. Draw a three-dimensional structure, using solid and striped wedge-shaped bonds where appropriate, for each of the following molecules.
   (a) CH_3OH
   (b) $H_2C_2O_4$
   (c) $C_2H_5OCH_3$
   (d) CH_3CO_2H
   (e) $CH_3CO_2C_2H_5$
   (f) $(CH_3)_2CHNH_2$

18. Identify the functional groups present in the molecule L-cysteine (Fig. 30.12).

19. Propose a way to synthesize benzoic acid from an alcohol.

20. Write a complete balanced equation for each of the following reactions.
   (a) Ethanol reacts with acetic acid.
   (b) 1-Butyne reacts with 2 mol of iodine.
   (c) Propene is burned in air.
   (d) Propanol is treated with limited H_2SO_4.
   (e) Propene is treated with water in dilute acid.

21. Show by means of chemical reactions how nicotine could be extracted from tobacco and then regenerated as a free base.

Additional Exercises

22. Why is ethanol soluble in water whereas its structural isomer dimethyl ether is not?

23. Indicate the types of hybridized orbitals used and the molecular geometry about each carbon atom in each of the following molecules.
   (a) $CH_3CH{=}CH_2$
   (b) $H_2C{=}C{=}O$
   (c) C_2H_2
   (d) H_2NCONH_2
   (e) CH_3CO_2H
   (f) CH_3COCH_3

24. Cyclohexane is a "puckered" (bent) six-membered ring, whereas benzene is a planar six-membered ring. Explain the difference on the basis of carbon atom hybridization.

25. How much acetic acid, in grams, is in exactly 1 quart of vinegar if the vinegar contains 3.00% acetic acid by volume? The density of acetic acid is 1.049 g/mL. (Conversion factors that may be helpful are given in Appendix B.)

26. Ethylene can be produced by the pyrolysis of ethane.

$$C_2H_6 \xrightarrow{\triangle} C_2H_4 + H_2$$

How many pounds of hydrogen does the pyrolysis of 1 ton of ethane produce?

27. When solid calcium carbide, CaC_2, is added to water, acetylene gas is produced. What volume of this gas at STP results from the hydrolysis of 21.7 g of CaC_2?

28. Hydrogen gas reduces C_2H_2 to ethane. How many grams of magnesium would have to react with hydrochloric acid to provide enough hydrogen to reduce the acetylene produced in Exercise 27?

29. Assuming a value of $n = 6$ in the formula for nylon, calculate how many pounds of hexamethylenediamine would be needed to produce 1000 lb of nylon.

30. How much ethyl acetate can be produced when 10.0 g of acetic acid reacts with 10.0 g of ethanol?

31

Biochemistry

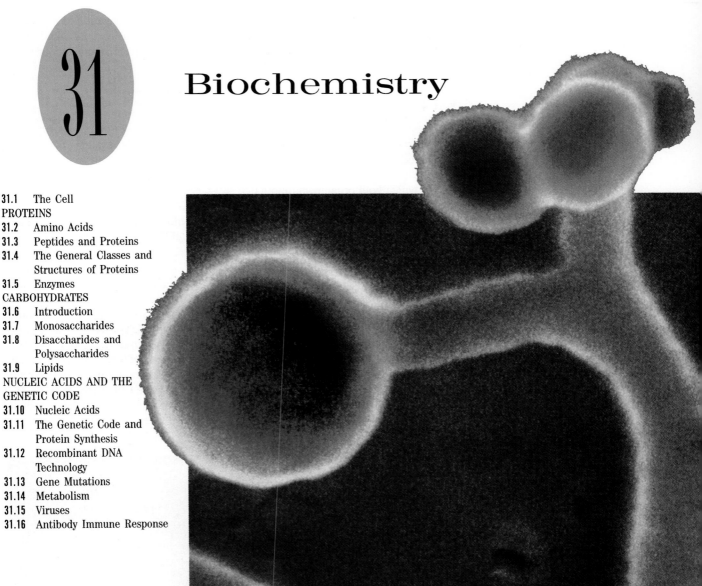

*AIDS virus particles being ejected from a tube that extends
from the surface of an infected cell.*

Biochemistry is the study of the chemical composition and structure of living organisms and the reactions that take place within them. Considering the diverse and complex functions of a cell, it is not surprising to find that its molecules are among the most complicated substances known.

Biomolecules are often divided into four major classes—proteins, carbohydrates, nucleic acids, and lipids—according to their structures or functions. Proteins, carbohydrates, and nucleic acids are often found in the form of macromolecules with molecular masses in the range 10^4–10^6, or larger, which form by the polymerization of monomers of relatively low molecular masses. Molecules of lipids are considerably smaller than those of the other three classes. However, they can associate to form clusters of molecules of enormous size.

31.1 The Cell

All cells are somewhat similar. They contain the same or similar systems of enzymes and the same kind of genetic material. The principal constituent of all living matter is water. The majority of plants and animals are 60–90% water, most of which is the solvent in which both organic and inorganic substances are dissolved and transported in the cell or through the organism.

An understanding of the role played by water in biological systems requires that a distinction be made between substances that are **hydrophilic** (literally, "water-loving") and those that are **hydrophobic** ("water-hating"). Recall from the Lewis structure of water that it is a polar molecule (see Section 8.3) and, as a solvent, it readily dissolves both polar and ionic substances (see Section 12.8). In general, the less polar a substance is, the more hydrophobic it is. The nonpolar hydrocarbons are excellent examples of hydrophobic compounds; they are almost totally immiscible with water. Some biomolecules contain polar or ionic substituents that impart hydrophilic character, and they are therefore water-soluble. Those biomolecules that do not contain polar or ionic substituents are hydrophobic; they are effectively insoluble in water and tend to escape from an aqueous environment. We have all seen oil floating on water, not mixing readily with it.

Cells are commonly divided into two classes. **Eukaryotic cells** such as that represented in Fig. 31.1(a) contain a nucleus. **Prokaryotic cells** do not contain a nucleus

Figure 31.1

(a) A eukaryotic cell. (b) A prokaryotic cell.

(a)   (b)

[Fig. 31.1(b)] and are restricted to certain microorganisms such as blue-green algae and bacteria.

The nucleus of eukaryotes contains the chromosomes, which are composed mainly of two substances: deoxyribonucleic acid (DNA) and protein. The nucleus stores the genetic information in DNA that enables the cell to replicate itself and to synthesize the various proteins that it needs for biological activity.

All cells are surrounded by a cell membrane, which is the "skin" or envelope containing the cell contents. The cell membrane insulates the contents of the cell from surrounding fluids and actively controls what enters and what leaves the cell.

The **cytoplasm** is the entire contents of the cell, except the nucleus. It can be divided into the **cytosol** (the water-soluble contents of the cell) and a variety of small organs, such as the ribosomes, mitochondria, and chloroplasts, which are referred to as **cellular organelles.**

Ribosomes, the site of the directed polymerization (genetic coding) of amino acids to form enzymes and other proteins, are small spherical bodies that are present in all cells. **Mitochondria,** a cell's power plants, are present in eukaryotic cells. A variety of biomolecules (including carbohydrates, amino acids, and fatty acids) are oxidized to carbon dioxide and water in the mitochondria. Some of the energy released during this oxidation is stored as chemical energy through the synthesis of compounds called **nucleoside triphosphates;** adenosine triphosphate (ATP) and guanosine triphosphate (GTP) are examples. **Chloroplasts** are present in all plants and algae that are capable of converting light energy into chemical energy through photosynthesis. Light induces the chloroplasts to synthesize carbohydrates from carbon dioxide and water.

Proteins

Proteins are the most abundant cellular component. They include enzymes, antibodies, transport-facilitating molecules, and hormones, and some are even components of the cell skeleton. The word *protein* is derived from the Greek *proteios,* meaning "of first importance." Every protein molecule is a polymer of amino acids.

31.2 Amino Acids

Nearly all the proteins in the biological world are made from the same 20 amino acids, the **alpha-amino acids.** A single amino acid has as its center a tetrahedral carbon atom called the alpha (α) carbon (C_α). It is bonded covalently on one side to an amino group ($-NH_2$) and on the other side to a carboxyl group ($-CO_2H$). The third bond is always to hydrogen and the fourth bond is to the functional side chain (R). The structures of the α-amino acids differ only in the nature of the side chain (R) and can be represented by the following general structure:

$$\overset{\text{R}}{\underset{|}{H_2N-CH-CO_2H}}$$

However, it is important to recognize that the basic H_2N- end of this molecule acts as a proton acceptor and that the $-CO_2H$ end functions as a proton donor. The proton transfer forms a species called a **zwitterion** (from the German for "hybrid ion" or "dipolar ion"). Zwitterions are molecules that contain ionic charges but that are electrically neutral overall:

$$H_2\ddot{N}-\underset{\underset{R}{|}}{C}H-CO_2\,\text{(H)} \longrightarrow H_3N^+-\underset{\underset{R}{|}}{C}H-CO_2^-$$

Zwitterion

Figure 31.2

The 20 α-amino acids commonly found as constituents of proteins.

Nonpolar R Group

$$H_3N^+-\underset{\underset{H}{|}}{C}H-CO_2^-$$
Glycine (Gly)

$$H_3N^+-\underset{\underset{\underset{CH}{|}}{\overset{CH_3 \quad CH_2CH_3}{\diagdown\diagup}}}{C}H-CO_2^-$$
Isoleucine (Ile)

$$H_3N^+-\underset{\underset{CH_2}{|}}{\underset{\underset{\overset{CH}{|}}{\overset{CH_3 \quad CH_3}{\diagdown\diagup}}}{C}}H-CO_2^-$$
Leucine (Leu)

$$H_3N^+-\underset{\underset{\underset{CH}{|}}{\overset{CH_3 \quad CH_3}{\diagdown\diagup}}}{C}H-CO_2^-$$
Valine (Val)

$$H_3N^+-\underset{\underset{CH_3}{|}}{C}H-CO_2^-$$
Alanine (Ala)

Proline (Pro)

Aromatic R Group

$$H_3N^+-CH-CO_2^-$$
Phenylalanine (Phe)

$$H_3N^+-CH-CO_2^-$$
Tyrosine (Tyr)

$$H_3N^+-CH-CO_2^-$$
Tryptophan (Trp)

Amino acids are usually grouped on the basis of similarities in the structure of the side chain. The names and structures of the 20 most common α-amino acids found in biological systems are shown in Fig. 31.2.

A zwitterion is the dominant form of an amino acid in aqueous solution at or near neutral pH (pH = 7). In an acidic solution, however, the amino acid becomes positively charged as the carboxylate ion is protonated. Conversely, in a basic solution, the amino acid becomes negatively charged as the amino group is deprotonated. Alanine is a good example.

Figure 31.2 (Continued)

Carboxylic Acid or Amide R Group

Aspartic acid (Asp)   Asparagine (Asn)   Glutamic acid (Glu)   Glutamine (Gln)

Basic R Group

Lysine (Lys)   Arginine (Arg)   Histidine (His)

Alcoholic R Group   *Sulfur-Containing R Group*

Serine (Ser)   Threonine (Thr)   Cysteine (Cys)   Methionine (Met)

$$H_3N^+\text{—CH—CO}_2H \xrightleftharpoons[OH^-]{H^+} H_3N^+\text{—CH—CO}_2^- \xrightleftharpoons[H^+]{OH^-} H_2N\text{—CH—CO}_2^-$$

| Acidic solution | Neutral solution | Basic solution |

Cysteine and methionine, as shown in Fig. 31.2, both have a sulfur-containing side chain. Cysteine often links to another cysteine through formation of a disulfide bond (—S—S—), which is a covalent bond between the side chains, to form the amino acid cystine.

$$H_3N^+\text{—CH—CO}_2^- \qquad H_3N^+\text{—CH—CO}_2^-$$

Two cysteine molecules → Cystine

With the exception of glycine (in which the R group is a hydrogen atom and carbon has only three different kinds of atoms bonded to it), the α-amino acids are optically active (see Section 30.6). Every amino acid isolated from a naturally occurring protein is an L amino acid. Looking down the H—C bond of an L amino acid, we see that the —CO$_2^-$, —R, and —NH$_3^+$ substituents are arranged in a clockwise fashion. In a D amino acid these substituents are arranged in a counterclockwise manner (Fig. 31.3). Though occasionally found in nature, D amino acids are not found in proteins.

L isomer

D isomer

Figure 31.3

The molecular structures of the D and L isomers of an amino acid. In every case, these optical isomers are mirror images.

31.3 Peptides and Proteins

The structures of peptides and proteins were first determined by the German chemist Emil Fischer between 1900 and 1910. **Peptides** are molecules formed from two or more amino acids linked by covalent amide linkages that are given the special name **peptide bonds.** The nature of a peptide bond (in color) can be seen in the following structure for a dipeptide (two amino acids joined by a peptide bond).

$$H_3N^+\text{—CH—C—NH—CH—CO}_2^-$$

The name *peptide* is usually restricted to polymers made up of only a small number of amino acids. Such polymers are often called **oligopeptides** (from the Greek word *oligo,* meaning "few"). Polymers containing approximately 10–40 amino acid units are called **polypeptides.** Relatively large polymers containing 40–10,000 (or more) amino acid units are called **proteins.** Aspartame, the artificial sweetener sold under the brand name NutraSweet®, is the methyl ester of the dipeptide aspartylphenylalanine.

Phenylalanine
residue

Aspartic acid
residue

Aspartylphenylalanine methyl ester
(Aspartame)

The peptide bond results from the removal of the elements of H_2O from the carboxyl group of one amino acid and from the α-amino group of the other amino acid. The amino acid units in a peptide are called **residues.** The amino acid residue at the end of the peptide that has a free α-amino group is the **amino-terminal** (or **N-terminal**) residue; the residue at the opposite end, which has a free carboxyl group, is the **carboxyl-terminal** (or **C-terminal**) residue. Peptides and proteins are written and named beginning from the N-terminal residue. For example, starting with two different amino acids, glycine (Gly) and alanine (Ala), two different dipeptides can be formed.

Glycylalanine
(Gly-Ala)

Alanylglycine
(Ala-Gly)

The tetrapeptide

is made up of cysteine, valine, lycine, and phenylalanine bonded together by peptide bonds and is therefore called cysteinylvalyllysylphenylalanine, or Cys-Val-Lys-Phe. The four amino acids in this tetrapeptide are shown alternately in blue and red. The order of the residues in a peptide is called the **amino acid sequence.** Most protein molecules contain hundreds of amino acids linked one to another in a specific order. Any changes, even small ones, in the amino acid sequence can produce profound differences in the chemical and biological properties of the peptide.

It would be very useful to be able to synthesize any given protein, because the body's inability to synthesize one or more proteins is the cause of many diseases, such as hemophilia, sickle-cell anemia, and diabetes. Unfortunately, there are three major obstacles to the chemical synthesis of peptides or proteins. First, the order in which the amino acids are incorporated must be rigorously controlled. Second, reactions must be prevented from occurring at the amino acid side chains. Finally, the free energy for the reaction of the peptide with water is negative, so proteins decompose spontaneously (see Section 19.8).

$$H_3N^+\!-\!CH\!-\!\underset{\|}{C}\!-\!NH\!-\!CH\!-\!CO_2^- + H_2O \longrightarrow H_3N^+\!-\!CH\!-\!CO_2^- + H_3N^+\!-\!CH\!-\!CO_2^-$$
$$\Delta G° = -17 \text{ kJ}$$

Each of these problems has been solved for many syntheses. Peptides and proteins can be produced by chemical syntheses, but generally not yet in large amounts. However, genetic engineering techniques, which use bacterial cells to synthesize mammalian proteins, now make it possible to synthesize human insulin, interferon (produced by cells in response to viral infection), and other important proteins.

31.4 The General Classes and Structures of Proteins

The extraordinary variations possible in the structures of proteins allow for remarkable differences in their types and functions. Proteins can function in many different ways because their amino acid sequences and three-dimensional structures vary widely. Their structures can vary so much because the amino acids can be used in many different orders in a peptide chain of given length. For example, from the 20 most common amino acids there are 20^2 (400) possible dipeptides, 20^3 (8000) tripeptides, and 20^4 (160,000) tetrapeptides. Even for a protein as small as insulin, with only 51 amino acid units, there are 2.3×10^{66} possible amino acid sequences. What is truly remarkable is that the number of proteins found in living systems is limited to the tens of thousands instead of the astronomically large numbers that are mathematically possible. This is so because only certain amino acid sequences are capable of forming a stable three-dimensional structure that has a biological function.

Among the biologically important proteins (and their physiological functions) are the following seven types:

1. **Enzymes.** Enzymes catalyze biochemical reactions with a high degree of efficiency and specificity. This is the most varied and most highly specialized group of proteins (Section 31.5).

2. **Transport Proteins.** Proteins are involved in the transport of both organic and inorganic nutrients across cell membranes. They are also contained in blood plasma and act to transport specific molecules or ions from one organ to another.

3. **Nutrient and Storage Proteins.** Many plant seeds store nutrient proteins that are necessary for growth of the embryonic plant. Casein, the major protein of milk, is a nutrient protein, and ferritin, which stores iron in animal tissues, is a storage protein.

4. **Contractile Proteins.** Muscles are composed of fibrous bundles of the proteins actin and myosin, which are involved in the contraction and relaxation of muscle tissue.

5. **Structural Proteins.** Many proteins serve as supports to give biological structures strength or protection. The protein collagen has high tensile strength and is the

major component of tendons and cartilage. Leather is an example of almost pure collagen. Hair, fingernails, and feathers consist mainly of the protein keratin.

6. **Defense Proteins.** The antibodies (Section 31.16) produced by the immune response system are proteins that neutralize viruses, bacteria, and other "foreign" substances.

7. **Regulatory Proteins.** Some proteins bind to specific sites on the cell membrane or within the cell to regulate cellular or physiological activity. Among them are many hormones such as insulin, which regulates sugar metabolism, and human growth hormone, which is produced in the pituitary gland.

The **primary structure** of a protein, the organic chemical structure, is simply the sequence of amino acids, listed as though printed on ticker tape, starting with the N-terminal amino acid and proceeding through the C-terminal amino acid.

A polypeptide chain can fold upon itself to produce a **secondary structure,** in which the number of hydrogen bonds between peptide linkages is maximized.

$$\diagup N—H \cdots O=C \diagdown$$

There are only a limited number of secondary structures that a polypeptide chain can adopt that maximize the number of hydrogen bonds between peptide linkages. Two of the most common forms of secondary structure are the **α-helix** (Fig. 31.4) and the **β-pleated sheet** (Fig. 31.5). In the α-helix the polypeptide backbone forms a helical coil with approximately 3.6 amino acids per 360° turn. The α-helix is the dominant secondary structure in fibrous proteins such as collagen and the α-keratins of hair and wool.

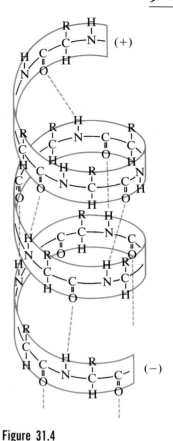

Figure 31.4

The α-helix structure of a peptide chain, one form of secondary structure of protein molecules. The hydrogen bonds that stabilize this structure are indicated by blue dashed lines.

Figure 31.5

The β-pleated sheet secondary structure of protein molecules.

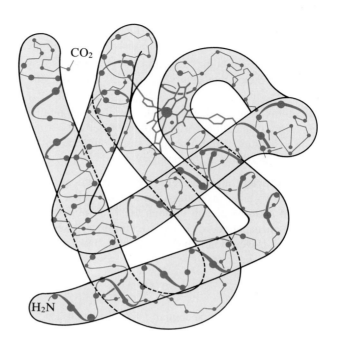

Figure 31.6

The tertiary structure of myoglobin, an oxygen-storing protein found in muscle tissue. The folded tertiary structure is shown, as well as the helical secondary structure (cylindrical regions). The primary structure is not shown in detail but as a series of red dots.

The β-pleated sheet structure results from hydrogen bonds between adjacent strands of a polypeptide backbone. Extended arrays of the β-pleated sheet secondary structure are found in the β-keratins, such as silk.

Proteins often contain regions where a helical or sheet structure is folded into a complex conformation known as the **tertiary structure** (Fig. 31.6). Interactions between amino acid side chains produce and stabilize this structure.

Many larger proteins contain more than one polypeptide chain. The **quaternary structure** of a protein describes how these independent molecules are related to each other. The oxygen-carrying protein hemoglobin (Section 26.5) consists of four separate polypeptide chains—two α subunits and two β subunits—held together in a quaternary structure.

Factors that **denature** a protein disturb its natural conformation, without chemically altering the primary structure, and lead to the loss of biological activity. A denatured protein has lost some or all of its secondary, tertiary, or quaternary structure. When food is cooked, its proteins are often denatured.

31.5 Enzymes

Enzymes are proteins that catalyze chemical reactions in living systems with remarkable efficiency. The enzyme carbonic anhydrase, for example, which catalyzes the reaction

$$CO_2 + 2H_2O \rightleftharpoons H_3O^+ + HCO_3^-$$

is such a good catalyst that a single molecule can transform over 36 million carbon dioxide molecules per minute into product. This corresponds to an increase of 10^7–10^8 in the rate of this reaction. One explanation for this efficiency is that the binding of the substrate (the molecule undergoing the reaction) to the enzyme may stretch or strain the substrate until its conformation more closely resembles the transition state for the reaction (see Section 14.6), thereby reducing the activation energy. Enzymes are not only efficient; they can also be remarkably selective. The ability of some enzymes to be specific for a very few substrates in a variety of substances with related structures suggests that the enzymes and substrate fit together somewhat like a lock and key. The enzyme activates only those substrates that fit, just as a lock is opened only by keys that fit.

In 1913 L. Michaelis and M. L. Menten suggested that enzyme-catalyzed reactions proceed through at least two steps. First, the substrate binds to the enzyme to form an enzyme–substrate complex. Second, within the complex the enzyme acts on the substrate to convert it into product. Many substances may bind to an enzyme, but only a limited number of them can react. The enzyme succinate dehydrogenase, for example, not only binds its normal substrate (succinate) but also binds other dicarboxylates, such as malonate, that do not react. By occupying a portion of the available binding sites on the enzyme, malonate slows down the rate of reaction (fewer molecules of enzyme are available to catalyze it). In effect, the activity of the enzyme is **inhibited.** Because the substrate (in this case, succinate) and the inhibitor (malonate) compete for the same binding sites on the enzyme, this form of enzyme inhibition is called **competitive inhibition.** Enzymes can also be inhibited by substances that have no resemblance to the substrate. Examples include heavy metal ions such as Ag^+, Pb^{2+}, and Hg^{2+}, which bind in either the presence or the absence of substrate. This form of enzyme inhibition is called **noncompetitive inhibition.**

For a cell to function at its maximum efficiency, the rates of its chemical reactions must be adjusted to its needs. Enzymes alone are not enough; the cell must also have control mechanisms that can turn enzyme activity on when the product of an enzyme-catalyzed reaction is needed and switch enzyme activity off when the product is present in excess. The cell can control the rate of enzyme-catalyzed reactions in four ways. First, it can influence the rate of a reaction by changing the concentration of the substrate. In the absence of substrate, the enzyme is effectively switched off. Second, the cell can produce natural inhibitors of enzyme activity, which operate by either competitive or noncompetitive inhibition mechanisms. Third, the cell can use **allosteric enzymes,** which contain two or more binding sites. Allosteric enzymes bind both a substrate molecule and a small molecule known as the **effector.** Binding of the effector is thought to alter the structure of the enzyme, thereby either switching on or switching off its activity. Binding of the effector usually does not influence the binding of the substrate; it either facilitates or prevents conversion of the substrate into product. There are several forms of control of allosteric enzymes. In so-called **feedback inhibition,** an enzyme involved in the synthesis of an end-product is inhibited by binding the end-product as an effector. Alternatively, when the synthesis of a particular product should occur only when the substrate is present in excess, an enzyme may exhibit **substrate activation,** wherein more than one substrate must bind to the enzyme before it is activated. Fourth, the cell can control the rate of an enzyme-catalyzed reaction by controlling the population of enzyme molecules. This can be done by controlling either the rate at which the enzyme is synthesized or the rate at which the enzyme is degraded or destroyed.

Carbohydrates

③① .6 Introduction

The name *carbohydrate* originally meant a compound with the empirical formula CH_2O; literally, a hydrate of carbon. This definition has since been broadened to include all aldehydes and ketones having two or more hydroxyl groups. Among the compounds that fall into the class of **carbohydrates** are starches, cellulose, glycogen, and sugars. Carbohydrates are an important source of energy for all organisms, and they form the supporting tissue of plants and some animals. Carbohydrates exist as monosaccharides, disaccharides, and polysaccharides.

③① .7 Monosaccharides

The simplest carbohydrates contain only a single aldehyde or ketone functional group (see Sections 30.11 and 30.12) and are known as **monosaccharides.** They are colorless, are crystalline, and frequently have a sweet taste. A monosaccharide is classified as either an **aldose** or a **ketose,** depending on whether it contains an aldehyde or a ketone functional group. With the exception of the simplest ketose (the three-carbon monosaccharide dihydroxyacetone), all of the monosaccharides are optically active. Although both D and L isomers are possible, the dominant form of carbohydrates isolated from natural sources is the D isomer. Structures of the D and L forms of the simplest aldose, glyceraldehyde, are

D-Glyceraldehyde   L-Glyceraldehyde

Monosaccharides can undergo a reversible intramolecular reaction to change from a linear structure to a cyclic structure. Glucose, an aldose, forms a six-membered **pyranose ring** (Fig. 31.7); fructose, a ketose, forms a five-membered **furanose ring** (Fig. 31.8). In each case two isomers known as the α and β forms are produced; they differ only in orientation of the —OH group at the first carbon atom, or C(1).

Glucose, $C_6H_{12}O_6$ (Fig. 31.7), also called **dextrose,** is the most abundant organic compound in nature. It is the sole component of the polysaccharides cellulose, starch, and glycogen. In medicine, glucose is often called blood sugar, because it is by far the most abundant carbohydrate in the bloodstream. Human blood normally contains about 1 gram of glucose per liter. Individuals suffering from diabetes are unable to assimilate glucose; they eliminate it through the kidneys. In 100 milliliters of a diabetic's urine, there may be as much as 8–10 grams of glucose, and its presence is one symptom of the disease. **Fructose** (Fig. 31.8), also called **levulose** or **fruit sugar,** has the same molecular formula as glucose but contains a ketone rather than an aldehyde functional group. Fructose occurs naturally in both fruits and honey and is found combined with glucose in

Figure 31.7

Glucose undergoes a reversible reaction leading to the formation of a stable six-membered glucopyranose ring. Two isomers, differing only in orientation at the C(1) atom, are formed.

the disaccharide sucrose, called cane sugar. Fructose is the sweetest of all sugars; a given mass of fructose is nearly twice as sweet as the same amount of sucrose.

31.8 Disaccharides and Polysaccharides

In addition to undergoing reversible reactions that lead to pyranose and furanose rings, monosaccharides can also polymerize to form chains. However, the polymerization reaction can be reversed only in the presence of acid or a suitable enzyme catalyst, so polysaccharides are relatively stable toward reaction with water.

The most important **disaccharide** is **sucrose,** or **cane sugar** (Fig. 31.9). The reaction of water and sucrose, $C_{12}H_{22}O_{11}$, yields a 50:50 mixture of the monosaccharides fructose and glucose (both $C_6H_{12}O_6$), a mixture often called **invert sugar,** which is a

Figure 31.8

Fructose undergoes a reversible reaction leading to the formation of α and β isomers of a five-membered fructofuranose ring. The two isomers differ in orientation of the —OH group around carbon 2.

Figure 31.9

The structure of the disaccharide sucrose, formed from reaction of α-D-glucopyranose with β-D-fructofuranose. (Carbon atoms in the rings are not shown.)

α-D-Glucopyranose

β-D-Fructofuranose

Sucrose

major component of honey. **Lactose,** or **milk sugar,** is a disaccharide that contains an α-D-glucopyranose ring and a β-D-galactopyranose ring (Fig. 31.10). Many individuals of African or Asian origin cannot digest milk because they lack enzymes that hydrolyze the β-linkage (the ether linkage between the rings) in lactose.

Three major classes of **polysaccharides** are formed by the polymerization of D-glucopyranose rings: starch, glycogen, and cellulose. **Starch** serves primarily as a long-term storage medium for food energy in plants. It accumulates in seeds, tubers, and fruits. Starch is often the main food supply for the young plant until the development of a leaf system enables the plant to manufacture its own food through photosynthesis.

Glycogen is a polysaccharide that serves the same function in animals as starch serves in plants. Glycogen is found primarily in liver, heart, and muscle tissue.

Cellulose is a linear polysaccharide of β-D-glucopyranose units (Fig. 31.11) found in plants. It is the principal component of the rigid cell wall of plant cells and provides structure rather than energy. The lack of an enzyme capable of cleaving the β-linkage in cellulose is the only thing that prevents humans from being able to digest cotton (which is at least 90% cellulose by weight) or the paper of this text. Most animals cannot digest cellulose because they lack suitable enzymes to catalyze its cleavage. Termites and the ruminant animals, such a cattle, sheep, and goats, are able to use cellulose as food

Figure 31.10

The structure of the disaccharide lactose, formed by reaction of β-D-galactopyranose with α-D-glucopyranose. (Carbon atoms in the rings are not shown.)

α-D-Glucopyranose

β-D-Galactopyranose

Lactose

Figure 31.11

The structure of cellulose, a linear polysaccharide formed by the polymerization of β-D-glucopyranose. (Carbon atoms in the rings are not shown.)

β-D-Glucopyranose unit

Cellulose

because bacteria in their digestive tracts contain enzymes that can cleave the β-linkages. Termites are commonly destroyed by killing these bacteria—they then starve to death.

Acid mucopolysaccharides are polysaccharides that contain N-acetylglucosamine and glucuronic acid. Hyaluronic acid is an example of an acid mucopolysaccharide. It consists of repeating units of N-acetylglucosamine linked to glucuronic acid (Fig. 31.12). Hyaluronic acid is a part of the connective tissue in the body and helps to hold

N-Acetylglucosamine

Glucuronic acid

Hyaluronic acid

Figure 31.12

The structures of N-acetylglucosamine (shown in blue), glucuronic acid (shown in red), and hyaluronic acid. (Carbon atoms in the rings and hydrogen atoms on these carbon atoms are not shown.)

Figure 31.13

The structures of a glucuronic acid sulfate unit (shown in red), a glucosamine sulfate unit (shown in blue), and heparin. (Carbon atoms in the rings and hydrogen atoms on these carbon atoms are not shown.)

cells together. Another acid mucopolysaccharide is heparin, an important blood antico-agulant. It contains a glucuronic acid sulfate unit and a glucosamine sulfate unit (Fig. 31.13).

Glycoproteins are protein molecules that have carbohydrate units attached to side chains of certain amino acid residues. Glycoproteins include protein blood-clotting materials and many of the cell membrane proteins. A very important glycoprotein is collagen, which is the most abundant protein in the human body, making up about one-third of its protein. It occurs in all organs, imparting strength and stiffness to them. Collagen is present in such diverse parts of the body as teeth, bones, cartilage, tendons, skin, and the lens of the eye.

31.9 Lipids

Lipids are more diverse than either proteins or carbohydrates: This class of biomolecules includes compounds of widely differing structures. Lipids are oily or greasy organic substances that are insoluble in water. They dissolve in relatively nonpolar solvents such as chloroform, $CHCl_3$, and diethyl ether, $(C_2H_5)_2O$.

In our coverage of esters in Section 30.14, we discussed **fatty acids.** One class of lipids consists of derivatives of long-chain carboxylic acids, or fatty acids, such as stearic acid, $C_{17}H_{35}CO_2H$.

$$CH_3CH_2CH_2CH_2CH_2CH_2CH_2CH_2CH_2CH_2CH_2CH_2CH_2CH_2CH_2CH_2CH_2CO_2H$$
Stearic acid

Although fatty acids are available to a cell from a wide variety of sources, the concentration of free fatty acid in the cell is negligible. Most fatty acids occur in plant and animal cells in the form of triesters (see Section 30.14) of the alcohol 1,2,3-propanetriol (glycerol).

$$CH_2OH$$
$$CHOH \qquad CH_3(CH_2)_{16}CO\overset{\displaystyle O\ \ CH_2OC(CH_2)_{16}CH_3}{\underset{CH_2OC(CH_2)_{16}CH_3}{}}$$
$$CH_2OH$$

Glycerol   Tristearylglycerol

Such lipids are commonly known as **triglycerides,** although the proper name is **triacyl-glycerols.** The primary function of these triglycerides is the long-term storage of food energy. Triglycerides formed from saturated fatty acids, such as tristearylglycerol, are typically solids at normal temperatures (see Section 30.14) and are known as **fats.** Triglycerides formed from unsaturated fatty acids, which contain one or more carbon–carbon double bonds, are more frequently liquids at room temperature and are known as **oils;** examples include cottenseed oil, linseed oil, and palm oil.

One of the characteristic reactions of fats and oils is **saponification,** which is the reaction of the triester in the presence of aqueous base to form glycerol and a salt of the fatty acid. The salts of the fatty acids are soaps (Section 12.25).

$$CH_3(CH_2)_{16}CO\overset{\displaystyle O\ \ CH_2OC(CH_2)_{16}CH_3}{\underset{CH_2OC(CH_2)_{16}CH_3}{}} + 3NaOH(aq) \longrightarrow \quad\begin{array}{l}CH_2OH\\ CHOH\\ CH_2OH\end{array} + 3CH_3(CH_2)_{16}CO_2{}^-Na^+(aq)$$

A soap

A second class of lipids are the **phosphoglycerides,** or **glycerophosphatides,** which are major components of cell membranes. These lipids can be thought of as derivatives of phosphoric acid and glycerol. They have the following structure:

$$\begin{array}{l} R-\overset{\displaystyle O}{\overset{\|}{C}}-O-CH_2 \\ R-\underset{\underset{\displaystyle O}{\|}}{C}-O-CH \qquad\ \overset{\displaystyle O}{\underset{\underset{\displaystyle OH}{|}}{}} \\ \qquad\qquad\quad CH_2-O-P-OX \end{array}$$

A phosphoglyceride

(where X is choline, ethanolamine, or serine). They consist of a hydrophobic hydrocarbon backbone with a hydrophilic head that is charged. Among the most important of the phosphoglycerides are the **phosphatidyl cholines,** or **lecithins,** of which the following is a representative example:

$$\underset{\substack{\text{Nonpolar} \\ \text{hydrophobic} \\ \text{tail}}}{\underbrace{\begin{array}{l} \text{CH}_3(\text{CH}_2)_{16}\overset{\text{O}}{\overset{\|}{\text{C}}}\text{O}\,\text{CH}_2 \\ \text{CH}_3(\text{CH}_2)_{16}\overset{}{\text{C}}\text{O}\,\text{CH} \\ \phantom{CH_3(CH_2)_{16}}\overset{\|}{\text{O}}\quad \text{CH}_2 \end{array}}} \underset{\substack{\text{Charged} \\ \text{hydrophilic head}}}{\underbrace{\begin{array}{l} \text{O} \\ \text{OPOCH}_2\text{CH}_2\text{N(CH}_3)_3{}^+ \\ \text{O}^- \end{array}}}$$

Like soaps, phosphatidyl cholines contain a highly charged hydrophilic head and a nonpolar hydrophobic tail. These lipids can spontaneously group to form **micelles,** in which the ionic heads face the surrounding water and the nonpolar tails form a hydrophobic pocket (Fig. 31.14). Alternatively, they can form bilayers, which serve as the basis for membranes that separate the cell from its surroundings or segment the interior of the cell (Fig. 31.15).

Other lipids do not contain a fatty acid. These include substances such as the **fatty alcohols** (cetyl alcohol and myricyl alcohol, for example), which are long-chain alcohols.

$$\underset{\text{Cetyl alcohol}}{\text{CH}_3(\text{CH}_2)_{14}\text{CH}_2\text{OH}} \qquad \underset{\text{Myricyl alcohol}}{\text{CH}_3(\text{CH}_2)_{29}\text{CH}_2\text{OH}}$$

With fatty acids, these fatty alcohols form esters (Section 30.14) known as **waxes.** Lipids also include the **terpenes,** among them pigments such as β-carotene, fat-soluble vitamins such as vitamin A, and forms of natural rubber (Section 30.19).

Figure 31.14

The phosphatidyl cholines, which possess a charged hydrophilic head and a nonpolar hydrophobic tail, can associate to form micelles in which the hydrophilic heads are oriented toward the surrounding water molecules and the hydrophobic tails share a region of the solution where water molecules are partially excluded.

Hydrophobic region

Hydrophilic head of phospholipid molecule

Hydrophobic tail of phospholipid molecule

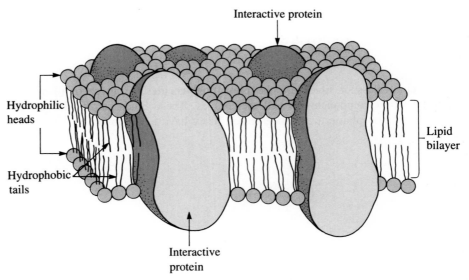

Interactive protein

Hydrophilic heads

Hydrophobic tails

Lipid bilayer

Interactive protein

Figure 31.15

The phosphatidyl cholines can associate to form bilayers that serve as the basis for cell membranes. The nonpolar tails associate to form hydrophobic pockets, and the hydrophilic heads point toward the polar solvent, water. Membranes may also contain other lipids, such as cholesterol, and proteins that are involved in the transport of molecules across the cell membrane.

Figure 31.16

The steroids represent a class of compounds all of which have the same essential fused-ring structure. The steroids function as important components of cell membranes, such as cholesterol; as precursors in the synthesis of vitamins, such as vitamin D_2; as hormones, such as the male and female sex hormones testosterone and estradiol-17; and as ingredients of oral contraceptives.

Cholesterol

Testosterone

Estradiol-17

A remarkably diverse group of lipids, **steroids,** can be synthesized from terpenes by a complex set of reactions. Among the steroids are such compounds as cholesterol, an important component of cell membranes, and the sex hormones testosterone and estradiol-17 (Fig. 31.16).

Nucleic Acids and the Genetic Code

31.10 Nucleic Acids

Understanding the chemical nature of nucleic acids is the basis for understanding biochemical genetics. The central dogma of molecular genetics defines three major steps in the processing of the genetic information contained in **nucleic acids:** replication, transcription, and translation (Section 31.11). The most important nucleic acids are macromolecules of very high molecular mass, the sole function of which is the storage and processing of genetic information. There are two types of such nucleic acids: **ribonucleic acids (RNA)** and **deoxyribonucleic acids (DNA).** While both types of nucleic acids are synthesized in the nucleus of the cell and the DNA remains in the nucleus, RNA is located in and functions primarily in the cell cytoplasm.

Figure 31.17

The five most common nitrogen-containing bases found in nucleic acids are (a) the pyrimidines uracil (U), thymine (T), and cytosine (C) and (b) the purines adenine (A) and guanine (G).

Uracil (U)   Thymine (T)   Cytosine (C)

(a)

Adenine (A)   Guanine (G)

(b)

The ribonucleic acids (RNA) are built on the framework of a β-D-ribofuranose ring, and the deoxyribonucleic acids (DNA) contain a modified ribofuranose ring in which the —OH group on the second, or 2′, carbon is replaced by a hydrogen atom.

β-D-Ribofuranose   2-Deoxy-β-D-ribofuranose

Nucleosides are formed by combining one of these monosaccharides with a cyclic nitrogen-containing base. These bases are divided into two families, the pyrimidines and the purines. The **pyrimidines** are six-membered nitrogen-containing cyclic compounds [Fig. 31.17(a)], and the **purines** are pyrimidines with five-membered nitrogen-contain-

Figure 31.18

The progression from base to nucleoside to nucleotide. Uracil is the original base, uridine the nucleoside, and uridine monophosphate the nucleotide.

Uracil   Uridine   Uridine monophosphate

ing rings fused to them [Fig. 31.17(b)]. **Nucleotides** are phosphate esters of nucleosides. For example, the base uracil, which is found only in RNA, not in DNA, can be joined to a ribofuranose ring at the 1′ carbon to form the nucleoside **uridine.** This nucleoside can then combine with the phosphate ion, PO_4^{3-}, to form the nucleotide **uridine mono-phosphate** (Fig. 31.18).

Nucleic acids are formed by polymerization of nucleotides. Polymerization occurs by reaction of the 3′ hydroxyl group of one nucleotide with the acidic phosphate that is attached to the 5′ carbon of another to form an ester. Figure 31.19 shows a segment of

Figure 31.19

The structure of a tetranucleotide segment of a single strand of deoxy-ribonucleic acid (DNA). Reading from the 5′ end to the 3′ end, this tetranucleotide can be symbolized as T-A-C-G. (Carbon atoms in the rings are not shown.)

Figure 31.20

Schematic diagram of the structure of DNA. The sugar–phosphate backbone is shown in black, whereas the purine and pyrimidine bases are shown in various colors. Dotted lines show hydrogen bonds.

a DNA chain containing the four nucleotides that are found in deoxyribonucleic acids. The sequence of nucleotides in Fig. 31.19, reading from the 5′ end of this chain to the 3′ end, can be symbolized as T-A-C-G. This figure shows the tetranucleotide as it would exist at or near neutral pH. The phosphodiester linkages between adjacent nucleosides in nucleic acids are strong acids. The phosphate groups should therefore be expected to carry a negative charge in aqueous solution at or near neutral pH. The nucleic acids are therefore normally found associated either with highly charged positive proteins known as **histones** or with cations such as the Mg^{2+} ion.

There are several important structural differences between the nucleic acids DNA and RNA. Each RNA nucleotide contains an —OH group on the 2′ carbon of the furanose ring, but DNA nucleotides do not. Furthermore, the nitrogen-containing bases used to form nucleotides are different. DNA contains exclusively the two purines adenine (A) and guanine (G) and the two pyrimidines thymine (T) and cytosine (C). RNA contains the pyrimidine uracil (U) instead of thymine and often a number of other nucleotides. Evidence suggests, however, that these additional nucleotides are formed by modification of adenine, guanine, cytosine, or uracil after the RNA polymer is produced.

In 1953 J. D. Watson and F. H. C. Crick proposed a mechanism for the storage of genetic information based on the structure of DNA. For this work they subsequently received the Nobel prize. According to Watson and Crick, DNA is composed of two strands, running in opposite directions, that are bridged by hydrogen bonds between specific pyrimidine groups on one strand and purine groups on the other (Fig. 31.20). These two strands are twisted into a double α-helix structure with approximately 10 nucleotide pairs per 360° turn (Fig. 31.21). The strongest hydrogen bonds form between

Figure 31.21

The double helix structure of deoxyribonucleic acid (DNA). (left) Model of the double-stranded α-helix. (right) Schematic drawing.

Figure 31.22
The hydrogen bonds in A-T and G-C base pairs. (Carbon atoms in the ring are not shown.)

adenine and thymine and between guanine and cytosine (Fig. 31.22). Wherever adenine is found on one strand, thymine is found on the other, and wherever guanine is found on one strand, cytosine is found on the other. The DNA helix can accommodate only a purine base opposite a pyrimidine; this results exclusively in A-T or G-C hydrogen-bonded interactions. The sequence of nucleotides on one strand of the double helix determines the sequence on the other, and it is the *sequence* of bases that determines what information is stored.

31.11 The Genetic Code and Protein Synthesis

Modern genetics, and much of modern biochemistry, rest on the theory that the double helix of DNA serves as the medium for storing the information necessary to control the sequence in which amino acids are incorporated during protein biosynthesis. To transmit this information during cell division, the DNA molecule must be capable of faultless **replication,** meaning "copying" or "reproduction," so that each of the new cells gets a perfect copy of the information (Fig. 31.23). To be useful to the cell, the information coded within the structure of the DNA double helix must be capable of being **transcribed,** meaning "rewritten," thereby passing the information contained in DNA to another nucleic acid called messenger RNA (m-RNA). Finally, a mechanism must exist to **translate** this code from one "language" to another during assembly of the protein—specifically from the language of nucleic acids to a completely different language, the amino acid sequence of a protein.

We can summarize the three processes of replication, transcription, and translation as follows:

$$\text{DNA} \xrightarrow{\text{Replication}} \text{DNA} \xrightarrow{\text{Transcription}} \text{m-RNA} \xrightarrow{\text{Translation}} \text{Protein}$$

Figure 31.23

Autoradiograph of replicating DNA from *E. coli*. Replication started in the bacterium at 12 o'clock and produced the two strands that converge in the circle at 3 o'clock on the large loop.

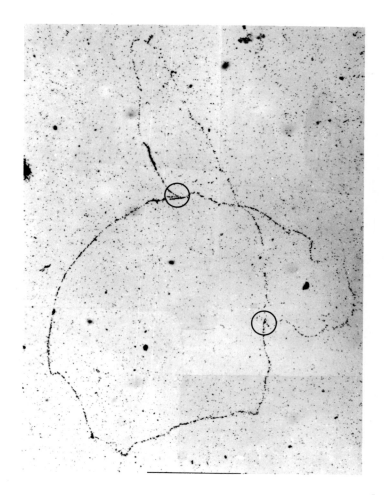

These three processes are very important in understanding the relationship between heredity and protein synthesis and thus are considered central to the subject of molecular biology. We will now consider each of the three processes in greater detail.

The successful replication of the DNA double helix is based on the preference of adenine (A) on one strand of a double helix for thymine (T) on the complementary strand and on the preference of guanine (G) for cytosine (C) on the complementary strand. The first step in the replication of DNA during cell division involves the binding of certain proteins that separate a portion of the double helix into two single strands of DNA. Each strand is then copied by the formation of new segments with A in the strand bonded to T in the new segment, G to C, T to A, and C to G. Replication proceeds until two identical copies of the original DNA molecule are formed. Replication is a semiconservative process; each resulting double strand contains one strand from the parent DNA molecule (Fig. 31.24).

In its sequence of bases, DNA stores the information that enables a cell to synthesize any of several thousand different proteins. This information is processed in a two-step mechanism. In transcription, an RNA complement of one strand of the DNA double helix is synthesized under the control of certain enzymes. This segment of RNA carries the message contained in the DNA molecule, so it is called **messenger RNA,** or

Figure 31.24

The replication of the DNA double helix. Both strands are copied simultaneously. One new strand is a continuous strand (the leading strand), and one new strand is fragmented (Okazaki fragments; the lagging strand). The fragmented strand is then joined together. The overall process is semiconservative, because each copy retains one strand from the parent molecule.

Original strand

Continuous new strand
$3' \longleftarrow 5'$

Fragmented new strand
$5' \longrightarrow 3'$

DNA double helix

New m-RNA

m-RNA. Just as the two strands of the DNA double helix run in opposite directions, the m-RNA segment synthesized during transcription is a reversed copy of the original DNA strand (Fig. 31.25), with one major difference—RNA contains the nucleotide uracil, whereas DNA contains thymine. Thus the base pairs used during transcription are A-U and G-C.

Now that the basic information from DNA is transcribed onto a messenger RNA segment, we must have a system for translating that information into an amino acid sequence, a protein. The second step in the mechanism of processing the information contained within the DNA double helix is therefore called **translation.** During translation the m-RNA segment serves as the template on which the protein is synthesized. The synthesis of a protein takes place in a ribosome (Section 31.1), which contains both proteins and a second form of RNA known as **ribosomal RNA, or r-RNA.** The first step in translation, then, is binding of the m-RNA segment to a ribosome. The amino acids are transported to the ribosome by a third form of RNA known as **transfer RNA,** or **t-RNA.** The t-RNA molecules are the smallest of all the nucleic acid structures. Individual t-RNA molecules, each carrying an amino acid, enter the ribosome and bind to the m-RNA chain at specific positions through hydrogen bonds analogous to those linking the base pairs in the DNA double helix. The amino acids are then joined to form a polypeptide chain. The process is repeated, increasing the size of the polypeptide chain. The elongation of the chain continues until a "chain termination" group of bases on the m-RNA is encountered, whereupon the ribosome releases both the finished polypeptide chain and the m-RNA segment.

The sequence of nucleotides in a DNA strand is the basis for coding the sequence of amino acids in proteins. Each sequence of three adjacent nucleotides (a code word or **codon**) is specific for a single amino acid. There are 64 possible codons and only 20 amino acids to be coded. Among the codons are three that signal chain termination: UAA, UGA, and UAG (Table 31.1).

The identity of the amino acid coded by any three-nucleotide sequence, or codon, on an m-RNA segment can be determined from the genetic code dictionary in Table 31.1. The structure of a single strand of DNA is always written with the 5′ end at the left and the 3′ end at the right—that is, in the 5′ → 3′ direction.

Figure 31.25

The transcription of a sequence of messenger RNA on the template of one strand of a DNA double helix. Note that the messenger RNA chain is the complement of the DNA strand being copied.

Table 31.1		The Amino Acids Coded by Specific Triplets (Codons) of Nucleotide Residues on Messenger RNA			
First Position (5′ end)	Second Position				Third Position (3′ end)
	U	C	A	G	
U	Phe	Ser	Tyr	Cys	U
	Phe	Ser	Tyr	Cys	C
	Leu	Ser	Term[a]	Term[a]	A
	Leu	Ser	Term[a]	Trp	G
C	Leu	Pro	His	Arg	U
	Leu	Pro	His	Arg	C
	Leu	Pro	Gln	Arg	A
	Leu	Pro	Gln	Arg	G
A	Ile	Thr	Asn	Ser	U
	Ile	Thr	Asn	Ser	C
	Ile	Thr	Lys	Arg	A
	Met	Thr	Lys	Arg	G
G	Val	Ala	Asp	Gly	U
	Val	Ala	Asp	Gly	C
	Val	Ala	Glu	Gly	A
	Val	Ala	Glu	Gly	G

[a]The three codons UAA, UGA, and UAG code for the termination of the polypeptide chain.

Example 31.1

What is the sequence of amino acids coded by the following sequence of nucleotides on a strand of DNA, reading from the 5′ end to the 3′ end?

$$^{5'}\text{A-T-C-G-C-T-A-C-G-A-A-T}^{3'}$$

The m-RNA segment that forms on this DNA template is the complement of this sequence and runs in the opposite direction. Thus the m-RNA chain, reading from the 3′ end to the 5′ end, would be U-A-G-C-G-A-U-G-C-U-U-A. Reading this message in the other direction, from the 5′ to the 3′ end, yields the triplets AUU, CGU, AGC, and GAU, which code for the sequence Ile-Arg-Ser-Asp, reading from the N- to the C-terminal amino acid.

All of the information necessary for the synthesis of the 2000–3000 different proteins found in the simplest cell is contained in the DNA molecules of the cell's **chromosomes.** The portion of the DNA molecule that codes for a single polypeptide chain is known as a **gene.** Each gene is specific for the synthesis of a single kind of protein, although multiple copies of a gene may be found on a chromosome.

To put the vast amount of information carried by DNA into perspective, consider that the entire genetic material of humans, which is called the **human genome,** consists of 3 billion nucleotides! These 3 billion units are contained in the 23 pairs of human chromosomes, which are strands of DNA associated with proteins varying in length from 50 million to 500 million nucleotides. This DNA contains (houses) the information for approximately 100,000 genes. Even so, about 95% of DNA is thought to be ''junk.'' It may have some as-yet-unknown function, but it does not code for any particular gene.

As the 1990s continue, two rather controversial topics have arisen concerning DNA: the human genome project and DNA ''fingerprinting.'' The aim of the human genome project is to determine the sequence of all the base pairs in the human genome. This task will be time-consuming and extremely costly. Current estimates suggest a cost of $200 million per year for 15 years. Many scientists feel that the benefits will not justify the cost, but advocates predict that the resulting information will have great impact on our ability to control major human diseases. DNA fingerprinting or profiling is based on the fact that considerable variation is found in the DNA of each individual. This is not surprising given the incredible amount of genetic information stored in DNA. Thus DNA typing has great potential to be useful in forensics (legal settings where identification of criminals is crucial). However, because this typing is an experimental determination, appropriate standards for both the analytical and interpretational aspects must be developed. Only then can DNA fingerprinting be admitted as evidence in court.

31.12 Recombinant DNA Technology

We have noted that DNA contains subunits, repeated many times, that are used to store the information necessary for life. DNA specifies all our physical characteristics. DNA molecules are divided into regions called genes, each of which is responsible for specific characteristics of an organism. For example, certain genes are responsible for determining eye color and others for determining blood type.

In the mid-1970s, scientists discovered how to cut DNA strands and to transfer particular pieces, containing specific information, from one organism to another, thereby changing the characteristics of the second organism. This procedure has come to be known as **recombinant DNA technology.**

The recipient organisms are most often bacteria. As the bacteria reproduce, the fragment of transferred DNA and the recipient organism are both duplicated **(cloned)** many times, producing millions of identical cells called a **clone of cells.** Thus it is possible to obtain millions of copies of a particular piece of a DNA chain by placing it in a bacterial cell and allowing the cell to multiply. This gene cloning is part of a process known as **genetic engineering.**

Several steps are necessary in carrying out these procedures:

1. Lyze (break open) live donor cells.
2. Remove genetic material from the cells.
3. Cut specific genes of interest away from the other parts of the DNA chain.
4. Splice the cut-away DNA sections into small DNA molecules, called **cloning vehicles,** that can penetrate the walls of a live host cell.
5. Transfer the cloning vehicle and the genes spliced into it into the host cell, which might be a single-celled bacterial organism or yeast.
6. Allow the host cell to multiply to a clone that has millions of identical cells.

Through these steps, a gene can be transferred into a cell where it would never occur naturally. Gene cloning is a procedure for transferring small pieces of genetic information from one organism to another, thereby altering the characteristics of the recipient organism in predictable and (it is hoped) useful ways.

There have been notable successes in recombinant DNA technology. Improvement in the isolation of human growth hormone and in the manufacture of insulin are two examples. The insulin gene in human DNA contains information for producing insulin. Before gene cloning was developed, insulin could be obtained only by an expensive process of extracting it from the pancreas of hogs and cattle. Now, through gene cloning techniques, large quantities of insulin are produced much more easily inside bacteria, using human insulin genes. This has the added advantage that the product is identical to human insulin, which is important to the many diabetic persons who are allergic to foreign insulin.

Another example is the use of genetically altered bacteria to inhibit frost damage in plants, which causes an estimated $1.6 billion in annual damage to agriculture in the United States. The first two authorized outdoor tests of the procedure, in 1987, involved spraying strawberries and potatoes with bacteria altered to eliminate frost-inducing characteristics.

Research is proceeding with great caution. Gene transplantation provides the potential for control of the genetic makeup of plants and animals, including human beings. Some applications would necessitate choices that raise profound ethical and moral issues.

㉛.13 Gene Mutations

Gene mutations are substitutions, deletions, or additions of one or more nucleotides in the DNA molecule. **Mutations** may be either beneficial or harmful to a living species.

An example of gene mutation results in **sickle-cell anemia,** which affects approximately three of every thousand Americans of African descent (Fig. 31.26). In sickle-cell anemia, the red blood cells contain an abnormal hemoglobin (a large protein) in which just one negatively charged glutamic acid residue at the sixth position of the beta chain of normal adult hemoglobin is replaced by an uncharged valine residue.

Normal adult hemoglobin:	Val-His-Leu-Thr-Pro-Glu-Glu-Lys . . .
Abnormal adult hemoglobin:	Val-His-Leu-Thr-Pro-Val -Glu-Lys . . .
	1 2 3 4 5 6 7 8

The difference in the electrical charge causes the abnormal hemoglobin to have a hydrophobic section (neutral Val), whereas the normal hemoglobin has a corresponding

Figure 31.26

Photo of normal (circular) red blood cells and (crescent-shaped) sickled cells from sickle-cell anemia.

hydrophilic section (negative Glu). This difference causes the abnormal hemoglobin, particularly in its deoxygenated form, to be considerably less soluble in water than normal hemoglobin is. The abnormal hemoglobin tends to precipitate in the red blood cells, causing the cells to "sickle" and sometimes burst. The sickled cells block the flow of blood to the capillaries, resulting in the painful effects of sickle-cell anemia.

Persons with sickle-cell trait (one abnormal gene) or sickle-cell anemia (two abnormal genes), for reasons not well understood, have a high resistance to malaria, illustrating that even the same gene mutation can have both beneficial and harmful effects. It is particularly striking that both these effects of the sickle-cell mutation arise from the substitution of a *single* nucleotide base in the gene that controls the synthesis of the beta chain of a hemoglobin molecule that contains a total of 574 amino acid residues.

31.14 Metabolism

The term **metabolism** is used to describe the chemical reactions that take place in living organisms. Metabolism includes the reactions in the cell that produce energy, capture nutrients for the synthesis of biomolecules, degrade macromolecules to produce the basic building blocks for future construction, and shuffle intermediates between more abundant and less abundant species. Metabolism results in either the synthesis or the degradation of a compound. **Anabolic pathways** result in the synthesis of a substance, and **catabolic pathways** lead to the degradation of a substance.

The energy required for the growth and maintenance of cells is provided by metabolic reactions of three general types: photosynthesis, respiration, and fermentation. **Photosynthesis** is an endothermic process by which the chloroplasts of green plants and algae convert light into chemical energy. Photosynthetic reactions lead to the reaction of carbon dioxide and water producing oxygen and a carbohydrate, such as glucose.

$$6CO_2 + 6H_2O \xrightarrow{\text{Light}} C_6H_{12}O_6 + 6O_2 \qquad \Delta G° = 2870 \text{ kJ mol}^{-1}$$

Respiration is a set of reactions that provide energy through the metabolic degradation, or catabolism, of organic compounds. The reactions involved in respiration can be divided into two categories: (1) those that can occur in the absence of molecular oxygen **(anaerobic reactions),** and (2) those that require oxygen **(aerobic reactions).** Anaerobic pathways typically do not lead to a net oxidation or reduction of a metabolic intermediate; they liberate significantly smaller amounts of energy than do the oxidation–reduction reactions that accompany aerobic pathways. **Fermentation** can be aerobic or anaerobic, but it does not involve an electron transport chain as respiration does.

The sequence of reactions involved in the anaerobic degradation of glucose is known collectively as **glycolysis.** Glycolysis ultimately degrades a single molecule of glucose into two pyruvate ions, with the release of more than 200 kilojoules of energy per mole of glucose consumed.

Glucose   Pyruvate ion

Anaerobic organisms, such as the yeast cells used in the production of alcohol by the fermentation of sugars, convert the pyruvate produced in glycolysis to acetaldehyde and then to ethanol.

Aerobic organisms ultimately convert pyruvate into carbon dioxide and water through a sequence of reactions known as the **citric acid cycle** or the **Krebs cycle.** The net reaction in aerobic organisms is the opposite of the photosynthetic reaction and liberates approximately 2870 kilojoules per mole of glucose consumed.

$$C_6H_{12}O_6 + 6O_2 \longrightarrow 6CO_2 + 6H_2O \qquad \Delta G° = -2870 \text{ kJ mol}^{-1}$$

About 50% of the energy released during the degradation of glucose is lost in the form of heat. The remainder is stored as chemical energy through the synthesis of nucleoside triphosphates such as **adenosine triphosphate, ATP.**

ATP and the related triphosphates GTP, CTP, and UTP can react with water to produce adenosine diphosphate, ADP (or GDP, CDP, or UDP) and the phosphate ion, with the release of approximately 31 kilojoules per mole of the triphosphate. The nucleoside diphosphates, such as ADP, can undergo further reaction to form nucleoside monophosphates, such as AMP, with the release of an additional 30 kilojoules per mole. The nucleoside triphosphates, and to some extent the diphosphates, serve as the cell's short-term energy-storage mechanism. ATP, for example, is synthesized from AMP and ADP during the degradation of carbohydrates, proteins, and lipids. When the cell needs energy either to drive a chemical reaction, such as the synthesis of proteins from amino acids, or for a mechanical process, such as the contraction of a muscle, ATP or its equivalent is consumed.

Glycolysis and the citric acid cycle are important means of producing biological energy in the form of ATP, but these pathways have other functions as well. There are several points where intermediates are produced that can be used in the synthesis of amino acids, or where intermediates from degradation of amino acids and proteins can be inserted for eventual conversion to carbohydrates. The metabolism of carbohydrates and the metabolism of proteins are therefore intimately related, as are those of carbohydrates and the complex lipids.

The complete degradation of either carbohydrates or lipids leads eventually to the same products: carbon dioxide and water. However, $2\frac{1}{2}$ times more energy per gram is released during the oxidation of fats. In times of plenty (that is, when biological energy is abundant), the cell first stores this energy by synthesizing ATP from ADP and/or AMP. Once this short-term storage capacity is exceeded, the cell may store additional energy by synthesizing carbohydrates. These carbohydrates may then be linked to form polysaccharides such as glycogen and starch, which serve as a more efficient means of storing energy for times of shortage. In times of extreme plenty, the cell stores excess energy in the form of complex lipids, or fats. Each of these forms of storage—ATP, carbohydrate, polysaccharide, and lipid—represents a progressively more efficient means of storing excess energy during times of plenty to provide for times of shortage that could come.

31.15 Viruses

Viruses consist of a protein coat, called a **capsid,** around a nucleic acid core. Viruses are much smaller than bacteria, ranging in size from 0.02 to 0.04 micrometers (μm) compared to about 1 μm for a prokaryotic cell and 10 to 20 μm for a eukaryotic cell (Section 31.1).

The overall shapes of viruses vary, depending largely on the arrangement of the capsids. Common shapes include rods, filaments, and spheres (Fig. 31.27).

When infecting an organism, a virus invades certain of the organism's cells and interrupts the transcription and translation function of the cell (Section 31.11). Instead of producing cellular DNA and proteins, the cell produces copies of the virus's DNA and the proteins of its coat; thus many copies of the virus are replicated. Cells reproduce the virus until they become filled with the virus and burst, releasing new virus to continue

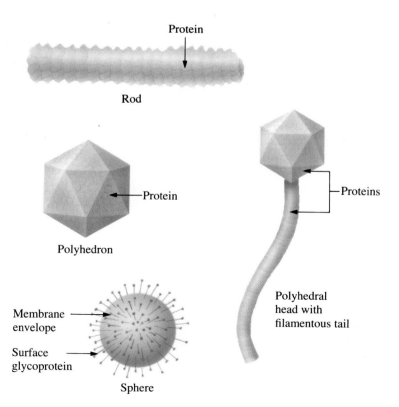

Figure 31.27

Some typical shapes of viruses.

the infection. Infection by viruses is responsible for many diseases—for example, measles, smallpox, mumps, influenza, and rabies in animals; and tobacco mosaic and tomato bushy stunt in plants.

㉛.16 Antibody Immune Response

The body has two basic defense mechanisms against infections. The first results when white blood cells ingest and destroy foreign matter. The second occurs when special cells in the body produce **antibodies** (an **antibody immune response**), large protein molecules that combine with and deactivate antigens. **Antigens** are materials that the body considers foreign; they include bacteria, viruses, and other substances. Antibodies are manufactured by **lymphocytes,** cells that are produced in bone marrow and in the lymphatic tissues (the lymph nodes, the spleen, and the thymus) when the cells are stimulated by the presence of an antigen. The antibodies function by forming complexes with the antigens that are then destroyed by cells of the body's immune system.

The bloodstream carries the antibodies to the body tissues. The antibody proteins released into the bloodstream are called **immunoglobulins,** the most common of which are the **gamma globulins.** Gamma globulin antibodies, which have been studied extensively, have been found to consist of pairs of high and low molecular mass peptide chains, arranged in a Y shape.

Many of the amino acid sequences are similar for various antibodies, but short variable regions exist in both the heavy (high molecular mass) and the light (low molecular mass) chains. The antigens bond to these variable regions. The formation of the antibody–antigen complexes is responsible for the destruction of the antigen. A single kind of antibody binds only to one kind of antigen. Huge numbers of kinds of antigens exist, but fortunately, the body can manufacture so many different variable regions that binding can occur for almost every antigen. The number of antibodies that can be synthesized by the body is enormous—trillions of antibodies and millions of different types each minute or two. When a particular antigen shows up, the appropriate lymphocytes are activated and synthesize many additional copies of the proper antibody.

The invasion of a certain class of human white blood cells, the helper T-lymphocytes, by the human immunodeficiency viruses HIV-1 and HIV-2 (and perhaps other HIV viruses) leads to the condition called **acquired immune deficiency syndrome, AIDS.** The infecting virus destroys these T-lymphocyte cells and, thus, the body's ability to produce certain antibodies. Death from AIDS results from the body's inability to defend itself from other infections because it cannot produce these antibodies to fight these new infections.

For Review

Summary

Molecules present in living organisms are called biomolecules and are often divided into four classes—proteins, carbohydrates, lipids, and nucleic acids—each having its own structure and functions.

Proteins are polymers composed of **amino acids,** molecules with the general formula H_3N^+—CHR—CO_2^-. The 20 amino acids that are genetically coded into proteins are distinguished by the nature of the R side chain on the α-carbon. Most amino acids are optically active. The combination of two or more amino acids by formation of **peptide bonds,**

$$\underset{\overset{\displaystyle \|}{}}{-C}-NH-$$

$$O$$

produces a **peptide.** Proteins are large **polypeptides** that can fulfill a variety of functions because their structures vary widely. The **primary structure** of a protein is the order in which its amino acids are connected. The **secondary structure** is produced by the folding of the chain of amino acids to maximize hydrogen bonding between peptide bonds; the **α-helix** and the **β-pleated sheet** are common secondary structures. The **tertiary structure** results when a helical or sheet structure is folded into a complex conformation that is produced and stabilized by interactions between amino-acid side chains. The **quaternary structure** describes how separate polypeptide chains within a large protein are related to each other. One of the most remarkable classes of proteins consists of the **enzymes,** which are catalysts of biochemical reactions.

Carbohydrates are aldehydes or ketones that have two or more —OH groups and that can be energy sources or energy stores in plants and animals. The simplest carbohydrates are the **monosaccharides,** such as the sugars glucose and fructose. **Disaccharides** are dimers composed of two monosaccharides; sucrose, for example, consists of glucose and fructose. **Starch** (a food storage carbohydrate found in plants), **glycogen** (a food storage carbohydrate found in animals), and **cellulose** (the carbohydrate that is the structural component of plants) are all **polysaccharides,** large polymers formed from glucose.

Fats and **oils** are members of the class of molecules known as **complex lipids,** esters formed from long-chain carboxylic acids (**fatty acids**) and glycerol. The closely related **phosphoglycerides** serve as the basis for cell membranes. **Simple lipids,** which include vitamin A and the steroids, do not contain fatty acids.

Nucleic acids are polymers of very high molecular masses that store and transfer genetic information. They also determine which proteins are synthesized by a cell. A nucleic acid consists of a polymeric chain of alternating phosphate groups and ribofuranose rings with nitrogen-containing bases bonded to the rings. The **DNA** polymer is a **double helix** that is held together by hydrogen bonds between pairs of specific bases, one on each strand of the helix. This base pairing makes each strand a complement of the other. The sequence of groups of three adjacent nucleotides (**codons**) in a DNA strand is the basis for coding the sequence of amino acids in proteins.

Protein synthesis is carried out in the body through a series of steps referred to as **replication, transcription,** and **translation.**

Gene mutations, such as those that occur in sickle-cell anemia, are substitutions, deletions, or additions of one or more nucleotides in the DNA molecule. Mutations can have both harmful and beneficial effects.

Research with **recombinant DNA** is a relatively new field that seeks to alter the nature of the protein being synthesized by cleaving the DNA chain, inserting a new piece of DNA in the opening, and resealing the chain.

Viruses (consisting of a protein coat, called a capsid, around a nucleic acid core) are responsible for a number of diseases that result from infection of cells by the viruses. The body sets up a defense against chronic infections through an **antibody immune response.**

The possible benefits to society from research in such fields as recombinant DNA are virtually without limit. Important moral and ethical choices must be made, and the work must proceed with caution and good judgment.

Key Terms and Concepts

acquired immune deficiency syn-
    drome, AIDS (31.16)
adenosine triphosphate, ATP (31.14)
aerobic reaction (31.14)
aldose (31.7)
α-helix (31.4)
amino acid (31.2)
amino acid sequence (31.3)
anabolic pathway (31.14)
anaerobic reaction (31.14)
antibody (31.16)
antibody immune response (31.16)
antigen (31.16)
β-pleated sheet (31.4)
carbohydrate (31.6)
catabolic pathway (31.14)
cell (31.1)
cellulose (31.8)
chloroplasts (31.1)
chromosome (31.11)
cloning (31.12)
codon (31.11)
cytoplasm (31.1)
cytosol (31.1)
deoxyribonucleic acid, DNA (31.10)

disaccharide (31.8)
double helix (31.10)
enzyme (31.4, 31.5)
eukaryotic (31.1)
fatty acids (31.9)
gene (31.11)
gene cloning (31.12)
gene mutation (31.13)
genetic code (31.11)
glycolysis (31.14)
glycoprotein (31.8)
hydrophilic (31.1)
hydrophobic (31.1)
immunoglobulin (31.16)
inhibition (31.5)
ketose (31.7)
lipid (31.9)
metabolism (31.14)
mitochondria (31.1)
monosaccharide (31.7)
nucleic acid (31.10)
nucleoside (31.10)
nucleotide (31.10)
oligopeptide (31.3)
peptide (31.3)

photosynthesis (31.14)
polypeptide (31.3)
polysaccharide (31.8)
primary structure (31.4)
prokaryotic (31.1)
protein (31.2, 31.3, 31.4)
protein structure (31.4)
protein synthesis (31.11)
purine (31.10)
pyrimidine (31.10)
quaternary structure (31.4)
recombinant DNA (31.12)
replication (31.11)
ribonucleic acid, RNA (31.10,
    31.11)
ribosomes (31.1)
saponification (31.9)
secondary structure (31.4)
steroids (31.9)
terpenes (31.9)
tertiary structure (31.4)
transcription (31.11)
translation (31.11)
virus (31.15)
zwitterion (31.2)

Exercises

Answers for selected even-numbered exercises marked by red numbers appear at the end of the book. The worked-out solutions to all even-numbered exercises appear in the *Solutions Guide*.

1. List the four principal chemical constituents of living cells. Identify the specific functions of each of these constituents.
2. Define *hydrophilic* and *hydrophobic*. What factor or factors determine whether a compound is hydrophilic or hydrophobic? Give an example of each class of compound.

Proteins

3. Define the following: amino acid, peptide, and protein.
4. Distinguish among the primary, secondary, tertiary, and quaternary structures of a protein.
5. Define what is meant by *denaturation*.
6. Define the following: enzyme, substrate, and product.
7. Describe what happens to the rate of an enzyme-catalyzed reaction from the instant that the enzyme and substrate are mixed until the substrate is consumed.
8. Into what simpler components may a protein be reduced?
9. Write the structure of the tripeptide Cys-Lys-Glu at neutral pH.

10. Write symbolic formulas for all of the possible tripeptides that could be formed from the amino acids Gly, Ala, and Val.
11. Describe the process of protein synthesis by the body and indicate its significance.
12. Fungal lactase, a blue protein found in wood-rotting fungi, contains approximately 0.397% copper by mass. If the molecular mass of fungal lactase is approximately 64,000 amu, how many copper atoms are there in each protein molecule?

Carbohydrates

13. What is the literal meaning of *carbohydrate,* and how did this name arise?
14. Which carbon atoms in glucose are asymmetric (Section 30.6)?
15. How does a pyranose differ from a furanose?
16. Write the name and formula for one example each of a monosaccharide, a disaccharide, and a polysaccharide.
17. What is the difference between the α and β isomers of glucopyranose?
18. How many grams of invert sugar can be produced by the reaction of 1.00 g of sucrose, $C_{12}H_{22}O_{11}$, with water?

Lipids

19. Write the general formula for a neutral fat. How do fats and oils differ in composition?
20. Define saponification and write an equation for the saponification of tripalmitylglycerol, the triester of palmitic acid, $CH_3(CH_2)_{14}CO_2H$.
21. Explain why the triacylglycerols do not form micelles.
22. The molecular mass of an unknown triglyceride can be estimated by determining the mass of KOH required to saponify a known mass of lipid. What is the molecular mass of a triglyceride if 3.12 mg of the triglyceride requires 0.590 mg of KOH for saponification?

Nucleic Acids

23. What is the connection between nucleic acids, amino acids, and proteins?
24. Write the complete structure of the following segment of DNA, reading from the 5′ end to the 3′ end: G-T-C-A.
25. If a single strand of DNA contains the nucleotide sequence A-G-G-C-T-C-A-G-C-T-A-G, reading from the 5′ to the 3′ carbon, what would be the sequence of nucleotides on the complementary strand of the DNA double helix, reading in the same direction?
26. What would be (a) the product of replication and (b) the product of transcription of the following fragment of a DNA molecule?

    5′   G-T-C-A-A-T-G-G-A   3′

27. What is the difference between the nucleotides adenosine monophosphate and deoxyadenosine monophosphate?
28. Complete the following table.

	DNA	RNA
Sugar unit		
Purine bases		
Pyrimidine bases		

29. What is a virus? What is its effect within the body?
30. Explain how sickle-cell anemia occurs.
31. Contrast cysteine and cystine.

32. How does the body build a defense against chronic infection?

Additional Exercises

33. Discuss the manner in which the energy requirements of a cell are satisfied.
34. How would you explain the observation that proteins can contain additional amino acids that are structurally related to the 20 genetically coded amino acids?
35. What sequence of amino acids would be specified by a single strand of DNA containing the nucleotide sequence A-G-G-C-T-C-A-G-C-T-A-G, reading from the 5′ to the 3′ carbon?
36. What evidence do we have that a twenty-first genetically coded amino acid will not be found?
37. Would the alanine in a solution with a pH of 5.0 migrate toward a positive electrode, migrate toward a negative electrode, or show no preference for either electrode upon electrolysis of the solution?
38. The synthesis of organic molecules in nature from carbon dioxide and water is an endothermic process. What is the source of the required energy?
39. Distinguish between aerobic and anaerobic processes.
40. What is recombinant DNA technology, and what are some of its consequences for society? What ethical and moral concerns arise? Cite examples of potential benefits and of potential problems.
41. In what sense can sucrose be considered an anhydride?
42. The degradation of both fatty acids, such as palmitic acid, and carbohydrates, such as glucose, leads to the formation of carbon dioxide and water. However, the degradation of palmitic acid produces $2\frac{1}{2}$ times as much energy as that of glucose, per gram of substance consumed. Explain this observation in terms of the average oxidation numbers of the carbon atoms in fatty acids, carbohydrates, and carbon dioxide.
43. If the degradation of 1 mol of glucose and that of 1 mol of palmitic acid yield 38 and 129 mol of ATP, respectively, calculate the moles of ATP produced per gram of lipid or carbohydrate consumed. The formula of palmitic acid is $CH_3(CH_2)_{14}CO_2H$.

Appendixes

Appendix A: Chemical Arithmetic

ⒶA.1 Exponential Arithmetic

Exponential notation is used to express very large and very small numbers as a product of two numbers. The first number of the product, the *digit term,* is usually a number not less than 1 and not greater than 10. The second number of the product, the *exponential term,* is written as 10 with an exponent. Some examples of exponential notation are

$$1000 = 1 \times 10^3 \qquad 0.01 = 1 \times 10^{-2}$$
$$100 = 1 \times 10^2 \qquad 0.001 = 1 \times 10^{-3}$$
$$10 = 1 \times 10^1 \qquad 2386 = 2.386 \times 1000 = 2.386 \times 10^3$$
$$1 = 1 \times 10^0 \qquad 0.123 = 1.23 \times 0.1 = 1.23 \times 10^{-1}$$
$$0.1 = 1 \times 10^{-1}$$

The power (exponent) of 10 is equal to the number of places the decimal is shifted to give the digit number. The exponential method is a particularly useful notation for very large and very small numbers. For example, $1{,}230{,}000{,}000 = 1.23 \times 10^9$ and $0.00000000036 = 3.6 \times 10^{-10}$.

1. **Addition of Exponentials.** Convert all numbers to the same power of 10, add the digit terms of the numbers, and, if appropriate, convert the digit term back to a number between 1 and 10 by adjusting the exponential term.

Add 5.00×10^{-5} and 3.00×10^{-3}.

$$3.00 \times 10^{-3} = 300 \times 10^{-5}$$
$$(5.00 \times 10^{-5}) + (300 \times 10^{-5}) = 305 \times 10^{-5} = 3.05 \times 10^{-3}$$

Example A.1

---

2. **Subtraction of Exponentials.** Convert all numbers to the same power of 10, take the difference of the digit terms, and, if appropriate, convert the digit term back to a number between 1 and 10 by adjusting the exponential term.

Subtract 4.0×10^{-7} from 5.0×10^{-6}.

$$4.0 \times 10^{-7} = 0.40 \times 10^{-6}$$

$$(5.0 \times 10^{-6}) - (0.40 \times 10^{-6}) = 4.6 \times 10^{-6}$$

Example A.2

---

3. Multiplication of Exponentials. Multiply the digit terms in the usual way and add the exponents of the exponential terms.

Example A.3

Multiply 4.2×10^{-8} by 2×10^3.

$$(4.2 \times 10^{-8}) \times (2 \times 10^3) = (4.2 \times 2) \times 10^{(-8)+(+3)} = 8.4 \times 10^{-5}$$

---

4. Division of Exponentials. Divide the digit term of the numerator by the digit term of the denominator and subtract the exponents of the exponential terms.

Example A.4

Divide 3.6×10^{-5} by 6×10^{-4}.

$$\frac{3.6 \times 10^{-5}}{6 \times 10^{-4}} = \left(\frac{3.6}{6}\right) \times 10^{(-5)-(-4)} = 0.6 \times 10^{-1} = 6 \times 10^{-2}$$

---

5. Squaring of Exponentials. Square the digit term in the usual way and multiply the exponent of the exponential term by 2.

Example A.5

Square the number 4.0×10^{-6}.

$$(4.0 \times 10^{-6})^2 = 4 \times 4 \times 10^{2\times(-6)} = 16 \times 10^{-12} = 1.6 \times 10^{-11}$$

---

6. Cubing of Exponentials. Cube the digit term in the usual way and multiply the exponent of the exponential term by 3.

Example A.6

Cube the number 2×10^4.

$$(2 \times 10^4)^3 = 2 \times 2 \times 2 \times 10^{3\times4} = 8 \times 10^{12}$$

---

7. Taking Square Roots of Exponentials. If necessary, decrease or increase the exponential term so that the power of 10 is evenly divisible by 2. Extract the square root of the digit term and divide the exponential term by 2.

Example A.7

Find the square root of 1.6×10^{-7}.

$$1.6 \times 10^{-7} = 16 \times 10^{-8}$$
$$\sqrt{16 \times 10^{-8}} = \sqrt{16} \times \sqrt{10^{-8}} = \sqrt{16} \times 10^{-8/2} = 4.0 \times 10^{-4}$$

A.2 Significant Figures

A beekeeper reports that he has 525,341 bees. The last three figures of the number are obviously inaccurate, for during the time the keeper was counting the bees, some of them died and others hatched; this makes it quite difficult to determine the exact number of bees. It would have been more accurate if the beekeeper had reported the number 525,000. In other words, the last three figures are not significant, except to set the position of the decimal point. Their exact values have no meaning. In reporting any information as numbers, use only as many significant figures as the accuracy of the measurement warrants.

The importance of significant figures lies in their application to fundamental computation. In addition and subtraction, the last digit that is retained in the sum or difference should correspond to the first doubtful decimal place (indicated by underscoring in the following example).

Add 4.383 g and 0.0023 g.

$$4.38\underline{3} \text{ g}$$
$$0.002\underline{3}$$
$$\overline{4.38\underline{5} \text{ g}}$$

**Example
A.8**

In multiplication and division, the product or quotient should contain no more digits than the least number of significant figures in the numbers involved in the computation.

Multiply 0.6238 by 6.6.

$$0.623\underline{8} \times 6.\underline{6} = 4.\underline{1}$$

**Example
A.9**

In rounding off numbers, increase the last digit retained by 1 if it is followed by a number larger than 5 or by a 5 followed by other nonzero digits. Do not change the last digit retained if the following digits are less than 5. If the last digit retained is followed by 5, increase the last digit retained by 1 if it is odd and leave the last digit retained unchanged if it is even.

Ⓐ.3 The Use of Logarithms and Exponential Numbers

The common logarithm of a number (log) is the power to which 10 must be raised to equal that number. For example, the common logarithm of 100 is 2 because 10 must be raised to the second power to equal 100. Additional examples follow.

Number	Number Expressed Exponentially	Common Logarithm
1000	10^3	3
10	10^1	1
1	10^0	0
0.1	10^{-1}	-1
0.001	10^{-3}	-3

What is the common logarithm of 60? Because 60 lies between 10 and 100, which have logarithms of 1 and 2, respectively, the logarithm of 60 must lie between 1 and 2. The logarithm of 60 is 1.7782; that is,

$$60 = 10^{1.7782}$$

The common logarithm of a number less than 1 has a negative value. The logarithm of 0.03918 is -1.4069; or

$$0.03918 = 10^{-1.4069} = \frac{1}{10^{1.4069}}$$

To obtain the common logarithm of a number, use the *log* button on your calculator. To calculate a number from its logarithm, enter the logarithm into your calculator and either push the *antilog* button, take the inverse log of the logarithm, or calculate 10^x (where x is the logarithm of the number).

The natural logarithm of a number (ln) is the power to which e must be raised to equal the number; e is the contant 2.7182818. For example, the natural logarithm of 10 is 2.303; that is,

$$10 = e^{2.303} = 2.7182818^{2.303}$$

To obtain the natural logarithm of a number, use the *ln* button on your calculator. To calculate a number from its natural logarithm, enter the natural logarithm and take the inverse ln of the natural logarithm, or calculate e^x (where x is the natural logarithm of the number).

Logarithms are exponents; thus operations involving logarithms follow the same rules as operations involving exponents.

1. The logarithm of a product of two numbers is the sum of the logarithms of the two numbers: $\log xy = \log x + \log y$, or $\ln xy = \ln x + \ln y$.
2. The logarithm of the number resulting from the division of two numbers is the difference between the logarithms of the two numbers: $\log x/y = \log x - \log y$, or $\ln x/y = \ln x - \ln y$.
3. The logarithm of the square root of a number is one-half of the logarithm of the number: $\log x^{1/2} = 1/2 \log x$, or $\ln x^{1/2} = 1/2 \ln x$.
4. The logarithm of the cube root of a number is one-third of the logarithm of the number: $\log x^{1/3} = 1/3 \log x$, or $\ln x^{1/3} = 1/3 \ln x$.

Ⓐ.4 The Solution of Quadratic Equations

Any quadratic equation can be expressed in the following form:

$$ax^2 + bx + c = 0$$

In order to solve a quadratic equation, use the following formula:

$$x = \frac{-b \pm \sqrt{b^2 - 4ac}}{2a}$$

Solve the quadratic equation $3x^2 + 13x - 10 = 0$.

Example A.10

Substituting the values $a = 3$, $b = 13$, and $c = -10$ in the formula, we obtain

$$x = \frac{-13 \pm \sqrt{(13)^2 - 4 \times 3 \times (-10)}}{2 \times 3}$$

$$x = \frac{-13 \pm \sqrt{169 + 120}}{6} = \frac{-13 \pm \sqrt{289}}{6} = \frac{-13 \pm 17}{6}$$

The two roots are therefore

$$x = \frac{-13 + 17}{6} = 0.67 \qquad \text{and} \qquad x = \frac{-13 - 17}{6} = -5$$

Equations constructed on physical data always have real roots, and of these real roots, usually only those having positive values are of any significance.

Appendix B: Units and Conversion Factors

Units of Length

Meter (m) = 39.37 inches (in.)
           = 1.094 yards (yd)
Centimeter (cm) = 0.01 m
Millimeter (mm) = 0.001 m
Kilometer (km) = 1000 m
Angstrom unit (Å) = 10^{-8} cm
                  = 10^{-10} m

Yard = 0.9144 m
Inch = 2.54 cm (definition)
Mile (U.S.) = 1.60934 km

Units of Volume

Liter (L) = 0.001 m^3 = 1000 cm^3
        = 1.057 (U.S.) quarts
Milliliter (mL) = 0.001 L = 1 cm^3

Liquid quart (U.S.) = 0.9463 L
                = 32 (U.S.) liquid ounces
                = $\frac{1}{4}$ (U.S.) gallon
Dry quart = 1.1012 L
Cubic foot (U.S.) = 28.316 L

Units of Mass

Gram (g) = 0.001 kg
Milligram (mg) = 0.001 g
Kilogram (kg) = 1000 g = 2.205 lb
Ton (metric) = 1000 kg = 2204.62 lb

Ounce (oz) (avoirdupois) = 28.35 g
Pound (lb) (avoirdupois) = 0.45359237 kg
Ton (short) = 2000 lb = 907.185 kg
Ton (long) = 2240 lb = 1.016 metric ton

Units of Energy

4.184 joule (J) = 1 thermochemical calorie (cal) = 4.184×10^7 erg
Erg = 10^{-7} J
Electron-volt (eV) = $1.60217733 \times 10^{-19}$ J = 23.061 kcal mol^{-1}
Liter atmosphere = 24.217 cal = 101.32 J

Units of Pressure

Torr = 1 mmHg
Atmosphere (atm) = 760 mm Hg = 760 torr = 101,325 N m^{-2} = 101,325 Pa
Pascal (Pa) = kg m^{-1} s^{-2} = N m^{-2}

Appendix C: General Physical Constants

Avogadro's number	6.0221367×10^{23} mol^{-1}
Electron charge, e	$1.60217733 \times 10^{-19}$ coulomb (C)
Electron rest mass, m_e	9.109390×10^{-31} kg
Proton rest mass, m_p	$1.6726231 \times 10^{-27}$ kg
Neutron rest mass, m_n	$1.6749286 \times 10^{-27}$ kg
Charge-to-mass ratio for electron, e/m_e	$1.75881962 \times 10^{11}$ coulomb kg^{-1}
Faraday constant, F	9.6485309×10^4 coulomb/equivalent
Planck constant, h	$6.6260755 \times 10^{-34}$ J s
Boltzmann constant, k	1.380658×10^{-23} J K^{-1}
Gas constant, R	8.205784×10^{-2} L atm mol^{-1} K^{-1}
	$= 8.314510$ J mol^{-1} K^{-1}
Speed of light (in vacuum), c	2.99792458×10^8 m s^{-1}
Atomic mass unit ($= \frac{1}{12}$ the mass of an atom of the ^{12}C nuclide), amu	$1.6605402 \times 10^{-27}$ kg
Rydberg constant, R_∞	1.0973731534×10^7 m^{-1}

Appendix D: Solubility Products

Substance	K_{sp} at 25°C	Substance	K_{sp} at 25°C
Aluminum		Bismuth	
Al(OH)$_3$	1.9×10^{-33}	BiO(OH)	1×10^{-12}
Barium		BiOCl	7×10^{-9}
BaCO$_3$	8.1×10^{-9}	Bi$_2$S$_3$	7.3×10^{-91}
BaC$_2$O$_4 \cdot 2$H$_2$O	1.1×10^{-7}	Cadmium	
BaSO$_4$	1.08×10^{-10}	Cd(OH)$_2$	1.2×10^{-14}
BaCrO$_4$	2×10^{-10}	CdS	2.8×10^{-35}
BaF$_2$	1.7×10^{-6}	CdCO$_3$	2.5×10^{-14}
Ba(OH)$_2 \cdot 8$H$_2$O	5.0×10^{-3}	Calcium	
Ba$_3$(PO$_4$)$_2$	1.3×10^{-29}	Ca(OH)$_2$	7.9×10^{-6}
Ba$_3$(AsO$_4$)$_2$	1.1×10^{-13}	CaCO$_3$	4.8×10^{-9}

Solubility Products (Continued)

Substance	K_{sp} at 25°C	Substance	K_{sp} at 25°C
$CaSO_4 \cdot 2H_2O$	2.4×10^{-5}	Hg_2Cl_2	1.1×10^{-18}
$CaC_2O_4 \cdot H_2O$	2.27×10^{-9}	Hg_2Br_2	1.26×10^{-22}
$Ca_3(PO_4)_2$	1×10^{-25}	Hg_2I_2	4.5×10^{-29}
$CaHPO_4$	5×10^{-6}	Hg_2CO_3	9×10^{-17}
CaF_2	3.9×10^{-11}	Hg_2SO_4	6.2×10^{-7}
Chromium		Hg_2S	8×10^{-52}
$Cr(OH)_3$	6.7×10^{-31}	Hg_2CrO_4	2×10^{-9}
Cobalt		HgS	2×10^{-59}
$Co(OH)_2$	2×10^{-16}	Nickel	
$CoS(\alpha)$	4.5×10^{-27}	$Ni(OH)_2$	1.6×10^{-14}
$CoS(\beta)$	6.7×10^{-29}	$NiCO_3$	1.36×10^{-7}
$CoCO_3$	1.0×10^{-12}	$NiS(\alpha)$	2×10^{-27}
$Co(OH)_3$	2.5×10^{-43}	$NiS(\beta)$	8×10^{-33}
Copper		Potassium	
$CuCl$	1.85×10^{-7}	$KClO_4$	1.07×10^{-2}
$CuBr$	5.3×10^{-9}	K_2PtCl_6	1.1×10^{-5}
CuI	5.1×10^{-12}	$KHC_4H_4O_6$	3×10^{-4}
$CuSCN$	4×10^{-14}	Silver	
Cu_2S	1.2×10^{-54}	$\frac{1}{2}Ag_2O\ (Ag^+ + OH^-)$	2×10^{-8}
$Cu(OH)_2$	5.6×10^{-20}	$AgCl$	1.8×10^{-10}
CuS	6.7×10^{-42}	$AgBr$	3.3×10^{-13}
$CuCO_3$	1.37×10^{-10}	AgI	1.5×10^{-16}
Iron		$AgCN$	1.2×10^{-16}
$Fe(OH)_2$	7.9×10^{-15}	$AgSCN$	1.0×10^{-12}
$FeCO_3$	2.11×10^{-11}	Ag_2S	8×10^{-58}
FeS	8×10^{-26}	Ag_2CO_3	8.2×10^{-12}
$Fe(OH)_3$	1.1×10^{-36}	Ag_2CrO_4	9×10^{-12}
Lead		$Ag_4Fe(CN)_6$	1.55×10^{-41}
$Pb(OH)_2$	2.8×10^{-16}	Ag_2SO_4	1.18×10^{-5}
PbF_2	3.7×10^{-8}	Ag_3PO_4	1.8×10^{-18}
$PbCl_2$	1.7×10^{-5}	Strontium	
$PbBr_2$	6.3×10^{-6}	$Sr(OH)_2 \cdot 8H_2O$	3.2×10^{-4}
PbI_2	8.7×10^{-9}	$SrCO_3$	9.42×10^{-10}
$PbCO_3$	1.5×10^{-13}	$SrCrO_4$	3.6×10^{-5}
PbS	6.5×10^{-34}	$SrSO_4$	2.8×10^{-7}
$PbCrO_4$	1.8×10^{-14}	$SrC_2O_4 \cdot H_2O$	5.61×10^{-8}
$PbSO_4$	1.8×10^{-8}	Thallium	
$Pb_3(PO_4)_2$	3×10^{-44}	$TlCl$	1.9×10^{-4}
Magnesium		$TlSCN$	5.8×10^{-4}
$Mg(OH)_2$	1.5×10^{-11}	Tl_2S	9.2×10^{-31}
$MgCO_3 \cdot 3H_2O$	$ca\ 1 \times 10^{-5}$	$Tl(OH)_3$	1.5×10^{-44}
$MgNH_4PO_4$	2.5×10^{-13}	Tin	
MgF_2	6.4×10^{-9}	$Sn(OH)_2$	5×10^{-26}
MgC_2O_4	8.6×10^{-5}	SnS	6×10^{-35}
Manganese		$Sn(OH)_4$	1×10^{-56}
$Mn(OH)_2$	4.5×10^{-14}	Zinc	
$MnCO_3$	8.8×10^{-11}	$ZnCO_3$	6×10^{-11}
MnS	4.3×10^{-22}	$Zn(OH)_2$	4.5×10^{-17}
Mercury		ZnS	1×10^{-27}
$Hg_2O \cdot H_2O$	1.6×10^{-23}		

Appendix E: Formation Constants for Complex Ions

Equilibirum	K_f
$Al^{3+} + 6F^- \rightleftharpoons [AlF_6]^{3-}$	5×10^{23}
$Cd^{2+} + 4NH_3 \rightleftharpoons [Cd(NH_3)_4]^{2+}$	4.0×10^6
$Cd^{2+} + 4CN^- \rightleftharpoons [Cd(CN)_4]^{2-}$	1.3×10^{17}
$Co^{2+} + 6NH_3 \rightleftharpoons [Co(NH_3)_6]^{2+}$	8.3×10^4
$Co^{3+} + 6NH_3 \rightleftharpoons [Co(NH_3)_6]^{3+}$	4.5×10^{33}
$Cu^+ + 2CN^- \rightleftharpoons [Cu(CN)_2]^-$	1×10^{16}
$Cu^{2+} + 4NH_3 \rightleftharpoons [Cu(NH_3)_4]^{2+}$	1.2×10^{12}
$Fe^{2+} + 6CN^- \rightleftharpoons [Fe(CN)_6]^{4-}$	1×10^{37}
$Fe^{3+} + 6CN^- \rightleftharpoons [Fe(CN)_6]^{3-}$	1×10^{44}
$Fe^{3+} + 6SCN^- \rightleftharpoons [Fe(NCS)_6]^{3-}$	3.2×10^3
$Hg^{2+} + 4Cl^- \rightleftharpoons [HgCl_4]^{2-}$	1.2×10^{15}
$Ni^{2+} + 6NH_3 \rightleftharpoons [Ni(NH_3)_6]^{2+}$	1.8×10^8
$Ag^+ + 2Cl^- \rightleftharpoons [AgCl_2]^-$	2.5×10^5
$Ag^+ + 2CN^- \rightleftharpoons [Ag(CN)_2]^-$	1×10^{20}
$Ag^+ + 2NH_3 \rightleftharpoons [Ag(NH_3)_2]^+$	1.6×10^7
$Zn^{2+} + 4CN^- \rightleftharpoons [Zn(CN)_4]^{2-}$	1×10^{19}
$Zn^{2+} + 4OH^- \rightleftharpoons [Zn(OH)_4]^{2-}$	2.9×10^{15}

Appendix F: Ionization Constants of Weak Acids

Acid	Formula	K_a at 25°C
Acetic	CH_3CO_2H	1.8×10^{-5}
Arsenic	H_3AsO_4	4.8×10^{-3}
	$H_2AsO_4^-$	1×10^{-7}
	$HAsO_4^{2-}$	1×10^{-13}
Arsenous	H_3AsO_3	5.8×10^{-10}
Boric	H_3BO_3	5.8×10^{-10}
Carbonic	H_2CO_3	4.3×10^{-7}
	HCO_3^-	7×10^{-11}

Ionization Constants of Weak Acids (Continued)

Acid	Formula	K_a at 25°C
Cyanic	HCNO	3.46×10^{-4}
Formic	HCO_2H	1.8×10^{-4}
Hydrazoic	HN_3	1×10^{-4}
Hydrocyanic	HCN	4×10^{-10}
Hydrofluoric	HF	7.2×10^{-4}
Hydrogen peroxide	H_2O_2	2.4×10^{-12}
Hydrogen selenide	H_2Se	1.7×10^{-4}
	HSe^-	1×10^{-10}
Hydrogen sulfate ion	HSO_4^-	1.2×10^{-2}
Hydrogen sulfide	H_2S	1.0×10^{-7}
	HS^-	1.0×10^{-19}
Hydrogen telluride	H_2Te	2.3×10^{-3}
	HTe^-	1×10^{-5}
Hypobromous	HBrO	2×10^{-9}
Hypochlorous	HClO	3.5×10^{-8}
Nitrous	HNO_2	4.5×10^{-4}
Oxalic	$H_2C_2O_4$	5.9×10^{-2}
	$HC_2O_4^-$	6.4×10^{-5}
Phosphoric	H_3PO_4	7.5×10^{-3}
	$H_2PO_4^-$	6.3×10^{-8}
	HPO_4^{2-}	3.6×10^{-13}
Phosphorous	H_3PO_3	1.6×10^{-2}
	$H_2PO_3^-$	7×10^{-7}
Sulfurous	H_2SO_3	1.2×10^{-2}
	HSO_3^-	6.2×10^{-8}

Appendix G: Ionization Constants of Weak Bases

Base	Ionization Equation	K_b at 25°C
Ammonia	$NH_3 + H_2O \rightleftharpoons NH_4^+ + OH^-$	1.8×10^{-5}
Dimethylamine	$(CH_3)_2NH + H_2O \rightleftharpoons (CH_3)_2NH_2^+ + OH^-$	7.4×10^{-4}
Methylamine	$CH_3NH_2 + H_2O \rightleftharpoons CH_3NH_3^+ + OH^-$	4.4×10^{-4}
Phenylamine (aniline)	$C_6H_5NH_2 + H_2O \rightleftharpoons C_6H_5NH_3^+ + OH^-$	4.6×10^{-10}
Trimethylamine	$(CH_3)_3N + H_2O \rightleftharpoons (CH_3)_3NH^+ + OH^-$	7.4×10^{-5}

Appendix H: Standard Electrode (Reduction) Potentials

Half-reaction	$E°$, V	Half-reaction	$E°$, V
$Li^+ + e^- \longrightarrow Li$	-3.09	$SnS + 2e^- \longrightarrow Sn + S^{2-}$	-0.94
$K^+ + e^- \longrightarrow K$	-2.925	$Cr^{2+} + 2e^- \longrightarrow Cr$	-0.91
$Rb^+ + e^- \longrightarrow Rb$	-2.925	$Fe(OH)_2 + 2e^- \longrightarrow Fe + 2OH^-$	-0.877
$Ra^{2+} + 2e^- \longrightarrow Ra$	-2.92	$SiO_2 + 4H_3O^+ + 4e^- \longrightarrow Si + 6H_2O$	-0.86
$Ba^{2+} + 2e^- \longrightarrow Ba$	-2.90	$NiS + 2e^- \longrightarrow Ni + S^{2-}$	-0.83
$Sr^{2+} + 2e^- \longrightarrow Sr$	-2.89	$2H_2O + 2e^- \longrightarrow H_2 + 2OH^-$	-0.828
$Ca^{2+} + 2e^- \longrightarrow Ca$	-2.87	$Zn^{2+} + 2e^- \longrightarrow Zn$	-0.763
$Na^+ + e^- \longrightarrow Na$	-2.714	$Cr^{3+} + 3e^- \longrightarrow Cr$	-0.74
$La^{3+} + 3e^- \longrightarrow La$	-2.52	$HgS + 2e^- \longrightarrow Hg + S^{2-}$	-0.72
$Ce^{3+} + 3e^- \longrightarrow Ce$	-2.48	$[Cd(NH_3)_4]^{2+} + 2e^- \longrightarrow Cd + 4NH_3$	-0.597
$Nd^{3+} + 3e^- \longrightarrow Nd$	-2.44	$Ga^{3+} + 3e^- \longrightarrow Ga$	-0.53
$Sm^{3+} + 3e^- \longrightarrow Sm$	-2.41	$S + 2e^- \longrightarrow S^{2-}$	-0.48
$Gd^{3+} + 3e^- \longrightarrow Gd$	-2.40	$[Ni(NH_3)_6]^{2+} + 2e^- \longrightarrow Ni + 6NH_3$	-0.47
$Mg^{2+} + 2e^- \longrightarrow Mg$	-2.37	$Fe^{2+} + 2e^- \longrightarrow Fe$	-0.440
$Y^{3+} + 3e^- \longrightarrow Y$	-2.37	$[Cu(CN)_2]^- + e^- \longrightarrow Cu + 2CN^-$	-0.43
$Am^{3+} + 3e^- \longrightarrow Am$	-2.32	$Cr^{3+} + e^- \longrightarrow Cr^{2+}$	-0.41
$Lu^{3+} + 3e^- \longrightarrow Lu$	-2.25	$Cd^{2+} + 2e^- \longrightarrow Cd$	-0.403
$\frac{1}{2}H_2 + e^- \longrightarrow H^-$	-2.25	$Se + 2H_3O^+ + 2e^- \longrightarrow H_2Se + 2H_2O$	-0.40
$Sc^{3+} + 3e^- \longrightarrow Sc$	-2.08	$[Hg(CN)_4]^{2-} + 2e^- \longrightarrow Hg + 4CN^-$	-0.37
$[AlF_6]^{3-} + 3e^- \longrightarrow Al + 6F^-$	-2.07	$ClO_4^- + H_2O + 2e^- \longrightarrow ClO_3^- + 2OH^-$	-0.36
$Pu^{3+} + 3e^- \longrightarrow Pu$	-2.07	$PbSO_4 + 2e^- \longrightarrow Pb + SO_4^{2-}$	-0.356
$Th^{4+} + 4e^- \longrightarrow Th$	-1.90	$In^{3+} + 3e^- \longrightarrow In$	-0.342
$Np^{3+} + 3e^- \longrightarrow Np$	-1.86	$[Ag(CN)_2]^- + e^- \longrightarrow Ag + 2CN^-$	-0.31
$Be^{2+} + 2e^- \longrightarrow Be$	-1.85	$Co^{2+} + 2e^- \longrightarrow Co$	-0.277
$U^{3+} + 3e^- \longrightarrow U$	-1.80	$[SnF_6]^{2-} + 4e^- \longrightarrow Sn + 6F^-$	-0.25
$Hf^{4+} + 4e^- \longrightarrow Hf$	-1.70	$Ni^{2+} + 2e^- \longrightarrow Ni$	-0.250
$SiO_3^{2-} + 3H_2O + 4e^- \longrightarrow Si + 6OH^-$	-1.70	$Sn^{2+} + 2e^- \longrightarrow Sn$	-0.136
$Al^{3+} + 3e^- \longrightarrow Al$	-1.66	$CrO_4^{2-} + 4H_2O + 3e^- \longrightarrow Cr(OH)_3 + 5OH^-$	-0.13
$Ti^{2+} + 2e^- \longrightarrow Ti$	-1.63	$Pb^{2+} + 2e^- \longrightarrow Pb$	-0.126
$Zr^{4+} + 4e^- \longrightarrow Zr$	-1.53	$MnO_2 + 2H_2O + 2e^- \longrightarrow Mn(OH)_2 + 2OH^-$	-0.05
$ZnS + 2e^- \longrightarrow Zn + S^{2-}$	-1.44	$[HgI_4]^{2-} + 2e^- \longrightarrow Hg + 4I^-$	-0.04
$Cr(OH)_3 + 3e^- \longrightarrow Cr + 3OH^-$	-1.3	$2H_3O^+ + 2e^- \longrightarrow H_2 + 2H_2O$	0.00
$[Zn(CN)_4]^{2-} + 2e^- \longrightarrow Zn + 4CN^-$	-1.26	$NO_3^- + H_2O + 2e^- \longrightarrow NO_2^- + 2OH^-$	$+0.01$
$Zn(OH)_2 + 2e^- \longrightarrow Zn + 2OH^-$	-1.245	$[Ag(S_2O_3)_2]^{3-} + e^- \longrightarrow Ag + 2S_2O_3^{2-}$	$+0.01$
$[Zn(OH)_4]^{2-} + 2e^- \longrightarrow Zn + 4OH^-$	-1.216	$[Co(NH_3)_6]^{3+} + e^- \longrightarrow [Co(NH_3)_6]^{2+}$	$+0.1$
$CdS + 2e^- \longrightarrow Cd + S^{2-}$	-1.21	$S + 2H_3O^+ + 2e^- \longrightarrow H_2S + 2H_2O$	$+0.141$
$[Cr(OH)_4]^- + 3e^- \longrightarrow Cr + 4OH^-$	-1.2	$Sn^{4+} + 2e^- \longrightarrow Sn^{2+}$	$+0.15$
$[SiF_6]^{2-} + 4e^- \longrightarrow Si + 6F^-$	-1.2	$Cu^{2+} + e^- \longrightarrow Cu^+$	$+0.153$
$V^{2+} + 2e^- \longrightarrow V$	$ca\ -1.18$	$Co(OH)_3 + e^- \longrightarrow Co(OH)_2 + OH^-$	$+0.17$
$Mn^{2+} + 2e^- \longrightarrow Mn$	-1.18	$[HgBr_4]^{2-} + 2e^- \longrightarrow Hg + 4Br^-$	$+0.21$
$[Cd(CN)_4]^{2-} + 2e^- \longrightarrow Cd + 4CN^-$	-1.03	$AgCl + e^- \longrightarrow Ag + Cl^-$	$+0.222$
$[Zn(NH_3)_4]^{2+} + 2e^- \longrightarrow Zn + 4NH_3$	-1.03	$Hg_2Cl_2 + 2e^- \longrightarrow 2Hg + 2Cl^-$	$+0.27$
$FeS + 2e^- \longrightarrow Fe + S^{2-}$	-1.01	$ClO_3^- + H_2O + 2e^- \longrightarrow ClO_2^- + 2OH^-$	$+0.33$
$PbS + 2e^- \longrightarrow Pb + S^{2-}$	-0.95	$Cu^{2+} + 2e^- \longrightarrow Cu$	$+0.337$

Standard Electrode (Reduction) Potentials (Continued)

Half-reaction	$E°$, V	Half-reaction	$E°$, V
$[Fe(CN)_6]^{3-} + e^- \longrightarrow [Fe(CN)_6]^{4-}$	+0.36	$NO_3^- + 4H_3O^+ + 3e^- \longrightarrow NO + 6H_2O$	+0.96
$[Ag(NH_3)_2]^+ + e^- \longrightarrow Ag + 2NH_3$	+0.373	$Pd^{2+} + 2e^- \longrightarrow Pd$	+0.987
$O_2 + 2H_2O + 4e^- \longrightarrow 4OH^-$	+0.401	$Br_2(l) + 2e^- \longrightarrow 2Br^-$	+1.0652
$[RhCl_6]^{3-} + 3e^- \longrightarrow Rh + 6Cl^-$	+0.44	$ClO_4^- + 2H_3O^+ + 2e^- \longrightarrow ClO_3^- + 3H_2O$	+1.19
$Ag_2CrO_4 + 2e^- \longrightarrow 2Ag + CrO_4^{2-}$	+0.446	$Pt^{2+} + 2e^- \longrightarrow Pt$	ca +1.2
$NiO_2 + 2H_2O + 2e^- \longrightarrow Ni(OH)_2 + 2OH^-$	+0.49	$ClO_3^- + 3H_3O^+ + 2e^- \longrightarrow HClO_2 + 4H_2O$	+1.21
$Cu^+ + e^- \longrightarrow Cu$	+0.521	$O_2 + 4H_3O^+ + 4e^- \longrightarrow 6H_2O$	+1.23
$TeO_2 + 4H_3O^+ + 4e^- \longrightarrow Te + 6H_2O$	+0.529	$MnO_2 + 4H_3O^+ + 2e^- \longrightarrow Mn^{2+} + 6H_2O$	+1.23
$I_2 + 2e^- \longrightarrow 2I^-$	+0.5355	$Cr_2O_7^{2-} + 14H_3O^+ + 6e^- \longrightarrow 2Cr^{3+} + 21H_2O$	+1.33
$[PtBr_4]^{2-} + 2e^- \longrightarrow Pt + 4Br^-$	+0.58	$Cl_2 + 2e^- \longrightarrow 2Cl^-$	+1.3595
$MnO_4^- + 2H_2O + 3e^- \longrightarrow MnO_2 + 4OH^-$	+0.588	$HClO + H_3O^+ + 2e^- \longrightarrow Cl^- + 2H_2O$	+1.49
$[PdCl_4]^{2-} + 2e^- \longrightarrow Pd + 4Cl^-$	+0.62	$Au^{3+} + 3e^- \longrightarrow Au$	+1.50
$ClO_2^- + H_2O + 2e^- \longrightarrow ClO^- + 2OH^-$	+0.66	$MnO_4^- + 8H_3O^+ + 5e^- \longrightarrow Mn^{2+} + 12H_2O$	+1.51
$[PtCl_6]^{2-} + 2e^- \longrightarrow [PtCl_4]^{2-} + 2Cl^-$	+0.68	$Ce^{4+} + e^- \longrightarrow Ce^{3+}$	+1.61
$O_2 + 2H_3O^+ + 2e^- \longrightarrow H_2O_2 + 2H_2O$	+0.682	$HClO + H_3O^+ + e^- \longrightarrow \frac{1}{2}Cl_2 + 2H_2O$	+1.63
$[PtCl_4]^{2-} + 2e^- \longrightarrow Pt + 4Cl^-$	+0.73	$HClO_2 + 2H_3O^+ + 2e^- \longrightarrow HClO + 3H_2O$	+1.64
$Fe^{3+} + e^- \longrightarrow Fe^{2+}$	+0.771	$Au^+ + e^- \longrightarrow Au$	ca +1.68
$Hg_2^{2+} + 2e^- \longrightarrow 2Hg$	+0.789	$NiO_2 + 4H_3O^+ + 2e^- \longrightarrow Ni^{2+} + 6H_2O$	+1.68
$Ag^+ + e^- \longrightarrow Ag$	+0.7991	$PbO_2 + SO_4^{2-} + 4H_3O^+ + 2e^- \longrightarrow$ $PbSO_4 + 6H_2O$	+1.685
$Hg^{2+} + 2e^- \longrightarrow Hg$	+0.854		
$HO_2^- + H_2O + 2e^- \longrightarrow 3OH^-$	+0.88	$H_2O_2 + 2H_3O^+ + 2e^- \longrightarrow 4H_2O$	+1.77
$ClO^- + H_2O + 2e^- \longrightarrow Cl^- + 2OH^-$	+0.89	$Co^{3+} + e^- \longrightarrow Co^{2+}$	+1.82
$2Hg^{2+} + 2e^- \longrightarrow Hg_2^{2+}$	+0.920	$F_2 + 2e^- \longrightarrow 2F^-$	+2.87
$NO_3^- + 3H_3O^+ + 2e^- \longrightarrow HNO_2 + 4H_2O$	+0.94		

Appendix I: Standard Molar Enthalpies of Formation, Standard Molar Free Energies of Formation, and Absolute Standard Entropies [298.15 K (25°C), 1 atm]

Substance	$\Delta H_f°$, kJ mol^{-1}	$\Delta G_f°$, kJ mol^{-1}	$S_{298}°$, J K^{-1} mol^{-1}
Aluminum			
Al(s)	0	0	28.3
Al(g)	326	286	164.4
Al$_2$O$_3$(s)	−1676	−1582	50.92
AlF$_3$(s)	−1504	−1425	66.44
AlCl$_3$(s)	−704.2	−628.9	110.7

Standard Molar Enthalpies of Formation, Standard Molar Free Energies of Formation, and Absolute Standard Entropies [298.15 K (25°C), 1 atm] (Continued)

Substance	ΔH_f°, kJ mol^{-1}	ΔG_f°, kJ mol^{-1}	S_{298}°, J K^{-1} mol^{-1}
$AlCl_3 \cdot 6H_2O(s)$	−2692	—	—
$Al_2S_3(s)$	−724	−492.4	—
$Al_2(SO_4)_3(s)$	−3440.8	−3100.1	239
Antimony			
$Sb(s)$	0	0	45.69
$Sb(g)$	262	222	180.2
$Sb_4O_6(s)$	−1441	−1268	221
$SbCl_3(g)$	−314	−301	337.7
$SbCl_5(g)$	−394.3	−334.3	401.8
$Sb_2S_3(s)$	−175	−174	182
$SbCl_3(s)$	−382.2	−323.7	184
$SbOCl(s)$	−374	—	—
Arsenic			
$As(s)$	0	0	35
$As(g)$	303	261	174.1
$As_4(g)$	144	92.5	314
$As_4O_6(s)$	−1313.9	−1152.5	214
$As_2O_5(s)$	−924.87	−782.4	105
$AsCl_3(g)$	−258.6	−245.9	327.1
$As_2S_3(s)$	−169	−169	164
$AsH_3(g)$	66.44	68.91	222.7
$H_3AsO_4(s)$	−906.3	—	—
Barium			
$Ba(s)$	0	0	66.9
$Ba(g)$	175.6	144.8	170.3
$BaO(s)$	−558.1	−528.4	70.3
$BaCl_2(s)$	−860.06	−810.9	126
$BaSO_4(s)$	−1465	−1353	132
Beryllium			
$Be(s)$	0	0	9.54
$Be(g)$	320.6	282.8	136.17
$BeO(s)$	−610.9	−581.6	14.1
Bismuth			
$Bi(s)$	0	0	56.74
$Bi(g)$	207	168	186.90
$Bi_2O_3(s)$	−573.88	−493.7	151
$BiCl_3(s)$	−379	−315	177
$Bi_2S_3(s)$	−143	−141	200
Boron			
$B(s)$	0	0	5.86
$B(g)$	562.7	518.8	153.3
$B_2O_3(s)$	−1272.8	−1193.7	53.97
$B_2H_6(g)$	36	86.6	232.0
$B(OH)_3(s)$	−1094.3	−969.01	88.83
$BF_3(g)$	−1137.3	−1120.3	254.0
$BCl_3(g)$	−403.8	−388.7	290.0
$B_3N_3H_6(l)$	−541.0	−392.8	200
$HBO_2(s)$	−794.25	−723.4	40

Standard Molar Enthalpies of Formation, Standard Molar Free Energies of Formation, and Absolute Standard Entropies [298.15 K (25°C), 1 atm] (Continued)

Substance	ΔH_f°, kJ mol^{-1}	ΔG_f°, kJ mol^{-1}	S_{298}°, J K^{-1} mol^{-1}
Bromine			
$Br_2(l)$	0	0	152.23
$Br_2(g)$	30.91	3.142	245.35
$Br(g)$	111.88	82.429	174.91
$BrF_3(g)$	−255.6	−229.5	292.4
$HBr(g)$	−36.4	−53.43	198.59
Cadmium			
$Cd(s)$	0	0	51.76
$Cd(g)$	112.0	77.45	167.64
$CdO(s)$	−258	−228	54.8
$CdCl_2(s)$	−391.5	−344.0	115.3
$CdSO_4(s)$	−933.28	−822.78	123.04
$CdS(s)$	−162	−156	64.9
Calcium			
$Ca(s)$	0	0	41.6
$Ca(g)$	192.6	158.9	154.78
$CaO(s)$	−635.5	−604.2	40
$Ca(OH)_2(s)$	−986.59	−896.76	76.1
$CaSO_4(s)$	−1432.7	−1320.3	107
$CaSO_4 \cdot 2H_2O(s)$	−2021.1	−1795.7	194.0
$CaCO_3(s)$ (calcite)	−1206.9	−1128.8	92.9
$CaSO_3 \cdot 2H_2O(s)$	−1762	−1565	184
Carbon			
$C(s)$ (graphite)	0	0	5.740
$C(s)$ (diamond)	1.897	2.900	2.38
$C(g)$	716.681	671.289	157.987
$CO(g)$	−110.52	−137.15	197.56
$CO_2(g)$	−393.51	−394.36	213.6
$CH_4(g)$	−74.81	−50.75	186.15
$CH_3OH(l)$	−238.7	−166.4	127
$CH_3OH(g)$	−200.7	−162.0	239.7
$CCl_4(l)$	−135.4	−65.27	216.4
$CCl_4(g)$	−102.9	−60.63	309.7
$CHCl_3(l)$	−134.5	−73.72	202
$CHCl_3(g)$	−103.1	−70.37	295.6
$CS_2(l)$	89.70	65.27	151.3
$CS_2(g)$	117.4	67.15	237.7
$C_2H_2(g)$	226.7	209.2	200.8
$C_2H_4(g)$	52.26	68.12	219.5
$C_2H_6(g)$	−84.68	−32.9	229.5
$CH_3COOH(l)$	−484.5	−390	160
$CH_3COOH(g)$	−432.25	−374	282
$C_2H_5OH(l)$	−277.7	−174.9	161
$C_2H_5OH(g)$	−235.1	−168.6	282.6
$C_3H_8(g)$	−103.85	−23.49	269.9
$C_6H_6(g)$	82.927	129.66	269.2
$C_6H_6(l)$	49.028	124.50	172.8
$CH_2Cl_2(l)$	−121.5	−67.32	178

Standard Molar Enthalpies of Formation, Standard Molar Free Energies of Formation, and Absolute Standard Entropies [298.15 K (25°C), 1 atm] (Continued)

Substance	ΔH_f°, kJ mol^{-1}	ΔG_f°, kJ mol^{-1}	S_{298}°, J K^{-1} mol^{-1}
$CH_2Cl_2(g)$	−92.47	−65.90	270.1
$CH_3Cl(g)$	−80.83	−57.40	234.5
$C_2H_5Cl(l)$	−136.5	−59.41	190.8
$C_2H_5Cl(g)$	−112.2	−60.46	275.9
$C_2N_2(g)$	308.9	297.4	241.8
$HCN(l)$	108.9	124.9	112.8
$HCN(g)$	135	124.7	201.7
Chlorine			
$Cl_2(g)$	0	0	222.96
$Cl(g)$	121.68	105.70	165.09
$ClF(g)$	−54.48	−55.94	217.8
$ClF_3(g)$	−163	−123	281.5
$Cl_2O(g)$	80.3	97.9	266.1
$Cl_2O_7(l)$	238	—	—
$Cl_2O_7(g)$	272	—	—
$HCl(g)$	−92.307	−95.299	186.80
$HClO_4(l)$	−40.6	—	—
Chromium			
$Cr(s)$	0	0	23.8
$Cr(g)$	397	352	174.4
$Cr_2O_3(s)$	−1140	−1058	81.2
$CrO_3(s)$	−589.5	—	—
$(NH_4)_2Cr_2O_7(s)$	−1807	—	—
Cobalt			
$Co(s)$	0	0	30.0
$CoO(s)$	−237.9	−214.2	52.97
$Co_3O_4(s)$	−891.2	−774.0	103
$Co(NO_3)_2(s)$	−420.5	—	—
Copper			
$Cu(s)$	0	0	33.15
$Cu(g)$	338.3	298.5	166.3
$CuO(s)$	−157	−130	42.63
$Cu_2O(s)$	−169	−146	93.14
$CuS(s)$	−53.1	−53.6	66.5
$Cu_2S(s)$	−79.5	−86.2	121
$CuSO_4(s)$	−771.36	−661.9	109
$Cu(NO_3)_2(s)$	−303	—	—
Fluorine			
$F_2(g)$	0	0	202.7
$F(g)$	78.99	61.92	158.64
$F_2O(g)$	−22	−4.6	247.3
$HF(g)$	−271	−273	173.67
Hydrogen			
$H_2(g)$	0	0	130.57
$H(g)$	217.97	203.26	114.60
$H_2O(l)$	−285.83	−237.18	69.91
$H_2O(g)$	−241.82	−228.59	188.71
$H_2O_2(l)$	−187.8	−120.4	110
$H_2O_2(g)$	−136.3	−105.6	233

Standard Molar Enthalpies of Formation, Standard Molar Free Energies of Formation, and Absolute Standard Entropies [298.15 K (25°C), 1 atm] (Continued)

Substance	ΔH_f°, kJ mol^{-1}	ΔG_f°, kJ mol^{-1}	S_{298}°, J K^{-1} mol^{-1}
HF(g)	−271	−273	173.67
HCl(g)	−92.307	−95.299	186.80
HBr(g)	−36.4	−53.43	198.59
HI(g)	26.5	1.7	206.48
H$_2$S(g)	−20.6	−33.6	205.7
H$_2$Se(g)	30	16	218.9
Iodine			
I$_2$(s)	0	0	116.14
I$_2$(g)	62.438	19.36	260.6
I(g)	106.84	70.283	180.68
IF(g)	95.65	−118.5	236.1
ICl(g)	17.8	−5.44	247.44
IBr(g)	40.8	3.7	258.66
IF$_7$(g)	−943.9	−818.4	346
HI(g)	26.5	1.7	206.48
Iron			
Fe(s)	0	0	27.3
Fe(g)	416	371	180.38
Fe$_2$O$_3$(s)	−824.2	−742.2	87.40
Fe$_3$O$_4$(s)	−1118	−1015	146
Fe(CO)$_5$(l)	−774.0	−705.4	338
Fe(CO)$_5$(g)	−733.9	−697.26	445.2
FeCl$_2$(s)	−341.79	−302.30	117.95
FeCl$_3$(s)	−399.49	−334.00	142.3
FeO(s)	−272	—	—
Fe(OH)$_2$(s)	−569.0	−486.6	88
Fe(OH)$_3$(s)	−823.0	−696.6	107
FeS(s)	−100	−100	60.29
Fe$_3$C(s)	25	20	105
Lead			
Pb(s)	0	0	64.81
Pb(g)	195	162	175.26
PbO(s) (yellow)	−217.3	−187.9	68.70
PbO(s) (red)	−219.0	−188.9	66.5
Pb(OH)$_2$(s)	−515.9	—	—
PbS(s)	−100	−98.7	91.2
Pb(NO$_3$)$_2$(s)	−451.9	—	—
PbO$_2$(s)	−277	−217.4	68.6
PbCl$_2$(s)	−359.4	−314.1	136
Lithium			
Li(s)	0	0	28.0
Li(g)	155.1	122.1	138.67
LiH(s)	−90.42	−69.96	25
Li(OH)(s)	−487.23	−443.9	50.2
LiF(s)	−612.1	−584.1	35.9
Li$_2$CO$_3$(s)	−1215.6	−1132.4	90.4
Manganese			
Mn(s)	0	0	32.0
Mn(g)	281	238	173.6

Standard Molar Enthalpies of Formation, Standard Molar Free Energies of Formation, and Absolute Standard Entropies [298.15 K (25°C), 1 atm] (Continued)

Substance	ΔH_f°, kJ mol^{-1}	ΔG_f°, kJ mol^{-1}	S_{298}°, J K^{-1} mol^{-1}
MnO(s)	−385.2	−362.9	59.71
MnO$_2$(s)	−520.03	−465.18	53.05
Mn$_2$O$_3$(s)	−959.0	−881.2	110
Mn$_3$O$_4$(s)	−1388	−1283	156
Mercury			
Hg(l)	0	0	76.02
Hg(g)	61.317	31.85	174.8
HgO(s) (red)	−90.83	−58.555	70.29
HgO(s) (yellow)	−90.46	−57.296	71.1
HgCl$_2$(s)	−224	−179	146
Hg$_2$Cl$_2$(s)	−265.2	−210.78	192
HgS(s) (red)	−58.16	−50.6	82.4
HgS(s) (black)	−53.6	−47.7	88.3
HgSO$_4$(s)	−707.5	—	—
Nitrogen			
N$_2$(g)	0	0	191.5
N(g)	472.704	455.579	153.19
NO(g)	90.25	86.57	210.65
NO$_2$(g)	33.2	51.30	239.9
N$_2$O(g)	82.05	104.2	219.7
N$_2$O$_3$(g)	83.72	139.4	312.2
N$_2$O$_4$(g)	9.16	97.82	304.2
N$_2$O$_5$(g)	11	115	356
NH$_3$(g)	−46.11	−16.5	192.3
N$_2$H$_4$(l)	50.63	149.2	121.2
N$_2$H$_4$(g)	95.4	159.3	238.4
NH$_4$NO$_3$(s)	−365.6	−184.0	151.1
NH$_4$Cl(s)	−314.4	−201.5	94.6
NH$_4$Br(s)	−270.8	−175	113
NH$_4$I(s)	−201.4	−113	117
NH$_4$NO$_2$(s)	−256	—	—
HNO$_3$(l)	−174.1	−80.79	155.6
HNO$_3$(g)	−135.1	−74.77	266.2
Oxygen			
O$_2$(g)	0	0	205.03
O(g)	249.17	231.75	160.95
O$_3$(g)	143	163	238.8
Phosphorus			
P$_4$(s)	0	0	164
P$_4$(g)	58.91	24.5	280.0
P(g)	314.6	278.3	163.08
PH$_3$(g)	5.4	13	210.1
PCl$_3$(g)	−287	−268	311.7
PCl$_5$(g)	−375	−305	364.5
P$_4$O$_6$(s)	−1640	—	—
P$_4$O$_{10}$(s)	−2984	−2698	228.9
HPO$_3$(s)	−948.5	—	—
H$_3$PO$_2$(s)	−604.6	—	—
H$_3$PO$_3$(s)	−964.4	—	—

Standard Molar Enthalpies of Formation, Standard Molar Free Energies of Formation, and Absolute Standard Entropies [298.15 K (25°C), 1 atm] (Continued)

Substance	ΔH_f°, kJ mol^{-1}	ΔG_f°, kJ mol^{-1}	S_{298}°, J K^{-1} mol^{-1}
$H_3PO_4(s)$	−1279	−1119	110.5
$H_3PO_4(l)$	−1267	—	—
$H_4P_2O_7(s)$	−2241	—	—
$POCl_3(l)$	−597.1	−520.9	222.5
$POCl_3(g)$	−558.48	−512.96	325.3
Potassium			
$K(s)$	0	0	63.6
$K(g)$	90.00	61.17	160.23
$KF(s)$	−562.58	−533.12	66.57
$KCl(s)$	−435.868	−408.32	82.68
Silicon			
$Si(s)$	0	0	18.8
$Si(g)$	455.6	411	167.9
$SiO_2(s)$	−910.94	−856.67	41.84
$SiH_4(g)$	34	56.9	204.5
$H_2SiO_3(s)$	−1189	−1092	130
$H_4SiO_4(s)$	−1481	−1333	190
$SiF_4(g)$	−1614.9	−1572.7	282.4
$SiCl_4(l)$	−687.0	−619.90	240
$SiCl_4(g)$	−657.01	−617.01	330.6
$SiC(s)$	−65.3	−62.8	16.6
Silver			
$Ag(s)$	0	0	42.55
$Ag(g)$	284.6	245.7	172.89
$Ag_2O(s)$	−31.0	−11.2	121
$AgCl(s)$	−127.1	−109.8	96.2
$Ag_2S(s)$	−32.6	−40.7	144.0
Sodium			
$Na(s)$	0	0	51.0
$Na(g)$	108.7	78.11	153.62
$Na_2O(s)$	−415.9	−377	72.8
$NaCl(s)$	−411.00	−384.03	72.38
Sulfur			
$S_8(s)$ (rhombic)	0	0	254
$S(g)$	278.80	238.27	167.75
$SO_2(g)$	−296.83	−300.19	248.1
$SO_3(g)$	−395.7	−371.1	256.6
$H_2S(g)$	−20.6	−33.6	205.7
$H_2SO_4(l)$	−813.989	690.101	156.90
$H_2S_2O_7(s)$	−1274	—	—
$SF_4(g)$	−774.9	−731.4	291.9
$SF_6(g)$	−1210	−1105	291.7
$SCl_2(l)$	−50	—	—
$SCl_2(g)$	−20	—	—
$S_2Cl_2(l)$	−59.4	—	—
$S_2Cl_2(g)$	−18	−32	331.4
$SOCl_2(l)$	−246	—	—
$SOCl_2(g)$	−213	−198	309.7
$SO_2Cl_2(l)$	−394	—	—
$SO_2Cl_2(g)$	−364	−320	311.8

Standard Molar Enthalpies of Formation, Standard Molar Free Energies of Formation, and Absolute Standard Entropies [298.15 K (25°C), 1 atm] (Continued)

Substance	ΔH_f°, kJ mol^{-1}	ΔG_f°, kJ mol^{-1}	S_{298}°, J K^{-1} mol^{-1}
Tin			
Sn(s)	0	0	51.55
Sn(g)	302	267	168.38
SnO(s)	−286	−257	56.5
SnO$_2$(s)	−580.7	−519.7	52.3
SnCl$_4$(l)	−511.2	−440.2	259
SnCl$_4$(g)	−471.5	−432.2	366
Titanium			
Ti(s)	0	0	30.6
Ti(g)	469.9	425.1	180.19
TiO$_2$(s)	−944.7	−889.5	50.33
TiCl$_4$(l)	−804.2	−737.2	252.3
TiCl$_4$(g)	−763.2	−726.8	354.8
Tungsten			
W(s)	0	0	32.6
W(g)	849.4	807.1	173.84
WO$_3$(s)	−842.87	−764.08	75.90
Zinc			
Zn(s)	0	0	41.6
Zn(g)	130.73	95.178	160.87
ZnO(s)	−348.3	−318.3	43.64
ZnCl$_2$(s)	−415.1	−369.43	111.5
ZnS(s)	−206.0	−201.3	57.7
ZnSO$_4$(s)	−982.8	−874.5	120
ZnCO$_3$(s)	−812.78	−731.57	82.4
Complexes			
[Co(NH$_3$)$_4$(NO$_2$)$_2$]NO$_3$, *cis*	−898.7	—	—
[Co(NH$_3$)$_4$(NO$_2$)$_2$]NO$_3$, *trans*	−896.2	—	—
NH$_4$[Co(NH$_3$)$_2$(NO$_2$)$_4$]	−837.6	—	—
[Co(NH$_3$)$_6$][Co(NH$_3$)$_2$(NO$_2$)$_4$]$_3$	−2733	—	—
[Co(NH$_3$)$_4$Cl$_2$]Cl, *cis*	−997.0	—	—
[Co(NH$_3$)$_4$Cl$_2$]Cl, *trans*	−999.6	—	—
[Co(en)$_2$(NO$_2$)$_2$]NO$_3$, *cis*	−689.5	—	—
[Co(en)$_2$Cl$_2$]Cl, *cis*	−681.1	—	—
[Co(en)$_2$Cl$_2$]Cl, *trans*	−677.4	—	—
[Co(en)$_3$](ClO$_4$)$_3$	−762.7	—	—
[Co(en)$_3$]Br$_2$	−595.8	—	—
[Co(en)$_3$]I$_2$	−475.3	—	—
[Co(en)$_3$]I$_3$	−519.2	—	—
[Co(NH$_3$)$_6$](ClO$_4$)$_3$	−1035	−227	636
[Co(NH$_3$)$_5$NO$_2$](NO$_3$)$_2$	−1089	−418.4	350
[Co(NH$_3$)$_6$](NO$_3$)$_3$	−1282	−530.5	469
[Co(NH$_3$)$_5$Cl]Cl$_2$	−1017	−582.8	366
[Pt(NH$_3$)$_4$]Cl$_2$	−728.0	—	—
[Ni(NH$_3$)$_6$]Cl$_2$	−994.1	—	—
[Ni(NH$_3$)$_6$]Br$_2$	−923.8	—	—
[Ni(NH$_3$)$_6$]I$_2$	−808.3	—	—

Appendix J: Composition of Commercial Acids and Bases

Acid or Base	Density, g/ml	Percentage by Mass	Molarity	Normality
Hydrochloric acid	1.19	38%	12.4	12.4
Nitric acid	1.42	70%	15.8	15.8
Sulfuric acid	1.84	95%	17.8	35.6
Acetic acid	1.05	99%	17.3	17.3
Aqueous ammonia	0.90	28%	14.8	14.8

Appendix K: Half-Life Times for Several Radioactive Isotopes

Isotope	Half-Life	Type of Emission[a]	Isotope	Half-Life	Type of Emission[a]
$^{14}_{6}C$	5730 yr	(β^-)	$^{206}_{83}Bi$	6.243 d	$(E.C.)$
$^{13}_{7}N$	9.97 m	(β^+)	$^{210}_{83}Bi$	5.01 d	(β^-)
$^{15}_{9}F$	5×10^{-22} s	(p)	$^{212}_{83}Bi$	60.5 m	$(\alpha$ or $\beta^-)$
$^{24}_{11}Na$	14.97 hr	(β^-)	$^{210}_{84}Po$	138.4 d	(α)
$^{32}_{15}P$	14.28 d	(β^-)	$^{212}_{84}Po$	3×10^{-7} s	(α)
$^{40}_{19}K$	1.26×10^9 yr	$(\beta^-$ or $E.C.)$	$^{216}_{84}Po$	0.16 s	(α)
$^{49}_{26}Fe$	0.08 s	(β^+)	$^{218}_{84}Po$	3.11 m	(α)
$^{60}_{26}Fe$	1.5×10^6 yr	(β^-)	$^{215}_{85}At$	1.0×10^{-4} s	(α)
$^{60}_{27}Co$	5.2 yr	(β^-)	$^{218}_{85}At$	1.6 s	(α)
$^{87}_{37}Rb$	4.7×10^{10} yr	(β^-)	$^{220}_{86}Rn$	55.6 s	(α)
$^{90}_{38}Sr$	29 yr	(β^-)	$^{222}_{86}Rn$	3.82 d	(α)
$^{115}_{49}In$	4.4×10^{14} yr	(β^-)	$^{224}_{88}Ra$	3.66 d	(α)
$^{131}_{53}I$	8.040 d	(β^-)	$^{226}_{88}Ra$	1590 yr	(α)
$^{142}_{58}Ce$	5×10^{15} yr	(α)	$^{228}_{88}Ra$	5.75 yr	(β^-)
$^{208}_{81}Tl$	3.052 m	(β^-)	$^{228}_{89}Ac$	6.13 hr	(β^-)
$^{210}_{82}Pb$	22.6 yr	(β^-)	$^{228}_{90}Th$	1.912 yr	(α)
$^{212}_{82}Pb$	10.6 hr	(β^-)	$^{232}_{90}Th$	1.4×10^{10} yr	(α)
$^{214}_{82}Pb$	26.8 m	(β^-)	$^{233}_{90}Th$	23 m	(β^-)

Half-Life Times for Several Radioactive Isotopes (Continued)

Isotope	Half-Life	Type of Emission[a]	Isotope	Half-Life	Type of Emission[a]
$^{234}_{90}Th$	24.10 d	(β^-)	$^{241}_{95}Am$	458 yr	(α)
$^{233}_{91}Pa$	27 d	(β^-)	$^{242}_{96}Cm$	162.8 d	(α)
$^{233}_{92}U$	1.62×10^5 yr	(α)	$^{243}_{97}Bk$	4.5 hr	$(\alpha$ or $E.C.)$
$^{234}_{92}U$	2.45×10^5 yr	(α)	$^{253}_{99}Es$	20.47 d	(α)
$^{235}_{92}U$	7.04×10^8 yr	(α)	$^{254}_{100}Fm$	3.24 hr	$(\alpha$ or $S.F.)$
$^{238}_{92}U$	4.51×10^9 yr	(α)	$^{255}_{100}Fm$	20.1 hr	(α)
$^{239}_{92}U$	23.54 m	(β^-)	$^{256}_{101}Md$	76 m	$(\alpha$ or $E.C.)$
$^{239}_{93}Np$	2.3 d	(β^-)	$^{254}_{102}No$	55 s	(α)
$^{239}_{94}Pu$	2.411×10^4 yr	(α)	$^{257}_{103}Lr$	0.65 s	(α)
$^{240}_{94}Pu$	6.58×10^3 yr	(α)	$^{260}_{105}Unp$	1.5 s	$(\alpha$ or $S.F.)$
$^{241}_{94}Pu$	14.4 yr	$(\alpha$ or $\beta^-)$	$^{263}_{106}Unh$	0.8 s	$(\alpha$ or $S.F.)$

[a] $E.C.$ = electron capture, $S.F.$ = spontaneous fission; yr = years, d = days, hr = hours, m = minutes, s = seconds.

Photo Credits

Glossary

Absolute entropy The entropy change of a substance taken from absolute zero to a given temperature (T). (19.13)

Absolute zero The temperature at which all possible heat has been removed from an object. (10.5)

Acid A compound that donates a proton (hydrogen ion, H^+) to another compound. (2.10)

Acid–base reaction Reaction occurring when a proton is transferred from a Brønsted acid to a Brønsted base. (2.11)

Acquired immune deficiency syndrome (AIDS) The invasion of a certain class of human white blood cells, the T-lymphocytes, by the HIV virus, leading to a fatal inability to produce antibodies against disease. (31.16)

Activated complex An unstable combination of reacting molecules that is intermediate between reactants and products. (14.6)

Activation energy (E_a) The minimum energy necessary to form an activated complex in a reaction. (14.7)

Addition polymer A polymer formed by an addition reaction. (30.19)

Addition reaction Reaction of two or more substances to give another substance. (2.11)

Adhesive force Force of attraction between two separate phases. (11.11)

Aerobic decomposition The decomposition of matter in the presence of oxygen. (29.9)

Alkyl group A substituent that contains one less hydrogen than the corresponding alkane. (30.2)

Alpha decay The loss of an alpha particle during radioactive decay. (24.6)

Alpha (α) particle A helium nucleus; that is, a helium atom that has lost two electrons. (5.4)

Amino acid A substance containing both an amine group and a carboxylic acid group. Proteins are composed of amino acids. (31.2)

Amorphous solid A solid that lacks a crystalline structure. (11.12)

Amphiprotic A species that may either gain or lose a proton in reaction. (16.2)

Amphoteric behavior The behavior of elements that can exhibit the properties of either a metal or a nonmetal. (16.5)

Anaerobic decomposition The decomposition of matter in the absence of oxygen. (29.9)

Anion A negative ion. (7.1)

Anode The electrode at which oxidation takes place in an electrochemical cell. (20.1)

Antibonding orbital Molecular orbital located outside of the region between two nuclei. Electrons in an antibonding orbital destabilize the molecule. (9.1)

Arrhenius equation ($k = A \times e^{-E_a/RT}$) Expresses the relationship between the rate constant and the activation energy of a reaction. (14.7)

Asymmetric carbon A carbon atom that is bonded to four different groups within a molecule. (30.6)

Atom The smallest particle of an element that can enter into a chemical combination. (1.6)

Atomic mass unit (amu) A unit of mass equal to $\frac{1}{12}$ of the mass of a ^{12}C atom. (2.2)

Atomic number (Z) The number of protons in the nucleus of an atom. (2.3)

Atomic mass (atomic weight) The average mass of an atom expressed in amu. (2.3)

Aufbau process Process by which chemists illustrate the electronic structures of the elements by "building" them in atomic order, adding one proton to the nucleus and one electron to the proper subshell at a time. (5.12)

Avogadro's law Equal volumes of all gases, measured under the same conditions of temperature and pressure, contain the same number of molecules. (10.7)

Avogadro's number The number of atoms contained in exactly 12 grams of ^{12}C, equal to 6.022×10^{23} atoms. (3.4)

Azeotropic mixture A solution that forms a vapor with the same concentration as the solution, distilling without a change in concentration. (12.16)

Azimuthal quantum number (l) A quantum number distinguishing the different shapes of orbitals. (5.10)

Band The orbitals, or energy levels, that extend through a crystal. The way in which these bands are filled or not filled with electrons determines whether the substance is a metal, a semiconductor, or an insulator. (9.15)

Barometer A device used to measure air pressure. (10.2)

Base A compound that accepts a proton (hydrogen ion, H^+). (2.10)

Beta decay The breakdown of a neutron into a proton, which remains in the nucleus, and an electron, which is emitted as a beta particle. (24.6)

Beta (β) particle An electron emitted during radioactive decay. (5.4)

Bimolecular reaction The collision and combination of two reactants to give an activated complex in an elementary reaction. (14.10)

Binary compound A compound containing two different elements. (2.8)

Biological oxygen demand (BOD) A measure of the volume of oxygen gas taken up by a given amount of water in five days at 20°C, indicating the quantity of microorganisms in the sample. (29.10)

Body-centered cubic structure A crystalline structure that has a cubic unit cell with lattice points at the corners and in the center of the cell. (11.14)

Boiling point The temperature at which the vapor pressure of a liquid equals the pressure of the gas above it. (11.6)

Boiling-point elevation $(\Delta T = K_b m)$ The elevation of the boiling point of a liquid by addition of a solute. (12.15)

Bond angle The angle between any two covalent bonds that include a common atom. (8.1)

Bond distance The distance between the nuclei of two bonded atoms. (8.1)

Bond energy The energy required to break a covalent bond in a gaseous substance. (7.9)

Bond order In a Lewis formula, the number of bonding pairs of electrons between two atoms. The molecular-orbital bond order is the net number of pairs of bonding electrons, or the difference between the number of bonding and antibonding electrons divided by two. (9.3)

Bonding orbital Molecular orbital located between two nuclei. Electrons in a bonding orbital stabilize a molecule. (9.1)

Born–Haber cycle Cyclic process used to relate the enthalpy of formation (ΔH_f) of a compound to its lattice energy (U), the ionization energy (I), the electron affinity $(E.A.)$, the enthalpy of sublimation (ΔH_s), and the bond dissociation energy (D) of its constituents. (11.20)

Boyle's law The volume of a given mass of gas held at constant temperature is inversely proportional to the pressure under which it is measured. $PV = k$. (10.3)

Bragg equation $(n\lambda = 2d \sin\theta)$ An equation that relates the angles (θ) at which X rays of wavelength λ are scattered by planes with a separation d. (11.21)

Brønsted acid A compound that donates a proton to another compound. (16.1)

Brønsted base A compound that accepts a proton. (16.1)

Buffer capacity The amount of an acid or base that can be added to a volume of a buffer solution before its pH changes significantly. (17.9)

Buffer solution A mixture of a weak acid or a weak base and its salt. The pH of a buffer resists change when small amounts of acid or base are added. (17.9)

Calorie A non-SI unit representing the amount of heat or other energy necessary to raise the temperature of one gram of water one degree Celsius. 1 cal = 4.184 J. (4.1)

Calorimetry The process of measuring the amount of heat involved in a chemical or physical change. (4.2)

Catalysis The effect of a catalyst in increasing the speed of a chemical reaction. (14.13)

Catalyst A substance that changes the speed of a chemical reaction without affecting the yield or undergoing permanent chemical change. (14.13)

Cathode The electrode at which reduction takes place in an electrochemical cell. (20.1)

Cathode ray Stream of particles (electrons) emanating from the negative electrode in an evacuated glass tube. (5.1)

Cathodic protection Method of preventing corrosion of iron or steel by connecting a metal that is more active than iron to it. (21.16)

Cation A positive ion. (7.1)

Cell potential The difference in potential between the two electrodes of a cell. (20.2)

Chain mechanism A series of elementary reactions that repeat over and over to produce a product. (14.12)

Chain reaction Repeated fission caused when the neutrons released in fission bombard other atoms. (24.9)

Charles's law The volume of a given mass of gas is directly proportional to its Kelvin temperature when the pressure is held constant. $V/T = k$. (10.4)

Chelating ligand A ligand that is attached to a central metal ion by bonds from two or more donor atoms. (26.1)

Chemical change Change producing a different kind of matter from an original kind of matter. (1.4)

Chemical property Behavior that is related to the change of one kind of matter into another kind. Examples include metallic–nonmetallic or acid–base behavior. (1.4)

Chemical thermodynamics The chemical science that deals with the energy transfers and transformations that accompany chemical and physical changes. (4.3, 19.1)

Cis **configuration** Configuration of a geometrical isomer in which two groups are on the same side of an imaginary reference line on the molecule. (26.4, 30.3)

Cloning The exact duplication of a cell's DNA and, therefore, of an organism's characteristics. (31.12)

Colligative properties Properties of a solution that depend only on the concentration of a solute species. (12.4)

Colloid Insoluble particles (larger than simple molecules) in a stable suspension. (12.23)

Common ion effect The shift in equilibrium caused by the addition of a substance with an ion in common with the substances in equilibrium. (17.8)

Compound A pure substance with an invariant composition that can be decomposed, producing either elements or other compounds, by chemical change. (1.5)

Concentration The relative amounts of solute and solvent present in a solution. (3.8)

Condensation The change from a vapor to a condensed state (solid or liquid). (11.5)

Condensation polymer A polymer formed by linking together molecules in a reaction that eliminates small molecules such as water. (30.20)

Conjugate acid Substance formed when a base gains a proton (hydrogen ion). Considered an acid because it can lose a proton (hydrogen ion) to re-form the base. (16.1)

Conjugate base Substance formed when an acid loses a proton (hydrogen ion). Considered a base because it can gain a proton (hydrogen ion) to re-form the acid. (16.1)

Constant boiling solution A solution that forms a vapor with the same concentration as the solution, distilling without a change in concentration. (12.16)

Coordinate covalent bond A bond formed when one atom provides both electrons in a shared pair. (7.4)

Coordination compound (complex) A molecule or ion formed by the bonding of a metal atom or ion to two or more ligands by coordinate covalent bonds. (26.1)

Coordination number The number of atoms closest to any given atom in a crystal or to the central metal atom in a complex (26.1). (11.14)

Coordination sphere The central metal atom or ion plus the attached ligands of a complex. (26.1)

Coulomb The quantity of electricity involved when a current of one ampere flows for one second. (20.5)

Covalent bond Bond formed when pairs of electrons are shared between atoms. (7.3)

Covalent radius Half the distance between the nuclei of two identical atoms when they are joined by a single covalent bond. (6.3)

Critical pressure The pressure required to liquefy a gas at its critical temperature. (11.9)

Critical temperature The temperature above which a gas cannot be liquefied, no matter how much pressure is applied. (11.9)

Crystal defect A variation in the regular arrangement of the atoms or molecules of a crystal. (11.13)

Crystal field splitting (10Dq) The difference in energy between the metal's e_g and t_{2g} orbitals in a coordination complex. (26.7)

Crystal field stabilization energy (CFSE) A measure of the increased stability of a complex showing crystal field splitting. (26.8)

Crystalline solid A homogeneous solid in which the atoms, ions, or molecules assume ordered positions. (11.12)

Cubic closest packed structure A crystalline structure in which planes of closest packed atoms or ions are stacked ABCABC. (11.14)

Dalton's law The total pressure of a mixture of ideal gases is equal to the sum of the partial pressures of the component gases. (10.11)

Daughter nuclide A nuclide produced by the radioactive decay of another nuclide. May be stable or may decay further. (24.6)

Decomposition reaction Reaction in which one compound breaks down into two or more substances. (2.11)

Degenerate orbitals Orbitals having the same energy. (5.10)

Density Mass of a unit volume of a substance. (1.13)

Diamagnetic substance A substance that contains no unpaired electrons. Diamagnetic substances are repelled by a magnetic field. (26.9)

Diffusion The movement of gas molecules through the gas. (10.1)

Dipole The separation of charge in a bond or a molecule with a positively charged end and a negatively charged end. (7.5)

Dipole-induced dipole attraction An intermolecular attraction between a dipole and a second dipole induced by the first. (11.3)

Dipole–dipole attraction The intermolecular attraction of two permanent dipoles. (11.2)

Diprotic acid An acid containing two ionizable hydrogen atoms per molecule. A diprotic acid ionizes in two steps. (16.8)

Dissociation constant (K_d) The equilibrium constant for the decomposition of a complex ion into its components in solution. (18.1)

Double bond A covalent bond in which two pairs of electrons are shared between two atoms. (7.3)

Einstein equation Equation for determining the amount of energy resulting from the conversion of matter to energy. $E = mc^2$. (24.2)

Electrode A system in which a conductor is in contact with a mixture of oxidized and reduced forms of some chemical species. (20.3)

Electrode potential The difference between the charge on an electrode and the charge in the solution. (20.3)

Electrolysis The input of electrical energy as a direct current to force a nonspontaneous reaction to occur. (20.12)

Electrolyte An ionic or covalent compound that melts to give a liquid that contains ions or that dissolves to give a solution that contains ions. (2.10, 12.8)

Electrolytic conduction The movement of ions through a molten substance, a solution, or (occasionally) a solid. (12.8)

Electromotive force (emf) The difference in potential between two half-cells. (20.7)

Electron A small, negatively charged subatomic particle. (2.3)

Electron affinity A measure of the energy involved when an electron is added to a gaseous atom to form a negative ion. (6.3)

Electron capture Capture of an electron by an unstable nucleus. The electron converts a proton to a neutron in the nucleus. (24.6)

Electron configuration Electronic structure of an atom. (6.2)

Electronegativity The relative attraction of an atom for the electrons in a covalent bond. (7.5)

Element A pure substance that cannot be decomposed by a chemical change. (1.5)

Elementary reaction A reaction that cannot be broken down into smaller steps. (14.8)

Empirical formula A formula showing the composition of a compound given as the simplest whole-number ratio of atoms. (2.1)

End point The point during a titration when an indicator shows that the amount of reactant necessary for a complete reaction has been added to a solution. (3.13)

Endothermic process A chemical reaction or physical change that occurs with the absorption of heat. (4.1)

Energy The capacity to do work. (1.2)

Enthalpy change (ΔH) The heat lost or absorbed by a system under constant pressure during a reaction or other change. (4.4, 19.5)

Enthalpy of fusion (ΔH_{fus}) The energy needed to change a given quantity of a substance from the solid state to the liquid state at a constant temperature. (4.4)

Enthalpy of reaction The heat lost or absorbed by a system in a reaction. (4.4)

Enthalpy of vaporization (ΔH_{vap}) The energy needed to evaporate a given quantity of liquid at a constant specified temperature. (4.4)

Entropy (S) The randomness, or amount of disorder, of a system. (19.7)

Entropy change (ΔS) The change in entropy that accompanies a chemical or physical change. ΔS is given by the sum of the entropies of the products of a chemical change minus the sum of the entropies of the reactants. $\Delta S = \Sigma S_{products} - \Sigma S_{reactants}$. (19.7)

Equilibrium The state at which the conversion of reactants into products and the conversion of products back into reactants occur simultaneously at the same rate. (15.1)

Equilibrium constant (K) The value of the reaction quotient for a system at equilibrium. (15.2)

Equivalent An equivalent of an acid is the amount of acid required to provide one mole of protons (hydrogen ions) in a reaction; an equivalent of a base is the amount of base required to react with one mole of protons (hydrogen ions). (16.13) An equivalent of an oxidizing agent or of a reducing agent is the amount of the agent that combines with or releases one mole of electrons, respectively. (20.15)

Eutrophication The process by which a lake grows rich in nutrients and gradually fills with organic sediment and plants. (29.9)

Evaporation The change of a liquid into a gas. (11.5)

Excited state State in which an atom or molecule picks up outside energy, causing an electron to move into a higher-energy orbital. (5.7)

Exothermic process A chemical reaction or physical change that produces heat. (4.1)

Expansion work Work transferred between a system and its surroundings as the system expands or contracts against a constant pressure. (19.2)

Extensive property A property of a substance that depends on the amount of substance. (1.4)

Face-centered cubic structure A crystalline structure consisting of a cubic unit cell with lattice points on the corners and in the center of each face. (11.14)

Faraday (F) The charge on one mole of electrons. $1 F = 96,485$ coulombs. (20.5)

Faraday's law The amount of a substance undergoing a chemical change at each electrode during electrolysis is directly proportional to the quantity of electricity that passes through the electrolytic cell. (20.15)

First ionization energy The energy required to remove the most loosely bound electron from a gaseous atom. (6.3)

First law of thermodynamics The total amount of energy in the universe is constant. (19.3)

Fission The splitting of a heavier nucleus into two or more lighter nuclei, usually accompanied by the conversion of mass into large amounts of energy. (24.9)

Formal charge The charge on the species that would result if the electrons in a covalently bonded atom were shared evenly. (7.7)

Formation constant (K_f) The equilibrium constant for the formation of a complex ion from its components in solution. (18.11)

Formula mass The sum of the atomic masses of the atoms found in one formula unit of an ionic compound. (3.2)

Free energy change (ΔG) A predictor of the spontaneity of a chemical reaction at constant temperature. $\Delta G = \Delta H - T\Delta S$. (19.8)

Freezing point The temperature at which the solid and liquid phases of a substance are in equilibrium. (11.8)

Freezing-point depression ($\Delta T = K_f m$) The lowering of the freezing point of a liquid by addition of a solute. (12.17)

Frequency factor (A) In the Arrhenius equation, a constant indicating how many collisions have the correct orientation to lead to products. (14.7)

Functional group A part of an organic molecule responsible for chemical behavior of the molecule. (30.1)

Fusion The combining of very light nuclei into heavier nuclei, accompanied by the conversion of mass into large amounts of energy. (24.10)

Galvanic cell A device in which chemical energy is converted into electrical energy. Also called a voltaic cell. (20.1)

Gamma (γ) ray High-energy electromagnetic radiation. (5.4)

Gas The state in which matter has neither a definite volume nor shape. (1.2)

Gas constant (R) Constant derived from the ideal gas equation, $PV = nRT$. $R = 0.08206$ L atm/mol K or 8.314 L kPa/mol K. (10.8)

Gay-Lussac's law The volume of gases involved in a reaction, at constant temperature and pressure, can be expressed as a ratio of small whole numbers. (10.6)

Gene cloning A procedure for transferring small pieces of genetic information from one organism to another, thereby producing many copies of the second organism as it replicates. (31.12)

Genetic code The information coded in a DNA molecule that is replicated when new cells are produced. (31.11)

Geometrical isomers Isomers that differ only in the way that atoms are oriented in space relative to each other. (26.4, 30.3)

Glass An amorphous solid. (11.12)

Graham's law The rates of diffusion of gases are inversely proportional to the square roots of their densities (or their molecular masses). (10.12)

Gram (g) A unit of measure for mass. $1 \text{ g} = 1 \times 10^{-3}$ kg. (1.12)

Ground state State in which the electrons in an atom, ion, or molecule are in the lowest energy orbitals possible. (5.7)

Half-cell An electrode containing both an oxidized and a reduced species. (20.1)

Half-life ($t_{1/2}$) The time required for half of the atoms in a radioactive sample to decay. (24.4)

Half-life of a reaction ($t_{1/2}$) The time required for half of the original concentration of the limiting reactant to be consumed. (14.5)

Half-reaction One of the two parts (oxidation or reduction) of an oxidation–reduction reaction. (20.1)

Hard water Water containing dissolved calcium, magnesium, and/or iron salts. (29.12)

Heat The form of energy that gives a substance its temperature (4.1)

Heat capacity A property of a body of matter that represents the quantity of heat required to increase its temperature by one degree Celsius (or kelvin). (4.1)

Heisenberg uncertainty principle It is impossible to determine accurately both the momentum and the position of a particle simultaneously. (5.9)

Henry's law The mass of a gas that dissolves in a definite volume of liquid is directly proportional to the pressure of the gas, provided that the gas does not react with the solvent. (12.2)

Hess's law If a process can be written as the sum of several stepwise processes, the enthalpy change of the total process equals the sum of the enthalpy changes of the various steps. (4.5)

Heterogeneous catalyst A catalyst present in a different phase from the reactants, furnishing a surface at which a reaction can occur. (14.13)

Heterogeneous equilibrium An equilibrium between two or more different phases, involving a boundary surface between the two phases. (15.12)

Heteronuclear diatomic molecule A diatomic molecule composed of two different elements. (9.14)

Hexagonal closest packed structure A crystalline structure in which close packed layers of atoms or ions are stacked ABABAB; the unit cell is hexagonal. (11.14)

Homogeneous catalyst A catalyst present in the same phase as the reactants. (14.13)

Homogeneous equilibrium An equilibrium within a single phase. (15.12)

Homonuclear diatomic molecule A molecule composed of two identical atoms. (9.1)

Hund's rule Every orbital in a subshell is singly occupied with one electron before any one orbital is doubly occupied, and all electrons in singly occupied orbitals have the same spin. (5.11)

Hybridization A model that describes the changes in the atomic orbitals of an atom when it forms a covalent compound. (8.5)

Hydrocarbon A compound composed only of hydrogen and carbon. The major component of fossil fuels. (4.6, 30.1)

Hydrogen bond The strong electrostatic attraction that occurs between molecules in which hydrogen is in a covalent bond with a highly electronegative element (fluorine, oxygen, nitrogen, or chlorine). (11.4)

Hydrogen salt A salt in which only part of the acidic hydrogens of a polyprotic acid are replaced by a cation. (16.11)

Hydronium ion (H_3O^+) A water molecule with an added proton (hydrogen ion). (2.11)

Ideal gas A gas that follows Boyle's law, Charles's law, and Avogadro's law perfectly. (10.8, 10.13)

Ideal gas equation $PV = nRT$. (10.8)

Ideal solution A solution formed with no accompanying energy change, when the intermolecular attractive forces between the molecules of the solvent are the same as those between the molecules in the separate components. (12.7)

Insulator A crystal that has bands that are completely filled or completely empty, with large energy gaps between them. An insulator does not conduct electricity. (9.15)

Intensive property A property of a substance that is independent of the amount of substance. (1.4)

Intermolecular force The attractive force between two molecules. (11.2)

Internal energy (E) The total of all possible kinds of energy present in a substance or substances. (4.3)

International System of Units (SI Units) An updated version of the metric system used by scientists, adopted by the Institute of Standards and Technology in 1964. (1.8)

Interstitial site A position between the regular positions in an array of atoms or ions that can be occupied by other atoms or ions. (11.13)

Intramolecular force The attractive force between the atoms making up a molecule. (11.2)

Ion Charged particle resulting from the loss or gain of one or more electrons from an atom or a molecule. (2.5)

Ion activity The effective concentration of any particular kind of ion in solution. It is less than indicated by the actual concentration of a solution. (12.27)

Ion exchange A method of softening water by filtering it through layers of sodium aluminosilicates (zeolites), which exchange sodium or hydrogen ions for Ca^{2+}, Mg^{2+}, or Fe^{2+} in the water. (29.13)

Ion product for water (K_w) The equilibrium constant for the autoionization of water. At 25°C, $K_w = 1.00 \times 10^{-14}$ $(mol/L)^2$. (17.1)

Ion–dipole attraction The electrostatic attraction between an ion and the dipole of a molecule. (11.2)

Ion-induced dipole attraction An intermolecular attraction between an ion and a dipole induced by the ion. (11.3)

Ionic bond Bond due to the electrostatic attraction between positive and negative ions in an ionic compound. (7.1)

Ionic compound A compound composed of ions. (2.6)

Ionic radius The radius of an ion. (6.3)

Ionization constant The equilibrium constant for the ionization of a weak acid or base. (17.4, 17.7)

Ionization energy The amount of energy required to remove an electron from a gaseous atom. (6.3)

Isoelectronic species A group of ions, atoms, or molecules that have the same number of electrons. (6.3)

Isomorphous structures Two elements or compounds that crystallize with the same structure. (11.14)

Isotopes Atoms with the same atomic number and different numbers of neutrons. (3.3)

Joule The SI unit of energy. One joule is the kinetic energy of an object with a mass of 2 kilograms moving with a velocity of one meter per second. 1 J = 1 kg m²/s² and 4.184 J = 1 cal. (4.1)

K_a The equilibrium constant for the reaction of an acid with water. (17.3)

K_b The equilibrium constant for the reaction of a base with water. (17.7)

Kelvin (K) The SI unit of temperature. 273.15 K = 0° Celsius. (1.14)

Kilogram Standard SI unit of mass. Approximately 2.2 pounds. (1.12)

Kinetic energy (KE) The kinetic energy of a moving body, in joules, is equal to $\frac{1}{2}mu^2$ (m = mass; u = speed in meters per second). (10.14)

Kinetic-molecular theory Theory that explains the properties of an ideal gas and assumes that such a gas consists of continuously moving molecules of negligible size. (10.13)

Lattice energy *(U)* The energy required to separate the ions or molecules in a mole of a compound by infinite distances. (11.19, 11.20)

Lattice point A point in a space lattice. (11.17)

Law of definite proportion All samples of a pure compound contain the same elements in the same proportion by mass. (3.6)

Law of mass action When a reversible reaction has attained equilibrium at a given temperature, the reaction quotient remains constant. (15.2)

Le Châtelier's principle When a stress is applied to a system in equilibrium, the equilibrium shifts in a way that tends to minimize the effect of the stress. (15.8)

Lewis acid Any species that can accept a pair of electrons and form a coordinate covalent bond. (16.14)

Lewis base Any species that can donate a pair of electrons and form a coordinate covalent bond. (16.14)

Lewis structure Diagram showing shared and unshared pairs of electrons in an atom, molecule, or ion. (7.3)

Lewis symbol The symbol for an element or monatomic ion that uses a dot to represent each valence electron in the element or ion. (7.1)

Ligand An ion or neutral molecule attached to the central metal ion in a coordination compound. (26.1)

Limiting reagent The reactant that is completely consumed by a chemical reaction. The amount of the limiting reagent limits the amount of product that can be formed. (3.12)

Liquid The state in which matter takes the shape of its container, assumes a horizontal upper surface, and has a fairly definite volume. (1.2)

Liter (L) Unit of volume. $1 \text{ L} = 1000 \text{ cm}^3$. (1.11)

London dispersion force The attraction between two rapidly fluctuating, temporary dipoles. Significant only if atoms are very close together. (11.3)

Magnetic quantum number *(m)* Quantum number signifying the orientation of an orbital around the nucleus. (5.10)

Mass The quantity of matter contained by an object. Mass is measured by the force required to change the speed or direction of its movement. (1.2)

Mass defect The difference between the calculated and experimental mass of a nucleus. (24.2)

Mass number *(A)* The sum of the numbers of neutrons and protons in the nucleus of an atom. (2.3, 24.1)

Matter Anything that occupies space and possesses mass. (1.2)

Melting point The temperature at which the solid and liquid phases of a substance are in equilibrium. (11.8)

Metal A substance that is malleable and ductile, has a characteristic luster, and is generally a good conductor of heat and electricity. (2.4) The bands of a metal are partially filled. (9.15)

Metallic conduction The movement of electrons through a metal, with no changes in the metal and no movement of the metal atoms. (9.15)

Metathesis reaction A reaction in which two or more compounds exchange parts. (2.11)

Meter Standard metric and SI unit of length. Approximately 1.094 yards (1.11)

Miscibility The ability of a liquid to mix with another liquid. (12.3)

Mixture Matter that can be separated into its components by physical means. (1.5)

Molality (m) The number of moles of solute dissolved in exactly one kilogram of solvent. (12.12)

Molar mass Mass in grams of one mole of an element or compound. Numerically equal to the molecular mass of a molecule or the atomic mass of an atom. (3.5)

Molar volume The volume of one mole of an ideal gas (22.4 liters at STP). (10.9)

Molarity (M) The number of moles of solute dissolved in one liter of solution. (3.8)

Mole (mol) The number of atoms contained in exactly 12 grams of ^{12}C (Avogadro's number). $1 \text{ mol} = 6.022 \times 10^{23}$ atoms, molecules, or ions. (3.4, 3.5)

Mole fraction *(X)* The number of moles of a component of a solution divided by the total number of moles of all components. (12.13)

Molecular formula A formula indicating the composition of a molecule of a compound and giving the actual number of atoms of each element in a molecule of the compound. (2.1)

Molecular orbital The discrete energy and region of space in which an electron can be found around the nuclei of the atoms in a molecule. (9.1)

Molecular structure The three-dimensional, geometrical arrangement of the atoms in a molecule. (8.1)

Molecular mass (molecular weight) The average mass of a molecule expressed in amu. (3.5)

Molecule A bonded collection of two or more atoms of the same or different elements. (1.6)

Monoprotic acid An acid containing one ionizable hydrogen atom per molecule. (16.8)

Nernst equation Used to calculate potential values at other than standard conditions. At 25°C, $E = E° - RT/nF \ln Q$. (20.6)

Neutralization A reaction that occurs when stoichiometrically equivalent quantities of an acid and a base are mixed. (16.4)

Neutron An uncharged subatomic particle with a mass of 1.0087 amu. (2.3)

Nonelectrolyte A compound that does not ionize when dissolved in water. (2.10, 12.8)

Nonmetal An element that is a gas, a liquid, or is brittle and nonductile as a solid, has no luster, and is a poor conductor of heat and electricity. (2.4)

Normal boiling point The temperature at which a liquid's vapor pressure equals 1 atm (760 torr). (11.6)

Normality (N) The number of equivalents of solute dissolved in one liter of solution. (16.13, 20.15)

Nuclear binding energy The energy produced by the loss of mass accompanying the formation of an atom from protons, electrons, and neutrons. (24.2)

Nuclear force The force of attraction between nucleons that holds a nucleus together. (24.1)

Nucleon Collective term for protons and neutrons. (24.1)

Nucleus The very heavy, positively charged body located at the center of an atom. (2.3)

Nuclide The nucleus of a particular isotope. (24.1)

Octahedral hole An octahedral space between six atoms or ions in a crystal. (11.15)

Optical isomers Molecules that are nonsuperimposable mirror images and that are optically active. (26.4, 30.6)

Optically active molecules Molecules that rotate the plane of vibration of plane-polarized light. (30.6)

Orbital A three-dimensional region around the nucleus in which an electron moves; can hold up to two electrons. (5.9)

Order of a reaction With respect to one of the reactants, the order of a reaction is equal to the power to which the concentration of that reactant is raised in the rate equation. (14.4)

Osmosis The tendency of a solvent to diffuse through a semipermeable membrane from the less concentrated to the more concentrated solution. (12.19)

Osmotic pressure (π) The pressure required to stop the osmosis from a pure solvent into a solution. $\pi = MRT$. (12.19)

Oxidation The loss of electrons or an increase in oxidation number. (2.11)

Oxidation number The charge on the species that would result if the electrons in a bond were assigned to the more electronegative atom. (7.11)

Oxidation–reduction reaction Reaction in which oxidation numbers change as electrons are lost by one atom and gained by another. (2.11)

Oxidizing agent The substance in an oxidation–reduction reaction that gains electrons and the oxidation number of which is reduced. (2.11)

Oxyacid A hydroxide of a nonmetal. (6.5)

Paramagnetic substance A substance containing unpaired electrons. Paramagnetic substances are attracted to a magnetic field. (26.9)

Parent nuclide An unstable nuclide that changes spontaneously into another (daughter) nuclide. (24.6)

Partial pressure The pressure exerted by an individual gas in a mixture of gases. (10.11)

Pauli exclusion principle No two electrons in the same atom can have the same set of four quantum numbers. (5.11)

Percent yield The actual yield of an experiment divided by the theoretical yield and multiplied by 100. (3.11)

Periodic law The properties of the elements are periodic functions of their atomic numbers. (6.1)

pH The negative logarithm of the concentration of hydronium ions in a solution. (17.1)

Photon A quantum of light or other electromagnetic radiation. The energy of a photon equals the product of Planck's constant and its frequency. (5.8)

Physical change A change in the state or properties of a particular kind of matter that does not involve a chemical change. (1.4)

Physical property A characteristic of a substance that can change without signaling a change of one kind of matter into another. Examples include color, hardness, and physical state. (1.4)

Pi (π) bond A covalent bond formed by side-by-side overlap of atomic orbitals. The electron density is found above and below the internuclear axis. (8.4)

Pi (π) orbital A molecular orbital formed by side-by-side overlap of atomic orbitals, in which the electron density is found above and below the internuclear axis. (9.1)

pOH The negative logarithm of the concentration of hydroxide ions in a solution. (17.1)

Polar covalent bond Covalent bond between atoms of different electronegativities; a covalent bond with a positive end and a negative end. (7.5)

Polydentate ligand A ligand that is attached to a central metal ion by bonds from several donor atoms. (26.1)

Polymer A compound of high molecular mass that is built up of a large number of simple molecules, or monomers. (2.10)

Polymorphism The assumption of two or more crystal structures by the same substance. (11.17)

Positron An atomic particle with the same mass as an electron but with one unit of positive charge. (24.5)

Pressure Force exerted on a unit area. The SI unit of pressure is the pascal (Pa). $Pa = 1 \, newton/m^2$. (10.2)

Principal quantum number *(n)* Quantum number specifying the shell of an electron in an atom or a monatomic ion. (5.10)

Proton A nuclear particle that has a mass of 1.0073 amu and carries a charge of $+1$. (2.3)

Quantized A description of the discrete, or individual, values by which the energy of an electron can vary. (5.7)

Rad (radiation absorbed dose) A unit of radiation dosage; the amount of radiation that deposits 1×10^2 J of energy per kilogram of tissue. (24.16)

Radioactive decay The spontaneous change of an unstable nuclide (parent) into another nuclide (daughter). (24.6)

Radioactivity The spontaneous decomposition of an unstable element, with the simultaneous emission of rays or particles. (5.4)

Radius ratio In an ionic compound, the radius of the positive ion, $r+$, divided by the radius of the negative ion, $r-$. (11.16)

Raoult's law The vapor pressure of the solvent in an ideal solution (P_{solv}) is equal to the mole fraction of the solvent (X_{solv}) times the vapor pressure of the pure solvent ($P°_{solv}$). (12.14)

Rate constant The proportionality constant in the relationship between reaction rate and concentrations of reactants. (14.3)

Rate equations Equations giving the relationship between reaction rate and concentrations of reactants. (14.3)

Rate-determining step The slowest elementary reaction in a reaction path, which determines the maximum rate of the overall reaction. (14.12)

Reaction mechanism The stepwise sequence of elementary reactions in an overall reaction. (14.8, 14.12)

Reaction quotient (Q) A ratio of the product of molar concentrations of the products to that of the reactants, each concentration being raised to the power equal to the coefficient in the equation. For the reaction $aA + bB + \cdots \rightarrow cC + dD + \cdots$, $Q = [C]^c[D]^d \, . \, . \, . \, / [A]^a[B]^b \, . \, . \, .$ (15.2)

Recombinant DNA DNA produced by cutting a DNA chain and inserting particular pieces from another organism, changing the characteristics of the original DNA. (31.12)

Reducing agent The substance in an oxidation–reduction reaction that gives up electrons and the oxidation number of which is increased. (2.11)

Reduction The gain of electrons or a decrease in oxidation number. (2.11)

Rem (roentgen equivalent in man) A unit of radiation dosage that includes a biological factor referred to as the RBE (relative biological effectiveness). $rems = RBE \times rads$. (24.16)

Resonance forms Two or more Lewis structures having the same arrangement of atoms but different arrangements of electrons. (7.8)

Resonance hybrid The average of the resonance forms shown by the individual Lewis structures. (7.8)

Reversible reaction A chemical reaction that can proceed in either direction (2.11)

Salt An ionic compound composed of cations and anions other than hydroxide or oxide ions. (9.2, 16.11)

Saturated solution A solution in which no more solute can be dissolved. (12.1)

Second law of thermodynamics Any spontaneous change that occurs in the universe must be accompanied by an increase in the entropy of the universe. (19.10)

Semiconductor A substance that contains a full band and an empty band, with small energy gaps between the bands. It is a poor conductor. (9.15)

Semi-metal Substances possessing some of the properties of both metals and nonmetals. (6.5)

Shell All of the orbitals in an atom or monatomic ion with the same value of n. (5.10)

Sigma (σ) bond A covalent bond formed by overlap of atomic orbitals along the internuclear axis. The electron density is found along the axis of the bond. (8.4)

Sigma (σ) orbital A molecular orbital in which the electron density is found along the axis of the bond. (9.1)

Simple cubic structure A crystalline structure with a cubic unit cell with lattice points only on the corners. (11.14)

Single bond A bond in which a single pair of electrons is shared between two atoms. (7.3)

Solid The state in which matter is rigid, has a definite shape, and has a fairly constant volume. (1.2)

Solid solution A homogeneous and stable solution of one solid substance in another. (12.6)

Solubility product (K_{sp}) The equilibrium constant for the dissolution of a slightly soluble electrolyte. (18.1)

Solution A homogeneous mixture of a solute in a solvent. (12.1)

Space lattice All points within a crystal that have identical environments. (11.17)

Specific heat A property of a substance that represents the quantity of heat required to raise the temperature of one gram of the substance one degree Celsius (or one kelvin). (4.1)

Spectrum The component colors, or wavelengths, of light or other forms of electromagnetic radiation. (5.8)

Spin quantum number (s) Number specifying the direction of the spin of an electron around its own axis. (5.10)

Spontaneous process A physical or chemical change that occurs without the addition of energy. (12.7) $\Delta G < 0$ for a spontaneous process. (19.6)

Stability curve A plot of the number of neutrons versus the number of protons for stable nuclei. (24.3)

Standard conditions (STP) 273.15 K (0°C) and one atmosphere of pressure (760 torr or 101.325 kilopascals). (10.9)

Standard electrode potential ($E°$) Potential measured with respect to a standard hydrogen electrode at 25°C with 1 M concentration of each ion in solution and 1 atm of pressure of each gas involved. (20.3)

Standard hydrogen electrode Assigned an electrode potential of exactly zero. The potential of all other electrodes is reported relative to that of the standard hydrogen electrode. (20.3)

Standard molar enthalpy of formation ($\Delta H_f°$) The enthalpy change of a chemical reaction in which one mole of a pure substance is formed from the free elements in their most stable states under standard state conditions. (4.4)

Standard molar entropy ($S_{298}°$) Actual entropy content of one mole of a substance in a standard state. (19.7)

Standard state 298.15 K (25 degrees Celsius) and one atmosphere of pressure. (4.4)

State function A property of a system that is not dependent on the way in which the system gets to the state in which it exhibits that property. (19.4)

Strong acid An acid that gives a 100% yield of hydronium ions when dissolved in water. (16.3)

Strong base A base that gives a 100% yield of hydroxide ions when dissolved in water. (16.3)

Strong electrolyte An electrolyte that gives a 100% yield of ions when dissolved in water. (2.10)

Structural isomers Two substances that have the same molecular formula but have different physical and chemical properties because their component atoms are arranged differently. (30.1)

Sublimation The passing of a solid directly to the vapor state without first melting. (11.5)

Subshell A set of degenerate orbitals with the same values of n and l. (5.10)

Substitution reaction A reaction in which one atom replaces another in a molecule. (30.1)

Supersaturated solution A solution that contains more solute than it would if the dissolved solute were in equilibrium with the undissolved solute. (12.1)

Surface tension The force that causes the surface of a liquid to contract, reducing its surface area to a minimum. (11.11)

Surroundings The universe outside a thermodynamic system. (4.3)

System The substance or substances involved in a reaction or change that is being studied. (4.3)

Termolecular reaction An elementary reaction involving the simultaneous collision of any combination of three molecules, ions, or atoms. (14.11)

Ternary compound A compound containing three different elements. (6.5)

Tetrahedral hole A tetrahedral space formed by four atoms or ions in a crystal. (11.15)

Theoretical yield The calculated yield of a reaction based on the assumptions that there is only one reaction involved, that all the reactant is converted into product, and that all the product is collected. (3.11)

Third law of thermodynamics The entropy of any pure, perfect crystalline element or compound at absolute zero (0 K) is equal to zero. (19.13)

Three-center bond The bonding of three atoms by one pair of electrons in a molecular orbital formed from the overlap of three atomic orbitals. (25.2)

Answers to Selected Even-Numbered Exercises

Chapter 1

18. (a) 5; (b) 2; (c) 3; (d) 5 **20.** (a) 2; (b) 5; (c) 1; (d) 3; (e) 4; (f) 2; (g) 6 **22.** (a) 370; (b) 0.166; (c) 6500; (d) 15; (e) 0.918; (f) 148; (g) 3400 **26.** 1.00 g/mL; 0.810 g/mL **30.** (a) 3.58×10^{-3} g; (b) 3.712×10^{-4} km; (c) 1344 mL; (d) 83.5 mL; (e) 0.1743 m; (f) 3.451×10^4 mg; (g) 2.78×10^{-1} m^3; (h) 1300 g **34.** 16 m **36.** 64.4 kg **38.** 5470 yd; 3.107 mi **40.** 4.9 pints **42.** 221 kg **44.** 60.6 km/h **46.** 1.85 km **48.** 328 ft **50.** 3.0×10^4 mL **52.** 110 pm; 4.33×10^{-9} in. **54.** 1.74 g/cm^3 **56.** (a) 10.2 cm^3; (b) 96.2 cm^3; (c) 3.3 L **58.** 98.6°F; 310.2 K **60.** 19°C **62.** Nitrogen: -321°F, 77 K; oxygen: -297°F, 90 K **66.** 1.1 g/cm^3 **68.** 343 m/s **70.** 1.0 L

Chapter 2

66. (c) 36 molecules of water

Chapter 3

2. (a) 256.528 amu; 256.528 g/mol; (b) 97.9952 amu; 97.9952 g/mol; (c) 201.7083 amu; 201.7083 g/mol; (d) 72.150 amu; 72.150 g/mol; (e) 378.103 amu; 378.103 g/mol; (f) 369.219 amu; 369.219 g/mol **4.** One molecule of carbon dioxide **6.** 3; 5 **8.** (a) One mole of carbon dioxide; (b) One mole of carbon dioxide **10.** (a) 48.9; (b) 3.84 g **12.** Calculation shows 6.0×10^{22} atoms for each; no—twice as many molecules of P$_4$ (1.5×10^{22} molecules of P$_4$ and 7.5×10^{21} molecules of S$_8$) **14.** Molecular mass of methane **16.** No change **18.** 3.441×10^{-22} g **20.** (a) 0.594 mol; (b) 2.33×10^{-5} mol; (c) 64 mol; (d) 0.202 mol; (e) 5.6×10^{-3} mol **22.** 0.050 mol of calcium **28.** (a) 11.016% Li; 50.893% S; 38.090% O; (b) 81.9581% Bi; 2.3552% C; 15.6866% O; (c) 37.017% C; 2.21883% H; 18.5003% N; 42.2644% O; (d) 49.481% C; 5.19040% H; 28.8512% N; 16.4778% O; (e) 60.0017% C; 4.47558% H; 35.5226% O **30.** (a) 38.8%; (b) 84.2%; (c) 69.241% **32.** (a) CH; (b) C$_6$H$_6$ **34.** CH$_3$; C$_2$H$_6$ **36.** NaNH$_4$HPO$_4$ **38.** Na$_2$S$_2$O$_3 \cdot$5H$_2$O **40.** C$_5$H$_7$N; C$_{10}$H$_{14}$N$_2$ **42.** (a) C$_5$H$_8$O$_2$; (b) CHCl; (c) CH$_2$; (d) CH; (e) C$_3$H$_3$N **44.** Fe + Cl$_2 \longrightarrow$ FeCl$_2$ **46.** MgCO$_3$ **48.** (a) 4.00 g; (b) 0.034 g; (c) 0.39 g; (d) 125 g; (e) 0.513 g **50.** (a) 1.00 mol; 164 g; (b) 0.118 mol; 7.09 g; (c) 0.012 mol; 1.5 g; (d) 0.012 mol; 1.2 g; (e) 0.012 mol; 4.1 g **52.** 18.4 M **54.** 6.202 g **56.** 1.954×10^{-2} M **58.** 0.217 mol; 15.4 g **60.** 680 g **62.** (a) 3537 g; (b) 36.8 g; (c) 0.200 mol **64.** (a) 132 g; (b) 2.55 mol **66.** (a) 1.814 mol; (b) 3.657 g **68.** (a) 1.275×10^{23}; (b) 53.74 g **70.** 225 g **72.** SiO$_2$ + 3C $\longrightarrow$ SiC + 2CO; 4.50 kg **74.** 0.2106 g **76.** 94% **78.** 48.3% **80.** 0.766 kg **82.** 78.2% **84.** (a) Cr; (b) 40% **86.** Na$_2$C$_2$O$_4$; 86.6% **88.** 1.33 g **90.** 0.337 M **92.** 4.00×10^2 mL

94. 0.2511 M **96.** (a) 0.717 M; (b) 4.28% **98.** Na; NaOH **100.** 8 **102.** 2.22 g **104.** (a) 24.5 kg; (b) 25.0 kg **106.** 37.6% **108.** 3.97×10^3 L **110.** 95 kg **112.** GaBr$_3$

Chapter 4

4. (a) 8.66°C; (b) 18.1°C; (c) 15°C **6.** (a) 920 J °C^{-1}; (b) 7.1×10^4 J; (c) 4.66×10^5 J **8.** 0.2520 Calories lb^{-1} °F^{-1} **10.** (a) 82°C **12.** Smaller **14.** (a) Smaller; (b) 4.55 J °C^{-1}; (c) 56.5°C **16.** 1.8 kJ; 0.49 J g^{-1} °C^{-1} **18.** (a) Endothermic; (b) 660 J **20.** -4.9 kJ **22.** Cu **28.** 1.09×10^4 kJ **30.** 0.125 mol **32.** 41.4 kJ **34.** 28.2 kJ **36.** 33.1 kJ mol^{-1} **38.** -2984 kJ **40.** 1.28 kg **42.** 0.042 g **44.** 66.4 kJ; no **46.** -520.0 kJ **48.** -982.8 kJ **50.** (a) 62.438 kJ; (b) 31.4 kJ; (c) 42.6 kJ; (d) 24.3 kJ **52.** CH$_4$ **54.** (a) C$_2$H$_5$OH(l) + 3O$_2$(g) $\longrightarrow$ 2CO$_2$(g) + 3H$_2$O(g); -1234.8 kJ; (b) -21.16 kJ; (c) 1.487 times farther **56.** 0.25 g **58.** 16 kJ; 3.7 Calories **62.** 31 g **64.** (a) Fe + Cl$_2 \longrightarrow$ FeCl$_2$; -338 kJ; (b) No, ΔH is not equal to ΔH$_f^\circ$ **66.** 18 kJ **68.** (a) 131.30 kJ; (b) -90.2 kJ mol^{-1}; -38.0 kJ mol^{-1}; (c) -638.4 kJ **70.** 67.1 kJ

Chapter 5

10. -0.2776 eV **12.** 5.08×10^{-5}; 9600 times larger (or 9.60×10^3 times larger, to show the number of significant figures justified) **14.** (a) 13.595 eV; 2.1782×10^{-18} J per atom; (b) 13.60 eV; 2.179×10^{-18} J per atom **16.** 48.36 eV; 7.748×10^{-18} J **18.** From $n = 5$ to $n = 4$, 0.3060 eV; from $n = 5$ to $n = 1$, 13.06 eV **20.** 2.961×10^{-19} J; 4.469×10^{14} s^{-1} **22.** (a) 4.800×10^{-7} m; yes; (b) 6.246×10^{14} s^{-1}; (c) 4.138×10^{-19} J; (d) No; 1.6336×10^{-18} J is required **30.** $3d$; 5 **34.** (a) 2; (b) 1; 3; 5; (c) 3; 2; 1; (d) i, 0; ii, 1; iii, 2; (e) i < ii < iii; no **40.** b; a **46.** 4.949×10^{14} s^{-1}

Chapter 6

No answers are provided for this chapter since the exercises do not require calculations.

Chapter 7

4. 3$-$; 1$-$; 2$+$; 1$-$; 3$+$; 1$+$; 3$-$; 2$-$; 2$-$; 2$+$; 1$+$

6. $:\ddot{\text{Cl}}:^-$; Na$^+$; Mg^{2+}; Ca^{2+}; K$^+$; $:\ddot{\text{Br}}:^-$; Sr^{2+}; and $:\ddot{\text{F}}:^-$

8. (a) Mg$^{2+}:\ddot{\text{S}}:^{2-}$; (b) [Al^{3+}]$_2$[$:\ddot{\text{O}}:^{2-}$]$_3$; (c) Ga^{3+}[$:\ddot{\text{Cl}}:^-$]$_3$; (d) [K$^+$]$_2:\ddot{\text{O}}:^{2-}$; (e) [Li$^+$]$_3:\ddot{\text{N}}:^{3-}$; (f) K$^+:\ddot{\text{F}}:^-$

10. (a) AlP; (b) $MgCl_2$; (c) Na_3P; (d) Al_2S_3;   **16.** Ionic: VO_2, $FeBr_2$, K_2O, $MgCl_2$, CaO; covalent: F_2CO, NCl_3, NO, HBr, IBr, CO_2

18. For H_2:   H : H

For HBr: H : Br :

For PCl_3:
: Cl :
|
: P—Cl :
|
: Cl :

For SF_2:   : F : S : F :

For $SiCl_4$:
: Cl :
|
: Cl—Si—Cl :
|
: Cl :

For H_3O^+:
$$\left[\begin{array}{c} H \\ | \\ H{-}O{-}H \end{array} \right]^+$$

For NH_4^+:
$$\left[\begin{array}{c} H \\ | \\ H{-}N{-}H \\ | \\ H \end{array} \right]^+$$

For BF_4^-:
$$\left[\begin{array}{c} : F : \\ | \\ : F{-}B{-}F : \\ | \\ : F : \end{array} \right]^-$$

20. For N_2:   : N≡N :

For CO: : C≡O :

For CN^-:   : C≡N : $^-$

For NO^+:   : N≡O : $^+$

For HCCH: H—C≡C—H

For HCN: H—C≡N :

For C_2^{2-}:   : C≡C : $^{2-}$

22.   : P≡P :

24. (a)
H
|
H—C—S—H
|
H   : O
| ‖
H—N—C—C—O—H
|
H

(b)
H : O   H
| ‖ |
H—N—C—N—H

(c)
H : O : O
| ‖   ‖
H—C—C—C—O—H
|
H

(d)
: O
‖
H   C—H
\ / \
: N   C
| ‖
C   C
‖   / \
O   N   H
|
H

(e)
: O
‖
H—O—C—O—H

26. For methane (CH_4):
H
|
H—C—H
|
H

For ethylene (C_2H_4):
H   H
\   /
C=C
/   \
H   H

For ethane (C_2H_6):
H H
| |
H—C—C—H
| |
H H

For hydrogen cyanide (HCN):   H—C≡N :

For propyne (H_3CCCH):
H
|
H—C—C≡C—H
|
H

For diacetylene (HCCCCH):   H—C≡C—C≡C—H

28. a, c

30.
: O   : O
‖   ‖
: O   O : ⟷ : O   O :

32.
$$\left[\begin{array}{c} N \\ : O \quad O : \end{array} \right]^- \longleftrightarrow \left[\begin{array}{c} N \\ : O \quad O : \end{array} \right]^-$$

34. (a) 0; (b) 0; (c) 0; (d) 0, 0

36. For F_2CO: F, 0; C, 0; O, 0

For NO^-: N, −1; O, 0

For BF_4^-: B, −1; F, 0

For ClNO: Cl, 0; N, 0; O, 0

For H_2CCH_2: H, 0; C, 0

For ClF_3: Cl, 0; F, 0

For SeF_6: Se, 0; F, 0

38.   : Cl—N=O :

46. For a nonpolar single bond: H—H

For a nonpolar double bond: : O = O :

For a nonpolar triple bond: H—C≡C—H

48. NO_3^-, CO_2, H_2S, BH_4^- **50.** (a) C=C; (b) C=N; (c) C≡O; (d) H—F; (e) O—H; (f) C—O;   **52.** N≡N, 945.408 kJ per mol of bonds; O=O, 498.34 kJ per mol of bonds; N=O, 631.62 kJ per mol of bonds   **54.** The S—F bond in SF_6 **56.** 128 kJ; 136.94 kJ   **58.** 386 kJ   **60.** 4.807×10^{-6}, 2080 cm^{-1} **62.** 6.65×10^{13} s^{-1} **64.** $CH_3C≡N$:   **68.** F, -1; Li, $+1$; Mg, $+2$; Cs, $+1$; O, -2; Al, $+3$; Ca, $+2$ **70.** (a) -1; (b) $+4$; (c) -3; (d) $+3$ and $+5$; (e) -2; (f) $+6$; (g) $+5$; (h) -1 **72.** -3; $+1$; -3; -1; $+3$; $+5$; $-1/3$; $+5$; $+3$ **74.** $PbCl_4$, PbS_2, K_2PbCl_6 **76.** Average oxidation number: $+3$; individual oxidation numbers: -1, $+5$ **84.** (a) $2Mg + O_2 \longrightarrow 2MgO$; (b) $2Al + 3Cl_2 \longrightarrow 2AlCl_3$; (c) $16K + S_8 \longrightarrow 8K_2S$; (d) $3Mg + N_2 \longrightarrow Mg_3N_2$; (e) $P_4O_6 + 2O_2 \longrightarrow P_4O_{10}$; (f) $Ca + 2HBr \longrightarrow CaBr_2 + H_2$; (g) $2Cs + 2H_2O \longrightarrow 2CsOH + H_2$; (h) $2Li + 2HI \longrightarrow 2LiI + H_2$; (i) $Sr + 2CH_3CO_2H \longrightarrow Sr(CH_3CO_2)_2 + H_2$; (j) $2Al + 3SnCl_4 \longrightarrow 2AlCl_3 + 3SnCl_2$; (k) $Mg + PbO \longrightarrow MgO + Pb$ **86.** $H_2 + F_2 \longrightarrow 2HF$ **88.** (a) $6HBr + In_2O_3 \longrightarrow 2InBr_3 + 3H_2O$; (b) $Mg(OH)_2(s) + 2HClO_4(aq) \longrightarrow Mg^{2+}(aq) + 2ClO_4^-(aq) + 2H_2O(l)$; (c) $Al(OH)_3(s) + 3HNO_3(aq) \longrightarrow Al^{3+}(aq) + 3NO_3^-(aq) + 3H_2O(l)$; (d) $Li_2O(s) + 2CH_3CO_2H(l) \longrightarrow 2LiCH_3CO_2 + H_2O$; (e) $SrO(s) + H_2SO_4(l) \longrightarrow SrSO_4 + H_2O$ **92.** For H_2: Oxidation number (ON), 0; formal charge (FC), 0; For BeH_2: ON, -1; FC, 0; For H_2O: ON, $+1$; FC, 0

98.

102. Na, $+1$; Al, $+3$; F, -1 **104.** K, 28.7%; H, 1.48%; P, 22.8%; O, 47.0%   **106.** $LiNO_3$; $Ca(ClO_4)_2$; K_2SO_4; $Ca(OH)_2$; $(NH_4)_2SO_4$; $AlPO_4$; $(NH_4)_3PO_4$ **108.** (a) $Ca(OH)_2 + 2HCl \longrightarrow CaCl_2 + 2H_2O$; (b) $Sr(OH)_2 + 2HNO_3 \longrightarrow Sr(NO_3)_2 + 2H_2O$; (c) $8Ca + S_8 \longrightarrow 8CaS$; (d) $12Cs + P_4 \longrightarrow 4Cs_3P$; (e) $2In + 3SnSO_4 \longrightarrow In_2(SO_4)_3 + 3Sn$; (f) $Si + 2F_2 \longrightarrow SiF_4$; (g) $2K(s) + 2H_2O(l) \longrightarrow 2KOH(aq) + H_2$; (h) $H_2 + Br_2 \longrightarrow 2HBr$; (i) $2P + 5F_2 \longrightarrow 2PF_5$; (j) $16Sb + 5S_8 \longrightarrow 8Sb_2S_5$; (k) $2Al(s) + 6HClO_4(aq) \longrightarrow 2Al(ClO_4)_3(aq) + 3H_2$

Chapter 8

2. (a) Octadedral; (b) trigonal bipyramidal; (c) tetrahedral; (d) linear; (e) trigonal planar   **4.** (a) square pyramidal; (b) trigonal bipyramidal; (c) T-shaped; (d) trigonal pyramidal; (e) seesaw; (f) square planar; (g) linear; (h) bent (109.5° angle)   **6.** (a) Bent (120° angle); (b) linear; (c) trigonal planar; (d) trigonal pyramidal; (e) tetrahedral; (f) seesaw   **8.** (a) Tetrahedral; (b) trigonal planar; (c) bent (109.5°); (d) trigonal planar; (e) bent (109.5°); (f) bent (120°); (g) CH_3 carbon, tetrahedral; others, linear; (h) tetrahedral; (i) end carbons, trigonal planar; middle carbon, linear   **10.** (c)   **12.** All contain polar bonds; none has a dipole moment   **14.** All contain polar bonds; a, c, d, e, f have dipole moments   **16.** P   **26.** (a) sp^3d^2; (b) sp^3d; (c) sp^3; (d) sp; (e) sp^2 **28.** (a) sp^3d^2; (b) sp^3d; (c) sp^3; (d) sp^3d; (e) sp^3d^2; (f) sp^3d **30.** (a) sp^2, p orbitals on

N and O; (b) sp, p orbitals on C and S; (c) sp^2, p orbitals on C and O; (d) sp^3, no π bonds; (e) sp^3, no π bonds; (f) sp^3d, no π bonds   **32.** (a) sp^3; (b) sp^3; (c) sp^3; (d) sp^2; (e) sp^3; (f) sp^2; (g) CH_3 carbon, sp^3; other carbons, sp; (h) sp^3; (i) End carbons, sp^2; middle carbon, sp **36.** Group VA (Group 15)

Chapter 9

No answers are provided for this chapter since the exercises do not require calculations.

Chapter 10

2. 715 mm   **4.** 0.974 atm; 740 mmHg; 98.6 kPa   **6.** 146.3 atm; 1.112×10^5 torr   **8.** 0.0468 atm.; 4.75 kPa   **10.** (a) 150 torr; (b) 150 torr   **12.** 3.24 L   **14.** 2.13×10^3 L   **18.** 635 mL   **20.** 9°C   **22.** 273 K; 0°C   **24.** 3.73 cm   **28.** At 300°C, $P = 0.917$ atm; mass = 0.86 g   **30.** At the same pressure, $1/V$ would be twice as large.   **32.** 0.355 mol   **34.** 2.12 mol   **36.** 420 K or 147°C   **38.** 135 atm   **40.** (a) 5.78 L; (b) 0.774 L; (c) 1.10×10^3 L; (d) 16.1 L; (e) 303 L; (f) 0.61 L   **42.** 1.70 g/L; 1.46 g/L   **44.** 1.25 g/L   **46.** 3 atm   **48.** Yes ($P_{O_2} = 1.3$ atm, 3.8% of the total pressure)   **50.** 3.48 L   **52.** 0.538 L   **54.** 271 mL   **56.** 7.00 L of O_2; 14.0 L of CO_2 **58.** 20.0 L   **60.** 3.34 tanks   **62.** 31.0 g/mol   **64.** 30.0 g/mol; NO   **66.** C_3H_6 **68.** 13.0 L   **70.** 11.5 kg   **72.** 1.30×10^3 L   **74.** 2.16 g   **76.** 8.52×10^{-2} mL   **88.** 66.0   **96.** 29°C   **98.** 2×10^{-10} atm   **100.** C_4H_8 **102.** 0.69 L   **104.** 30.3 L   **106.** 177 g   **108.** XeF_2 **110.** 397 mL

Chapter 11

58. Face-centered cubic   **60.** (a) 4.95 Å; (b) 11.3 g cm^{-3} **62.** TiO_2 **64.** 4; sp^3 for both   **66.** Co_3O_4 **70.** (a) ZnS structure; (b) CaF_2 structure; (c) NaCl structure; (d) ZnS structure; (e) NaCl structure; (f) CaF_2 structure; (g) NaCl structure; (h) CsCl structure; (i) NaCl structure; (j) NaCl structure; (k) ZnS structure   **72.** (a) MnF_3; (b) 6; (c) 4.02 Å; (d) 2.86 g/cm^3 **74.** 1.48 Å   **76.** 6.023×10^{23} **78.** 890 kJ/mol   **80.** 0.722 Å   **88.** 780 kJ   **90.** Ethyl ether, ~17°C; ethyl alcohol, ~45°C; water, ~86°C; ~65°C   **98.** 3.57 Å   **100.** 50.84%, $+3$

Chapter 12

26. 0.025 M   **28.** (a) 5.04×10^{-3} M; (b) 0.499 M; (c) 9.087 M; (d) 9.74 M; (e) 1.1×10^{-3} M   **30.** (a) Na_2CO_3, 0.0119; H_2O, 0.9881; (b) H_2SO_4, 0.0666; H_2O, 0.933; (c) NaCl, 0.0027; H_2O, 0.997; (d) $C_{18}H_{21}NO_3$, 0.05433; C_2H_5OH, 0.9457; (e) C_5H_9N, 0.00426; $CHCl_3$, 0.996   **32.** 42 g   **34.** 19.9 g   **36.** 1.75×10^{-3} M   **38.** 4.2×10^{-3} m   **40.** 0.561 m   **42.** 1.03 M   **44.** 49.6 mL   **46.** 0.91 L   **48.** H_2, 0.78; CO, 0.038; CO_2, 0.18   **50.** 0.39; 0.27; 0.34   **52.** (a) 54% $NaNO_3$, 46% H_2O; (b) 14 m   **64.** 2.1×10^2 amu   **66.** 144 amu   **68.** 0.87°C   **70.** Dissolve 284 g of glycerin in 1.00 kg of water;

−5.73°C **72.** S_8 **74.** 13,900 amu **76.** 54 g **84.** 43%
90. 47 M; 4.3 m; 0.44% **92.** 243 amu **94.** 6.59%; 0.442 m
96. 0.282 M **98.** 15.5 mL **100.** No **102.** $C_{12}H_{10}$
104. $C_6H_{12}O_6$

Chapter 13

8. $Ca(l) + 2CsCl(l) \longrightarrow 2Cs(g) + CaCl_2(l)$ **14.** Yes; H^+ is the
Lewis acid and H^- is the Lewis base. **16.** 0.23 g

22. Cathode: $2 Li^+ + 2e^- \longrightarrow 2Li(l)$
Anode: $\qquad\quad 2Cl^- \longrightarrow Cl_2(g) + 2e^-$

Overall: $2Li^+ + 2Cl^- \longrightarrow 2Li(l) + Cl_2(g)$

30. 0.5035 g **34.** (a) Ba; (b) Na_2CO_3; (c) $BeCl_2$; (d) Rb;
(e) Al^{3+}; (f) Xe **36.** $Ca + 2H_2O \longrightarrow Ca(OH)_2 + H_2$
40. $MgSO_4 \cdot 7H_2O$

48. (a) Cl; (b) Cl; (c) $:\overset{..}{F}—Al\overset{\overset{\displaystyle\cdot\cdot}{\displaystyle F}\,\cdot}{\underset{\underset{\displaystyle\cdot\cdot}{\displaystyle F}\,\cdot}{}}$

(d) Na, basic; Al, amphoteric; Cl, acidic **52.** (a) $Al_2O_3 \cdot$
$2H_2O + 6NaF + 6HF \longrightarrow 2Na_3AlF_6 + 5H_2O(g)$; (b) $4Al(s) +$
$3O_2 \longrightarrow 2Al_2O_3$; (c) $2Al(s) + 3Cl_2 \longrightarrow 2AlCl_3$; (d) $Al_2S_3 +$
$6H_2O \longrightarrow 2Al(OH)_3 + 3H_2S$; (e) $Al(OH)_3 + HNO_3 \longrightarrow$
$Al^{3+} + 3NO_3^- + 3H_2O$ **54.** (a) 2.33 h; (b) 5.32×10^4 L
60. 222 L; 344 L **62.** 3.85 g/L

Chapter 14

4. Rate $= k[NO]^2[Cl_2]$; $k = 9.12$ L^2 mol^{-2} h^{-1} **6.** 2×10^{-8}
mol L^{-1} s^{-1} **8.** Rate $= k[NOCl]^2$; $k = 4.0 \times 10^{-8}$ L mol^{-1} s^{-1}
10. Rate $= k[I^-][OCl^-]$; $k = 6.1 \times 10^{-2}$ L mol^{-1} s^{-1}
12. 2.5×10^{-2} yr^{-1} **14.** (a) $t_{1/2} = 3.2 \times 10^4$ s;
(b) 2.0×10^{-2} mol **16.** 1.21×10^{-4} yr^{-1} **18.** (a) Second
order; (b) 0.231 L mol^{-1} s^{-1} **20.** 19.7 min; 34.0 min **26.** 4
times faster; 128 times faster **28.** 3.8×10^{15} s^{-1} **30.** 43 kJ
mol^{-1} **40.** Rate $= k[penicillinase][penicillin]$; $k = 1.0 \times 10^7$ L
mol^{-1} min^{-1}

Chapter 15

8. (a) $Q = 0.23$, shifts left; (b) $Q = 0$, shifts right; (c) $Q = 640$,
shifts right **10.** 4 **12.** $K = 1.8 \times 10^{-14}$ mol L^{-1} **14.** 2.0
mol^2 L^{-2} **16.** 507 g **18.** 1.9×10^3 atm^{-1} **20.** H_2, F_2, $1.6 \times$
10^{-7} M; HF, 0.50 M **22.** (a) Cl_2, 0.028 M; NO, 0.056 M;
NOCl, 1.9 M; (b) Cl_2, 0.044 M; NO, 0.088 M; NOCl, 3.9 M;
(c) Cl_2, 2.2×10^{-5} M; NO, 2.0 M; NOCl, 2.0 M; (d) Cl_2,
0.036 M; NO, 0.072 M; NOCl, 3.9 M; (e) Cl_2, 0.5 M; NO,
9.9×10^{-3} M; NOCl, 1.5 M **24.** (a) NH_3, 0.13 M; N_2, 0.13
M; H_2, 1.3 M; (b) converges very slowly; SO_3, 0.67 M; SO_2,
0.77 M; O_2, 0.38 M; (c) Cl_2, 0.0043 M; NO, 0.038 M; NOCl,
0.52 M **26.** 1.17×10^{-3} M **28.** PCl_5, 0.063 M; PCl_3, 0.0366
M; Cl_2, 0.0366 M **30.** (a) 0.33 mol; (b) 0.50 mol **32.** b, c, g
34. (a) Cl_2, 0.072 atm; NO, 0.14 atm; NOCl, 1.9 atm; (b) Cl_2,
0.11 atm; NO, 0.22 atm; NOCl, 3.8 atm; (c) Cl_2, 6.0×10^{-3}

atm; NO, 0.031 atm; NOCl, 0.52 atm; (d) Cl_2, 0.11 atm; NO,
0.22 atm; NOCl, 3.8 atm; (e) Cl_2, 0.5 atm; NO, 0.042 atm;
NOCl, 1.5 atm **36.** 34% **42.** $P_{N_2O_4} = 8.0$ atm; $P_{NO_2} =$
1.0 atm **44.** 0.50 M **46.** $K_p = 3.06$ atm^2 **50.** 33 g
56. 1.0 atm **58.** (a) First order; (b) 0.294 h^{-1}; (c) 0.588 h^{-1}
60. (a) Rate $= k[H_2O_2][HI]$; (b) $K = [HI]/[H_3O^+][I^-]$; (c) Rate $=$
$kK[H_3O^+][I^-][H_2O_2] = k'[H_3O^+][I^-][H_2O_2]$ **62.** (a) [Sucrose] $=$
1.65×10^{-7} M; [glucose] $=$ [fructose] $= 0.150$ M; (b) $6.5 \times$
10^{11} s (21,000 years!)

Chapter 16

2. (a) $H_3O^+ \longrightarrow H^+ + H_2O$; (b) $HCl \longrightarrow H^+ + Cl^-$;
(c) $H_2O \longrightarrow H^+ + OH^-$; (d) $CH_3CO_2H \longrightarrow H^+ + CH_3CO_2^-$;
(e) $NH_4^+ \longrightarrow H^+ + NH_3$; (f) $HSO_4^- \longrightarrow H^+ + SO_4^{2-}$
4. (a) H_2O; (b) HF; (c) H_3O^+; (d) H_2SO_4; (e) H_2CO_3; (f) NH_4^+;
(g) NH_3; (h) H_2; (i) HN^{2-} **6.** (a) NH_3; (b) Cl^-; (c) NO_3^-;
(d) ClO_4^-; (e) $CH_3CO_2^-$; (f) CN^- **8.** (a) H_2SO_4, HNO_3, HCl;
CaO, $Ca(OH)_2$, NaOH; (b) H_3PO_4, NH_4NO_3, $(NH_4)_2SO_4$;
(c) NH_3, Na_2CO_3 **10.** (a) acid, HNO_3; CB, NO_3^-; base, H_2O;
CA, H_3O^+; (b) acid, H_2O; CB, OH^-; base, CN^-; CA, HCN;
(c) acid, H_2SO_4; CB, HSO_4^-; base, Cl^-; CA, HCl; (d) acid,
HSO_4^-; CB, SO_4^{2-}; base, OH^-; CA, H_2O; (e) acid, H_2O; CB,
OH^-; base, O^{2-}; CA, OH^-; (f) acid, $[Al(H_2O)_6]^{3+}$; CB,
$[Al(H_2O)_5(OH)]^{2+}$; base, $[Cu(H_2O)_3(OH)]^+$; CA, $[Cu(H_2O)_4]^{2+}$;
(g) acid, H_2S; CB, HS^-; base, NH_2^-; CA, NH_3 **14.** a, b, e
16. 0.1 **18.** NH_4^+ **22.** (a) H_2O; (b) HF; (c) H_2S; (d) HI
24. (a) $Cl^- < H_2O < OH^- < H^-$; (b) $ClO_4^- < ClO_3^- <$
$ClO_2^- < ClO^-$; (c) $HTe^- < HS^- < PH_2^- < NH_2^-$; (d) $ClO_2^- <$
$BrO_2^- < IO_2^-$ **26.** CN^-

32. $Ca^{2+} \left[:\overset{..}{\underset{..}{O}}:\right]^{2-} + :\overset{..}{O}=C=\overset{..}{O}: \longrightarrow Ca^{2+} \left[:\overset{..}{\underset{..}{O}}=\overset{\overset{\textstyle :\overset{..}{O}:}{|}}{C}—\overset{..}{\underset{..}{O}}\right]^{2-}$

Lewis base   Lewis acid

36. $Al(OH)_4^- + CO_2 \longrightarrow Al(OH)_3 + HCO_3^-$ **40.** $H_3AsO_4 +$
$H_2O \longrightarrow H_3O^+ + H_2AsO_4^-$; $H_2AsO_4^- + H_2O \longrightarrow H_3O^+ +$
$HAsO_4^{2-}$; $HAsO_4^{2-} + H_2O \longrightarrow H_3O^+ + AsO_4^{3-}$; amphiprotic:
$H_2AsO_4^-$, $HAsO_4^{2-}$ **48.** (a) 2.5 N; (b) 0.075 N; (c) 0.015 N;
(d) 0.4829 N **50.** 22.8 mL **52.** 0.191 N **54.** 1.22×10^{-2}
M; 0.904 g/L **60.** (a) H_2O, $Fe_3(SO_4)_2$; (b) Li_2SiO_3; (c) H_2,
NaCN; (d) Na_2CO_3, NH_3; (e) $Li_3N + 2NH_3 \longrightarrow 3LiNH_2$;
(f) $BaO + Cl_2O_7 \longrightarrow Ba(ClO_4)_2$; (g) $NaF + H_3PO_4 \longrightarrow$
$NaH_2PO_4 + HF$; (h) $MgH_2 + H_2S \longrightarrow MgS + 2H_2$;
(i) $NaCH_3 + NH_3 \longrightarrow NaNH_2 + CH_4$; (j) $KHCO_3 + KHS \longrightarrow$
$K_2CO_3 + H_2S$; (k) $H_2SO_4 + NaCH_3CO_2 \longrightarrow CH_3CO_2H +$
$NaHSO_4$ **64.** $2Na + 2NH_3 \longrightarrow 2NaNH_2 + H_2$

Chapter 17

6. $[H_3O^+] = [OH^-] = 3.101 \times 10^{-7}$ M; pH $=$ pOH $= 6.5085$
8. $[H_3O^+] = 1.82 \times 10^{-9}$ M; $[OH^-] = 5.49 \times 10^{-6}$ M
10. 1×10^{-8} M; pOH $= 6$ **12.** $[H_3O^+] = 1 \times 10^{-2}$ M;
$[OH^-] = 1 \times 10^{-12}$ M **16.** (a) $[H_3O^+] = 0.085$ M; $[NO_3^-] =$
0.085 M; (b) $[CO^{2+}] = 1.248$ M; $[Cl^-] = 2.496$ M;
(c) $[Fe(H_2O)_6^{3+}] = 0.214$ M; $[SO_4^{2-}] = 0.321$ M
22. (a) 1.82×10^{-5}; (b) 4.5×10^{-4} **24.** (a) 1.8×10^{-5} M;

(b) 6×10^{-6} M **26.** (a) 2.36×10^{-3} M; (b) 8.1×10^{-3} M; (c) 1.4×10^{-2} M **28.** 8.7×10^{-3} M; 2.1% **30.** 7.2×10^{-2} M; 14% **32.** 2.3×10^{-3} M **34.** 1×10^{-7} M **36.** (a) pH = 2.80; pOH = 11.20; (b) pH = 2.60; pOH = 11.40 **38.** (a) pH = 2.31; pOH = 11.69; (b) pH = 1.21; pOH = 12.79 **40.** pH = 2.69 **42.** 2.41 **44.** $K_{H_2CO_3} = 4.3 \times 10^{-7}$; $K_{HCO_3^-} = 7.0 \times 10^{-11}$; $K_1 \cdot K_2 = 3.0 \times 10^{-17}$ **46.** $[H_3O^+] = [HS^-]$ **48.** $[H_3O^+] = [NO_2^-] = 7.5 \times 10^{-3}$ M; $[OH^-] = 1.3 \times 10^{-12}$ M; $[HNO_2] = 0.126$ M; $[HBrO] = 0.10$ M; $[BrO^-] = 3 \times 10^{-8}$ M **50.** $[H_3O^+] = [Hgly] = 0.018$ M; $[OH^-] = 5.6 \times 10^{-13}$ M; $[H_2gly^+] = 0.072$ M; $[gly^-] = 2.5 \times 10^{-10}$ M **52.** $[H_3O^+] = [C_6H_4(CO_2H)(CO_2)^-] = 2.8 \times 10^{-3}$ M; $[OH^-] = 3.6 \times 10^{-12}$ M; $[C_6H_4(CO_2H)_2] = 7.2 \times 10^{-3}$ M; $[C_6H_4(CO_2^-)_2] = 3.9 \times 10^{-6}$ M **58.** (a) 9×10^{-4} M; (b) 2×10^{-3} M **60.** (a) 4.5×10^{-3} M; (b) 4.07×10^{-4} M **62.** (a) pH = 11.0; pOH = 3.0; (b) pH = 11.3; pOH = 2.7 **64.** (a) pH = 11.65; pOH = 2.35; (b) pH = 10.61; pOH = 3.390 **66.** 1.5×10^{-3} M **68.** 11.16 **70.** $[H_3O^+] = 3.9 \times 10^{-13}$ M; $[OH^-] = [HPO_4^{2-}] = 2.6 \times 10^{-2}$ M; $[PO_4^{3-}] = 2.4 \times 10^{-2}$ M; $[H_2PO_4^-] = 1.6 \times 10^{-7}$ M; $[H_3PO_4] = 8.0 \times 10^{-18}$ M; $[Na^+] = 0.150$ M **72.** (a) pH = 11.18; pOH = 2.82; (b) pH = 11.63; pOH = 2.37; (c) pH = 11.12; pOH = 2.88; (d) pH = 10.62; pOH = 3.38; (e) pH = 10.44; pOH = 3.56 **80.** 11 to 1 **82.** 7.72 **84.** 12.70 **86.** 4.5 **88.** 1.8 mol; 0.57 mol **90.** 5.444; 5.434 **92.** HCO_2H **96.** (a) 1.4×10^{-11}; (b) 1×10^{-1}; (c) 2.2×10^{-11}; (d) 5.6×10^{-10}; (e) 1.4×10^{-11}; (f) 1.7×10^{-13} **98.** 3.18 **100.** 1×10^{-5}; 4.3×10^{-12} **102.** 5.0 **108.** 3.0–4.9 **116.** 12.01; 1.0×10^{-2} M **118.** $[C_7H_4NSO_3H] = 3.9 \times 10^{-5}$ M; $[Na(C_7H_4NSO_3)] = 2.5 \times 10^{-11}$ M **120.** 4.51; 4.82

Chapter 18

10. (a) Precipitates; (b) Does not precipitate; (c) Does not precipitate; (d) Precipitates **12.** (a) 1.5×10^{-4}; (b) 4.6×10^{-17}; (c) 1.36×10^{-4}; (d) 7.9×10^{-10} **14.** (a) 2.1×10^{-11} M; (b) 1.3×10^{-4} M; (c) 1.6×10^{-4} M; (d) 2.1×10^{-4} M **16.** No; $[SO_4^{2-}] = 4.9 \times 10^{-3}$ M **18.** 7.6×10^{-3} M **20.** 6.2×10^{-5} M **22.** (a) 5.7×10^{-7} M; (b) 6.6×10^{-12} M; (c) 1.6×10^{-11} M **24.** 4.0×10^{-6} M **26.** Yes **28.** 0.89 **30.** (a) Yes; (b) 0.93 **32.** (a) 5×10^{-12} M; (b) 2×10^{-16} M **34.** 1×10^{-5} M **36.** 4.2×10^{-5} M **38.** 100% **40.** 0.008% **44.** 3×10^{-21} M **46.** 0.014 M **48.** $[Ag^+] = 5.5 \times 10^{-9}$ M; $[CN^-] = 1 \times 10^{-10}$ M; $[Ag(CN)_2^-] = 5.5 \times 10^{-9}$ M **50.** (a) $CoSO_3$, $PbCO_3$, Tl_2S; (b) Tl_2S **52.** 2×10^{-2} mol **54.** 0.80 g **56.** 12.40 **58.** 2.2×10^{-3} g **60.** 3×10^{-3} M **62.** 0.040 M **64.** 8×10^{-9} M; 1×10^{-10} M

Chapter 19

2. (a) $\Delta E = 870$ J; (b) $q = -3000$ J; (c) $w = -550$ J; (d) $\Delta E = 575$ J **6.** 3.10 J; increase **8.** -2.48 kJ **10.** 0 **14.** (a) (1) -89.4 kJ; (2) 164 kJ; (3) -238 kJ; (4) 180.5 kJ; (b) 1, 3 **16.** 90.83 kJ **18.** -335 kJ **20.** 67.1 kJ **28.** (a) (1) -531.8 J K^{-1}; (2) -34 J K^{-1}; (3) 15.3 J K^{-1}; (4) 290 J K^{-1}; (b) 3, 4 **30.** -47 J K^{-1} **32.** -68.7 J K^{-1} **38.** (a) (1) -78.8; (2) 159; (3) -159; (4) 173.1 kJ; (b) 1, 3 **44.** (a) -1.6 kJ; (b) 1.9 kJ; -11.9 kJ; the reaction is spontaneous at 100.0°C, but not at 0.00°C **46.** (a) -89.7 kJ; (b) 618.6 K (345.4°C)

50. (a) -30.3 kJ; (b) 2.03×10^5 **52.** No; $\Delta H > 0$, $\Delta S < 0$ **54.** 314 K (41°C) **56.** -79.9 kJ **58.** 5.35×10^{15}; exothermic **60.** (a) 131.30 kJ; (b) -90.2 kJ mol^{-1}; -38.0 kJ mol^{-1}; (c) -638.4 kJ **62.** 1.3×10^{-5} atm **64.** -163 J K^{-1} **66.** 307.3 kJ

Chapter 20

10. (a) $+1.40$ V; (b) -0.17 V; (c) $+1.37$ V **12.** (a) $+0.356$ V; (b) -0.74 V **14.** (a) $+0.23$ V; (b) $+1.4$ V; (c) $+0.43$ V **16.** (a) 2.041 V; (b) 12.25 V **18.** $Fe|Fe^{2+}||Ag^+|Ag$ **22.** (a) -0.195 V; (b) -0.836 V; (c) 1.13 V **24.** $+1.28$ V **26.** (a) $+1.16$ V; (b) $+1.36$ V **28.** -1.124 V **30.** (a) $+0.78$ V; -150 kJ; 2.4×10^{26}; (b) $+1.38$ V; -799 kJ; 9.62×10^{139}; (c) -0.5297 V; 102.2 kJ; 1.229×10^{-18} **32.** -348 kJ; 1.05×10^{61} **34.** 7.8×10^{-4} M **36.** (a) Yes; (b) No; (c) Yes; (d) No; (e) Yes **44.** 9.648×10^4 C **46.** (a) 1.60; (b) 2.000; (c) 0.690; (d) 7.31×10^{-3}; (e) 0.18; (f) 0.10; (g) 9.046×10^{-3} **48.** 3.0 mol; 3.0 faraday; 2.9×10^5 C **50.** 65.3 mol; 65.3 faraday; 6.30×10^6 C **52.** 111 g **54.** 1.2×10^{-3} mol **56.** 0.140 faraday; 30 min **58.** 198 kg **68.** (a) ii; (b) Dish A contains Hg_2^{2+} and Hg^{2+}; Dish B contains NO_3^-, H_3O^+, and HNO_2; (c) 0.92 V; (d) -3.9 kJ; (e) 4.7; (f) 0.23; (g) 0.60 mol; (h) 1.9×10^3 s; (i) i **72.** 1.76×10^{-10} **74.** 1.60×10^7 **78.** 4.48 h **80.** 0.20

Chapter 21

18. 3.2 g **24.** -2.900 kJ; yes **28.** 3.6 g **30.** 310 kJ **38.** SF_6; 26.2 g **40.** 8.44 g; 5.91 L **50.** 297 mL **52.** $H_2 + I_2 \longrightarrow 2HI$ **58.** XeF_4 **62.** 3.71×10^3 m^3 **64.** $I_2 + 3Cl_2 \longrightarrow 2ICl_3$ **66.** 13.97 kJ; endothermic **68.** 1.23×10^2

Chapter 22

12. 1.92×10^{-3} L **24.** 281 mol **28.** 1.56 L **44.** 1.561×10^{-1} M **46.** 25.8 L **70.** 1.47×10^{-5} **72.** 23.7 amu; due to HF dimers **74.** $CdCl_2$ **78.** (a) -296.83 kJ; (b) -197.8 kJ; (c) -132.5 kJ

Chapter 23

12. 1.5×10^{24} **14.** 0.434 kg **18.** -905.5 kJ; -114.1 kJ **24.** 291 mL **26.** 28 tons **42.** 18.74 g **48.** 9.857 g **50.** 4×10^{-6} M **52.** $P_{N_2O_4} = 8.0$ atm; $P_{NO_2} = 1.0$ atm **54.** 13.55 g **56.** 8.16×10^{-3}

Chapter 24

6. 0.8 MeV **8.** 2.3%; 2.0×10^{-18}% **10.** 0.97 (97%) **12.** 2×10^3 yr **14.** 28.8 yr **34.** 2.8×10^9 yr

Chapter 25

26. (a) $\Delta H° = 87$ kJ; $\Delta G° = 44$ kJ; (b) $\Delta H° = -109.9$ kJ;

$\Delta G° = -154.7$ kJ; (c) $\Delta H° = -510$ kJ; $\Delta G° = -601.5$ kJ
36. 92.0 g; Si_3H_8 **42.** (a) -48 kJ; (b) $+436$ kJ **44.** SiS_2
46. $B_{10}H_{14}$

Chapter 26

28. Tetrahedral; $NiCl_2[P(CH_3)_3]_2$ **30.** $[NiCl_4]^{2-}$, tetrahedral; $[MnCl_6]^{4-}$, octahedral; $[ScCl_6]^{3-}$, octahedral

Chapter 27

40. 2.57% **42.** 3.5×10^4 ft^3 **48.** 14.5897% **66.** 136 g
68. 1.1×10^{-11} M **76.** 29.319%; RbCl

Chapter 28

24. 1.3×10^3 lb **34.** 4.9 kg; 11 lb **40.** 25.83% **48.** 2.8×10^{-6} **60.** 2.8×10^{-32} M **64.** 0.040 M **66.** 0.174 V

Chapter 29

6. (a) Air, 1.30; hydrogen, 0.0900; helium, 0.179;
(b) Hydrogen, 1.21; helium, 1.12; 92.6% **10.** (a) CCl_4, 140 lb;
HF, 18.2 lb; (b) CCl_4, 159 lb; HF, 41.4 lb **22.** Na^+, 0.4593
M; Cl^-, 0.5354 M

Chapter 30

14. (a) -99.76 kJ; -134.2 kJ; (b) -638 kJ; -1235 kJ
16. (a) alkane; (b) alcohol; (c) ketone; (d) carboxylic acid;
(e) amine; (f) ether; (g) aldehyde **26.** 134.08 lb **28.** 16.5 g
30. 14.7 g

Chapter 31

12. 4 **18.** 1.05 **22.** 890 g/mol (tripalmitylglycerol)

Index

Covalent and Ionic Radii of the Elements

Numerical values of radii are in angstrom units

Periods	1 IA	2 IIA	3 IIIB	4 IVB	5 VB	6 VIB	7 VIIB	8 VIII	9 VIII
1	**H** 0.3 +1 ?	Metals							
2	**Li** 1.52 +1 0.60	**Be** 1.11 +2 0.31					Transition metals		
3	**Na** 1.86 +1 0.95	**Mg** 1.60 +2 0.65							
4	**K** 2.31 +1 1.33	**Ca** 1.97 +2 0.99	**Sc** 1.60 +3 0.81	**Ti** 1.46 +4 0.64	**V** 1.31 +5 0.4	**Cr** 1.25 +6 0.52	**Mn** 1.29 +2 0.80	**Fe** 1.26 +2 0.75	1.26 +2 0.72
5	**Rb** 2.44 +1 1.48	**Sr** 2.15 +2 1.13	**Y** 1.80 +3 0.93	**Zr** 1.57 +4 0.87	**Nb** 1.43 +5 0.69	**Mo** 1.36 +6 0.62	**Tc** 1.3	**Ru** 1.33	1.34
6	**Cs** 2.62 +1 1.69	**Ba** 2.17 +2 1.35	**La** 1.88 +3 1.15	**Hf** 1.57 +4 0.84	**Ta** 1.43 +5 0.68	**W** 1.37 +6 0.68	**Re** 1.37	**Os** 1.34	1.35
7	**Fr** 2.7	**Ra** 2.20 +2 1.52	**Ac** 2.0 +3 1.11						